Digital Logic: Analysis, Application & Design

The Saunders College Publishing Series in Electronics Technology

Garrod/Borns: DIGITAL LOGIC: ANALYSIS, APPLICATION & DESIGN
ISBN 0-03-023099-3

Harrison: TRANSFORM METHODS IN CIRCUIT ANALYSIS
ISBN 0-03-020724-X

Hazen: EXPERIENCING ELECTRICITY AND ELECTRONICS
Conventional Current Version ISBN 0-03-007747-8
Electron Flow Version ISBN 0-03-03427-2

Hazen: EXPLORING ELECTRONIC DEVICES
ISBN 0-03-028533-X

Hazen: FUNDAMENTALS OF DC AND AC CIRCUITS
ISBN 0-03-028538-0

Ismail/Rooney: DIGITAL CONCEPTS AND APPLICATIONS
ISBN 0-03-026628-9

Kale: INDUSTRIAL CIRCUITS AND AUTOMATED MANUFACTURING
ISBN 0-03-013609-1

Laverghetta: ANALOG COMMUNICATIONS FOR TECHNOLOGY
ISBN 0-03-029403-7

Ludeman: INTRODUCTION TO ELECTRONIC DEVICES AND CIRCUITS
ISBN 0-03-009538-7

Oppenheimer: SURVEY OF ELECTRONICS
ISBN 0-03-020842-4

Prestopnik: DIGITAL ELECTRONICS: CONCEPTS AND APPLICATIONS FOR DIGITAL DESIGN
ISBN 0-03-026757-9

Spiteri: ROBOTICS TECHNOLOGY
ISBN 0-03-020858-0

SAUNDERS COLLEGE PUBLISHING

A Division of Holt, Rinehart and Winston, Inc.

Philadelphia Fort Worth Chicago San Francisco
Montreal Toronto London Sydney Tokyo

Digital Logic: ANALYSIS, APPLICATION & DESIGN

Susan A. R. Garrod

Robert J. Borns

PURDUE UNIVERSITY

Text Typeface: Times Roman
Compositor: Maryland Composition
Senior Acquisitions Editor: Barbara Gingery
Managing Editor: Carol Field
Project Editor: Anne Gibby
Copy Editor: Elaine Honig
Manager of Art and Design: Carol Bleistine
Art and Design Coordinator: Doris Bruey
Text Designer: Rita Naughton
Cover Designer: Lawrence R. Didona
Text Artwork: GRAFACON
Director of EDP: Tim Frelick
Production Manager: Bob Butler
Marketing Manager: Denise Watrobsky

Cover Credit: IBM token ring chip/courtesy IBM Corporation

Printed in the United States of America

Digital Logic: Analysis, Application & Design

ISBN: 0-03-023099-3

Library of Congress Catalog Card Number: 90-052901

1123 039 987654321

This book is dedicated to our children,
John and Joanna, and to our students. Their interest
in learning has been our inspiration to write.

Preface

PURPOSE OF THE TEXT

DIGITAL LOGIC: ANALYSIS, APPLICATION & DESIGN provides a comprehensive study of digital logic technology. In today's globally competitive market, it is imperative that engineering and technology students have textbooks that include a thorough coverage of both the fundamentals and the latest developments in the technology. The fundamentals of digital logic are presented to establish a foundation for the study of circuit analysis, application, and design. Numerous examples, figures, review questions, troubleshooting problems, and designs of varying difficulty aid students in the learning process.

Programmable logic devices have been included in the text as one of the most important new advancements in digital electronics. The analysis, application, and design of problems with programmable logic devices provides a technical progression of the digital electronics into the 1990s and better prepares students for the field of logic circuit application and design. Numerous programming examples are included in the text and in the appendices so that students can work with these devices in the laboratory.

An important component in the learning process is hands-on laboratory experience. It is intended that the text material be reinforced through laboratory activities in the accompanying laboratory manual. The laboratory manual is structured around the analysis, application, design, and troubleshooting of TTL and CMOS circuits and programmable logic devices.

Students should view digital logic as a starting point to establish their expertise in electrical or computer science fields. Digital logic has served both authors to launch their respective research and teaching interests in the related fields of telecommunications and computer networking. The basic concepts of digital logic are prevalent in the advanced applications and research projects that the authors encounter. In addition to teaching digital logic, Professor Garrod developed and teaches a senior level digital telecommunications course. She has experience with advanced digital communication network architectures and digital communication satellite applications through her work at the National Aeronautic and Space Administration (NASA). Professor Borns has over five years of experience in semiconductor memory research and development with IBM Corporation, and has been involved in digital communications as a consultant for IBM. He teaches fundamental digital logic, and a senior level computer local area networking (LAN) course that he developed.

INTENDED AUDIENCE

This text is written primarily for students of electrical engineering technology or electrical engineering at ABET-accredited institutions. The text may also be used by students in other areas of engineering or technology to provide in-depth coverage of digital electronics as a technical elective to complement their major discipline.

Material is presented from basic concepts and definitions to advanced design through examples and applications to allow all students, especially those with no prior knowledge in digital logic, to proceed independently through the material. A thorough coverage of Boolean logic fundamentals is achieved by the use of both examples and logic relationships. Application and design topics are all related to practical approaches and problem solving using available TTL logic circuitry and programmable logic devices.

All topics in this text, including the material in programmable logic devices, are included in the first two courses in digital electronics taken by all electrical engineering technology students at Purdue University. The students enroll in these courses as first- and second-semester freshmen. The material has been tested in the lecture and laboratory portions of the courses, and is at an appropriate level to provide the depth and breadth of topic coverage that is required by the bachelor's degree program at Purdue University. At the completion of the material in this text, students will have sufficient background knowledge to proceed to an advanced digital design course or to any beginning microprocessor course, as well as begin work in the digital electronics field.

ORGANIZATION AND USE OF THE TEXT

The text is divided into several sections to assist in the learning and mastery of the vast array of topics related to the study of digital logic. The material is presented to establish topical relationships and to develop a clear understanding of how to apply the concepts learned in actual digital design and analysis situations. The major sections of the text and the chapters that are included in the section are as follows:

DIGITAL LOGIC FUNDAMENTALS

1. Digital Logic and Technology
2. Number Systems and Arithmetic

COMBINATIONAL LOGIC

3. Logic Functions and Combinational Logic Circuits

ADVANCED COMBINATIONAL LOGIC DESIGN WITH MEDIUM SCALE INTEGRATION (MSI) LOGIC CIRCUITS

4. Multiplexers and Demultiplexers
5. Decoders, Encoders, and Code Converters
6. Arithmetic Circuits

SEQUENTIAL LOGIC

7. Monostable and Astable Circuits
8. Latches
9. Flip-Flops

ADVANCED SEQUENTIAL LOGIC DESIGN

10. Counter Circuits
11. Shift Registers

LSI LOGIC AND MEMORY

12. Programmable Logic Devices and Semiconductor Logic
13. Semiconductor Memory Technology
14. Logic Design with Microprocessors

LOGIC FAMILY PERFORMANCE AND INTERFACING

15. Logic Families, Interfacing, and Device Selection
16. Analog/Digital Conversion

LOGIC SYSTEM DESIGN

17. Digital Logic Design Projects

APPENDICES

A. Interpreting Data Sheet Information
B. Data Transmission
C. Programmable Logic Device Development Systems
D. Programmable Logic Device Example Problems: LC9000 Source File Listings and LC9000 Document File Listings
E. Semiconductor Memory Data Book Specifications

The text can be used in its entirety in a two-semester course, or it can be selectively arranged for use in a one-semester course. The method of organization also allows the text to be used later by students as an application reference guide.

Topics are discussed concisely and labeled for quick and direct referencing. The sections on logic design, LSI logic, memories, logic families, interfacing, and system design will be useful references far beyond the initial course.

Recommended Two-Semester Use of the Text

The following chapter sequence is recommended in a two-semester course taught to freshmen or sophomore students:

First Semester—Combinational Logic

DIGITAL LOGIC FUNDAMENTALS

1. Digital Logic and Technology
2. Number Systems and Arithmetic

COMBINATIONAL LOGIC

3. Logic Functions and Combinational Logic Circuits

ADVANCED COMBINATIONAL LOGIC DESIGN WITH MEDIUM SCALE INTEGRATION (MSI) LOGIC CIRCUITS

4. Multiplexers and Demultiplexers
5. Decoders, Encoders, and Code Converters
6. Arithmetic Circuits
12. Programmable Logic Devices and Semiconductor Logic (first half of the chapter on combinational logic)

APPENDIX

A. Interpreting Data Sheet Information

Second Semester—Sequential Logic

SEQUENTIAL LOGIC

7. Monostable and Astable Circuits
8. Latches
9. Flip-Flops

ADVANCED SEQUENTIAL LOGIC DESIGN

10. Counter Circuits
11. Shift Registers

LSI LOGIC AND MEMORY

12. Programmable Logic Devices and Semiconductor Logic (second half of the chapter on sequential logic)
13. Semiconductor Memory Technology
14. Logic Design with Microprocessors

LOGIC FAMILY PERFORMANCE AND INTERFACING

15. Logic Families, Interfacing, and Device Selection
16. Analog/Digital Conversion

LOGIC SYSTEM DESIGN

17. Digital Logic Design Projects

APPENDICES

B. Data Transmission
E. Semiconductor Memory Data Book Specifications

Recommended One-Semester Use of the Text

The following chapter sequence is recommended for a one-semester course taught to sophomore students:

DIGITAL LOGIC FUNDAMENTALS

1. Digital Logic and Technology
2. Number Systems and Arithmetic

COMBINATIONAL LOGIC

3. Logic Functions and Combinational Logic Circuits

ADVANCED COMBINATIONAL LOGIC DESIGN WITH MEDIUM SCALE INTEGRATION (MSI) LOGIC CIRCUITS

4. Multiplexers and Demultiplexers
5. Decoders, Encoders, and Code Converters
6. Arithmetic Circuits

SEQUENTIAL LOGIC

7. Monostable and Astable Circuits
8. Latches
9. Flip-Flops

ADVANCED SEQUENTIAL LOGIC DESIGN

10. Counter Circuits
11. Shift Registers

LSI LOGIC AND MEMORY

12. Programmable Logic Devices and Semiconductor Logic

LOGIC FAMILY PERFORMANCE AND INTERFACING

15. Logic Families, Interfacing, and Device Selection

LOGIC SYSTEM DESIGN

17. Digital Logic Design Projects

Coverage of Programmable Logic Devices (PLDs)

We encourage faculty who have not previously included programmable logic devices (PLDs) to consider using the material in this text in their own course. The material is presented here as we present it to our freshmen students. Within one week of using the programmable logic devices in the laboratory, the majority of the students elect to implement future logic circuit designs with the programmable devices, rather than with traditional hardware. Seeing our students enthusiastically undertake projects using PLDs is testimony to the success we have had in this area. When given a choice between using PLDs or conventional IC logic, most students select the PLD approach.

Special assistance was provided by Jim Forbis of Programmable Logic Technologies during development of the PLD material. The PLD programming in the text is performed with products developed by Programmable Logic Technologies. These software and hardware systems were selected specifically for their use in educational settings. The cost, simplicity, and reliability of the systems were the three main criteria used to make the selection. Additional information on PLD systems can be found in Appendix C of this text.

ACKNOWLEDGMENTS

We would like to thank our own first professors in digital electronics: John Lindenlaub and David Meyer, School of Electrical Engineering, Purdue University, for providing our first glimpse of this fascinating world of digital electronics. Their masterful teaching and technical ingenuity inspired us to contribute to this field of learning by writing this text.

We would like to recognize and thank several of our students who assisted in the development of the textbook and laboratory manual: Sang The Bui, Chuck Burt, Frederick W. Cheng, Gregg Cromer, Joel Frick, Matt Hillier, Damon Hoyda, George Knish, Dale Nussel, Jay Oliver, Kurt Reichert, Scott M. Whitlock, and Don Wyatt. We greatly appreciate their interest in this project.

We would like to thank our colleagues on the faculty of Purdue University who have provided helpful comments and input. In addition, we would like to thank our many colleagues at other colleges and universities for their support, encouragement and resourceful comments: Ernie Sharp, George Mason, Harold Hultman, Jerry Humphrey, John L. Morgan, Marybelle Beigh, Al McHenry, Samuel Derman, Donald Dorn, Surinder Jain, Albert Grubbs, John C. Debo, and David Hata.

With great appreciation we thank our editor, Barbara Gingery, and project editor, Anne Gibby. They have been consistent managers and supporters of this work. We would also like to thank Laura Shur and the staff at Saunders College Publishing. They have made every effort to accommodate our ideas and to ensure that a high quality textbook was produced.

Finally, we would like to thank Sally J. Roth for providing valuable consulting during the project, Sandra K. Roth, our legal counsel, and David J. Drake for his encouragement to complete this project (to begin the next writing endeavor!). We especially thank our children, John and Joanna. Their enthusiasm, creativity, positive outlook on life, and interest in learning provided the needed inspiration, while their sound sleeping habits enabled us to work well into the night to complete this project.

Any comments by students or faculty using the text are welcomed.

We would like to include your ideas in the next edition of the text. Please feel free to contact us or to send us your comments at Purdue University, Knoy Hall, West Lafayette, Indiana 47907, (317) 494-7483.

Susan A. R. Garrod
Purdue University

Robert J. Borns
Purdue University

December 1990

Contents

Chapter 6 Arithmetic Circuits *328*

Part 4 SEQUENTIAL LOGIC *390*

Chapter 7 Monostable and Astable Circuits *392*

Part 6 LSI LOGIC AND MEMORY 630

Chapter 12 Programmable Logic Devices and Semiconductor Logic 632

Chapter 13 Semiconductor Memory Technology 730

Chapter 14 Logic Design with Microprocessors 776

Part 7 LOGIC FAMILY PERFORMANCE AND INTERFACING *802*

Chapter 15 Logic Families, Interfacing, and Device Selection *804*

APPENDICES

Digital Logic:

Analysis, Application & Design

Part 1

DIGITAL LOGIC FUNDAMENTALS

Chapter 1

Digital Logic and Technology

Upon completing and mastering the material in this chapter, you should be able to understand the basics of digital logic and technology in the areas of analysis, application, and design:

ANALYSIS

1. Define the difference between digital and analog information.
2. Understand the rationale for digital logic.
3. Know the history and development of digital circuits.
4. Explain how digital circuits are integrated and manufactured into ICs.
5. Represent digital logic levels as binary numbers and waveforms.
6. Classify waveforms as ideal or nonideal, periodic or aperiodic.
7. Define TTL input and output voltages.
8. Know the types of tools available for digital analysis, testing, and troubleshooting.

APPLICATION

9. Identify ICs by the printed coding information.
10. Differentiate between the different types of IC packages available.
11. Explain the difference among design, analysis, testing, and troubleshooting.

DESIGN

12. Understand how the representation of information in digital form provides a powerful tool for the design of advanced circuits and systems.

Currently we live in an information age. During every day of our life we are provided with a tremendous amount of information from our surroundings: Television, radio, and the printed media provide almost instantaneous access to worldwide events. Some of this information, which is received by our senses (sight, sound, etc.), is conditioned, analyzed, and stored by the brain. For example, light energy is continuously received by the eyes, in turn this energy is converted into another form, and finally it is processed by the brain. The brain then changes this information into a form that can be more easily stored and analyzed.

In electronics it is very useful to represent or code information such as voltage or current into another form, referred to as **digital**. As indicated, the brain codes information into a form that is advantageous for analysis and storage. Similarly, the coding of information into a digital code provides a powerful tool to analyze and design a wide range of complex electronic circuits and systems. Digital systems are replacing analog systems because of their ability to process information quickly.

Digital logic is used in almost every product and technology. Computers, calculators, television, audio and video recordings, compact discs, long distance telephone service, automobile control systems, and satellite systems use digital logic.

This chapter introduces the student to digital logic and provides an insight into how such a simple concept, representing information with only combinations of 0's and 1's, can be used to design and build complex systems and products.

1-1 DIGITAL AND ANALOG INFORMATION

The field of electronics that represents information in digital form is known as digital electronics. Digital electronics are used in communications systems, computers, control systems, automobile manufacturing, medical instrumentation, consumer electronics, stereo and video equipment, and virtually every field of technology.

Most information commonly encountered falls into a broad category known as **analog** information. Any type of data or information that is variable and continuous is classified as analog. Since the information is continuous, there is an infinite number of data points associated with analog information. A clock with a conventional dial and hands is a good example of a device that provides analog information. There is an infinite number of positions that the clock's hands can assume. Each position represents a measure of time, and the continuous nature of an analog clock's hands allows for fractional parts of minutes and seconds to be displayed.

Another way to represent time on a clock is to display a limited number of codes or **digits.** Thus, a **digital clock** has a limited or **discrete** number of times that can be displayed to *represent* time values. For example, a simple digital clock can be constructed to display only the numbers 1 through 12. It is possible to determine the time, but only in 1 hour measurements. When the digital clock displays a "2," it is impossible to tell if the time is exactly 2 o'clock or if, in fact, the time is almost 3 o'clock. The time can be anywhere from 2 o'clock to a fraction of a second before 3 o'clock. The accuracy of this simple clock can be 1 hour. Adding more digits to display minutes improves the accuracy of the clock but adds to the complexity of the clock.

What is the advantage of the simple 12-number digital clock? It provides an easy and quick way to determine the time. Although trivial now, determining time from an analog clock takes some effort and thought process. A 4-year-old child has difficulty interpreting an analog clock, but the same child can easily analyze a 12-number clock that displays the digits to determine time. Equally important is the ability to represent and store a large quantity of continuous information (time) with only 12 different codes.

Digital electronics is the field of electronics that utilizes the representation of information in digital form. The clock example illustrates several important points that relate to digital electronics.

1. Digital coding allows for the representation of *continuous analog* information into *discrete digital* information.
2. Digital coding provides a powerful method to represent information in a form (code) for *analysis* and *storage*.
3. Analog information can be converted (coded) to a digital form to simplify processing that information.
4. The coding of information from an analog to a digital form results in the loss of some accuracy.
5. The accuracy of digital information can be improved by adding additional digits of the code to represent the analog information.

Section Self-Test

Categorize the following as analog or digital:

1. Speed
2. Temperature
3. Number of seconds in a minute
4. Binary numbers

ANSWERS (Not necessarily in the order of the questions)

• Analog • Digital • Analog • Digital

1-2 BINARY DIGITAL LOGIC

Digital logic is the representation of information using only two binary digits, a 0 and a 1. Complex circuits and systems can be designed and built by applying the principles of digital logic.

In an analog world more information is available than is needed or can be processed. Every day, people automatically process and analyze a large amount of analog information. Much information processing is in the form of yes/no decisions. For example, a television program is to be televised at 7 P.M. today, but you don't know which channel it is on. Your first yes/no decision may involve whether to use a television program guide.

The decision is made not to use it. You turn on the television at 7 P.M., decide to use the automatic channel selector, and scan the channels to find the program. You make a rapid series of yes/no decisions for each channel encountered, and finally stop at the channel that has the program of interest. You are making **logical** decisions that are simple in nature, either yes or no, and that in combination allow you to complete the more complex task of finding the right channel.

Information represented by two possible conditions, or **states,** such as yes/no, true/false, on/off, high/low, and so on, is referred to as **binary. Logic** is the application of a set of rules to determine if a given statement is true or false. It is useful to represent binary information with the digits 0 and 1. With this convention, **digital binary logic** is the representation of information with two allowed states, 0 and 1. Digital binary logic is commonly referred to simply as **digital logic.**

It is advantageous to represent or process analog information digitally, and this property of having only two possible states makes digital information and logic a powerful tool for information processing, circuit and system design, and information storage.

Section Self-Test

1. What is meant by the term "states"?
2. Why is digital logic referred to as "binary"?

ANSWERS

- States are the conditions that circuits or devices are in. A switch has an "on" state and "off" state. Binary logic has a 1 state and a 0 state.
- Digital logic is binary since there are only two possible states, a 1 or a 0.

1-3 THE HISTORY OF DIGITAL LOGIC

Digital logic has its roots in mathematics. It evolved to the point where it was utilized to construct the first digital computer about 50 years ago. Today's personal computers are based on the principles of digital logic.

Digital logic is used extensively in the electronics industry since the two digital states of 0 and 1 are used to represent the physical action of a switch in its open or closed position. A 0 represents an open switch with no electric current flow, and a 1 represents a closed switch with current flow. A digital computer uses the relationship between a physical device (switch) and its representation (digital logic) to perform calculations and make decisions.

The first mechanical computing device was proposed in 1835 by Charles Babbage, an English mathematician. In 1944 Harvard University researchers built the first automated electromechanical digital computer, which used relay circuits to represent the two digital digits, 0 and 1.

Two years later researchers at the University of Pennsylvania built the first electronic digital computer using vacuum tube circuitry, the now famous ENIAC (electronic numerical integrator and computer). ENIAC used a tremendous amount of power, the circuitry filled an entire room, and it had very limited computational capacity and speed by today's standards.

Section Self-Test

1. What physical device was used to represent a binary 1 or 0 in the first computational device?
2. What physical device was used to represent a binary 1 or 0 with the ENIAC computer?

ANSWERS • Vacuum tube • Relay switch

1-4 DIGITAL CIRCUIT MANUFACTURING

All of today's digital circuits are miniaturized using semiconductor technology. The resulting chips are packaged into several different types of ICs for use in digital applications.

Digital logic rapidly developed with the invention of the transistor in the early 1950s. The **transistor** is a low-powered and extremely reliable electronic device that can function as a switch with two logic states.

The first digital logic circuits were built on circuit boards by combining single or **discrete components** like transistors, inductors, capacitors, and resistors. These circuits are referred to as **component board circuits.** Almost any type of digital circuit can be built using a combination of these components.

Further engineering research and development produced **integrated circuits,** also known as **ICs** or **chips. Integration** is the process by which discrete components can be manufactured into circuitry on a single piece of **semiconductor material.** Although the most common semiconductor material used is **silicon,** some devices are fabricated using gallium arsenide or germanium as the semiconductor materials.

Integration provides several advantages over component board digital circuits: ICs have reduced the cost of digital circuits, are more reliable, require less power to operate, and make it possible to build very complex circuits in a small amount of physical space.

Further advancements in semiconductor technology allowed for integration of more devices into the semiconductor device to the point that entire digital circuits were produced. As more and more devices were integrated into a single silicon chip, a classification scheme was developed to describe the level of integration by the number of transistors integrated per chip.

The five classifications of semiconductor integration are **small scale integration (SSI), medium scale integration (MSI), large scale integration (LSI), very large scale integration (VLSI),** and **ultra large scale integration (ULSI).** Table 1-1 summarizes semiconductor classification.

One of the basic logic devices, the **logic gate,** can be integrated with just a few integrated transistors, diodes, resistors, and capacitors. However, many of today's more complex semiconductor chips have over 1 million transistors per chip, and 10 million transistor chips are currently in the experimental stage.

One important example of a VLSI or ULSI chip is a **microprocessor.** A microprocessor is a type of IC that can be programmed to perform specific logic functions for a particular circuit application. Microprocessors are discussed in Chapter 14.

TABLE 1-1 Integrated Circuit Classification

Classification	Transistors	Typical IC
SSI	10 or less	54/74 logic gates
MSI	10 to 100	Counters, adders
LSI	100 to 1000	Small memory ICs, gate arrays
VLSI	1000 to 1 million	Large memory ICs, microprocessors
ULSI	1 million and up	Multifunction ICs

FIGURE 1-1(a) A Semiconductor Chip (Courtesy IBM Corporation)

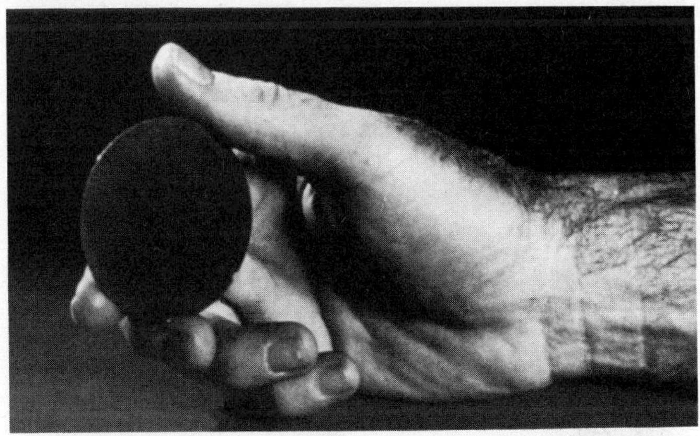

FIGURE 1-1(b) A semiconductor wafer (Courtesy IBM Corporation)

1.4.1 Integrated Circuit Packaging

Logic gates are not normally produced individually. SSI and MSI ICs are fabricated using semiconductor technology and contain typically from two to eight logic gates. The standard component used to package the IC is the **dual-in-line package,** or **DIP.** Many common digital logic gate ICs are packaged in a 16-pin DIP. The body of the DIP is typically plastic or ceramic, and the pins are corrosive-resistant metal. DIPs adhere to strict standards regarding package size and number of pins. More complex digital ICs may have a larger DIP package size or additional pins.

In addition to DIP packaging, **small outline ICs,** or **SOICs** are manufactured. This type of package can be soldered directly to the surface of a **printed circuit board,** or **PC board,** at the next stage of manufacturing. This is accomplished with **surface mount technology, SMT,** and SOICs are commonly referred to as **surface mount devices,** or **SMDs.** Soldering DIP packages requires circuit boards with holes for the pins.

Other types of IC packages exist, including **plastic leadless chip carrier, PLCC,** and **flat pack ICs.** Each type of package has its unique advantages and disadvantages. There is a packaging section in IC data books that describes the types of packages available for each type of IC that should be

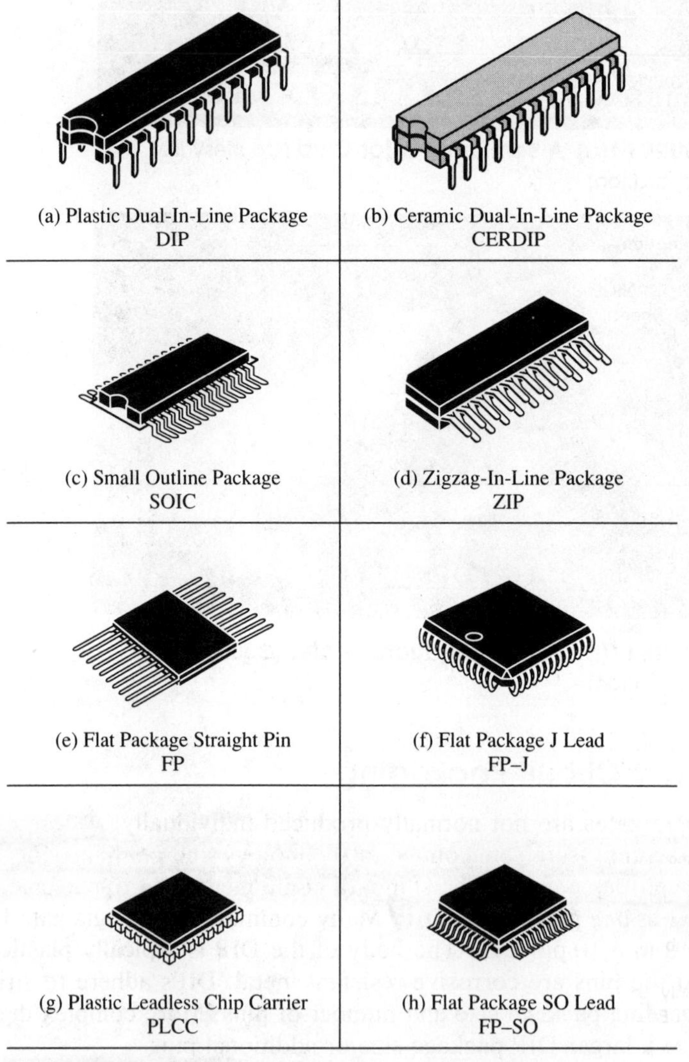

FIGURE 1-2 IC Packaging (Courtesy Hitachi America, Ltd.)

consulted for detailed part mechanical specifications. Figure 1-2 illustrates the different types of IC packaging commercially available.

1.4.2 IC Identification

After an IC is packaged, the package is marked for identification. The most important marking is the IC identification number. This number varies with the type and function of the IC. The numbering system is standardized by function within a logic family, independent of the manufacturer. The coding from a typical IC is shown in Figure 1-3. The "SN" indicates that the IC

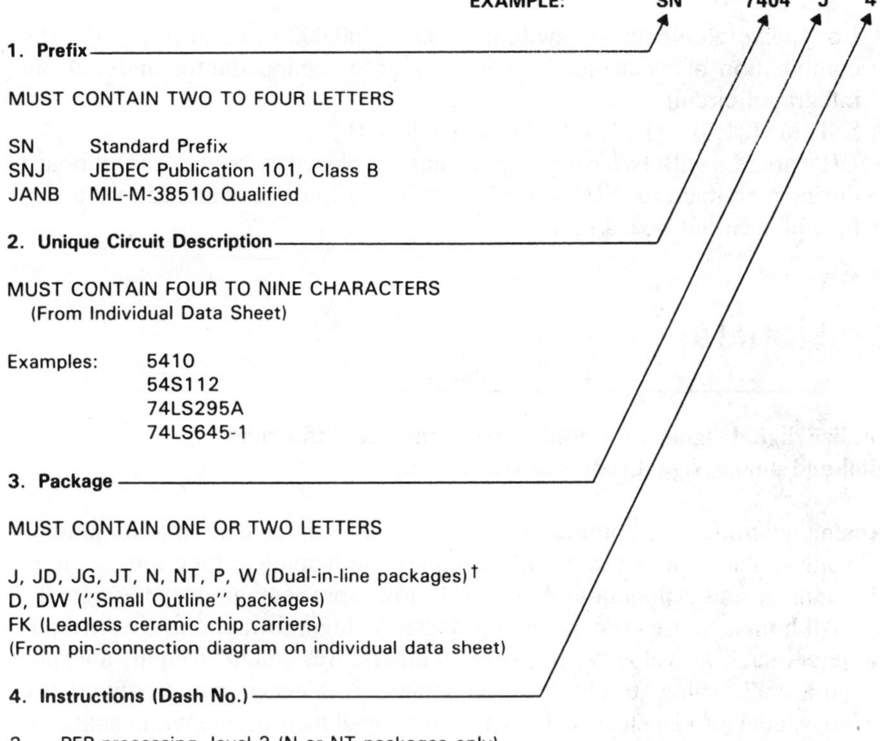

†These circuits in dual-in-line packages are shipped in one of the carriers shown below. Unless a specific method of shipment is specified by the customer (with possible additional costs), circuits will be shipped in the most practical carrier. Please contact your TI sales representative for the method that will best suit your particular needs.

Dual-in-line (D, DW, J, JD, JG, JT, N, NT, P, W)
- Slide Magazines
- A-Channel Plastic Tubing
- Tape and Reel
- Barnes Carrier (W only)
- Sectioned Cardboard Box
- Individual Plastic Box

FIGURE 1-3 IC Number Coding (Courtesy Texas Instruments)

is manufactured by Texas Instruments, Inc. The "74" refers to a type of digital logic known as commercial grade TTL. The "04" refers to the function of the IC; in this case, an inverter gate.

Also included in the marking is the manufacturer's code or logo, and often a code to identify when and where the IC was manufactured.

Section Self-Test

1. Define the following terms:
   (a) transistor (b) VLSI (c) integration (d) IC
2. List the different levels of integration and the number of equivalent gates associated with each.
3. List and explain the difference between DIPs and SMDs.

ANSWERS

- Low-powered electronic switch; 1,000 to 100,000 transistors per IC; the combination of electronic components onto semiconductor material; an integrated circuit
- SSI, MSI, LSI, VLSI, ULSI (see Table 1-1)
- DIPs are ICs with two rows of pins that are placed through a circuit board during manufacture. SMDs are ICs with pins that are soldered to the surface of a circuit board in use.

1-5 ANALOG SIGNALS

In order to utilize digital signals, we need to recognize the differences between digital and analog signal representation.

Analog quantities are continuous functions that can have an infinite number of values. The signals are usually complex mathematical functions such as the sinusoid and exponential. Figure 1-4 shows some common analog signals.

All human senses receive and process analog information. Physical parameters such as velocity, pressure, temperature, sound, weight, and position are all analog. In electrical technology it is necessary to convert the analog signal into an electrical quantity for signal measurement and analysis. An analog **transducer** is used to convert physical analog quantities into electrical analog quantities, such as current, voltage, and resistance.

Current and voltage are commonly displayed or graphed over a time interval, producing analog waveforms. Figure 1-5 shows a periodic voltage waveform that varies from 0 to 5 volts within a fixed time interval of 100 ms. If the analog value varies in a pattern that repeats, it is referred to as a **periodic signal,** and the smallest interval that repeats is known as the **period** of the signal, represented by a capital letter **T.** If a waveform does not have a pattern that repeats, then it is referred to as **aperiodic.** The period of the waveform in Figure 1-5 is T = 100 ms.

Many signals that are studied in digital electronics have very small periods. Standardized time units and abbreviations are used to represent the

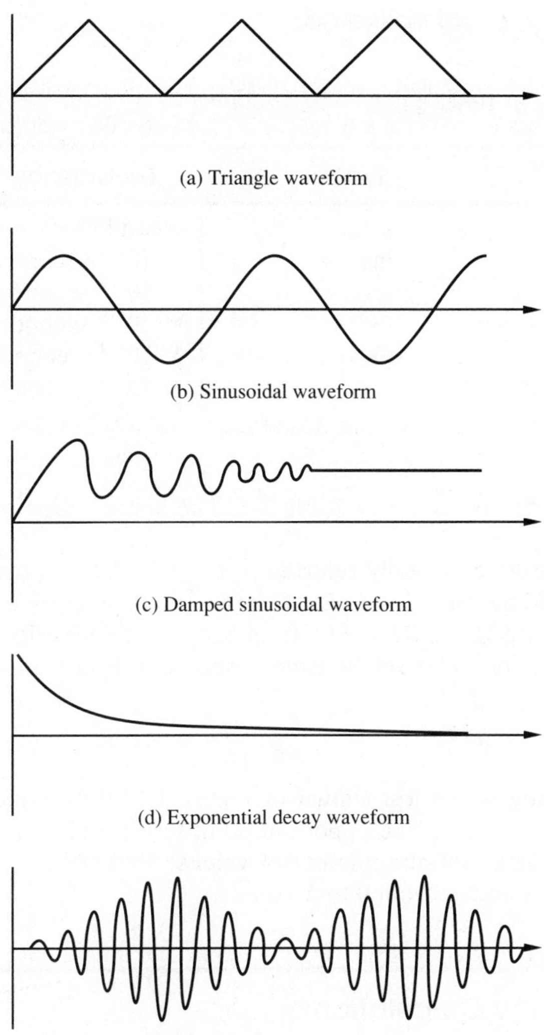

FIGURE 1-4 Analog Signals

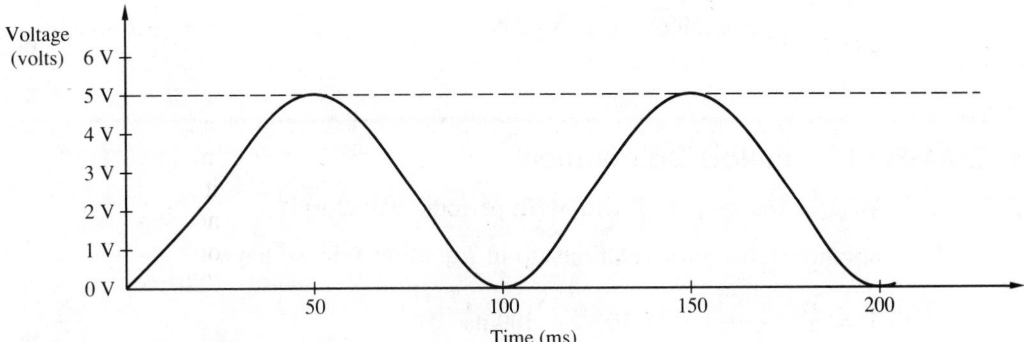

FIGURE 1-5 Periodic Analog Sine Waveform

TABLE 1-2 Units of Time

Time Unit	Symbol	Equivalence
Second	s	1 second
Millisecond	ms	1×10^{-3} seconds
Microsecond	μs	1×10^{-6} seconds
Nanosecond	ns	1×10^{-9} seconds
Picosecond	ps	1×10^{-12} seconds
Femtosecond	fs	1×10^{-15} seconds

small units of time, as shown in Table 1-2. The abbreviation for second is s.

A signal is more commonly referred to by its frequency rather than by its period. The **frequency** of the waveform is represented by a small letter **f,** and the units are **Hertz (Hz).** The frequency of the waveform is the reciprocal of the period. This relationship is shown in Equation 1-1.

Eq. 1-1 $$f = \frac{1}{T}\ \text{Hz}$$

For the analog waveform shown in Figure 1-5, the frequency is $f = 1/T = 1/100$ ms $= 10$ Hz. The important point to remember here is that an analog voltage has an infinite number of values; for Figure 1-5 there is an infinite number of values from 0 to 5 volts.

■ EXAMPLE 1-1 Frequency Calculation

What is the frequency of a sine wave that has a period of 200 μs?

Solution: Using Equation 1-1, we find that the frequency is

$$\frac{1}{200 \times 10^{-6}} = 5000\ \text{Hz} = 5\ \text{KHz}$$

■

■ EXAMPLE 1-2 Period Calculation

What is the period of a 10 MHz periodic waveform?

Solution: Using the relationship in Equation 1-1, we have

$$T = \frac{1}{f} = \frac{1}{1 \times 10^{7}} = 10^{-7} = 100\ \text{ns}$$

■

TABLE 1-3 Units of Frequency

Frequency Unit	Symbol	Equivalence
Hertz	Hz	1 Hertz
Kilohertz	KHz	1×10^3 Hertz
Megahertz	MHz	1×10^6 Hertz
Gigahertz	GHz	1×10^9 Hertz
Terahertz	THz	1×10^{12} Hertz

Since the frequency of a waveform is the reciprocal of the period, the frequencies of the waveforms commonly encountered in digital electronics are very large quantities. Table 1-3 shows the frequency units and abbreviations used.

Typical analog signals include AC power, radio signals, and television signals. AC electrical power in the United States is 60 Hz. The electrical power in Europe is 50 Hz. **Amplitude modulated (AM)** radio signals are between 530 and 1600 KHz. **Frequency modulated (FM)** radio signals are between 88 and 108 MHz. **Very high frequency (VHF)** and **ultra high frequency (UHF)** television signals are above 6 GHz.

■ EXAMPLE 1-3 Period Calculations

What are the periods of the upper and lower FM frequencies?

Solution:

Lower frequency period: $\dfrac{1}{88 \text{ MHz}} = 11.36 \text{ ns}$

Upper frequency period: $\dfrac{1}{108 \text{ MHz}} = 9.26 \text{ ns}$ ■

Section Self-Test

1. List four analog signals.
2. Explain how analog information, such as temperature, is converted to an analog electrical quantity.
3. As the frequency of a signal increases, does the period increase or decrease? Explain.

ANSWERS

- FM radio, UHF television, cellular telephones, microwave satellites.
- A transducer is used to convert analog quantities into electrical signals.
- The period decreases, according to Equation 1-1 (inversely proportional).

1-6 DIGITAL SIGNALS

Analog circuits are necessary blocks of any electrical system. However, it is advantageous to represent many of the analog quantities and parameters digitally. The representation of a continuous analog voltage digitally (with two unique logic states) makes it possible to build complex systems such as computers.

Digital quantities are **discrete signals** that can assume only certain voltage values. The binary numbers 0 and 1 are used to represent these discrete signal voltages, or **digital voltages.** These digital voltages are commonly referred to as **logic levels.**

1.6.1 Logic Levels

Positive logic is defined as assigning the binary digit 0 to the low level voltage and the binary digit 1 to the high level voltage. One example of positive logic would be the assignment of 5 volts as a high logic level, or binary 1, and the assignment of 0 volts as a low logic level, or binary 0, as shown in Table 1-4. The terms **"0"** and **"LOW"** are used interchangeably to indicate a low level voltage, and the terms **"1"** and **"HIGH"** are used interchangeably to indicate a high level voltage, using the positive logic convention.

Negative logic is defined as assigning the binary digit 0 to the high voltage and the binary digit 1 to the low voltage, as shown in Table 1-5.

TABLE 1-4 Positive Logic

Voltage (volts)	Binary	Term
+5	1	HIGH
0	0	LOW

TABLE 1-5 Negative Logic

Voltage (volts)	Binary	Term
+5	0	LOW
0	1	HIGH

Positive and negative logic can also be represented graphically as shown in Figure 1-6.

Positive logic is predominately used in the design of digital circuitry and will be the logic convention used throughout this text. Negative logic is often used in other areas of electrical technology, such as communications. Thus, it is important to determine which logic convention is being used before proceeding to analyze any digital waveforms or circuitry.

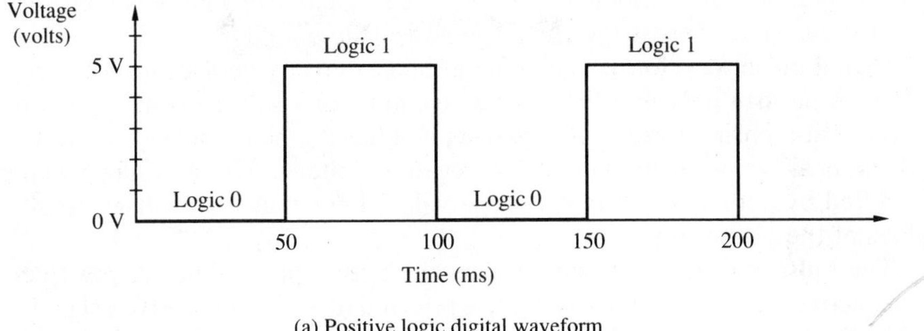

(a) Positive logic digital waveform

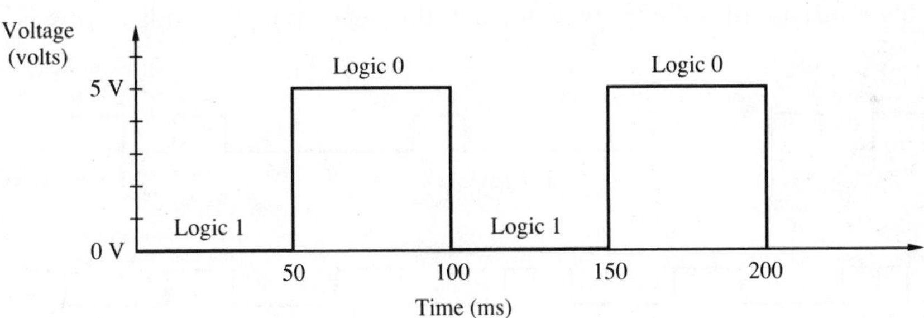

(b) Negative logic digital waveform

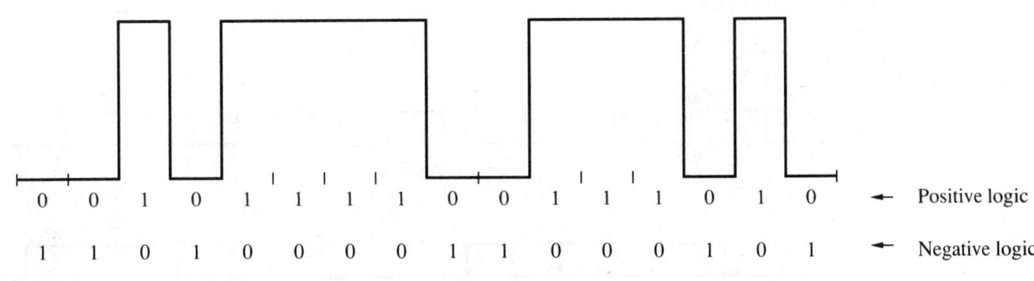

(c) Graphic representation of 16-bits of data

FIGURE 1-6 Digital Waveforms: Positive and Negative Logic

1.6.2 Digital Waveforms

A **digital waveform** is the graphical representation of the logic levels with respect to time. The waveform assumes only two discrete values and is referred to as a **pulse waveform.**

Digital waveforms can be classified as periodic or aperiodic using the same definitions given for analog waveforms. Figure 1-7 shows both periodic and aperiodic digital waveforms.

The period, T, and the frequency, f, can be specified for digital waveforms only if they are periodic functions. The frequency of a pulse waveform can also be referred to as the **pulse repetition rate,** or **PRR.**

Digital pulse waveforms can be identified as positive pulses or negative pulses. A **positive pulse** has the low voltage at 0 volts and the peak value of the pulse at a positive value. A **negative pulse** has the high voltage at 0 volts and the peak value of the pulse at a negative voltage. These voltages can be shifted by adding a constant voltage value, known as a **DC offset,** to all values of the waveform.

The **pulse width,** t_w, is specified as the active pulse time. A positive pulse, active when the voltage is high, is referred to as an **active HIGH signal.** A negative pulse, active when the voltage is low, is referred to as an **active LOW signal.**

Another important definition that is related to pulse width and describes the characteristic of a digital waveform is the **duty cycle.** The duty cycle is

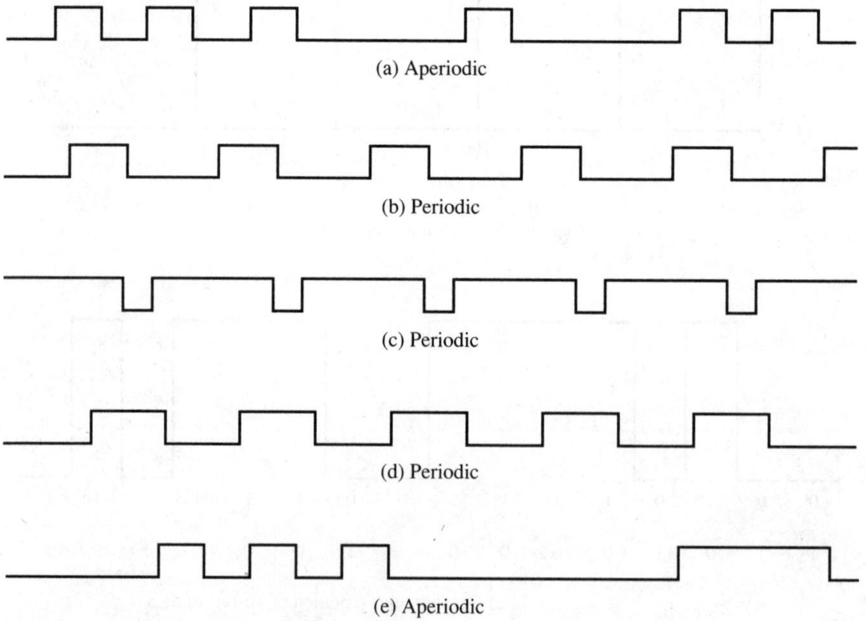

FIGURE 1-7 Digital Waveforms

the percent a waveform is **active** within a period. Equation 1-2 defines the duty cycle of a digital waveform. Waveforms with a 50% duty cycle are defined as **square waves.** A square wave is at the high voltage level 50% of the time and at the low voltage level 50% of the time.

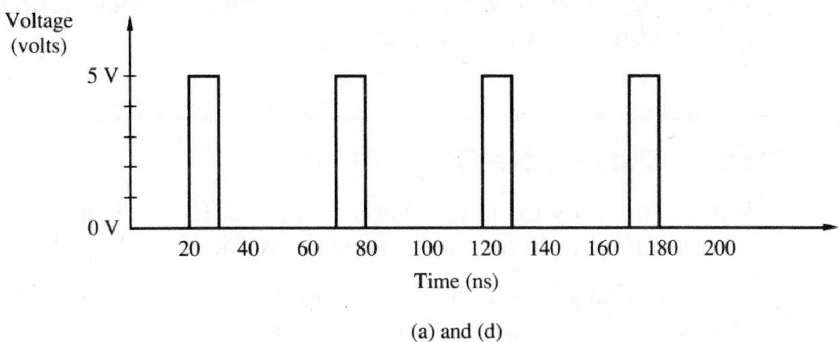

(a) and (d)

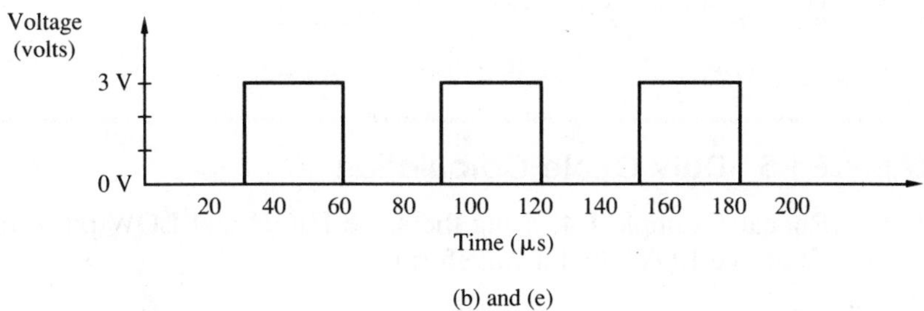

(b) and (e)

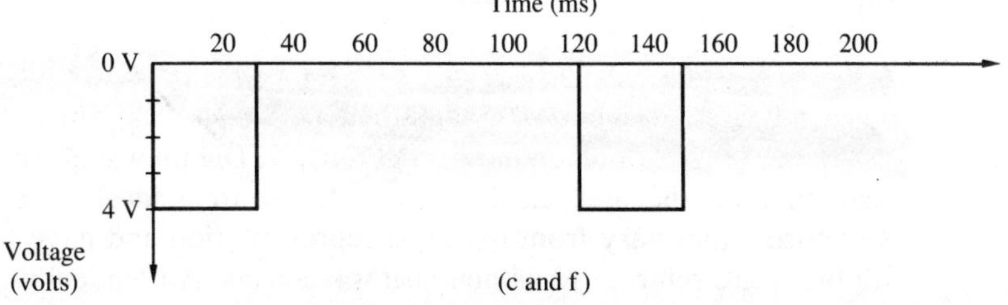

(c and f)

FIGURE 1-8 Periodic Digital Waveforms. (a) 5 V positive pulse: 0 V DC offset, t_w = 10 ns, 20% duty cycle, T = 50 ns, f = PRR = 20 MHz; (b) 3 V positive pulse: 0 V DC offset, T_w = 30 μs, 50% duty cycle, T = 60 μs, f = PRR = 16.67 KHz; (c) 4 V negative pulse: 0 V DC offset, t_w = 30 ms, 25% duty cycle, T = 120 ms, f = PRR = 8.33 Hz; (d) 5 V negative pulse: +5 V DC offset, t_w = 40 ns, 80% duty cycle, T = 50 ns, f = PRR = 20 MHz; (e) 3 V negative pulse: +3 V DC offset, t_w = 30 μs, 50% duty cycle, T = 60 μs, f = PRR = 16.67 KHz; (f) 4 V positive pulse: −4 V DC offset, t_w = 90 ms, 75% duty cycle, T = 120 ms, f = PRR = 8.33 Hz

Eq. 1-2

$$\text{Duty cycle (\%)} = \frac{t_w}{T} \times 100\%$$

$$= \left(\frac{t_{active}}{T}\right) \times 100\%$$

Figure 1-8 shows several digital waveforms and their period, frequency, pulse width, duty cycle, and DC offset.

■ EXAMPLE 1-4 Duty Cycle Calculation

What is the duty cycle of a periodic active HIGH digital waveform that is a logic HIGH for 6 ms, and a logic LOW for 10 ms?

Solution: Using Equation 1-2, we find that the waveform is active for 6 ms, and the period is 6 ms + 10 ms = 16 ms.

$$\text{Duty cycle} = \frac{6}{16} \times 100\% = 37.5\%$$

■

■ EXAMPLE 1-5 Duty Cycle Calculation

Repeat Example 1-4, using the same HIGH and LOW pulse times, but for an active LOW digital waveform.

Solution:

$$\text{Duty cycle} = \frac{10}{16} \times 100 = 62.5\%$$

■

In actual digital waveforms the pulse cannot rise or fall instantaneously. The pulse will rise and fall more gradually in actual circuits. Thus, it is necessary to define the **rise time, t_r,** and the **fall time, t_f.** Digital waveforms shown with instantaneous rise and fall times are referred to as **ideal waveforms.** Digital waveforms that vary from the ideal representation and have finite rise and fall times are referred to as **nonideal waveforms.** A nonideal pulse typical of those found in actual digital circuits is shown in Figure 1-9.

The rise time is defined as the time it takes the pulse to rise from 10% of its peak value to 90% of its peak value. The fall time is defined as the time it takes the pulse to fall from 90% of its peak value to 10% of its peak value. Typical values for digital signal rise and fall times are a few nanoseconds, depending on the logic device or circuitry. The pulse width is defined as the time the pulse amplitude is greater than or equal to 50% of its peak value. Rise time, fall time, and pulse width are all shown graphically in Figure 1-9.

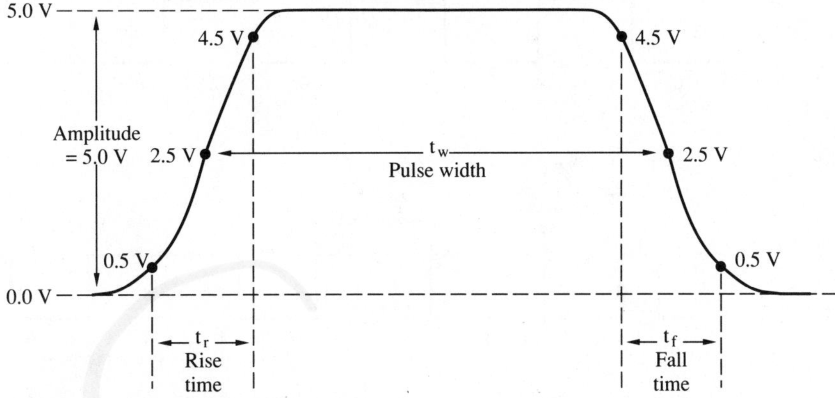

FIGURE 1-9 Nonideal Pulse

EXAMPLE 1-6 Periodic Waveforms

Draw and label two periods of a digital waveform with a 50% duty cycle, a pulse width of 100 ns, a rise time of 10 ns, and a fall time of 20 ns.

Solution:

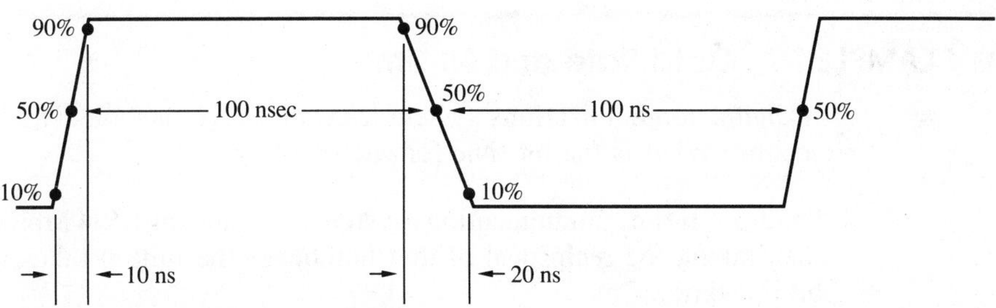

FIGURE 1-10 Example 1-6 Waveform

■

Most of the digital waveforms used in this text will be shown as ideal waveforms. In practice, each waveform will have a rise time and a fall time, but it is not necessary to illustrate this on each waveform drawn. The purpose of most digital waveforms is to show when an input or output is either a LOW or a HIGH over an interval of time.

In Figure 1-11 the relation among digital logic levels, the binary bits 0 and 1, and digital waveforms is illustrated. In Figure 1-11(a) a square wave is shown. Notice that a square wave alternates between 0 and 1. The waveform in Figure 1-11(b) illustrates a binary bit pattern. The minimum time that the waveform is at either a HIGH or a LOW is known as the **bit time,**

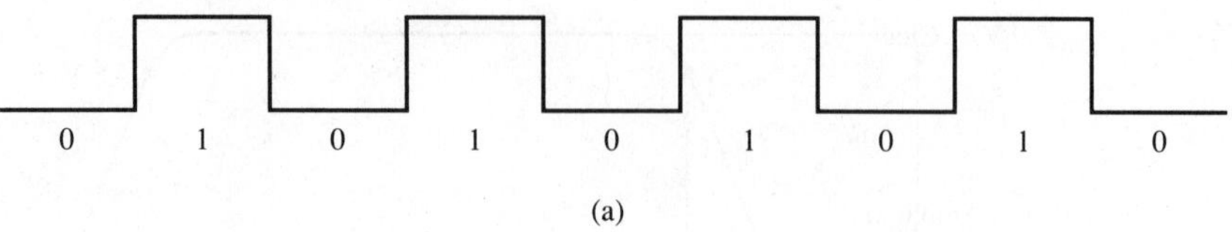

(a)

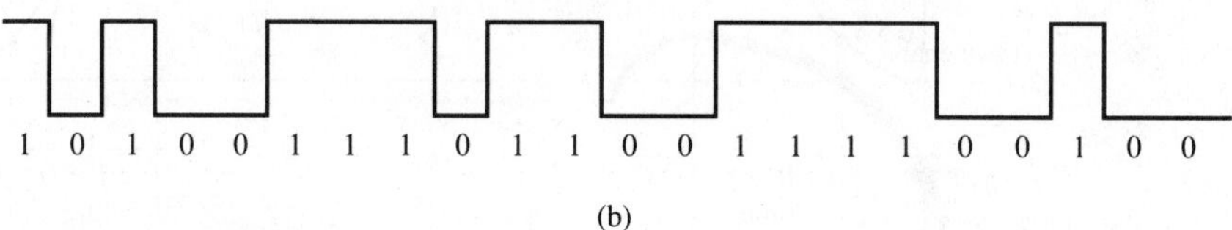

(b)

FIGURE 1-11 Binary and Graphical Representation of Logic Levels

that is, the time it takes to represent 1 bit of data. The **data rate** is a measure of the number of bits of data transmitted per second. If the waveform stays at a logic level for more than 1 bit time, it is useful to repeat the binary bit so that there is a binary bit shown for each bit time.

■ EXAMPLE 1-7 Data Rate and Bit Time

A digital communications system transmits 1,544,000 bits (1.544 Mbits) per second. What is the bit time for each bit?

Solution: If the communications system can transmit 1.544 Mbits per second, then taking the reciprocal of that number is the time it takes to transmit 1 bit (bit time). Thus,

$$\left[\frac{1.544 \times 10^6}{\text{s}}\right]^{-1} = \text{X s/bit}$$

$$\text{X} = 647.67 \times 10^{-9}\ \text{s}$$

$$= 648\ \text{ns}$$

■

Graphs of multiple digital waveforms are known as **timing diagrams.** The timing relationship of one waveform to another is the primary information being supplied with such a diagram, and no DC offset is implied. The waveforms in a timing diagram are often called **timing signals.** Figure 1-12 shows a typical timing diagram. Timing diagrams are supplied with digital ICs, memories, logic, and microprocessors.

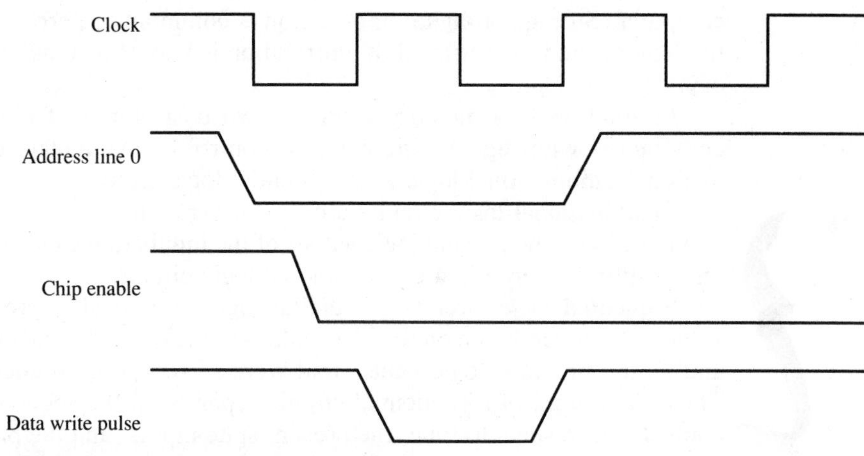

FIGURE 1-12 Digital Timing Diagram

Section Self-Test

1. Can aperiodic digital waveforms have a period and duty cycle? Explain.
2. What is the difference between an ideal waveform and nonideal waveform?
3. How do you represent a 0 and a 1 with positive logic, using 0 and 5 volts?
4. How do you represent a 0 and a 1 with negative logic, using 0 and 5 volts?

ANSWERS (Not necessarily in the right order)

- Logic 0 = 5 volts, logic 1 = 0 volts
- Logic 0 = 0 volts, logic 1 = 5 volts
- No. They have no repetitive pattern and no period, T.
- Nonideal waveforms take into account physical parameters such as rise and fall times that ideal waveforms ignore.

1-7 DIGITAL CIRCUITS

Digital circuits use logic gates as the basic building blocks. Memory elements are digital circuits that can save binary data. Two large classes of digital circuits are combinational and sequential circuits.

One of the basic digital logic elements that can be constructed with the combination of logic gates is a **memory element.** A memory element is a digital circuit that can remember or **store** a logic level of 0 or 1. The stored information can then be **retrieved** and used. In combination, memory elements can store a large amount of information. The printing on this page, for example, was stored and retrieved from memory elements in a personal computer. Storage of digital information is commonly referred to as **writing** to memory, and the retrieval of information is known as **reading** from memory.

In addition to a memory element, two basic types of circuits can be constructed with digital logic gates to control or manipulate digital information: combinational logic and sequential logic circuits.

Combinational logic circuits are digital logic circuits that have outputs that depend on the present logic values of the inputs to the circuit. No digital information is stored in a combinational logic circuit.

Sequential logic circuits are digital logic circuits that produce output values that depend both on the logic values of the present inputs to the circuit and on the previous logic values that were stored in the sequential circuit. Thus, the output of a sequential circuit depends on the sequence of inputs applied with respect to time, the present state inputs, and the previous state inputs.

Section Self-Test

1. What is the difference between retrieval and storage of information?
2. Explain the basic difference between combinational logic and sequential logic.

ANSWERS

- Storage is the process of writing information to a memory element.
- Retrieval is the process of reading information from a memory element. Combinational circuits have no memory and are not time sequence dependent.

1-8 DIGITAL LOGIC FAMILIES

Digital ICs are manufactured with different electrical operating parameters and are categorized by these electrical characteristics into logic families. TTL and CMOS are the two most widely used logic families.

Integrated circuits are manufactured according to specific electrical and mechanical specifications. The ICs are classified into **logic families** and **subfamilies** according to their specific electrical parameters. Each logic family is named according to the type of circuitry used to fabricate the logic gates for that family. The two most widely used logic families are **TTL, transistor-transistor logic,** and **CMOS, complementary metal-oxide semiconductor.** These logic families, along with others, are described in detail in Chapter 15.

1.8.1 Transistor-Transistor Logic Input and Output Voltages

Input and output voltage levels are one of the major parameters of interest for a logic family. TTL, for example, has a defined voltage range for input

TABLE 1-6 TTL Voltage Levels

Signal	Parameter	Defined Voltage Range (volts)
Input LOW	V_{IL}	0.0–0.8
Input HIGH	V_{IH}	2.0–5.0
Output LOW	V_{OL}	0.0–0.4
Output HIGH	V_{OH}	2.4–5.0

LOW voltage, input HIGH voltage, output LOW voltage, and output HIGH voltage. These voltage levels, also known as **signal levels,** are defined in Table 1-6.

Integrated circuits that meet the input and output voltage specifications listed in Table 1-6 are referred to as having **TTL logic levels,** or as being **TTL compatible.** Notice that the input and output HIGH and LOW are defined as ranges, as illustrated in Figure 1-13. Input or output voltages that fall within the shaded region of Figure 1-13 are undefined voltages and cannot be distinguished as a logic LOW or logic HIGH by the IC's circuitry. Thus, the farther the input and output voltages are from the undefined voltage region, and still within the TTL voltage definitions, the easier it is for circuitry to differentiate a logic LOW (0), or a logic HIGH (1).

1.8.2 Logic Family Applications

Digital logic families are selected for use in digital logic designs based on the type of application. Automobiles, for example, are required to work in a harsh environmental application, with temperatures ranging from −30° to over 150°F. Thus, an IC logic family would be selected that could operate over a wide temperature range.

Some other important logic family parameters considered for an application are voltage and current levels, power consumption, circuit speed, noise immunity, and cost. A complete discussion of logic families can be found in Chapter 15.

1.8.3 Logic Family Design

Design is the process by which a circuit needed for a given application is conceived, analyzed, and ultimately constructed. A design can be as simple as a few logic gates, or as complex as several million gates in a multifunction logic system.

Throughout this text fundamental analysis and design techniques will be presented in each chapter. Logic family selection, for example, is one

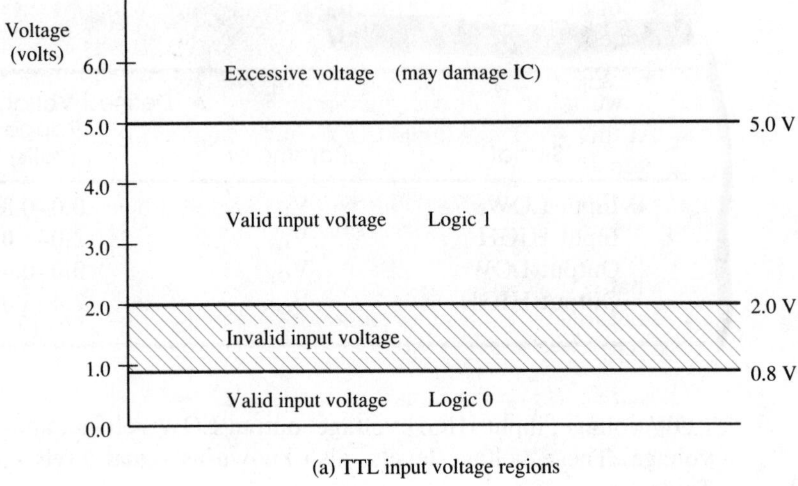

(a) TTL input voltage regions

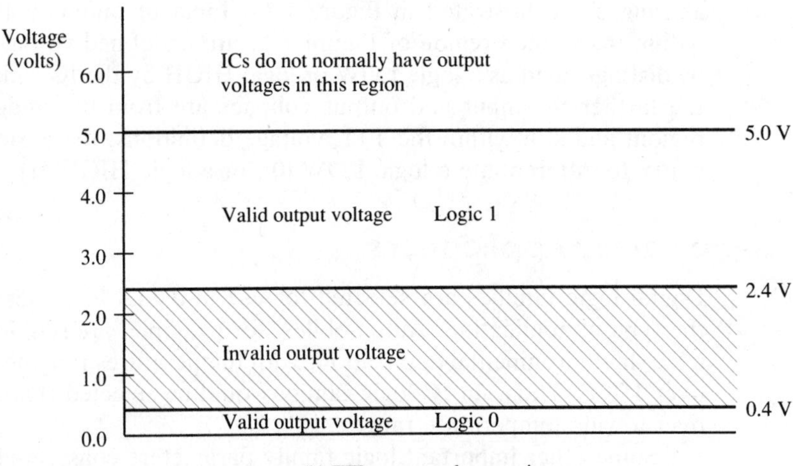

(b) TTL output voltage regions

FIGURE 1-13 TTL Input and Output Voltage Specifications

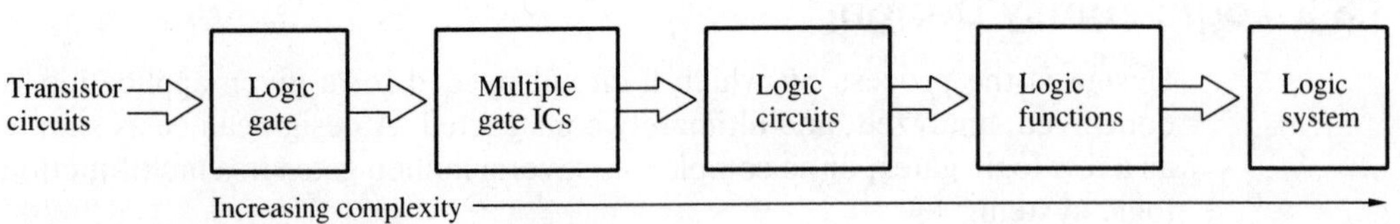

FIGURE 1-14 Digital Circuit Functionality

aspect of digital design. Most digital logic systems are designed using only components of one type of logic family. Thus, you will hear of designs being "TTL" or "CMOS." This indicates that logic ICs from the TTL or CMOS family were used to build the circuitry.

At this point it is important to have an overall concept of digital circuit functionality from the transistor level up to digital logic systems. Figure 1-14 illustrates this progression. Refer back to this figure throughout the course to chart your understanding of digital logic functionality.

Section Self-Test

1. What is a logic family?
2. What are the two major digital logic families?
3. What is meant by the term "TTL compatible"?

- ICs are categorized according to their electrical parameters into logic families.
- TTL and CMOS
- TTL compatible devices have input and output voltages that meet the TTL voltage specifications.

1-9 CIRCUIT ANALYSIS, TESTING, AND TROUBLESHOOTING

It would be ideal if every circuit designed and built operated correctly. Unfortunately, this is often not the case. Circuit analysis, testing, and troubleshooting are used by engineers, technologists, and technicians to correct malfunctioning circuits.

Analysis is the process by which a circuit is theoretically checked for proper operation. The question being examined is, "Does the circuit, when checked by pencil and paper analysis or computer simulation, operate to meet the defined application?" The circuit operation should be predicted and analyzed before any extensive hardware troubleshooting is conducted.

Testing is the laboratory procedure used to verify that a circuit is operating according to its design specifications. If there are eight possible output combinations, all eight should be tested for proper operation.

Troubleshooting is a laboratory technique used to detect, isolate, and correct problems in a circuit. The circuit may be improperly wired; not be powered properly; contain a malfunctioning IC; or, in fact, be improperly designed. Thus, troubleshooting is only efficient when accompanied by an understanding of the application, analysis, and design aspects of the circuit.

1.9.1 Design and Analysis Tools

The basic design tools are a pencil, paper, data books, and a calculator. Personal computers and design software can also be used when available.

Some software includes the ability to draw circuits on a computer screen, known as **schematic capture.** Analysis can be done on a computer with the use of **logic simulation** software.

1.9.2 Testing and Troubleshooting Tools

Testing and troubleshooting are laboratory activities. A textbook can be very effective in describing design and analysis, but laboratory experimentation is necessary to learn good testing and troubleshooting techniques.

A **breadboard** is a type of circuit board that allows for the temporary insertion and removal of ICs and wires to build, test, and troubleshoot digital designs. Often the breadboard will be combined with a power supply, input switches, output lights (LEDs), and a clock (digital waveform generator) into a **prototype board.**

When taking basic measurements on digital circuits, one finds that the electrical analysis centers around determining the logic levels at the inputs and outputs of the circuitry and on comparing the logic levels with the expected levels.

A **logic probe** is an inexpensive hardware tool that has indicator lights and a circuit probe tip for determining logic levels. The probe indicates if a pin or wire is a logic HIGH, LOW, pulsing LOW and HIGH, or some unknown logic level.

A **voltmeter** can be used like a logic probe, but it provides additional information about the actual amount of voltage at a particular point. (Refer to Table 1-6 on TTL input and output voltage levels.)

Digital waveforms can be displayed with the use of an **oscilloscope.** A dual trace oscilloscope can display two digital waveforms and the timing relationship between them, and a four trace scope can display four waveforms.

Logic analyzers are special types of oscilloscopes with multiple trace capabilities specifically designed to display digital timing waveforms. Logic analyzers can display from 8 to 32 digital waveforms simultaneously for digital circuit analysis. Many PCs now have special hardware and software that can be used to display and analyze digital waveforms similar to a logic analyzer.

One special type of logic analyzer specifically designed for use in microprocessor and memory applications is a **signature analyzer.** A signature analyzer can be used to test and troubleshoot microprocessor circuits. It differs from a standard logic analyzer in that it has some automatic test features to read and write data to memories and to perform other types of specialized tests.

Another type of laboratory equipment often used in digital design is the **pulse counter.** A pulse counter can be used to count changes in digital waveforms, known as **pulses,** to determine how many times a circuit pulsed. It can also be used to provide frequency information.

Section Self-Test

1. Explain the difference between analysis and troubleshooting.
2. List three different design and analysis tools.
3. List six different test and troubleshooting tools.

ANSWERS

- Analysis is the process of checking a circuit or design for proper theoretical operation. Troubleshooting is a laboratory procedure to detect and correct malfunctioning circuits.
- Computer simulation, paper calculations, data books
- Oscilloscope, logic probe, voltmeter, signature analyzer, logic analyzer, pulse counter

SUMMARY

ANALYSIS

Digital logic is the representation of information with the use of the binary digits 0 and 1. Since analog information is continuous in nature, it is often difficult to analyze, manipulate, and store. This difficulty can be reduced by representing information digitally.

Digital information can be represented numerically by the binary bits 0 and 1 or graphically as waveforms. Waveforms are characterized as either nonideal or ideal and periodic or aperiodic.

APPLICATION

Digital logic is the basis for computers. Semiconductor integration provides a means by which millions of bits of memory storage and complex circuitry can be placed into a small electronic component, an IC. Integrated circuits are manufactured in many different types of packages and coded according to function and type.

DESIGN

Good design techniques are very important when working with digital circuits. Testing and troubleshooting are laboratory activities used to verify the operation of a circuit or to find and correct problems with a circuit. A variety of tools, including a logic probe, voltmeter, and oscilloscope, can be used in the laboratory for testing and troubleshooting.

In addition, the concepts of digital logic analysis, application, and design are presented in this chapter. These important concepts and the detailed techniques that apply to each will be the focal point for our study of digital logic throughout this text.

PROBLEMS

1-1 Digital and Analog Information

1. List five examples of analog devices, and explain why each is analog.
2. Is a "digital" wristwatch an analog device or digital device? Explain.
3. List and explain five reasons to represent information in digital form.

1-2 Binary Digital Logic

*4. Which of the following decisions could be classified as binary?
   a. deciding to walk or drive to the store
   b. selecting an entrée from a menu
   c. turning a light switch on or off
   d. adjusting light intensity with a dimmer switch

1-3 The History of Digital Logic

5. a. Explain the origins of digital logic.
   b. Draw a time line of the major events that led to the development of digital logic as we know it today.
6. Do some library research and determine the computational capabilities of ENIAC. Compare these capabilities with those of a personal computer commonly available today.

1-4 Digital Circuit Manufacturing

7. Locate the following ICs in a data book. Specify their function and classify them according to their level of integration (SSI, MSI, LSI, VLSI):

7400	7445	74150
7402	7447	74154
7404	7473	74193
7408	7485	74198
7432	7493	74381

*8. Classify each of the following according to their level of integration:
   a. microprocessor
   b. counter IC
   c. adder IC
   d. logic gate
   e. 4 Mbit memory IC

* See Answers to Selected Problems

9. Refer to a TTL data book and identify the following ICs:
   54LS04 7404 74H138 54L00

1-5 Analog Signals

*10. Find the period of a signal with a frequency of:
   (a) 1 KHz (b) 10 KHz (c) 100 KHz (d) 1 MHz

11. Find the frequency of a signal with the following period:
   (a) 5 s (b) 5 ms (c) 5 μs (d) 5 ns (e) 5 ps

*12. A quality stereo system has a frequency response from 20 to 20,000 Hz. What periods do these frequencies correspond to?

1-6 Digital Signals

13. For the digital pulse given below, find the following:
   (a) t_r (b) t_f (c) t_w

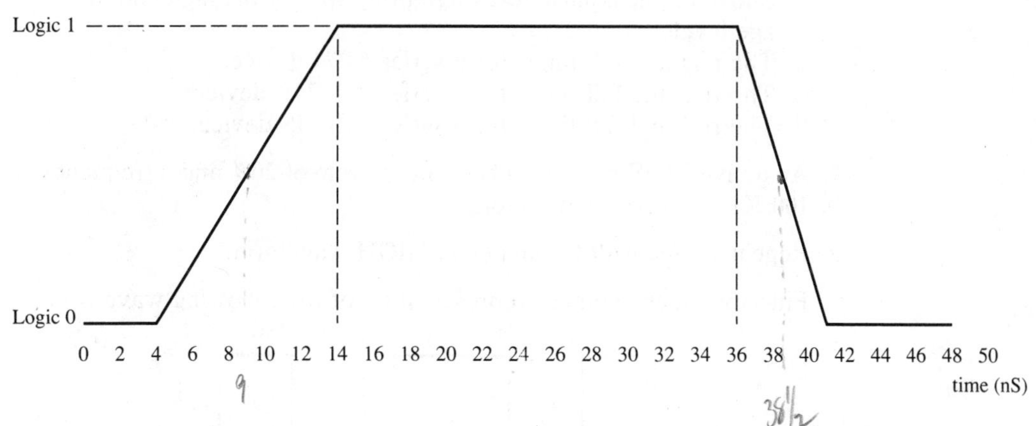

14. Draw a positive logic digital waveform with:
   a. logic HIGH = 3.5 V, logic LOW = 0.0 V, f = 1000 Hz, duty cycle = 50%
   b. logic 1 = 5.0 V, logic 0 = 0.2 V, T = 0.01 ms, duty cycle = 80%

15. Draw the following waveforms:
   a. 4.0 V positive pulse, PRR = 1 MHz, duty cycle = 20%, +1.0 V DC offset
   b. 5.0 V negative pulse, f = 50 KHz, duty cycle = 60%, +5.0 V DC offset

*16. a. Given the following positive logic waveform, write down the equivalent logic values, 0 and 1 for each part of the waveform numbered:

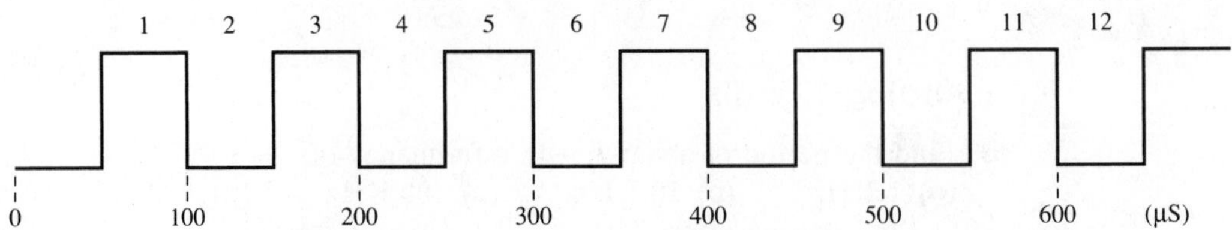

b. What is the period of the waveform?
c. What is the frequency of the waveform?
d. What is the duty cycle of the waveform?
e. What is this waveform commonly called?
f. If the frequency of the waveform doubled, what would be the new period?

17. Construct a digital waveform for the following logic values, using 5.0 V = 1, and 0.0 V = 0:
(a) 001100110011 (b) 0111010 (c) 1111011101

18. Use a TTL data book to look up the following information:
a. Show a typical pulse test waveform. Specify the high and low voltage levels.
b. The rise and fall times for a series 54/74 device.
c. The rise and fall times for a series 54L/74L device.
d. The rise and fall times for a series 54S/74S device.

*19. An active LOW waveform has a duty cycle of 20% and a frequency of 100 KHz. Draw the waveform.

20. Repeat Problem 19 for an active HIGH waveform.

21. Find the binary number representation of the following waveform:

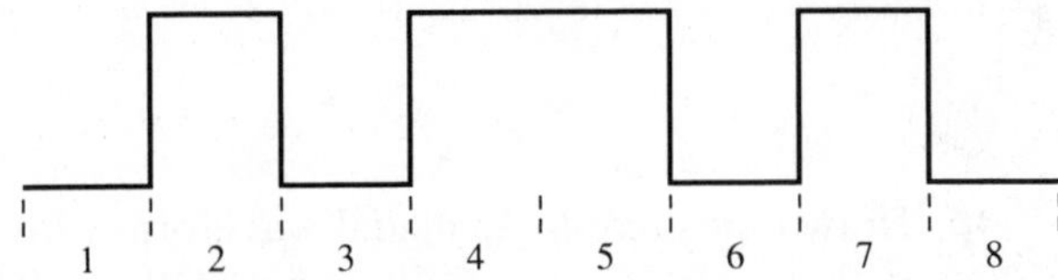

*22. A square wave has a frequency of 25 KHz. What is the pulse width and period of the waveform?

1-7 Digital Circuits

23. List five devices that have memory. What are the characteristics of devices that have memory?

1-8 Digital Logic Families

24. a. Refer to a TTL data book. Look at the functional index and list all the TTL technologies (subfamilies) listed.
    b. Which TTL subfamily has the most ICs available?
    c. Which TTL subfamily has the least ICs available?

25. Refer to a TTL data book, and locate the following device: SN7400.
    a. Is this IC a SSI, MSI, or LSI device?
    b. What are the *minimum* V_{IH} values?
    c. Why isn't a maximum value specified for V_{IH}?
    d. What are the *maximum* V_{IL} values?
    e. Why isn't a minimum value specified for V_{IL}?

1-9 Circuit Analysis, Testing, and Troubleshooting

26. Explain the *advantages* of using a logic probe over using a voltmeter for troubleshooting.

27. Explain the *disadvantages* of using a logic probe over using a voltmeter for troubleshooting.

28. Explain why it is important to analyze a digital circuit thoroughly before proceeding to troubleshoot the circuit if a problem exists.

Chapter 2

Number Systems and Arithmetic

Upon completing and mastering the material in this chapter, you should be able to perform the following functions in preparation for analysis, application, and design of digital electronic circuits:

ANALYSIS

1. Count in binary numbers.
2. Represent binary numbers as voltage waveforms.
3. Convert between decimal and binary numbers.
4. Count in hexadecimal numbers.
5. Convert between hex, binary, and decimal numbers.
6. Represent decimal numbers in 8421 BCD and Excess-3 codes.
7. Add, subtract, multiply, and divide in binary.
8. Represent negative binary numbers in their one's and two's complement form.
9. Add and subtract in BCD.
10. Represent negative decimal numbers in their nine's and ten's complement form.

Binary numbers are used in digital electronics, computer applications, and data communications applications to represent the logic HIGH and logic LOW states of the digital circuits. All information in a digital system is encoded and transmitted as binary numbers. The binary number system, binary codes, and binary arithmetic are studied in this chapter to understand their applications in digital logic circuits. The concepts covered in this chapter will be applied in many logic circuit examples throughout the text.

2-1 BINARY NUMBER SYSTEM

The binary number system is used to represent the voltage levels of a digital system. The binary and decimal number systems are studied to enable students to count in binary numbers, represent binary numbers as digital waveforms, and convert between decimal and binary numbers.

A binary digital waveform is a signal with two discrete or allowed voltage levels. The allowed voltage levels are referred to as a **logic HIGH** or a **logic LOW.**

The **binary number system** is used to represent binary voltage levels and binary waveforms in a numerical form. By using the binary number system, one can easily specify the binary voltage levels with numbers rather than as a waveform.

The binary number system is a **weighted base-2** number system with only two allowable values, 0 and 1. The **binary digits** or **bits** represent the logic LOW as a 0 and the logic HIGH as a 1. By comparison, the **decimal** number system is a **weighted base-10** code consisting of values 0 through 9.

In a weighted code such as the decimal or binary codes the weight of each bit position is the $(\text{base})^n$, where n is 0, 1, 2, 3, and so on, for integer values and -1, -2, -3, and so on, for fractional values. In the decimal number system the weight of each bit is 10^n, thus giving the one's, ten's, hundred's, and so on, positions. In the binary number system the weight of each bit position is 2^n. Figure 2-1 lists the weights of the digits for both the binary and decimal number systems.

When counting in binary, the bit values of 0 and 1 first occupy the **least significant bit (LSB)** position. Since there are no other values that can be used, the count continues by moving to the next **most significant bit (MSB).** To count up, the next MSB is a 1 while the LSB position repeats the pattern of 0 and 1. Before moving to a more significant bit position, one must use all possible combinations of digits in the LSB positions of the number. Table 2-1 shows the sequence of binary digits when counting from 0 through 15.

It can be seen from Table 2-1 that n bits can represent 2^n values ranging from 0 to $2^n - 1$. For example, 4 bits are required to represent 16 numbers,

Binary Bit Weights

... 2^3	2^2	2^1	2^0	.	2^{-1}	2^{-2}	2^{-3} ...
... 8	4	2	1	.	1/2	1/4	1/8 ...

Binary point

Decimal Digit Weights

... 10^3	10^2	10^1	10^0	.	10^{-1}	10^{-2}	10^{-3} ...
... 1000	100	10	1	.	1/10	1/100	1/1000 ...

Decimal point

FIGURE 2-1 Binary and Decimal Digit Weights

the values 0 through 15, in the binary number system. Some basic facts about the binary number system should be kept in mind:

1. n bits can represent 2^n numbers with values ranging from 0 through $2^n - 1$.
2. All even numbers have a 0 in the LSB.

TABLE 2-1 Binary and Decimal Codes

Binary (base 2) Bit Weights				Decimal (base 10) Digit Weights	
2^3	2^2	2^1	2^0	10^1	10^0
			0		0
			1		1
		1	0		2
		1	1		3
	1	0	0		4
	1	0	1		5
	1	1	0		6
	1	1	1		7
1	0	0	0		8
1	0	0	1		9
1	0	1	0	1	0
1	0	1	1	1	1
1	1	0	0	1	2
1	1	0	1	1	3
1	1	1	0	1	4
1	1	1	1	1	5

3. All odd numbers have a 1 in the LSB.
4. Multiplication by 2 is equivalent to inserting a 0 into the LSB position and shifting all the other bits to the left toward the MSB.
5. Division by 2 is equivalent to inserting a 0 in the MSB position and shifting all other bits to the right toward the LSB. Dividing odd numbers by 2 produces a fractional result.

2.1.1 Waveform Representation of Binary Numbers

Digital electronics and computer applications represent binary values as voltage levels in order to process the data. These levels can be graphically represented as digital waveforms. Since the binary number system is only a mathematical representation of the binary digital waveform, it is necessary to be able to convert the numbers to voltage waveforms. Each bit in a binary number is represented by a waveform. Assuming positive logic, a 1 represents the high voltage level and a 0 represents the low voltage level. As an example, a counter that counts up from 0 through 15 requires 4 bits to represent the 16 different values of the count sequence. Four waveforms are needed to represent the numbers.

Figure 2-2 shows the waveforms and the corresponding bit values representing the numbers 0 through 15. Note that each waveform has a 50% duty cycle and that the frequency of each waveform decreases by one half as the bit position becomes more significant.

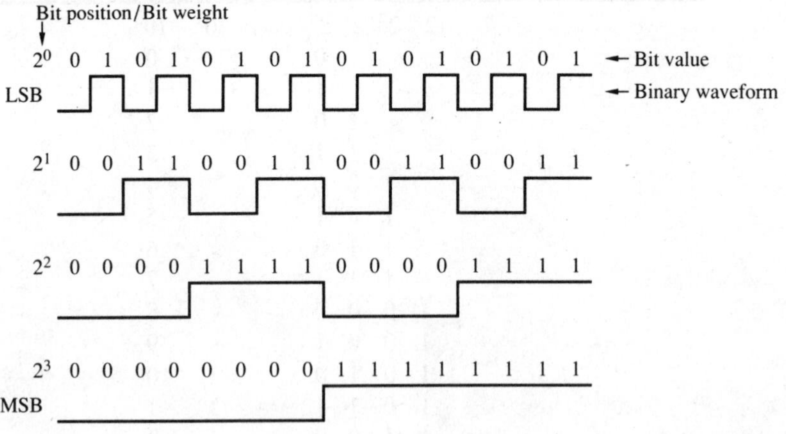

FIGURE 2-2 Binary Numbers and Waveform: Representation of Numbers 0 through 15.

2.1.2 Binary to Decimal Conversion

Binary numbers are converted to decimal numbers by multiplying the value of the binary bit times the weight of the bit position and then summing the results. This technique is referred to as **bit weight expansion.** It is used to convert binary integers to decimal integers and to convert binary fractions to decimal fractions.

■ EXAMPLE 2-1 Binary to Decimal Conversion

Problem: Convert the following binary numbers to decimal numbers.

Solution: Multiply the value of each bit position and sum the results.

Bit Weights

$2^4\ 2^3\ 2^2\ 2^1\ 2^0 \cdot 2^{-1}\ 2^{-2}\ 2^{-3}\ 2^{-4}$

$(1\ 0\ 1\ 1\ 0\ .)_2$

$1 \times 2^4 + 0 \times 2^3 + 1 \times 2^2 + 1 \times 2^1 + 0 \times 2^0 =$
$2^4 + 2^2 + 2^1 = (22)_{10}$ ■

■ EXAMPLE 2-2 Binary to Decimal Conversion

$(0\ 1\ 1\ 0\ 1\ .)_2$

$0 \times 2^4 + 1 \times 2^3 + 1 \times 2^2 + 0 \times 2^1 + 1 \times 2^0 =$
$2^3 + 2^2 + 1 = (13)_{10}$ ■

■ EXAMPLE 2-3 Binary to Decimal Conversion

$(.1\ 0\ 1)_2$

$1 \times 2^{-1} + 0 \times 2^{-2} + 1 \times 2^{-3} = 2^{-1} + 2^{-3} = (.625)_{10}$ ■

■ EXAMPLE 2-4 Binary to Decimal Conversion

$(1\ 0\ 1\ 0\ 0\ .\ 1\ 1)_2$

$1 \times 2^4 + 0 \times 2^3 + 1 \times 2^2 + 0 \times 2^1 + 0 \times 2^0 +$
$1 \times 2^1 + 1 \times 2^{-2} = 2^4 + 2^2 + 2^{-1} + 2^{-2} = (20.75)_{10}$ ■

2.1.3 Decimal to Binary Conversion

Conversion from the decimal number system to the binary number system requires two separate methods: one for integer conversion and one for fractional conversion. Decimal values containing both integer and fractional parts are converted to binary by applying each technique separately to the integer and fractional part of the number. Any value that is an integer in one number system will remain so in another number system, and similarly for fractions.

Decimal (base-10) integers are converted to binary (base-2) integers by a method of **repeated division by 2.** The integer is divided by 2 and the remainder, either a 0 or a 1, is the binary value for the bit position of the LSB. The quotient resulting from the first division is the next value to be divided by 2. The remainder from the second division process becomes the second bit of the binary number, and so on. Successive divisions produce the bit values to occupy positions moving away from the binary point to the MSB. The division process is continued until the quotient is 0 and no further division can take place.

■ EXAMPLE 2-5 Decimal to Binary Integer Conversion

Problem: Convert the following decimal integers to binary integers.

Solution: Divide by 2. The remainder is the binary bit value.

$(53)_{10} = (110101)_2$

DIVISION	REMAINDER	
2 | 53	1	LSB position
2 | 26	0	
2 | 13	1	
2 | 6	0	
2 | 3	1	
2 | 1	1	MSB position
0		

Check: Multiply the resulting binary number by bit weights to verify the answer.

$$(110101)_2 = 2^5 + 2^4 + 2^2 + 2^0$$

$$= 32 + 16 + 4 + 1 = (53)_{10}$$

Results are verified as correct. ■

■ EXAMPLE 2-6 Decimal to Binary Integer Conversion

$(29)_{10} = (11101)_2$

DIVISION	REMAINDER	
2 | 29	1	LSB position
2 | 14	0	
2 | 7	1	
2 | 3	1	
2 | 1	1	MSB position
0		

■

Decimal (base-10) fractions are converted to binary (base-2) fractions by a method of **repeated multiplication by 2.** The fraction is multiplied by 2. The carry-out into the first integer position, either a 0 or a 1, is the bit value for the MSB of the binary fraction. The fractional result from the first multiplication is then multiplied by 2 and its carry-out into the integer portion of the number is the next bit value. Each successive multiplication produces binary bit values to occupy positions moving away from the decimal point to the LSB. The multiplication process continues until the fractional part of the number is 0, or until the desired level of accuracy has been met. The accuracy of the number can be verified by expanding the result by bit weights.

■ EXAMPLE 2-7 Decimal to Binary Fraction Conversion

Problem: Convert the following decimal fractions to binary fractions.

Solution: Multiply the fraction by 2. The carry-out is the bit value.

$(.75)_{10} =$ $(.1\ 1)_2$

MULTIPLICATION	CARRY-OUT	
$.75 \times 2 = 1.50$	1	MSB
$.5 \times 2 = 1.0$	1	LSB

■

■ EXAMPLE 2-8 Decimal to Binary Fraction Conversion

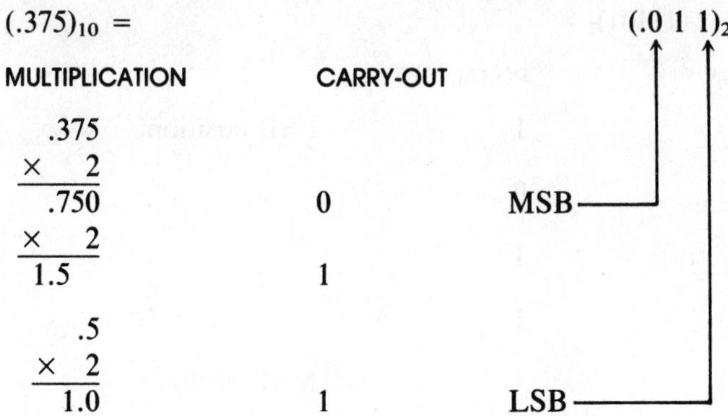

$(.375)_{10}$ =
$(.0\ 1\ 1)_2$
MULTIPLICATION
CARRY-OUT
.375
× 2
.750
0
MSB
× 2
1.5
1
.5
× 2
1.0
1
LSB

■

■ EXAMPLE 2-9 Decimal to Binary Conversion

Problem: Convert the following decimal value to a binary value and determine the accuracy of the resulting number.

Solution: The integer and fraction must be converted separately.

$(50.14)_{10} = (50)_{10} + (.14)_{10}$

Integer:

$(50)_{10} = (110010)_2$

DIVISION	REMAINDER	
2 ⌊ 50	0	LSB position
2 ⌊ 25	1	
2 ⌊ 12	0	
2 ⌊ 6	0	
2 ⌊ 3	1	
2 ⌊ 1	1	MSB position
0		

Fraction:

$(.14)_{10} = (.001000111101)_2$

MULTIPLICATION	CARRY-OUT	
.14 × 2 = .28	0	MSB position
× 2 = .56	0	
× 2 = 1.12	1	
.12 × 2 = .24	0	
× 2 = .48	0	
× 2 = .96	0	
× 2 = 1.92	1	
.92 × 2 = 1.84	1	
.84 × 2 = 1.68	1	
.68 × 2 = 1.36	1	
.36 × 2 = .72	0	
× 2 = 1.44	1	LSB position

Result:

$(50.14)_{10} = (110010.001000111101)_2$

Accuracy Check: Check the accuracy of the resulting binary number by converting it back to its decimal value by expanding the number by bit weights.

$$(110010.001000111101)_2$$

$$= 2^5 + 2^4 + 2^1 + 2^{-3} + 2^{-7} + 2^{-8} + 2^{-9} + 2^{-10} + 2^{-12}$$

$$= (50.1398925)_{10}$$

■

Section Self-Test

1. How many bits are required to represent the number $(2000)_{10}$ in binary?
2. Convert $(1111.11)_2$ to decimal.
3. Convert $(1111.11)_{10}$ to binary.

ANSWERS (Not necessarily in the order of the questions)

- 15.75
- 10001010111.00011100001
- 11

2-2 HEXADECIMAL CODE

The hexadecimal code is a weighted base-16 code that represents four binary bits with one digit. The hexadecimal code is used often in digital electronics, microprocessor, computer, and data communication applications to simplify the representation of binary values.

The hexadecimal or **hex code** has 16 digits—the numbers 0 through 9 and the letters A through F. Four binary bits can be represented by one hexa-

TABLE 2-2 Number System Comparison: Decimal, Binary, and Hexadecimal Numbers

Decimal (base 10)	Binary (base 2)	Hexadecimal (base 16)
0	0000 0000	0 0
1	0000 0001	0 1
2	0000 0010	0 2
3	0000 0011	0 3
4	0000 0100	0 4
5	0000 0101	0 5
6	0000 0110	0 6
7	0000 0111	0 7
8	0000 1000	0 8
9	0000 1001	0 9
10	0000 1010	0 A
11	0000 1011	0 B
12	0000 1100	0 C
13	0000 1101	0 D
14	0000 1110	0 E
15	0000 1111	0 F
16	0001 0000	1 0
17	0001 0001	1 1
18	0001 0010	1 2
19	0001 0011	1 3
20	0001 0100	1 4

$\ldots 16^3 \quad 16^2 \quad 16^1 \quad 16^0 \; . \; 16^{-1} \quad 16^{-2} \quad 16^{-3} \ldots$

FIGURE 2-3 Hexadecimal Digit Weights

decimal digit. Table 2-2 shows the relationship among the decimal, binary, and hexadecimal codes.

The hexadecimal code is a **weighted base-16** code. Each digit has a weight of 16^n. For integers, n is 0, 1, 2, 3, and so on. For fractions, n is −1, −2, −3, and so on. The digit weights of the hexadecimal code are shown in Figure 2-3.

When counting in hex, one must use each character of the number system in the least significant weighted positions before advancing to higher weighted positions. In Table 2-2, notice that after the value $(0F)_{16}$ the next value is $(10)_{16}$, and after $(1F)_{16}$ the next value is $(20)_{16}$.

2.2.1 Hex to Binary Conversion

To convert a hexadecimal number to a binary number, replace each hex digit with the equivalent 4-bit binary code.

■ EXAMPLE 2-10 Hex to Binary Code Conversion

Problem: Convert hex numbers to binary numbers.

Solution: Replace each hex character with the corresponding 4-bit binary code.

$(ABC.D)_{16} =$

$(1010\ 1011\ 1100.1101)_2$ ■

■ EXAMPLE 2-11 Hex to Binary Code Conversion

$(F156)_{16} =$

$(1111\ 0001\ 0101\ 0110)_2$ ■

2.2.2 Binary to Hex Conversion

To convert from binary to hex, write the binary value in groups of 4 bits, beginning at the binary point and moving out. Add leading 0's or trailing 0's, if necessary, to complete the group of 4 bits farthest from the binary point on both the integer and fractional sides of the number. Then replace each group of four binary bits with the corresponding hex character.

■ EXAMPLE 2-12 Binary to Hex Code Conversion

Problem: Convert binary numbers to hex numbers.

Solution: Write the binary number as groups of 4 bits, beginning at the binary point. Add leading 0's to the integer and trailing 0's to the fraction if required to complete the group of 4 bits. Replace each group of 4 bits with the corresponding hex character.

$(1101011.1001111)_2 =$

$(110\ 1011.1001\ 111)_2 =$

$(0110\ 1011.1001\ 1110)_2 =$

$(6B.9E)_{16}$ ■

■ EXAMPLE 2-13 Binary to Hex Code Conversion

$(11110111.010001)_2 =$

$(1111\ 0111.0100\ 01)_2 =$

$(1111\ 0111.0100\ 0100)_2 =$

$(F7.44)_{16}$ ■

2.2.3 Hex to Decimal Conversion

Hex numbers are converted to decimal numbers by expanding the hex number by digit weights in a manner similar to the technique used to convert binary numbers to decimal numbers. To convert from the hexadecimal code to the decimal number system, multiply each hex value by the weight of the digit and sum the results. The value of the hex characters is equal to their decimal value for the characters 1 through 9. The characters A, B, C, D, E, and F have the value 10, 11, 12, 13, 14, and 15, respectively.

■ EXAMPLE 2-14 Hex to Decimal Conversion

Problem: Convert hex numbers to decimal numbers.

Solution: Multiply the value of each hex character by the weight of the digit and sum.

$(156.32)_{16} =$

$1 \times 16^2 + 5 \times 16^1 + 6 \times 16^0 + 3 \times 16^{-1} + 2 \times 16^{-2}$

$= 256 + 80 + 6 + \frac{3}{16} + \frac{2}{256}$

$= (342.1953)_{10}$ ■

■ EXAMPLE 2-15 Hex to Decimal Conversion

$(ABC.D)_{16} =$

$10 \times 16^2 + 11 \times 16^1 + 12 \times 16^0 + 13 \times 16^{-1}$

$= 2560 + 176 + 12 + \frac{13}{16}$

$= (2748.812)_{10}$ ■

2.2.4 Decimal to Hex Conversion

To convert decimal integers to hexadecimal integers, divide the decimal value repeatedly by 16. The remainder is the hex digit, beginning with the least significant digit in the integer. Then divide the quotient of the first division by 16 to obtain the second hex digit. Repeat the division process until the quotient is 0. The final remainder is the most significant hex digit in the integer result. This procedure is similar to the conversion from the decimal number system to the binary number system.

To convert a decimal fraction to a hexadecimal fraction, multiply the decimal fraction repeatedly by 16. The carry-out of the fraction is the hex digit, beginning with the most significant digit in the fraction. The fractional result from the first multiplication is then multiplied by 16 and its carry-out into the integer portion of the number is the next bit value. The process continues until the desired level of accuracy is met. This procedure is similar to the conversion from decimal fractions to binary fractions.

It is also possible to convert decimal numbers to hexadecimal numbers by first converting to the binary number and then converting the binary to hex.

■ EXAMPLE 2-16 Decimal to Hex Integer Conversion

Problem: Convert decimal integers to hex integers

Solution: Divide the decimal integer by 16. The remainder is the hex digit, beginning with the least significant hex digit. Repeat by dividing the quotient by 16 to obtain all the hex digits.

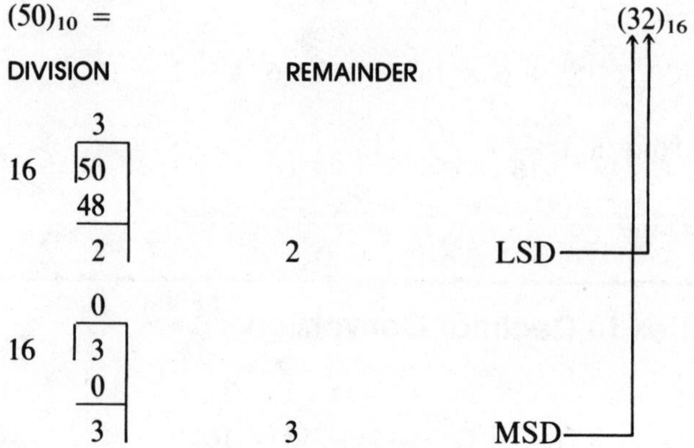

■ **EXAMPLE 2-17 Decimal to Hex Fraction Conversion**

Problem: Convert decimal fractions to hex fractions.

Solution: Multiply the decimal fraction by 16. The carry-out of the fraction is the hex digit, beginning with the most significant hex digit in the fraction.

$(.14)_{10}$ = $(.23D)_{16}$

MULTIPLICATION	CARRY-OUT	
.14 × 16 = 2.24	2	MSD
.24 × 16 = 3.84	3	
.84 × 16 = 13.44	D	LSD

Accuracy Check:

$(.23D7)_{16}$ =

$2 \times 16^{-1} + 3 \times 16^{-2} + 13 \times 16^{-3} + 7 \times 16^{-4}$

$= (.1399993)_{10}$ ■

■ EXAMPLE 2-18 Decimal to Hex Conversion through Binary

Problem: Convert a decimal number, containing an integer and a fraction, to the hex number by first converting to binary.

Solution: Follow the decimal-to-binary conversion procedures. Then convert the binary to hex.

$(50.14)_{10} =$

$(50)_{10} = (1100010)_2$ See Example 2-9

$(.14)_{10} = (.00100111101)_2$ See Example 2-9

Binary Result:

$(50.14)_{10} = (1100010.001000001)_2$

$(11\ 0010.0010\ 0011\ 1101)_2 =$

$(0011\ 0010.0010\ 0011\ 1101)_2 =$

$(32.23D)_{16}$

Hex Result:

$(50.14)_{10} = (32.23D)_{16}$ ■

Section Self-Test

1. How many hex digits are required to represent the number $(5000)_{10}$?
2. What is the maximum decimal value represented by four hex digits?
3. Convert $(1492)_{10}$ to hex.

ANSWERS (Not necessarily in the order of the questions)

• 5D4 • 65,535 • 4

2-3 BINARY CODES

Special binary codes have been designed to represent decimal numbers and alphanumeric characters. These codes are used extensively in digital logic and computer communication applications. The binary codes will be used extensively in digital logic circuit applications in Chapter 5, "Decoders, Encoders, and Code Converters," and in Chapter 6, "Arithmetic Circuits," as well as in general examples throughout the text.

2.3.1 8421 Binary Coded Decimal

The **8421 binary coded decimal** code is used to represent each decimal character, 0 through 9, with a 4-bit binary code. Decimal numbers can be easily converted to a binary code by replacing the decimal character by the appropriate 4-bit binary code. This eliminates the need to perform the division or multiplication processes needed to convert a decimal number to the binary number system. The 8421 code is an alternate way to represent a decimal number in a binary format.

The 8421 BCD code, or **BCD code** as it is also known, has ten valid 4-bit binary codes representing the decimal numbers 0 through 9. There are six invalid 4-bit binary codes that are not part of the BCD code. Table 2-3 lists the 8421 BCD code.

Table 2-4 compares the decimal, BCD, and binary and hex representations of equivalent values. The 8421 BCD code and the binary number system have equivalent representations only for the values 0 through 9.

To convert from a decimal value to the 8421 BCD representation, replace each decimal digit with the equivalent 4-bit BCD value. Both integers and fractions can be converted using this simple technique.

TABLE 2-3 8421 BCD Code

Decimal	8421 BCD
0	0000
1	0001
2	0010
3	0011
4	0100
5	0101
6	0110
7	0111
8	1000
9	1001
Invalid 8421 BCD Codes	
	1010
	1011
	1100
	1101
	1110
	1111

TABLE 2-4 Decimal, BCD, Binary, and Hex Numbers

Decimal	BCD	Binary	Hex
0	0000	00	0
1	0001	01	1
2	0010	10	2
3	0011	11	3
4	0100	100	4
5	0101	101	5
6	0110	110	6
7	0111	111	7
8	1000	1000	8
9	1001	1001	9
10	0001 0000	1010	A
11	0001 0001	1011	B
12	0001 0010	1100	C
13	0001 0011	1101	D
14	0001 0100	1110	E
15	0001 0101	1111	F
16	0001 0110	10000	10
17	0001 0111	10001	11
18	0001 1000	10010	12
19	0001 1001	10011	13
20	0010 0000	10100	14

■ EXAMPLE 2-19 Decimal to BCD Conversion

Problem: Convert decimal numbers to BCD; convert BCD numbers to decimal.

Solution: Replace each decimal character with its 4-bit BCD code. Replace each 4-bit BCD code with its decimal character.

$(1990)_{10}$ =

$(0001\ 1001\ 1001\ 0000)_{BCD}$ ■

■ EXAMPLE 2-20 Decimal to BCD Conversion

$(20.57)_{10}$ =

$(0010\ 0000.0101\ 0111)_{BCD}$ ■

■ EXAMPLE 2-21 BCD to Decimal Conversion

Problem: Convert BCD numbers to decimal.

Solution: Replace each 4-bit BCD code with its decimal character.

$(0010\ 1001\ 0001.0110)_{BCD}$ =

$(291.6)_{10}$ ■

■ EXAMPLE 2-22 BCD to Decimal Conversion

$(1001\ 0010.1000\ 0111)_{BCD}$ =

$(92.87)_{10}$ ■

2.3.2 Excess-3 Binary Coded Decimal

The **Excess-3** code is a binary code that also represents each decimal character with a 4-bit binary code. The Excess-3 code is derived from the 8421 BCD code by adding 3, $(0011)_2$, to each 8421 BCD value.

TABLE 2-5 Excess-3 Code

Decimal	Excess-3
0	0011
1	0100
2	0101
3	0110
4	0111
5	1000
6	1001
7	1010
8	1011
9	1100
Invalid Excess-3 Codes	
	0000
	0001
	0010
	1101
	1110
	1111

TABLE 2-6 Decimal, 8421 BCD, and Excess-3 Codes

Decimal	8421 BCD	Excess-3
0	0000	0011
1	0001	0100
2	0010	0101
3	0011	0110
4	0100	0111
5	0101	1000
6	0110	1001
7	0111	1010
8	1000	1011
9	1001	1100

The Excess-3 code is shown in Table 2-5. Like the 8421 BCD code, the Excess-3 code also has six invalid 4-bit binary numbers that are not included in the code. The 4-bit binary codes that are not part of the Excess-3 code are also shown in Table 2-5.

Decimal numbers can be converted to Excess-3 by forming the 8421 BCD code and then adding $(0011)_2$ to each digit. Table 2-6 shows the relationship among the decimal, 8421 BCD, and Excess-3 codes.

■ EXAMPLE 2-23 Decimal to Excess-3 Conversion

Problem: Convert between Excess-3 and Decimal numbers.

Solution: Replace each decimal digit by its Excess-3 code.

$(1990)_{10}$ =

$(0100\ 1100\ 1100\ 0000)_{x-3}$ ■

■ EXAMPLE 2-24 Decimal to Excess-3 Conversion

Problem: Convert between Excess-3 and Decimal numbers.

Solution: Replace each 4-bit Excess-3 code by its decimal character.

$(20.57)_{10}$ =

$(0101\ 0033\ .\ 1000\ 1010)_{x-3}$ ■

■ EXAMPLE 2-25 Excess-3 to Decimal Conversion

Problem: Convert between Excess-3 and Decimal numbers.

Solution: Replace each 4-bit Excess-3 code by its decimal character.
$(0101\ 1100\ 0100\ .\ 1001)_{X-3}$

$(291.6)_{10}$ ■

A special feature of the Excess-3 code is its **self-complementing** property when forming the **nine's complement** of decimal numbers. The nine's complement is a representation of negative decimal numbers. The nine's complement can be found for each decimal digit by subtracting the value of the digit from 9. With the Excess-3 code, the nine's complement can be formed simply by inverting the value of each bit. The ability to form the nine's complement easily is beneficial when performing arithmetic operations directly on Excess-3 values. The Excess-3 code and the self-complementing feature will be discussed further in Section 2.5.3.

2.3.3 Gray Code

The **Gray code** is a special binary code that allows only a single bit to change from one consecutive number to another. See Table 2-7.

TABLE 2-7 Decimal, Gray Code, and Binary Values

Decimal	Gray	Binary
0	0000	0
1	0001	1
2	0011	10
3	0010	11
4	0110	100
5	0111	101
6	0101	110
7	0100	111
8	1100	1000
9	1101	1001
10	1111	1010
11	1110	1011
12	1010	1100
13	1011	1101
14	1001	1110
15	1000	1111
16	11000	10000

The purpose of the Gray code is to minimize encoding errors by allowing only 1 bit value to change from one number to the next. The Gray code can minimize glitches, or unwanted voltage level spikes, caused when more than one bit in a code does not change at precisely the same instant. For instance, in the binary number system the change from $(0111)_2$ to $(1001)_2$ requires that 3 bits change simultaneously. In the Gray code the equivalent numbers are $(0100)_{Gray}$ and $(1100)_{Gray}$, and only the MSB changes when advancing from one number to the next.

2.3.4 Alphanumeric Binary Codes

Several **alphanumeric binary codes** exist for the purpose of transmitting written information via a computer. Each key on a keyboard must have a binary code assigned to it so that the computer can identify each character. These include all letters, numbers, punctuation, function control characters, and page format characters, such as the space, backspace, and line feed.

The two most common alphanumeric codes are the ASCII and EBCDIC codes. ASCII (American Standard Code for Information Interchange) is a 7-bit binary code capable of representing 2^7 or 128 characters. The ASCII code is specified in Table 2-8. Note that the code is specified as a hexadecimal value. This can be converted to binary if necessary.

TABLE 2-8 ASCII Code

HEX	Character	HEX	Character	HEX	Character
0	NUL	12	DC2	24	$
1	SOH	13	DC3	25	%
2	STX	14	DC4	26	&
3	ETX	15	NAK	27	'
4	EOT	16	SYN	28	(
5	ENQ	17	ETB	29	)
6	ACK	18	CAN	2A	*
7	BEL	19	EM	2B	+
8	BS	1A	SUB	2C	,
9	HT	1B	ESC	2D	—
A	LF	1C	FS	2E	.
B	VT	1D	GS	2F	/
C	FF	1E	RS	30	0
D	CR	1F	US	31	1
E	S0	20	SP	32	2
F	S1	21	!	33	3
10	DLE	22	"	34	4
11	DC1	23	#	35	5

TABLE 2-8 ***(continued)***

HEX	Character	HEX	Character	HEX	Character
36	6	54	T	72	r
37	7	55	U	73	s
38	8	56	V	74	t
39	9	57	W	75	u
3A	:	58	X	76	v
3B	;	59	Y	77	w
3C	<	5A	Z	78	x
3D	=	5B	[	79	y
3E	>	5C	‘	7A	z
3F	?	5D	]	7B	{
40	∂	5E	^	7C	|
41	A	5F	-	7D	}
42	B	60		7E	~
43	C	61	a	7F	DEL
44	D	62	b		
45	E	63	c		
46	F	64	d		
47	G	65	e		
48	H	66	f		
49	I	67	g		
4A	J	68	h		
4B	K	69	i		
4C	L	6A	j		
4D	M	6B	k		
4E	N	6C	l		
4F	O	6D	m		
50	P	6E	n		
51	Q	6F	o		
52	R	70	p		
53	S	71	q		

Although there are only 7 bits in the ASCII code, an eighth **parity bit** is often added as the most significant bit. This parity bit is used for detecting errors during transmission. Additional information about parity is found in Chapter 5, "Decoders, Encoders, and Code Converters."

EBCDIC (Extended Binary Coded Decimal Information Code) is an 8-bit binary code capable of representing 2^8 or 256 characters. The EBCDIC is specified in Table 2-9 in a hexadecimal format. EBCDIC is not transmitted with a parity bit.

TABLE 2-9 EBCDIC Code

HEX	Character	HEX	Character	HEX	Character
00	NUL	29		32	SYN
01	SOH	2A	SM	33	
02	STX	2B		34	PN
03	ETX	2C		35	RS
04	PF	2D	ENQ	36	UC
05	PT	2E	ACK	37	EOT
06	LC	2F	BEL	38	
07	DEL	90		39	
08	VT	91	j	3A	
09	RLF	92	k	3B	NAK
0A	SMM	93	l	3C	DC4
0B		94	m	3D	NL
0C	FF	95	n	3E	
0D	CR	96	o	3F	SUB
0E	SO	97	p	40	SP
0F	S1	98	q	41	
10	DLE	99	r	42	
11	DC1	9A		43	
12	DC2	9B		44	
13	DC3	9C		45	
14	RES	9D		46	
15		9E		47	
16	BS	9F		48	
17	L	A0		49	
18	CAN	A1	~	4A	¢
19	EM	A2	s	4B	.
1A	CC	A3	t	4C	<
1B		A4	u	4D	(
1C	FS	A5	v	4E	+
1D	GS	A6	w	4F	|
1E		A7	x	50	&
1F	US	A8	y	51	
20	DS	A9	z	52	
21	SOS	AA		53	
22	FS	AB		54	
23		AC		55	
24	BYP	AD		56	
25	LF	AE		57	
26	ETB	AF		58	
27	ESC	30		59	
28		31		5A	!

TABLE 2-9 (*continued*)

HEX	Character	HEX	Character	HEX	Character
5B	$	62		89	i
5C	*	63		8A	
5D	)	64		8B	
5E	;	65		8C	
5F	¬	66		8D	
C0	{	67		8E	
C1	A	68		8F	
C2	B	69		E0	\
C3	C	6A		E1	
C4	D	6B	,	E2	S
C5	E	6C	%	E3	T
C6	F	6D		E4	U
C7	G	6E	>	E5	V
C8	H	6F	?	E6	W
C9	I	70		E7	X
CA		71		E8	Y
CB		72		E9	Z
CC		73		EA	
CD		74		EB	
CE		75		EC	
CF		76		ED	
D0	}	77		EE	
D1	J	78		EF	
D2	K	79	▲	F0	0
D3	L	7A	:	F1	1
D4	M	7B	#	F2	2
D5	N	7C	∂	F3	3
D6	O	7D	▲	F4	4
D7	P	7E	=	F5	5
D8	Q	7F	’’	F6	6
D9	R	80		F7	7
DA		81	a	F8	8
DB		82	b	F9	9
DC		83	c	FA	
DD		84	d	FB	
DE		85	e	FC	
DF		86	f	FD	
60	-	87	g	FE	
61	/	88	h	FF	

■ EXAMPLE 2-26 ASCII and EBCDIC Coding of Alphanumeric Information

Problem: Encode the following line in ASCII and then in EBCDIC.

Solution: Refer to Tables 2-8 and 2-9 for the ASCII and EBCDIC code for each character.
"The weekend is here at last!"

ASCII in hex code:

22 54 68 65 20 77 65 65 6B 65 6E 64 20
" T h e space w e e k e n d space

69 73 20 68 65 72 65 20 62 74 20
i s space h e r e space a t space

6C 61 73 74 21 22
l a s t ! "

EBCDIC in hex code:

7F E3 88 85 40 A6 85 85 92 85 95 84 40
" T h e space w e e k e n d space

89 A2 40 88 85 99 85 40 81 A3 40
i s space h e r e space a t space

93 81 A2 A3 5A 7F
l a s t ! " ■

Section Self-Test

1. Convert $(308.56)_{10}$ to 8421 BCD.
2. Convert $(450.34)_{10}$ to Excess-3.
3. When counting up in binary from 0 to 7, which number changes will have glitches if all the bits do not change simultaneously?

ANSWERS (Not necessarily in the same order)

- 1 to 2, 3 to 4, 5 to 6
- 0011 0000 1000.0101 0110
- 0111 1000 0011.0110 0111

2-4 BINARY ARITHMETIC

The arithmetic processes of addition, subtraction, multiplication, and division can be performed on binary numbers just as they are performed on decimal numbers. Specific rules govern the procedures for each arithmetic process, but many are very similar to the rules followed in decimal arithmetic calculations.

The arithmetic processes covered in the following sections begin with the discussion of addition, subtraction, multiplication, and division for unsigned numbers. Following that, the signed-number arithmetic processes using complements are presented. Finally, special arithmetic processes using the hexadecimal and 8421 BCD codes are covered. The arithmetic concepts covered in this chapter will be used extensively in Chapter 6 in the application and design of digital logic arithmetic circuits.

2.4.1 Binary Addition

Addition is the most important binary arithmetic process because it can be used to perform all other arithmetic operations of subtraction, multiplication, and division. For instance, subtraction can be performed by changing the sign of a number and adding. Multiplication can be performed by repeated additions by the same value. Division can be performed by repeated subtraction by the same value, but the subtraction can be performed as an addition. Thus, it is important to understand binary addition processes thoroughly.

Binary addition follows four basic rules. The rules are shown in Figure 2-4.

In binary arithmetic, when two 1's are added, the result is a sum plus a carry-out to the next bit location. This is equivalent to the binary count sequence progressing from $(1)_2$ to $(10)_2$ or from $(11)_2$ to $(100)_2$.

The addition of two 1's in the same bit position results in a 0 in that bit position, plus a carry-out of 1 to the next MSB position. The addition of three 1's results in a sum value of 1 plus a carry-out of 1.

Several examples follow to illustrate the rules for binary addition.

$$\begin{array}{r} 0 \\ +0 \\ \hline 0 \end{array} \qquad \begin{array}{r} 0 \\ +1 \\ \hline 1 \end{array} \qquad \begin{array}{r} 1 \\ +0 \\ \hline 1 \end{array} \qquad \begin{array}{r} 1 \\ +1 \\ \hline \mathbf{1}\ \ 0 \end{array} \qquad \begin{array}{r} 1 \\ 1 \\ +1 \\ \hline \mathbf{1}\ \ 1 \end{array}$$

Sum   Sum   Sum   **Carry out** + Sum   **Carry out** + Sum

FIGURE 2-4 Rules for Binary Addition

■ EXAMPLE 2-27 Binary Addition

Problem: Add the following binary numbers.

Solution: Follow the rules of binary addition. Recall that adding two 1's generates a 0 plus a carry-out, and adding three 1's generates a 1 plus a carry-out.

```
                     1     Carry-out
  1001010      1001010
+   10011    +   10011
-------      -------
               1011101
```

■

■ EXAMPLE 2-28 Binary Addition

```
              111111     Carry-out
  1111111    1111111
+ 1110101  + 1110101
-------    --------
            11110100
```

■

■ EXAMPLE 2-29 Binary Addition

```
             1           Carry-out
  1000000    1000000
+ 1100011  + 1100011
-------    --------
            10100011
```

■

2.4.2 Unsigned Binary Subtraction

Binary subtraction on unsigned numbers can be performed by following four basic rules. The rules for binary subtraction are shown in Figure 2-5.

Whenever the value of the number being subtracted (the subtrahend) is less than the value of the number it is being subtracted from (the minuend) no borrow will occur. If the subtrahend is greater than the minuend, a borrow-in is required in order to perform the subtraction.

In cases when a borrow is needed and the next most significant bit in the minuend is a 0, the borrow must be taken from the next bit that is a 1, as shown in Figure 2-5.

				Borrow in
Values to be subtracted:	0	1	1	1 0
	− 0	− 0	− 1	− 1
Result:	0	1	0	1

```
                    1  Borrow in
   1 0 0          1̸ 0̸ 0
 −     1        −     1
 ---------      ---------
                    1 1
```

FIGURE 2-5 Rules for Binary Subtraction

EXAMPLE 2-30 Binary Subtraction

Problem: Subtract the following binary numbers.

Solution: Follow the binary subtraction rules using a borrow from bit positions to subtract a 1 from a 0.

```
                0 1         1      Borrow
  10110010      1̸ 0 1 1 0 0 1̸ 0
 − 1010001    −   1 0 1 0 0 0 1
 ---------    -----------------
                  1 1 0 0 0 0 1
```

EXAMPLE 2-31 Binary Subtraction

```
                  0 1 1 1          Borrow
  11100000    1 1 1̸ 0̸ 0̸ 0 0 0
 −   11100    −       1 1 1 0 0
 ---------    -----------------
              1 1 0 0 0 1 0 0
```

EXAMPLE 2-32 Binary Subtraction

```
                0 1 1 1 1 1 1      Borrow
  1000000       1̸ 0̸ 0̸ 0̸ 0̸ 0̸ 0
 − 101011     −   1 0 1 0 1 1
 ---------    -----------------
                    1 0 1 0 1
```

Subtraction is often performed by changing the sign of the number and adding, or, in other words, adding the complement. Signed binary subtraction using the complement method is covered in detail in Section 2.4.7.

2.4.3 Binary Multiplication

Binary multiplication follows the same rules as decimal multiplication. Figure 2-6 lists the four rules for binary multiplication.

$0 \times 0 = 0$	$0 \times 1 = 0$
$1 \times 0 = 0$	$1 \times 1 = 1$

FIGURE 2-6 Binary Multiplication Rules

■ EXAMPLE 2-33 Binary Multiplication

Problem: Multiply the following binary numbers.

Solution: Follow the binary multiplication rules.

```
 100011
×    10
1000110
```

■

■ EXAMPLE 2-34 Binary Multiplication

```
  101010
×     11
  101010
+101010
 1111110
```

■

■ EXAMPLE 2-35 Binary Multiplication

```
   100100
 ×   1011
   100100
  100100
+ 100100
110001100
```

■

Multiplication is performed in microprocessors by a series of additions. For instance, Example 2-34 would be computed as shown in Example 2-36.

■ EXAMPLE 2-36 Binary Multiplication by Addition

Problem: Multiply the binary numbers through addition.

Solution: Follow the binary rules for addition.

EQUIVALENT OPERATIONS:

```
  101010        101010
×     11      + 101010
  ------      + 101010
  101010      --------
+101010        1111110
--------
 1111110
```

■

2.4.4 Binary Division

The rules for binary division are the same as those for decimal division.

■ EXAMPLE 2-37 Binary Division

Problem: Divide the binary numbers.

Solution: Follow the rules of binary division.

```
                  11
110 ÷ 10 = 10/ 110
                11
               ---
                 10
                 10
                ---
                 00
```

■

■ EXAMPLE 2-38 Binary Division

```
                     100
10100 ÷ 101 = 101/ 10100
                   101
                   ---
                     00
```

■

■ EXAMPLE 2-39 Binary Division

```
                    100.1
1001 ÷ 10 = 10/ 1001.0
                 10
                 0 1 0
                   1 0
                   0 0
```

■

Division operations performed by a microprocessor are accomplished by a series of subtractions. These subtractions are computed by using a series of complement additions, as will be seen in Section 2.4.7. Therefore, all arithmetic processes can be performed by addition.

2.4.5 Signed Binary Numbers

A binary number can be represented as either a positive or negative value. Several standard notations exist to specify the sign of binary numbers in arithmetic processes. The common representation of signed binary numbers is either in the form of sign-and-magnitude, or in the complement form, either one's complement or two's complement.

Sign-and-magnitude (SAM) representation of a binary number requires that a **sign bit** be added as the MSB. This bit position is used only to represent the sign of the number. A 0 signifies a positive number, whereas a 1 signifies a negative number. The remaining bits are used to represent the **magnitude** of the number. Only the sign bit changes to distinguish a positive number from a negative number.

■ EXAMPLE 2-40 Sign-and-Magnitude Notation

Problem: Determine the binary sign-and-magnitude notation for positive and negative numbers.

Solution: The MSB is the sign bit; the remaining bits are the magnitude. Positive numbers have a sign bit of 0. Negative numbers have a sign bit of 1. The magnitude is in the true form.

$(5)_{10} = (101)_2$ SAM: $+5 = 0101$

$-5 = 1101$ ■

■ EXAMPLE 2-41 Sign-and-Magnitude Notation

$(12)_{10} = (1100)_2$ SAM: $+12 = 01100$

$-12 = 11100$ ■

■ EXAMPLE 2-42 Sign-and-Magnitude Notation

$(31)_{10} = (11111)_2$ SAM: $+31 = 011111$

$-31 = 111111$ ■

A **folded binary code** is one that uses the SAM notation, and therefore is said to be **symmetrical** around 0. Table 2-10 shows an example of a folded binary code. Folded binary codes are used in communications encoding.

2.4.6 One's and Two's Complement Notation

Complement notation refers to **complementing, or changing the sign** of the number to be subtracted. One's and two's complement notation is often used in microprocessor arithmetic systems. With subtraction using complement notation, the minus sign is eliminated by changing the sign of the number and adding. This enables subtraction processes to be performed according to the rules of binary addition. Two forms of the complement notation exist: one's complement and two's complement.

One's complement is formed by subtracting each bit from 1. An equiv-

TABLE 2-10 Folded Binary Code—SAM Notation

Decimal	Binary
+5	0101
+4	0100
+3	0011
+2	0010
+1	0001
+0	0000
−0	1000
−1	1001
−2	1010
−3	1011
−4	1100
−5	1101

TABLE 2-11 Forming the One's and Two's Complement

One's Complement	Two's Complement
Invert each bit value.	Add 1 to the one's complement. Shortcut method: 1. Begin at the LSB position, and move toward the MSB to the first 1. 2. Keep all bit values the same up to and including the first 1. 3. Invert all remaining bit values.

alent way to form the one's complement is to invert each bit; change all 1's to 0's and all 0's tc 1's. **Two's complement** is formed by forming the one's complement and then adding 1.

In the complement notation, positive numbers have a sign bit of 0 and are expressed in their true form. Negative numbers have a sign bit of 1 and are expressed in their complement form. Table 2-11 summarizes the steps to form the one's complement and two's complement.

A shortcut method to form the two's complement is also included in Table 2-11. It is as follows: Examine the bits of the number, beginning with the LSB and moving toward the MSB. Do not change any bits up to and including the first 1. After the first 1, invert all bits in the higher weighted positions.

■ EXAMPLE 2-43 One's Complement Notation

Problem: Determine the 8-bit one's complement notation of the signed numbers and compare it to the SAM notation.

Solution: Positive numbers remain in their true form with a sign bit of 0. Negative numbers are in the one's complement with a sign bit of 1.

$(5)_{10} = (101)_2$

One's complement (8-bit form):

$+5 = 00000101$
$-5 = 11111010$

SAM (8-bit form):

$+5 = 0000101$

$-5 = 1000101$ ■

■ EXAMPLE 2-44 One's Complement Notation

$(12)_{10} = (1100)_2$

One's complement (8-bit form):

$+12 = 00001100$

$-12 = 11110011$

SAM (8-bit form):

$+12 = 00001100$

$-12 = 10001100$ ■

■ EXAMPLE 2-45 One's Complement Notation

$(31)_{10} = (11111)_2$

One's complement (8-bit form):

$+31 = 00011111$

$-31 = 11100000$

SAM (8-bit form):

$+31 = 00011111$

$-31 = 10011111$ ■

■ EXAMPLE 2-46 Two's Complement Notation

Problem: Determine the 8-bit two's complement notation of the signed numbers and compare it to the one's complement and SAM notation.

Solution: Positive numbers remain in their true form with a sign bit of 0. Negative numbers are in the two's complement with a sign bit of 1.

$(5)_{10} = (101)_2$

Two's complement (8-bit form):

$+5 = 00000101$

$-5 = 11111011$

One's complement (8-bit form):

+5 = 00000101

−5 = 11111010

SAM (8-bit form):

+5 = 00000101

−5 = 10000101 ■

■ EXAMPLE 2-47 Two's Complement Notation

$(12)_{10} = (1100)_2$

Two's complement (8-bit form):

+12 = 00001100

−12 = 11110100

One's complement (8-bit form):

+12 = 00001100

−12 = 11110011

SAM (8-bit form):

+12 = 00001100

−12 = 10001100 ■

■ EXAMPLE 2-48 Two's Complement Notation

$(31)_{10} = (11111)_2$

Two's complement (8-bit form):

+31 = 00011111

−31 = 11100001

One's complement (8-bit form):

+31 = 00011111

−31 = 11100000

SAM (8-bit form):

+31 = 00011111

−31 = 10011111 ■

2.4.7 Signed Binary Arithmetic

All binary arithmetic operations can be performed as addition processes. Complement notation is used to represent negative numbers. Positive numbers remain in their true form. Either the one's or two's complement form may be used.

Subtraction operations are performed through complement addition. The subtraction is changed to addition by changing the sign of the number to be subtracted. This is equivalent to forming the complement of the number to be subtracted, also known as the subtrahend.

Microprocessor and digital systems perform addition and subtraction in one's or two's complement arithmetic. The rules for one's complement and two's complement subtraction are outlined in Table 2-12. Either complement can be used in the binary arithmetic operation so long as it is followed throughout the computation.

The procedures for sign-and-magnitude notation require that negative numbers be converted to their complement. Then the procedures can be followed for complement arithmetic. Negative results would be in their complement format, and they must be converted back to sign-and-magnitude notation.

A condition that can occur with signed-number arithmetic is **overflow,** when the sign bit of the result is incorrect because the magnitude of the result "overflowed" into the sign bit position of the final number. An over-

TABLE 2-12 One's and Two's Complement Subtraction

One's Complement Method	Two's Complement Method
1. Eliminate the subtraction by forming the **one's complement of the subtrahend.**	1. Eliminate the subtraction by forming the **two's complement of the subtrahend.**
2. **Add** the values.	2. **Add** the values.
3. If a carry-out of the MSB occurs, **perform an "end-around carry"** by adding this value to the LSB.	3. If a carry-out of the MSB occurs, **drop the carry-out.**
4. Check the sign bit for **overflow,** which occurs if when **adding two numbers of the same sign, the result is the opposite sign.**	4. Check the sign bit for **overflow,** which occurs if when **adding two numbers of the same sign, the result is the opposite sign.**
5. Positive results are in their true form. Negative results are in their **one's complement** form.	5. Positive results are in their true form. Negative results are in their **two's complement** form.

flow condition occurs when the magnitude of the result requires more bit positions than were allowed in the particular format being used. This can result only when two numbers of the same sign are being added: two positive numbers or two negative numbers.

Overflow is a critical condition that must be monitored in any digital or microprocessor system performing arithmetic operations. In digital systems arithmetic circuits store the results of each operation in registers of a fixed capacity or bit length. If a result requires more capacity than the register has available, it **overflows** the register. The value in the register is not correct, and the resulting MSB stored in the register will not be the correct sign bit for the computation.

Overflow can be detected if two positive numbers being added produce a result with a negative sign bit or if two negative numbers being added produce a result with a positive sign bit.

To eliminate the overflow condition, one must use larger registers so that additional bits can be allocated to the magnitude position of the number. This can be done in the hand calculations of binary arithmetic operations by adding leading 0's to positive numbers and by adding leading 1's to negative numbers to increase the number of bits in the representation of the number.

When using the complement notation, one commonly understands that negative numbers are specified in their complement notation. The same complement must be used throughout the entire computation.

EXAMPLE 2-49 One's Complement Subtraction

Problem: Perform the signed binary addition and subtraction using the one's complement rules. All negative numbers are expressed in their one's complement form. All positive numbers are expressed in their true form.

Solution: Complement the subtrahend only to perform the subtraction operation following the rules of complement addition. Do not complement any negative numbers; only complement the number to be subtracted. Add the numbers. If a carry-out occurs, add it to obtain the final result. Check the result for an overflow condition.

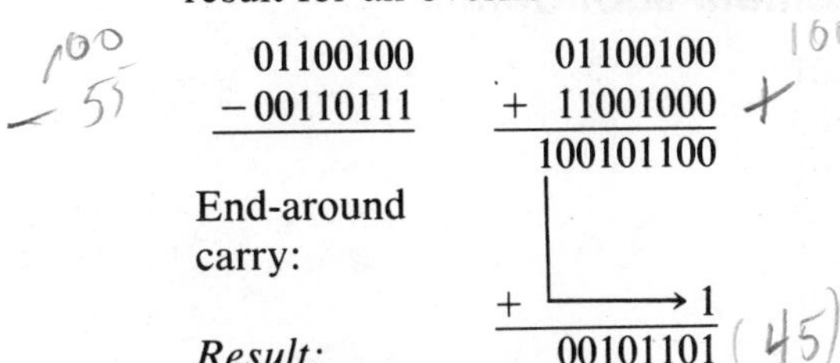

The result is a positive value in the true form. Overflow could not have occurred since a positive number was added to a negative number. ■

■ EXAMPLE 2-50 One's Complement Subraction

	1111 11 carry-out
01011101	01011101
−10010000	+01101111
Result:	11001100

Addition of two positive numbers produced a negative result. Therefore, **overflow occurred.** ■

■ EXAMPLE 2-51 Two's Complement Subtraction

Problem: Perform the signed binary additions and subtractions using the two's complement rules. All negative numbers are expressed in their complement form. All positive numbers are expressed in their true form.

Solution: Complement the subtrahend only to perform the subtraction operation following the rules of complement addition. Do not complement any negative numbers; only complement the number to be subtracted. Add the numbers. Drop a carry-out if it occurs. Check the result for an overflow condition.

10011110	10011110
−01011001	+ 10100111
Drop the carry-out:	~~1~~11000101
Result:	11000101

The result is a negative value in the two's complement form. ■

■ EXAMPLE 2-52 Two's Complement Subtraction

11101001	11101001
−11000011	+ 00111100
Drop the carry-out:	~~1~~00100101
Result:	00100101

The result is a positive value in the true form. Overflow could not have occurred because a negative number was added to a positive number. ■

Section Self-Test

1. One's complement arithmetic: 1101011 − 0110101
2. Two's complement arithmetic: 0101100 − 0110101
3. Correct the first problem so that overflow would not occur, and recompute the result.

ANSWERS (Not necessarily in the same order)

- 11101011 − 00110101 = 10110110
- 1110111
- 0110110

2-5 ARITHMETIC USING BCD AND BINARY CODES

Arithmetic processes can be performed directly on binary codes, rather than on just those values represented by the binary number system. The addition and subtraction processes in hexadecimal and 8421 BCD are covered in the following sections.

2.5.1 Hexadecimal Arithmetic

Addition of hexadecimal numbers is easily performed by converting the numbers to their binary equivalent, performing the arithmetic computations in binary, and then converting the result back to the appropriate code.

■ EXAMPLE 2-53 Hexadecimal Addition and Subtraction

Problem: Perform the arithmetic operations on the hex numbers.

Solution: Convert the hex numbers to binary. Perform the operation using the binary arithmetic rules. Convert the binary result to the hex notation.

```
                11 carry-out
 2F1      0010 1111 0001
+503     +0101 0000 0011
----     ---------------
 7F4      0111 1111 0100
```

The result is a positive number. ■

■ EXAMPLE 2-54 Hexadecimal Addition and Subtraction

B17	1011 0001 0111
−F2C	−1111 0010 1100
Form two's complement:	1011 0001 0111
	+0000 1101 0100
	1011 1110 1011

The result is a negative number in the two's complement form.

Convert result to hex: $(\text{BEB})_{16}$ ■

2.5.2 8421 BCD Arithmetic

Arithmetic operations can be performed on the BCD and complement representation of each decimal digit without requiring that the entire value be converted to the binary number system. However, the addition of BCD numbers requires special rules to prevent the occurrence of results containing invalid codes.

In the 8421 BCD code each decimal digit, 0 through 9, is represented by four binary bits. The 4-bit binary combinations for values greater than 9 are invalid in the 8421 BCD code. **When adding BCD numbers, a correction must be performed by adding 6, or $(0110)_2$,** to each group of BCD bits where a computation gives a result greater than 9, or where a carry-out to the next decimal digit occurs. By adding 6, the six invalid states are "skipped" in the sequence of numbers, so that the results are valid.

■ EXAMPLE 2-55 8421 BCD Arithmetic

Problem: Perform the addition and subtraction operations on the BCD numbers.

Solution: Add the numbers following the rules of binary arithmetic. Add $(0110)_2$ to any 4-bit group that has an invalid BCD result or that has a decimal carry-out.

$(146)_{10} + (259)_{10} = (405)_{10}$

0001 0100 0110	Form BCD
+0010 0101 1001	
0011 1001 1111	
+ 0110	Correction
0011 1010 0101	
+ 0110	Correction
0100 0000 0101	$= (405)_{10}$

■

■ EXAMPLE 2-56 8421 BCD Arithmetic

$(52)_{10} + (199)_{10} = (251)_{10}$

```
  0000 0101 0010    Form BCD
+ 0001 1001 1001
  --------------
  0001 1110 1011
+      0110 0110    Correction
  --------------
  0010 0101 0001 = (251)10
```

■

■ EXAMPLE 2-57 8421 BCD Arithmetic

$(8)_{10} + (8)_{10} = (16)_{10}$

```
       1000    Form BCD
+      1000
  ---------
  0001 0000
+      0110    Correction
  ---------
  0001 0110 = (16)10
```

■

2.5.3 Nine's and Ten's Complement Subtraction

Subtraction of BCD numbers can also be performed by the addition of the complements of the values, just as the complements of binary numbers are added to eliminate the subtraction process. However, decimal arithmetic requires the use of **nine's and ten's complements** rather than the one's and two's complements used with the binary number system.

The nine's complement is formed by subtracting each decimal digit from 9. The ten's complement if formed by adding 1 to the nine's complement result. When forming the ten's complement of numbers with more than one digit, add only the 1 to the nine's complement result in the one's digit, not to each digit. Table 2-13 displays the decimal, BCD, and binary representations of the nine's and ten's complements.

Notice that the nine's complement of the 8421 BCD code is **not formed by inverting the bits of the BCD value.** In **self-complementing BCD codes,** such as **Excess-3,** one can form the nine's complement by inverting each bit of the Excess-3 code for each decimal digit. Table 2-14 illustrates the self-complementing property of the Excess-3 code.

Specific procedures are defined for adding the nine's and ten's complement to perform the subtraction process on BCD numbers. The nine's complement method is similar to the one's complement method. If a carry-out of the MSB occurs in nine's complement addition, an end-around carry is performed to add the 1 to the LSB for the final result. The ten's complement method is similar to the two's complement method. Any carry-out of the MSB position is dropped in ten's complement arithmetic.

TABLE 2-13 Nine's and Ten's Complements

Decimal	BCD	Nine's Complement	Ten's Complement
0	0000	1001	1010
1	0001	1000	1001
2	0010	0111	1000
3	0011	0110	0111
4	0100	0101	0110
5	0101	0100	0101
6	0110	0011	0100
7	0111	0010	0011
8	1000	0001	0010
9	1001	0000	0001

TABLE 2-14 Excess-3 Self-Complementing Code

Decimal	Excess-3	Nine's Complement	Ten's Complement
0	0011	1100	1101
1	0100	1011	1100
2	0101	1010	1011
3	0110	1001	1010
4	0111	1000	1001
5	1000	0111	1000
6	1001	0110	0111
7	1010	0101	0110
8	1011	0100	0101
9	1100	0011	0100

When performing BCD signed arithmetic operations, apply the rules for BCD addition. Any 4-bit value that is an invalid BCD code or an operation that generates a decimal carry must have $(0110)_2$ added to obtain the correct BCD result.

■ EXAMPLE 2-58 BCD Subtraction Using the Nine's Complement

Problem: Subtract the BCD numbers using the complement rules for addition.

Solution: Convert the decimal number to BCD. Eliminate the subtraction by converting the subtrahend to the complement form. Add and perform any correction required by adding $(0110)_2$.

$(18)_{10} - (14)_{10} = (4)_{10}$

FORM BCD	NINE'S COMPLEMENT
0001 1000	0001 1000
−0001 0100	+1000 0101
	1001 1101
Correction:	+ 0110
	1010 0011
Correction:	+0110
	1 0000 0011
End-around carry:	→ 1
	0000 0100

Result: $(04)_{10}$ ■

■ EXAMPLE 2-59 BCD Subtraction Using the Ten's Complement

$(20)_{10} - (2)_{10} = (18)_{10}$

FORM BCD	TEN'S COMPLEMENT
0010 0000	0010 0000
−0000 0010	+1001 1000
	1011 1000
Correction:	+0110
Drop carry:	~~1~~ 0001 1000

Result: $(18)_{10}$ ■

Section Self-Test

1. Hexadecimal arithmetic: $(F4)_{16} - (3C)_{16}$ = (two's complement form)
2. BCD addition: (1001 0111) + (0011 0011) =
3. BCD subtraction: (1001 0111) − (0011 0011) = (nine's complement form)

ANSWERS (Not necessarily in the same order)

• (0001 0011 0000) • $(B8)_{16}$ • (0110 0100)

SUMMARY

Binary numbers are used to represent data in a digital system. The binary values of 1 and 0 correspond to the two allowed states in digital electronics. The binary number system is a weighted base-2 system, in which n bits can represent 2^n numbers.

Decimal numbers can be represented in a binary format. Simple techniques can be used to convert between the binary and decimal forms of a number.

The hexadecimal code is used as a shorthand notation for the binary code. Four binary bits can be represented by one hex digit. The hexadecimal code is a weighted base-16 number system. Numbers can be converted among the hex, binary, and decimal formats.

Special binary codes are used to represent decimal numbers and alphanumeric characters. The binary coded decimal, or BCD codes, represent each decimal digit 0 through 9 with a 4-bit binary code. The 8421 BCD code is the most common binary coded decimal format.

The Excess-3 BCD code is a self-complementing BCD code. The self-complementing feature of the Excess-3 code is convenient in arithmetic operations.

ASCII and EBCDIC are the two most common alphanumeric codes in use in computer systems. ASCII encodes each character with a 7-bit word, and EBCDIC encodes each character with an 8-bit word.

The Gray code is an unweighted binary code that allows only one bit in the word to change from one consecutive word to the next. This encoding technique eliminates glitches that can occur when a code requires several bits to change simultaneously when moving from one number to a consecutive number.

The binary number system is used in all arithmetic operations of addition, subtraction, multiplication, and division. Signed-number arithmetic operations can be accomplished entirely through addition by representing a number in its one's or two's complement form. BCD and hex numbers can also be added directly without converting back to binary.

The number systems, codes, and arithmetic procedures presented in this chapter are used frequently in digital electronics and microprocessor applications. They do not constitute all the codes and procedures used; rather, they form the basis for many other procedures that have been developed for special applications.

A thorough understanding of the codes and arithmetic procedures of this chapter is essential for further work in digital electronics, leading to more advanced work with microprocessor systems and applications.

The concepts and material covered in this chapter are applied in digital logic circuit designs in Chapter 5, "Decoders, Encoders, and Code Converters," Chapter 6, "Arithmetic Circuits," and elsewhere throughout the text. The student can refer to examples in Chapter 2 for a review of any material related to binary number systems or codes.

PROBLEMS

2-1 Binary Number System

*1. What sequence of binary numbers is represented by the following voltage waveforms? (Assume a high voltage level signifies a high logic level.)

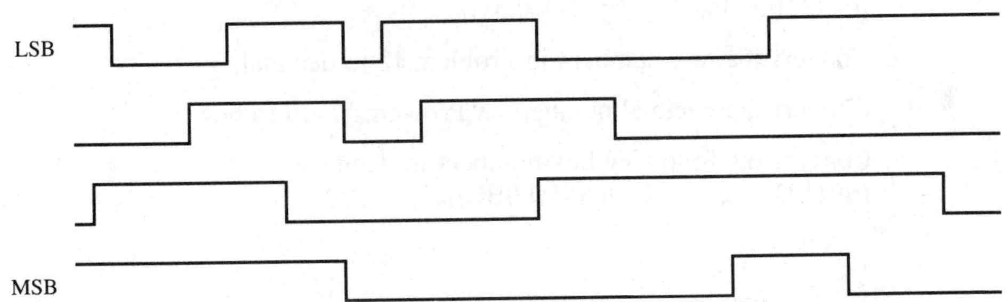

*2. For each of the binary numbers represented in Problem 1, find the decimal equivalent.

3. What is the maximum value that can be represented by:
   a. 12 bits in the binary number system?
   b. 16 bits?
   c. 32 bits?

*4. How many bits are required to represent the decimal value 2000 as a binary number?

---

* See Answers to Selected Problems.

5. Convert each of the following binary numbers to decimal:
   (a) $(101001)_2$ (b) $(11.01101)_2$

6. Convert each of the following binary numbers to decimal:
   (a) $(100100111.10011)_2$ (b) $(1001111.11)_2$

7. Convert the following decimal integers to binary integers:
   (a) $(500)_{10}$ (b) $(59)_{10}$

8. Convert the following decimal fractions to binary fractions:
   (a) $(.0857)_{10}$ (b) $(.34)_{10}$

9. Convert the following decimal numbers to binary:
   (a) $(125.0357)_{10}$ (b) $(1002.45)_{10}$

*10. Convert the following decimal numbers to binary:
   (a) $(56.879)_{10}$ (b) $(2029.56)_{10}$

2-2 Hexadecimal Codes

11. Convert each of the binary numbers given in Problems 5 and 6 to the hexadecimal code.

*12. Convert the following hex numbers to binary:
   (a) $(23F.45)_{16}$ (b) $(A040.51)_{16}$

13. Convert the hex numbers in Problem 12 to decimal.

14. Convert the decimal numbers in Problems 7–10 to hex.

15. Convert the following hex numbers to decimal:
   (a) $(103.2)_{16}$ (b) $(A45D.0BC)_{16}$

2-3 Binary Codes

16. Convert each of the decimal numbers in Problems 7–10 to 8421 BCD.

*17. Convert each of the decimal numbers in Problems 7–10 to Excess-3.

18. Draw the waveforms for binary numbers 0 through 15, and show where glitches would occur if all bits did not change simultaneously.

19. Draw the waveforms for the Gray code for numbers 0 through 15, and compare to the binary waveforms in Problem 18.

*20. What is the maximum value that can be represented by 12 bits in the 8421 BCD code?

21. Determine the bit sequence for the following statement: "Digital electronics are logical!"
   a. Encode in ASCII
   b. Encode in EBCDIC

2-4 Binary Arithmetic

*22. Perform the unsigned binary arithmetic operations:

(a)
```
  1101011
 +1011001
 --------
```
(b)
```
  10000001
 -  111011
 ---------
```

23. Perform the unsigned binary arithmetic operations:

(a)
```
  1001110
 + 110110
 --------
```
(b)
```
  10010011
 - 1100100
 ---------
```

*24. Perform the unsigned binary arithmetic:

(a)
```
  1001001
 ×     10
 --------
```
(b) 101)‾110001

25. Perform the unsigned binary arithmetic:

(a)
```
  1110011
 ×  11011
 --------
```
(b) 111)‾100111

26. Compute the following signed binary numbers using one's complement arithmetic:

(a)
```
  100100111
 -010110011
 ----------
```
(b)
```
  011110111
 +110010011
 ----------
```

27. Compute the following signed binary numbers using one's complement arithmetic:

(a)
```
  100111000
 -111001101
 ----------
```
(b)
```
  101100001
 -010110011
 ----------
```

28. Compute the following signed binary numbers using two's complement arithmetic:

(a)
```
  100100111
 +010110011
 ----------
```
(b)
```
  011110111
 -110010011
 ----------
```

29. Compute the following signed binary numbers using two's complement arithmetic:

(a) 100111000 +111001101 (b) 101100001 −011110000

30. Which calculations in Problems 26–29 resulted in an overflow condition?

31. How is an overflow condition detected?

32. How is an overflow condition corrected?

2-5 Arithmetic Using BCD and Binary Codes

33. Compute each of the following signed hexadecimal numbers:

(a) 35A +2E4 (b) FF1B +A12D

34. Compute each of the following signed hexadecimal numbers:

(a) 103E +D5FA (b) 6789 +BA10

*35. Compute each of the following signed hexadecimal numbers:

(a) F84 −A09 (b) 29E6 −5F58

36. Compute each of the following signed hexadecimal numbers:

(a) 7298 −8043 (b) 596E −28F3

37. Add the following numbers using BCD arithmetic:

(a) 7298 +8043 (b) 59 +28

38. Add the following numbers using BCD arithmetic:

(a) 3208 + 459 (b) 289 + 38

39. Compute the following signed numbers using 8421 BCD arithmetic and the nine's complement method for performing the subtraction:

(a) 702 −489 (b) 200 −374

40. Compute the following signed numbers using 8421 BCD arithmetic and the nine's complement method for performing the subtraction:

(a) $\begin{array}{r} 362 \\ -934 \\ \hline \end{array}$ (b) $\begin{array}{r} 144 \\ -144 \\ \hline \end{array}$

41. Use 8421 BCD arithmetic and the ten's complement method for computing each of the values given in Problem 40.

Part 2

COMBINATIONAL LOGIC

Part 1 DIGITAL LOGIC FUNDAMENTALS

Chapter 1 Digital Logic and Technology
Chapter 2 Number Systems and Arithmetic

Part 2 COMBINATIONAL LOGIC

Chapter 3 Logic Functions and Combinational Logic Circuits

Part 3 ADVANCED COMBINATIONAL LOGIC DESIGN WITH MEDIUM SCALE INTEGRATION (MSI) LOGIC CIRCUITS

Chapter 4 Multiplexers and Demultiplexers
Chapter 5 Decoders, Encoders, and Code Converters
Chapter 6 Arithmetic Circuits

Part 4 SEQUENTIAL LOGIC

Chapter 7 Monostable and Astable Circuits
Chapter 8 Latches
Chapter 9 Flip-Flops

Part 5 ADVANCED SEQUENTIAL LOGIC DESIGN

Chapter 10 Counter Circuits
Chapter 11 Shift Registers

Part 6 LSI LOGIC AND MEMORY

Chapter 12 Programmable Logic Devices and Semiconductor Logic
Chapter 13 Semiconductor Memory Technology
Chapter 14 Logic Design with Microprocessors

Part 7 LOGIC FAMILY PERFORMANCE AND INTERFACING

Chapter 15 Logic Families, Interfacing, and Device Selection
Chapter 16 Analog/Digital Conversion

Part 8 LOGIC SYSTEM DESIGN

Chapter 17 Digital Logic Design Projects

Chapter 3

Logic Functions and Combinational Logic Circuits

Upon completing and mastering the material in this chapter, you should be able to use combinational logic functions and circuits in the areas of analysis, application, and design:

ANALYSIS

1. Understand the seven basic logic functions.
2. Represent logic functions with truth tables.
3. Represent logic functions with standard and IEEE logic gate symbols.
4. Represent logic functions with equations.
5. Analyze logic circuits with logic levels.
6. Analyze logic circuits with pulsed operation.
7. Analyze logic circuits using truth tables.
8. Simplify logic equations with Boolean algebra.
9. Apply DeMorgan's Theorems to simplify circuits.
10. Analyze and simplify circuits using K-maps.
11. Analyze combinational logic circuits.
12. Perform waveform analysis of combinational circuits.
13. Analyze and simplify circuits using equivalent and alternate gates.

APPLICATION

14. Define logic functions for specific digital applications.
15. Karnaugh map logic functions for digital applications.

DESIGN

16. Design combinational circuits with logic gates and functions.
17. Design circuits with SOP equations.
18. Design circuits with POS equations.
19. Design and build logic circuits for specific logic applications.
20. Understand how POS and SOP equations apply to programmable logic device design.

TROUBLESHOOTING

21. Understand the correct procedure to use when troubleshooting combinational logic circuits.

This text covers many aspects of digital logic analysis, application, and design. Chapter 3, which studies the basics of logic functions and combinational logic, is the cornerstone for future digital logic work. All remaining chapters in this text will build on the fundamentals presented here. For example, Chapters 4, 5, and 6 deal with advanced combinational logic topics, such as multiplexers, demultiplexers, decoders, encoders, and arithmetic circuits. Chapters 7 through 11 cover sequential logic circuits—logic circuits whose operation is dependent on the sequence of inputs. Chapter 12 introduces programmable logic devices that can be programmed and erased to perform any of the previously studied logic functions.

3-1 LOGIC FUNCTION REPRESENTATION

Digital logic is the representation of quantities with two logic states: a logic HIGH and a logic LOW. Logic functions perform the operations to process the digital logic waveforms. Seven basic logic functions form all operations in digital electronics. Logic functions can be used alone in simple applications or combined to form complex digital circuits, such as adders, decoders, encoders, multiplexers, demultiplexers, counters, and storage registers.

There are seven basic logic functions that are used to form all logic functions in digital electronics. The basic logic functions, each of which corresponds to a **logic gate,** are the fundamental building blocks of digital electronics. Each logic function is represented by its **symbol, logic equation, name,** and **truth table.**

A **logic symbol** is a unique pictorial representation of the logic function. Each logic function or gate has a standard symbol, just as in analog circuitry each component has a standard symbol. Standard digital symbols are shown in Figure 3-1.

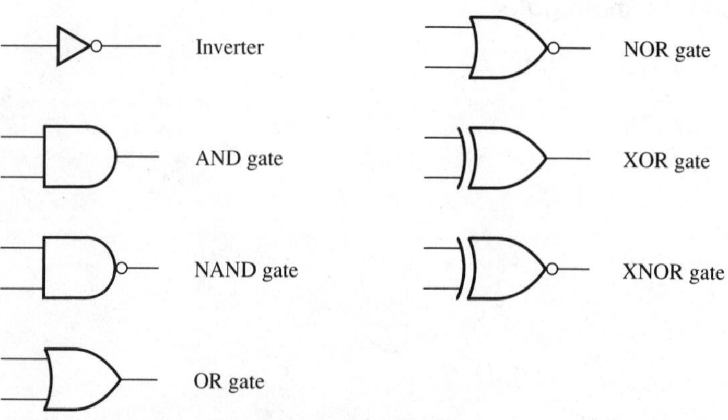

FIGURE 3-1 Standard Digital Symbols

It is important to recognize and associate each digital logic symbol with the digital function the symbol represents. Since entire logic circuits are drawn with logic symbols, one needs to remember each symbol and function in order to understand and interpret logic circuit diagrams.

In addition to symbolic representation, **logic equations** are used to represent the logic functions. Again, each function has a unique logic equation to describe its operation. Capital letters are used most often to designate logic gate inputs and outputs.

Logic functions are also defined by a **truth table.** A truth table lists all possible input combinations into a gate or circuit and the resulting outputs. For "n" input **variables**, 2^n input combinations are possible. These input combinations are listed in binary counting order in a truth table. A two-input truth table, also known as a two-variable truth table, will have four possible input combinations, and a three-variable truth table will have eight input combinations.

The seven basic logic functions are the inverter or NOT, AND, NAND, OR, NOR, Exclusive-OR, and Exclusive-NOR. Each of these will be explained in detail in the following sections.

In summary, each logic function can be represented with a logic equation, gate name, gate symbol, and truth table. It is important to become familiar with each logic function and its many representations, as they will be used when describing digital logic circuitry.

Section Self-Test

1. What are the seven basic logic functions?
2. List four ways to describe a logic function.
3. How many input combinations will a four-variable truth table have?

ANSWERS (Not necessarily in the same order as the questions)

- 16
- Truth table, equation, symbol, gate name
- Inverter, AND, NAND, OR, NOR, XOR, XNOR

3-2 INVERTER FUNCTION

An inverter is a logic gate with one input and one output. The inverter produces an output that is the opposite logic level of the input. If a logic LOW is input, the output is a logic HIGH. If a logic HIGH is input, the output is a logic LOW. Thus, the inverter inverts, or complements the input. The inverter is also known as a NOT gate, which performs the NOT function.

Figure 3-2 shows the logic symbol, equation, and truth table for an inverter. In this figure A is the input and Y is the output. The output equation is $Y = \overline{A}$, read as "A inverted," "A bar," or "A NOT."

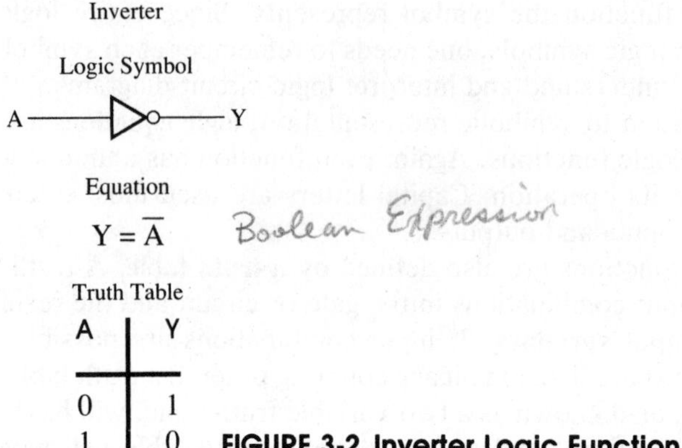

FIGURE 3-2 Inverter Logic Function

The truth table for the inverter lists the input states and resulting output. **The output of the inverter is always the opposite of the input.**

One transistor-transistor logic (TTL) integrated circuit (IC) that performs the inverter function is the 7404. The 7404 is an IC that contains six inverter gates, and thus is known as a **HEX inverter.** The data sheet for the 7404 Hex inverter IC is shown in Figure 3-3.

The 7404 has 14 pins, with pin 7 as the voltage ground input and pin 14 as the supply voltage V_{CC} input. The six inverter gates on the 7404 are to be used individually, with each gate having its own input and output pin. A logic circuit designer can use any or all of the inverter gates on the chip.

Section Self-Test

1. What is a TTL IC number for an inverter IC?
2. How many inverters are in each inverter IC?
3. If an inverter has an input C and an output Z, what is the equation for the output?

ANSWERS (Not necessarily in the order of the questions)

• 74LS04 • 6 • $Z = \overline{C}$

3-3 AND FUNCTION

An AND gate has two or more inputs and one output. The only time a logic HIGH is output is when all inputs are HIGH. If at least one of the inputs is a logic 0, the output is a logic 0.

SN5404, SN54LS04, SN54S04, SN7404, SN74LS04, SN74S04 HEX INVERTERS

DECEMBER 1983 – REVISED MARCH 1988

- **Package Options Include Plastic "Small Outline" Packages, Ceramic Chip Carriers and Flat Packages, and Plastic and Ceramic DIPs**
- **Dependable Texas Instruments Quality and Reliability**

description

These devices contain six independent inverters.

The SN5404, SN54LS04, and SN54S04 are characterized for operation over the full military temperature range of −55°C to 125°C. The SN7404, SN74LS04, and SN74S04 are characterized for operation from 0°C to 70°C.

FUNCTION TABLE (each inverter)

INPUTS A	OUTPUT Y
H	L
L	H

logic symbol† (military)

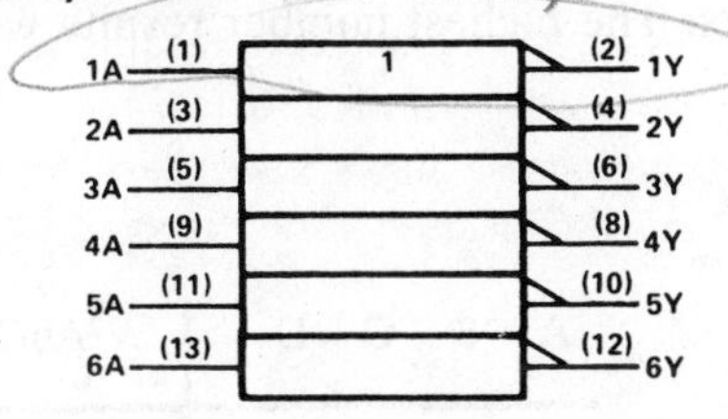

†This symbol is in accordance with ANSI/IEEE Std. 91-1984 and IEC Publication 617-12.
Pin numbers shown are for D, J, and N packages.

logic diagram (positive logic)

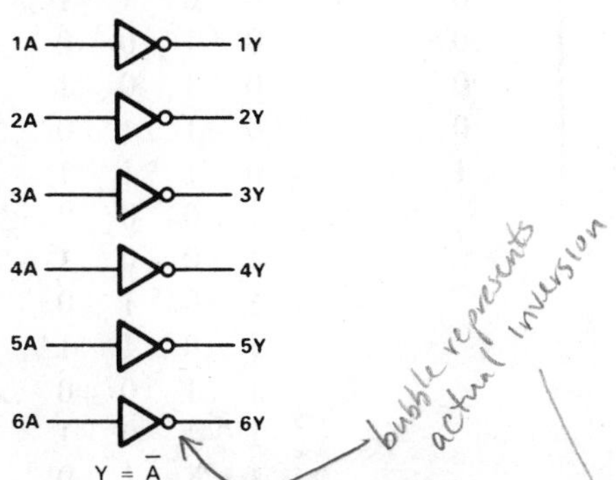

SN5404 . . . J PACKAGE
SN54LS04, SN54S04 . . . J OR W PACKAGE
SN7404 . . . N PACKAGE
SN74LS04, SN74S04 . . . D OR N PACKAGE
(TOP VIEW)

Pin	Name	Pin	Name
1	1A	14	VCC
2	1Y	13	6A
3	2A	12	6Y
4	2Y	11	5A
5	3A	10	5Y
6	3Y	9	4A
7	GND	8	4Y

SN5404 . . . W PACKAGE
(TOP VIEW)

Pin	Name	Pin	Name
1	1A	14	1Y
2	2Y	13	6A
3	2A	12	6Y
4	VCC	11	GND
5	3A	10	5Y
6	3Y	9	5A
7	4A	8	4Y

SN54LS04, SN54S04 . . . FK PACKAGE
(TOP VIEW)

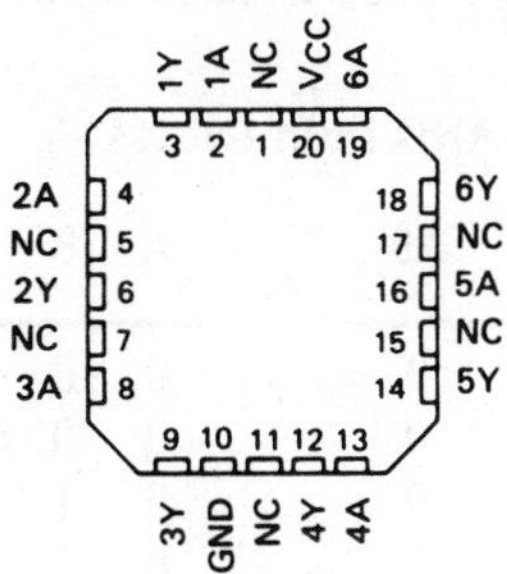

NC - No internal connection

FIGURE 3-3 7404 Hex Inverter Data Sheet (Courtesy Texas Instruments)

is a buffer

AND

Logic Symbol

A, B → Y

Equation

Y = AB

Truth Table

A	B	Y
0	0	0
0	1	0
1	0	0
1	1	1

FIGURE 3-4 AND Logic Function

Figure 3-4 shows the logic symbol, equation, and truth table for a 2-input AND gate. For the 2-input AND gate, the output is AB, commonly pronounced "A AND B." The output of a 4-input AND gate would be "A AND B AND C AND D." It is also common to write the output of an AND function as A×B or A·B. The AND function is commutative, as AB = BA.

The truth tables for two, three, and four input AND gates are shown in Table 3-1. **The only time the AND function is HIGH is when all inputs are HIGH.**

The number of input combinations in the truth table corresponds to the number of input variables raised to the power of 2. Thus, a two input AND gate has 2^2 or four possible input combinations; a 3-input AND gate has eight possible input combinations. Each input has a corresponding output. Note that the inputs follow a binary counting order. The input side of a truth table is produced by starting with a binary 0 and counting up in binary to the highest number for the given inputs. The highest number results when 1's are in each input position.

TABLE 3-1 AND Truth Tables

A	B	AB
0	0	0
0	1	0
1	0	0
1	1	1

A	B	C	ABC
0	0	0	0
0	0	1	0
0	1	0	0
0	1	1	0
1	0	0	0
1	0	1	0
1	1	0	0
1	1	1	1

A	B	C	D	ABCD
0	0	0	0	0
0	0	0	1	0
0	0	1	0	0
0	0	1	1	0
0	1	0	0	0
0	1	0	1	0
0	1	1	0	0
0	1	1	1	0
1	0	0	0	0
1	0	0	1	0
1	0	1	0	0
1	0	1	1	0
1	1	0	0	0
1	1	0	1	0
1	1	1	0	0
1	1	1	1	1

SN5408, SN54LS08, SN54S08, SN7408, SN74LS08, SN74S08
QUADRUPLE 2-INPUT POSITIVE-AND GATES
DECEMBER 1983 – REVISED MARCH 1988

- **Package Options Include Plastic "Small Outline" Packages, Ceramic Chip Carriers and Flat Packages, and Plastic and Ceramic DIPs**
- **Dependable Texas Instruments Quality and Reliability**

description

These devices contain four independent 2-input AND gates.

The SN5408, SN54LS08, and SN54S08 are characterized for operation over the full military temperature range of −55°C to 125°C. The SN7408, SN74LS08 and SN74S08 are characterized for operation from 0° to 70°C.

FUNCTION TABLE (each gate)

INPUTS		OUTPUT
A	B	Y
H	H	H
L	X	L
X	L	L

logic symbol†

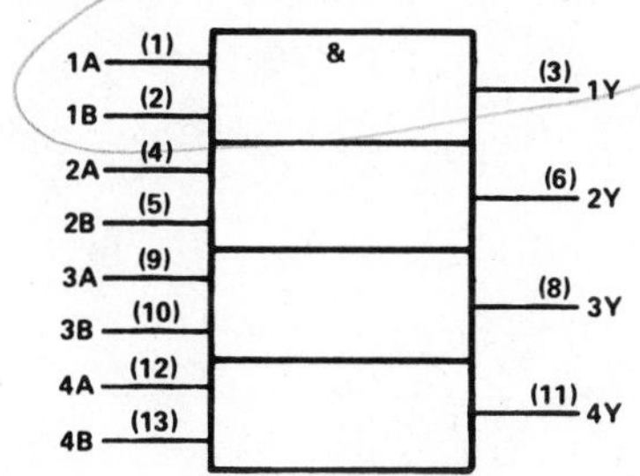

†This symbol is in accordance with ANSI/IEEE Std 91-1984 and IEC Publication 617-12.
Pin numbers shown are for D, J, N, and W packages.

SN5408, SN54LS08, SN54S08 . . . J OR W PACKAGE
SN7408 . . . J OR N PACKAGE
SN74LS08, SN74S08 . . . D, J OR N PACKAGE
(TOP VIEW)

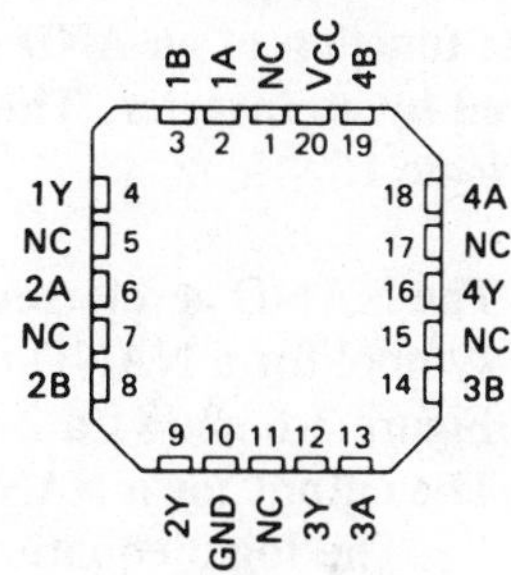

SN54LS08, SN54S08 . . . FK PACKAGE
(TOP VIEW)

NC – No internal connection

logic diagram (positive logic)

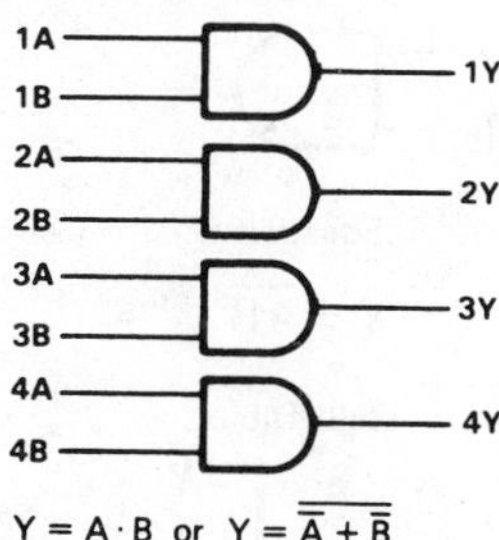

$Y = A \cdot B$ or $Y = \overline{\overline{A} + \overline{B}}$

FIGURE 3-5 7408 Quad 2-Input AND Data Sheet (Courtesy Texas Instruments)

Several different TTL ICs are used to implement the AND function. A 7408 contains four two-input AND gates and is known as a **quadruple** or **quad** two-input AND IC. A 7411 is a triple three-input AND IC. A 7421 is a dual four-input AND IC. All data sheets can be found in a TTL data book. The data sheet for the 7408 quad two-input AND IC is shown in Figure 3-5.

Section Self-Test

1. Write the output equation for an AND gate with three inputs, D, E, and F.
2. How many AND gates are in a TTL 7408 IC?
3. For a two input AND gate, if both of the inputs are HIGH, what is the output?

ANSWERS (Not necessarily in the order of the questions)

• 4 • HIGH • DEF

3-4 NAND FUNCTION

NAND means "NOT AND," and its output is the exact opposite of an AND gate. A NAND gate has two or more inputs and one output and has the opposite function of an AND gate. The NAND functions as an AND gate followed by an inverter. The only time a logic 0 is output is when all inputs are logic 1.

The NAND is referred to as the **complement** function of the AND. The logic symbol for a NAND is an AND gate with an inverter bubble on the output. Figure 3-6 shows a 2-input NAND logic symbol, equation, and truth table. **The output for a NAND is LOW only when all inputs are high.**

The logic equation for the NAND is formed by placing a bar over the

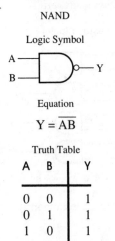

NAND

Logic Symbol

Equation

$$Y = \overline{AB}$$

Truth Table

A	B	Y
0	0	1
0	1	1
1	0	1
1	1	0

FIGURE 3-6 NAND Logic Function

combined input terms, such as $\overline{AB}$, $\overline{ABC}$, or $\overline{ABCD}$. The output of a 2-input NAND is commonly pronounced "A NAND B," or "AB bar."

The truth tables for two-, three-, and four-input NAND gates are shown in Table 3-2. The output is the complement of the AND function.

TABLE 3-2 NAND Truth Tables

A	B	$\overline{AB}$
0	0	1
0	1	1
1	0	1
1	1	0

A	B	C	$\overline{ABC}$
0	0	0	1
0	0	1	1
0	1	0	1
0	1	1	1
1	0	0	1
1	0	1	1
1	1	0	1
1	1	1	0

A	B	C	D	$\overline{ABCD}$
0	0	0	0	1
0	0	0	1	1
0	0	1	0	1
0	0	1	1	1
0	1	0	0	1
0	1	0	1	1
0	1	1	0	1
0	1	1	1	1
1	0	0	0	1
1	0	0	1	1
1	0	1	0	1
1	0	1	1	1
1	1	0	0	1
1	1	0	1	1
1	1	1	0	1
1	1	1	1	0

Common TTL ICs containing NAND gates have either one, two, three, or four NAND gates per IC, depending on the number of inputs per gate. Specialized NAND gates may have eight or more inputs.

The 7400 is a quadruple (quad) 2-input NAND gate IC and has four 2-input NAND gates per package. The 7410 is a triple 3-input NAND gate IC with three 3-input NAND gates per package. The 7420 is a dual 4-input NAND gate IC, and the 7430 contains a single 8-input NAND gate. The data sheet for the 7400 quad 2-input NAND IC is shown in Figure 3-7.

When designing a logic circuit, one selects the ICs that will provide the necessary number of gates to build the circuit. If, for example, a circuit requires six 2-input NAND gates, nine 3-input NAND gates, and two 4-input NAND gates, two 7400s, three 7410s, and one 7420 will be needed. Notice that a total of 17 gates are required, and the six ICs selected provide 19 NAND gates. Two of the 2-input gates from one of the 7400 ICs will be unused at this time.

Section Self-Test

1. How many different input combinations does a 4-input NAND gate truth table have?
2. What must the logic value of each NAND input be so that the output is LOW?
3. What TTL IC is a quad NAND?

ANSWERS (Not necessarily in the order of the questions)

- 16
- 74LS00
- 1

SN5400, SN54LS00, SN54S00, SN7400, SN74LS00, SN74S00
QUADRUPLE 2-INPUT POSITIVE-NAND GATES

DECEMBER 1983—REVISED MARCH 1988

- **Package Options Include Plastic "Small Outline" Packages, Ceramic Chip Carriers and Flat Packages, and Plastic and Ceramic DIPs**
- **Dependable Texas Instruments Quality and Reliability**

description

These devices contain four independent 2-input-NAND gates.

The SN5400, SN54LS00, and SN54S00 are characterized for operation over the full military temperature range of −55°C to 125°C. The SN7400, SN74LS00, and SN74S00 are characterized for operation from 0°C to 70°C.

FUNCTION TABLE (each gate)

INPUTS		OUTPUT
A	B	Y
H	H	L
L	X	H
X	L	H

logic symbol†

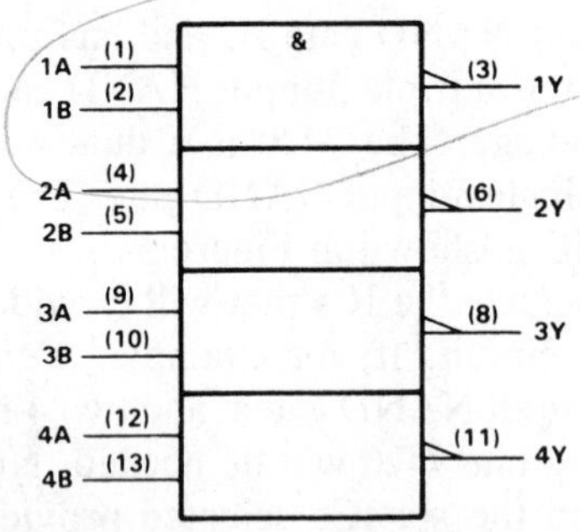

†This symbol is in accordance with ANSI/IEEE Std. 91-1984 and IEC Publication 617-12.

Pin numbers shown are for D, J, and N packages.

SN5400 . . . J PACKAGE
SN54LS00, SN54S00 . . . J OR W PACKAGE
SN7400 . . . N PACKAGE
SN74LS00, SN74S00 . . . D OR N PACKAGE
(TOP VIEW)

1A	1	14	V_{CC}
1B	2	13	4B
1Y	3	12	4A
2A	4	11	4Y
2B	5	10	3B
2Y	6	9	3A
GND	7	8	3Y

SN5400 . . . W PACKAGE
(TOP VIEW)

1A	1	14	4Y
1B	2	13	4B
1Y	3	12	4A
V_{CC}	4	11	GND
2Y	5	10	3B
2A	6	9	3A
2B	7	8	3Y

SN54LS00, SN54S00 . . . FK PACKAGE
(TOP VIEW)

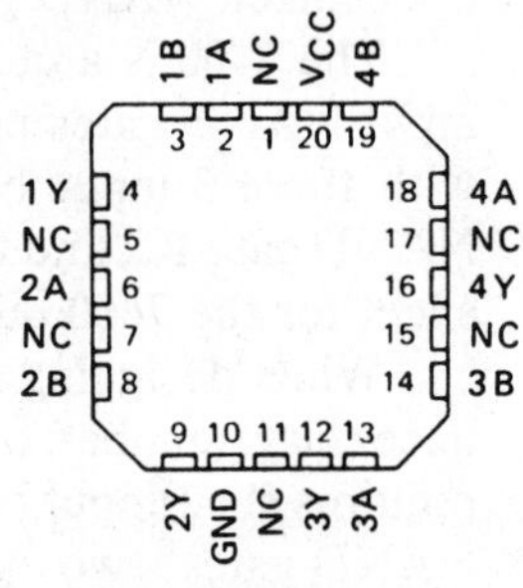

NC - No internal connection

logic diagram (positive logic)

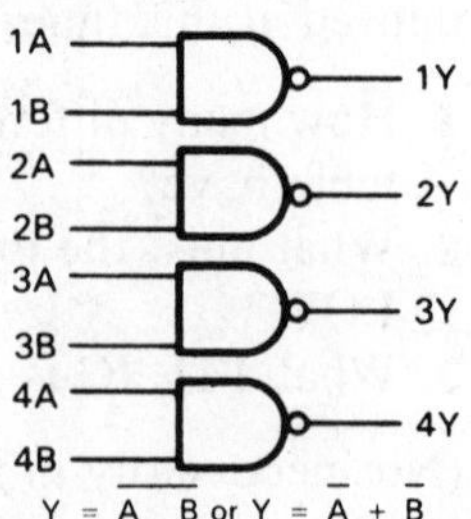

$Y = \overline{A \cdot B}$ or $Y = \overline{A} + \overline{B}$

FIGURE 3-7 7400 Quad 2-Input NAND Data Sheet (Courtesy Texas Instruments)

3-5 OR FUNCTION

The OR gate is a logic gate with two or more inputs and one output. The operation of an OR gate is such that if any of the inputs are a logic 1, the output is a logic 1. The only time an OR gate has a LOW or 0 output is when all inputs are LOW.

In Figure 3-8 a 2-input OR gate symbol, logic equation, and truth table are shown. **The output of an OR function is LOW only when all inputs are LOW.** The output A + B is pronounced "A OR B," and the output D + E + F is pronounced "D OR E OR F."

The OR function is commutative since the output does not depend on the order of the variables ORed together. Therefore, (A + B) = (B + A), and (D + E + F) will equal (F + D + E) or any other ORed combination of the three variables. Notice that parentheses are used to group variables in these logic equations, just as in standard algebra.

The truth tables for two, three, and four input OR gates are shown in Table 3-3. The output is HIGH when at least one of the inputs is HIGH. **The OR function is LOW only when all inputs are LOW.**

The 7432 IC has four 2-input OR gate. It is the only commonly available TTL IC that contains only OR gates. The data sheet for the 7432 quad 2-input OR IC is shown in Figure 3-9.

OR functions of two or more inputs can be constructed by combining the OR gates as shown in Example 3-1.

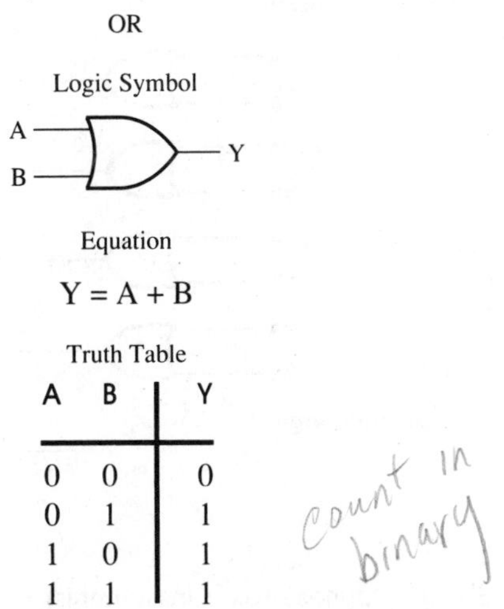

A	B	Y
0	0	0
0	1	1
1	0	1
1	1	1

FIGURE 3-8 OR Logic Function

SN5432, SN54LS32, SN54S32, SN7432, SN74LS32, SN74S32
QUADRUPLE 2-INPUT POSITIVE-OR GATES

DECEMBER 1983 – REVISED MARCH 1988

- **Package Options Include Plastic "Small Outline" Packages, Ceramic Chip Carriers and Flat Packages, and Plastic and Ceramic DIPs**
- **Dependable Texas Instruments Quality and Reliability**

description

These devices contain four independent 2-input OR gates.

The SN5432, SN54LS32 and SN54S32 are characterized for operation over the full military range of −55°C to 125°C. The SN7432, SN74LS32 and SN74S32 are characterized for operation from 0°C to 70°C.

FUNCTION TABLE (each gate)

INPUTS		OUTPUT
A	B	Y
H	X	H
X	H	H
L	L	L

logic symbol†

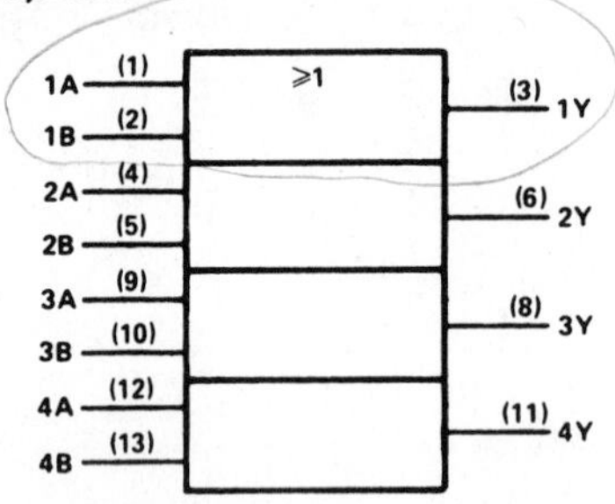

† This symbol is in accordance with ANSI/IEEE Std 91-1984 and IEC Publication 617-12.
Pin numbers shown are for D, J, N, or W packages.

SN5432, SN54LS32, SN54S32 . . . J OR W PACKAGE
SN7432 . . . N PACKAGE
SN74LS32, SN74S32 . . . D OR N PACKAGE
(TOP VIEW)

1A	1	14 VCC
1B	2	13 4B
1Y	3	12 4A
2A	4	11 4Y
2B	5	10 3B
2Y	6	9 3A
GND	7	8 3Y

SN54LS32, SN54S32 . . . FK PACKAGE
(TOP VIEW)

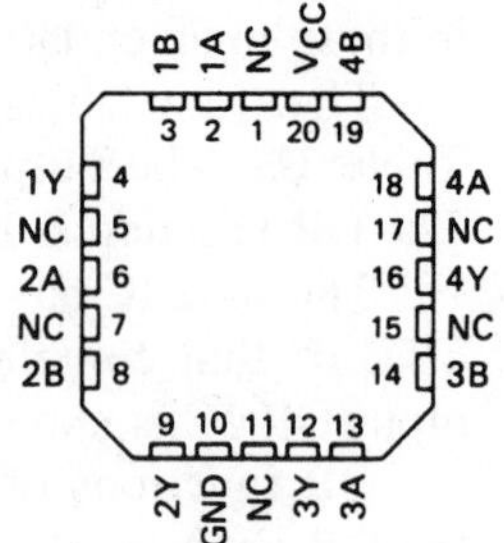

NC - No internal connection

logic diagram

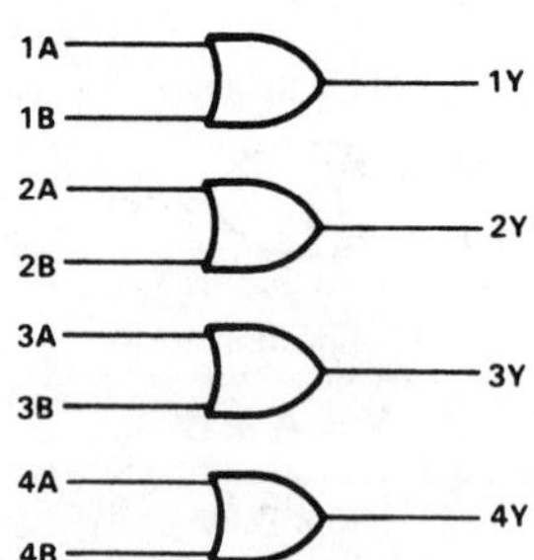

positive logic

$$Y = A + B \text{ or } Y = \overline{\overline{A} \cdot \overline{B}}$$

FIGURE 3-9 7432 Quad 2-Input OR Data Sheet (Courtesy Texas Instruments)

TABLE 3-3 OR Truth Tables

A B	A + B
0 0	0
0 1	1
1 0	1
1 1	1

A B C	A + B + C
0 0 0	0
0 0 1	1
0 1 0	1
0 1 1	1
1 0 0	1
1 0 1	1
1 1 0	1
1 1 1	1

A B C D	A + B + C + D
0 0 0 0	0
0 0 0 1	1
0 0 1 0	1
0 0 1 1	1
0 1 0 0	1
0 1 0 1	1
0 1 1 0	1
0 1 1 1	1
1 0 0 0	1
1 0 0 1	1
1 0 1 0	1
1 0 1 1	1
1 1 0 0	1
1 1 0 1	1
1 1 1 0	1
1 1 1 1	1

■ EXAMPLE 3-1 OR Function

Problem: Produce a circuit equivalent to a 4-input OR gate using a 7432 IC.

Solution: Logically, the OR function is associative such that (A + B + C + D) = (A + B) + (C + D). Three 2-input OR gates can be used to construct the 4-input OR function. The circuit and wiring diagram for the 7432 is shown in Figure 3-10. One OR gate on the 7432 will be unused. ■

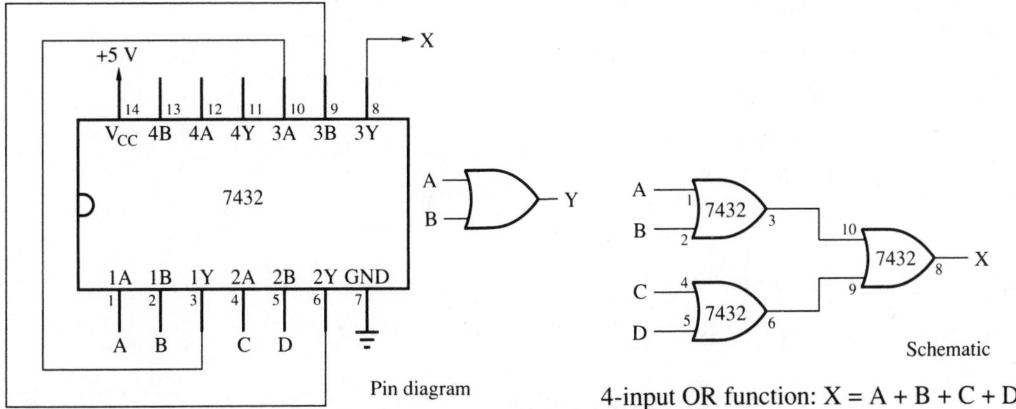

FIGURE 3-10 7432 IC Used to Construct a 4-Input OR Function

Section Self-Test

1. List all commonly available TTL OR ICs
2. What must be the logic values of the inputs to an OR gate so that the output is 0?
3. How many 2-input OR gates will it take to produce the following equation?

$$X = A + B + C + D + E + F + G$$

ANSWERS (Not necessarily in the same order as the questions)

• 6 • 0 • 74LS32

3-6 NOR FUNCTION

The NOR function means "NOT OR." The NOR functions as an OR followed by an inverter. The output of a NOR gate is HIGH only when both inputs are LOW. Since the truth table for a NOR is the opposite of an OR, the NOR and the OR are complementary functions.

The gate symbol for a NOR gate is made by adding an inverter bubble to the output of an OR gate symbol to indicate the complement function of an OR gate.

A 2-input NOR gate symbol, equation, and truth table are shown in Figure 3-11. **The only time the NOR function is HIGH is when all inputs are LOW.**

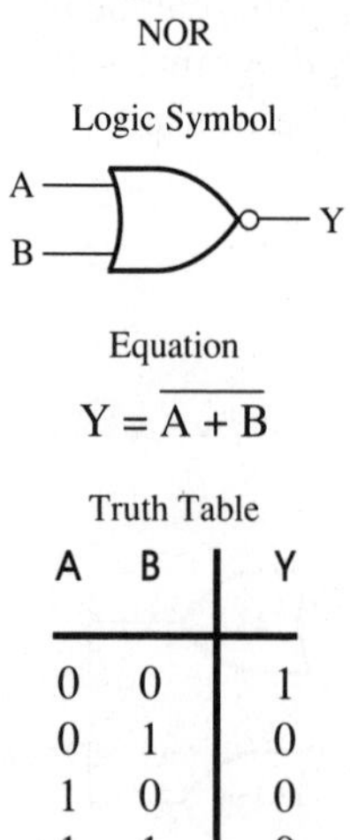

A	B	Y
0	0	1
0	1	0
1	0	0
1	1	0

FIGURE 3-11 NOR Logic Function

TABLE 3-4 NOR Truth Tables

A B	$\overline{A + B}$
0 0	1
0 1	0
1 0	0
1 1	0

A B C	$\overline{A + B + C}$
0 0 0	1
0 0 1	0
0 1 0	0
0 1 1	0
1 0 0	0
1 0 1	0
1 1 0	0
1 1 1	0

A B C D	$\overline{A + B + C + D}$
0 0 0 0	1
0 0 0 1	0
0 0 1 0	0
0 0 1 1	0
0 1 0 0	0
0 1 0 1	0
0 1 1 0	0
0 1 1 1	0
1 0 0 0	0
1 0 0 1	0
1 0 1 0	0
1 0 1 1	0
1 1 0 0	0
1 1 0 1	0
1 1 1 0	0
1 1 1 1	0

The logic equation for a NOR gate has a bar over the entire output equation to indicate that the entire OR function is complemented to produce the NOR function. The output of a 3-input NOR gate will be $\overline{A + B + C}$, and is pronounced "(A OR B OR C) NOT," or "A NOR B NOR C"; the latter, using the NOR terminology, is preferred.

The truth tables for two, three, and four input NOR gates are shown in Table 3-4. Compare the truth tables for OR and NOR functions to verify their complementary output relationship.

■ EXAMPLE 3-2 NOR Function

Problem: A 0 and two 1's are input into a 3-input NOR gate. Analyze the operation by determining:
(a) What is the output?
(b) How many possible input combinations does this problem have?

Solution: Referring to the NOR truth table in Table 3-4, we find that the output will be 0 and that there are three input combinations of two 1's and a 0 that can produce this output: 011, 101, 110. ■

Common TTL ICs containing NOR gates may have either two, three, or four NOR gates per IC, depending on the number of inputs per gate. The

SN5402, SN54LS02, SN54S02, SN7402, SN74LS02, SN74S02
QUADRUPLE 2-INPUT POSITIVE-NOR GATES

DECEMBER 1983—REVISED MARCH 1988

- **Package Options Include Plastic "Small Outline" Packages, Ceramic Chip Carriers and Flat Packages, and Plastic and Ceramic DIPs**
- **Dependable Texas Instruments Quality and Reliability**

description

These devices contain four independent 2-input-NOR gates.

The SN5402, SN54LS02, and SN54S02 are characterized for operation over the full military temperature range of −55°C to 125°C. The SN7402, SN74LS02, and SN74S02 are characterized for operation from 0°C to 70°C.

FUNCTION TABLE (each gate)

INPUTS		OUTPUT
A	B	Y
H	X	L
X	H	L
L	L	H

SN5402 . . . J PACKAGE
SN54LS02, SN54S02 . . . J OR W PACKAGE
SN7402 . . . N PACKAGE
SN74LS02, SN74S02 . . . D OR N PACKAGE
(TOP VIEW)

Signal	Pin	Pin	Signal
1Y	1	14	V_{CC}
1A	2	13	4Y
1B	3	12	4B
2Y	4	11	4A
2A	5	10	3Y
2B	6	9	3B
GND	7	8	3A

SN5402 . . . W PACKAGE
(TOP VIEW)

Signal	Pin	Pin	Signal
1A	1	14	4Y
1B	2	13	4B
1Y	3	12	4A
V_{CC}	4	11	GND
2Y	5	10	3B
2A	6	9	3A
2B	7	8	3Y

logic symbol†

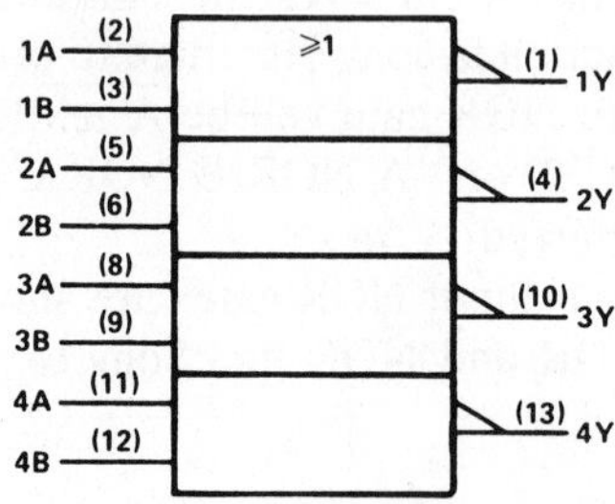

†This symbol is in accordance with ANSI/IEEE Std. 91-1984 and IEC Publication 617-12.
Pin numbers shown are for D, J, and N packages.

SN54LS02, SN54S02 . . . FK PACKAGE
(TOP VIEW)

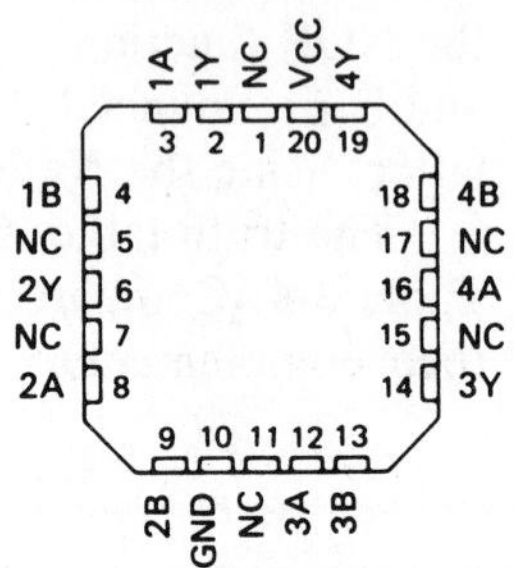

NC - No internal connection

logic diagram (positive logic)

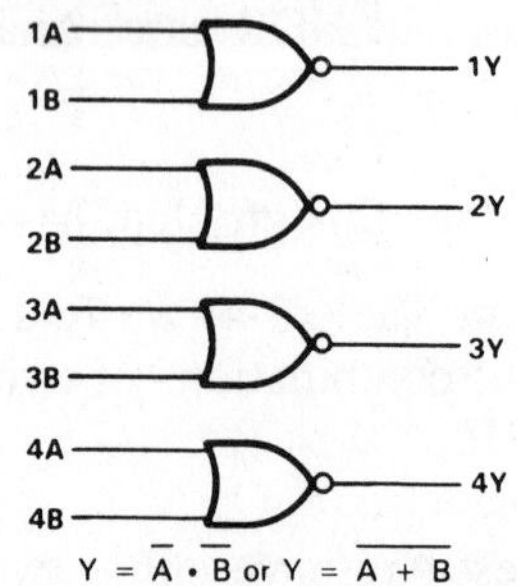

$Y = \overline{A} \cdot \overline{B}$ or $Y = \overline{A + B}$

FIGURE 3-12 7402 Quad 2-Input NOR Data Sheet (Courtesy Texas Instruments)

7402 is a 14-pin TTL IC with four 2-input NOR gates. The data sheet for the 7402 quad 2-input NOR IC is shown in Figure 3-12.

It is interesting to note that the input and output pin assignments differ from the input and output pin assignments for a 7400 quad 2-input NAND IC. On the 7402, pins 2 and 3 are the inputs and pin 1 is the output for the first NOR gate. The 7400 has pins 1 and 2 as inputs, and pin 3 as the output for the first NAND gate. It is important to remember to refer to the pin specifications for ICs before attempting to wire circuits. It is also helpful to label pin numbers and gate numbers on any schematic as shown in Figure 3-13 to aid in wiring the circuits.

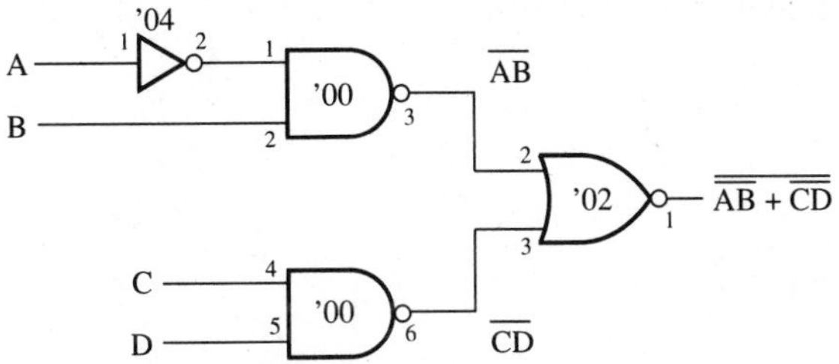

FIGURE 3-13 Labeled Logic Schematic

The 7427 is a triple 3-input NOR gate IC. The 7425 is a dual 4-input NOR gate IC, and the 74260 is a dual 5-input NOR gate IC. Refer to a TTL data book for the pin diagram and technical specifications for each IC.

Section Self-Test

1. What is the equation for a 3-input NOR gate?
2. When is the output of a NOR gate 0?
3. When is the output of a NOR gate HIGH?

ANSWERS (Not necessarily in the same order as the questions)

- When any input is a 1
- When all inputs are 0
- $\overline{A + B + C}$

3-7 EXCLUSIVE FUNCTIONS: XOR AND XNOR

The Exclusive-OR gate is a logic gate with two inputs and one output. The Exclusive-OR is an "inequality" function. The output of an Exclusive-OR gate is HIGH when the inputs are not equal to each other. If both inputs are HIGH, or if both inputs are LOW, the output of the Exclusive-OR gate is LOW. By definition, an exclusive gate has only two inputs.

The complement gate to an Exclusive-OR gate is the Exclusive-NOR, or XNOR. The XNOR is an "equality" function. The only time the output of an Exclusive-NOR gate is HIGH is when both inputs are equal, either HIGH or LOW.

The gate symbol for an Exclusive-OR gate is similar to the symbol for an OR gate but has an additional curved line added across the inputs to indicate the exclusive function. The Exclusive-OR gate is designated as **XOR.**

The logic equation operand for the XOR function is the OR operand, "+," with a circle drawn around it, as in $A \oplus B$. The equation is pronounced "A Exclusive-OR B." The gate symbol, equation, and truth table for an XOR gate is shown in Figure 3-14.

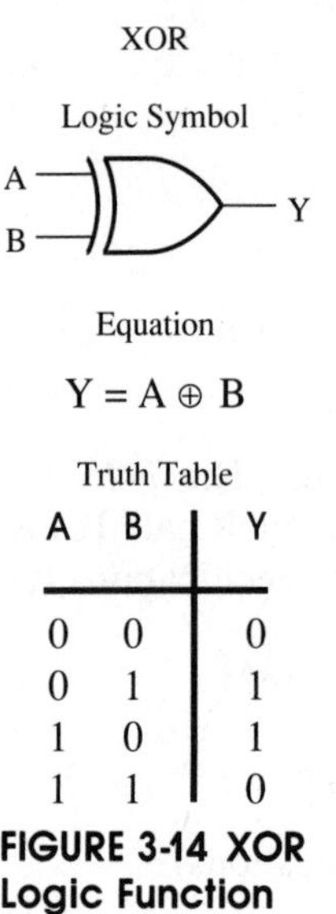

A	B	Y
0	0	0
0	1	1
1	0	1
1	1	0

FIGURE 3-14 XOR Logic Function

The XOR TTL IC is the 7486. The 7486 has four 2-input Exclusive-OR gates. The data sheet for the 7486 is shown in Figure 3-15.

The gate symbol for an XNOR gate is formed by placing the inverter bubble on the output of an XOR gate. As with the XOR, the XNOR function is only a two-input operation.

The logic equation operand is a circle-dot symbol, "$\odot$." However, the preferred way to indicate the Exclusive-NOR in equation form is to complement the XOR function by placing a bar over the XOR equation. Thus, $A \odot B = \overline{A \oplus B}$. The equation $\overline{A \oplus B}$ is pronounced "A Exclusive-NOR B." The gate symbol, equation, and truth table for a XNOR gate are shown in Figure 3-16.

SN5486, SN54LS86A, SN54S86, SN7486, SN74LS86A, SN74S86 QUADRUPLE 2-INPUT EXCLUSIVE-OR GATES

DECEMBER 1972—REVISED MARCH 1988

- **Package Options Include Plastic "Small Outline" Packages, Ceramic Chip Carriers and Flat Packages, and Standard Plastic and Ceramic 300-mil DIPs**
- **Dependable Texas Instruments Quality and Reliability**

TYPE	TYPICAL AVERAGE PROPAGATION DELAY TIME	TYPICAL TOTAL POWER DISSIPATION
'86	14 ns	150 mW
'LS86A	10 ns	30.5 mW
'S86	7 ns	250 mW

SN5486, SN54LS86A, SN54S86 . . . J OR W PACKAGE
SN7486 . . . N PACKAGE
SN74LS86A, SN74S86 . . . D OR N PACKAGE
(TOP VIEW)

Pin	Name	Pin	Name
1	1A	14	V_{CC}
2	1B	13	4B
3	1Y	12	4A
4	2A	11	4Y
5	2B	10	3B
6	2Y	9	3A
7	GND	8	3Y

SN54LS86A, SN54S86 . . . FK PACKAGE
(TOP VIEW)

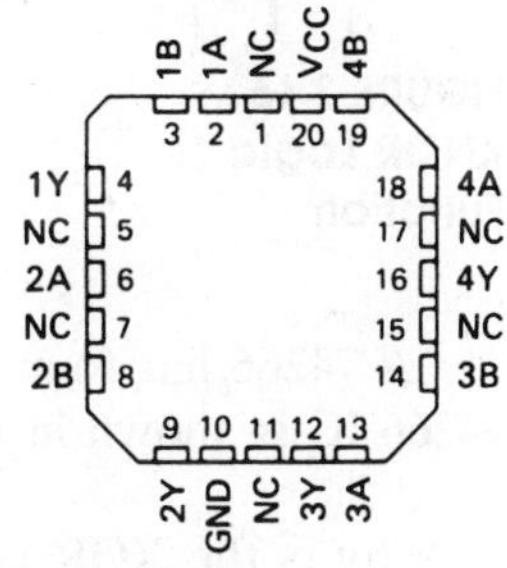

NC - No internal connection

description

These devices contain four independent 2-input Exclusive-OR gates. They perform the Boolean functions $Y = A \oplus B = \overline{A}B + A\overline{B}$ in positive logic.

A common application is as a true/complement element. If one of the inputs is low, the other input will be reproduced in true form at the output. If one of the inputs is high, the signal on the other input will be reproduced inverted at the output.

The SN5486, 54LS86A, and the SN54S86 are characterized for operation over the full military temperature range of $-55\,°C$ to $125\,°C$. The SN7486, SN74LS86A, and the SN74S86 are characterized for operation from $0\,°C$ to $70\,°C$.

exclusive-OR logic

An exclusive-OR gate has many applications, some of which can be represented better by alternative logic symbols.

EXCLUSIVE-OR

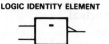

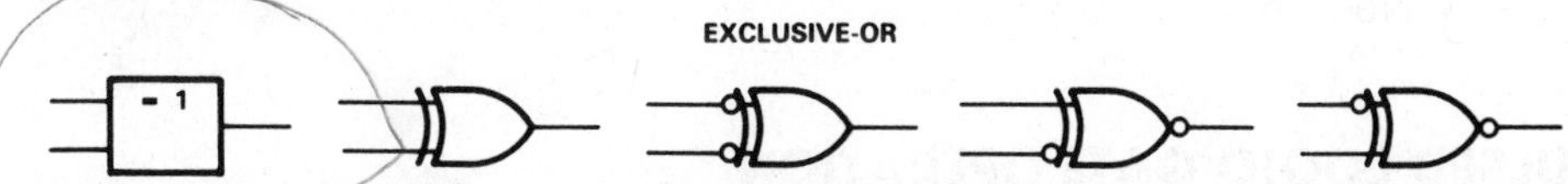

These are five equivalent Exclusive-OR symbols valid for an '86 or 'LS86A gate in positive logic; negation may be shown at any two ports.

LOGIC IDENTITY ELEMENT	EVEN-PARITY	ODD-PARITY ELEMENT
=	2k	2k + 1
The output is active (low) if all inputs stand at the same logic level (i.e., A = B).	The output is active (low) if an even number of inputs (i.e., 0 or 2) are active.	The output is active (high) if an odd number of inputs (i.e., only 1 of the 2) are active.

FIGURE 3-15 7486 Quad 2-Input XOR Data Sheet (Courtesy Texas Instruments)

XNOR

Logic Symbol

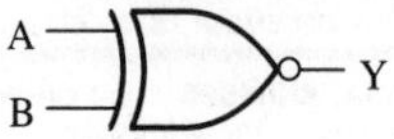

A, B → Y

Equation

$Y = \overline{A \oplus B}$

Truth Table

A	B	Y
0	0	1
0	1	0
1	0	0
1	1	1

FIGURE 3-16 XNOR Logic Function

A 74266 has four 2-input Exclusive-NOR gates. The data sheet for the 74266 IC is shown in Figure 3-17.

Section Self-Test

1. Why is the XOR called an "inequality" function and the XNOR called an "equality" function?
2. Can an exclusive gate have three inputs?
3. Are the XOR and XNOR complement functions?

ANSWERS (Not necessarily in the order of the questions)

- The XOR is HIGH when the inputs are not equal; the XNOR is HIGH when the inputs are equal.
- Yes
- No

3-8 PULSED LOGIC GATE OPERATION

Pulse analysis is a verification of the logic gate or circuit under actual operating conditions. As the input waveforms change, the output waveform can be determined from the logic expression or truth table for the gate.

A truth table is used to define a logic function. Each input combination has a corresponding output. The application of constant or **steady state** values

SN54LS266, SN74LS266
QUADRUPLE 2-INPUT EXCLUSIVE-NOR GATES WITH OPEN-COLLECTORS OUTPUTS

DECEMBER 1972 – REVISED MARCH 1988

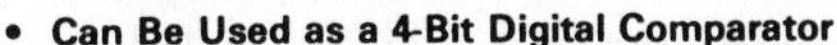

- **Can Be Used as a 4-Bit Digital Comparator**
- **Input Clamping Diodes Simplify System Design**
- **Fully Compatible with Most TTL Circuits**

FUNCTION TABLE

INPUTS		OUTPUT
A	B	Y
L	L	H
L	H	L
H	L	L
H	H	H

H = high level, L = low level

SN54LS266 . . . J OR W PACKAGE
SN74LS266 . . . D OR N PACKAGE
(TOP VIEW)

	Pin	Pin	
1A	1	14	V_{CC}
1B	2	13	4B
1Y	3	12	4A
2Y	4	11	4Y
2A	5	10	3Y
2B	6	9	3B
GND	7	8	3A

SN54LS266 . . . FK PACKAGE
(TOP VIEW)

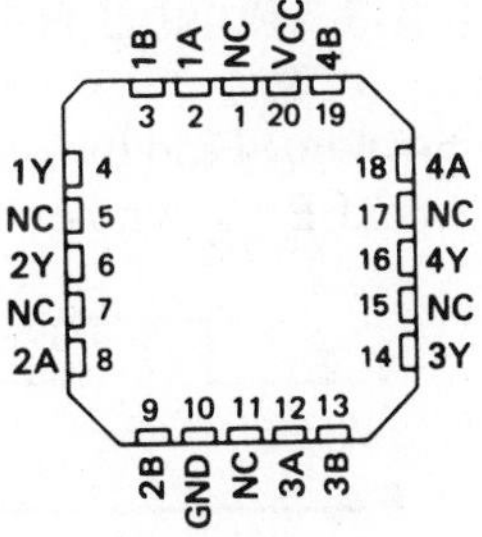

NC – No internal connection

description

The 'LS266 is comprised of four independent 2-input exclusive-NOR gates with open-collector outputs. The open-collector outputs permit tying outputs together for multiple-bit comparisons.

logic symbol (each gate)

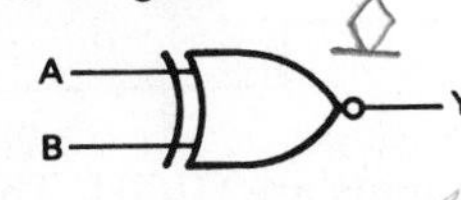

logic symbol†

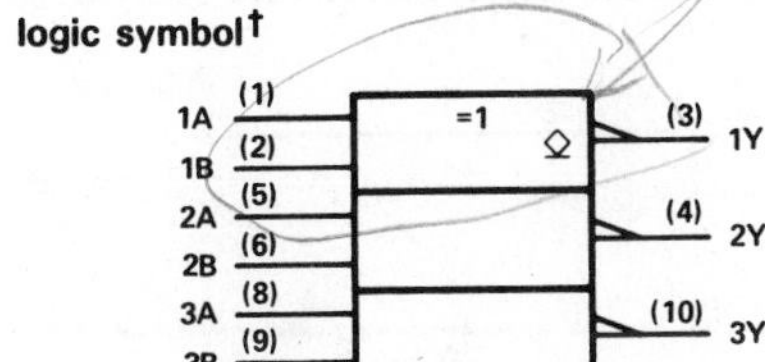

positive logic: $Y = \overline{A \oplus B} = AB + \overline{A}\overline{B}$

†This symbol is in accordance with ANSI/IEEE Std. 91-1984 and IEC Publication 617-12.

Pin numbers shown are for D, J, N, and W packages.

schematic of inputs and outputs

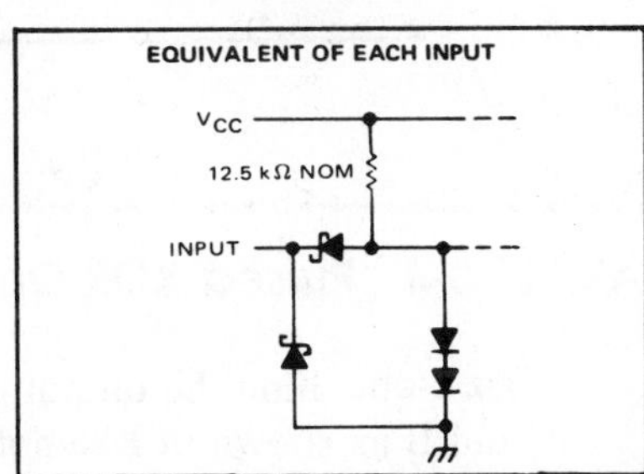

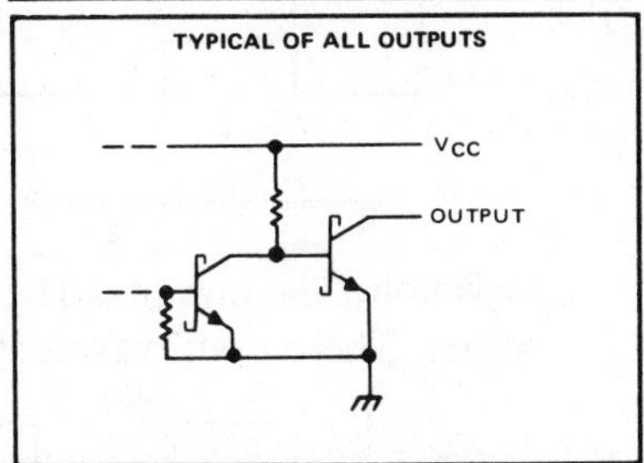

FIGURE 3-17 74266 Quad 2-Input XNOR Data Sheet (Courtesy Texas Instruments)

to a logic gate is sometimes referred to as **static operation.** For example, if a 0 is placed on one input to a NAND, and a 1 is placed on the other input of a NAND, the output is defined by the truth table as a 1.

It is also possible to operate logic gates by inputting digital waveforms into the gate inputs. This is known as **pulsed operation.** The outputs for each gate are still defined by the truth tables, but the waveforms must be analyzed with respect to time to determine an output waveform. This technique is referred to as **pulsed analysis.**

In the laboratory pulsed analysis is performed using an oscilloscope or logic analyzer. Pulsed operation is also used to determine the physical parameters of a gate or circuit, such as the time it takes for a signal to travel through a gate. This time is known as **propagation delay.**

■ EXAMPLE 3-3 Pulsed NAND Operation

Problem: Find the output waveform for a 2-input NAND gate with the inputs A and B shown here:

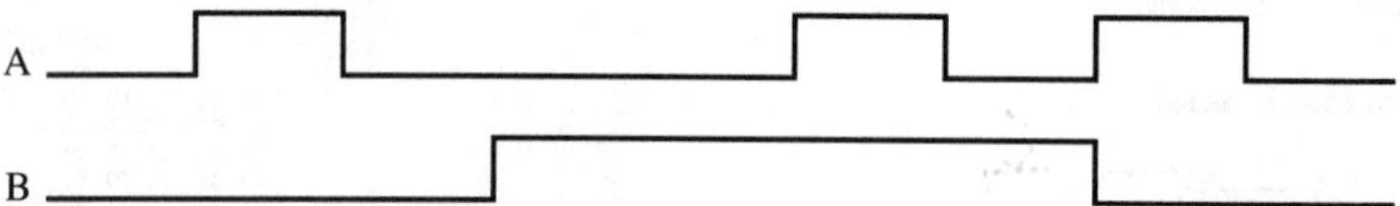

Solution: The output is LOW only when both inputs are HIGH. The resulting output waveform follows.

$\overline{AB}$ ■

■ EXAMPLE 3-4 Pulsed XOR Operation

Problem: Find the output pulsed waveform for an XOR gate with inputs A and B as shown in Example 3-3.

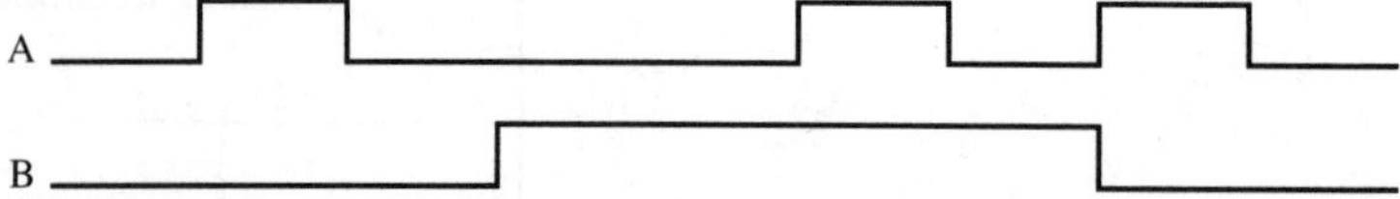

Solution: The output is HIGH when the two input signals do not equal each other. The output waveform follows.

■

Section Self-Test

1. What is meant by the term "pulsed operation"?
2. What is meant by the term "static operation"?
3. Will any logic gate accept a pulsed input?

ANSWERS (Not necessarily in the order of the questions)

- Yes
- Constant input voltages applied to the inputs of the logic function
- Time-varying input voltages applied to the inputs of the logic function

3-9 COMBINATIONAL LOGIC CIRCUITS

The basic logic gates of NOT, AND, NAND, OR, NOR, XOR, and XNOR are used to form all other digital logic functions. These functions can be built from individual gates or they can be manufactured as special-function integrated circuits.

In this section the seven basic logic gates are combined to form logic functions. For each of these functions, a circuit, logic equation, and truth table are derived to define the operation of the newly formed function.

3.9.1 Combinational Logic Circuit Functions and Truth Table Analysis

Combinational logic circuits are constructed by connecting together basic logic gates to form new logic functions. The logic expression of the resulting circuit can be determined by following the outputs of the logic gates as they connect to inputs of other logic gates.

The **combinational circuits** are analyzed from the inputs to the outputs. When first learning combinational circuit analysis, it is helpful to write the logic equation and analyze the output at each gate in the circuit before obtaining the final result.

Digital logic circuits can be analyzed using a truth table to specify all possible input combinations and the output result for each input combination. Each gate in the circuit can be analyzed to determine the final output.

To analyze the circuit operation, one applies each input combination to the circuit in order to determine the output. Intermediate nodes can be analyzed to simplify the process of predicting the output function. A truth table is used to perform the analysis in several examples that follow.

■ EXAMPLE 3-5 Combinational Logic Circuit Analysis

Problem: Analyze the circuit to determine the logic equation and the output.

Solution: Label each gate output as a node in the circuit. Write the output equation of each gate as a function of its inputs to eventually arrive at the final output equation. Analyze the logic state of each gate and record the results in a truth table. Finally, record the circuit output in the last column in the table.

■

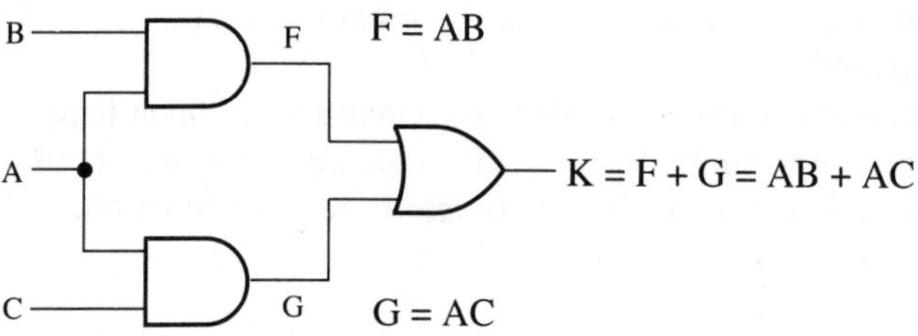

Inputs			Intermediate nodes		Output
A	B	C	F	G	K
0	0	0	0	0	0
0	0	1	0	0	0
0	1	0	0	0	0
0	1	1	0	0	0
1	0	0	0	0	0
1	0	1	0	1	1
1	1	0	1	0	1
1	1	1	1	1	1

$K = AB + AC$

FIGURE 3-18 Combinatorial Circuit Example 3-5

EXAMPLE 3-6 Circuit Analysis

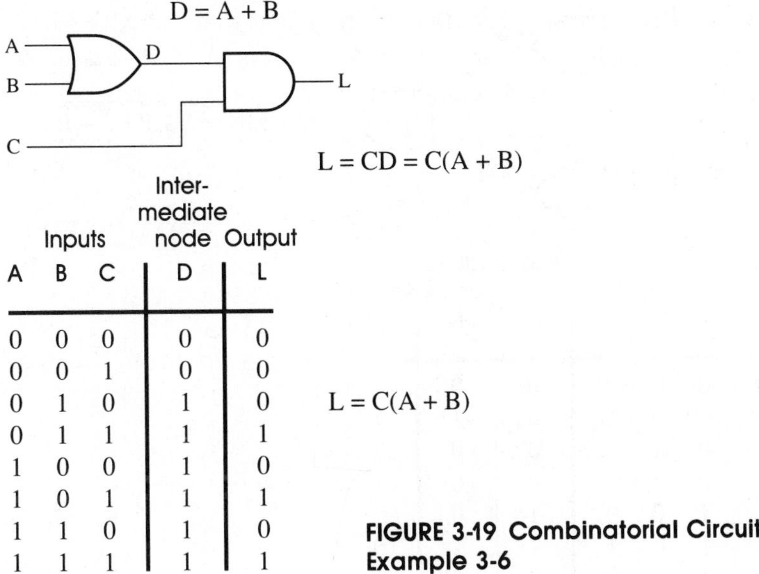

Inputs			Intermediate node	Output
A	B	C	D	L
0	0	0	0	0
0	0	1	0	0
0	1	0	1	0
0	1	1	1	1
1	0	0	1	0
1	0	1	1	1
1	1	0	1	0
1	1	1	1	1

FIGURE 3-19 Combinatorial Circuit Example 3-6

EXAMPLE 3-7 Circuit Analysis

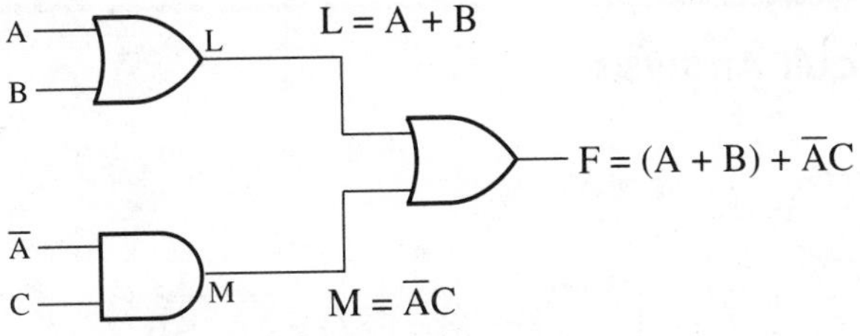

Inputs			Intermediate nodes		Output
A	B	C	L	M	F
0	0	0	0	0	0
0	0	1	0	1	1
0	1	0	1	0	1
0	1	1	1	1	1
1	0	0	1	0	1
1	0	1	1	0	1
1	1	0	1	0	1
1	1	1	1	0	1

$F = A + B + \overline{A}C$

Note: $F = A + B + C$ by inspection of the truth table.

FIGURE 3-20 Combinatorial Circuit Example 3-7

EXAMPLE 3-8 Circuit Analysis

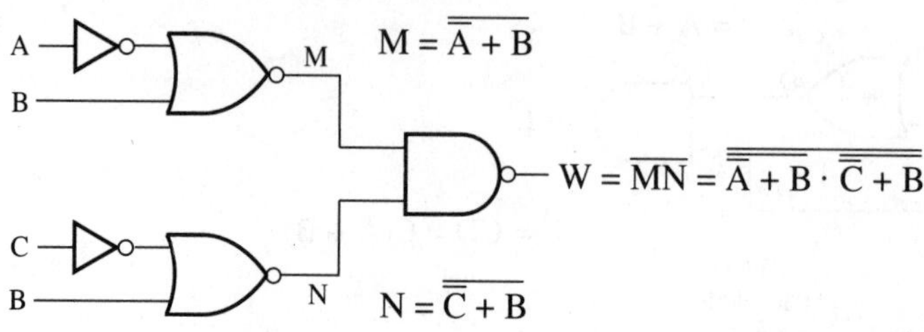

Inputs			Intermediate nodes		Output
A	B	C	M	N	W
0	0	0	0	0	1
0	0	1	0	1	1
0	1	0	0	0	1
0	1	1	0	0	1
1	0	0	1	0	1
1	0	1	1	1	0
1	1	0	0	0	1
1	1	1	0	0	1

$W = \overline{\overline{\overline{A} + B} \cdot \overline{\overline{C} + B}}$

FIGURE 3-21 Combinatorial Circuit Example 3-8

EXAMPLE 3-9 Circuit Analysis

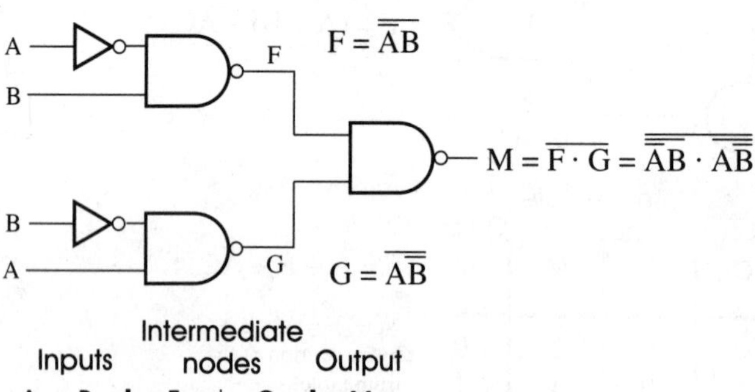

Inputs		Intermediate nodes		Output
A	B	F	G	M
0	0	1	1	0
0	1	0	1	1
1	0	1	0	1
1	1	1	1	0

$M = \overline{\overline{\overline{A}B} \cdot \overline{A\overline{B}}}$

Note: $M = A \oplus B$ by inspection of the truth table.

FIGURE 3-22 Combinatorial Circuit Example 3-9

The combinational circuits in the previous examples consist of several **levels** of logic gates. The levels are numbered, beginning with level 1 at the output, and increasing the count toward the input. Any inverters at the input level are not counted as a separate level.

The total number of levels indicates the maximum number of gates that a digital signal must pass through before it is seen at the output. Figure 3-23 illustrates a four level digital circuit.

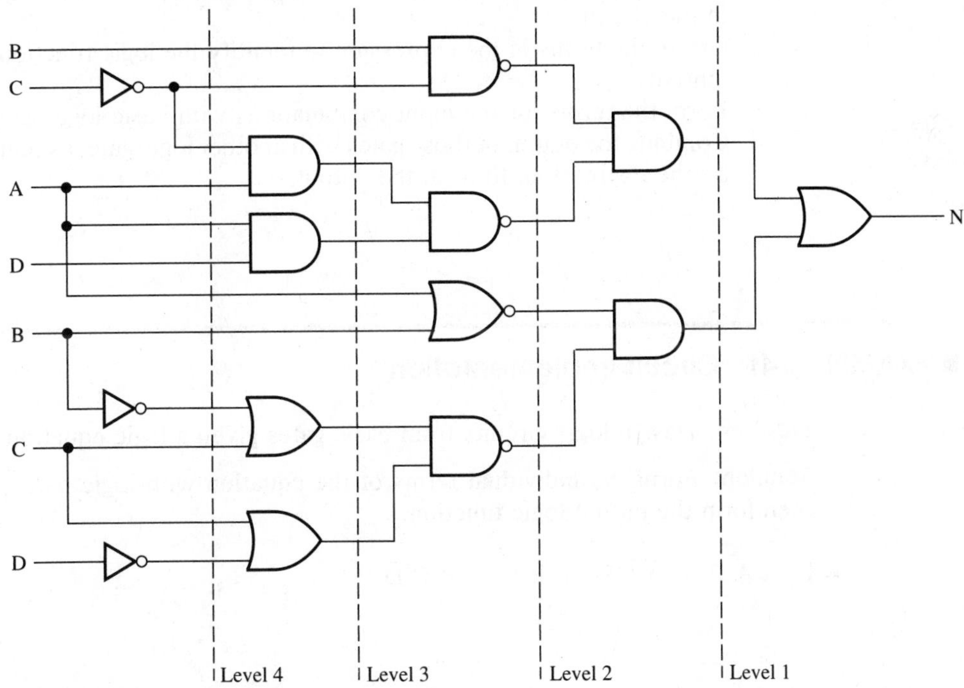

FIGURE 3-23 Four-Level Digital Circuit

■ EXAMPLE 3-10 Digital Circuit Levels

Problem: Determine the number of levels in each of the circuits in Examples 3-5 through 3-9.

Solution: Beginning at the output, count the maximum number of gates to the inputs. (Remember, input inverters do not count)

CIRCUIT	NUMBER OF LEVELS
Example 3-5	2
Example 3-6	2
Example 3-7	2
Example 3-8	2
Example 3-9	2

■

3.9.2 Logic Circuits from Boolean Equations

A logic circuit can be constructed from a logic expression by forming the terms in the logic expression with the basic logic gates and combining the outputs of those gates with other logic gates to form the final circuit output. The following procedure summarizes the steps:

1. Identify the input variables, both true and inverted forms, as required in the circuit.
2. Group the terms in the expression to identify the logic functions required.
3. Form the terms for the input combinations with basic logic gates.
4. Combine the output of those gates with another logic gate, as required by the expression, to form the output.

■ EXAMPLE 3-11 Circuit Implementation

Problem: Design logic circuits from basic gates given a logic equation.

Solution: Form the individual terms of the equation with logic gates, and then form the output logic function.

$$L = \overline{A}\,B + \overline{A\,C}\,D + B\,C + B\,C\,\overline{D}$$

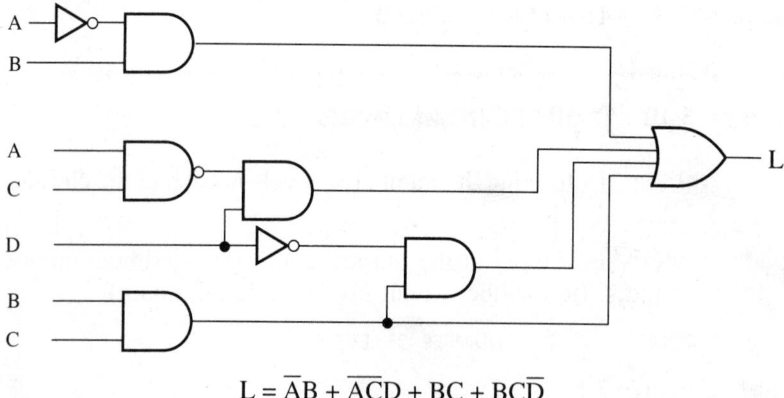

FIGURE 3-24 Circuit Implementation Example 3-11 ■

EXAMPLE 3-12 Circuit Implementation

$$M = (A + \overline{B})(A + \overline{B + C})(\overline{\overline{B} + D})$$

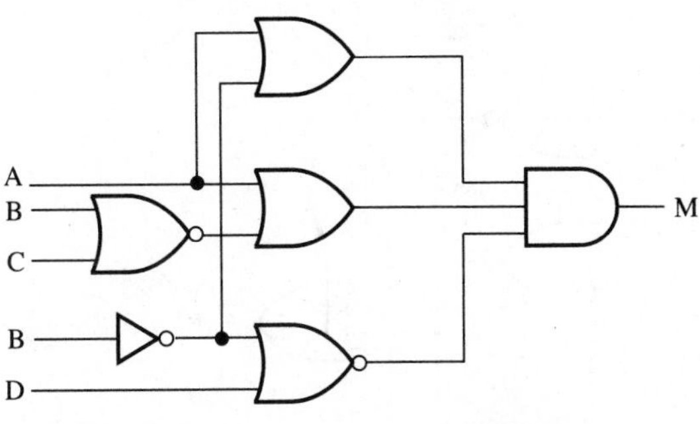

$$M = (A + \overline{B})(A + \overline{B + C})(\overline{\overline{B} + D})$$

FIGURE 3-25 Circuit Implementation Example 3-12

EXAMPLE 3-13 Circuit Implementation

$$N = \overline{\overline{A\,\overline{B}}\ \overline{B\,\overline{C}\,D}\ \overline{A\,D}\ \overline{\overline{B}\,\overline{D}}}$$

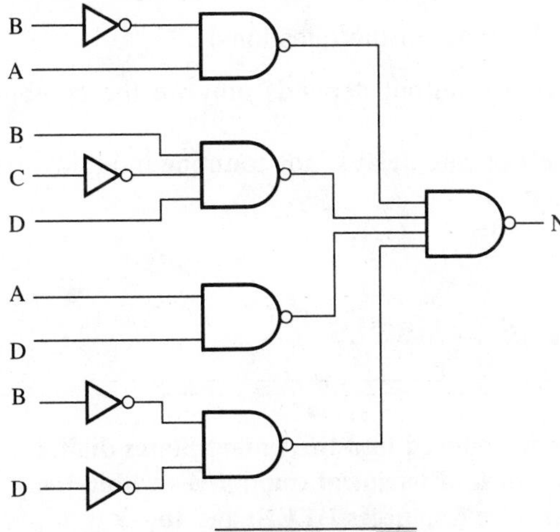

$$N = \overline{\overline{A\overline{B}}\ \overline{B\overline{C}D}\ \overline{AD}\ \overline{\overline{B}\,\overline{D}}}$$

FIGURE 3-26 Circuit Implementation Example 3-13

■ EXAMPLE 3-14 Circuit Implementation

$$P = \overline{\overline{(B + \overline{C} + D)} + \overline{(\overline{A} + \overline{B} + C + D)} + \overline{(A + \overline{B} + \overline{C} + \overline{D})} + \overline{(A + C)}}$$

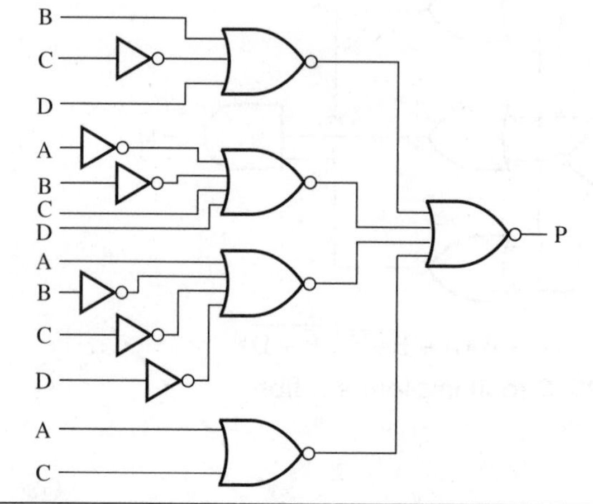

$P = \overline{\overline{(B + \overline{C} + D)} + \overline{(\overline{A} + \overline{B} + C + D)} + \overline{(A + \overline{B} + \overline{C} + \overline{D})} + \overline{(A + C)}}$

FIGURE 3-27 Circuit Implementation Example 3-14 ■

Section Self-Test

1. What is the definition of a combinational circuit?
2. What does it mean to say a circuit has five levels of logic?
3. Is it possible to construct a truth table from a digital circuit?

ANSWERS (Not necessarily in the order of the questions)

- A digital circuit whose output depends only on the combination of the input states.
- There are five levels of gate delays, not counting input inverters, from the inputs to the output.
- Yes

3-10 IEEE/ANSI LOGIC GATE SYMBOLS

In 1973 new logic symbols were introduced into the United States digital electronics industry through the work of technical committees within the Institute of Electrical and Electronics Engineers (IEEE) and the American National Standards Institute (ANSI). The finalized standard, released internationally in 1984, is referred to as IEEE Standard 91-1984.

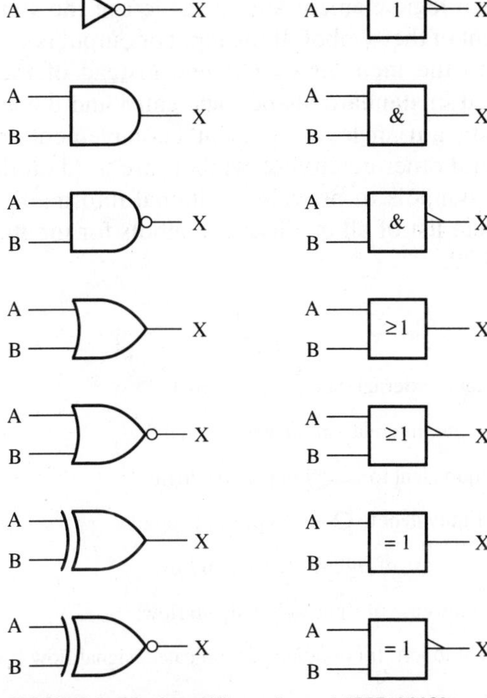

FIGURE 3-28 Traditional and IEEE/ANSI Logic Gate Symbols

The standard logic symbols still predominate in digital technology, but the new IEEE/ANSI symbols are becoming more widely used in many data books and military applications since the U.S. government now requires all military contract work to use the new symbols.

The new IEEE/ANSI symbols provide more information than the standard shape logic symbols, especially for more complex logic devices such as flip-flops, shift registers, decoders, counters, multiplexers, demultiplexers, and adders. Enough information is provided with the symbol to lessen the need to refer to the TTL data book for logic device operation. Traditional logic symbols and new IEEE/ANSI standard logic symbols for each of the seven basic logic functions are shown in Figure 3-28.

3.10.1 Qualifying Symbols and Symbol Composition

Each of the IEEE standard symbols uses a rectangular symbol for each logic element or gate. The shape of this symbol can be a square or any other sized rectangle,.as there is no exact shape specified.

The inputs of each logic element are on the left of the symbol, and the outputs are on the right of the symbol. If the input or output is complemented, a triangle is added to the input or output line instead of the open circle inversion symbol used in standard shape logic gates and devices.

In addition to using a triangle to represent a complement or **active-LOW** input or output, several other qualifying symbols are used on the inputs and outputs of the logic symbols to provide additional information concerning the device. A complete list of all qualifying symbols for inputs and outputs is shown in Figure 3-29.

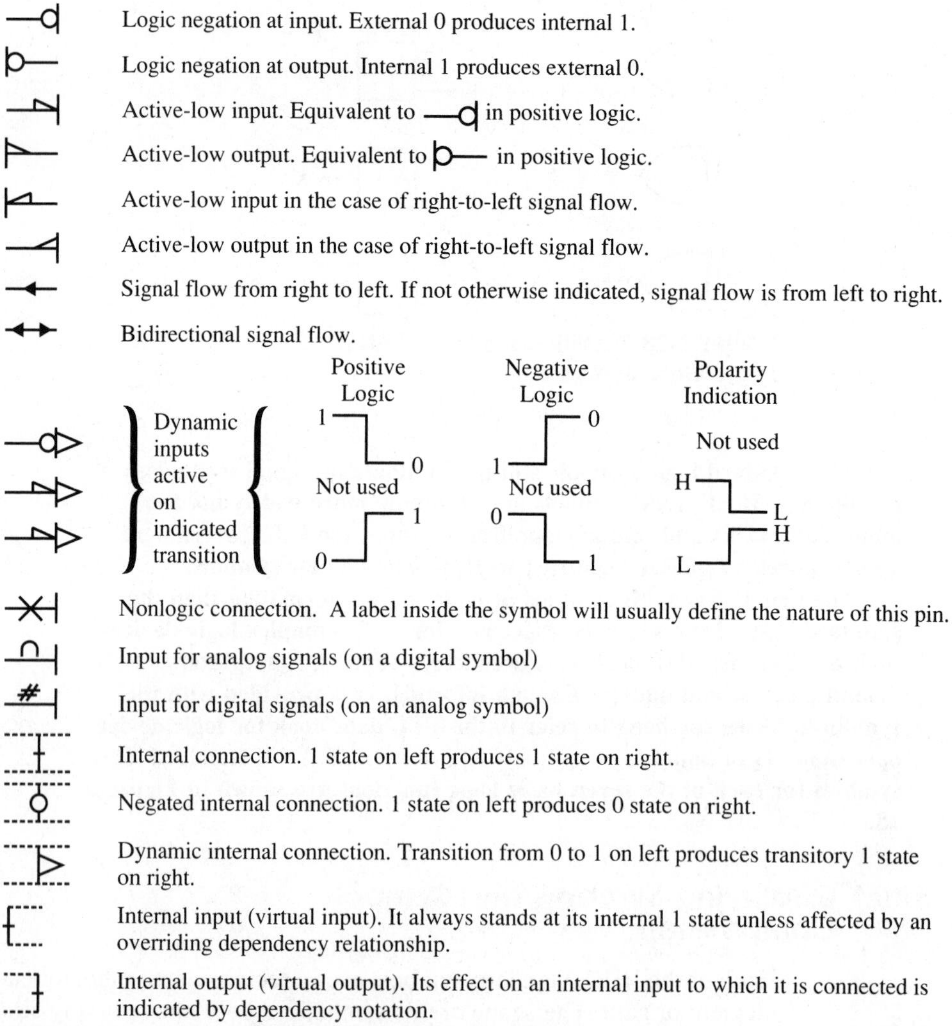

Logic negation at input. External 0 produces internal 1.

Logic negation at output. Internal 1 produces external 0.

Active-low input. Equivalent to in positive logic.

Active-low output. Equivalent to in positive logic.

Active-low input in the case of right-to-left signal flow.

Active-low output in the case of right-to-left signal flow.

Signal flow from right to left. If not otherwise indicated, signal flow is from left to right.

Bidirectional signal flow.

Dynamic inputs active on indicated transition

	Positive Logic	Negative Logic	Polarity Indication
	1 → 0	1 → 0	Not used
	Not used	Not used	H → L
	0 → 1	0 → 1	L → H

Nonlogic connection. A label inside the symbol will usually define the nature of this pin.

Input for analog signals (on a digital symbol)

Input for digital signals (on an analog symbol)

Internal connection. 1 state on left produces 1 state on right.

Negated internal connection. 1 state on left produces 0 state on right.

Dynamic internal connection. Transition from 0 to 1 on left produces transitory 1 state on right.

Internal input (virtual input). It always stands at its internal 1 state unless affected by an overriding dependency relationship.

Internal output (virtual output). Its effect on an internal input to which it is connected is indicated by dependency notation.

FIGURE 3-29 IEEE Input/Output Qualifying Symbols

Symbol	Description	CMOS Example	TTL Example
&	AND gate or function.	'HC00	SN7400
≥1	OR gate or function. The symbol was chosen to indicate that at least one active input is needed to activate the output.	'HC02	SN7402
= 1	Exclusive OR. One and only one input must be active to activate the output.	'HC86	SN7486
=	Logic identity. All inputs must stand at the same state.	'HC86	SN74180
2k	An even number of inputs must be active.	'HC280	SN74180
2k + 1	An odd number of inputs must be active.	'HC86	SN74ALS86
1	The one input must be active.	'HC04	SN7404
▷ or ◁	A buffer or element with more than usual output capability (symbol is oriented in the direction of signal flow).	'HC240	SN74S436
⎍	Schmitt trigger; element with hysteresis.	'HC132	SN74LS18
X/Y	Coder, code converter (DEC/BCD, BIN/OUT, BIN/7-SEG, etc.).	'HC42	SN74LS347
MUX	Multiplexer/data selector.	'HC151	SN74150
DMUX or DX	Demultiplexer.	'HC138	SN74138
Σ	Adder.	'HC283	SN74LS385
P – Q	Subtracter.	*	SN74LS385
CPG	Look-ahead carry generator.	'HC182	SN74182
π	Multiplier.	*	SN74LS384
COMP	Magnitude comparator.	'HC85	SN74LS682
ALU	Arithmetic logic unit.	'HC181	SN74LS381
⎍	Retriggerable monostable.	'HC123	SN74LS422
1⎍	Nonretriggerable monostable (one-shot).	'HC221	SN74121
G ⎍⎍	Astable element. Showing waveform is optional.	*	SN74LS320
! G ⎍⎍	Synchronously starting astable.	*	SN74LS624
G ! ⎍⎍	Astable element that stops with a completed pulse.	*	*
SRGm	Shift register. m = number of bits.	'HC164	SN74LS595
CTRm	Counter. m = number of bits; cycle length = 2^m.	'HC590	SN74LS590
CTR DIVm	Counter with cycle length = m.	'HC160	SN74LS668
RCTRm	Asynchronous (ripple-carry) counter; cycle length = 2^m.	'HC4020	*
ROM	Read-only memory.	*	SN74187
RAM	Random-access read/write memory.	'HC189	SN74170
FIFO	First-in, first-out memory.	*	SN74LS222
I = 0	Element powers up cleared to 0 state.	*	SN74AS877
I = 1	Element powers up set to 1 state.	'HC7022	SN74AS877
Φ	Highly complex function; "gray box" symbol with limited detail shown under special rules.	*	SN74LS608

FIGURE 3-30 IEEE General Qualifying Symbols

The basic logic function of each symbol is specified by a **general qualifying symbol.** Each general qualifying symbol is placed near the top center or geometric center of a symbol or symbol element. The general qualifying symbols are listed in Figure 3-30.

3.10.2 IEEE/ANSI Logic Symbol Usage

Throughout this text most logic functions will be represented by traditional logic symbols and notation. When appropriate, the new logic symbols will be shown to familiarize the student with their use.

For the seven basic logic functions, the new symbols do not offer any advantage over the traditional shaped logic symbols. For more complex ICs, **dependency notation** provides significant justification for using the new symbols, as the complete operation of the device can be specified.

Dependency notation provides a method for designating the relationship between inputs and outputs without showing all internal connections. To date, 11 types of dependency have been defined for the IEEE standard. Readers are encouraged to refer to IEEE specification standard 91-1984 for more information on dependency notation.

Section Self-Test

Determine if the following statements are true or false.

1. A cross is placed at the output of IEEE logic symbols to denote the complement function.
2. The IEEE logic symbol for an Exclusive–OR gate has an = 1 in the symbol.
3. The —◁ symbol indicates that a HIGH on the input will produce a LOW internally on the device.

ANSWERS

• True • True • False

3-11 BOOLEAN ALGEBRA

Boolean algebra is a systematic algebraic formulation of mathematical postulates and symbols that can be used to describe and simplify logic functions. It is very useful in the simplification of logic equations, which in turn can simplify the circuitry needed to perform a given logic function. In addition, Boolean relationships can be used to substitute one type of gate for another, which is a very useful technique to optimize the construction of digital logic circuitry. Once the basic Boolean algebraic laws are understood, the principles can be applied to a large number of practical digital logic applications.

3.11.1 Historical Perspective

The original mathematical theory on Boolean algebra was introduced by George Boole (1815–1864), an English mathematics professor, in a work entitled "An Investigation into the Laws of Thought," published in 1854.

Edward V. Huntington (1874–1952) presented some additional postulates, called Huntington's postulates, that expanded on the original theory of Boole.

Claude E. Shannon (1916) did some additional research in the area of two-valued Boolean algebra, known as switching algebra, that led to the practical form of Boolean algebra used today in the area of digital circuits.

3.11.2 Boolean Algebraic Laws

The basic laws of Boolean algebra are mathematically equivalent to the rules of standard variable algebra, with the exception of the meaning of operator symbols. As mentioned, the logical AND function is denoted by a dot "·," or by dropping the dot operand and placing the variable letters of the equation together. Thus, "A AND B AND C," is written as A·B·C, or ABC. Groups of ANDed variables are also known as **product terms.** AC, A·B·C, WXYZ, and (A·B) are all product terms.

The logical OR function is denoted by a plus, "+." Thus, "A OR B OR C" is written as A + B + C. Groups of ORed variables are also known as **sum terms.** Thus, A + B, D + E + F, and (W + X + Y + Z) are all examples of sum terms.

Finally, the complement is designated by the use of a bar "–" over the variable or expression to be complemented. Thus, the complement of A is $\overline{A}$, and the complement of (A + B)C is $\overline{(A + B)C}$. The bar in equation form corresponds to the inverter bubble symbol placed on the input or output of a logic gate.

Parentheses are used as in normal algebra to designate groups of variables to aid in equation manipulation. Variables can also be combined algebraically with the logic levels 0 and 1 in Boolean equations.

As in standard algebra, there is a **Commutative Law** for Boolean algebra. The Commutative Laws for two-variable logical operations are shown in Equations 3-1 through 3-6.

Eq. 3-1	$AB = BA$	AND operation
Eq. 3-2	$\overline{AB} = \overline{BA}$	NAND operation
Eq. 3-3	$A + B = B + A$	OR operation
Eq. 3-4	$\overline{A + B} = \overline{B + A}$	NOR operation
Eq. 3-5	$A \oplus B = B \oplus A$	XOR operation
Eq. 3-6	$\overline{A \oplus B} = \overline{B \oplus A}$	XNOR operation

The **Associative Law** also applies to Boolean logic operations. The Associative Law for three-variable operations are shown in Equations 3-7 through 3-10.

Eq. 3-7	$A(BC) = (AB)C$	AND
Eq. 3-8	$\overline{A(BC)} = \overline{(AB)C}$	NAND
Eq. 3-9	$(A + B) + C = A + (B + C)$	OR
Eq. 3-10	$\overline{(A + B) + C} = \overline{A + (B + C)}$	NOR

The **Distributive Law** applies to certain three-variable AND/OR Boolean expressions as shown in Equations 3-11 and 3-12.

Eq. 3-11 $\quad A(B + C) = AB + AC$

Eq. 3-12 $\quad (A + B)(C + D) = AC + AD + BC + BD$

The Commutative, Associative, and Distributive laws can also be demonstrated with logic gates. Figure 3-31 illustrates the gate equivalent circuits for Equation 3-11.

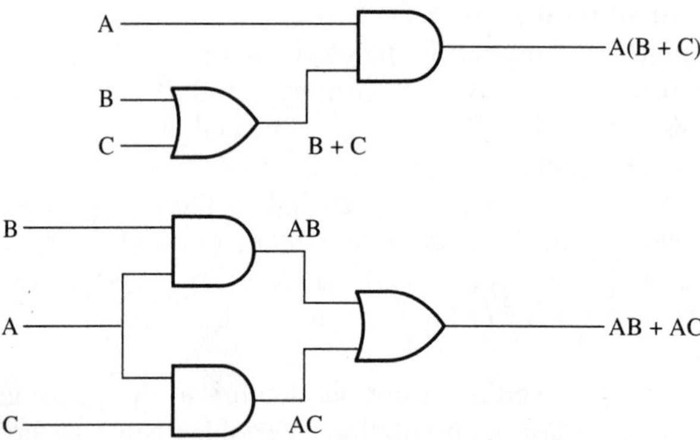

FIGURE 3-31 Distributive Law Equivalent Circuits

Truth tables can also be used to prove any of the Boolean theorems and identities.

■ EXAMPLE 3-15 Truth Table Verification of the Distributive Law

Problem: Prove the Boolean algebra Distributive Law with the use of a truth table. Show

$A(B + C) = AB + AC$

Solution: Set up a three-variable truth table with the input variables A, B, and C. A three-variable truth table has eight possible input combinations, ranging from 000 to 111. Determine the output resulting from the equation, A(B + C) and the outputs resulting from the equation, AB + AC. If the Distributive Law is correct, the two output results will be equal. To simplify the truth table analysis, analyze the intermediate terms as well as the final result.

The resulting truth table is shown in Table 3-5. It can be seen that Output #1 is equal to Output #2, and therefore the Distributive Law is valid.

TABLE 3-5 Truth Table to Verify the Distributive Law

Input Variables				Output #1			Output #2
A	B	C	B + C	A(B + C)	AB	AC	AB + AC
0	0	0	0	0	0	0	0
0	0	1	1	0	0	0	0
0	1	0	1	0	0	0	0
0	1	1	1	0	0	0	0
1	0	0	0	0	0	0	0
1	0	1	1	1	0	1	1
1	1	0	1	1	1	0	1
1	1	1	1	1	1	1	1

■

It has been demonstrated that the Distributive Law is valid by the use of a truth table. Thus, the combinational logic circuits must also be functionally equivalent.

Functionally equivalent circuits output the same logic levels when the inputs to each circuit are the same. It is important to note that many possible digital circuits will perform the equivalent logic function. Skills must be developed to recognize, translate between, and select the appropriate digital circuit for an application.

Both circuits in Figure 3-31 perform the same logic function, but one requires three gates and the other requires only two gates. Circuit minimization techniques will be examined in detail, beginning with a firm understanding of Boolean algebra to simplify logic equations and recognize equivalent logic gates for circuit implementation.

3.11.3 Boolean Identities and Theorems

In addition to the basic Commutative, Associative, and Distributive laws, several Boolean identities and theorems are very useful in simplifying Boo-

TABLE 3-6 Boolean Identities, Theorems, and Rules

Eq. 3-13	$\overline{\overline{A}} = A$
Eq. 3-14	$A + A = A$
Eq. 3-15	$A + \overline{A} = 1$
Eq. 3-16	$A + 0 = A$
Eq. 3-17	$A + 1 = 1$
Eq. 3-18	$A + AB = A$
Eq. 3-19	$A + \overline{A}B = A + B$
Eq. 3-20	$A(A + B) = A$
Eq. 3-21	$A(\overline{A} + B) = AB$
Eq. 3-22	$A \cdot A = A$
Eq. 3-23	$A \cdot \overline{A} = 0$
Eq. 3-24	$A \cdot 0 = 0$
Eq. 3-25	$A \cdot 1 = A$
Eq. 3-26	$(A + B)(A + \overline{B}) = A$
Eq. 3-27	$A\,B + A\,\overline{B} = A$
Eq. 3-28	$(A + B)(A + C) = A + BC$
Eq. 3-29	$A \oplus B = A\,\overline{B} + \overline{A}\,B$
Eq. 3-30	$\overline{A \oplus B} = \overline{A}\,\overline{B} + A\,B$

lean logic equations and logic circuits. Table 3-6 lists the major Boolean identities, theorems, and relationships used for equation and circuit simplification.

The Boolean algebraic relationships shown in Table 3-8 are very useful in the simplification of Boolean equations and digital logic circuits. Each of the variables in the equations can represent any single variable, or a group of variables. Thus, $ABC + \overline{ABC} = 1$, according to Equation 3-15. Using Equation 3-18, CD + CDA equals CD.

Any of the Boolean relationships can be derived with a truth table. Therefore, if one forgets a particular relationship, a truth table can be constructed to determine the Boolean identity.

■ EXAMPLE 3-16 Theorem A·0 = 0

Problem: Verify the specified Boolean theorem.

Solution: Analyze the function in the theorem with a truth table.

Truth Table Analysis

A	0	A·0
0	0	0
1	0	0

Note that the output is always 0. Therefore, the theorem is verified. ■

■ EXAMPLE 3-17 Theorem A + AB = A

Truth Table Analysis

A	B	AB	A + AB
0	0	0	0
0	1	0	0
1	0	0	1
1	1	1	1

Note that the column for A + AB is equal to the column for A. Therefore, the theorem is verified. ■

It is also important to note that any of the Boolean algebraic relationships can be shown with logic gates. For example, Equation 3-13, $\overline{\overline{A}} = A$, can be illustrated with two inverters as shown in Figure 3-32.

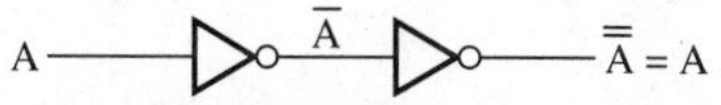

A —▷○— $\overline{A}$ —▷○— $\overline{\overline{A}} = A$

FIGURE 3-32 Circuit Implementation, $\overline{\overline{A}} = A$

Any two complements performed on a logic variable or input will result in the true or original logic variable or value. This fact can be used to simplify logic equations or logic circuits.

■ EXAMPLE 3-18 Circuit Simplification Using Boolean Algebra Theorems

Problem: Simplify the logic circuit in Figure 3-33 using Boolean algebra theorems.

Solution: First, recognize that the NOT symbol on the output of the NAND gate and the NOT symbol on the input of the OR gate cancel. The first circuit modification is shown in Figure 3-33(b).

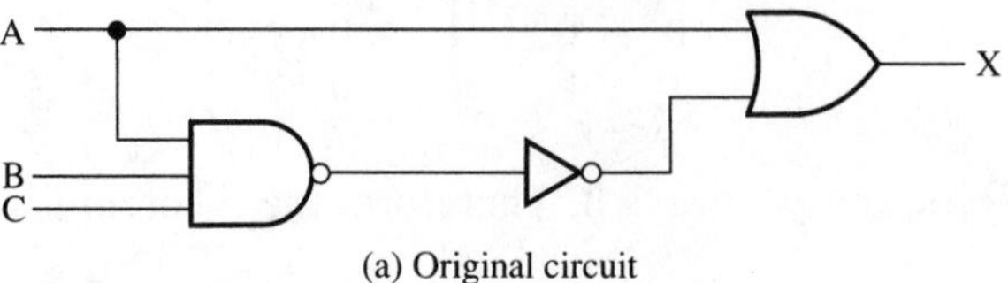

(a) Original circuit

FIGURE 3-33 Example Problem 3-18

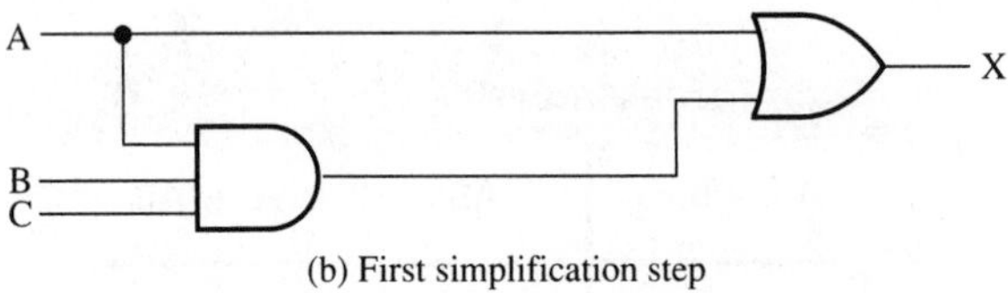

(b) First simplification step

The Boolean equation for the simplified circuit of Figure 3-33(b) is ABC + A. Using Equation 3-18, A + ABC = A. Thus, no logic gates are needed to perform this logic function, as the output X equals the input A. The final circuit simplification is shown in Figure 3-33(c). ■

A ——— X

(c) Final simplification

3.11.4 DeMorgan's Theorems

DeMorgan's Theorems, first proposed by an English mathematician and logician, Augustus DeMorgan (1806–1871), and later expanded on by George Boole, are two very important Boolean algebra theorems. DeMorgan's theorems can be used to simplify expressions involving both AND and OR operations. The theorems, stated in equation form in Equations 3-31 and 3-32, are shown in the form of logic gates in Figure 3-34.

Eq. 3-31	$\overline{A + B} = \overline{A}\,\overline{B}$	DeMorgan's Theorem 1
Eq. 3-32	$\overline{A\,B} = \overline{A} + \overline{B}$	DeMorgan's Theorem 2

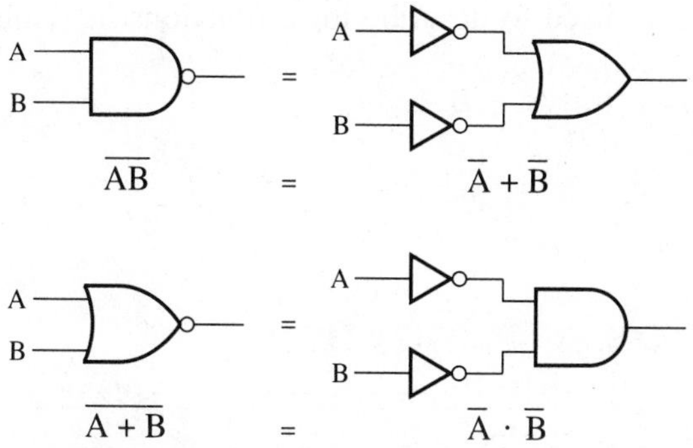

$\overline{AB} = \overline{A} + \overline{B}$

$\overline{A + B} = \overline{A} \cdot \overline{B}$

FIGURE 3-34 Logic Circuit Implementation of DeMorgan's Theorems

DeMorgan's Theorems can be expanded to two or more variables. In equation form for four variables in Equations 3-33 and 3-34.

Eq. 3-33 $\overline{A + B + C + D} = \overline{A}\,\overline{B}\,\overline{C}\,\overline{D}$ DeMorgan Theorem 1

Eq. 3-34 $\overline{A\,B\,C\,D} = \overline{A} + \overline{B} + \overline{C} + \overline{D}$ DeMorgan Theorem 2

DeMorgan's Theorems state that an inversion process on the output of a logic gate can be converted to the input of the logic gate if the function is changed to its **dual.** In other words, the AND must be changed to the OR, and the OR function must be changed to the AND.

A naming convention often associated with DeMorgan's Theorems is the following:

Break the bar; change the sign.
Make the bar; change the sign.

An equivalent convention that applies to the conversion of logic gates is:

Invert the inputs; invert the outputs; change the gate to its dual function.

DeMorgan's Theorems will be applied to equations and circuits as a useful technique to obtain alternative gates and alternative circuit implementation. The objective of using DeMorgan's Theorems in circuit design is to minimize the number of ICs required in a logic circuit.

Section Self-Test

1. What is Boolean algebra?
2. (a) $A + 1 = ??$ (b) $A0 = ??$ (c) $A + \overline{A}B = ??$
3. What are DeMorgan's Theorems in Boolean equation form for two variables?

ANSWERS

- A type of algebra used to describe logic functions in symbolic equation form.
- (a) 1 (b) 0 (c) A + B
- $\overline{A + B} = \overline{A}\,\overline{B}$
  $\overline{AB} = \overline{A} + \overline{B}$

3-12 BOOLEAN EQUATION SIMPLIFICATION

It is important to become familiar with the Boolean theorems so that one can apply them to logic equations for simplification. Boolean simplification techniques are used not only to reduce the number of ICs needed to construct a logic circuit, but also to simplify the logic equations input into programmable logic devices (PLDs).

Several examples are presented to demonstrate how to use the Boolean theorems to simplify equations. The applicable Boolean Equations 3-1 through 3-32 that were used to simplify the equation are specified.

■ EXAMPLE 3-19 Boolean Simplification

Simplify $A + \overline{A}B + \overline{A}BC$

SIMPLIFICATION STEPS	EQUATION USED
$A + \overline{A}B + \overline{A}BC$	
$A + \overline{A}B(1 + C)$	Eq. 3-18
$A + \overline{A}B\,1$	Eq. 3-17
$A + \overline{A}B$	Eq. 3-25
$A + B$	Eq. 3-19

■

■ EXAMPLE 3-20 Boolean Simplification

Simplify $\overline{A}\,\overline{B}\,\overline{C} + \overline{A}\,\overline{B}\,C + A\,\overline{B}\,\overline{C}$

SIMPLIFICATION STEPS	EQUATION USED
$\overline{A}\,\overline{B}\,\overline{C} + \overline{A}\,\overline{B}\,C + A\,\overline{B}\,\overline{C}$	
$\overline{A}\,\overline{B} + A\,\overline{B}\,\overline{C}$	Eq. 3-27
$\overline{B}(\overline{A} + A\,\overline{C})$	Factor out $\overline{B}$

SIMPLIFICATION STEPS	EQUATION USED
$\overline{B}(\overline{A} + \overline{\overline{A}}\,\overline{C})$	Eq. 3-13
$\overline{B}(\overline{A} + \overline{C})$	Eq. 3-19
$\overline{A}\,\overline{B} + \overline{B}\,\overline{C}$	Eq. 3-11 ■

■ EXAMPLE 3-21 Boolean Simplification

Simplify $ABCD + \overline{ABCD}$

SIMPLIFICATION STEPS	EQUATION USED
$A\,B\,C\,D + \overline{A\,B\,C\,D}$	
1	Eq. 3-15 ■

■ EXAMPLE 3-22 Boolean Simplification

Simplify $(\overline{A} + \overline{B} + \overline{C})(\overline{A} + \overline{B} + C)(A + \overline{B} + \overline{C})$

SIMPLIFICATION STEPS	EQUATIONS USED
$(\overline{A} + \overline{B} + \overline{C})(\overline{A} + \overline{B} + C)(A + \overline{B} + \overline{C})$	
$(\overline{A} + \overline{B} + \overline{C})(\overline{A} + \overline{B} + C)(A + \overline{B} + \overline{C}))(\overline{A} + \overline{B} + \overline{C})$	Eq. 3-22
$[(\overline{A} + \overline{B} + \overline{C})(\overline{A} + \overline{B} + C)][(A + \overline{B} + \overline{C})(\overline{A} + \overline{B} + \overline{C})]$	
$[\overline{A} + \overline{B}][\overline{B} + \overline{C}]$	Eq. 3-26
$[\overline{B} + \overline{A}][\overline{B} + \overline{C}]$	Eq. 3-3
$\overline{B} + \overline{A}\,\overline{C}$	Eq. 3-28 ■

■ EXAMPLE 3-23 Boolean Simplification

Simplify $\overline{AB(CD + EF)}$

SIMPLIFICATION STEPS	EQUATION USED
$\overline{AB(CD + EF)}$	
$\overline{AB} + \overline{(CD + EF)}$	Eq. 3-23
$\overline{A} + \overline{B} + (\overline{CD})(\overline{EF})$	Eq. 3-32
	Eq. 3-31
$\overline{A} + \overline{B} + (\overline{C} + \overline{D})(\overline{E} + \overline{F})$	Eq. 3-32
$A + B + \overline{C}\,\overline{D} + \overline{C}\,\overline{F} + \overline{D}\,\overline{F}$	Eq. 3-12 ■

■ EXAMPLE 3-24 Boolean Simplification

Simplify $\overline{(\overline{A} + B + C + D)} + (A\,\overline{B}\,\overline{C}\,D)$

SIMPLIFICATION STEPS	EQUATION USED
$\overline{(\overline{A} + B + C + D)} + (A\,\overline{B}\,\overline{C}\,D)$	
$\overline{\overline{A}}\,\overline{B}\,\overline{C}\,\overline{D} + A\,\overline{B}\,\overline{C}\,D$	Eq. 3-31
$A\,\overline{B}\,\overline{C}\,\overline{D} + A\,\overline{B}\,\overline{C}\,D$	Eq. 3-13
$A\,\overline{B}\,\overline{C}$	Eq. 3-27

■

■ EXAMPLE 3-25 Boolean Simplification

Simplify $(\overline{A} + \overline{B})(A + \overline{B})(\overline{A} + B)$

SIMPLIFICATION STEPS	EQUATION USED
$(\overline{A} + \overline{B})(A + \overline{B})(\overline{A} + B)$	
$[(\overline{A} + \overline{B})(A + \overline{B})][(\overline{A} + B)(\overline{A} + \overline{B})]$	Eq. 3-22
$[\overline{B}][\overline{A}]$	Eq. 3-26
$\overline{A}\,\overline{B}$	Eq. 3-1

■

Section Self-Test

1. Simplify $AB + \overline{A\,B}$.
2. Simplify ABC0.
3. Simplify ABC1.

ANSWERS (Not necessarily in the order of the questions)

• ABC • 1 • 0

3-13 SUM OF PRODUCTS (SOP) AND PRODUCT OF SUMS (POS)

Two standard forms for logic expressions are used to specify logic functions. These standard forms for logic expressions aid the designer by simplifying the derivation of the equation and the design and implementation of the circuit. The standard expressions are the sum of products (SOP) expression and the product of sums (POS) expression.

An example of the **sum of products (SOP)** and **product of sums (POS)** expression forms are shown in Equations 3-35 and 3-36. The names of these standard expressions describe the form of the equation. The sum of products, or SOP expression, is a sum (OR) of several product (AND) terms. The product of sums, or POS, is a product (AND) of several sum (OR) terms.

Eq. 3-35, SOP $X = ABC + DEF$

Eq. 3-36, POS $Y = (A + B + C)(D + E + F)$

These standard forms are used for several reasons:

1. *Ease in derivation of the expression from the truth table or the circuit.* Each logic expression can be read directly from a truth table specification of a logic function or from a circuit schematic.
2. *Ease in circuit implementation.* Each expression can be implemented with just two levels of gates, not counting inverters at the input level.
3. *Ease in gate selection.* Each expression requires only AND gates, OR gates, and inverters for the basic circuit implementation. By applying DeMorgan's Theorems to the expressions, one can build the SOP form by using two levels of NAND gates and build the POS form by using two levels of NOR gates.
4. *Ease in circuit simplification.* The SOP and POS expressions can be easily manipulated with Boolean algebra and Karnaugh maps to simplify the expression and in turn simplify the circuit.
5. *Use in advanced logic applications.* The SOP form of the logic expression is used extensively to specify logic equations in advanced logic design, including programmable logic devices (PLDs).

3.13.1 Sum of Product Equations and Circuits

The Sum of Products expression is the equation of the logic function as read off the truth table to specify the input combinations when the output is a logic 1.

By examining the sum of product form of the expression in Equation 3-35, one can see that the output is a 1 whenever any single product term is a 1. Therefore, the SOP expression can be a sum of all input term combinations that result in an output of 1.

The unsimplified form of the SOP expression that contains terms for all possible input combinations that result in the output being a 1 is considered the **expanded** form of the SOP expression. The number of terms in the equation will equal the number of occurrences that the output is a 1 in the truth table. In many cases the equation can be simplified to reduce the number of terms or variables in the SOP equation.

Table 3-7 lists the rules to follow in order to derive the SOP equation directly from a truth table of a logic function.

The circuit required to implement the SOP equation consists of two levels of gates, not counting the input inverters. For the SOP equation, the two gate levels can be implemented as an **AND-OR circuit or a NAND-NAND circuit** by applying DeMorgan's Theorems to the original SOP expression.

TABLE 3-7 Rules for Deriving Sum of Products Equations from Truth Tables

1. When a variable is a **1,** write the variable in the equation in its **true form.**
2. When a variable is a **0,** write the variable in the equation in its **inverted form.**
3. Include all input terms that result in the output of the desired level. Do not include any other input terms in the equation.
4. Write each term of the individual **input combinations as a product.**
5. **Sum together all the terms specifying the input combinations.**
6. Rearrange and simplify the equation, if required, based on the rules of Boolean algebra.
7. Verify the equation by substituting input combinations from the truth table to obtain the correct output value.

EXAMPLE 3-26 Sum of Products Expressions and Circuits

Problem: Derive the SOP expression for the logic function specified in the truth table, and form an AND-OR circuit to implement the function.

Solution: Follow the rules listed in Table 3-7 to derive the SOP expression from the truth table and then to form a logic circuit from the expression. The AND-OR circuit is shown in Figure 3-35.

A	B	C	L
0	0	0	1
0	0	1	1
0	1	0	0
0	1	1	1
1	0	0	0
1	0	1	0
1	1	0	0
1	1	1	1

$$L = \overline{A}\,\overline{B}\,\overline{C} + \overline{A}\,\overline{B}\,C + \overline{A}\,B\,C + A\,B\,C$$

■

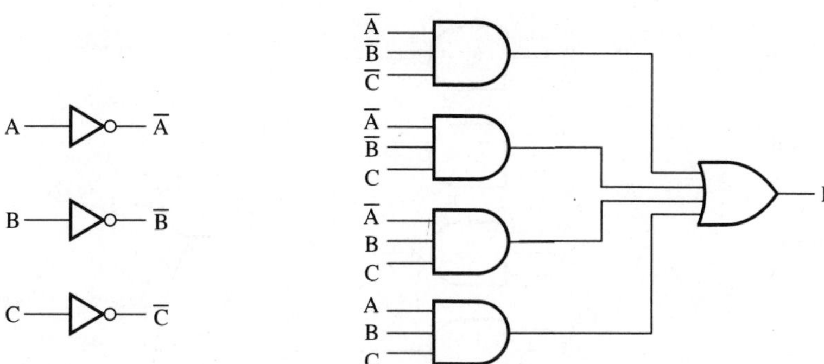

FIGURE 3-35 AND-OR Sum of Products (SOP) Circuit for Example 3-26

■ EXAMPLE 3-27 NAND-NAND SOP CIRCUIT

Problem: Derive the NAND-NAND SOP circuit corresponding to the SOP expression in Example 3-26.

Solution: Apply DeMorgan's Theorems to convert the AND-OR equation and the circuit obtained in Example 3-26 to the NAND-NAND form. The steps are as follows:

1. Invert the expression for L twice.
2. Keep the top inversion bar.
3. Apply DeMorgan's Theorems to the bottom inversion bar to eliminate the OR operations.
4. Design the NAND-NAND circuit from this equation.

$$L = \overline{A}\,\overline{B}\,\overline{C} + \overline{A}\,\overline{B}\,C + \overline{A}\,B\,C + A\,B\,C$$

$$L = \overline{\overline{\overline{A}\,\overline{B}\,\overline{C} + \overline{A}\,\overline{B}\,C + \overline{A}\,B\,C + A\,B\,C}}$$

$$L = \overline{(\overline{\overline{A}\,\overline{B}\,\overline{C}})\,(\overline{\overline{A}\,\overline{B}\,C})\,(\overline{\overline{A}\,B\,C})\,(\overline{A\,B\,C})}$$

The NAND-NAND SOP circuit for L is shown in Figure 3-36. The circuit is shown with the standard logic symbol for the NAND gate, as well as the "active-LOW OR" NAND symbol. Both circuits are built from the identical ICs. ■

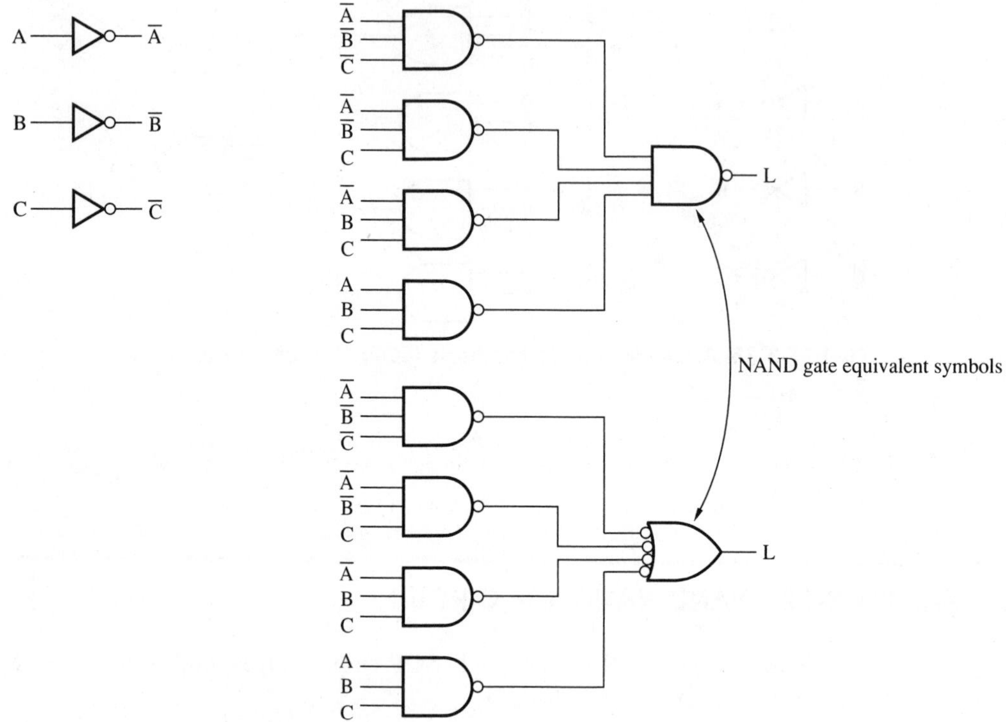

FIGURE 3-36 NAND-NAND SOP Circuit for Example 3-27

■ EXAMPLE 3-28 Active-LOW Sum of Products Expression Derived from a Truth Table

Problem: Derive the active-LOW SOP expression for M, defining the input combinations when M is 0, given the truth table for the function M.

Solution: The rules for the SOP equation hold for active-LOW as well as for active-HIGH SOP expressions. Any variable that appears in the truth table as a 0 is written in its inverted form, and any variable that appears in the truth table as a 1 is written in its true form. The product terms specify the input combinations that result in the output being a 0. The circuit for M is shown in Figure 3-37.

A	B	C	D	M
0	0	0	0	0
0	0	0	1	0
0	0	1	0	0
0	0	1	1	1
0	1	0	0	1
0	1	0	1	1
0	1	1	0	1
0	1	1	1	1
1	0	0	0	1
1	0	0	1	1
1	0	1	0	0
1	0	1	1	1
1	1	0	0	1
1	1	0	1	1
1	1	1	0	1
1	1	1	1	0

$$\overline{M} = \overline{A}\,\overline{B}\,\overline{C}\,\overline{D} + \overline{A}\,\overline{B}\,\overline{C}\,D + \overline{A}\,\overline{B}\,C\,\overline{D} + A\,\overline{B}\,C\,\overline{D} + A\,B\,C\,D$$

■

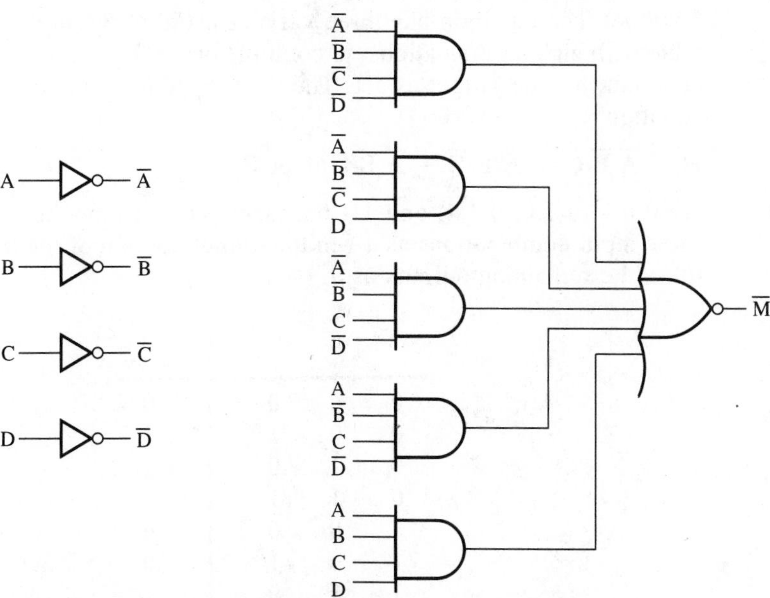

FIGURE 3-37 Active-LOW SOP Circuit Example 3-28

In some cases it may be necessary to derive the truth table from an SOP circuit or from a two-level AND-OR or NAND-NAND circuit. The equation can be obtained from the circuit by following the logic gate inputs and outputs.

The truth table can be derived from the equation. The input side of the truth table must list all possible input combinations with the variables used in the circuit.

Recall that in an SOP circuit any variable that is a 1 is written in its true form, and any variable that is a 0 is written in its inverted form. All AND terms in the equation should be identified and matched with the corresponding input variable combination of 1's and 0's. The output for the AND terms in the SOP expression is a 1.

After all 1's have been entered in the output column of the truth table, the 0's should be entered as the output result for all remaining input combinations.

■ EXAMPLE 3-29 Truth Table Derived from a Sum of Products Expression

Problem: Derive the truth table from the SOP expression.

$$H = \overline{A}\,\overline{B}\,C + \overline{A}\,B\,\overline{C} + \overline{A}\,B\,C + A\,B\,\overline{C}$$

Solution: The equation has three variables. Fill in the input side of a truth table with eight combinations, in counting order. For each AND term in the equation, list the output as a 1. The input combinations represented by the equation

$$H = \overline{A}\,\overline{B}\,C + \overline{A}\,B\,\overline{C} + \overline{A}\,B\,C + A\,B\,\overline{C}$$

are 0 0 1, 0 1 0, 0 1 1, and 1 1 0, respectively. Enter the output state for these input combinations as a 1 in the output column of the truth table, and fill in the remaining outputs as 0.

A	B	C	H
0	0	0	0
0	0	1	1
0	1	0	1
0	1	1	1
1	0	0	0
1	0	1	0
1	1	0	1
1	1	1	0

■

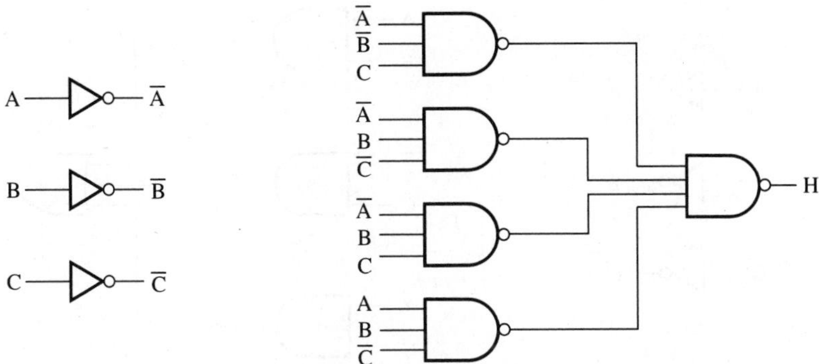

FIGURE 3-38 SOP Circuit for Example 3-29

■ EXAMPLE 3-30 Truth Table Derived from a Sum of Products Expression

Problem: Derive the truth table from the active-LOW SOP expression:

$$\overline{J} = A\,B + \overline{B}\,\overline{C} + \overline{A}\,C$$

Solution: The rules for the SOP expression are still followed, even with the active-LOW equation for J. An active-LOW SOP expression defines the input combinations that result in the output being a 0. Form the input side of the truth table with all possible combinations of the variables A, B, and C. Identify the input combinations represented by the product terms in the equation. The output state for the product terms in the SOP expression is a 0. Enter a 0 in the output column of the truth table for all the product terms in the SOP expression, and fill in the remaining outputs as 1's.

A	B	C	J
0	0	0	0
0	0	1	0
0	1	0	1
0	1	1	0
1	0	0	0
1	0	1	1
1	1	0	0
1	1	1	0

■

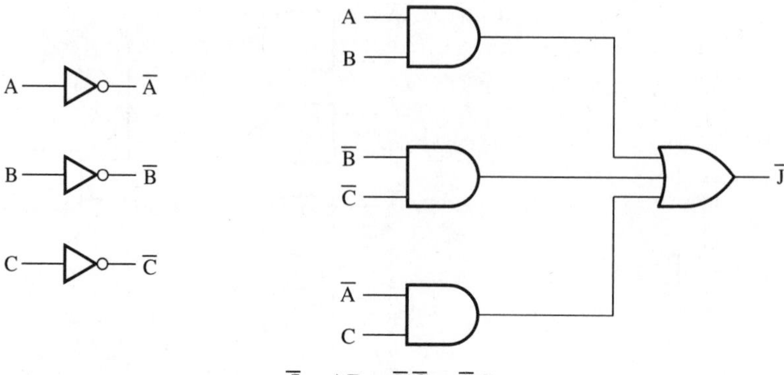

$\overline{J} = AB + \overline{B}\,\overline{C} + \overline{A}C$

FIGURE 3-39 Active-LOW SOP Circuit for Example 3-30

3.13.2 Product of Sums Equations and Circuits

The Product of Sums (POS) expression is the **active-LOW** equation of the logic function. It specifies the input combinations that result in a logic 0 output. The **POS is not the complement of the SOP expression.** It is active-LOW since the variables that are a 0 are written in their true form, and all variables that are a 1 are written in their inverted form.

The form of the POS expression, as a product of individual sum terms, results in an output of 0 of the expression whenever any sum term is a 0. Therefore, the POS expression is a product of all input term combinations that result in an output of 0. The input terms in their sum form are often referred to as **maxterms.**

The unsimplified form of the POS expression that contains terms for all possible input combinations that result in the output being a 0 is considered

TABLE 3-8 Rules for Deriving Product of Sums Expressions from Truth Tables

1. When a variable is a **1,** write the variable in the equation in its **inverted form.**
2. When a variable is a **0,** write the variable in the equation in its **true form.**
3. Include all input terms that result in the output of the desired level. Do not include any other input terms in the equation.
4. Write each term of the individual **input combinations as a sum.**
5. **AND together all terms specifying input combinations.**
6. Rearrange and simplify the equation, if required, based on the rules of Boolean algebra.
7. Verify the equation by substituting input combinations from the truth table to obtain the correct output value.

the **expanded** form of the POS expression. The number of terms in the equation equals the number of occurrences that the output is a 0 in the truth table. In many cases the expression can be simplified using Boolean algebra, but it still remains a POS equation.

Table 3-8 lists the rules for deriving the POS form of the logic equation directly from a truth table.

The circuits required to implement these statements have two levels of gates, not counting the input inverters. These two gate levels can be implemented as an **OR-AND circuit** or a **NOR-NOR circuit** by applying DeMorgan's Theorems to the original POS expression.

■ EXAMPLE 3-31 Product of Sums Expressions and Circuits

Problem: Derive the POS equation for the logic function specified in the truth table. Design an OR-AND circuit to implement the logic function.

Solution: Follow the rules listed in Table 3-8 to derive a POS expression from a truth table. In the expression any variable that was a 0 in the truth table is written in its true form, and any variable that was a 1 in the truth table is written in its inverted form. The OR-AND POS circuit is shown in Figure 3-40.

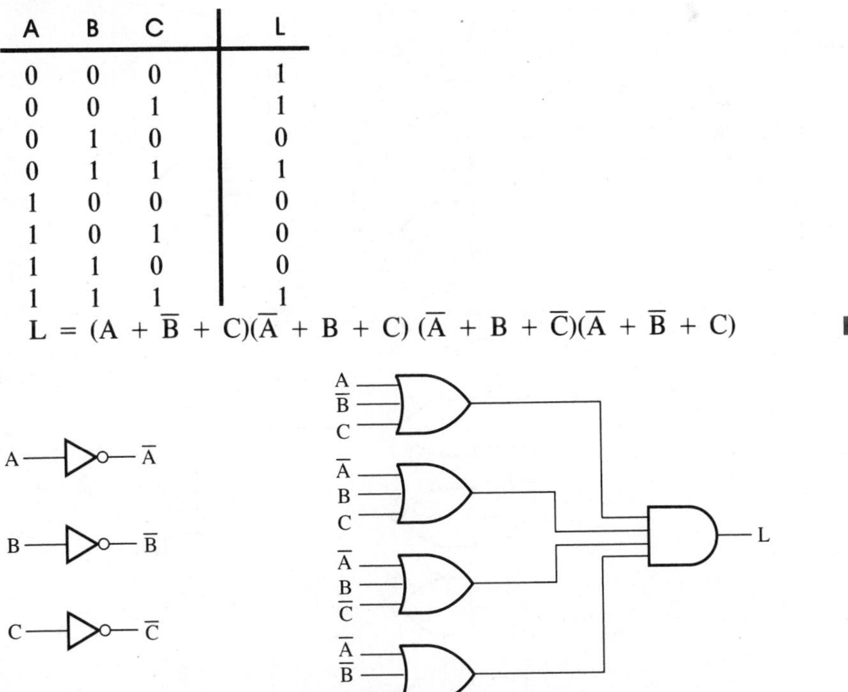

A	B	C	L
0	0	0	1
0	0	1	1
0	1	0	0
0	1	1	1
1	0	0	0
1	0	1	0
1	1	0	0
1	1	1	1

$$L = (A + \overline{B} + C)(\overline{A} + B + C)(\overline{A} + B + \overline{C})(\overline{A} + \overline{B} + C)$$ ■

FIGURE 3-40 OR-AND (Product of Sums) POS Circuit for Example 3-31

■ EXAMPLE 3-32 NOR-NOR Product of Sums Circuit

Problem: Convert the OR-AND POS circuit designed in Example 3-31 to a NOR-NOR POS circuit.

Solution: Apply DeMorgan's Theorem to convert the OR-AND circuit to a NOR-NOR circuit, according to the following steps:

1. Double invert the expression for L.
2. Keep the top inversion bar.
3. Apply DeMorgan's Theorem to the bottom inversion bar to eliminate the AND operations.
4. Design the NOR-NOR circuit from this equation.

$$L = (A + \overline{B} + C)(\overline{A} + B + C)(\overline{A} + B + \overline{C})(\overline{A} + \overline{B} + C)$$

$$L = \overline{\overline{(A + \overline{B} + C)(\overline{A} + B + C)(\overline{A} + B + \overline{C})(\overline{A} + \overline{B} + C)}}$$

$$L = \overline{\overline{(A + \overline{B} + C)} + \overline{(\overline{A} + B + C)} + \overline{(\overline{A} + B + \overline{C})} + \overline{(\overline{A} + \overline{B} + C)}}$$

The NOR-NOR POS circuit for L in Figure 3-41 is shown with the standard logic symbol for the NOR gate, as well as the "active-LOW AND" NOR symbol. Both circuits are built from identical ICs. ■

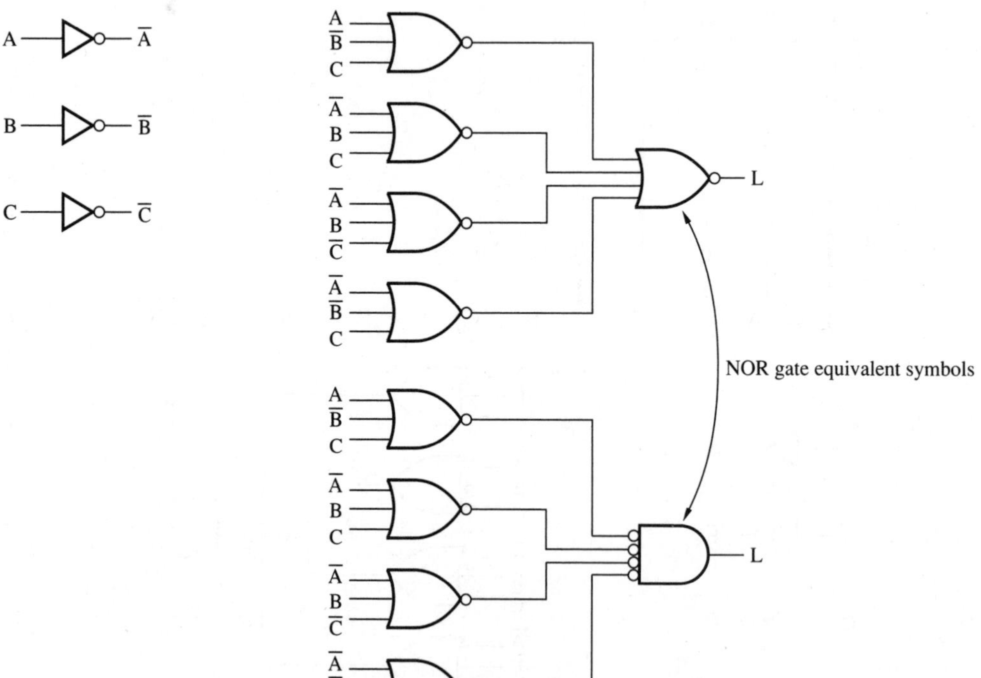

FIGURE 3-41 NOR-NOR POS Circuit for Example 3-32

■ EXAMPLE 3-33 Product of Sums Expressions and Circuits

Problem: Derive the POS equation and circuit for the logic function specified by the truth table.

Solution: Follow the same procedures described in Example 3-31 to form the POS expression. The NOR-NOR POS circuit is shown in Figure 3-42.

A	B	C	D	M
0	0	0	0	0
0	0	0	1	0
0	0	1	0	0
0	0	1	1	1
0	1	0	0	1
0	1	0	1	1
0	1	1	0	0
0	1	1	1	0
1	0	0	0	1
1	0	0	1	1
1	0	1	0	0
1	0	1	1	1
1	1	0	0	0
1	1	0	1	0
1	1	1	0	1
1	1	1	1	1

$$M = (A + B + C + D)(A + B + C + \overline{D})\,(A + B + \overline{C} + D)(A + \overline{B} + \overline{C} + D)$$

$$\cdot\,(A + \overline{B} + \overline{C} + \overline{D})(\overline{A} + B + \overline{C} + D)\,(\overline{A} + \overline{B} + C + D)(\overline{A} + \overline{B} + C + \overline{D})$$

■

In some cases it may be necessary to derive the truth table from a POS circuit or from a two-level OR-AND or NOR-NOR circuit. The equation can be obtained from the circuit by following the logic gate inputs and outputs.

The truth table can be derived from the equation. The input side of the truth table must list all possible input combinations with the variables used in the circuit.

Recall that in a POS circuit, any variable that is a 0 is written in its true form, and any variable that is a 1 is written in its inverted form. All OR terms in the equation should be identified and matched with the corresponding input variable combination of 1's and 0's. The output for each OR term in the POS expression is a 0.

After all 0's have been entered in the output column of the truth table, the 1's should be entered as the output result for all remaining input combinations.

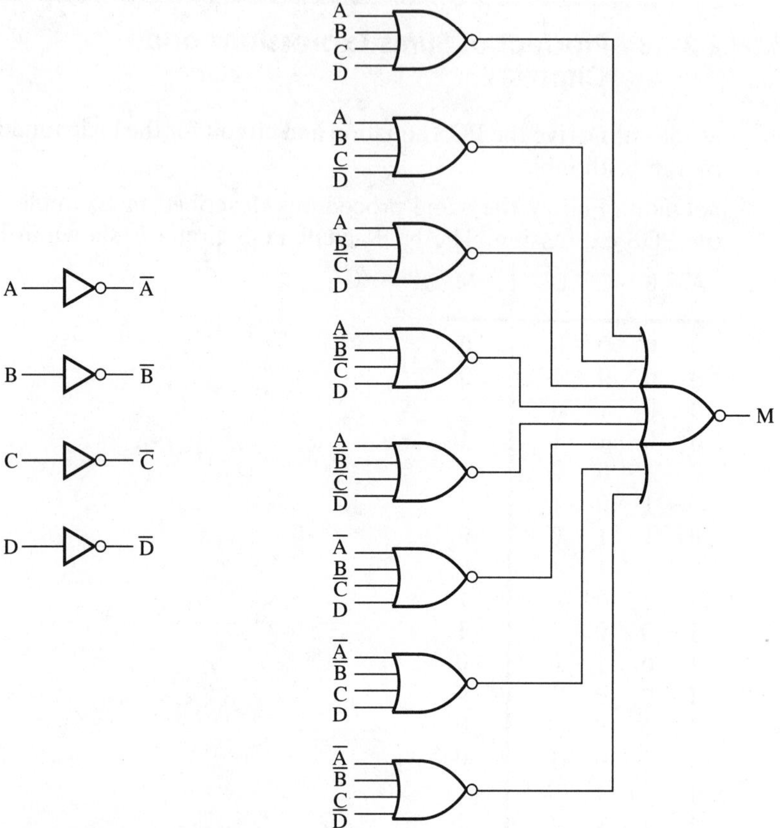

FIGURE 3-42 NOR-NOR POS Circuit for Example 3-33

■ EXAMPLE 3-34 Truth Table Derivation from a Product of Sums Expression

Problem: Derive the truth table from the POS equation.

$$G = (\overline{A} + \overline{B} + C)(A + \overline{B} + C)(A + B + \overline{C})$$

Solution: The equation has three variables. Fill in the input side of a truth table with eight combinations, in counting order. For each OR term in the equation, list the output as a 0. The input combinations represented by the equation

$$G = (\overline{A} + \overline{B} + C)(A + \overline{B} + C)(A + B + \overline{C})$$

are 1 1 0, 0 1 0, and 0 0 1, respectively. Enter the output state for these input combinations as a 0 in the output column of the truth table, and fill in the remaining outputs as 1. The POS circuit is shown in Figure 3-43.

A	B	C	G
0	0	0	1
0	0	1	0
0	1	0	0
0	1	1	1
1	0	0	1
1	0	1	1
1	1	0	0
1	1	1	1

■

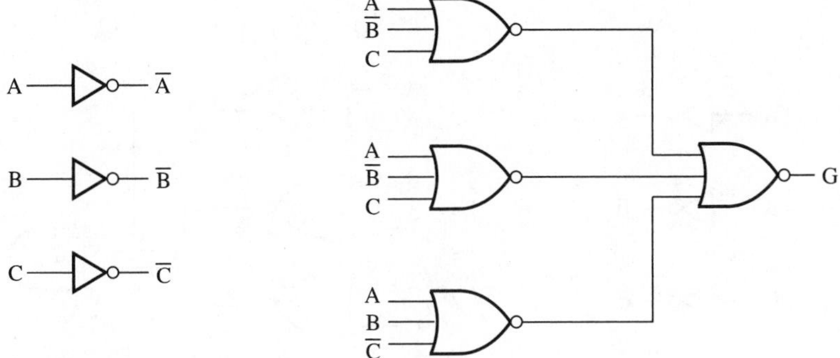

FIGURE 3-43 NOR-NOR POS CIRCUIT for Example 3-34

■ EXAMPLE 3-35 Truth Table Derived from a Product of Sums Expression

Problem: Derive the truth table for the POS logic expression.

$$K = (A + \overline{D})(\overline{B} + \overline{C})(A + C)(\overline{A} + B)$$

Solution: The procedures are the same as those followed for Example 3-34. The POS circuit is shown in Figure 3-44.

A	B	C	D	K
0	0	0	0	0
0	0	0	1	0
0	0	1	0	1
0	0	1	1	0
0	1	0	0	0
0	1	0	1	0
0	1	1	0	0
0	1	1	1	0
1	0	0	0	0
1	0	0	1	0
1	0	1	0	0
1	0	1	1	0
1	1	0	0	1
1	1	0	1	1
1	1	1	0	0
1	1	1	1	0

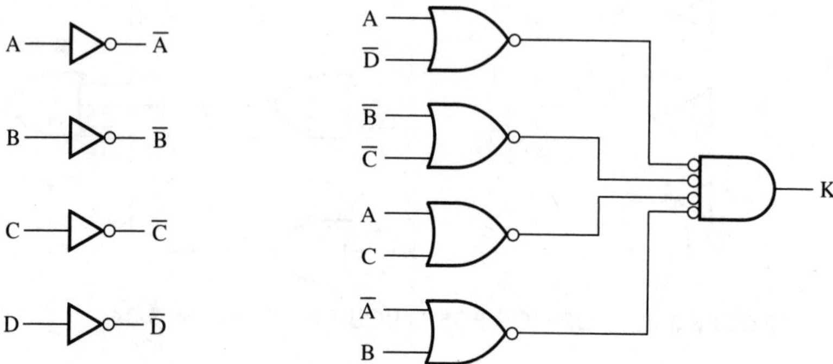

FIGURE 3-44 NOR-NOR POS Circuit for Example 3-35

Section Self-Test

Categorize each of the following equations as POS, SOP, or neither:

1. ABC + BC + D
2. (A + B)(B + C + D)E
3. ABC + (DE) + A(B + C)

ANSWERS (Not necessarily in the same order as the questions)

• SOP • POS • Neither

3-14 COMPARISON AND CONVERSION OF SUM OF PRODUCT AND PRODUCT OF SUMS EQUATIONS

Both POS and SOP forms of the logic expression are standard forms used extensively in logic design. Although many advanced logic applications specify the logic expression in the SOP or inverted SOP form, it is still necessary to be able to work with the POS form of the equation.

One form of the expression, either SOP or POS, usually results in a simpler expression for the logic function, and thus a simpler circuit to design with a minimal number of gates. As a rule of thumb, if the truth table specifies fewer 1's than 0's, the SOP form of the expression is the simplest. If the

TABLE 3-9 SOP and POS Procedures

SOP Procedure	POS Procedure
1. Derive the SOP expression using only those **input combinations that result in an output of logic 1.**	1. Derive the POS expression using only those **input combinations that result in the output being logic 0.**
2. Input variables of **1** are written in their **true form.**	2. Input variables of **0** are written in their **true form.**
3. Input variables of **0** are written in their **inverted form.**	3. Input variables of **1** are written in their **inverted form.**
4. Input variables are **ANDed** to form the input terms.	4. Input variables are **ORed** to form the input terms.
5. Input terms are **ORed** together to give the final output result.	5. Input terms are **ANDed** together to give the final output result.

Active-LOW SOP
1. Derive the active-LOW SOP expression by using only those **input combinations that give an output of 0.**
2. Follow the **same SOP procedures.**
3. Write the **output variable** in its **inverted form.**

truth table specifies fewer 0's than 1's, the POS or inverted SOP form of the expression is the simplest. (Further simplification techniques will be addressed later in the chapter).

Table 3-9 summarizes the procedures that have been studied for deriving SOP and POS expressions. The procedures are similar in content but are **duals** since variables are inverted and the mathematical form of one equation is a dual of the form used in the other equation.

When it is necessary to convert between the POS and SOP forms of the logic expression, the conversion can be easily accomplished by completing the truth table specification of the logic function. Once the truth table is determined, any form of the logic expression can be derived following the steps as specified in Table 3-9.

Since many advanced logic design applications, such as those associated with PLDs, require the specification of the logic function in either the SOP or active-LOW SOP form, one should be able to convert from a given POS equation to the equivalent SOP equation.

Section Self-Test

1. Convert AB + BC to POS form.
2. Convert AB + BC to inverted SOP form.
3. Convert (A + B)(B + C)(A + C) to SOP form.

ANSWERS (Not necessarily in the order of the questions)

- $\overline{A}\,\overline{B}\,\overline{C} + \overline{A}\,\overline{B}\,C + \overline{A}\,B\,\overline{C} + A\,\overline{B}\,\overline{C} + A\,\overline{B}\,C$
- $\overline{A}\,B\,C + A\,B\,\overline{C} + A\,B\,C$
- $(A + B + C)(A + B + \overline{C})(A + \overline{B} + C)(\overline{A} + B + C)(\overline{A} + B + \overline{C})$

3-15 EQUIVALENT GATES AND ALTERNATIVE GATE SELECTION

In addition to equivalent circuits, equivalent relationships exist between gates. If one gate's logic function can be represented by another gate or combination of gates, the gates are called equivalent gates or alternative gates.

In some applications the circuitry available to build the circuit may not include all possible logic functions. It is then necessary to implement the function with an alternative selection of gates. The alternative implementation of basic logic gates is an extension of Boolean algebra concepts.

3.15.1 Alternative Gate Selection

Alternative gate selection is used to minimize the number of ICs required to implement a particular logic function or Boolean equation. For example, a logic circuit may require one inverter and three NAND gates. Implemented directly, this circuit requires two ICs; a 7400 quad NAND, and a 7404 hex inverter.

Selecting alternative gates can reduce the number of chips required for this problem. If one applies Boolean relationships to a NAND gate, a NAND gate can be wired to function as an inverter by wiring the inputs together. In equation form, $\overline{A\,A} = \overline{A}$. A NAND gate can also be wired to function as an inverter by wiring one of the inputs HIGH. In equation form, $\overline{A\,1} = \overline{A}$.

Using a NAND gate with the inputs connected to function as an inverter allows the circuit to be built using only one IC, a 7400 quad NAND, as shown in Figure 3-45.

Additional equivalent gate relationships exist for other basic logic functions. Figure 3-46 illustrates the equivalent logic gate symbols for an inverter, AND, NAND, OR, NOR, XOR, and XNOR.

Alternative gate selection does not always result in using the minimum number of gates for a given logic circuit. It may be more advantageous to have a slightly larger number of gates, but to use fewer types of ICs to build a circuit. Often this can result in requiring a lower number of ICs being needed, as more of the gates per IC are actually used. This results in less unused gates per IC.

For the example circuit shown in Figure 3-47, there are six NOR gates, three inverters, and one AND gate. The alternative gates that perform the same logic function as an AND gate are two inverters and a NOR gate, as shown below. The AND gate in this circuit can be replaced by the equivalent

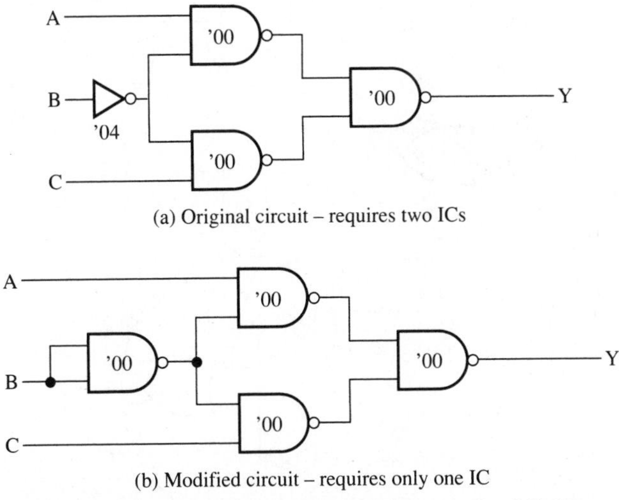

FIGURE 3-45 Alternative Gate Selection for Minimum IC Count

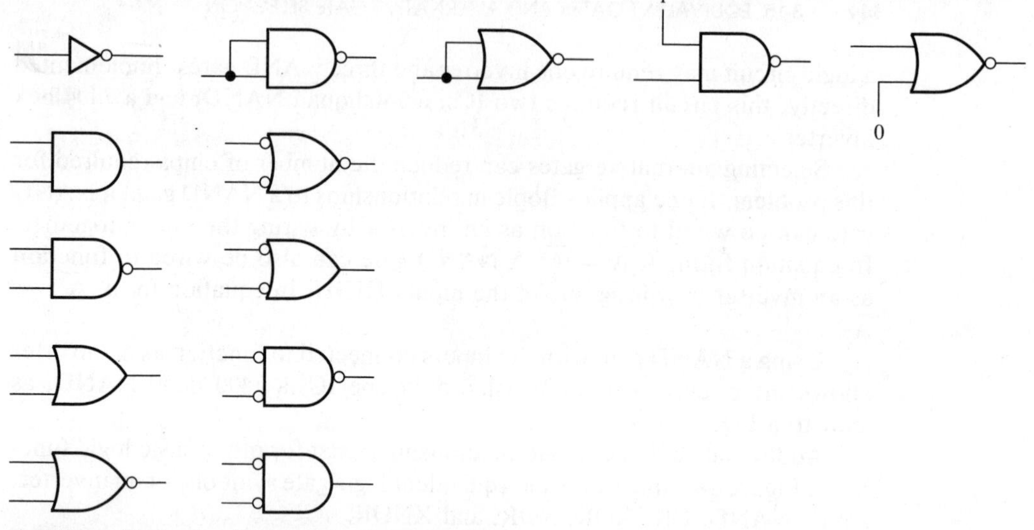

FIGURE 3-46 Equivalent Logic Gate Symbols

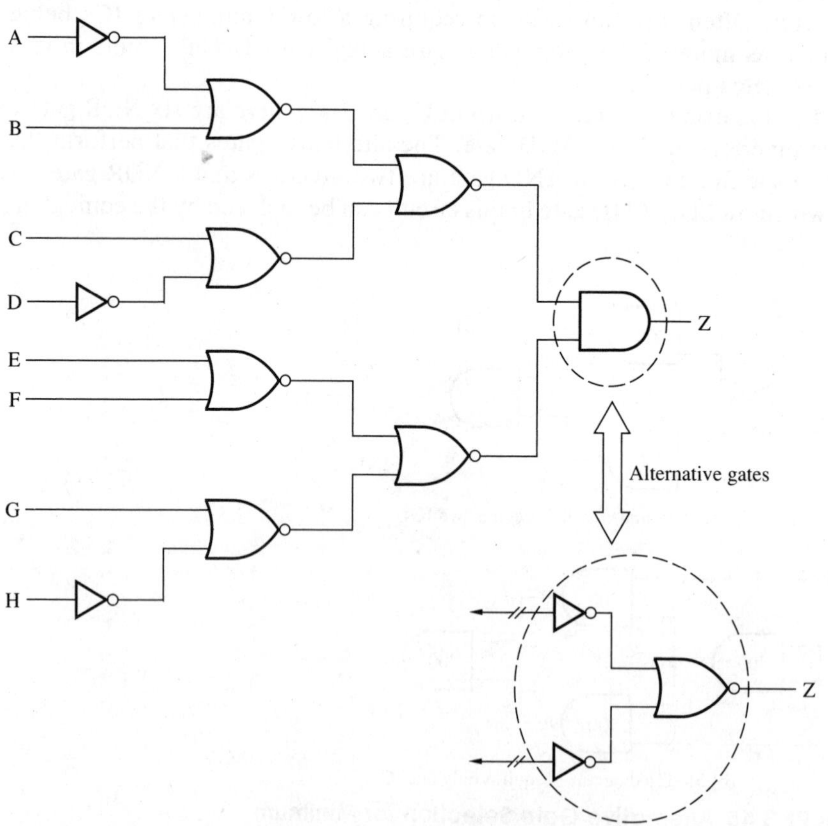

FIGURE 3-47 Equivalent Combinational Logic Circuits

combination of the two inverters and the NOR gate as shown in Figure 3-47. This equivalency is an application of DeMorgan Theorem 1.

The original circuit, implemented directly, would require four ICs (two 7402s, a 7404, and a 7408). The modified circuit would require only three ICs (two 7402s and a 7404) since the AND IC would no longer be needed.

Logic designers commonly draw logic circuits using both standard and equivalent logic gate representations. Recall that the inverted input or output symbol, an open dot or "bubble," can be placed on the input or output of any logic gate to indicate logic inversion. If the output of a gate that has an inverter symbol is connected to the input of another gate with the inverter symbol, the inversions, in effect, cancel and the circuit can be redrawn without the inversion symbols. This often results in simplified logic circuit schematics.

As shown in previous examples, it is advantageous to be able to substitute freely the alternative gate representations to simplify a logic circuit, reduce the number of ICs needed to construct logic circuits, or change Boolean equations into a form suitable for PLD logic circuit implementation.

3.15.2 NAND Equivalent Circuits

Another application of alternative gate selection often used is the construction of logic circuits using only NAND gates. This is possible since any of

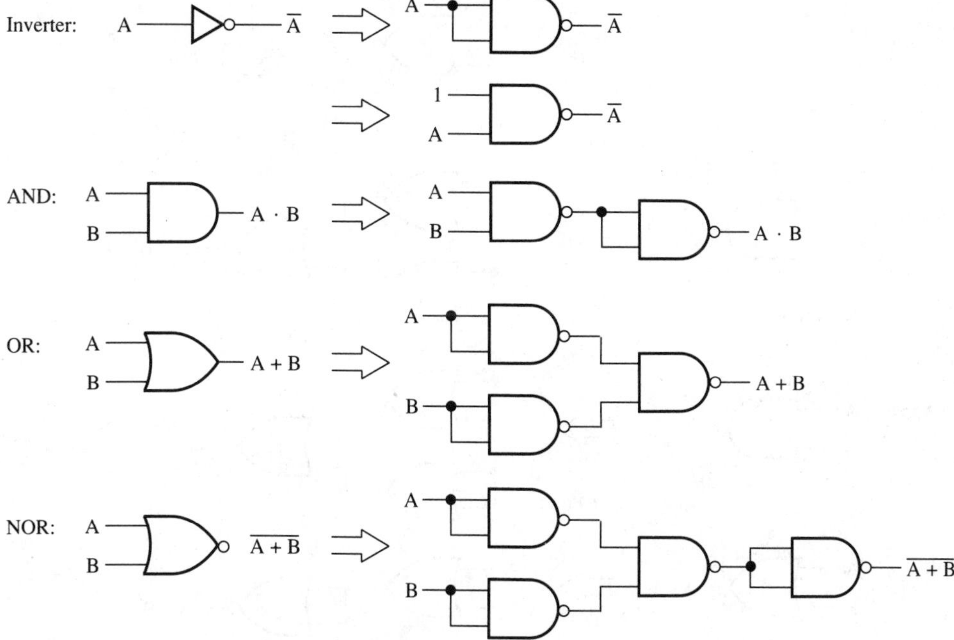

FIGURE 3-48 NAND Equivalent Gates

the basic logic functions can be produced by using only NAND gates. Figure 3-48 shows the construction of the inverter, AND, OR, and NOR gates utilizing only NAND gates. Thus, these equivalent gates are called **NAND equivalent gates.** The student should verify that XOR and XNOR gates can also be constructed with only NAND gates.

If only NAND gates are used to construct a circuit, this is known as a **NAND equivalent circuit.** This type of circuit is very useful in representing Boolean **SOP** equations.

3.15.3 NOR Equivalent Circuits

It is also useful to be able to construct logic circuits using only NOR gates. As with the NAND gate, all other basic logic functions can be constructed with only NOR gates. Figure 3-49 shows the construction of the **NOR equivalent gates** using an inverter, AND, NAND, and OR gates using only NOR gates.

If only NOR gates are used to construct a logic circuit, this is known as a **NOR equivalent circuit.** This type of circuit is useful in representing Boolean **POS** equations.

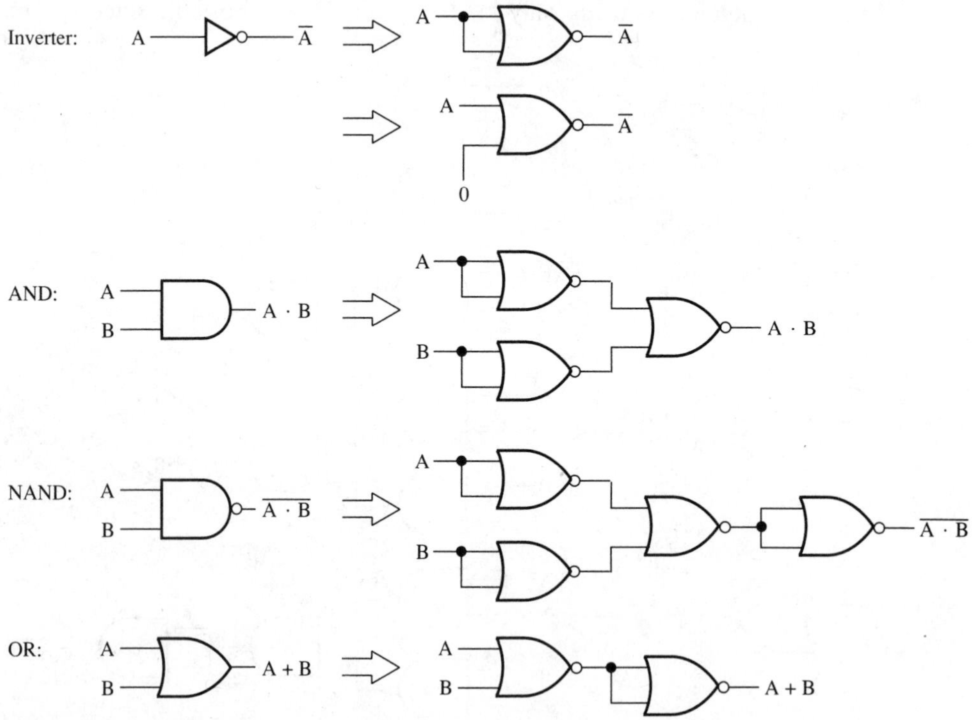

FIGURE 3-49 NOR Equivalent Gates

Section Self-Test

1. What are alternative gates?
2. Describe NAND and NOR equivalent circuits.
3. List two reasons to use alternative gates in a design.

ANSWERS (Not necessarily in the order of the questions)

- An equivalent circuit implementation of a logic function.
- NAND and NOR equivalent circuits can be obtained by applying Boolean algebra and DeMorgan's Theorems to obtain an alternate logic expression. NAND and NOR gates can form all combinational logic functions.
- Alternative gates can be used to minimize ICs or simplify the circuit implementation of a logic function.

3-16 KARNAUGH MAPPING

A Karnaugh map is a tool used in digital logic circuit analysis and design to simplify logic equations. It is a graphical representation of the output for each input combination for a given logic function, just as a truth table lists each output for all possible input combinations.

A **Karnaugh map,** or **K-map** as it is often referred to, is used to simplify a logic expression and derive either the simplified SOP or POS form of the expression from the truth table. The specific arrangement of the K-map eliminates the need for extensive use of Boolean algebra to simplify the equation. Instead, the simplification is done graphically using the K-map.

3.16.1 K-Map Relationship to Truth Tables

A truth table is a complete definition of the logic function, listing the output result for all possible combinations of input variables. A K-map contains the same information as a truth table, representing the logic function in a slightly different format.

The K-map contains a **cell** for each input combination. A logic function with n input variables has 2^n cells on the K-map. A two-variable K-map has 4 cells, a three-variable K-map has 8 cells, and a four-variable K-map has 16 cells. Occasionally, five-variable K-maps are formed by using two four-variable maps. Functions requiring larger K-maps are usually handled by computer simulation and Boolean algebra techniques.

The values of input variables are labeled along the outer edges of the map, and the cells of the map contain the output result for the corresponding input combination. Two-, three-, and four-variable K-maps are shown in Figure 3-50.

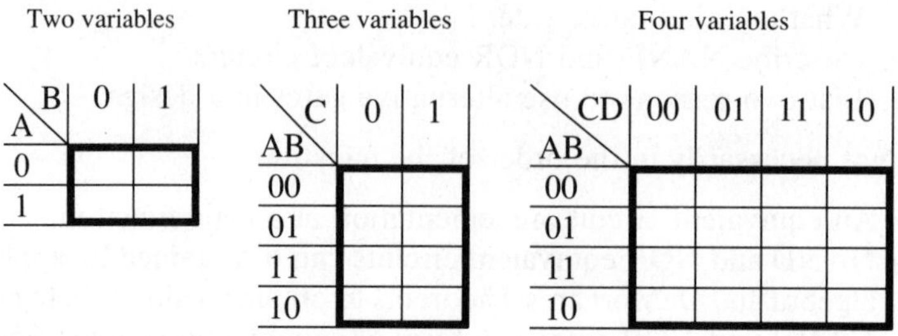

Two variables

A \ B	0	1
0		
1		

Three variables

AB \ C	0	1
00		
01		
11		
10		

Four variables

AB \ CD	00	01	11	10
00				
01				
11				
10				

FIGURE 3-50 Karnaugh Maps

The correct labeling of input values on the K-map is critical for using a K-map to simplify a logic function. The labeling is done to assure that there is **only one input variable that changes between adjacent cells.**

By labeling the K-map so that only one variable changes between ad jacent cells, the edges of the map can be wrapped around, as they are adjacent with the opposite edge on the map. Both the top and sides can be wrapped in this manner. In addition, on only four-variable K-maps the four corners can be wrapped and brought together, as if forming a sphere, since they are all adjacent by the ordering of the input variables.

The order of labeling on the cells of the K-map is not in counting order. Since most truth tables list the inputs in counting order, care must be taken when transferring the output values to the K-map. For convenience and ease in converting between the truth table and K-map, the input variables should be labeled in the top left corner of the K-map in the same order they are listed in the truth table.

3.16.2 Function Simplification

Logic functions represented on a K-map can be simplified by a graphical technique. By appropriately grouping the output 1's or 0's on the K-map, one can eliminate input variables and input terms from the final SOP or POS equation.

Only one output condition should be selected to specify the logic function. The logic functions can be simplified by grouping only the 1's to derive the SOP equation or only the 0's to derive the POS equation or the inverted SOP equation. A comparison should be made to determine which logic expression results in the simplest solution for the function prior to implementing the equation with a circuit.

The procedures for simplifying a logic function using a K-map are outlined in Table 3-10. Examples of the simplification procedure are shown in the following sections to derive SOP and POS logic functions.

TABLE 3-10 Function Simplification Using K-Maps

1. Enter the complete output specification for the logic function in the K-map for every possible input combination.
2. Select one output state to group, either the 1's or the 0's. All the oc curences of the selected output must be included in the groups formed to specify the function.
3. Group **adjacent** cells in groups of $\mathbf{2^n}$. Rectangular groups of 1, 2, 4, 8, and 16 are the only allowable groups on K-maps of up to four variables. See Figures 3-51 and 3-52.

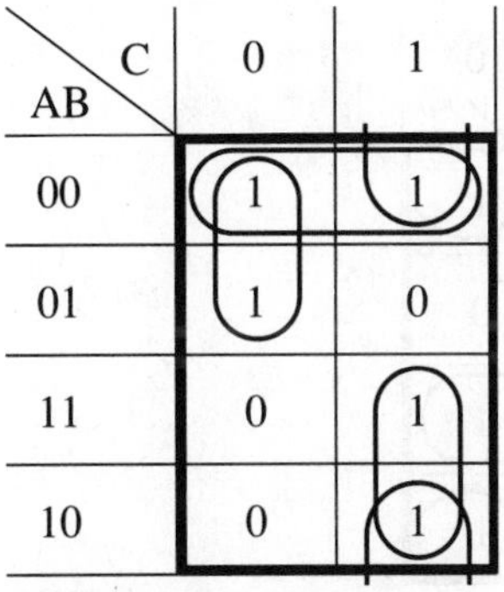

AB \ C	0	1
00	1	1
01	1	0
11	0	1
10	0	1

FIGURE 3-51 K-Map: Adjacent Cells

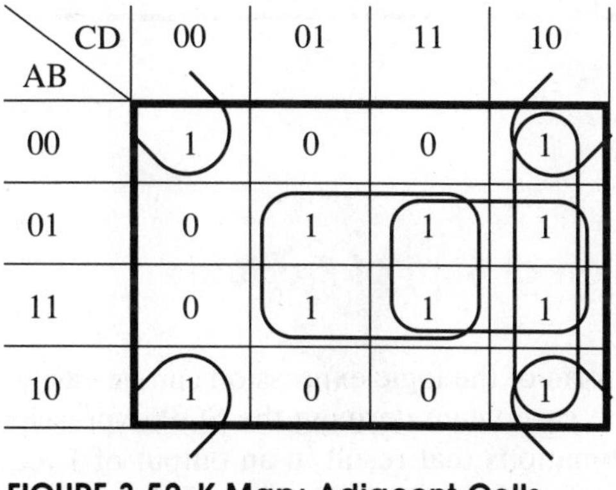

AB \ CD	00	01	11	10
00	1	0	0	1
01	0	1	1	1
11	0	1	1	1
10	1	0	0	1

FIGURE 3-52 K-Map: Adjacent Cells

4. The larger the group, the more input variables are eliminated. For a group containing 2^n cells, n input variables are eliminated.
5. The simplified terms contain **only the variables common to all outputs in the group.**

TABLE 3-10 (*continued*)

6. Each group represents a term in the function equation. The fewer number of groups, the fewer terms are needed in the final equation.
7. Groups can overlap. See Figure 3-53.
8. The first goal in grouping the outputs is to **minimize the number of groups.**
9. The second goal in grouping the outputs is to **maximize the size of the group** in order to minimize the number of input variables in each term.
10. There may be more than one correct grouping for a given function.

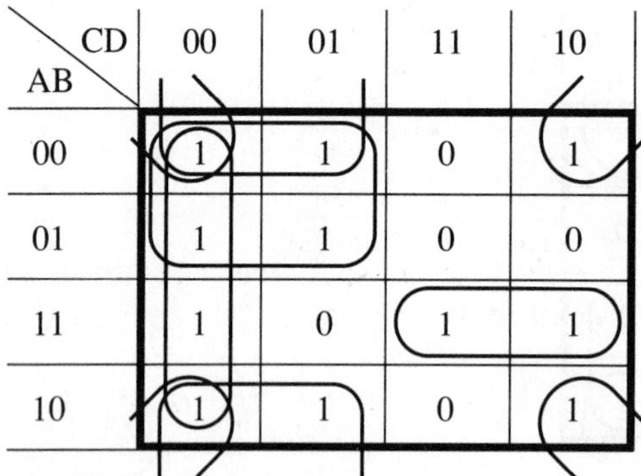

FIGURE 3-53 K-Map: Overlapping Groups

3.16.3 K-Map Simplification of Sum of Products Equations

The simplified SOP form of the logic expression can be easily obtained from the K-map. As in the case when deriving the SOP expression from a truth table, all input combinations that result in an output of 1 must be included in the equation. Therefore, when dealing with a K-map one must represent all cells with an output value of 1 in some grouping.

Since the values of the input variables are labeled at the edges of the K-map, the actual SOP expression can be written as if it was derived from a truth table. Those input variables of a value of 1 are written in their true form, and those of a value of 0 are written in their inverted form.

To simplify the equations, only those variables common to all 1's in the group are included in the AND terms. In other words, if an input variable changes between adjacent cells in a group, but the output remains the same, that input variable is not needed in the AND term.

Each group of adjacent cells on the K-map is specified by a separate AND term in the equation. The final equation is formed by ORing the individual AND terms.

When forming the simplified SOP expression with a K-map, the 1's are grouped in as large a group as possible to minimize the input variables in each term. Each output value of 1 is included in some group, but additional groups are not formed by unnecessary overlapping of extra groups, so that the number of AND terms in the final expression is minimized.

■ EXAMPLE 3-36 SOP Simplification Using K-Maps

Problem: Simplify the logic function specified in the truth table using a K-Map. Obtain the simplified SOP expression.

Solution: Group the adjacent 1's; maximize the size of the groups but minimize the number of groups. All 1's in the output must be included in a group, even if it is only a group of one cell. Each AND term is written with only the input variables common to the group. Form the final SOP expression by ORing all AND terms.

■

A	B	C	M
0	0	0	1
0	0	1	1
0	1	0	0
0	1	1	1
1	0	0	0
1	0	1	0
1	1	0	0
1	1	1	1

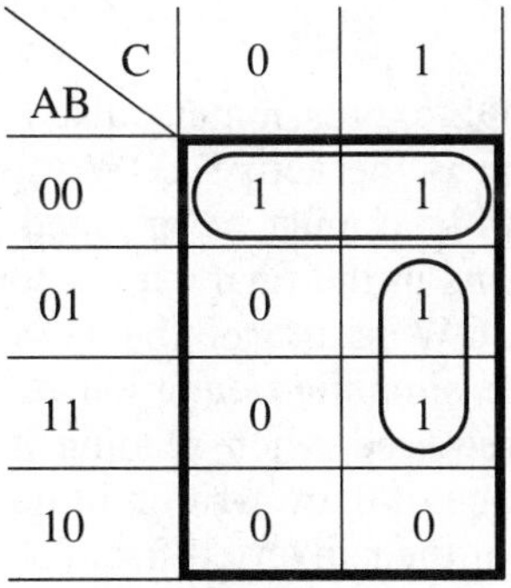

AB \ C	0	1
00	1	1
01	0	1
11	0	1
10	0	0

$$M = \overline{A}\,\overline{B} + B\,C$$

FIGURE 3-54 Example 3-36 K-Map and Truth Table

■ EXAMPLE 3-37 SOP Simplificaton Using K-Maps

A	B	C	D	N
0	0	0	0	1
0	0	0	1	1
0	0	1	0	1
0	0	1	1	0
0	1	0	0	1
0	1	0	1	1
0	1	1	0	0
0	1	1	1	0
1	0	0	0	1
1	0	0	1	1
1	0	1	0	1
1	0	1	1	0
1	1	0	0	0
1	1	0	1	1
1	1	1	0	0
1	1	1	1	1

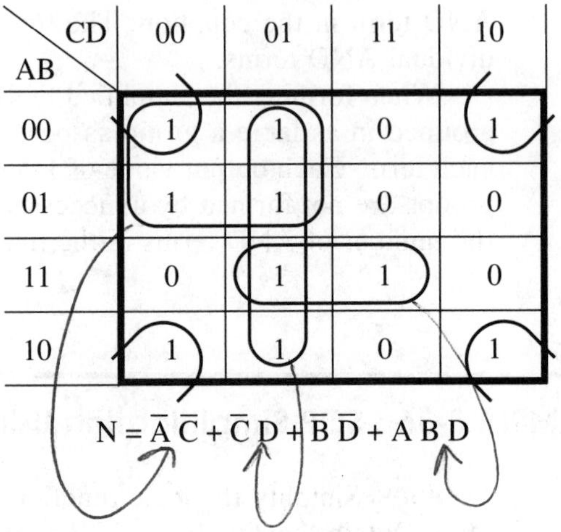

AB \ CD	00	01	11	10
00	1	1	0	1
01	1	1	0	0
11	0	1	1	0
10	1	1	0	1

$$N = \overline{A}\,\overline{C} + \overline{C}\,D + \overline{B}\,\overline{D} + A\,B\,D$$

FIGURE 3-55 Example 3-37 K-Map and Truth Table ■

3.16.4 K-Map Simplification of Product of Sum Equations

The simplified POS expression can also be obtained from the K-map. Since the POS equation is the active-LOW representation of the logic function, the output values of 0 must be grouped to minimize the number of input variables and terms in the final expression.

The active-LOW nature of the POS expression requires special care when reading the simplified equation off the K-map, in the same way as special care is required when reading it off the truth table. Those input variables of a value of 0 are written in their true form, and those of a value of 1 are written in their inverted form.

To simplify the equation, all occurrences of the output being a 0 must be included in some group to specify the function completely, even if it requires a group containing only one cell. Only those input variables common to all 0's in the group are included in the OR terms. In other words, if an input variable in a group of adjacent cells changes but the output remains a 0, that input variable is not needed in the OR term.

Each group of adjacent cells is specified by a separate OR term in the equation. The final equation is formed by ANDing the individual OR terms.

When forming the simplified POS expression with a K-map, the 0's are grouped in as large a group as possible to minimize the input variables in each term. Each output value of 0 is included in some group, but additional groups are not formed by unnecessary overlapping of extra groups, so that the number of OR terms in the final expression is minimized.

EXAMPLE 3-38 POS Simplification Using K-Maps

Problem: Use a K-map to obtain the simplified POS expression for the function specified in the truth table.

Solution: Group the adjacent 0's; maximize the size of the groups but minimize the number of groups. All 0's in the output must be included in a group, even if it is only a group of one cell. Each OR term is written with only the input variables common to the group. Form the final POS expression by ANDing all OR terms.

A	B	C	P
0	0	0	1
0	0	1	1
0	1	0	0
0	1	1	1
1	0	0	0
1	0	1	0
1	1	0	0
1	1	1	1

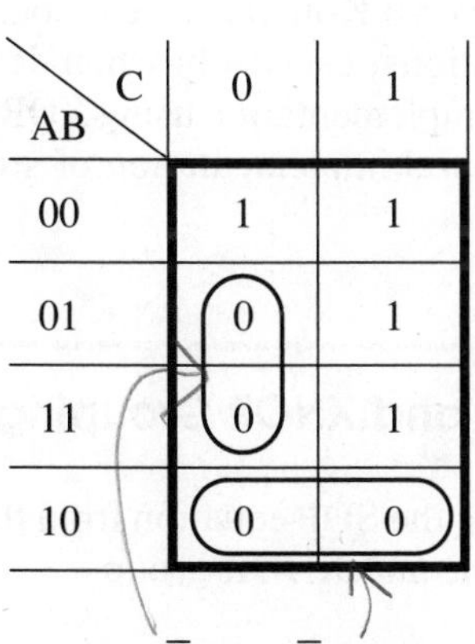

AB \ C	0	1
00	1	1
01	0	1
11	0	1
10	0	0

$$P = (\overline{B} + C)(\overline{A} + B)$$

FIGURE 3-56 Example 3-38 K-MAP and Truth Table

■ EXAMPLE 3-39 POS Simplification Using K-Maps

A	B	C	D	R
0	0	0	0	1
0	0	0	1	0
0	0	1	0	0
0	0	1	1	0
0	1	0	0	0
0	1	0	1	1
0	1	1	0	1
0	1	1	1	1
1	0	0	0	0
1	0	0	1	0
1	0	1	0	0
1	0	1	1	0
1	1	0	0	0
1	1	0	1	1
1	1	1	0	1
1	1	1	1	1

AB \ CD	00	01	11	10
00	1	0	0	0
01	0	1	1	1
11	0	0	1	1
10	0	0	0	0

$$R = (\overline{A} + C)(B + \overline{C})(B + \overline{D})(\overline{B} + C + D)$$

FIGURE 3-57 Example 3-39 K-Map and Truth Table ■

3.16.5 XOR and XNOR Groupings on K-Maps

Diagonal groups on a K-map can be recognized as XOR or XNOR functions. In some applications, especially when dealing with arithmetic circuit applications, circuit implementation using XOR or XNOR gates may be preferable to the more general implementation of standard SOP and POS equations.

■ EXAMPLE 3-40 XOR and XNOR Grouping of K-Maps

Problem: Derive the SOP equation from the K-map, and use Boolean algebra to form the XOR and XNOR groups.

Solution: None of the cells can be grouped as adjacent cells. Write the SOP expression, and factor out variables that are common to several AND terms. Regroup as Exclusive-OR and Exclusive-NOR functions.

A	B	C	E
0	0	0	1
0	0	1	0
0	1	0	0
0	1	1	1
1	0	0	0
1	0	1	1
1	1	0	1
1	1	1	0

AB \ C	0	1
00	1	0
01	0	1
11	1	0
10	0	1

$$E = \bar{A}\,\bar{B}\,\bar{C} + \bar{A}\,B\,C + A\,B\,\bar{C} + A\,\bar{B}\,C$$
$$= \bar{A}(\overline{B \oplus C}) + A(B \oplus C)$$
$$= \overline{A \oplus (B \oplus C)}$$

FIGURE 3-58 Example 3-40 K-Map and Truth Table ■

■ EXAMPLE 3-41 XOR and XNOR Grouping of K-Maps

A	B	C	D	F
0	0	0	0	1
0	0	0	1	0
0	0	1	0	0
0	0	1	1	1
0	1	0	0	0
0	1	0	1	1
0	1	1	0	1
0	1	1	1	0
1	0	0	0	0
1	0	0	1	1
1	0	1	0	1
1	0	1	1	0
1	1	0	0	1
1	1	0	1	0
1	1	1	0	0
1	1	1	1	1

AB \ CD	00	01	11	10
00	1	0	1	0
01	0	1	0	1
11	1	0	1	0
10	0	1	0	1

$$F = \bar{A}\,\bar{B}\,\bar{C}\,\bar{D} + \bar{A}\,\bar{B}\,C\,D + \bar{A}\,B\,\bar{C}\,D + \bar{A}\,B\,C\,\bar{D} + A\,B\,\bar{C}\,\bar{D} + A\,B\,C\,D + A\,\bar{B}\,\bar{C}\,D + A\,\bar{B}\,C\,\bar{D}$$

$$F = \bar{A}\,\bar{B}\,(\overline{C \oplus D}) + A\,B(\overline{C \oplus D}) + \bar{A}\,B(C \oplus D) + A\,\bar{B}(C \oplus D)$$
$$= (\overline{A \oplus B})(\overline{C \oplus D}) + (A \oplus B)(C \oplus D)$$
$$= \overline{(A \oplus B) \oplus (C \oplus D)}$$

FIGURE 3-59 Example 3-41 K-Map and Truth Table ■

3.16.6 Don't Care States on K-Maps

Truth table specifications for a logic function may not include all possible combinations of the binary digits for the input variables, yet they may still be complete specifications of the logic function for the prescribed application. Such is the case if the input variables are a specific code, such as the 8421 BCD code or the Excess-3 code.

In these situations certain input combinations will not occur due to the nature of the application. When **the input combinations cannot occur,** the output states are filled in on the truth table and in the K-map as a **X,** and are referred to as **don't care states.**

In a K-map simplification of a logic function with don't care states the X's are transferred to the K-map as the output result for the appropriate input combinations. When grouping the output states of interest, the X's can be used to enlarge group sizes to eliminate input variables from the terms in the equation. The output locations on the K-map can be treated individually as 1's or 0's, whichever is preferred for a particular grouping.

Only those X's that assist in simplifying the function should be included in the groupings. No additional X's should be added that will result in additional terms in the expression.

■ EXAMPLE 3-42 Don't Care States on K-Maps

Problem: Form the simplified SOP expression for the logic function specified in the truth table using a K-map and including the occurrence of don't care states.

Solution: The truth table specifying the logic function indicates that some input combinations are irrelevant or cannot occur. Therefore, the output is

A	B	C	J
0	0	0	1
0	0	1	1
0	1	0	0
0	1	1	1
1	0	0	0
1	0	1	X
1	1	0	X
1	1	1	X

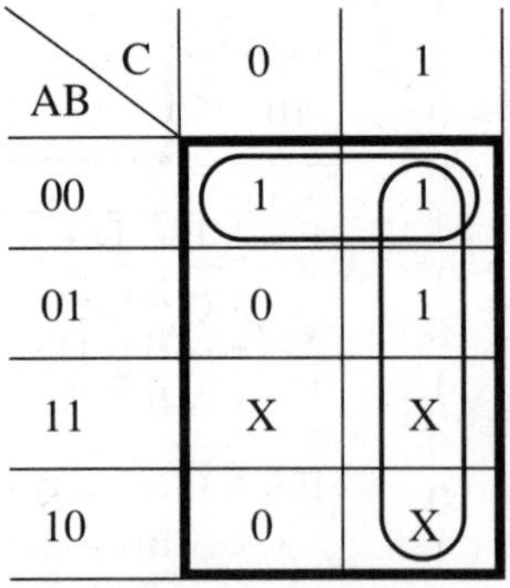

AB \ C	0	1
00	1	1
01	0	1
11	X	X
10	0	X

$$J = C + \overline{A}\,\overline{B}$$

FIGURE 3-60 Example 3-42 K-Map and Truth Table

entered as an X for a don't care state. Fill in the K-map with the output results from the logic function, including the don't care states. Simplify the logic function following the SOP rules, and include the don't care states only if they help to maximize the size of AND terms or minimize the number of AND terms to be ORed together.

■

■ EXAMPLE 3-43 Don't Care States on K-Maps

A	B	C	D	K
0	0	0	0	0
0	0	0	1	0
0	0	1	0	0
0	0	1	1	1
0	1	0	0	1
0	1	0	1	1
0	1	1	0	0
0	1	1	1	0
1	0	0	0	1
1	0	0	1	1
1	0	1	0	X
1	0	1	1	X
1	1	0	0	X
1	1	0	1	X
1	1	1	0	X
1	1	1	1	X

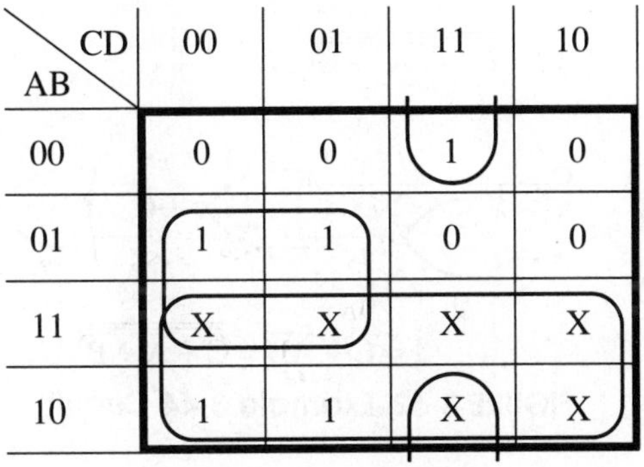

AB \ CD	00	01	11	10
00	0	0	1	0
01	1	1	0	0
11	X	X	X	X
10	1	1	X	X

$$K = A + B\overline{C} + \overline{B}CD$$

FIGURE 3-61 Example 3-43 K-Map and Truth Table

■

3.16.7 K-Map Application: Gate Minimization

Boolean algebra identities and theorems can be used to simplify logic equations, and in turn to simplify logic circuits. Section 3.15 explained the use of alternative gates to minimize circuits. K-maps can also be used to simplify circuits through the use of alternative gates.

In large scale designs circuit minimization is not a primary concern due to the use of medium scale integration (MSI), large scale integration (LSI), custom logic, and programmable logic devices (PLDs). However, the concept of circuit simplification and IC minimization are important in many small scale projects where cost and the IC count are primary concerns.

■ EXAMPLE 3-44 Minimizing the ICs for the SOP Expression Obtained in Example 3-42

Problem: Minimize the ICs used to implement the circuits in Examples 3-42 and 3-43 by selecting alternative gates for the functions.

Solution: The functions obtained in Examples 3-42 and 3-43, DeMorgan's Theorem, and Boolean algebra are applied to form an equivalent logic function that can be built using fewer ICs than the original expression.

$$J = C + \overline{A}\,\overline{B} = C + \overline{A + B}$$

$$J = \overline{\overline{C + \overline{A + B}}}$$

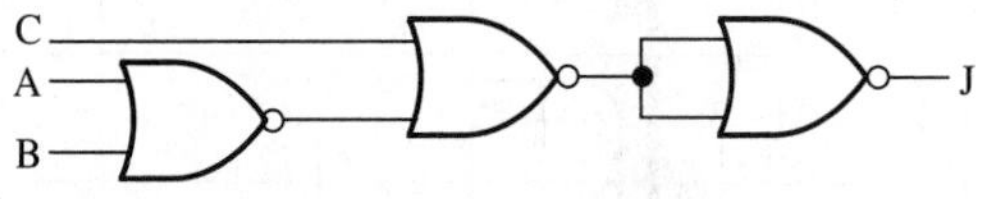

$$J = C + \overline{AB} = \overline{\overline{C + \overline{A + B}}}$$

FIGURE 3-62 Example 3-44 Circuit ■

■ EXAMPLE 3-45 Minimizing the ICs for the SOP Expression Obtained in Example 3-43

$$\overline{K} = C\,\overline{D} + B\,C + \overline{A}\,\overline{B}\,\overline{C}$$

$$K = \overline{C\,\overline{D} + B\,C + \overline{A + B + C}}$$

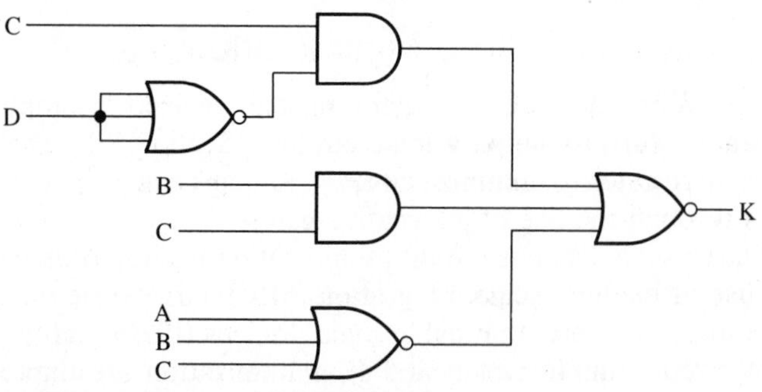

FIGURE 3-63 Example 3-45 Circuit ■

3.16.8 Alternative Forms of K-Maps

The form of the K-map that has been used throughout this chapter is a standard form selected for its ease in implementation with both truth tables and equations of logic functions. Other forms of K-maps also exist that are a slight variation of those shown, as illustrated in Figure 3-64. However, all K-maps have the same properties of adjacent cells, and the same rules are followed to minimize logic functions.

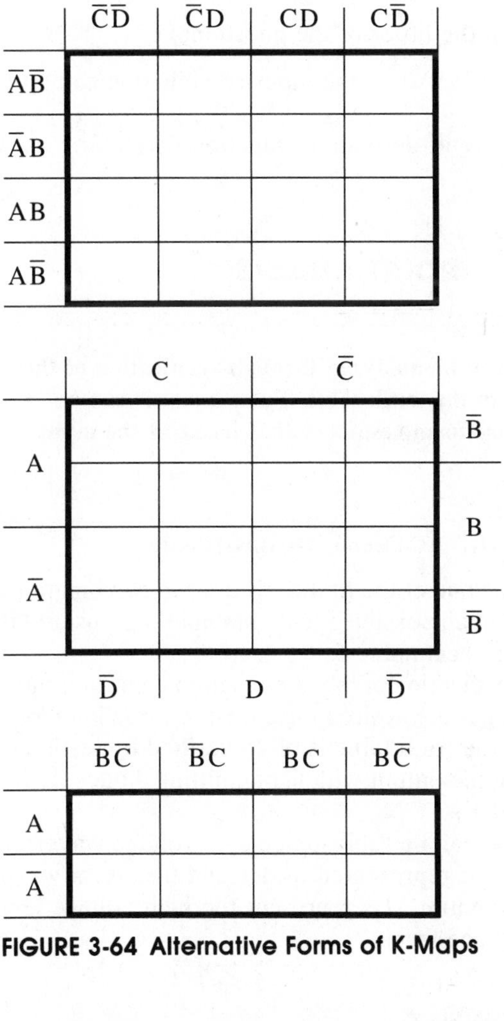

	$\overline{C}\overline{D}$	$\overline{C}D$	CD	$C\overline{D}$
$\overline{A}\overline{B}$				
$\overline{A}B$				
AB				
$A\overline{B}$				

	$\overline{B}\overline{C}$	$\overline{B}C$	BC	$B\overline{C}$
A				
$\overline{A}$				

FIGURE 3-64 Alternative Forms of K-Maps

The primary difference between the forms of K-maps is the labeling of input variables along the edges of the map. Instead of labeling the cell rows and columns with 0's and 1's to represent their logic value, other K-map forms label the cells with the true and inverted specification of the variable letter, according to the active-HIGH convention followed by the SOP equation format. Those input variables of a value of 1 are written in their true form, and those of a value of 0 are written in their inverted form. If the K-map is to be used to derive the POS expression of the function, the labeling of the input variables should be converted to avoid errors.

Section Self-Test

1. How many squares are in a four-variable K-map?
2. List three reasons to use a K-map in digital design.
3. What are don't care states?

ANSWERS (Not necessarily in the order of the questions)

- The output condition when the input combination cannot occur
- 16
- Simplification, circuit derivation, function derivation, as well as gate or IC minimization

3-17 COMBINATIONAL CIRCUIT ANALYSIS

Combinational logic circuits can be analyzed through verification of the circuit output corresponding to the truth table. Pulse analysis can be used to analyze the output waveform results of the circuit as the input waveforms are changed.

3.17.1 Waveform and Truth Table Comparisons

The truth table was one of the first tools used in combinational logic design. Its representation of all possible input combinations ensured that all possible output results were accounted for.

Truth table verification of the combinational logic circuit is an important step in determining if the desired logic function was implemented correctly. In the laboratory the truth table is often verified by testing the logic circuit and by monitoring the output with light emitting diodes (LEDs) to represent the output 0's and 1's.

The truth table can be represented as a voltage waveform. In the truth table logic levels are represented as 1's and 0's. As a waveform with the positive logic convention, 1's represent the high voltage level and 0's represent the low voltage level.

3.17.2 Pulse Circuit Analysis

The waveform representation of input variables in counting order has a periodic relationship with the least significant bit (LSB) having the highest frequency, or shortest period. The period doubles for each successive bit. Actual input waveforms for combinational logic circuits usually have no time relationship. Under normal operating conditions the inputs would seldom change in a counting order, and therefore the actual input waveforms would not be periodic.

Just as logic gates can be analyzed with pulse analysis (as discussed in Section 3.8), combinational logic circuits can be analyzed with pulse waveform analysis.

■ EXAMPLE 3-46 Pulsed Circuit Analysis for the Logic Function in Example 3-42

Problem: Determine the output waveform for the logic functions of Examples 3-42 and 3-43 for the given input waveforms.

Solution: The input waveforms are not in counting order. However, they produce input combinations that are listed in the truth table for the logic function. The output waveform is a graph of the output result when the inputs change as specified.

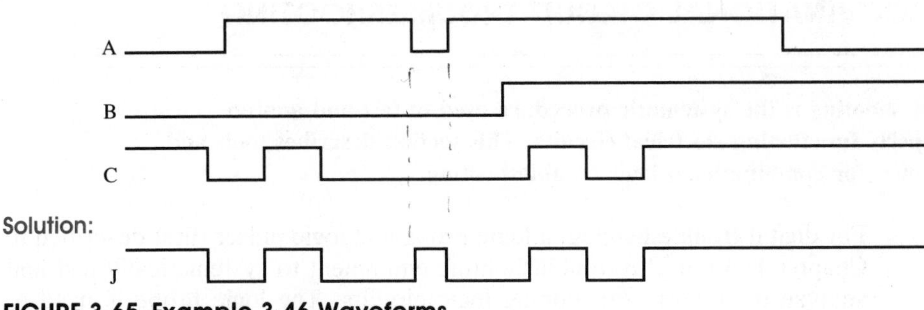

FIGURE 3-65 Example 3-46 Waveforms ■

■ EXAMPLE 3-47 Pulsed Circuit Analysis for the Logic Function Specified in Example 3-43

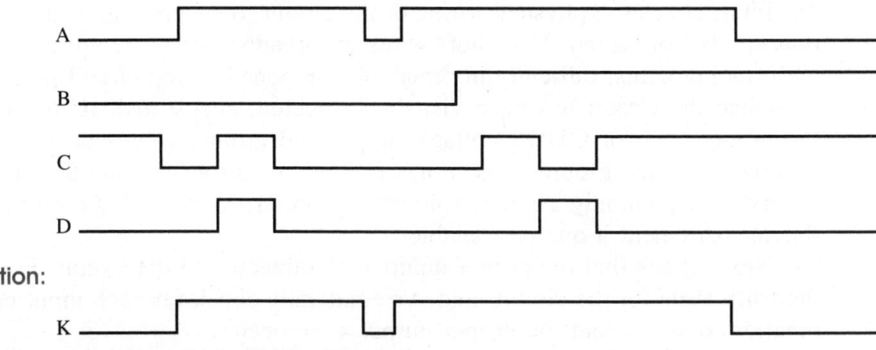

FIGURE 3-66 Example 3-47 Waveforms ■

Section Self-Test

1. A 2-input NAND gate has one input pulsed HIGH and LOW and the other input LOW. What is the output waveform?
2. Can any combinational circuit be analyzed with pulse analysis?

ANSWERS (Not necessarily in the order of the questions)

- NAND Inputs: A

  B

  NAND Output C

  The output is always a logic-HIGH according to the definition of the NAND.
- Yes, all combinational circuits can and should be analyzed with pulse analysis.

3-18 COMBINATIONAL CIRCUIT TROUBLESHOOTING

Troubleshooting is the systematic procedure used to test and analyze improperly functioning electrical circuits. This section describes tools and techniques for combinational logic troubleshooting.

For digital **troubleshooting,** a logic probe and logic pulser (first described in Chapter 1) are useful troubleshooting equipment to systematically test and analyze improperly functioning logic circuits. The logic probe is used to determine input and output logic levels, and a logic pulser can be used to **inject** input pulse waveforms for analysis of circuit outputs.

The first step in troubleshooting combinational circuits is the analysis of the circuit on paper using the techniques described in this chapter. This includes truth table and waveform analysis. Only when the expected outputs are understood can one successfully attempt troubleshooting.

First, check the physical wiring of the circuit to ensure that each IC pin is properly connected. Use short wires on breadboards to avoid problems with tracing wires, difficulty in replacing components, and circuit noise.

Once the circuit has been visually inspected, check each IC to verify the proper TTL or CMOS voltage supply and ground values on their respective V_{CC} and ground pins. For TTL, +5 volts for V_{CC} and 0 volts for ground are commonly used. A voltmeter is preferred over a logic probe for this measurement if one is available.

Next, check that the proper inputs are connected to the circuit. Follow the truth table for the circuit, and systematically check for each input combination to verify that the proper output state occurs.

When an incorrect output is found, analyze and perform troubleshooting from the improper output back through the logic levels to the inputs. At each stage, check that each gate in the circuit operates according to its respective truth table. This technique is called **fault isolation.**

Each problem is systematically traced back and isolated. For each fault found, either an input is incorrect or the gate is not functioning properly. The fault is then eliminated by correcting the improper inputs or by replacing the defective gate with another gate or a new IC.

Most problems will not be due to faulty components in beginning digital logic courses, but rather to incorrect circuit design, analysis, or faulty circuit construction.

Section Self-Test

1. If a combinational circuit has an output of logic 0 instead of logic 1 for a given set of inputs, list two possible problems that can be found with troubleshooting.
2. What is fault isolation?
3. If the inputs to a NOR gate are shorted, how can this be determined by troubleshooting?

ANSWERS (Not necessarily in the order of the questions)

- Inputs unconnected, or inputs incorrectly wired
- Determining where the fault is occurring in the circuit
- Inputs that are changed (i.e., at the input switches) will produce no change in output.

3-19 COMBINATIONAL LOGIC DESIGN

The purpose of the study of combinational logic is to design circuits to perform specific logic functions as required by applications. Truth tables, SOP and POS equations, and K-maps are all tools used to aid in the design and analysis of such circuits.

To accomplish digital logic circuit design, the application must be defined in a truth table to specify it in terms of logic functions. The functions must then be defined by equations, and the circuits must be built to produce the functions.

3.19.1 Logic Function Definition

Perhaps the most important part of any circuit design is to analyze and understand fully the required functions and performance of the end product. The design must be broken down into simpler functional blocks and defined according to the necessary circuit operations. This design procedure will be used throughout this book.

The first step in designing a digital circuit is to determine the number of input and output signals required for setting up the truth table. Once the number of individual inputs and outputs is determined, the actual input combinations that result in specific outputs can be identified. All possible input combinations are listed in the truth table. The resulting output signals are then listed in one or more output columns in the table. It is often helpful to add comments to the truth table to more clearly identify the output signals. Such comments are important in complex logic designs where a truth table is perhaps only an intermediate specification of signals in the entire design.

3.19.2 Logic Function Simplification

After each output signal is defined by a truth table, the output is K-mapped if the number of input variables in the system is 5 or less. The logic function can be simplified and specified as an SOP, POS, or active-LOW SOP equation.

For systems with greater than five input variables, K-mapping tech niques are no longer useful due to the large size of the K-map. Boolean algebra simplification may be employed, or a PLD solution may be appropriate. (In many applications requiring a large number of input variables, MSI and LSI circuitry is available to implement the function.) Such applications using multiplexers, decoders, encoders, arithmetic circuits, and PLDs will be covered in succeeding chapters.

3.19.3 Circuit Implementation of the Function

The logic circuit needed to implement the function can be designed based on the SOP or POS equation. The resulting circuit can be a standard two-level SOP or POS circuit, or alternative gates may be selected to minimize the number of chips or gates required in the design. In more complex designs the SOP equation of the logic function can be implemented with a PLD, as discussed in Chapter 12.

Several examples follow to show how an application can be defined in terms of a logic function, simplified, and implemented as a circuit.

■ EXAMPLE 3-48 Logic Design: Instant Replay Voting Machine

Problem: Sports fans want a vote in the instant replay decisions on a referee's calls, as does the coach from the home team. This voting machine allows a coach and three fans (in this case, Tom, Dick, and Harry) to vote on the referee's call. The decision is based on majority rule, but in the case of a tie, the coach's vote is the final decision. The voting machine must indicate whether or not a play stands as called by the referee. A 0 is cast to vote against the referee; a 1 is cast to vote in agreement with the referee. Perform the following steps:

1. Construct a truth table with all inputs and the vote output.
2. K-map the output and simplify the logic expression.
3. Minimize the chip count by substituting alternative gates as necessary.

Solution: Four inputs are required for the three fans and the one coach from the home team. Let the votes from the fans be represented by variables T, D, and H, and let the coach's vote be represented by the variable C. The only output variable is the vote, V. (See Figures 3-67 and 3-68.)

T	D	H	C	V
0	0	0	0	0
0	0	0	1	0
0	0	1	0	0
0	0	1	1	1
0	1	0	0	0
0	1	0	1	1
0	1	1	0	0
0	1	1	1	1
1	0	0	0	0
1	0	0	1	1
1	0	1	0	0
1	0	1	1	1
1	1	0	0	0
1	1	0	1	1
1	1	1	0	1
1	1	1	1	1

TD \ HC	00	01	11	10
00	0	0	1	0
01	0	1	1	0
11	0	1	1	1
10	0	1	1	0

$$V = HC + DC + TC + TDH$$

$$V = \overline{(\overline{HC})(\overline{DC})(\overline{TC})(\overline{TDH})}$$

FIGURE 3-67 Example 3-48 K-Map and Truth Table

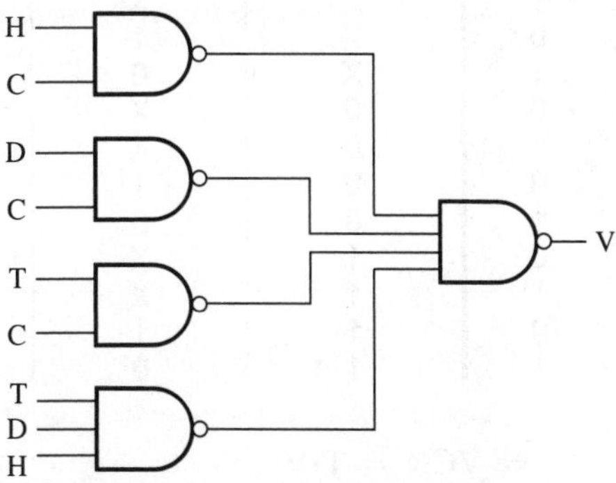

FIGURE 3-68 Example 3-48 Circuit

■

■ EXAMPLE 3-49 Home "Sound" System Controller

Problem: Four basic home appliances—the telephone, stereo, TV, and VCR, are usually located near each other, and the use of more than one simultaneously can be annoying. Design a controller that will produce signals to do the following:

1. Turn off the VCR when the TV is turned off.
2. Mute the TV or stereo when the telephone is lifted off the hook.
3. Mute the TV if the stereo is on.
4. Use the don't care states for the output whenever appropriate. For the final control circuit, a HIGH output indicates on; a LOW output indicates off or mute.

Each appliance will be turned on manually or by a preset timer, but the controller will either control the audio levels or turn the appliance off. The controller will not turn on any device.

Solution: Four inputs are needed: VCR (V), TV (T), stereo (S), and telephone (P)

For simplifying the design, the three output signals are those specified by the conditions in (1), (2), and (3). The three outputs in the truth table are VCR off (VCR), stereo mute (S mute), and TV mute (TV mute). (See Figure 3-69.)

VCR V	TV T	Stereo S	Phone P	VCR OFF (0=off)	Stereo mute S mute (0 mute)	TV mute (0 mute)
0	0	0	0	X	X	X
0	0	0	1	X	X	X
0	0	1	0	X	1	X
0	0	1	1	X	0	X
0	1	0	0	X	X	1
0	1	0	1	X	X	0
0	1	1	0	X	1	0
0	1	1	1	X	0	0
1	0	0	0	0	X	X
1	0	0	1	0	X	X
1	0	1	0	0	1	X
1	0	1	1	0	0	X
1	1	0	0	1	X	1
1	1	0	1	1	X	0
1	1	1	0	1	1	0
1	1	1	1	1	0	0

VCR off control: $= \text{VCR} = T \cdot V$
TV mute control: $= \text{TV mute} = \overline{V}T\overline{S}\overline{P} + VT\overline{S}\overline{P} = T\overline{S}\overline{P}$
Stereo mute control: $= \text{S mute} = \overline{P}$

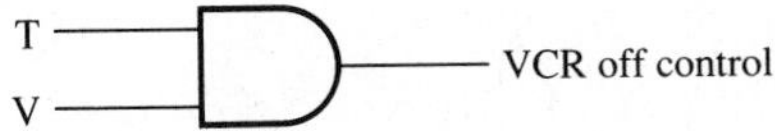

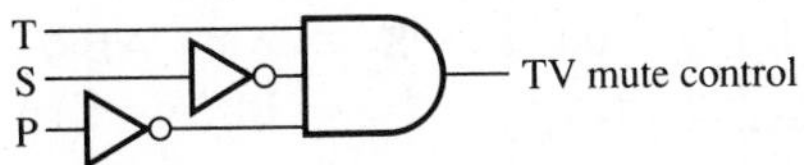

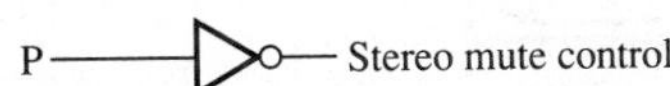

FIGURE 3-69 Example 3-49 Circuit

EXAMPLE 3-50 Two-Bit Adder

Problem: Design a logic circuit to add two 2-bit binary numbers and output the resulting number:

$$\begin{array}{rccc} & & A & B \\ + & & Y & Z \\ \hline & S_3 & S_2 & S_1 \end{array}$$

Solution: Four inputs are needed, one for each bit that is added. Three outputs are required for the sum bits and the carry-out bit. (See Figures 3-70, 3-71, and 3-72.)

A	B	Y	Z	S_3	S_2	S_1
0	0	0	0	0	0	0
0	0	0	1	0	0	1
0	0	1	0	0	1	0
0	0	1	1	0	1	1
0	1	0	0	0	0	1
0	1	0	1	0	1	0
0	1	1	0	0	1	1
0	1	1	1	1	0	0
1	0	0	0	0	1	0
1	0	0	1	0	1	1
1	0	1	0	1	0	0
1	0	1	1	1	0	1
1	1	0	0	0	1	1
1	1	0	1	1	0	0
1	1	1	0	1	0	1
1	1	1	1	1	1	0

FIGURE 3-70 Example 3-50 Truth Table

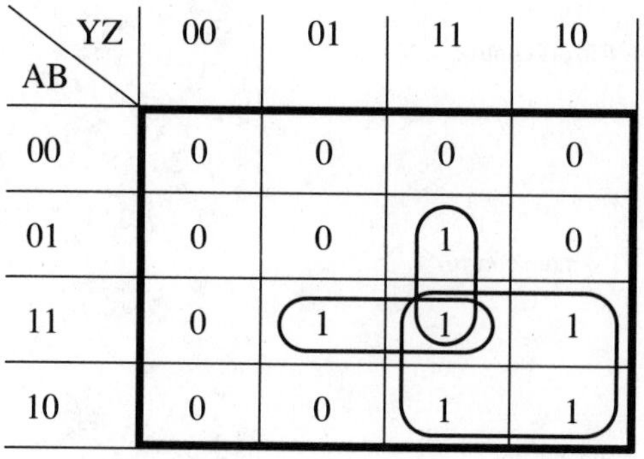

AB \ YZ	00	01	11	10
00	0	0	0	0
01	0	0	1	0
11	0	1	1	1
10	0	0	1	1

$$S_3 = AY + ABZ + BYZ$$
$$= BZ(A + Y) + AY$$

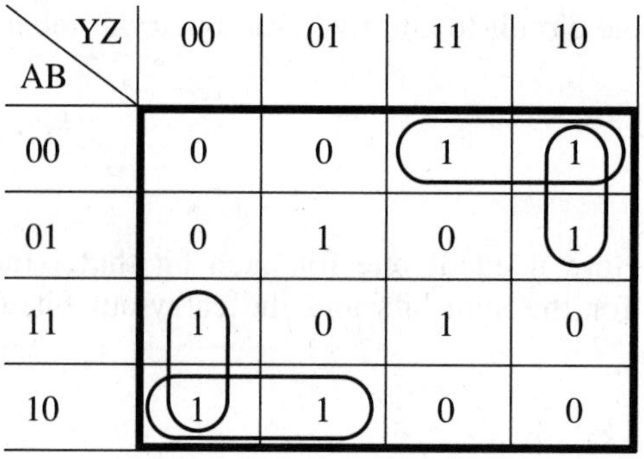

AB \ YZ	00	01	11	10
00	0	0	1	1
01	0	1	0	1
11	1	0	1	0
10	1	1	0	0

$$S_2 = \overline{A}\overline{B}Y + \overline{A}Y\overline{Z} + A\overline{Y}\overline{Z} + A\overline{B}\overline{Y} + \overline{A}B\overline{Y}Z + ABYZ$$
$$= (A \oplus Y) \oplus (BZ)$$

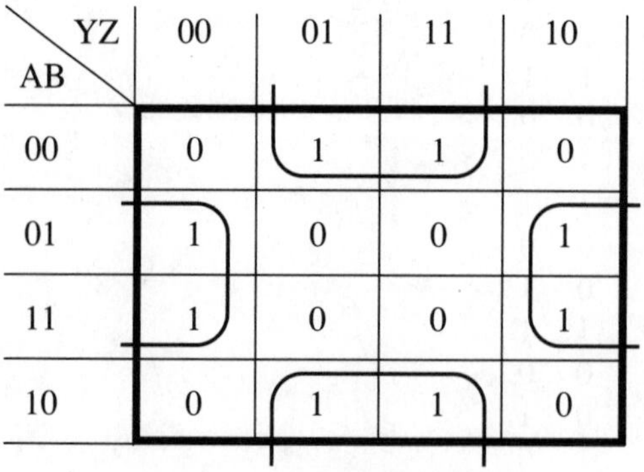

AB \ YZ	00	01	11	10
00	0	1	1	0
01	1	0	0	1
11	1	0	0	1
10	0	1	1	0

$$S_1 = B\overline{Z} + \overline{B}Z$$
$$= B \oplus Z$$

FIGURE 3-71 Example 3-50 K-Maps

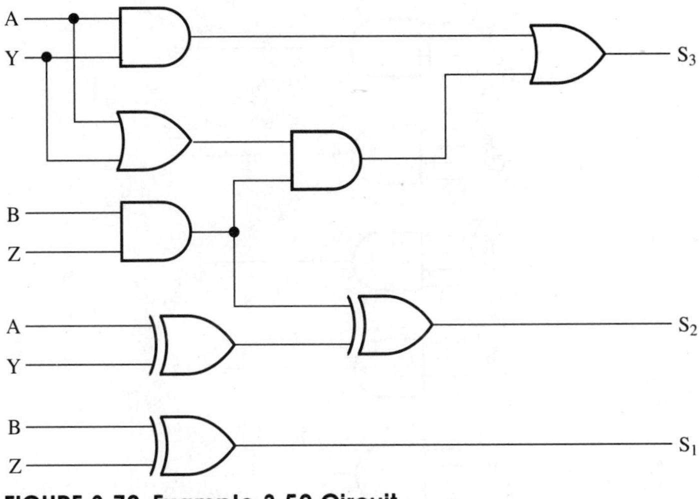

FIGURE 3-72 Example 3-50 Circuit

EXAMPLE 3-51 Decimal Decoder

Problem: Design a decoder circuit to decode decimal digits. When each digit is decoded, an LED should be lit that identifies only that digit.

Solution: Set up a truth table with four binary inputs and ten outputs, one for each decimal digit. The logic equations for each output are derived from the following function table. (See Figure 3-73.)

A	B	C	D	0	1	2	3	4	5	6	7	8	9
0	0	0	0	1	0	0	0	0	0	0	0	0	0
0	0	0	1	0	1	0	0	0	0	0	0	0	0
0	0	1	0	0	0	1	0	0	0	0	0	0	0
0	0	1	1	0	0	0	1	0	0	0	0	0	0
0	1	0	0	0	0	0	0	1	0	0	0	0	0
0	1	0	1	0	0	0	0	0	1	0	0	0	0
0	1	1	0	0	0	0	0	0	0	1	0	0	0
0	1	1	1	0	0	0	0	0	0	0	1	0	0
1	0	0	0	0	0	0	0	0	0	0	0	1	0
1	0	0	1	0	0	0	0	0	0	0	0	0	1

$0 = \overline{A}\,\overline{B}\,\overline{C}\,\overline{D}$ $\quad 4 = \overline{A}\,B\,\overline{C}\,\overline{D}$ $\quad 7 = \overline{A}\,B\,C\,D$

$1 = \overline{A}\,\overline{B}\,\overline{C}\,D$ $\quad 5 = \overline{A}\,B\,\overline{C}\,D$ $\quad 8 = A\,\overline{B}\,\overline{C}\,\overline{D}$

$2 = \overline{A}\,\overline{B}\,C\,\overline{D}$ $\quad 6 = \overline{A}\,B\,C\,\overline{D}$ $\quad 9 = A\,\overline{B}\,\overline{C}\,D$

$3 = \overline{A}\,\overline{B}\,C\,D$

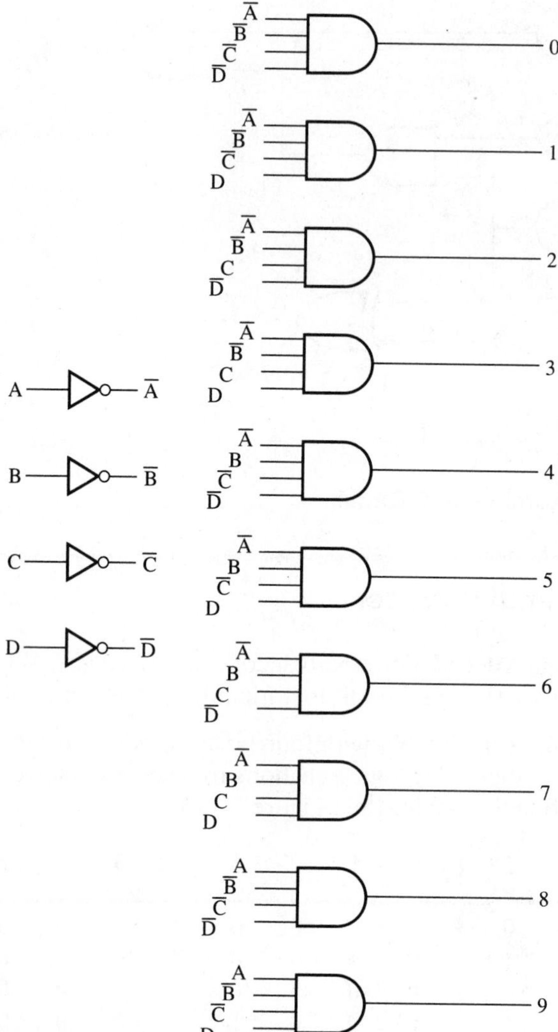

FIGURE 3-73 Example 3-51 Circuit

■

■ EXAMPLE 3-52 Decimal Encoder

Problem: Design an encoder circuit to encode ten separate input switches and output the binary value corresponding to each input switch.

Solution: Set up a truth table with ten inputs, one for each decimal digit, and four outputs, one for each binary bit. When a decimal digit input is activated, the 4-bit output is the binary equivalent of that decimal number.

Obtain the output equations from the truth table. A K-map is not practical since the problem has ten inputs! (See Figure 3-74.)

0	1	2	3	4	5	6	7	8	9	A	B	C	D
1	0	0	0	0	0	0	0	0	0	0	0	0	0
0	1	0	0	0	0	0	0	0	0	0	0	0	1
0	0	1	0	0	0	0	0	0	0	0	0	1	0
0	0	0	1	0	0	0	0	0	0	0	0	1	1
0	0	0	0	1	0	0	0	0	0	0	1	0	0
0	0	0	0	0	1	0	0	0	0	0	1	0	1
0	0	0	0	0	0	1	0	0	0	0	1	1	0
0	0	0	0	0	0	0	1	0	0	0	1	1	1
0	0	0	0	0	0	0	0	1	0	1	0	0	0
0	0	0	0	0	0	0	0	0	1	1	0	0	1

$A = 8 + 9$ $\qquad B = 4 + 5 + 6 + 7$

$C = 2 + 3 + 6 + 7$ $\qquad D = 1 + 3 + 5 + 7 + 9$

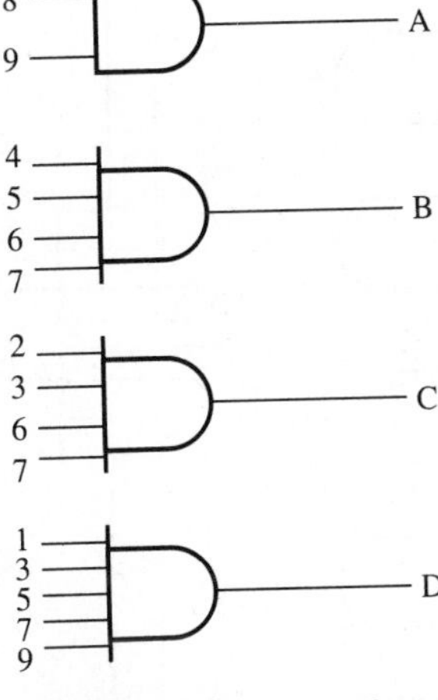

FIGURE 3-74 Example 3-52 Circuit

■

■ EXAMPLE 3-53 Three-Bit Programmable Function Generator

Problem: Design a programmable function generator that can be "hardware programmed" via eight DIP switches to produce any output function for a truth table of up to three input variables.

Solution: The truth table requires four inputs: the 3-input variables control the function generator, plus the eight data inputs generated by the DIP switch. (There are a total of 11 switches in this problem: 3 for the input variables and 8 for the "data" that will be routed to the output.) The output

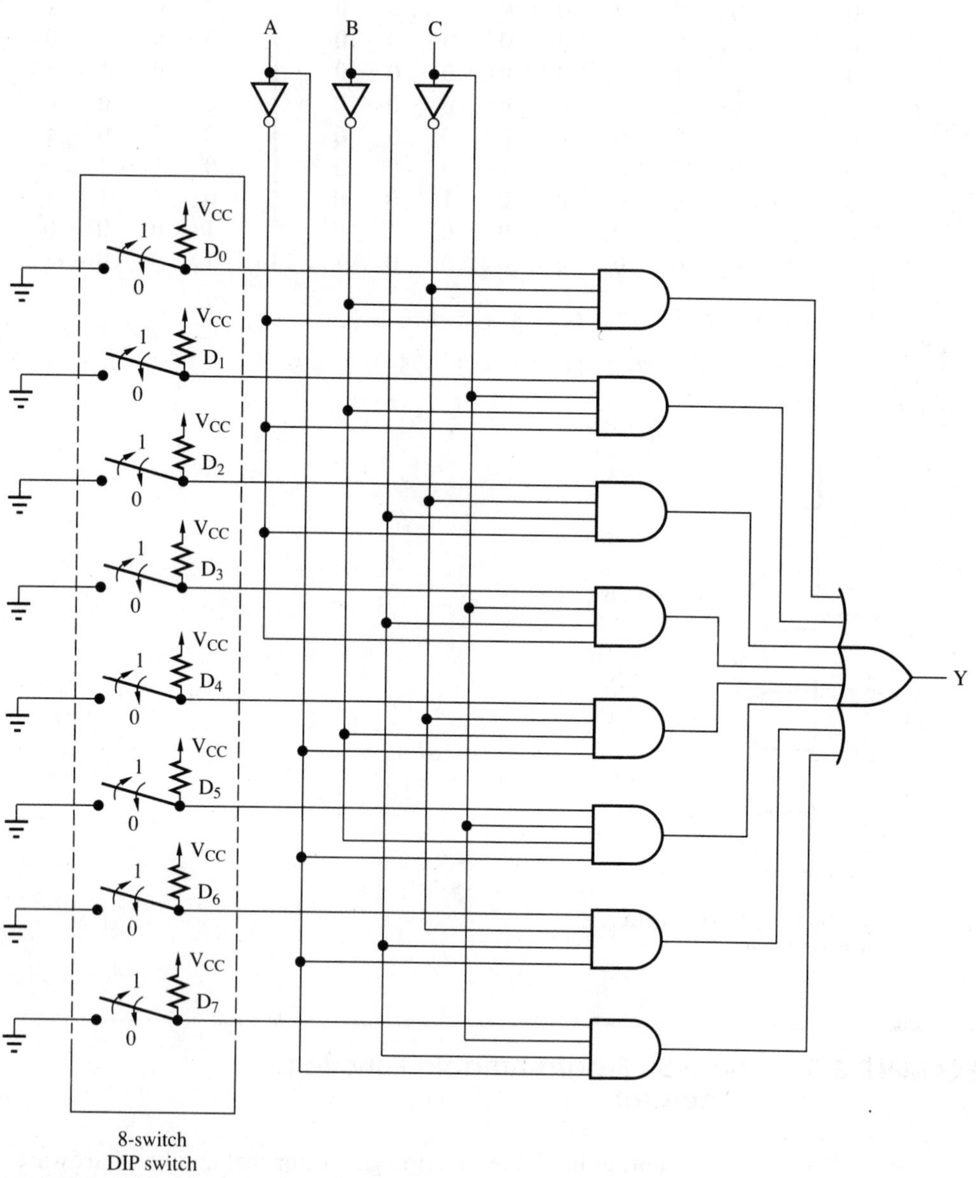

FIGURE 3-75 Example 3-53 Circuit

Y is derived as a function of the control input variables and the data values of the DIP switches. (See Figure 3-75.)

A	B	C	Data	Y
0	0	0	D_0	D_0
0	0	1	D_1	D_1
0	1	0	D_2	D_2
0	1	1	D_3	D_3
1	0	0	D_4	D_4
1	0	1	D_5	D_5
1	1	0	D_6	D_6
1	1	1	D_7	D_7

$$Y = \overline{A}\,\overline{B}\,\overline{C}\,D_0 + \overline{A}\,\overline{B}\,C\,D_1 + \overline{A}\,B\,\overline{C}\,D_2 + \overline{A}\,B\,C\,D_3$$

$$= A\,\overline{B}\,\overline{C}\,D_4 + A\,\overline{B}\,C\,D_5 + A\,B\,\overline{C}\,D_6 + A\,B\,C\,D_7$$

■

■ EXAMPLE 3-54 BCD to Excess-3 Code Converter

Problem: Design a code converter that will convert a single-digit binary coded decimal (BCD) value to Excess-3.

Solution: Set up a truth table with four inputs for the BCD digit and four outputs for the Excess-3 digit. The output is the Excess-3 equivalent code for the BCD input value. Obtain the output equations from a K-map. Use the don't care states to aid in the simplification of the output equations. (See Figures 3-76 and 3-77.)

A	B	C	D	J	K	L	M
0	0	0	0	0	0	1	1
0	0	0	1	0	1	0	0
0	0	1	0	0	1	0	1
0	0	1	1	0	1	1	0
0	1	0	0	0	1	1	1
0	1	0	1	1	0	0	0
0	1	1	0	1	0	0	1
0	1	1	1	1	0	1	0
1	0	0	0	1	0	1	1
1	0	0	1	1	1	0	0

AB \ CD	00	01	11	10
00	0	0	0	0
01	0	1	1	1
11	X	X	X	X
10	1	1	X	X

$M = \overline{D}$ by inspection of the truth table

$J = A + BC + BD$

AB \ CD	00	01	11	10
00	0	1	1	1
01	1	0	0	0
11	X	X	X	X
10	0	1	X	X

$K = \overline{B}C + \overline{B}D + \overline{A}B\overline{C}\overline{D}$

AB \ CD	00	01	11	10
00	1	0	1	0
01	1	0	1	0
11	1	0	1	0
10	1	0	1	0

$L = \overline{C}\overline{D} + CD$

$L = \overline{C \oplus D}$

FIGURE 3-76 Example 3-54 K-Maps and Equations

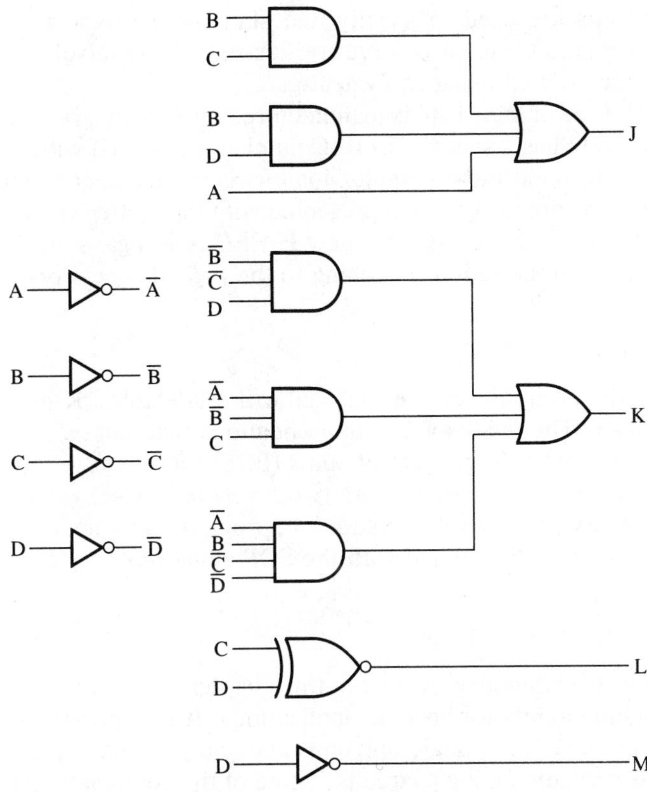

FIGURE 3-77 Example 3-54 Circuit ■

Section Self-Test

1. List the steps necessary to perform combinational logic design.
2. Why are K-maps for systems with more than five variables not used?
3. What is needed to construct a truth table for combinational logic design?

ANSWERS (Not necessarily in the same order as the questions)

- The graphical technique for K-maps of six variables or more requires more than three dimensions. (A five-variable K-map is a three dimensional map.)
- Input and output variable specifications
- Function definition, function simplification, and circuit implementation

SUMMARY

Digital circuits can be designed to perform any type of digital function through the use of seven basic logic functions: NOT, AND, NAND, OR, NOR, XOR, and XNOR. Each logic function can be represented by a logic gate, symbol, Boolean equation, and truth table. Algebraic laws and Boolean relationships are used to specify and simplify the logic functions. These Boolean relationships also serve to illustrate that equivalent logic circuits can be constructed using equivalent gates.

Each type of logic gate is manufactured into an integrated circuit, or IC, and each gate has a specific TTL IC number associated with it. The ICs are combined to build more complex logic circuits, using combinational logic. Entire digital circuits can be represented with logic gate symbols. In addition to the traditional logic symbols, new IEEE/ANSI logic symbols are used to specify more information pertaining to the logic device's operation.

ANALYSIS

Combinational circuits can be analyzed with truth tables, K-maps, and waveform pulses. The results are output equations that can be specified in sum of products (SOP) or product of sums (POS) form. These forms are useful for implementing the circuits with two levels of NAND gates or two levels of NOR gates, respectively. In addition, programmable logic devices (PLDs) can be directly programmed with the SOP equations.

APPLICATION

The analysis techniques learned in this chapter can be used to analyze and build digital circuits for specific applications. It is important to have a firm understanding of basic logic functions and analysis techniques to be able to design combinational logic circuits. Some of the combinational applications include multiplexers, demultiplexers, decoders, encoders, code converters, and various arithmetic circuits. Specific applications will be discussed in subsequent chapters.

DESIGN

Combinational circuits can be systematically designed by first understanding the intended application, and then defining the logic function. Next, each logic function is specified as a Boolean equation, simplified by one of the various means described (Boolean, K-map, truth table), and finally implemented with combinational logic. A wide variety of TTL ICs are available for IC implementation.

PROBLEMS

3-1 Logic Function Representation—Analysis Problems

1. a. Draw the traditional and IEEE/ANSI logic symbol for each of the seven basic logic gates (2-input gates).
   b. Write the logic equation for each gate next to its logic symbols.

2. Use your TTL data book and find an IC for each 2-input gate drawn in Problem 1.

3. Use your CMOS data book and find an IC for each 2-input gate drawn in Problem 1.

3-2 Inverter Function—Analysis Problems

4. List three TTL ICs that contain inverters. List the differences between each IC.

*5. Draw a logic schematic for three cascaded inverters, using a 7404. Label all pins, and write a truth table for the input and the output.

3-3 AND Function—Analysis Problems

6. Make a table of all available AND gate ICs. List the following in the table: IC number, technology (TTL sub-family), number of AND gates, number of inputs for each AND gate.

7. A 0, 1, and 1 are input into a 3-input AND gate. What is the output?

3-4 NAND Function—Analysis Problems

8. Look up a 7400 TTL IC in a data book or other reference.
   a. Identify the IC.
   b. Draw the traditional logic symbol.
   c. Draw the IEEE/ANSI logic symbol.
   d. Draw the IC, label each pin, and give a description of the function of each pin.

9. a. What TTL IC has the greatest number of NAND inputs?
   b. How many inputs does it have?
   c. Explain why there are no TTL ICs with more inputs than the answer to (b).

3-5 OR Function—Analysis Problems

10. Make a table of all available OR gate ICs. List the following in the table: IC number, technology (TTL subfamily), number of OR gates, and number of inputs for each OR gate.

---

* See Answers to Selected Problems.

*11. A digital circuit designer wants to OR 16 individual inputs.
  a. Show how this can be done with 7432 ICs.
  b. How many ICs would be needed?

3-6 NOR Function—Analysis Problems

12. a. Design a circuit that can NOR inputs A, B, and C. Use an actual IC, and show your schematic with pin numbers.
  b. If the output from the circuit in part (a) is NORed with input D, what is the final output equation?

3-7 Exclusive Gates: XOR and XNOR Functions—Analysis Problems

13. a. Use a TTL data book to find all exclusive gates with more than two inputs.
  b. How many TTL exclusive gates were found in part (a)? Explain.

14. Use exclusive gates to design a circuit that will turn on an LED when both inputs are the same.

15. Use exclusive gates to design a circuit that will turn on an LED when the inputs are different.

*16. Use other logic gates and exclusive gates to design a circuit that will turn on an LED when eight inputs are the same.

3-8 Pulsed Logic Gate Operation—Analysis Problems

17. Waveform A:

Waveform B:

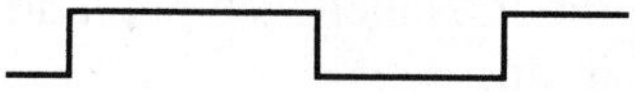

Given waveforms A and B shown as inputs into an AND gate, draw the resulting output waveform.

18. Repeat Problem 17 for an OR gate.

19. Repeat Problem 17 for a NAND gate.

*20. Repeat Problem 17 for a NOR gate.

21. Repeat Problem 17 for an XOR gate.

22. Repeat Problem 17 for an XNOR gate.

23. A 1 KHz square wave is input into one input of an XOR gate while the other input is grounded.

a. What is the frequency of the XOR output?
b. If the same frequency is input but the other input to the XOR is tied to V_{CC}, what is the frequency of the output?
c. Graph the 1 KHz input waveform and the answers to (a) and (b) with the same time base (as they would appear on an oscilloscope).

3-9 Combinational Logic Circuits—Analysis Problems

*24. Draw the following logic circuit, and label all pins and gates: two inputs, A, B. NANDed; three inputs B, C, D, NANDed; and the outputs of the NAND gates input into a NOR gate.

25. Determine the output equation and truth table for the circuit in Figure 3-78.

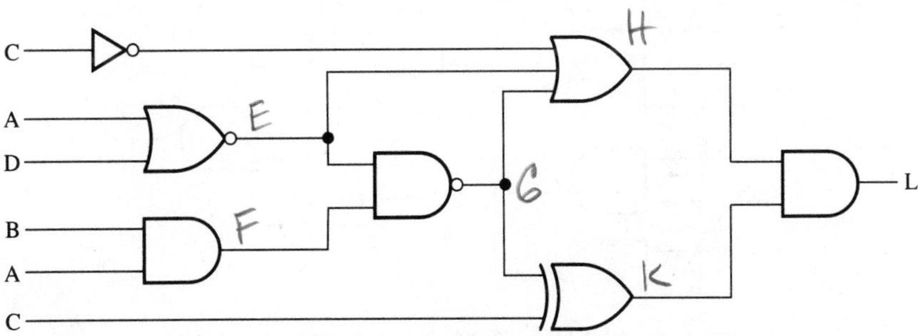

FIGURE 3-78 Problems 3-25, 3-29, 3-35, and 3-89

26. Determine the output equation and truth table for the circuit in Figure 3-79.

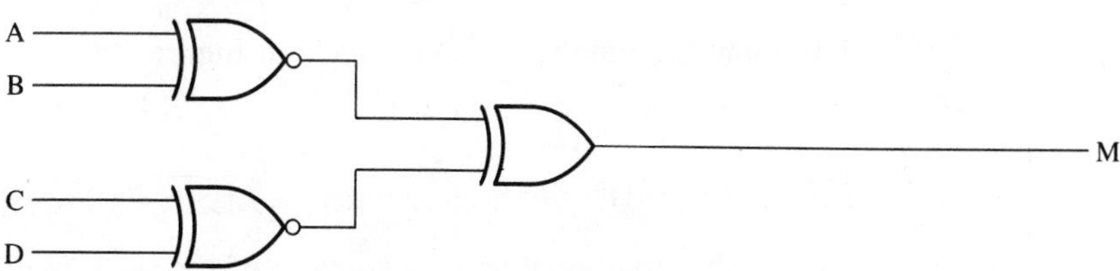

FIGURE 3-79 Problems 3-26, 3-30, 3-36, and 3-90

27. Determine the output equation and truth table for the circuit in Figure 3-80.

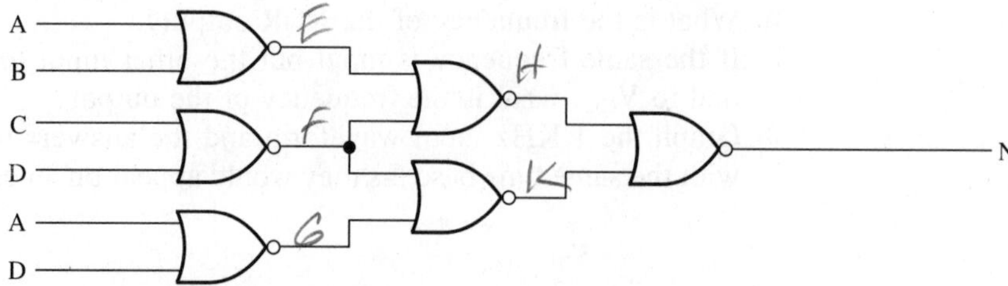

FIGURE 3-80 Problems 3-27, 3-31, 3-37, and 3-91

28. Determine the output equation and truth table for the circuit in Figure 3-81.

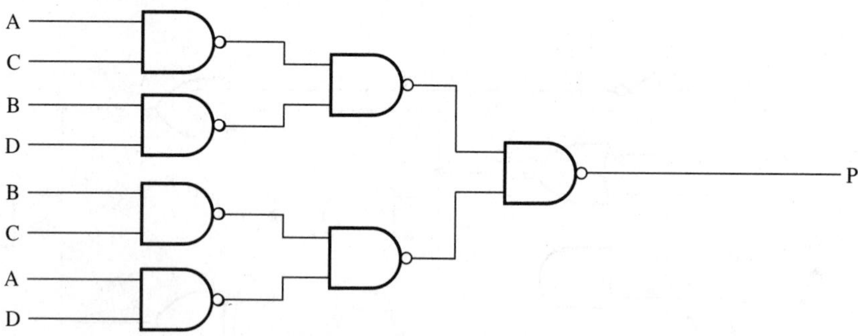

FIGURE 3-81 Problems 3-28, 3-32, 3-38, and 3-92

29. Determine the number of logic levels in Figure 3-78.

*30. Determine the number of logic levels in Figure 3-79.

31. Determine the number of logic levels in Figure 3-80.

32. Determine the number of logic levels in Figure 3-81.

3-10 IEEE/ANSI Logic Gate Symbols—Analysis Problems

35. Convert the traditional logic schematic of Figure 3-78 into an IEEE/ANSI logic schematic.

36. Convert the traditional logic schematic of Figure 3-79 into an IEEE/ANSI logic schematic.

37. Convert the traditional logic schematic of Figure 3-80 into an IEEE/ANSI logic schematic.

38. Convert the traditional logic schematic of Figure 3-81 into an IEEE/ANSI logic schematic.

3-11 Boolean Algebra—Analysis Problems

For Problems 3-39–3-42, prove the following Chapter 3 text equations using truth tables.

*39. $A(\overline{A} + B) = AB$ (Eq. 3-21)

40. $(A + B)(A + C) = A + BC$ (Eq. 3-28)

41. $\overline{A \oplus B} = \overline{A}\,\overline{B} + A\,B$ (Eq. 3-30)

42. $\overline{A + B + C + D} = \overline{A}\,\overline{B}\,\overline{C}\,\overline{D}$ (Eq. 3-33)

3-12 Boolean Equation Simplification—Application Problems

For Problems 3-43–3-51, simplify the Boolean expressions.

43. $\overline{X}\,\overline{Y}\,\overline{Z} + X\,\overline{Y}\,Z + X\,Y\,Z + X + Y\,\overline{Z}$

44. $\overline{A\,B + \overline{(A + B)}}$

*45. $\overline{(A + B)}(\overline{A} + \overline{B})$

46. $\overline{A}\,\overline{B}\,C + A\,\overline{B}$

47. $(A + B + \overline{C})(\overline{A} + B + \overline{C})$

48. $S\,T\,U + \overline{R}\,T\,U + \overline{Q}\,T\,U + Q\,R\,\overline{S}$

49. $(A + \overline{A})(A\,B\,\overline{C} + A\,B)$

*50. $(A + C)(B + C)(\overline{A} + \overline{C})$

51. $\overline{B} + ABC + \overline{A}C + \overline{A}\,\overline{B}$

For Problems 3-52 and 3-53, write the Boolean expression and circuit for the given truth table.

*52.

A	B	C	X
0	0	0	0
0	0	1	0
0	1	0	1
0	1	1	1
1	0	0	0
1	0	1	1
1	1	0	1
1	1	1	0

53.

Q	R	S	T	X
0	0	0	0	0
0	0	0	1	1
0	0	1	0	0
0	0	1	1	1
0	1	0	0	0
0	1	0	1	1
0	1	1	0	1
0	1	1	1	0
1	0	0	0	0
1	0	0	1	0
1	0	1	0	1
1	0	1	1	1
1	1	0	0	1
1	1	0	1	0
1	1	1	0	1
1	1	1	1	0

54. Draw the simplest logic circuit possible to implement the following Boolean expression:

$$\overline{(\overline{A} + B + C + D) + (A\,\overline{B}\,\overline{C}\,D)} = Q$$

55. Draw and label the logic circuit for the original Boolean expression given in Example 3-19.

56. Draw and label the logic circuit for the original Boolean expression given in Example 3-20.

57. Draw and label the logic circuit for the original Boolean expression given in Example 3-21.

58. Draw and label the logic circuit for the original Boolean expression given in Example 3-22.

59. Draw and label the logic circuit for the original Boolean expression given in Example 3-23.

60. Draw and label the logic circuit for the original Boolean expression given in Example 3-24.

*61. Draw and label a logic circuit to implement the following Boolean expression, using only 2-input NAND gates and inverters:

$$X = \overline{A}\,B\,C\,\overline{D}$$

62. Simplify the following equation, and draw the resulting logic schematic:

$$WXY + WZ + X\overline{Y} + \overline{W}XY + \overline{W}Z$$

63. Simplify the following equation, and draw the resulting logic schematic:

$$\overline{A\,B + \overline{(A + B)}}$$

3-13 Sum of Products and Product of Sums—Analysis and Application Problems

64. Convert the logic expression for the circuit in Problem 3-25 to SOP form.

65. Convert the logic expression for the circuit in Problem 3-26 to SOP form.

66. Convert the logic expression for the circuit in Problem 3-27 to SOP form.

67. Convert the logic expression for the circuit in Problem 3-28 to SOP form.

68. Convert the logic expression for the circuit in Problem 3-25 to POS form.

*69. Convert the logic expression for the circuit in Problem 3-26 to POS form.

70. Convert the logic expression for the circuit in Problem 3-27 to POS form.

71. Convert the logic expression for the circuit in Problem 3-28 to POS form.

72. Determine the logic functions, SOP and POS forms, for the K-map in Figure 3-82.

AB \ CD	00	01	11	10
00	0	1	1	0
01	1	0	1	0
11	0	1	1	1
10	0	0	0	0

FIGURE 3-82 Problems 3-72, 3-77, and 3-102 through 3-104

73. Determine the logic functions, SOP and POS forms, for the K-map in Figure 3-83.

EF \ GH	00	01	11	10
00	1	0	0	1
01	0	0	1	1
11	0	1	0	0
10	1	1	1	1

FIGURE 3-83 Problems 3-73, 3-78, and 3-105 through 3-107

*74. Determine the logic functions, SOP and POS forms, for the K-map in Figure 3-84.

JK \ LM	00	01	11	10
00	0	0	0	1
01	1	0	0	0
11	1	0	0	1
10	1	1	0	1

FIGURE 3-84 Problems 3-74 and 3-108 through 3-110

75. Determine the logic functions, SOP and POS forms, for the K-map in Figure 3-85.

PQ \ RS	00	01	11	10
00	1	1	0	0
01	1	1	1	0
11	0	0	1	0
10	1	1	1	0

FIGURE 3-85 Problems 3-75, and 3-111 through 3-113

76. Refer to your TTL data book, and find a single IC that can be used to implement an active-LOW SOP equation with six input variables and one output.

77. Determine the active-LOW SOP logic function form for the K-map in Figure 3-82.

78. Determine the active-LOW SOP logic function form for the K-map in Figure 3-83.

79. Implement the answer to Problem 77 using AND-OR-INVERT ICs. Show your labelled schematic.

80. Implement the answer to Problem 78 using AND-OR-INVERT ICs. Show your labelled schematic.

3-14 Comparison and Conversion of Sum of Products and Product of Sums Equations—Analysis and Application Problems

81. A circuit solution for a given application can be implemented using SOP, POS, or inverted SOP equations. Will each implementation require the same number of gates? Explain.

82. Find the SOP, POS, and inverted SOP equations for the truth table in Problem 52. Build the minimum circuit for each implementation using any of the seven basic gates. Which implementation uses the least number of gates?

83. Find the SOP, POS, and inverted SOP equations for the truth table in

Problem 53. Build the minimum circuit for each implementation using any of the seven basic gates. Which implementation uses the least number of gates?

3-15 Equivalent Gates and Alternative Gate Selection—Application Problems

84. Construct a 2-input NOR function using NAND gates, and draw the logic schematic using the IEEE/ANSI symbols.

85. Construct a 2-input NAND function using NOR gates, and draw the logic schematic using the IEEE/ANSI symbols.

*86. Build an XOR function with only NAND gates.

87. Build an XNOR function with only NOR gates.

88. List four reasons to use equivalent gates in a circuit.

3-16 Karnaugh Mapping—Application Problems

89. Simplify the circuit in Figure 3-78 using K-maps. Derive both the SOP and POS expressions.
    a. SOP equation form
    b. POS equation form

90. Simplify the circuit in Figure 3-79 using K-maps. Derive both the SOP and POS expressions.
    a. SOP equation form
    b. POS equation form

91. Simplify the circuit in Figure 3-80 using K-maps. Derive both the SOP and POS expressions.
    a. SOP equation form
    b. POS equation form

92. Simplify the circuit in Figure 3-81 using K-maps. Derive both the SOP and POS expressions.
    a. SOP equation form
    b. POS equation form

93. Draw a five-variable K-map for variables A, B, C, D, and E.

3-17 Combinational Circuit Analysis—Analysis Problems

94. Determine the simplified logic function of the circuit that produced the output waveform W for the given input waveforms (A, B, C, and D) as shown in Figure 3-86.

Truth Table:
D C B A | W

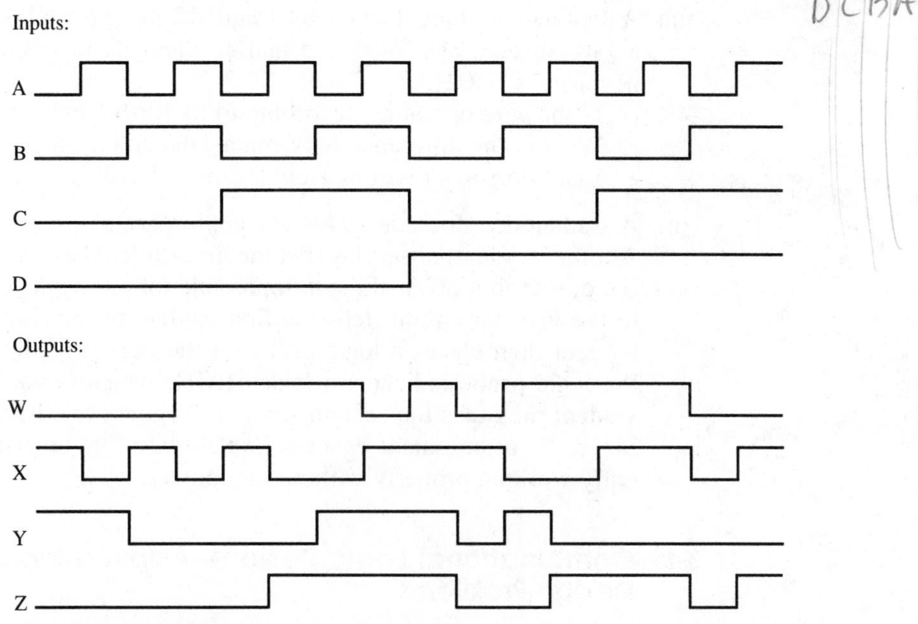

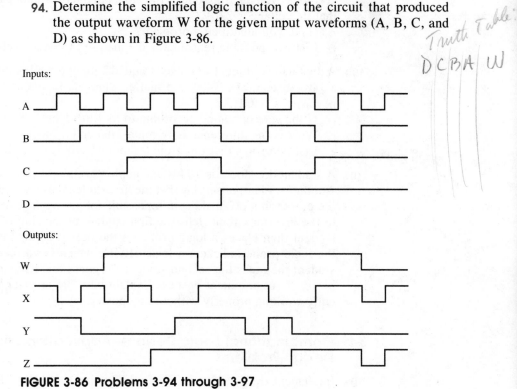

FIGURE 3-86 Problems 3-94 through 3-97

95. Determine the simplified logic function of the circuit that produced the output waveform X for the given input waveforms (A, B, C, and D) as shown in Figure 3-86.

96. Determine the simplified logic function of the circuit that produced the output waveform Y for the given input waveforms (A, B, C, and D) as shown in Figure 3-86.

*97. Determine the simplified logic function of the circuit that produced the output waveform Z for the given input waveforms (A, B, C, and D) as shown in Figure 3-86.

3-18 Combinational Circuit Troubleshooting—Troubleshooting Problems

98. Explain why the shortest possible wire lengths should be used on a breadboard when wiring digital circuits.

99. When troubleshooting a NOR gate that appears to be operating incorrectly, you measure one of the inputs to the two-input gate and find that its voltage is 2.0 V.
    a. Have you identified a problem?
    b. List two possible reasons for the measured voltage value.

100. A digital logic student who needs a quad 2-input NAND gate IC selects a 7401 instead of a 7400. No matter what the inputs are the output never goes HIGH.
    a. Is the gate operating according to its truth table?
    b. What is the difference between a 7400 and a 7401?
    c. List two ways that this troubleshooting problem can be solved.

101. A student breadboards a 7404 and applies ground to an inverter input. Another student, observing that the first student has a workbench with the power shut off, making it impossible for any voltage to be applied to the inverter circuit, tells the first student of the shut off. The first student then places a logic probe on the output of the inverter, and the logic probe indicates a logic HIGH, which is correct. The first student then tells the second student, "I guess this IC works without power." An argument ensues. Explain why the inverter was apparently working properly without any power.

3-19 Combinational Logic Design—Application and Design Problems

102. Implement the function in Figure 3-82 using the AND-OR-INVERT logic chip, 74LS54.

103. Implement the function in Figure 3-82 using only NAND gates. Specify the type and number of ICs used.

104. Implement the function in Figure 3-82 using only NOR gates. Specify the type and number of ICs used.

105. Implement the function in Figure 3-83 using the AND-OR-INVERT logic chip, 74LS54.

106. Implement the function in Figure 3-83, using only NAND gates. Specify the type and number of ICs used.

107. Implement the function in Figure 3-83 using only NOR gates. Specify the type and number of ICs used.

108. Implement the function in Figure 3-84 using the AND-OR-INVERT logic chip, 74LS54.

109. Implement the function in Figure 3-84 using only NAND gates. Specify the type and number of ICs used.

110. Implement the function in Figure 3-84 using only NOR gates. Specify the type and number of ICs used.

111. Implement the function in Figure 3-85 using the AND-OR-INVERT logic chip, 74LS54.

112. Implement the function in Figure 3-85 using only NAND gates. Specify the type and number of ICs used.

113. Implement the function in Figure 3-85 using only NOR gates. Specify the type and number of ICs used.

*114. Design a logic circuit to multiply two 2-bit binary numbers and output the resulting number.

115. Design a logic circuit to subtract two 2-bit binary numbers and output the resulting number.

116. Design a code converter that will convert a 4-bit binary code to Gray code.

117. Design a comparator that will determine whether two 2-bit binary numbers are equal to, greater than, or less than each other.

118. Design a number encrypter that will accept 4-bit binary numbers as the input and output of an encrypted number according to the following rules:
   a. Multiply odd numbers times 2 and then add 11.
   b. Divide even numbers by 2 and then add 5.

119. Design a number decipherer that will accept an encrypted number from Problem 3-118 and output the correct 4-bit binary number. Any invalid numbers should be noted by an alarm output.

Part 3

ADVANCED COMBINATIONAL LOGIC DESIGN WITH MEDIUM SCALE INTEGRATION (MSI) LOGIC CIRCUITS

Chapter 4

Multiplexers and Demultiplexers

Upon completing and mastering the material in this chapter, you should be able to perform the functions in the areas of analysis, application, and design of multiplexer and demultiplexer circuits:

ANALYSIS

1. Analyze the operation of multiplexer and demultiplexer ICs based on the function table specification in the data sheet.
2. List common TTL multiplexer and demultiplexer ICs.
3. Analyze the operation of logic circuits that include multiplexers and demultiplexers ICs.

APPLICATION

4. Define the operation of multiplexers in applications of data selection, cascaded operation, binary word multiplexing, time division multiplexing, and logic function generation.
5. Define the operation of demultiplexers in applications of data routing, time division multiplexing and demultiplexing, and cascaded operation.

DESIGN

6. Design multiplexers and demultiplexers from logic gates.
7. Design and build logic circuits that use multiplexers in applications of data selection, cascaded operation, binary word multiplexing, time division multiplexing, and logic function generation.
8. Design and build logic circuits that use demultiplexers in applications of data routing, time division multiplexing and demultiplexing, and cascaded operation.

TROUBLESHOOTING

9. Troubleshoot multiplexer circuits.
10. Troubleshoot demultiplexer circuits.

Multiplexers and demultiplexers are devices that are used primarily in data routing applications. Multiplexers accept data from several different sources and route the data to one output. Demultiplexers accept data from one input and route it to several outputs. This chapter studies data routing, time division multiplexing, data selection, and logic function generation applications of multiplexer and demultiplexer circuits.

Multiplexers and demultiplexers are commonly available as Medium Scale Integration (MSI) integrated circuits. MSI circuits are usually complex functions that are manufactured as standard operational blocks and available as a single chip integrated circuit. These devices can replace up to 100 basic logic gates, greatly reducing the total chip count in the finished design.

The type of devices that are fabricated as MSI circuits include multiplexers, demultiplexers, decoders, encoders, display drivers, comparators, error detection circuits, and arithmetic circuits. MSI logic circuits can be used alone, but they are more often incorporated into a larger system design. Chapters 4, 5, and 6, are devoted to MSI circuits and their use in logic hardware designs.

4-1 MULTIPLEXERS

Multiplexers accept data from one of many inputs and route the data to one output. A multiplexer can be thought of as an electronic switch, as shown in Figure 4-1. This simple function of selecting and routing data serves many purposes, such as routing data, generating logic functions, transmitting data from several sources on one common transmission line, and using display multiplexing.

4.1.1 Functional Description

A multiplexer has **data inputs**, **select inputs**, and an **output**. The **data inputs** are used to input the binary logic levels, or **data**, to be switched to the output of the multiplexer. A multiplexer has several data inputs, but only one data input can be switched to the output at any one time. Some multiplexers invert the data during the switching process, whereas others leave the data unchanged. Other than the possible inversion, the data is not altered as it is routed to the output of the multiplexer.

The **select inputs** are the **address inputs** for the multiplexer. The address on the select inputs determines which data input is switched to the output. Each data input requires its own **address**, which is a unique binary combination that is specified on the select inputs. For instance, data input 1, or D_1 as it is often labeled, has a 4-bit binary address of 0001. D_{15} has a binary

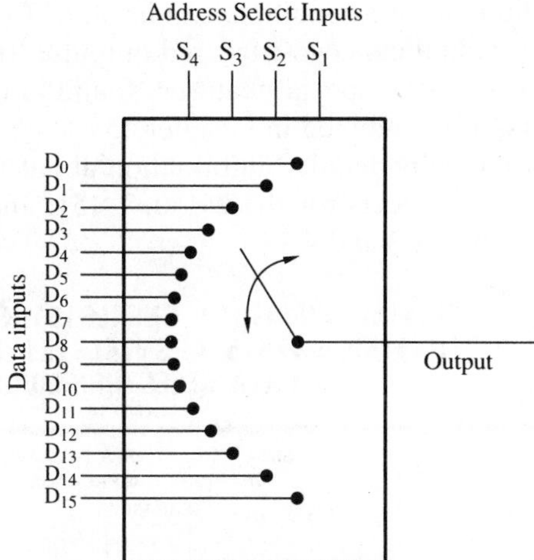

FIGURE 4-1 Multiplexer Block Diagram

address of 1111. The multiplexer is programmed through the select inputs to establish a connection between the output and addressed data input.

4.1.2 Integrated Circuit Specification

Many types of **multiplexer**, or **MUX**, circuits are available as a medium scale integration (MSI) IC. The multiplexers are specified by a designation that indicates the number of data inputs that can be routed to the output. For instance, an 8:1 MUX has eight data inputs.

ICs containing two multiplexers are labeled **dual**, and those containing four multiplexers are labeled **quad**. Table 4-1 lists a summary of common multiplexer circuits, the input to output designation, the number of data inputs, the select inputs, and whether the output is available in its true and/

TABLE 4-1 Common Multiplexer Circuits

IC	Data Inputs	Select Inputs	Output
74150 (16:1)	16	4	Inverted
74151 (8:1)	8	3	True and inverted
74152 (8:1)	8	3	Inverted
74153 (4:1 dual)	4 × 2	2	True
74157 (2:1 quad)	2 × 4	1	True

or inverted form. In addition to those multiplexers listed in Table 4-1, there are others with storage capabilities, edge-triggered outputs, tristate output, and open-collector outputs. These special features, found in many circuits as well as in multiplexers, are examined in Chapter 15.

The logic data book contains detailed information about the operation of each multiplexer. The data sheets for the 74150, 74151, and 74157 multiplexers are shown in Figures 4-2 and 4-3.

SN54150, SN54151A, SN54LS151, SN54S151, SN74150, SN74151A, SN74LS151, SN74S151 DATA SELECTORS/MULTIPLEXERS

DECEMBER 1972—REVISED MARCH 1988

- '150 Selects One-of-Sixteen Data Sources
- Others Select One-of-Eight Data Sources
- All Perform Parallel-to-Serial Conversion
- All Permit Multiplexing from N Lines to One Line
- Also For Use as Boolean Function Generator
- Input-Clamping Diodes Simplify System Design
- Fully Compatible with Most TTL Circuits

TYPE	TYPICAL AVERAGE PROPAGATION DELAY TIME DATA INPUT TO W OUTPUT	TYPICAL POWER DISSIPATION
'150	13 ns	200 mW
'151A	8 ns	145 mW
'LS151	13 ns	30 mW
'S151	4.5 ns	225 mW

description

These monolithic data selectors/multiplexers contain full on-chip binary decoding to select the desired data source. The '150 selects one-of-sixteen data sources; the '151A, 'LS151, and 'S151 select one-of-eight data sources. The '150, '151A, 'LS151, and 'S151 have a strobe input which must be at a low logic level to enable these devices. A high level at the strobe forces the W output high, and the Y output (as applicable) low.

The '150 has only an inverted W output; the '151A, 'LS151, and 'S151 feature complementary W and Y outputs.

The '151A and '152A incorporate address buffers that have symmetrical propagation delay times through the complementary paths. This reduces the possibility of transients occurring at the output(s) due to changes made at the select inputs, even when the '151A outputs are enabled (i.e., strobe low).

SN54150 . . . J OR W PACKAGE
SN74150 . . . N PACKAGE
(TOP VIEW)

Pin	Name	Pin	Name
1	E7	24	VCC
2	E6	23	E8
3	E5	22	E9
4	E4	21	E10
5	E3	20	E11
6	E2	19	E12
7	E1	18	E13
8	E0	17	E14
9	$\overline{G}$	16	E15
10	W	15	A
11	D	14	B
12	GND	13	C

SN54151A, SN54LS151, SN54S151 . . . J OR W PACKAGE
SN74151A . . . N PACKAGE
SN74LS151, SN74S151 . . . D OR N PACKAGE
(TOP VIEW)

Pin	Name	Pin	Name
1	D3	16	VCC
2	D2	15	D4
3	D1	14	D5
4	D0	13	D6
5	Y	12	D7
6	W	11	A
7	$\overline{G}$	10	B
8	GND	9	C

SN54LS151, SN54S151 . . . FK PACKAGE
(TOP VIEW)

Pin	Name	Pin	Name
3	D2	18	D5
2	D3	17	D6
1	NC	16	NC
20	VCC	15	D7
19	D4	14	A
4	D1	9	$\overline{G}$
5	D0	10	GND
6	NC	11	NC
7	Y	12	C
8	W	13	B

NC - No internal connection

FIGURE 4-2 74150/74151 Multiplexer Data Sheet (Courtesy Texas Instruments)

SN54150, SN54151A, SN54LS151, SN54S151, SN74150, SN74151A, SN74LS151, SN74S151 DATA SELECTORS/MULTIPLEXERS

logic symbols†

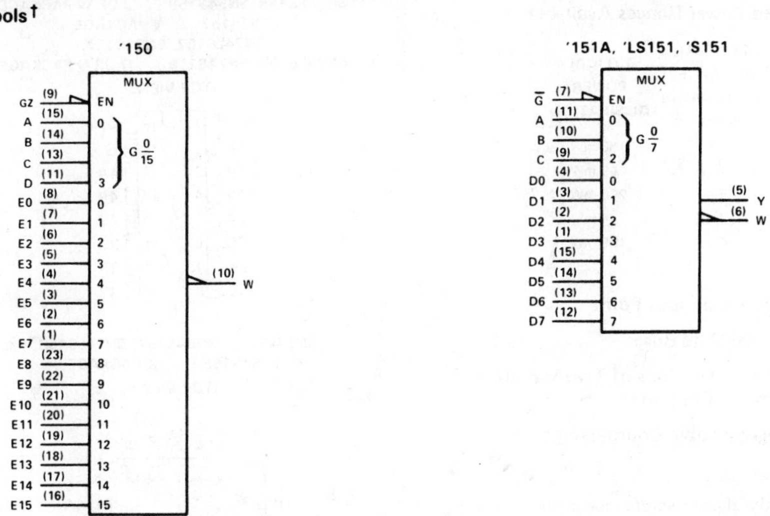

†These symbols are in accordance with ANSI/IEEE Std. 91-1984 and IEC Publication 617-12.
Pin numbers shown are D, J, N, and W packages.

'150 FUNCTION TABLE

INPUTS					OUTPUT
SELECT				STROBE	W
D	C	B	A	$\overline{G}$	
X	X	X	X	H	H
L	L	L	L	L	$\overline{E0}$
L	L	L	H	L	$\overline{E1}$
L	L	H	L	L	$\overline{E2}$
L	L	H	H	L	$\overline{E3}$
L	H	L	L	L	$\overline{E4}$
L	H	L	H	L	$\overline{E5}$
L	H	H	L	L	$\overline{E6}$
L	H	H	H	L	$\overline{E7}$
H	L	L	L	L	$\overline{E8}$
H	L	L	H	L	$\overline{E9}$
H	L	H	L	L	$\overline{E10}$
H	L	H	H	L	$\overline{E11}$
H	H	L	L	L	$\overline{E12}$
H	H	L	H	L	$\overline{E13}$
H	H	H	L	L	$\overline{E14}$
H	H	H	H	L	$\overline{E15}$

'151A, 'LS151, 'S151 FUNCTION TABLE

INPUTS				OUTPUTS	
SELECT			STROBE	Y	W
C	B	A	$\overline{G}$		
X	X	X	H	L	H
L	L	L	L	D0	$\overline{D0}$
L	L	H	L	D1	$\overline{D1}$
L	H	L	L	D2	$\overline{D2}$
L	H	H	L	D3	$\overline{D3}$
H	L	L	L	D4	$\overline{D4}$
H	L	H	L	D5	$\overline{D5}$
H	H	L	L	D6	$\overline{D6}$
H	H	H	L	D7	$\overline{D7}$

H = high level, L = low level, X = irrelevant
$\overline{E0}$, $\overline{E1}$ . . . $\overline{E15}$ = the complement of the level of the respective E input
D0, D1 . . . D7 = the level of the D respective input

FIGURE 4-2 ***(continued)***

SN54157, SN54LS157, SN54LS158, SN54S157, SN54S158, SN74157, SN74LS157, SN74LS158, SN74S157, SN74S158 QUADRUPLE 2-LINE TO 1-LINE DATA SELECTORS/MULTIPLEXERS

MARCH 1974 – REVISED MARCH 1988

- Buffered Inputs and Outputs
- Three Speed/Power Ranges Available

TYPES	TYPICAL AVERAGE PROPAGATION TIME	TYPICAL POWER DISSIPATION
'157	9 ns	150 mW
'LS157	9 ns	49 mW
'S157	5 ns	250 mW
'LS158	7 ns	24 mW
'S158	4 ns	195 mW

SN54157, SN54LS157, SN54S157,
SN54LS158, SN54S158 . . . J OR W PACKAGE
SN74157 . . . N PACKAGE
SN74LS157, SN74S157,
SN74LS158, SN74S158 . . . D OR N PACKAGE
(TOP VIEW)

Signal	Pin	Pin	Signal
$\overline{A}/B$	1	16	V_{CC}
1A	2	15	$\overline{G}$
1B	3	14	4A
1Y	4	13	4B
2A	5	12	4Y
2B	6	11	3A
2Y	7	10	3B
GND	8	9	3Y

applications

- Expand Any Data Input Point
- Multiplex Dual Data Buses
- Generate Four Functions of Two Variables (One Variable Is Common)
- Source Programmable Counters

SN54LS157, SN54S157, SN54LS158,
SN54S158 . . . FK PACKAGE
(TOP VIEW)

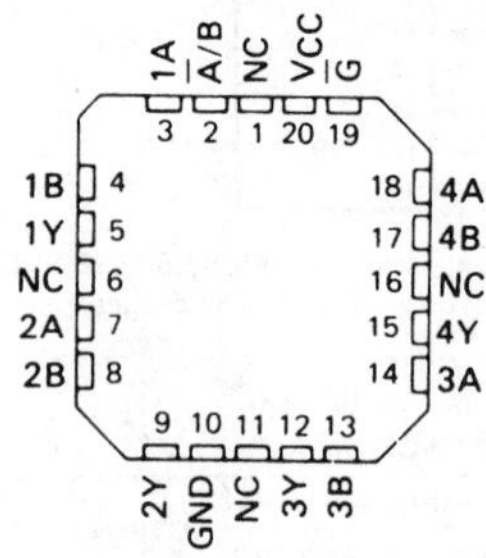

NC - No internal connection

description

These monolithic data selectors/multiplexers contain inverters and drivers to supply full on-chip data selection to the four output gates. A separate strobe input is provided. A 4-bit word is selected from one of two sources and is routed to the four outputs. The '157, 'LS157, and 'S157 present true data whereas the 'LS158 and 'S158 present inverted data to minimize propagation delay time.

FUNCTION TABLE

INPUTS				OUTPUT Y	
STROBE $\overline{G}$	SELECT $\overline{A}/B$	A	B	'157, 'LS157, 'S157	'LS158 'S158
H	X	X	X	L	H
L	L	L	X	L	H
L	L	H	X	H	L
L	H	X	L	L	H
L	H	X	H	H	L

H = high level, L = low level, X = irrelevant

absolute maximum ratings over operating free-air temperature range (unless otherwise noted)

Supply voltage, V_{CC} (See Note 1)	7 V
Input voltage: '157, 'S158	5.5 V
'LS157, 'LS158	7 V
Operating free-air temperature range: SN54'	−55°C to 125°C
SN74'	0°C to 70°C
Storage temperature range	−65°C to 150°C

NOTE 1: Voltage values are with respect to network ground terminal.

FIGURE 4-3 74157 Quad 2:1 Multiplexer Data Sheet (Courtesy Texas Instruments)

SN54157, SN54LS157, SN54LS158, SN54S157, SN54S158,
SN74157, SN74LS157, SN74LS158, SN74S157, SN74S158
QUADRUPLE 2-LINE TO 1-LINE DATA SELECTORS/MULTIPLEXERS

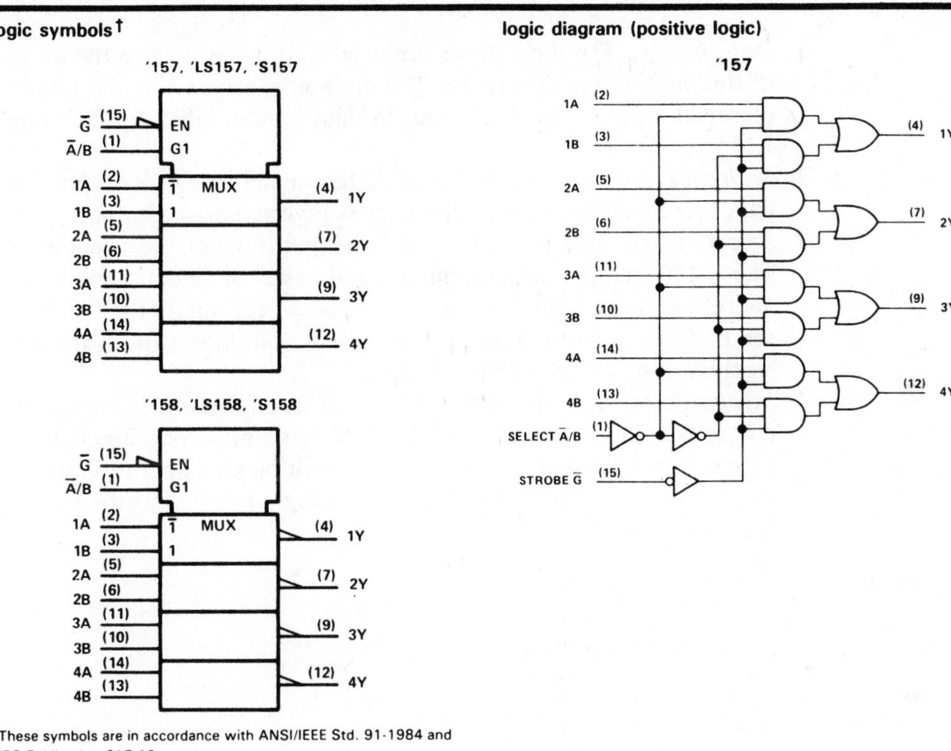

†These symbols are in accordance with ANSI/IEEE Std. 91-1984 and IEC Publication 617-12.
Pin numbers shown are for D, J, N, and W packages.

schematics of inputs and outputs

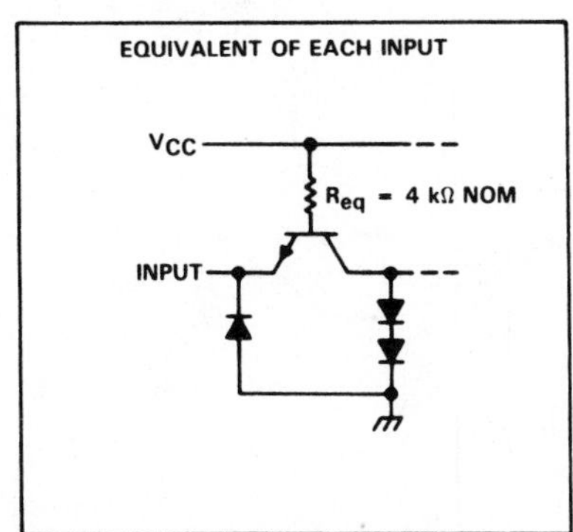

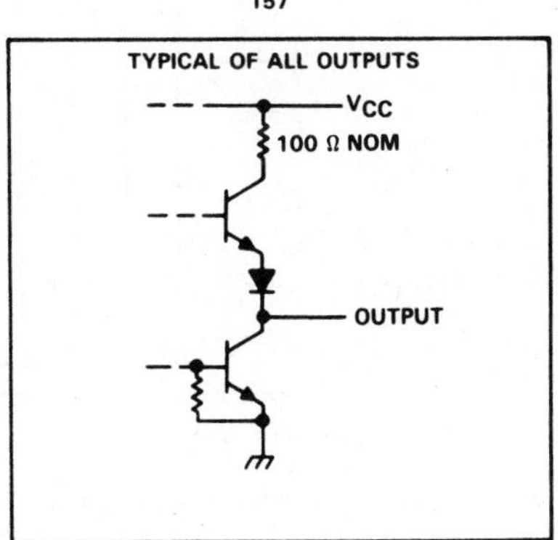

FIGURE 4-3 ***(continued)***

The operation of the multiplexer circuit is defined in the function table of the data sheet. The function table specifies all possible input conditions and the output results. As an example, the operation of the 74150 16:1 MUX is described in detail.

1. *Data inputs.* The data inputs are used to transfer data to the output of the multiplexer. There are 2^n data inputs, where n is the number of select inputs. The 74150 has 16 data inputs, labeled E0 through E15.
2. *Multiplexed data output.* The 74150 has an active-LOW output. The data routed through the multiplexer is inverted at the output.
3. *Select inputs.* The address of the data input is put on the select input. The 74150 has four select inputs to address 2^4 or 16 data inputs. The addresses range from 0000 to 1111. The select inputs for the 74150 are D, C, B, A, with D the most significant bit (MSB) and A the least significant bit (LSB) of the address.
4. *Strobe input.* The strobe input is used to engage or disengage the multiplexer from operation. The 74150 has one strobe input that is active-LOW, labeled G NOT. For the multiplexing operation to take place, this strobe input must be set to a logic-LOW, specified by the function table.

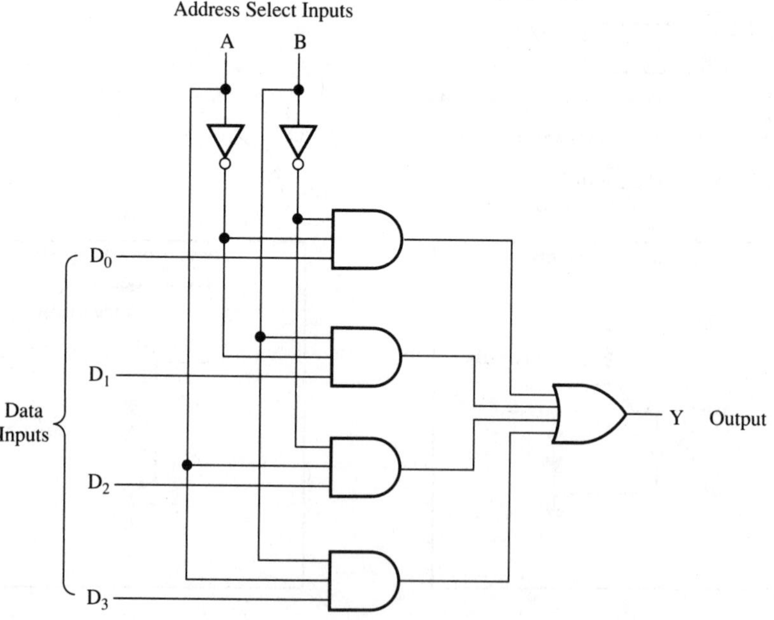

FIGURE 4-4 4:1 Multiplexer Built from Logic Gates

4.1.3 Gate Equivalent Circuits

A multiplexer is a simple two-level logic circuit comprised of one OR level and one AND level, plus the inverted and noninverted select inputs is an example of a 4:1 MUX built out of AND and OR gates.

The logic equation of the output is read off the truth table in the sum of products (SOP) form. The output equation has all input variable product terms ANDed with the respective data input. The logic output equation and truth table description of the operation appear in Figure 4-5. With an output equation of this form, multiplexers can generate any logic function, as will be seen in Section 4.2.5.

Multiplexer Truth Table

Select Inputs A	B	Output Y
0	0	D_0
0	1	D_1
1	0	D_2
1	1	D_3

Multiplexer logic expression $Y = \overline{A}\,\overline{B}\,D_0 + \overline{A}\,B\,D_1 + A\,\overline{B}\,D_2 + A\,B\,D_3$

FIGURE 4-5 4:1 Multiplexer Logic Expression and Truth Table

Section Self-Test

1. How many select inputs are required on a 16:1 MUX?
2. For the multiplexer shown in Figure 4-4, determine the sequence of data inputs routed to the output if the following addresses are applied to the select inputs A and B, respectively: 10; 11; 00; 11; 01.
3. Determine the MUX output equation for an 8:1 MUX. The output, X, is an inverted output, the data inputs are D_0 through D_7, and the select inputs are S_0 through S_2.

ANSWERS (Not necessarily in the order of the questions)

- D_2; D_3; D_0; D_3; D_1
- 4
- $X = \overline{S_2}\,\overline{S_1}\,\overline{S_0}\,\overline{D_0} + \overline{S_2}\,\overline{S_1}\,S_0\,\overline{D_1} + \overline{S_2}\,S_1\,\overline{S_0}\,\overline{D_2}$
  $\overline{S_2}\,S_1\,S_0\,\overline{D_3} + S_2\,\overline{S_1}\,\overline{S_0}\,\overline{D_4} + S_2\,\overline{S_1}\,S_0\,\overline{D_5}$
  $S_2\,S_1\,\overline{S_0}\,\overline{D_6} + S_2\,S_1\,S_0\,\overline{D_7}$

4-2 APPLICATION AND DESIGN USING MULTIPLEXERS

Multiplexers are versatile circuits that are used in applications such as data selection, cascaded operation, binary word multiplexing, time division multiplexing, and logic function generation.

Multiplexer application circuits can be designed based on the standard MUX circuits studied in Section 4.1. They can also be built from programmable logic devices (PLDs), which are presented in Chapter 12.

4.2.1 Data Selection

One important application for the MUX circuit is to control a single output channel shared by several individual devices transmitting data. In the 4:1 MUX example four different devices could share one output channel by multiplexing the outputs of those devices, which are tied to the data inputs of the multiplexer. The select inputs have the address of the corresponding data input to connect one device at a time to the MUX output.

The data from only one device is selected to be transmitted on the common channel at a given time, but the multiplexer can address any of the device outputs when necessary. This application, referred to as **data selection**, is commonly used to reduce the cost of separate transmission facilities.

■ EXAMPLE 4-1 Electronic Switch Applications

Refer to the diagrams in Figure 4-6 for example multiplexer configurations. ■

■ EXAMPLE 4-2 Data Selection Application

Problem: A 4:1 data selector is to transmit data from one of four data inputs to a single output. The input waveforms are given, and the circuit is shown in Figure 4-7. Determine the output waveform.

Solution: The output waveform, given in Figure 4-7, matches the input waveform of the selected device. ■

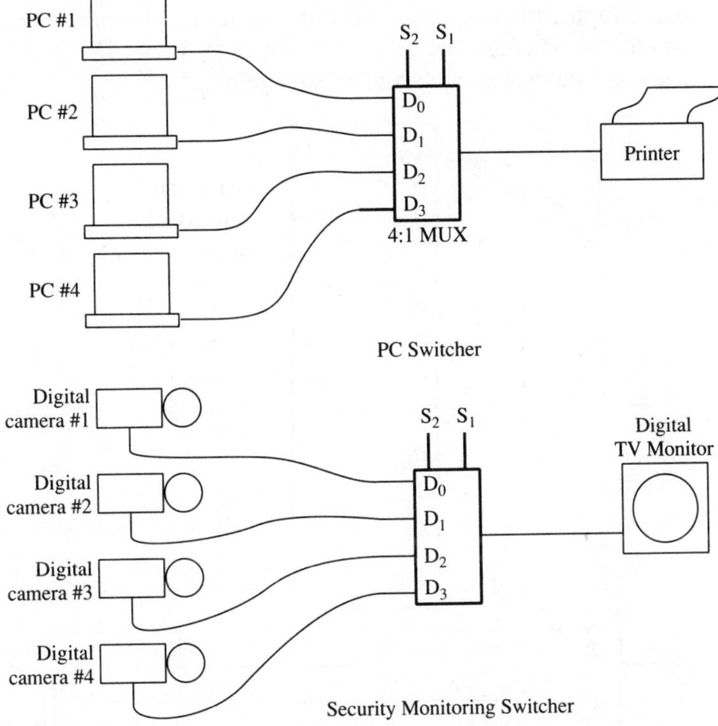

FIGURE 4-6 Electronic Switch Applications

4.2.2 Cascaded Operation

Multiplexers can be **cascaded** together to increase the number of data inputs that can be transferred to a single output. **Cascading** is a technique whereby several MUX chips are wired to work together. Only one multiplexer is actively transferring data to the output at any one time. Figures 4-8 through 4-11 show individual and cascaded MUX circuits that switch 8, 16, and 32 separate inputs to a single output.

When more than one multiplexer is cascaded together in a circuit, the enable or strobe inputs must be used as address inputs to provide the needed address bits. In Figure 4-9 16 data inputs are to be multiplexed to a single output using two 74151 8:1 MUXs. Each 74151 has three select inputs capable of addressing only 8 data inputs. In order to address 16 data inputs, four address bits are needed.

In the circuit in Figure 4-9 the address bits are S_3, S_2, S_1, and S_0. The three LSBs of the address, S_2, S_1, and S_0, are tied to the select inputs of each multiplexer, C, B, and A, respectively. The MSB, S_3, is connected to the active-LOW enable input of one multiplexer, and then is inverted and connected to the enable input of the second multiplexer.

By cascading the two multiplexers with the enable input serving as an address input, the addresses for data inputs D_0 through D_7 enable the first multiplexer, whereas the addresses for data inputs D_8 through D_{15} enable the second multiplexer, as shown in Table 4-2.

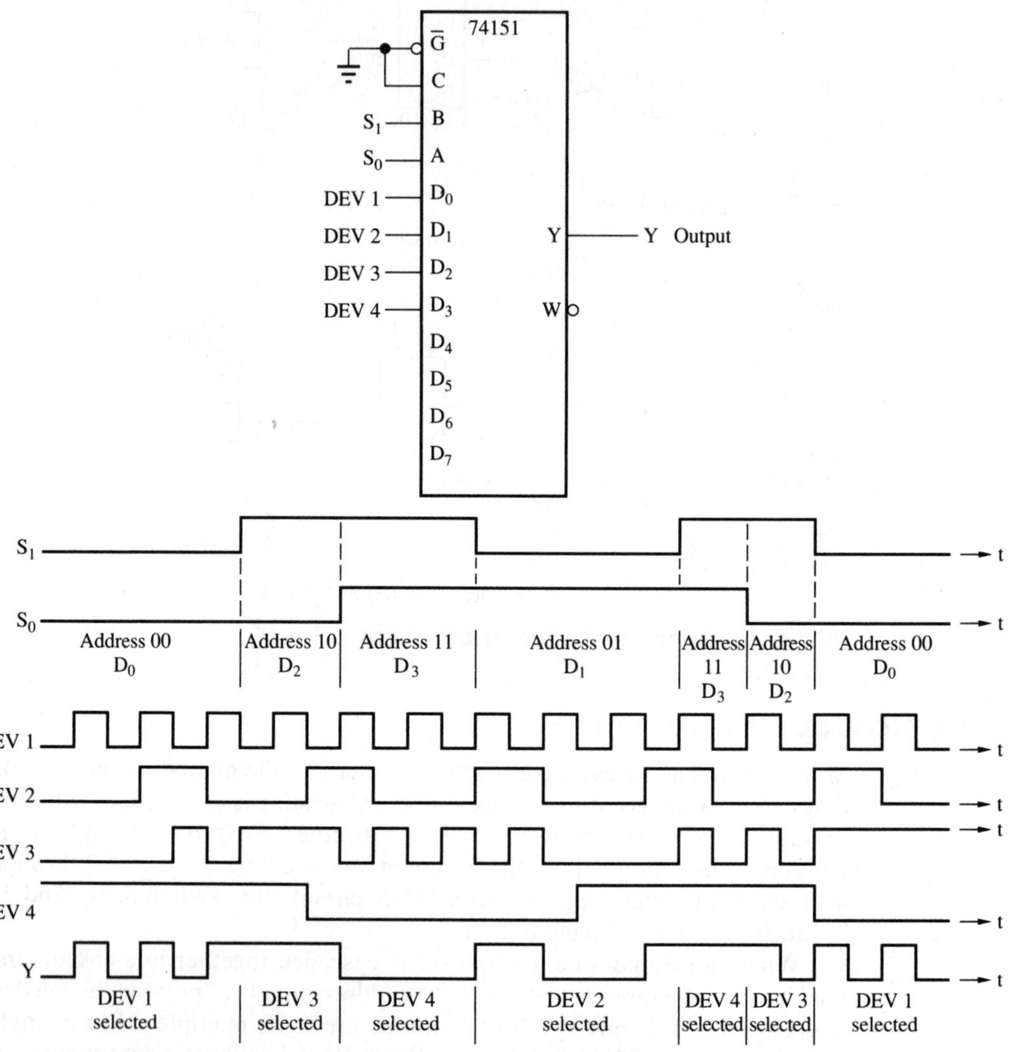

FIGURE 4-7 Data Selection Application

4.2.3 Binary Word Multiplexing

Binary word multiplexing is an application where all **the bits of a binary word are switched in parallel**, or simultaneously, through a MUX circuit. Binary words are typically a **4-bit nibble**, or an **8-bit byte**.

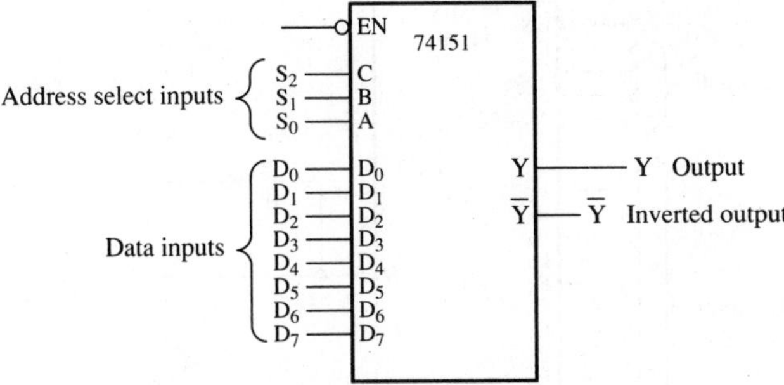

FIGURE 4-8 8:1 Multiplexer Using the 74151

Binary word multiplexing is important when data must remain in a parallel format, as opposed to a serial data stream generated from a single-output multiplexer. Common applications for word multiplexing include numerical applications where binary numbers or binary coded decimal (BCD) codes must be switched to a common output for display multiplexing or applications where binary data in nibble or byte formats must be switched to registers or to memory devices. Display multiplexing applications will be

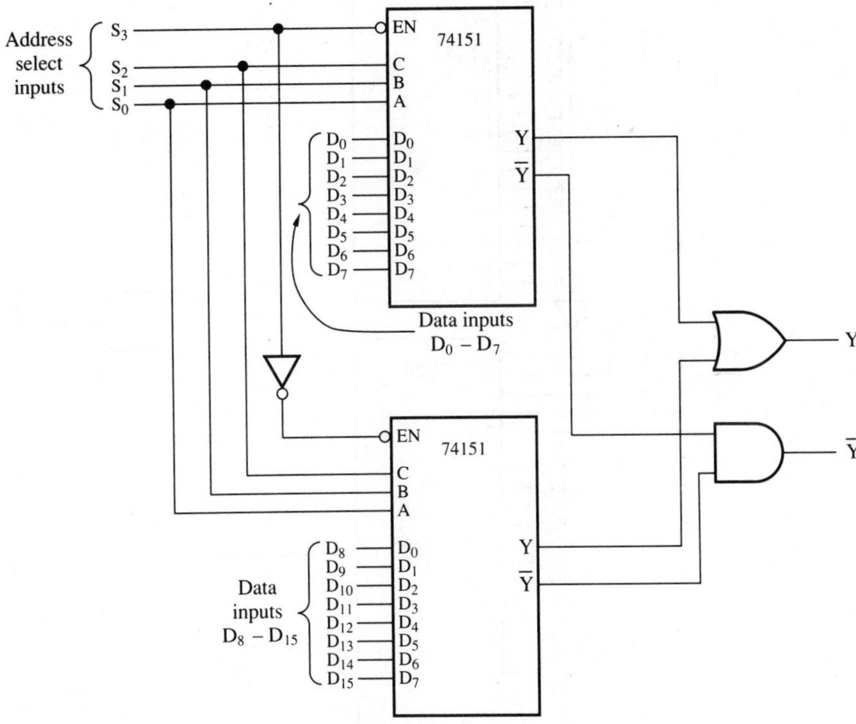

FIGURE 4-9 16:1 Multiplexer Using the 74151

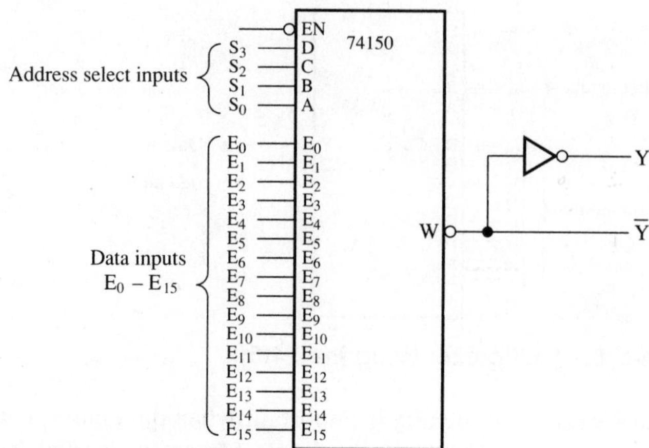

FIGURE 4-10 16:1 Multiplexer Using the 74150

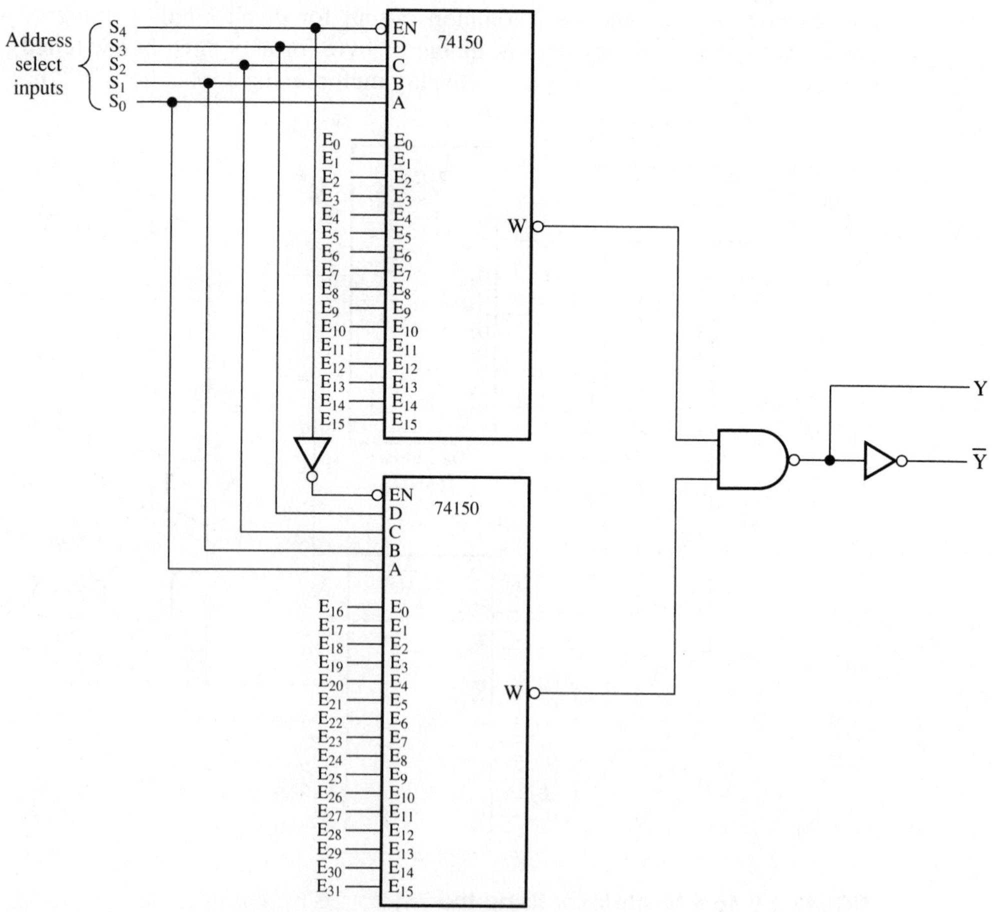

FIGURE 4-11 32:1 Multiplexer Using the 74150

TABLE 4-2 16:1 Cascaded Multiplexer Operation

	ENABLE INPUT	SELECT INPUTS			
MUX Inputs →	EN	C	B	A	
Address Bits→	S_3	S_2	S_1	S_0	
	0	0	0	0	Multiplexer #1 addresses for D_0 through D_7
	0	0	0	1	
	0	0	1	0	
	0	0	1	1	
	0	1	0	0	
	0	1	0	1	
	0	1	1	0	
	0	1	1	1	
	1	0	0	0	Multiplexer #2 addresses for D_8 through D_{15}
	1	0	0	1	
	1	0	1	0	
	1	0	1	1	
	1	1	0	0	
	1	1	0	1	
	1	1	1	0	
	1	1	1	1	

studied in Chapter 5. Nibble and byte multiplexing are examined in this section.

Figure 4-12 illustrates a 4-bit 2:1 MUX that can switch one of two 4-bit words to the four multiplexed outputs. This multiplexer is in fact four 2:1 MUXs, all controlled by the same select input to ensure that the four selected data inputs are switched to the outputs simultaneously.

■ EXAMPLE 4-3 Four-Bit Word Multiplexer

Problem: Determine the logic equations for the MUX outputs in Figure 4-12, assuming that the A word is switched to the output when the select input is a logic-HIGH, and that the B word is switched to the output when the select input is a logic-LOW.

Solution: The four MUX outputs are controlled by the same select input. The most significant data bit of the A or the B word is transferred to the

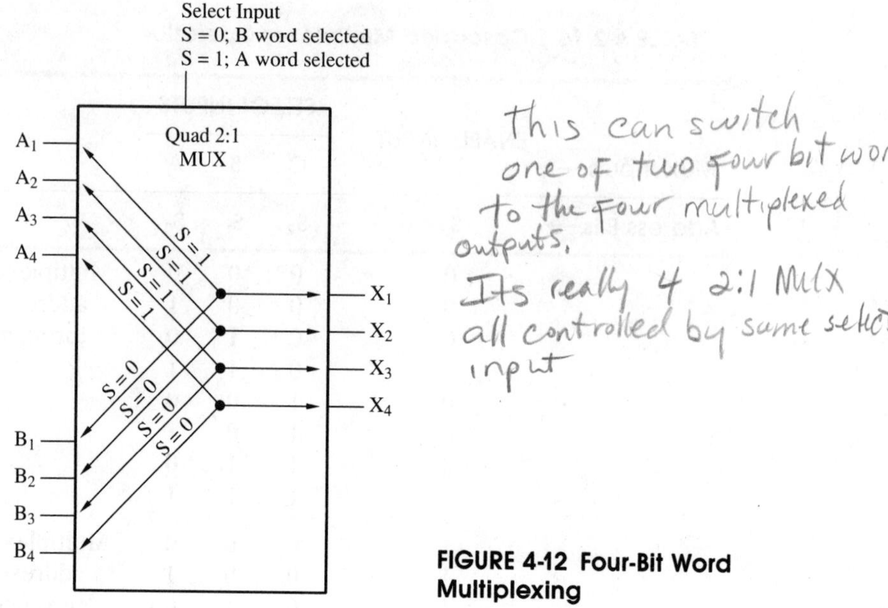

FIGURE 4-12 Four-Bit Word Multiplexing

MSB of the output. A truth table of the operation is constructed here, and the equations are derived from the truth table.

Select Input S	MUX Outputs X_4	X_3	X_2	X_1
0	B_4	B_3	B_2	B_1
1	A_4	A_3	A_2	A_1

$$X_4 = \overline{S}\,B_4 + S\,A_4$$

$$X_3 = \overline{S}\,B_3 + S\,A_3$$

$$X_2 = \overline{S}\,B_2 + S\,A_2$$

$$X_1 = \overline{S}\,B_1 + S\,A_1$$

■

Binary word multiplexing can be accomplished using the 74157 quad 2:1 MUX. The data sheets for the 74157 are in Figure 4-3. Several 74157s can be connected to operate in parallel to expand the size of the binary word that can be multiplexed.

■ EXAMPLE 4-4 Byte Multiplexing

Problem: Use the 74157 quad 2:1 MUX IC to switch one of two bytes of data to the output of the multiplexer.

Solution: Two 74157s are required to multiplex two individual bytes of data. The select inputs and enable inputs on the 74157s are tied common and controlled by the same select and enable inputs, respectively. The lower nibble of each byte is entered into one 74157, and the upper nibble of each byte is entered into the other 74157. The circuit is shown in Figure 4-13.

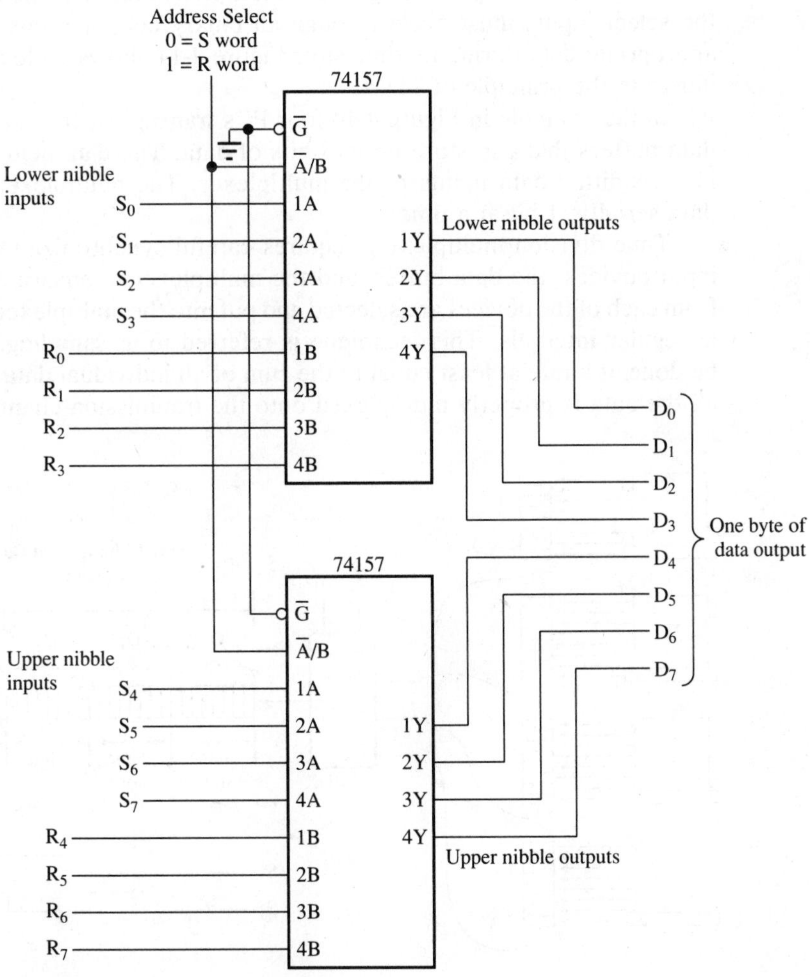

FIGURE 4-13 Byte Multiplexing

■

4.2.4 Time Division Multiplexing

Time division multiplexing, or **TDM**, is a complex form of data selection that is very important in digital transmission systems. Time division multiplexing is used extensively in public and private telephone networks for the transmission of many voice, data, and video messages on a common transmission line.

In TDM applications, just as in data selection applications, many devices share a single transmission line. Each device sharing the transmission line is assigned a **time slot** for transferring its data. The output multiplexed data is organized into a **frame**, which contains one slot of data from each device.

Time division multiplexing circuits require considerable control and synchronization for proper timing of the multiplexed inputs. The addresses on the select inputs must cycle through all binary combinations to select the appropriate data during its time slot. Figure 4-14 shows a block diagram to illustrate the principle of TDM.

In the example in Figure 4-14 four PCs transmit their data to individual data buffers that can store up to 8 bits of data. The data held in the buffer is transmitted data inputs of the multiplexer. The multiplexer outputs the data serially, 1 bit at a time.

Time division multiplexing requires careful synchronization among the input devices, the data buffer, and the multiplexer to ensure that data bits from each of the devices are selected and put into the multiplexed data stream at regular intervals. This technique is referred to as **sampling**, and it must be done at a rate at least equal to the sum of all individual data rates so that all the data is properly multiplexed onto the tranmission channel.

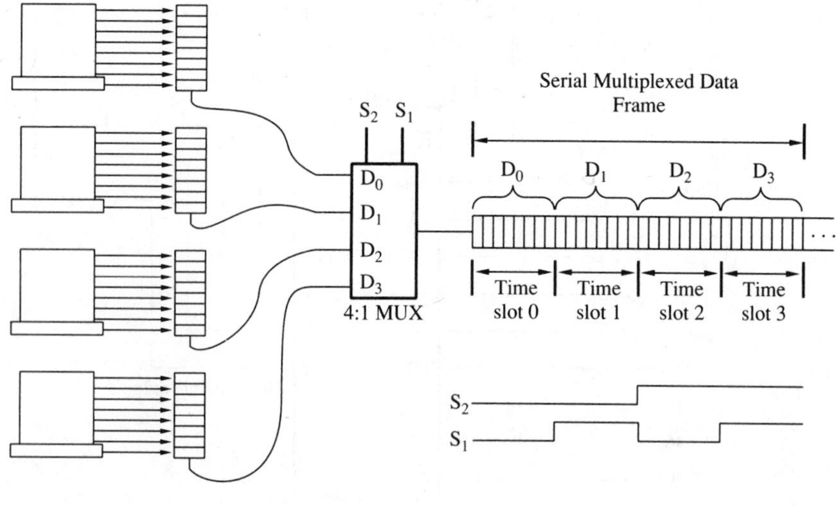

FIGURE 4-14 4:1 TDM Block Diagram

■ EXAMPLE 4-5 Time Division Multiplexing

Problem: Eight devices are to be time division multiplexed onto one common transmission line, as shown in Figure 4-15. The data rate of each device is 600 bits per second (bps). What is the total data rate of the multiplexed serial bit stream? How many time slots are in the frame?

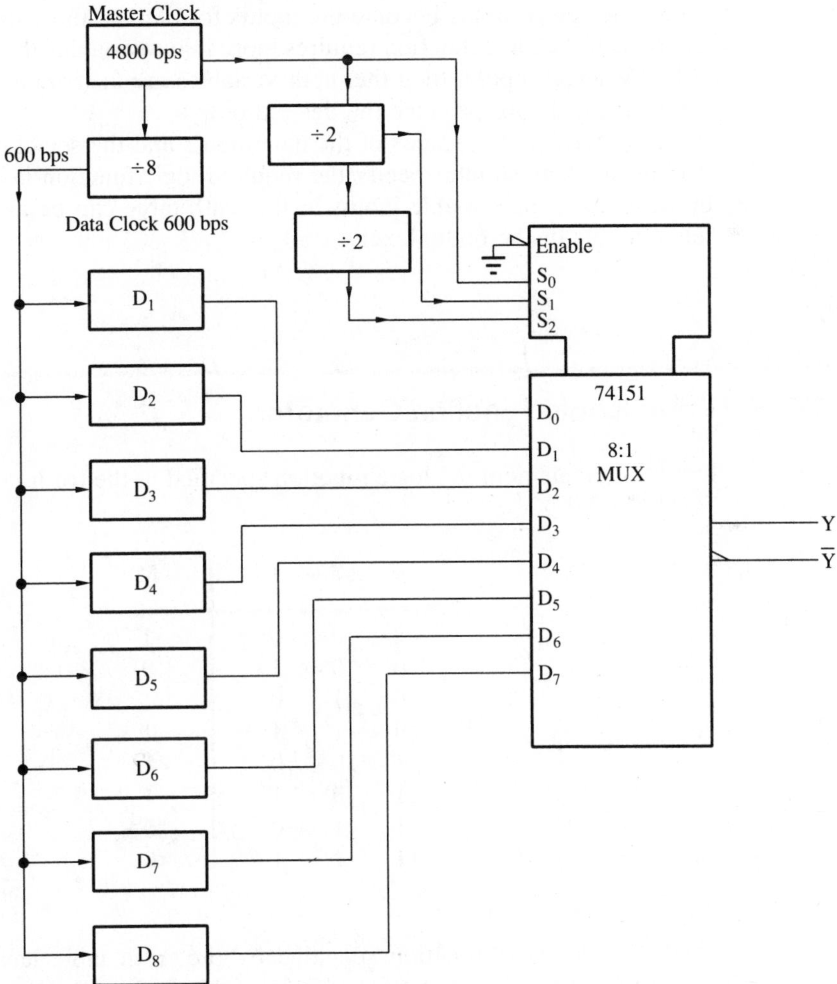

FIGURE 4-15 Time Division Multiplexing

Solution: Each device outputs data at 600 bps, so 8 times 600 bps is equal to 4800 bps, the data rate of the serial multiplexed data stream. There are eight time slots in the frame; one for each device. ■

4.2.5 Logic Function Generation

Another important application of the multiplexer is to operate as a logic function generator. The multiplexer output equation shown in Figure 4-5 is an SOP equation with a term for each input variable combination. Thus, the MUX output can represent the Boolean expression for any combinational logic function.

To use a multiplexer as a logic function generator, the logic function is formed by setting the data inputs D_0, D_1, D_2, or D_3 to the appropriate logic level. The select inputs become the inputs for the variables specified in the function. If the logic function requires more input variables than the number of MUX select inputs, then the input variables are also applied to the data inputs as needed to produce the desired output.

To determine the values of the data inputs and the select inputs for the multiplexer, one should specify the required logic function in a truth table. In most cases the variable inputs in the truth table can be assigned to the select inputs of the multiplexer.

■ EXAMPLE 4-6 Logic Function Generator

Problem: Implement the logic function specified in the truth table using the 74151 8:1 MUX.

R	S	T	M
0	0	0	1
0	0	1	0
0	1	0	1
0	1	1	1
1	0	0	0
1	0	1	1
1	1	0	0
1	1	1	0

Solution: The logic function specified by the truth table has three input variables and eight output states. The variable inputs, R, S, and T, are assigned to the select inputs of the multiplexer. The output states are assigned to the data input on the multiplexer. The address of the data input should be the R, S, T input variable combination required for that output state. The multiplexer circuit is shown in Figure 4-16.

Multiplexer Logic Function Generator

	Select Inputs			MUX Output	
	C	B	A	Y	
Input Variables →	**R**	**S**	**T**	**M** ← Output	
	0	0	0	1 = D_0	MUX
	0	0	1	0 = D_1	Data
	0	1	0	1 = D_2	Inputs
	0	1	1	1 = D_3	
	1	0	0	0 = D_4	
	1	0	1	1 = D_5	
	1	1	0	0 = D_6	
	1	1	1	0 = D_7	

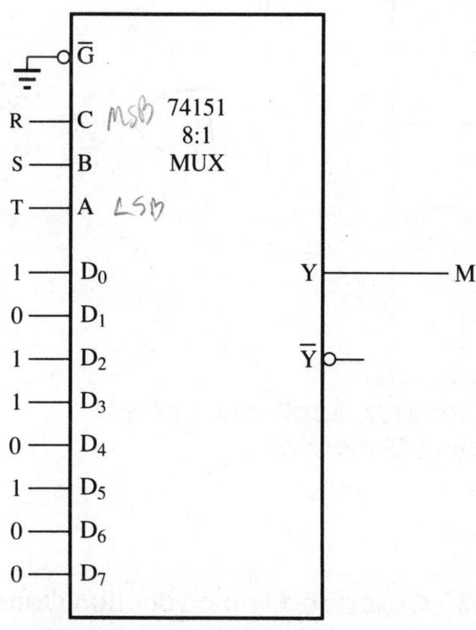

FIGURE 4-16 74151 MUX of a Three-Variable Logic Function Generator

■

■ EXAMPLE 4-7 Cascaded Logic Function Generator

Problem: Implement the same logic function specified in Example 4-6, this time using two 74153 4:1 MUXs cascaded together and any other logic gates as needed.

Solution: The cascaded configuration of two 74153 MUXs is easy to implement, especially since there are two 4:1 MUXs in this IC. Cascaded circuits require an enable input to control the operation of the multiplexers. The strobe input on the 74153 can be used as an enable input. The outputs of the cascaded multiplexers are ORed together to produce a single output function as required. The truth table for designing the circuit follows. The cascaded multiplexer circuit is shown in Figure 4-17.

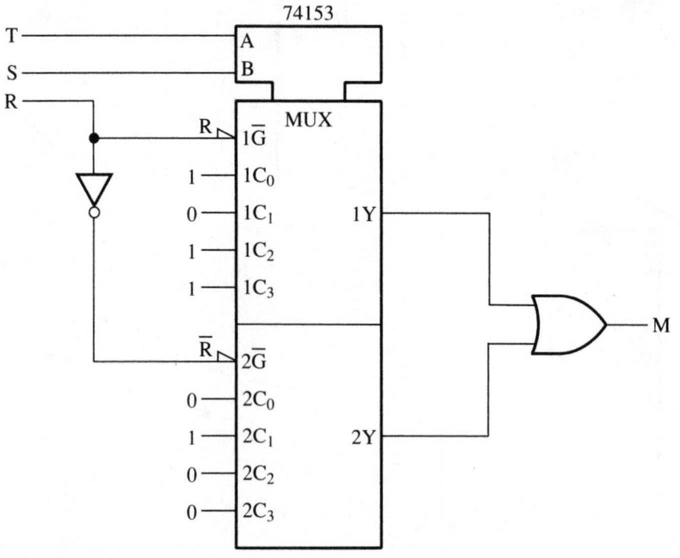

FIGURE 4-17 74153 Cascaded MUX Application of a Three-Variable Logic Function Generator

74153 Cascaded Logic Function Generator

Multiplier #1

	Strobe	Select Inputs		MUX Output	Data Inputs
MUX Inputs →	1G	B	A	1Y	
Input Variables →	**R**	**S**	**T**	**M**	
	0	0	0	1	$1 = 1C_0$
	0	0	1	0	$0 = 1C_1$
	0	1	0	1	$1 = 1C_2$
	0	1	1	1	$1 = 1C_3$

Multiplexer # 2

MUX Inputs →	2G	B	A	2Y	
Input Variables →	$\overline{R}$	S	T	M	
	0	0	0	0	$0 = 2C_0$
	0	0	1	1	$1 = 2C_1$
	0	1	0	0	$0 = 2C_2$
	0	1	1	0	$0 = 2C_3$

Logic function output: **M** = **1Y** + **2Y** ■

■ EXAMPLE 4-8 Logic Function Generator

Problem: Implement the same logic function specified in Example 4-6, this time using a single 74153 4:1 MUX and other logic gates as needed.

Solution: In this case there are only two select inputs in the multiplexer, which can address only four data inputs. The problem can be set up in a truth table to define the logic function, and then two of the input variables can be assigned to the two select inputs. The third is applied as needed to the data inputs.

In this example variable inputs R and S are assigned to the select inputs B and A, respectively. T must be applied to the data inputs, IC_0, IC_1, IC_2, and IC_3, as required to produce the output function M. (See Figure 4-18.)

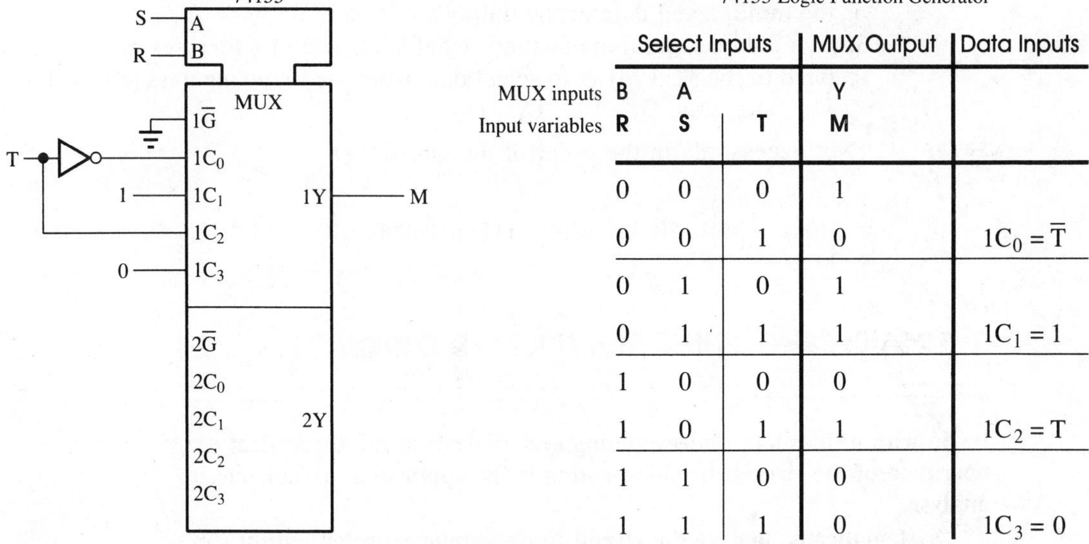

74153 Logic Function Generator

Select Inputs			MUX Output	Data Inputs
B	A		Y	
R	S	T	M	
0	0	0	1	
0	0	1	0	$1C_0 = \overline{T}$
0	1	0	1	
0	1	1	1	$1C_1 = 1$
1	0	0	0	
1	0	1	1	$1C_2 = T$
1	1	0	0	
1	1	1	0	$1C_3 = 0$

(MUX inputs: B, A; Input variables: R, S, T, M)

FIGURE 4-18 74153 MUX Application of a Three-Variable Logic Function Generator ■

Flexible MUX programmability could be provided by connecting DIP switches to the MUX inputs to generate the Boolean expression. The circuit in Figure 4-19 can represent any three-variable combinational logic function.

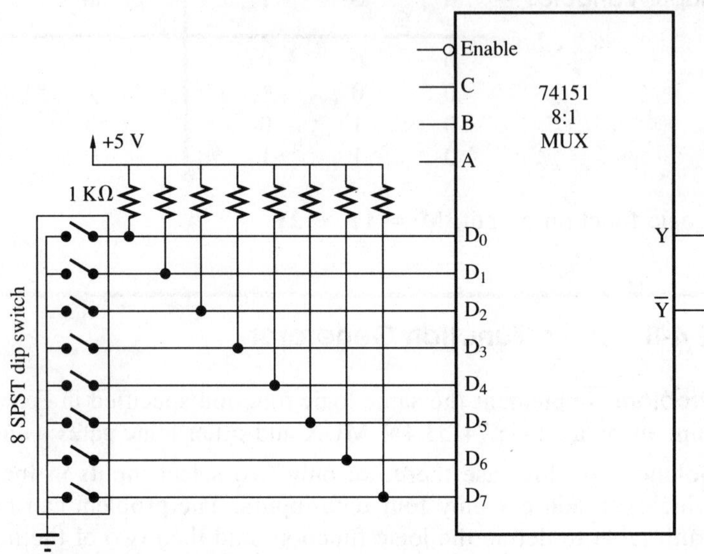

FIGURE 4-19 DIP Switch Programmable MUX Function Generator

Section Self-Test

1. What is the range of hexadecimal addresses required for the 32:1 cascaded MUX circuit shown in Figure 4-11?
2. Assume the 32:1 MUX circuit in Figure 4-11 is used in a TDM system. If each input device has a data rate of 64 Kbps, what is the data rate of the multiplexed data at the output?
3. In a data selection application, what sequence of addresses must be applied to the 32:1 MUX to select data from the following data inputs: D_{25}, D_{01}, D_{18}, D_{20}, D_{31}, D_{00}, D_{10}, D_{13}.

ANSWERS (Not necessarily in the order of the questions)

- 2.048 Mbps
- 11001, 00001, 10010, 10100, 11111, 00000, 01010, 01101
- 00 to 1F HEX

4-3 TROUBLESHOOTING MULTIPLEXER CIRCUITS

Begin with a thorough understanding and analysis of the theoretical operation of the circuit; troubleshooting is the application of logic circuit analysis.

Systematically analyze the circuit to determine expected output conditions for all input combinations. Compare expected results with observed results. It is critical to determine the required logic level of all

enable or strobe inputs. Once complete analysis has been conducted, focus troubleshooting to determine whether the wiring or the IC is faulty.

■ EXAMPLE 4-9 The Disorderly Data Selector

Problem: A data selector circuit using a 74151 is wired to produce an output according to the truth table in Figure 4-20. Four output states are correct—D_0, D_2, D_5, and D_7—but the remaining outputs are not selected appropriately.

Solution: Upon analyzing the circuit, one determines that the address inputs, L, M, and N, which are connected to the select inputs on the multiplexer, are backward. L should be connected to the C, the most significant select input, and N should be connected to A, the least significant select input. The corrected circuit is shown in Figure 4-20. ■

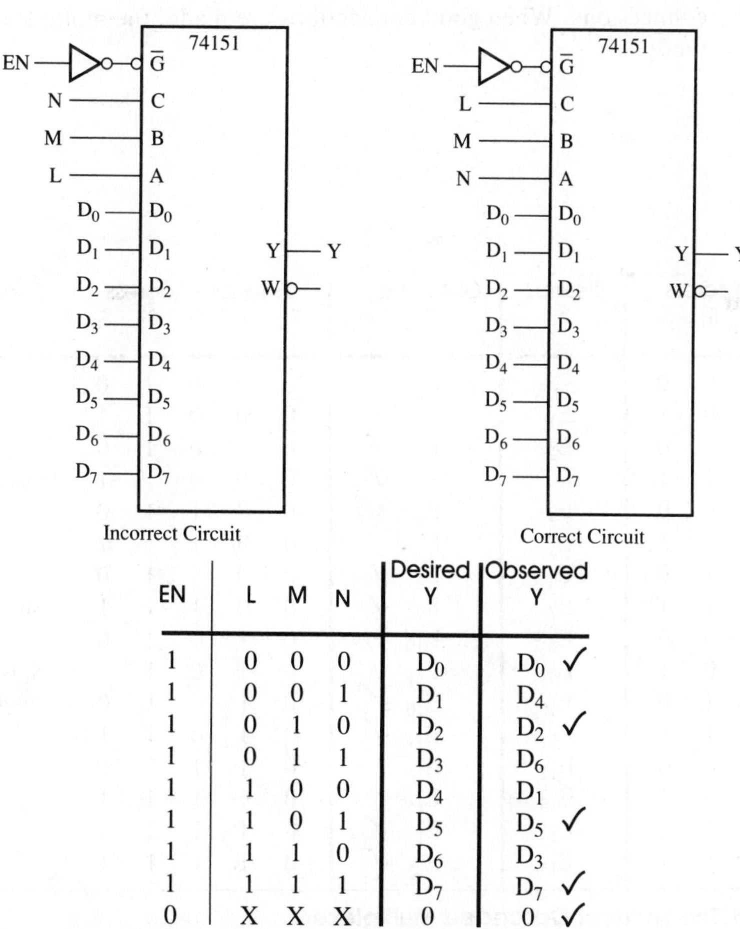

EN	L	M	N	Desired Y	Observed Y
1	0	0	0	D_0	D_0 ✓
1	0	0	1	D_1	D_4
1	0	1	0	D_2	D_2 ✓
1	0	1	1	D_3	D_6
1	1	0	0	D_4	D_1
1	1	0	1	D_5	D_5 ✓
1	1	1	0	D_6	D_3
1	1	1	1	D_7	D_7 ✓
0	X	X	X	0	0 ✓

FIGURE 4-20 The Disorderly Data Selector

EXAMPLE 4-10 The Shortcut Cascaded Multiplexer

Problem: A student incorrectly wires the cascaded multiplexer circuit of Figure 4-11 and obtains wild results. In hopes of receiving partial credit, the student notes that 12 output conditions are correct. The results are shown in Figure 4-21.

Solution: To correct the circuit and obtain full credit, the student should now record the addresses that had produced the observed results and compare those to the addresses that were required for the theoretical results. It can be seen that the observed results were generated when S_1 was always a logic HIGH level and S_2 was a logic HIGH for data inputs E_{16} to E_{31}. Now the student must determine if these select inputs were shorted high or left unconnected. A logic probe test on the pins of interest indicates no logic level was recorded. This is verified by a close inspection that shows loose connections. When good connections are made, the multiplexer works correctly.

Desired Address					Desired	Observed	Probable Address					Reasoning
S_4	S_3	S_2	S_1	S_0	Y	Y	S_4	S_3	S_2	S_1	S_0	
0	0	0	0	0	E_0	E_2	0	0	0	1	0	
0	0	0	0	1	E_1	E_3	0	0	0	1	1	
0	0	0	1	0	E_2	E_2 ✓	0	0	0	1	0	
0	0	0	1	1	E_3	E_3 ✓	0	0	0	1	1	Observe:
0	0	1	0	0	E_4	E_6	0	0	1	1	0	$S_1 = 1$
0	0	1	0	1	E_5	E_7	0	0	1	1	1	
0	0	1	1	0	E_6	E_6 ✓	0	0	1	1	0	
0	0	1	1	1	E_7	E_7 ✓	0	0	1	1	1	Suspicion:
0	1	0	0	0	E_8	E_{10}	0	1	0	1	0	
0	1	0	0	1	E_9	E_{11}	0	1	0	1	1	S_1 is floating or
0	1	0	1	0	E_{10}	E_{10} ✓	0	1	0	1	0	shorted HIGH
0	1	0	1	1	E_{11}	E_{11} ✓	0	1	0	1	1	on MUX #1
0	1	1	0	0	E_{12}	E_{14}	0	1	1	1	0	
0	1	1	0	1	E_{13}	E_{15}	0	1	1	1	1	
0	1	1	1	0	E_{14}	E_{14} ✓	0	1	1	1	0	
0	1	1	1	1	E_{15}	E_{15} ✓	0	1	1	1	1	

FIGURE 4-21 The Shortcut Cascaded Multiplexer

Desired Address					Desired	Observed	Probable Address					Reasoning
S_4	S_3	S_2	S_1	S_0	Y	Y	S_4	S_3	S_2	S_1	S_0	
1	0	0	0	0	E_{16}	E_{22}	1	0	1	1	0	
1	0	0	0	1	E_{17}	E_{23}	1	0	1	1	1	
1	0	0	1	0	E_{18}	E_{22}	1	0	1	1	0	Observe:
1	0	0	1	1	E_{19}	E_{23}	1	0	1	1	1	$S_2 = S_1 = 1$
1	0	1	0	0	E_{20}	E_{22}	1	0	1	1	0	
1	0	1	0	1	E_{21}	E_{23}	1	0	1	1	1	
1	0	1	1	0	E_{22}	E_{22} ✓	1	0	1	1	0	Suspicion:
1	0	1	1	1	E_{23}	E_{23} ✓	1	0	1	1	1	
1	1	0	0	0	E_{24}	E_{30}	1	1	1	1	0	S_1 & S_2 are floating
1	1	0	0	1	E_{25}	E_{31}	1	1	1	1	1	or are shorted
1	1	0	1	0	E_{26}	E_{30}	1	1	1	1	0	HIGH on MUX #2
1	1	0	1	1	E_{27}	E_{31}	1	1	1	1	1	
1	1	1	0	0	E_{28}	E_{30}	1	1	1	1	0	
1	1	1	0	1	E_{29}	E_{31}	1	1	1	1	1	
1	1	1	1	0	E_{30}	E_{30} ✓	1	1	1	1	0	
1	1	1	1	1	E_{31}	E_{31} ✓	1	1	1	1	1	

(Refer to the circuit in Figure 4-11.)

FIGURE 4-21 (*continued*) ■

Section Self-Test

Determine if the following statements are true or false:

1. Troubleshooting relies heavily on circuit analysis.
2. Loosely connected wires provide a logic HIGH at the input.
3. Floating inputs cause the output to respond as if a logic HIGH was applied to the input, although no logic level is applied.

ANSWERS (Not necessarily in the order of the questions)

- False
- True
- True

4-4 DEMULTIPLEXERS

A demultiplexer, or DMUX, performs the opposite operation from that of a multiplexer. A demultiplexer functions as an electronic switch to route an incoming data signal to one of several output lines, as shown in Figure 4-22. Demultiplexer circuits will be used in TDM applications and data routing applications, often in conjunction with multiplexers. In

addition, demultiplexer circuits perform a dual function as decoder circuits. Decoder circuits and applications will be examined in Chapter 5.

4.4.1 Functional Description

A **demultiplexer** has one data input, several data outputs, and select inputs to address the required data outputs. A demultiplexer, or **DMUX**, is specified by the input to output lines that are demultiplexed, such as the 1:4 DMUX shown in Figure 4-22.

The functional truth table for the demultiplexer has one data input, n select address inputs, and 2^n data outputs, as shown in Figure 4-23. The data input signal, D, can take on any allowable digital waveform values. The demultiplexer output equations can be derived from the truth table.

The output can be either active-HIGH or active-LOW, as shown in Figure 4-23. Active-HIGH DMUX circuits route the data to one output, and the remaining outputs are at a logic LOW. Active-LOW DMUX circuits route the data to the selected output and invert it, and the remaining outputs are held at a logic HIGH.

4.4.2 Integrated Circuit Specification

Many common demultiplexers are available as standard transistor-transistor logic (TTL) MSI logic circuits. The demultiplexer integrated circuits (ICs) also perform decoding functions, which will be studied in Chapter 5. Therefore, the ICs are specified as decoders/demultiplexers.

Table 4-3 lists the common TTL decoder/demultiplexer ICs, and Figures 4-24 through 4-25 show the data sheet specifications for selected ICs listed in Table 4-3. Those ICs that contain two separate decoders/demultiplexers are listed as dual devices.

TABLE 4-3 Common Decoders/Demultiplexers

IC	Decoder	DMUX	Output Active-State
74138	3:8	1:8	LOW
74154	4:16	1:16	LOW
74139	Dual 2:4	Dual 1:4	LOW
74155	Dual 2:4	Dual 1:4	LOW
74155	3:8	1:8	LOW

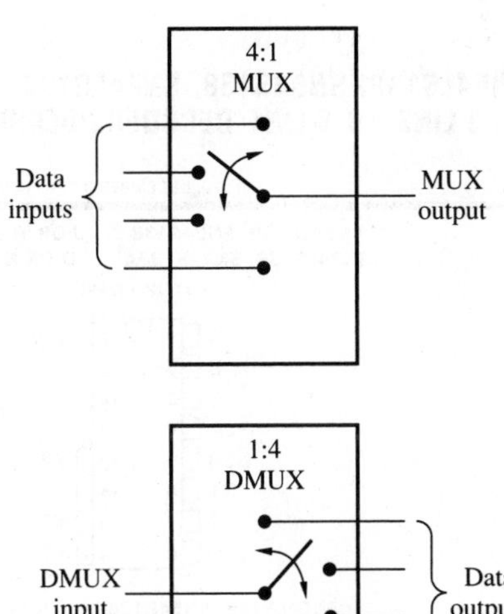

1:4
DMUX
DMUX
input
Data
outputs

FIGURE 4-22 MUX and DMUX Electronic Switches

In addition to those devices presented in Table 4-3, other decoders and demultiplexers exist with output functions, such as address latches, open-collector, or tristate outputs for special applications.

The demultiplexer operation is defined in the function table of the data

1:4 Demultiplexer

Active-HIGH Outputs

Data D	Address S_2	S_1	Outputs Y_0	Y_1	Y_2	Y_3
D	0	0	D	0	0	0
D	0	1	0	D	0	0
D	1	0	0	0	D	0
D	1	1	0	0	0	D

$$Y_0 = \overline{S_2}\,\overline{S_1}\,D \qquad Y_1 = \overline{S_2}\,S_1\,D$$

$$Y_2 = S_2\,\overline{S_1}\,D \qquad Y_3 = S_2\,S_1\,D$$

1:4 Demultiplexer

Active-LOW Outputs

Data D	Address S_2	S_1	Outputs Y_0	Y_1	Y_2	Y_3
D	0	0	$\overline{D}$	1	1	1
D	0	1	1	$\overline{D}$	1	1
D	1	0	1	1	$\overline{D}$	1
D	1	1	1	1	1	$\overline{D}$

$$\overline{Y_0} = \overline{S_2}\,\overline{S_1}\,D \qquad \overline{Y_1} = \overline{S_2}\,S_1\,D$$

$$\overline{Y_2} = S_2\,\overline{S_1}\,D \qquad \overline{Y_3} = S_2\,S_1\,D$$

FIGURE 4-23 Demultiplexer Function Tables and Equations

SN54LS138, SN54S138, SN74LS138, SN74S138A
3-LINE TO 8-LINE DECODERS/DEMULTIPLEXERS

DECEMBER 1972 – REVISED MARCH 1988

- **Designed Specifically for High-Speed:**
  Memory Decoders
  Data Transmission Systems
- **3 Enable Inputs to Simplify Cascading and/or Data Reception**
- **Schottky-Clamped for High Performance**

description

These Schottky-clamped TTL MSI circuits are designed to be used in high-performance memory decoding or data-routing applications requiring very short propagation delay times. In high-performance memory systems, these docoders can be used to minimize the effects of system decoding. When employed with high-speed memories utilizing a fast enable circuit, the delay times of these decoders and the enable time of the memory are usually less than the typical access time of the memory. This means that the effective system delay introduced by the Schottky-clamped system decoder is negligible.

The 'LS138, SN54S138, and SN74S138A decode one of eight lines dependent on the conditions at the three binary select inputs and the three enable inputs. Two active-low and one active-high enable inputs reduce the need for external gates or inverters when expanding. A 24-line decoder can be implemented without external inverters and a 32-line decoder requires only one inverter. An enable input can be used as a data input for demultiplexing applications.

All of these decoder/demultiplexers feature fully buffered inputs, each of which represents only one normalized load to its driving circuit. All inputs are clamped with high-performance Schottky diodes to suppress line-ringing and to simplify system design.

The SN54LS138 and SN54S138 are characterized for operation over the full military temperature range of −55°C to 125°C. The SN74LS138 and SN74S138A are characterized for operation from 0°C to 70°C.

SN54LS138, SN54S138 . . . J OR W PACKAGE
SN74LS138, SN74S138A . . . D OR N PACKAGE
(TOP VIEW)

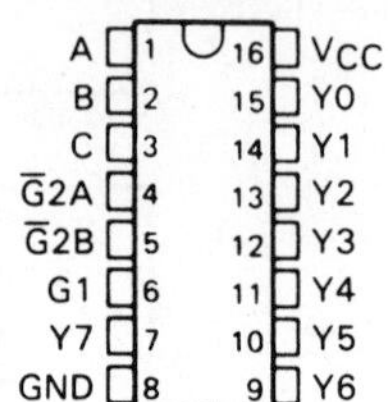

SN54LS138, SN54S138 . . . FK PACKAGE
(TOP VIEW)

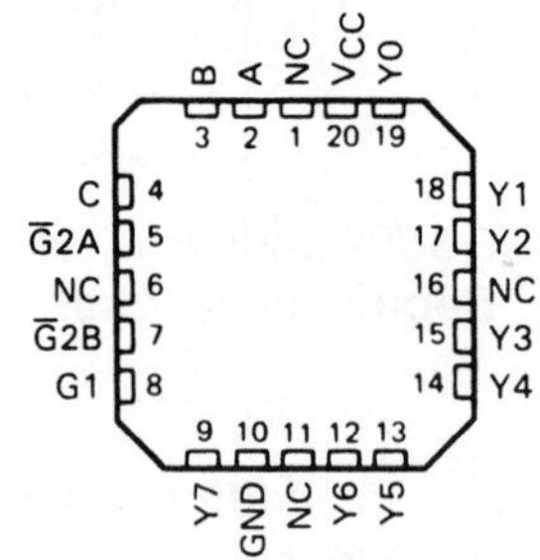

NC – No internal connection

logic symbols†

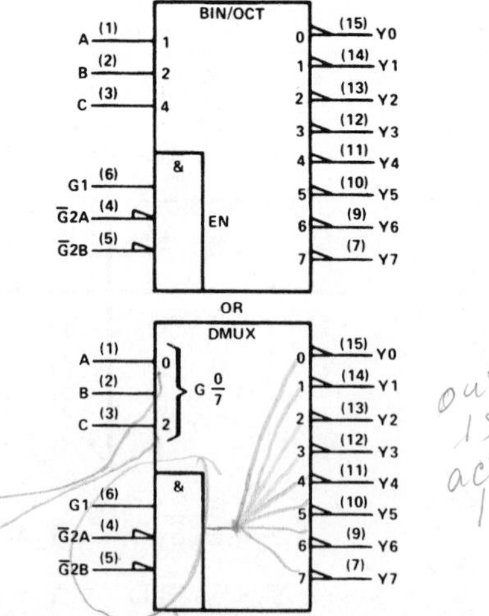

†These symbols are in accordance with ANSI/IEEE Std 91-1984 and IEC Publication 617-12.
Pin numbers shown are for D, J, N, and W packages.

FIGURE 4-24 74138 Decoder/Demultiplexer (Courtesy Texas Instruments)

SN54LS138, SN54S138, SN74LS138, SN74S138A
3-LINE-TO 8-LINE DECODERS/DEMULTIPLEXERS

logic diagram and function table

'LS138, SN54S138, SN74S138A

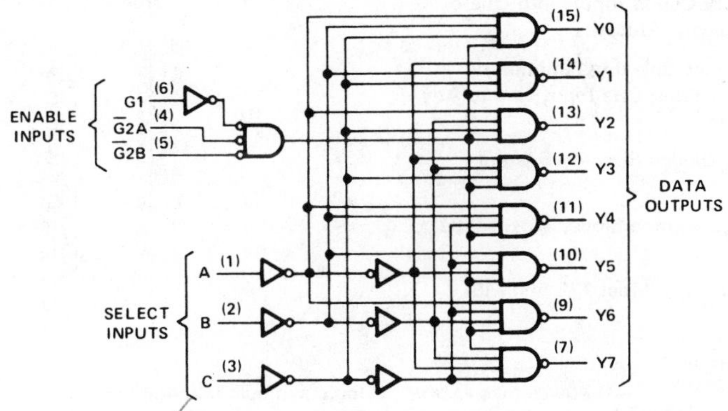

Pin numbers shown are for D, J, N, and W packages.

'LS138, SN54138, SN74S138A
FUNCTION TABLE

INPUTS					OUTPUTS							
ENABLE		SELECT										
G1	$\overline{G2}$*	C	B	A	Y0	Y1	Y2	Y3	Y4	Y5	Y6	Y7
X	H	X	X	X	H	H	H	H	H	H	H	H
L	X	X	X	X	H	H	H	H	H	H	H	H
H	L	L	L	L	L	H	H	H	H	H	H	H
H	L	L	L	H	H	L	H	H	H	H	H	H
H	L	L	H	L	H	H	L	H	H	H	H	H
H	L	L	H	H	H	H	H	L	H	H	H	H
H	L	H	L	L	H	H	H	H	L	H	H	H
H	L	H	L	H	H	H	H	H	H	L	H	H
H	L	H	H	L	H	H	H	H	H	H	L	H
H	L	H	H	H	H	H	H	H	H	H	H	L

*$\overline{G2} = \overline{G2A} + \overline{G2B}$
H = high level, L = low level, X = irrelevant

FIGURE 4-24 (*continued*)

sheet, which specifies the output results for all possible inputs. The operation of the 74138 1:8 DMUX (see Figure 4-24) will be described in detail.

1. *Enable inputs = data inputs.* The data input in DMUX circuits is labeled as an enable input. When the same IC is used as a decoder, these inputs function as true enable inputs. However, for demultiplexing functions, the enable inputs serve as the data inputs.

SN54154, SN74154
4-LINE TO 16-LINE DECODERS/DEMULTIPLEXERS

DECEMBER 1972 – REVISED MARCH 88

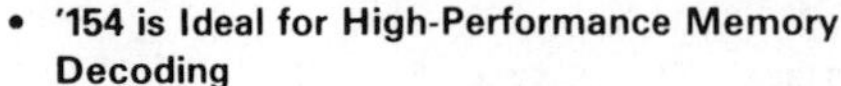

- **'154 is Ideal for High-Performance Memory Decoding**
- **Decodes 4 Binary-Coded Inputs into One of 16 Mutually Exclusive Outputs**
- **Performs the Demultiplexing Function by Distributing Data From One Input Line to Any One of 16 Outputs**
- **Input Clamping Diodes Simplify System Design**
- **High Fan-Out, Low-Impedance, Totem-Pole Outputs**
- **Fully Compatible with Most TTL and MSI Circuits**

TYPICAL AVERAGE PROPAGATION DELAY 3 LEVELS OF LOGIC	TYPICAL AVERAGE PROPAGATION DELAY STROBE	TYPICAL POWER DISSIPATION
23 ns	19 ns	170 mW

SN54154 . . . J OR W PACKAGE
SN74154 . . . N PACKAGE
(TOP VIEW)

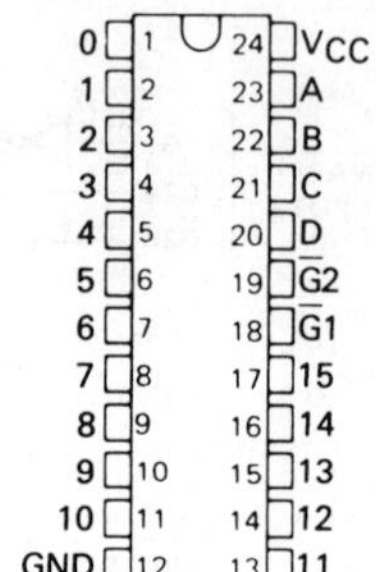

description

Each of these monolithic, 4-line-to-16-line decoders utilizes TTL circuitry to decode four binary-coded inputs into one of sixteen mutually exclusive outputs when both the strobe inputs, $\overline{G1}$ and $\overline{G2}$, are low. The demultiplexing function is performed by using the 4 input lines to address the output line, passing data from one of the strobe inputs with the other strobe input low. When either strobe input is high, all outputs are high. These demultiplexers are ideally suited for implementing high-performance memory decoders. For ultra-high speed systems, SN54S138/SN74S138 and SN54S139/SN74S139 are recommended.

These circuits are fully compatible for use with most other TTL circuits. All inputs are buffered and input clamping diodes are provided to minimize transmission-line effects and thereby simplify system design.

The SN54154 is characterized for operation over the full military temperature range of −55°C to 125°C. The SN74154 is characterized for operation from 0°C to 70°C.

logic symbols (alternatives)†

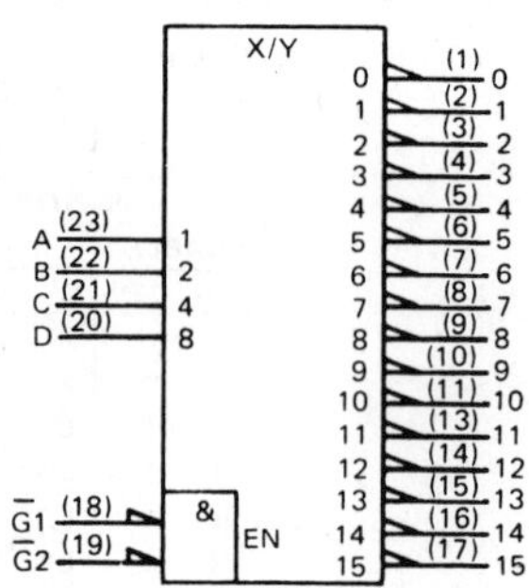

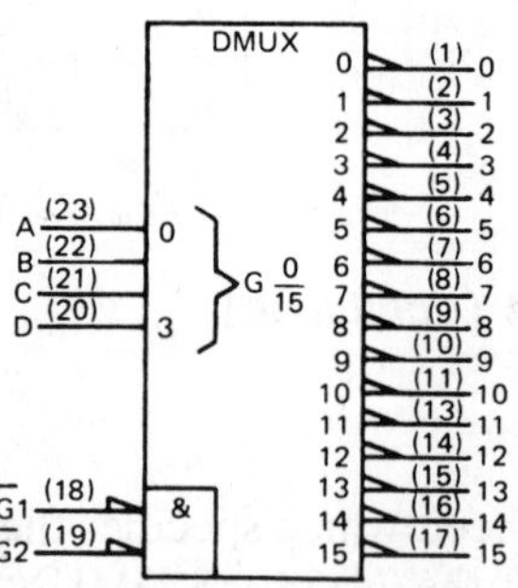

†These symbols are in accordance with ANSI/IEEE Std. 91-1984 and IEC Publication 617-12.

FIGURE 4-25 74154 Decoder/Demultiplexer (Courtesy Texas Instruments)

SN54154, SN74154
4-LINE TO 16-LINE DECODERS/DEMULTIPLEXERS

FUNCTION TABLE

INPUTS						OUTPUTS															
$\bar{G}1$	$\bar{G}2$	D	C	B	A	0	1	2	3	4	5	6	7	8	9	10	11	12	13	14	15
L	L	L	L	L	L	L	H	H	H	H	H	H	H	H	H	H	H	H	H	H	H
L	L	L	L	L	H	H	L	H	H	H	H	H	H	H	H	H	H	H	H	H	H
L	L	L	L	H	L	H	H	L	H	H	H	H	H	H	H	H	H	H	H	H	H
L	L	L	L	H	H	H	H	H	L	H	H	H	H	H	H	H	H	H	H	H	H
L	L	L	H	L	L	H	H	H	H	L	H	H	H	H	H	H	H	H	H	H	H
L	L	L	H	L	H	H	H	H	H	H	L	H	H	H	H	H	H	H	H	H	H
L	L	L	H	H	L	H	H	H	H	H	H	L	H	H	H	H	H	H	H	H	H
L	L	L	H	H	H	H	H	H	H	H	H	H	L	H	H	H	H	H	H	H	H
L	L	H	L	L	L	H	H	H	H	H	H	H	H	L	H	H	H	H	H	H	H
L	L	H	L	L	H	H	H	H	H	H	H	H	H	H	L	H	H	H	H	H	H
L	L	H	L	H	L	H	H	H	H	H	H	H	H	H	H	L	H	H	H	H	H
L	L	H	L	H	H	H	H	H	H	H	H	H	H	H	H	H	L	H	H	H	H
L	L	H	H	L	L	H	H	H	H	H	H	H	H	H	H	H	H	L	H	H	H
L	L	H	H	L	H	H	H	H	H	H	H	H	H	H	H	H	H	H	L	H	H
L	L	H	H	H	L	H	H	H	H	H	H	H	H	H	H	H	H	H	H	L	H
L	L	H	H	H	H	H	H	H	H	H	H	H	H	H	H	H	H	H	H	H	L
L	H	X	X	X	X	H	H	H	H	H	H	H	H	H	H	H	H	H	H	H	H
H	L	X	X	X	X	H	H	H	H	H	H	H	H	H	H	H	H	H	H	H	H
H	H	X	X	X	X	H	H	H	H	H	H	H	H	H	H	H	H	H	H	H	H

H = high level, L = low level, X = irrelevant

schematics of inputs and outputs

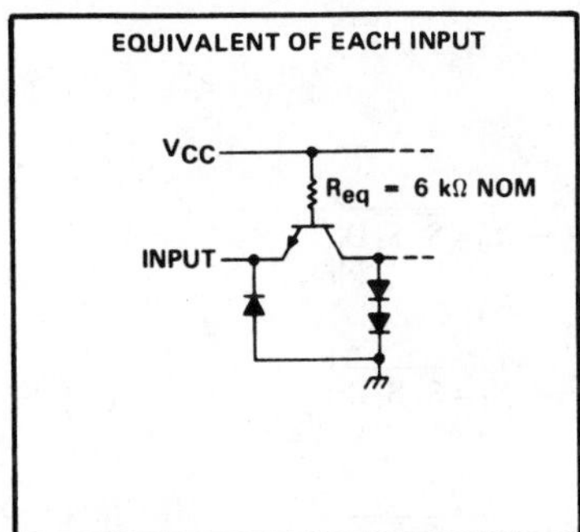

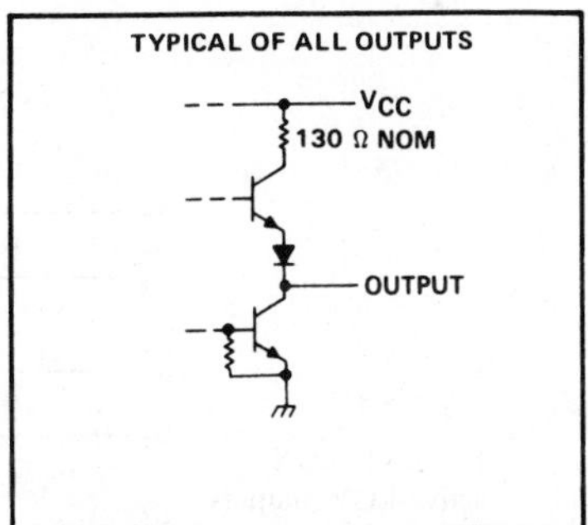

FIGURE 4-25 (*continued*)

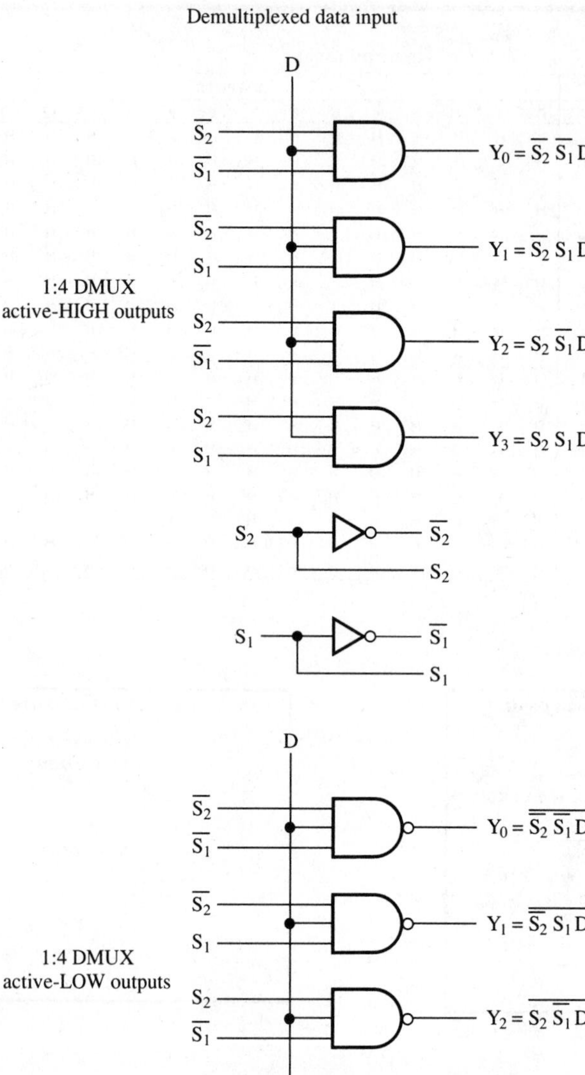

FIGURE 4-26 Demultiplexer Circuits

The 74138 has three enable inputs: G_1 is active-HIGH, $\overline{G_{2A}}$ and $\overline{G_{2B}}$ are active-LOW. When the 74138 is used for demultiplexing, any one of the enable inputs can serve as the data input. If G_1 is used, the resulting data at the output is inverted, due to the active-LOW outputs. If the $\overline{G_{2A}}$ or $\overline{G_{2B}}$ inputs are used, the data appears in its true form since it passes through two inversions between the input and output of the demultiplexer.

2. *Select inputs.* The address for the data output of the demultiplexed data is put in the select inputs. The 74138 has three select inputs, C, B, and A, with C the **MSB** of the select inputs. Three select inputs can address eight outputs. The addresses range from 000 to 111.
3. *Data outputs.* The demultiplexed data is routed to one data output while the other outputs remain in an inactive logic state. There are 2^n data outputs, where n is the number of select inputs. The 74138 has eight active-LOW outputs. The inactive outputs maintain a constant logic-HIGH state.

4.4.3 Gate Equivalent Circuits

The logic equations for a demultiplexer can be obtained from the function tables in Figure 4-26. The DMUX logic gate equivalent circuit is simply an AND gate array for each input combination to route the data, as shown in Figure 4-26.

Section Self-Test

Examine the data sheets for the 74155 to answer these self-test questions.

1. Which select inputs are used to operate the 74155 as a 1:4 DMUX?
2. Which select inputs are used to operate the 74155 as a 1:8 DMUX?
3. What input should be used as the data input so that the demultiplexed data appears in its true form at the outputs?

ANSWERS

(Not necessarily in the same order as the questions)

- 1C, $2\overline{C}$, B, A
- $1\overline{G}$, $2\overline{G}$
- B, A

4-5 APPLICATION AND DESIGN USING DEMULTIPLEXERS

Demultiplexer circuits are multipurpose AND-array circuits used extensively in data transmission and in data routing applications. The examples covered in this section use standard DMUX ICs. Complex demultiplexing circuits can be found in high speed data transmission circuits, but their operation is based on the fundamental principles of demultiplexers discussed in this chapter.

Demultiplexer circuits can also be built using programmable logic devices (PLDs). These devices will be studied in Chapter 12.

4.5.1 Data Routing

The demultiplexer routes a single data stream to one of several different outputs, as determined by the address on the select inputs. Only one data output is active with demultiplexed data; the other data outputs remain at a constant logic level as specified by the function table for the circuit.

Figure 4-27 shows an example of data from a PC being transmitted to a demultiplexer and then selectively routed to one of four devices: a plotter, a laser printer, a dot matrix line printer, and a dumb terminal.

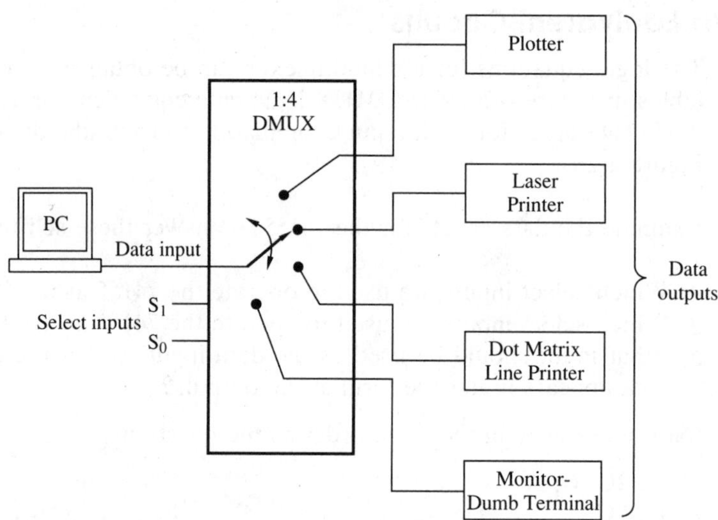

FIGURE 4-27 Demultiplexer Data Routing

■ EXAMPLE 4-11 Demultiplexer Data Routing

Problem: For the PC office equipment setup in Figure 4-27, use a 74138 demultiplexer to transmit data from the PC to the output devices as specified. The data should not be inverted during transmission to the output device.

Personal Computer Routing Specification Table

Address	Output Device
000	Laser printer
001	Dot matrix printer
010	Plotter
011	Dumb terminal—monitor
100	For future use
101	For future use
110	For future use
111	For future use

Solution: Problem specifications must be translated into a truth table for the 74138 DMUX circuit. The addresses will be placed in the select inputs. The $\overline{G_2}$ inputs can be connected together and used as the data input. The G_1 enable must be tied to a logic HIGH. The output devices must be connected to the output corresponding to their unique address, as listed here.

DMUX OUTPUT	DEVICE
Y_0	Laser printer
Y_1	Dot matrix printer
Y_2	Plotter
Y_3	Dumb terminal—monitor

The function table for the 74138 follows, and the circuit is shown in Figure 4-28.

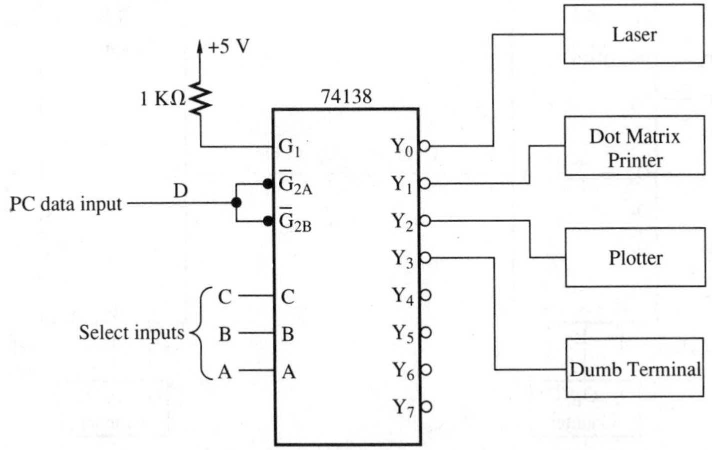

Note: See material in Appendix B for serial data transmission and the RS-232 standard. Serial data transmission should not be attempted at TTL voltage levels.

FIGURE 4-28 74138 PC Data Routing Application

74138 Function Table

G_1	$\overline{G_{2A}}$ $\overline{G_{2B}}$	C	B	A	Y_0	Y_1	Y_2	Y_3	Y_4	Y_5	Y_6	Y_7
1	D	0	0	0	D	1	1	1	1	1	1	1
1	D	0	0	1	1	D	1	1	1	1	1	1
1	D	0	1	0	1	1	D	1	1	1	1	1
1	D	0	1	1	1	1	1	D	1	1	1	1
1	D	1	0	0	1	1	1	1	D	1	1	1
1	D	1	0	1	1	1	1	1	1	D	1	1
1	D	1	1	0	1	1	1	1	1	1	D	1
1	D	1	1	1	1	1	1	1	1	1	1	D

4.5.2. Time Division Multiplexing and Demultiplexing

In TDM applications a MUX is used to transmit data serially from several sources so that the devices share one common transmission line. Each device must transmit its data during its assigned time slot. When several data signals are multiplexed together for transmission, a DMUX separates received signals and routes them to their final destination.

The MUX and DMUX must be operated synchronously to transmit data in the correct time slot for proper routing. One way of synchronizing the MUX and DMUX is to transmit a master clock signal. The clock signal drives counters that generate synchronous select inputs at the transmit and receive ends of the system, as shown in Figure 4-29.

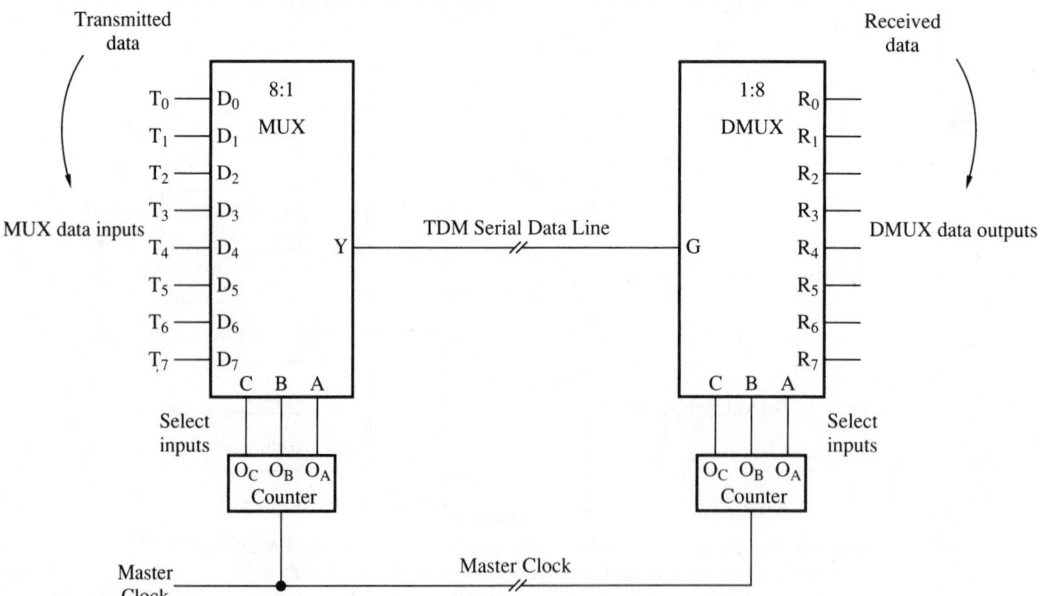

FIGURE 4-29 TDM Application

Transmit–MUX				Receive–DMUX										
Select Inputs			Transmitted MUX Data	Select Inputs			Received DMUX Data							
C	B	A	Y	C	B	A	R_0	R_1	R_2	R_3	R_4	R_5	R_6	R_7
0	0	0	T_0	0	0	0	T_0	0	0	0	0	0	0	0
0	0	1	T_1	0	0	1	0	T_1	0	0	0	0	0	0
0	1	0	T_2	0	1	0	0	0	T_2	0	0	0	0	0
0	1	1	T_3	0	1	1	0	0	0	T_3	0	0	0	0
1	0	0	T_4	1	0	0	0	0	0	0	T_4	0	0	0
1	0	1	T_5	1	0	1	0	0	0	0	0	T_5	0	0
1	1	0	T_6	1	1	0	0	0	0	0	0	0	T_6	0
1	1	1	T_7	1	1	1	0	0	0	0	0	0	0	T_7

FIGURE 4-29 TDM Application

■ EXAMPLE 4-12 Multiplexer/Demultiplexer System

Problem: Use the 74151 multiplexer and the 74138 demultiplexer to design a system that can transmit up to eight devices on a single transmission line.

Solution: The 74151 MUX is an 8:1 MUX with both true and inverted outputs. It can be interfaced easily with the 1:8 74138 DMUX, as shown in Figure 4-30. The signal out of the 74138 must be inverted in order for the final signal to be active-HIGH. The MUX and DMUX operate with common select inputs. This eliminates the need for a counter at the transmit and receive sites. ■

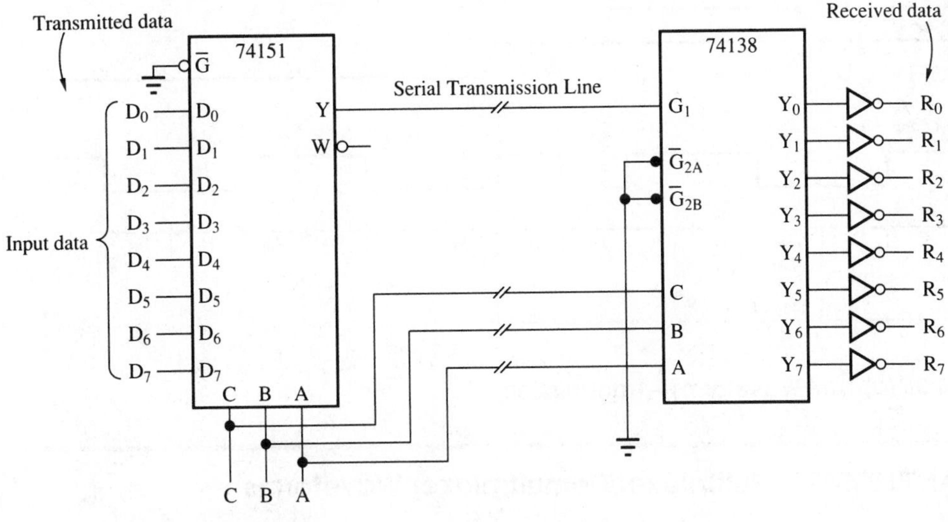

FIGURE 4-30 TDM Multiplexer/Demultiplexer System

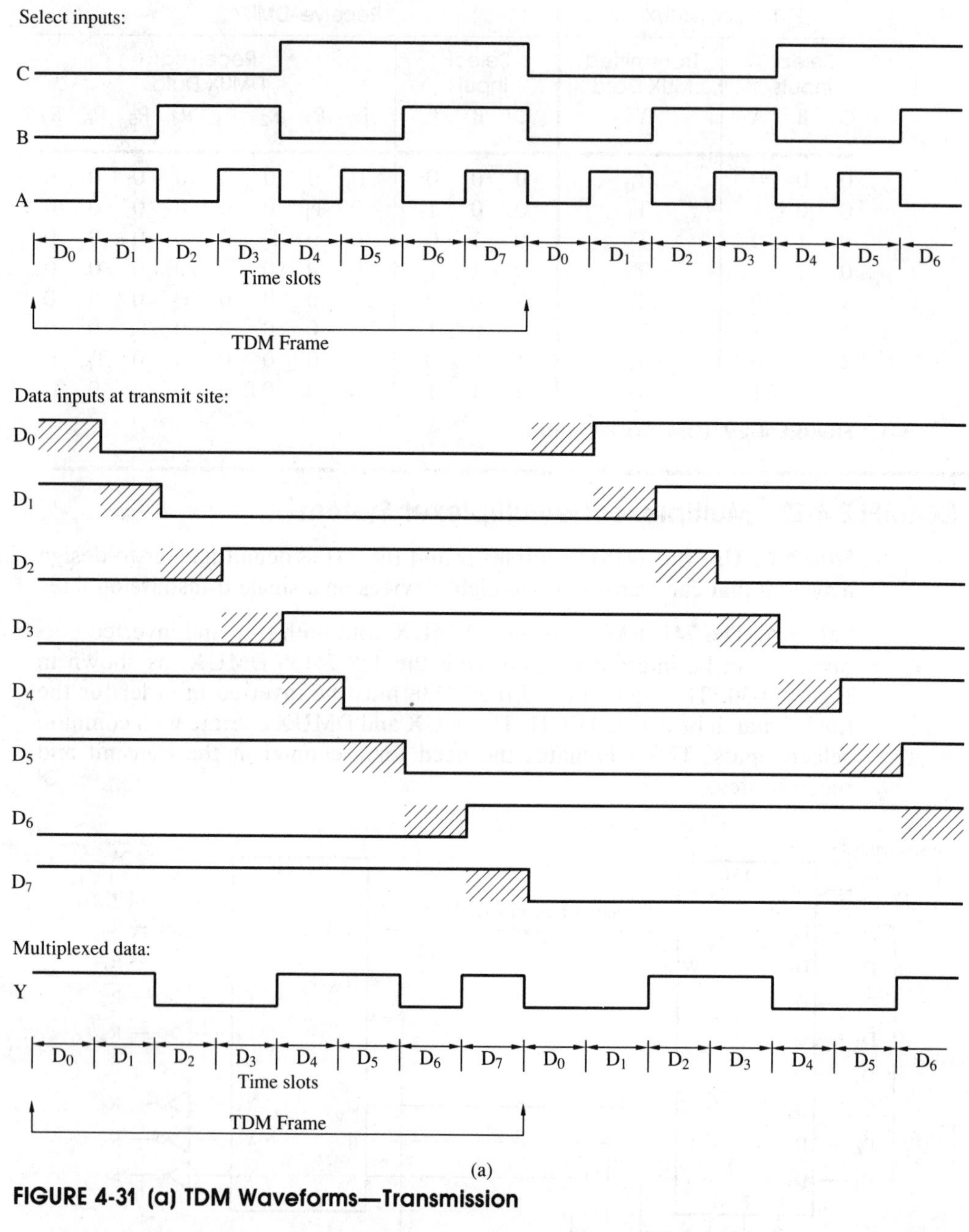

(a)

FIGURE 4-31 (a) TDM Waveforms—Transmission

■ EXAMPLE 4-13 Multiplexer/Demultiplexer Waveforms

Problem: Given the input waveforms for the TDM system in Example 4-12, determine the output waveforms that are demultiplexed at the receive site.

Solution: The input data is multiplexed and transmitted during the appropriate time slot according to the address in the select inputs at the transmit site [Figure 4-31(a)]. The data is received and demultiplexed according to the address in the select inputs at the receive site [Figure 4-31(b)]. The demultiplexed outputs are active only during their assigned time slot; at all other times they are inactive and remain at a logic LOW state. ■

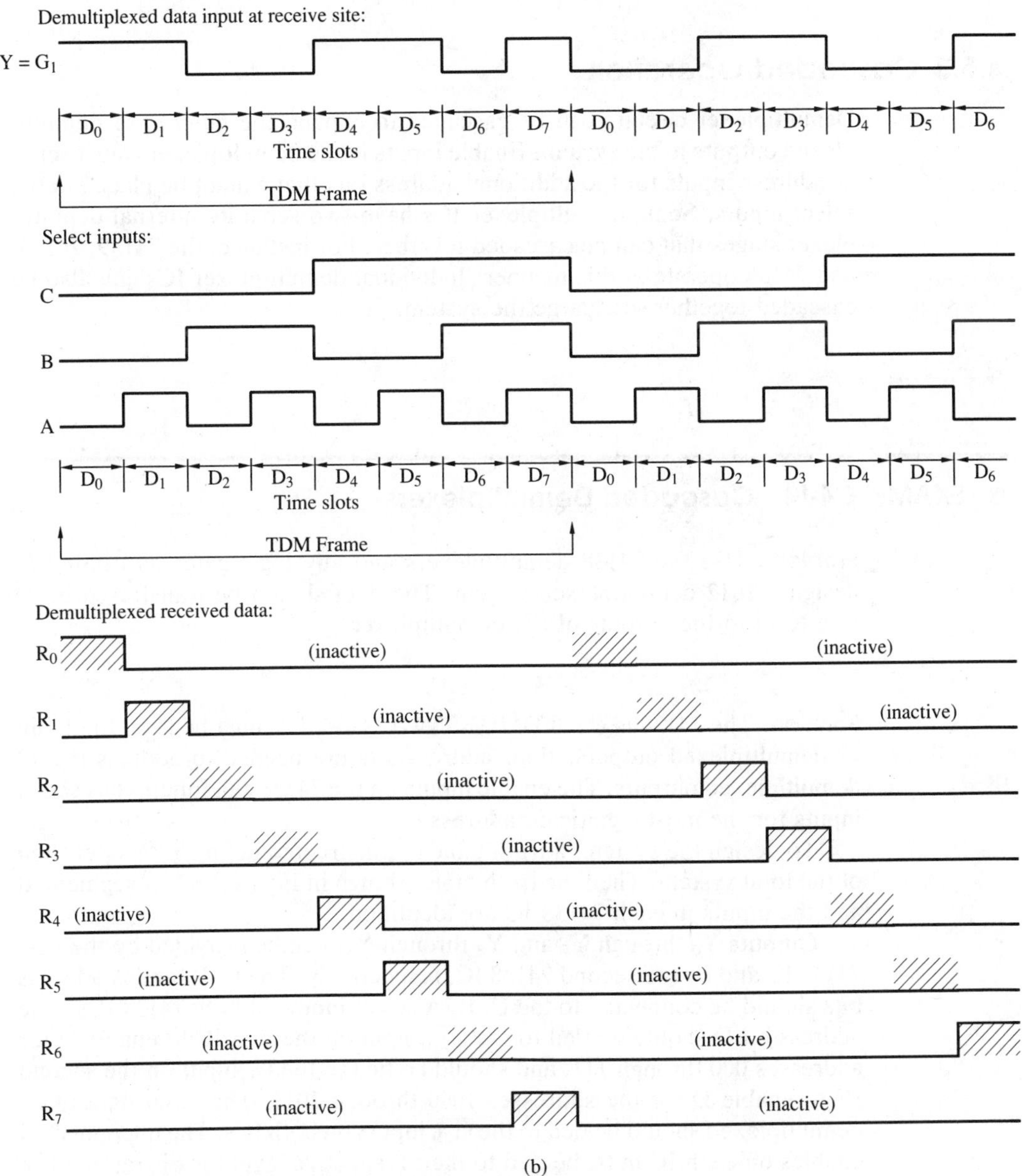

(b)

FIGURE 4-31 (b) TDM Waveforms—Reception

Solution: The input data is multiplexed and transmitted during the appropriate time slot according to the address in the select inputs at the transmit site [Figure 4-31(a)]. The data is received and demultiplexed according to the address in the select inputs at the receive site [Figure 4-31(b)]. The demultiplexed outputs are active only during their assigned time slot; at all other times they are inactive and remain at a logic-LOW state. ■

4.5.3 Cascaded Operation

Demultiplexer circuits can be cascaded to expand the number of demultiplexed outputs in the system. Enable inputs in the demultiplexers must serve as address inputs for the additional address bits that cannot be placed in the select inputs. Some demultiplexer ICs have two separate internal demultiplexer stages that can be cascaded together. For instance, the 74139, 74155, and 74156 operate in this manner. Individual demultiplexer ICs can also be cascaded together to enlarge the system.

■ EXAMPLE 4-14 Cascaded Demultiplexers

Problem: Use the 74138 demultiplexers and any logic gates as needed to design a 1:12 demultiplexer system. The data should be transferred in its true form to the outputs of the demultiplexer.

Solution: The 74138 is a 1:8 DMUX. Two 74138 ICs must be used to obtain 12 demultiplexed outputs. Four address bits are needed to address the 12 demultiplexed outputs. The enable inputs on the 74138 can function as select inputs for the most significant address bit.

To design the system, a truth table is constructed defining the operation of the total system. Then the truth table, shown in Figure 4-32, is segmented and the inputs in each 74138 IC are identified.

Outputs Y_0 through Y_7 and Y_8 through Y_{11} can be provided by the first 74138 IC and by the second 74138 IC, respectively. The C, B, and A address bits should be connected to the C, B, A select inputs of both 74138 ICs. The address bit D should be tied to the $\overline{G_{2A}}$ input on the first IC to enable D for addresses 000 through 111, and should be tied to the G_1 input on the second IC to enable D for the addresses 1000 through 1011. The input data to be demultiplexed should be tied to the $\overline{G_{2B}}$ inputs on both ICs. The unconnected enables on each IC must be tied to their respective level for operation. The circuit for the 1:12 DMUX is shown in Figure 4-33.

1:12 DMUX Function Table

G	Data Address D	C	B	A	Outputs Y_0	Y_1	Y_2	Y_3	Y_4	Y_5	Y_6	Y_7	Y_8	Y_9	Y_{10}	Y_{11}
d	0	0	0	0	d	1	1	1	1	1	1	1	1	1	1	1
d	0	0	0	1	1	d	1	1	1	1	1	1	1	1	1	1
d	0	0	1	0	1	1	d	1	1	1	1	1	1	1	1	1
d	0	0	1	1	1	1	1	d	1	1	1	1	1	1	1	1
d	0	1	0	0	1	1	1	1	d	1	1	1	1	1	1	1
d	0	1	0	1	1	1	1	1	1	d	1	1	1	1	1	1
d	0	1	1	0	1	1	1	1	1	1	d	1	1	1	1	1
d	0	1	1	1	1	1	1	1	1	1	1	d	1	1	1	1
d	1	0	0	0	1	1	1	1	1	1	1	1	d	1	1	1
d	1	0	0	1	1	1	1	1	1	1	1	1	1	d	1	1
d	1	0	1	0	1	1	1	1	1	1	1	1	1	1	d	1
d	1	0	1	1	1	1	1	1	1	1	1	1	1	1	1	d

FIGURE 4-32 1:12 Demultiplexer Function Table

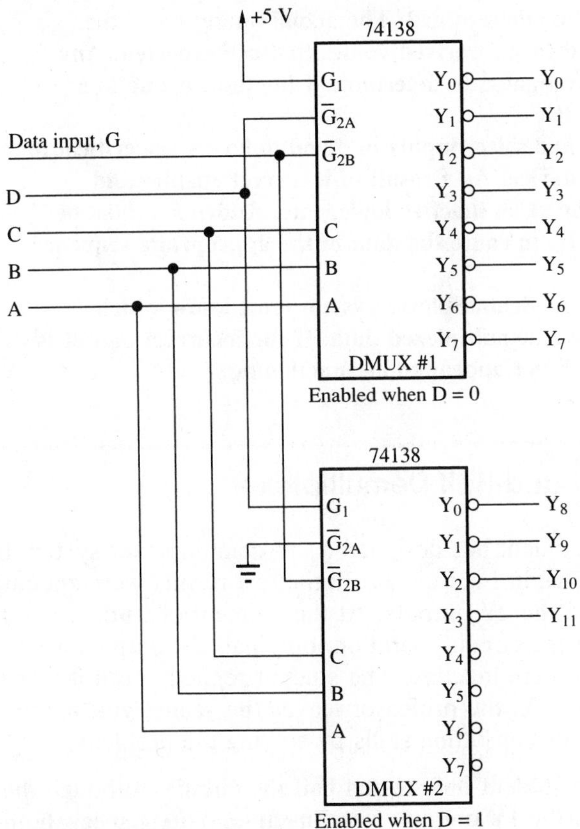

FIGURE 4-33 1:12 Demultiplexer

Section Self-Test

1. Why does a TDM system require common select inputs at both the transmit and receive sites?
2. What IC should have been used for the 1:12 DMUX to simplify the design greatly?
3. When using the 74155 in a 1:8 demultiplexing application, what input is the **data input**?

ANSWERS (Not necessarily in the order of the questions)

- 74154
- 1G and 2G connected together
- The common select inputs are required so that the data is demultiplexed and routed to the appropriate output.

4-6 TROUBLESHOOTING DEMULTIPLEXER CIRCUITS

Troubleshooting demultiplexer circuits is based on the analysis of the DMUX operation. As with multiplexer troubleshooting, output results for all input situations must be determined. The actual operation of the device must be compared to the derived values that are expected. Any discrepancy must be investigated to determine if the fault is due to a wiring error or a faulty IC.

The enable, strobe, and select inputs in demultiplexers are critical to proper operation of the device. As a result of incorrect enables and strobes all outputs will be at an inactive logic state. Addresses must be entered correctly to the IC to route the data in the appropriate sequence to the desired output.

Finally, the user of the demultiplexer system must know which output will have the active demultiplexed data. If the incorrect output is monitored, the device will not appear to be functioning.

■ EXAMPLE 4-15 Half-and-Half Demultiplexer

Problem: A student has designed a 1:8 demultiplexer system based on the 74155, as shown in Figure 4-34. Initial test results were encouraging as the student tested the 2Y outputs. At the moment of truth when the professor was verifying the circuit operation, only half the outputs were working and the other half were inactive. The student replied, "But it was just working a minute ago." As the professor leaves the scene, you see an opportunity to sharpen your consulting skills by solving the problem.

Solution: The student only tested half the circuit. Although the 2Y outputs were correct, the 1Y outputs were inactive. You suspect the problem is in the data input to the 1Y outputs. Close inspection of the function table for the 74155 shows that two inputs, $1\overline{G}$ and $2\overline{G}$, must be connected together to route the data to all eight outputs when they are addressed. There is no financial gain in this consulting position, but you chalk it up to your *pro bono* work. The corrected circuit is shown in Figure 4-34.

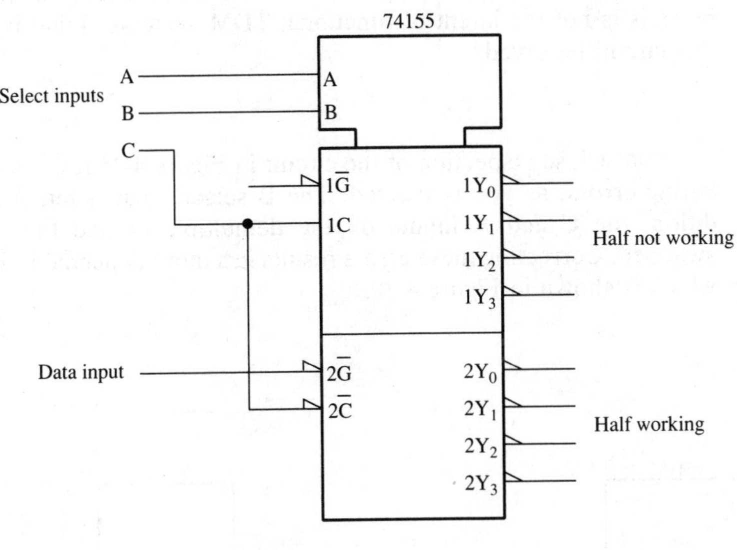

Incorrect Circuit

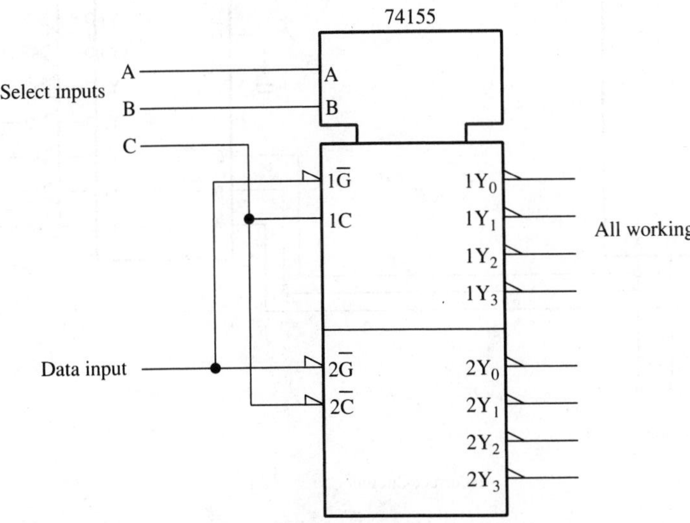

Correct Circuit

FIGURE 4-34 Half-and-Half Demultiplexer

■ EXAMPLE 4-16 Random Generator Time Division Multiplexing

Problem: The TDM circuit shown in Figure 4-35 produces the results shown in Figure 4-36. The data appears to be mixed up during the transmission, but this is not the intent of functional TDM systems. What is wrong? Can this circuit be saved?

Solution: Close inspection of the circuit in Figure 4-35 reveals a few critical wiring errors, as you suspected. The B select input is left floating. In addition, the C and A inputs on the demultiplexer had the address lines swapped. Correcting these errors results in a more dependable TDM system, which is shown in Figure 4-30.

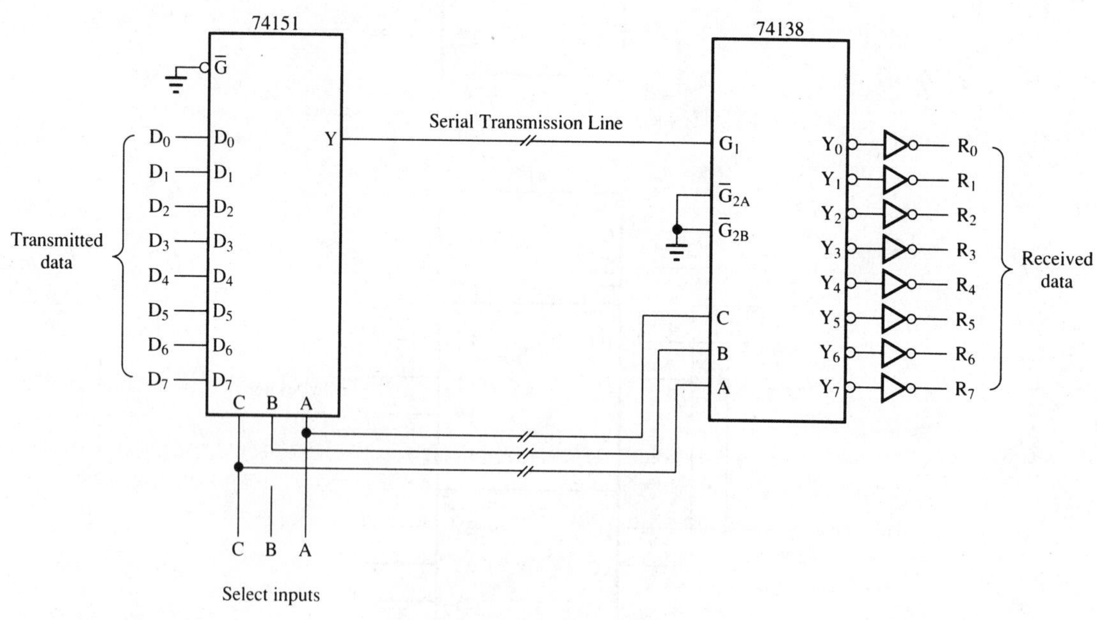

FIGURE 4-35 Random Generator TDM Circuit

Transmit–MUX				Receive–DMUX										
Select Inputs			Incorrect Transmitted MUX Data	Select Inputs			Incorrect Received DMUX Data							
C	B	A	Y	C	B	A	R_0	R_1	R_2	R_3	R_4	R_5	R_6	R_7
0	X	0	D_2	0	X	0	0	0	D_2	0	0	0	0	0
0	X	1	D_3	1	X	0	0	0	0	0	0	0	D_3	0
0	X	0	D_2	0	X	0	0	0	D_2	0	0	0	0	0
0	X	1	D_3	1	X	0	0	0	0	0	0	0	D_3	0
1	X	0	D_6	0	X	1	0	0	0	D_6	0	0	0	0
1	X	1	D_7	1	X	1	0	0	0	0	0	0	0	D_7
1	X	0	D_6	0	X	1	0	0	0	D_6	0	0	0	0
1	X	1	D_7	1	X	1	0	0	0	0	0	0	0	D_7

(Compare to correct TDM results in Figure 4-31.)

FIGURE 4-36 Random Generator Function Table

Section Self-Test

Determine if the following statements are true or false.

1. Time division multiplexing systems always transmit data in sequential order, regardless of how they are wired.
2. Inputs can be left unconnected if they are only to be a logic HIGH.
3. The 74156 can replace the 74155 with no changes to the circuit.

ANSWERS (Not necessarily in the order of the questions)

- False • False • False

SUMMARY

Multiplexers and demultiplexers are general purpose MSI logic devices used in a wide variety of logic applications. The primary applications of multiplexer and demultiplexer circuits were studied in this chapter through many examples dealing with analysis, application, design and troubleshooting. The major concepts are now summarized.

ANALYSIS

Multiplexers and demultiplexers are often described as electronic switches. The multiplexer switches one of several inputs to one output, and the demultiplexer routes one input to one of several outputs. Multiplexers are basic

AND-OR array circuits with a single output, and demultiplexers are an array of AND or NAND gates.

Many multiplexer and demultiplexer ICs that are available as MSI circuits are used to simplify the design and reduce the number of chips required in the final design. Common multiplexer and demultiplexer ICs examined in this chapter were the 74150, 74151, 74153, 74157, 74138, 74154, 74155, 74156, and 74139 devices.

Multiplexer and demultiplexer circuit analysis rely heavily on verifying the function table specified in the data sheet. All input conditions and output results are stated and must be verified through building and testing the logic circuits.

Troubleshooting the multiplexer and demultiplexer circuits focus on examining the differences that occur in actual operation of the logic circuit as opposed to the results indicated by the manufacturer's function table. Errors in circuit operation commonly result from incorrect addressing or enabling of the IC.

APPLICATION

Multiplexers are used commonly in applications of data selection, cascaded operation, binary word multiplexing, TDM, and logic function generation.

In data selection the multiplexer is used as a very basic electronic switch to select data for routing from an input to the output.

Cascaded operation of multiplexers allows the designer to expand the number of inputs that can be selected and routed to a single output.

Binary word multiplexing requires a group of multiplexers that are controlled by a common address input to route an entire binary word to the outputs. Binary words are commonly 4, 8, or 16 bits, so that the binary word multiplexers select from one of two binary words and route the bits to the outputs.

Time division multiplexing applications are used frequently in data transmission systems where many input devices must share a common transmission line. Time division multiplexing requires the synchronous routing of data from each of the demultiplexer's data inputs to the common output.

Logic functions can be generated with a multiplexer by applying constant logic levels to the data inputs. The multiplexer can easily implement logic functions requiring a single output.

Demultiplexers are used in applications of data routing, cascaded operation, and TDM and demultiplexing.

Data routing with a demultiplexer is an operation opposite from that of the multiplexer data selector. A demultiplexer functions as an electronic switch to route a single input to one of many output devices.

Cascaded operation of demultiplexers expands the number of data outputs to which data can be routed.

Time division multiplexing and demultiplexing is a complex data transmission application that requires the synchronous operation of a multiplexer to transmit the data and a demultiplexer to receive the data. The data originates from many different sources, is transmitted in a serial format on a common transmission line shared by the transmitting devices, and is separated out at the receive end by the demultiplexer.

DESIGN

Multiplexer and demultiplexer circuits can be designed from logic gates, based on the basic Boolean algebra equations derived to specify the operation. A programmable logic device, such as a PLD covered in Chapter 12, can be programmed to perform a multiplexing or demultiplexing function for a specific application.

Logic systems can be designed using multiplexer and demultiplexer ICs as functional blocks with additional logic circuitry added to the system. These design techniques enhance and expand the operation of the multiplexer and demultiplexer circuits in applications of data selection, data routing, cascaded operation, binary word multiplexing, logic function generation, and TDM.

PROBLEMS

4-1 Multiplexers—Analysis Problems

1. List three functional uses for a multiplexer, other than those specified in the chapter.

*2. Examine the data sheet for a 74151 in a logic data book.
   a. How long does it take for an input to be routed to the output? Give the typical and minimum values.
   b. What is this routing time parameter called?
   c. How can it limit the maximum data rate of the multiplexed serial bit stream?

3. Repeat Problem 2 for the 74150 multiplexer.

4. Define the data inputs, select inputs, enable inputs, and data outputs for the 74151, and describe their operation.

5. Repeat Problem 4 for the 74153.

6. Repeat Problem 4 for the 74157.

7. Determine the output logic equations for the 74157 multiplexed outputs.

8. Repeat Problem 7 using the 74153.

---

* *See* Answers to Selected Problems.

9. Repeat Problem 7 using the 74151.

*10. Determine the serial output waveforms, Y and W, for the circuit and input waveforms shown in Figure 4-37 (electronic switch application).

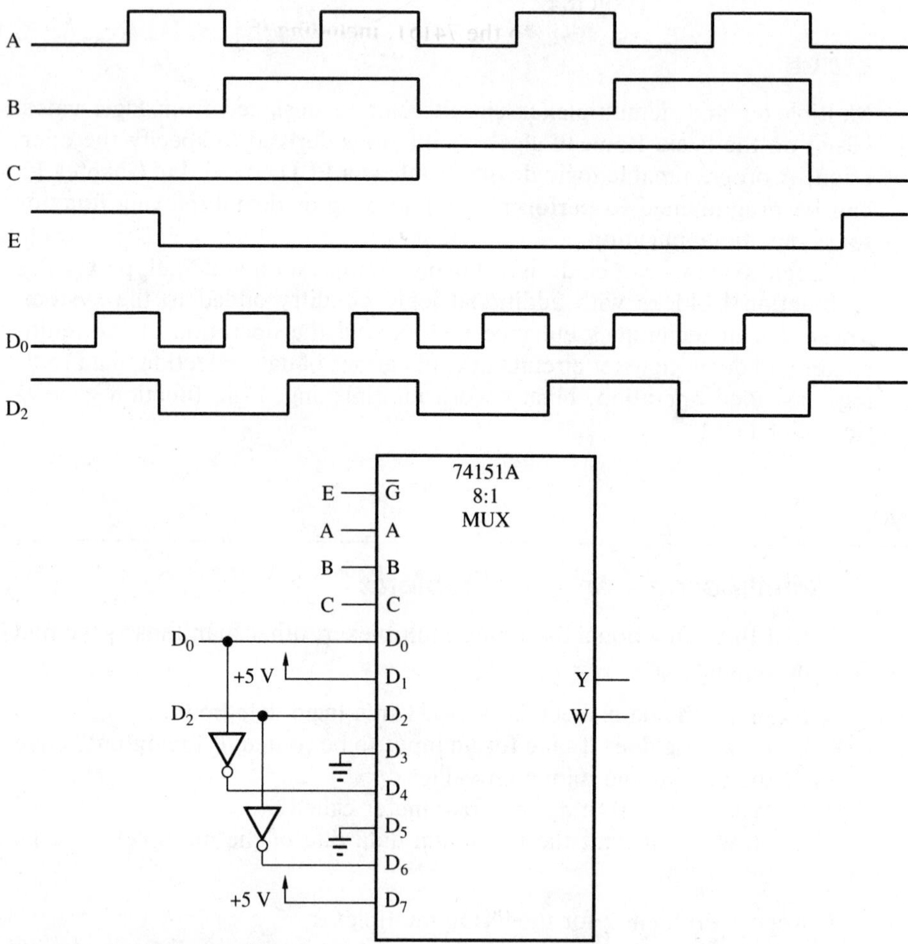

FIGURE 4-37 Problem 4-10

4-2 Application and Design Using Multiplexers—Design Problems

11. Specify all required connections in the 74153 multiplexer to use it for the application in Example 4-2.

12. Use a 74157 to implement Example 4-3.

*13. Modify Example 4-6 to output the complement of M as specified in the function table, using any additional logic gates.

*14. Repeat Problem 13 using no additional logic gates.

15. Six devices, A, B, C, D, E, and F, require multiplexing. Only a 74151 is available.
   a. Design a circuit to multiplex the devices in alphabetical order.
   b. Design a circuit to multiplex the devices in reverse alphabetic order.
   Specify all connections to the 74151, including the unused data inputs.

16. Repeat Problem 15 using a 74150.

17. Repeat Problem 15 using a 74153.

*18. Design a circuit that will transmit a 4-bit binary number generated by a counter to a display device. Between each number generated by the counter the multiplexer must transmit a clear value (0000) to the display device, without altering the count sequence of the counter. Use any MUX ICs that were presented in this chapter along with any logic gates. (*Hint:* Examine the 74157.)

19. Design a quad logic function generator to generate four separate two-variable Boolean functions. (*Hint:* Use 74157 and DIP switches.)

20. Implement a 3-input and 4-input XOR function with a multiplexer.
   a. $(A \oplus B) \oplus C$
   b. $((A \oplus B) \oplus C) \oplus D$

21. Design a programmable comparator that can be set to compare two 2-bit binary numbers. The comparator should have the capability of providing the output for $A > B$, $A = B$, or $A < B$, depending on the operation selected.

*22. Design a parallel-to-serial data converter to convert one byte of data from a parallel format to serial for transmission at a serial transmission rate of 1200 bits per second.

23. Design a controllable data router to transmit 4-bits of data serially to two separate output devices, with the capability of disabling the data from being switched to either or both outputs.

24. Implement the following logic functions with a multiplexer of your choice.
   a. $\overline{A}\,B\,C + A\,D + B\,C\,D + \overline{C}\,D = L$
   b. $(A + B + \overline{D})(C + A)(B + D) = K$
   c. $A\,\overline{B}\,\overline{C} + A\,\overline{B}\,C + \overline{A}\,\overline{B}\,C = M$

4-3 Troubleshooting Multiplexer Circuits—Troubleshooting Problems

25. Describe the results of incorrect addresses input on the select inputs of the 74150.

*26. Derive the function table for the 74150 that would result if all select inputs were left unconnected.

27. Derive the function table for the 74150 that would result if the B select input were left unconnected.

28. Describe the result of incorrect strobe inputs in the 74150.

29. Derive the function table for the 74150 if the strobe input were left unconnected.

30. Derive the function table for the 74153 if the 1G strobe were left unconnected.

31. Determine the output results for the problem in Example 4-7 if the variable R were not inverted in the second multiplexer.

4.4 Demultiplexers—Analysis Problems

*32. Examine the data sheet for the 74154 decoder/demultiplexer.
   a. What is the maximum delay to decode the address, or select inputs?
   b. What is the maximum delay to demultiplex a signal on the strobe input?

33. Examine the data sheets for the 74139 and the 74155 decoders/demultiplexers. What is the primary difference between these two ICs?

34. Derive the output expressions for the outputs of the 74155 operated as a 1:4 DMUX.

35. Derive the output expressions for the outputs of the 74155 operated as a 1:8 DMUX.

36. Derive the output expressions for the outputs of the 74139 operated as a 1:4 DMUX.

37. Derive the output expressions for the outputs of the 74139 operated as a 1:8 DMUX.

38. Define the data input(s), select inputs, enable inputs, and data outputs for the 74154, and describe their operation.

4-5 Application and Design Using Demultiplexers—Design Problems

*39. Design the circuitry needed to demultiplex the data signal of Example 4-2.

40. Design the circuitry to demultiplex the data generated in Problem 4-15.

41. Design the circuitry to multiplex the byte of data transmitted by the MUX circuit of Problem 4-22.

42. Demultiplex the serial data input signal shown below using the 74138 to obtain the parallel output signals for the specified waveforms. Specify all connections and waveforms for the circuit.

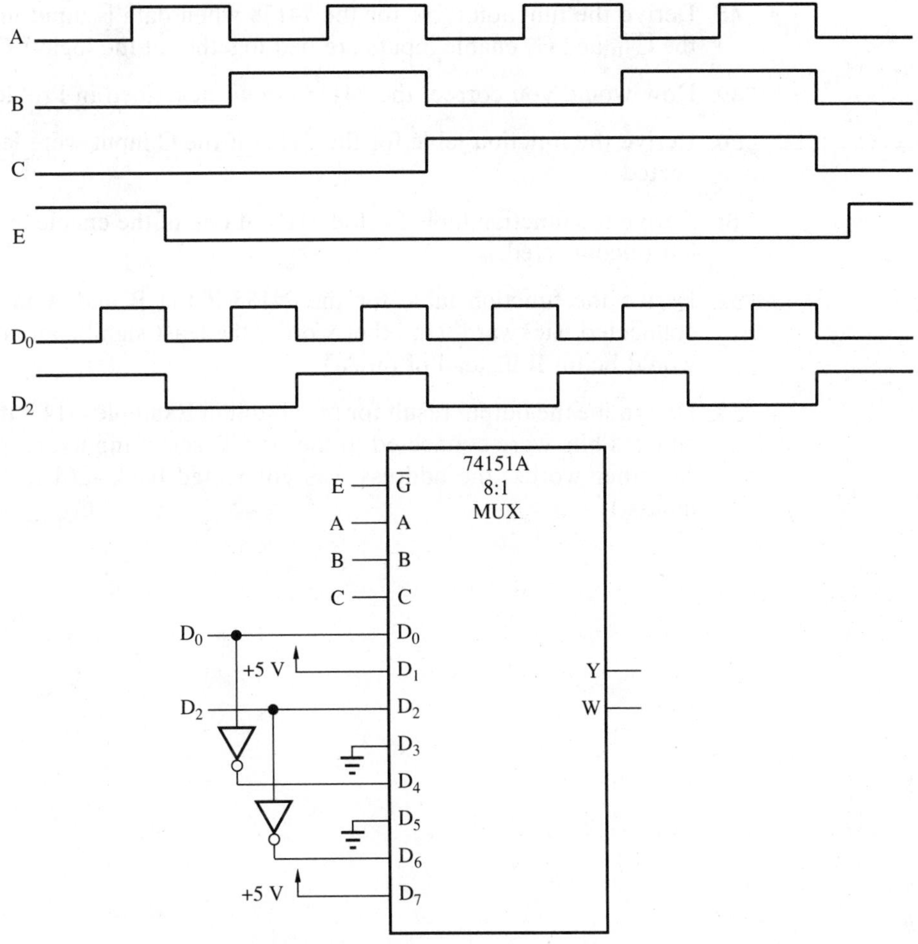

43. Repeat Example 4-14 using a 74155 demultiplexer.

4-6 Troubleshooting Demultiplexer Circuits—Troubleshooting Problems

*44. What is required by the 74156 decoder/demultiplexer in order to output logic-HIGHs?

45. Derive the function table for the 74156 if it replaces a 74155 in a circuit with no other modifications.

46. Describe the result of incorrectly connecting the select inputs in a decoder/demultiplexer IC.

47. Describe the result of incorrectly enabling a decoder/demultiplexer IC.

48. Derive the function table for the 74138 when data is input in $\overline{G_{2A}}$ and the $\overline{G_{2B}}$ and G_1 enable inputs are tied together at the logic-LOW level.

*49. How would you correct the 74138 circuit described in Problem 48.

50. Derive the function table for the 74154 if the C input were left unconnected.

51. Derive the function table for the 74154 if one of the enable inputs were left unconnected.

52. Derive the function table for the 74155 if the B and A inputs were connected backward. (In other words, the least significant address bit would be on B instead of on A.)

53. Determine the output result for the circuit in Example 4-14 if the DCBA address bits were connected to the ABCD select inputs, respectively. (In other words, the address was connected backward to the select inputs.)

Chapter 5

Decoders, Encoders, and Code Converters

Upon completing and mastering the material in this chapter, you should be able to perform the functions in the areas of analysis, application, and design of decoders, encoders, and code converter circuits:

ANALYSIS

1. Identify the primary code conversion applications.
2. Describe the differences among decoders, encoders, and code converters.
3. Analyze the operation of decoder, encoder, and code converter circuits.
4. Describe the difference between active-HIGH and active-LOW decoding.
5. Describe the difference between active-HIGH and active-LOW encoding.
6. Calculate the current drawn by LED displays.
7. Calculate the resistor value required to limit the current to a safe level so that the display is not damaged.
8. Describe priority encoding.

APPLICATION

9. Use decoder circuits for address decoding.
10. Cascade decoder circuits for expanded address decoding.
11. Use display decoder/drivers in applications requiring seven-segment displays.
12. Use multiplexer circuits with a display decoder/driver for display multiplexing applications.
13. Use decoders to generate logic functions.
14. Use encoder circuits for keyboard encoding.

DESIGN

15. Design code conversion circuits using general combinational logic design techniques.
16. Design decoder circuits that require decoder ICs be cascaded together.
17. Design encoder circuits that require encoder ICs be cascaded together.
18. Design display decoding circuits to display any defined character in a seven-segment display.

TROUBLESHOOTING

19. Analyze the cause of incorrect circuit operation.
20. Identify the circuit faults causing incorrect circuit operation.
21. Correct the circuit faults and test the circuit for proper operation.

Code conversion circuitry is a general category of logic circuits used to perform the operation of converting from one code to another. Code conversion is performed by decoder, encoder, and code converter circuits.

Code conversion operations, which occur extensively in digital applications, are required when signals are entered into a system or displayed as the output from a system. For instance, code conversion must take place each time a key is pressed on a computer keyboard, a telephone keypad, a microwave oven keypad, or any similar device where input values are entered into a system for processing. Code conversion is required to operate the electronic read-out displays that show numbers or letters on calculators, clocks, and the multitude of electronic displays. Very complex code conversion is necessary in order for many different computers or digital devices to communicate with each other.

This chapter studies the analysis, application, and design of decoder, encoder, and code converter circuits. The applications examined include keyboard encoding, display decoding, address decoding, memory address selection, function generation, error detection, and display multiplexing.

The basic theory and rationale for several digital codes covered in Chapter 2 should be reviewed as necessary to supplement the applications and design of code converter circuits in this chapter.

5-1 CODE CONVERSION CIRCUITS

Decoders, encoders, and code converter circuits are manufactured as medium scale integration (MSI) integrated circuits (ICs). Three types of MSI circuits are used for code conversion applications: decoders, encoders, and code converters.

Decoders convert a binary number or binary address to a single output bit. Encoders convert a single input bit to a binary number. Code converters convert from one binary code to another, such as converting from binary coded decimal (BCD) to binary.

Table 5-1 lists several of the most common code conversion circuits. The application of these circuits will be emphasized throughout this chapter.

The data sheets for several of these circuits are shown in Figures 5-1 through 5-5. Two important decoder circuits, the 74138 and the 74154, had their data sheets included in Chapter 4 since these circuits were also used as demultiplexers. Refer to Figure 4-24 for the data sheet for the 74138 decoder. Refer to Figure 4-25 for the data sheet for the 74154 decoder.

Section Self-Test

1. What types of circuits perform code conversion operations?
2. Cite the part numbers of three decoder circuits and their function.
3. Cite the part numbers of three code converter circuits and their function.

TABLE 5-1 Code Conversion Circuits

IC	Inputs:Outputs	Function
7442	4:10	BCD to decimal
74138	3:8	Binary to octal
74154	4:16	Binary to hexadecimal
74139	Dual 2:4	Two-bit decoding
74155	Dual 2:4	Two-bit decoding

DISPLAY DECODER/DRIVERS

IC	Inputs:Outputs	Function
7445	4:10	BCD to decimal
7446/7447	4:7-segment	BCD to seven-segment

ENCODERS

IC	Inputs:Outputs	Function
74147	10:4	Decimal to BCD
74148	8:3	Octal to binary

CODE CONVERTERS

IC	Inputs	Function
74184	6-bit	BCD to binary
74184	4-bit	BCD to nine's/ten's complement
74185	6-bit	Binary to BCD
74180	9-bit	Parity generator/checker

ANSWERS (Not necessarily in the same order as the questions)

- 74184 BCD to binary code converter
  74185 Binary to BCD code converter
  74180 Parity generator/checker
- Decoders, encoders, code converters
- 74138 3:8 binary to octal decoder
  74154 4:16 binary to hex decoder
  7447 BCD to seven segment display decoder/driver

SN5442A, SN54LS42, SN74442A, SN74LS42
4-LINE BCD TO 10-LINE DECIMAL DECODERS

MARCH 1974 REVISED MARCH 1988

- **All Outputs Are High for Invalid Input Conditions**
- **Also for Application as**
  4-Line-to-16-Line Decoders
  3-Line-to-8-Line Decoders
- **Diode-Clamped Inputs**

TYPES	TYPICAL POWER DISSIPATION	TYPICAL PROPAGATION DELAYS
'42A	140 mW	17 ns
'LS42	35 mW	17 ns

SN5442A, SN54LS42 . . . J OR W PACKAGE
SN7442A . . . N PACKAGE
SN74LS42 . . . D OR N PACKAGE
(TOP VIEW)

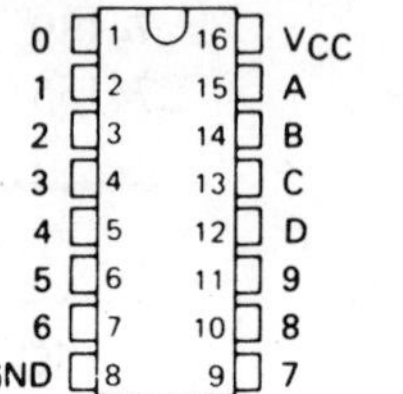

description

These monolithic BCD-to-decimal decoders consist of eight inverters and ten four-input NAND gates. The inverters are connected in pairs to make BCD input data available for decoding by the NAND gates. Full decoding of valid input logic ensures that all outputs remain off for all invalid input conditions.

The '42A and 'LS42 feature inputs and outputs that are compatible for use with most TTL and other saturated low-level logic circuits. DC noise margins are typically one volt.

The SN5442A and SN54LS42 are characterized for operation over the full military temperature range of −55 °C to 125 °C. The SN7442A and SN74LS42 are characterized for operation from 0 °C to 70 °C.

SN54LS42 . . . FK PACKAGE
(TOP VIEW)

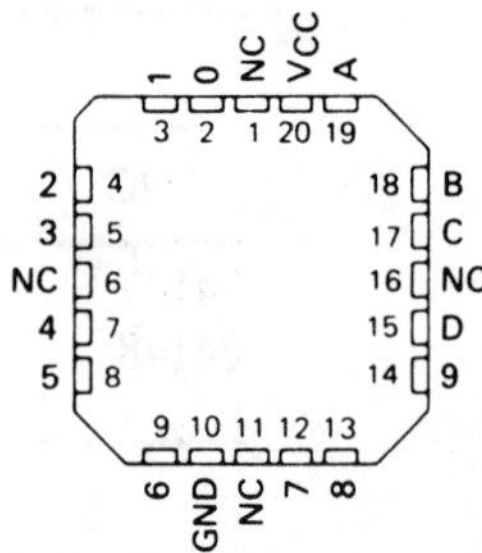

NC - No internal connection

logic symbol†

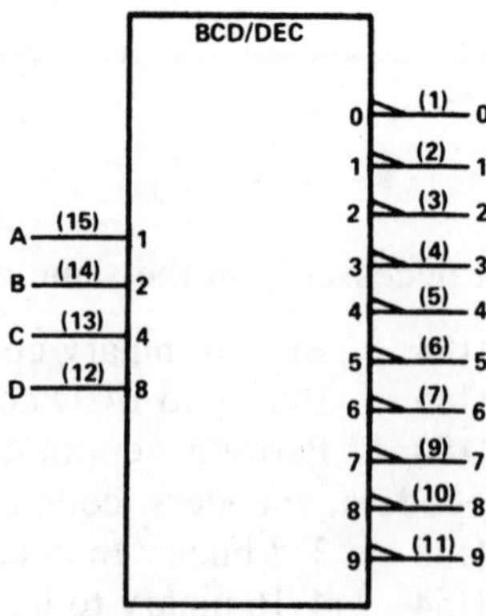

† This symbol is in accordance with ANSI/IEEE Std 91-1984 and IEC Publication 617-12.

FIGURE 5-1 7442 Data Sheets (Courtesy Texas Instruments)

SN5442A, SN54LS42, SN7442A, SN74LS42
4-LINE BCD TO 10-LINE DECIMAL DECODERS

logic diagram (positive logic)

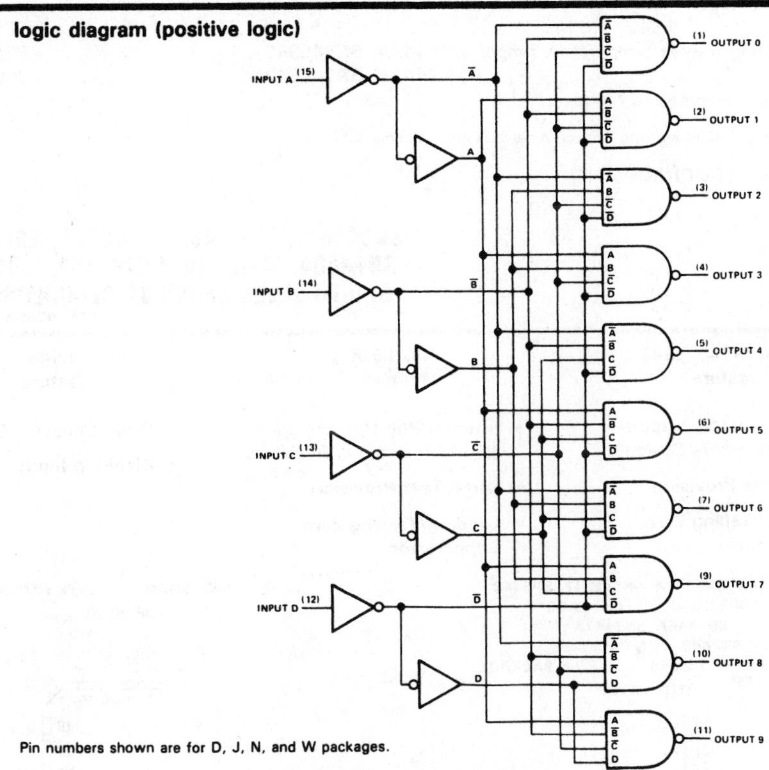

Pin numbers shown are for D, J, N, and W packages.

FUNCTION TABLE

NO.	BCD INPUT				DECIMAL OUTPUT									
	D	C	B	A	0	1	2	3	4	5	6	7	8	9
0	L	L	L	L	L	H	H	H	H	H	H	H	H	H
1	L	L	L	H	H	L	H	H	H	H	H	H	H	H
2	L	L	H	L	H	H	L	H	H	H	H	H	H	H
3	L	L	H	H	H	H	H	L	H	H	H	H	H	H
4	L	H	L	L	H	H	H	H	L	H	H	H	H	H
5	L	H	L	H	H	H	H	H	H	L	H	H	H	H
6	L	H	H	L	H	H	H	H	H	H	L	H	H	H
7	L	H	H	H	H	H	H	H	H	H	H	L	H	H
8	H	L	L	L	H	H	H	H	H	H	H	H	L	H
9	H	L	L	H	H	H	H	H	H	H	H	H	H	L
INVALID	H	L	H	L	H	H	H	H	H	H	H	H	H	H
	H	L	H	H	H	H	H	H	H	H	H	H	H	H
	H	H	L	L	H	H	H	H	H	H	H	H	H	H
	H	H	L	H	H	H	H	H	H	H	H	H	H	H
	H	H	H	L	H	H	H	H	H	H	H	H	H	H
	H	H	H	H	H	H	H	H	H	H	H	H	H	H

H = high level, L = low level

FIGURE 5-1 (*continued*)

absolute maximum ratings over operating free-air temperature range (unless otherwise noted)

Supply voltage, V_{CC} (see Note 1)		7 V
Input voltage: '42A		5.5 V
'LS42		7 V
Operating free-air temperature range:	SN5442A, SN54LS42	−55°C to 125°C
	SN7442A, SN74LS42	0°C to 70°C
Storage temperature range		−65°C to 150°C

NOTE 1: Voltage values are with respect to network ground terminal.

FIGURE 5-1 (*continued*)

SN5446A, '47A, '48, SN54LS47, 'LS48, 'LS49, SN7446A, '47A, '48, SN74LS47, 'LS48, 'LS49 BCD-TO-SEVEN-SEGMENT DECODERS/DRIVERS

MARCH 1974—REVISED MARCH 1988

'46A, '47A, 'LS47 feature

- **Open-Collector Outputs Drive Indicators Directly**
- **Lamp-Test Provision**
- **Leading/Trailing Zero Suppression**

'48, 'LS48 feature

- **Internal Pull-Ups Eliminate Need for External Resistors**
- **Lamp-Test Provision**
- **Leading/Trailing Zero Suppression**

'LS49 feature

- **Open-Collector Outputs**
- **Blanking Input**

SN5446A, SN5447A, SN54LS47, SN5448, SN54LS48 . . . J PACKAGE
SN7446A, SN7447A, SN7448 . . . N PACKAGE
SN74LS47, SN74LS48 . . . D OR N PACKAGE
(TOP VIEW)

Pin	Name	Pin	Name
1	B	16	VCC
2	C	15	f
3	$\overline{LT}$	14	g
4	$\overline{BI}/\overline{RBO}$	13	a
5	$\overline{RBI}$	12	b
6	D	11	c
7	A	10	d
8	GND	9	e

SN54LS47, SN54LS48 . . . FK PACKAGE
(TOP VIEW)

Pin	Name	Pin	Name
3	C	2	B
1	NC	20	VCC
19	f	4	$\overline{LT}$
5	$\overline{BI}/\overline{RBO}$	6	NC
7	$\overline{RBI}$	8	D
9	A	10	GND
11	NC	12	e
13	d	14	c
15	b	16	NC
17	a	18	g

SN54LS49 . . . J OR W PACKAGE
SN74LS49 . . . D OR N PACKAGE
(TOP VIEW)

Pin	Name	Pin	Name
1	B	14	VCC
2	C	13	f
3	$\overline{BI}$	12	g
4	D	11	a
5	A	10	b
6	e	9	c
7	GND	8	d

SN54LS49 . . . FK PACKAGE
(TOP VIEW)

Pin	Name	Pin	Name
3	C	2	B
1	NC	20	VCC
19	f	4	$\overline{BI}$
5	NC	6	D
7	NC	8	A
9	e	10	GND
11	NC	12	d
13	c	14	b
15	NC	16	a
17	NC	18	g

NC – No internal connection

FIGURE 5-2 (a) 7446, 7447, 7448, 7449 Data Sheets; (b) 7446, 7447, 7448, 7449 Data Sheets (Courtesy Texas Instruments)

SN5446A, '47A, '48, SN54LS47, 'LS48, 'LS49, SN7446A, '47A, '48, SN74LS47, 'LS48, 'LS49 BCD-TO-SEVEN-SEGMENT DECODERS/DRIVERS

- **All Circuit Types Feature Lamp Intensity Modulation Capability**

TYPE	DRIVER OUTPUTS				TYPICAL POWER DISSIPATION	PACKAGES
	ACTIVE LEVEL	OUTPUT CONFIGURATION	SINK CURRENT	MAX VOLTAGE		
SN5446A	low	open-collector	40 mA	30 V	320 mW	J, W
SN5447A	low	open-collector	40 mA	15 V	320 mW	J, W
SN5448	high	2-kΩ pull-up	6.4 mA	5.5 V	265 mW	J,W
SN54LS47	low	open-collector	12 mA	15 V	35 mW	J, W
SN54LS48	high	2-kΩ pull-up	2 mA	5.5 V	125 mW	J, W
SN54LS49	high	open-collector	4 mA	5.5 V	40 mW	J, W
SN7446A	low	open-collector	40 mA	30 V	320 mW	J, N
SN7447A	low	open-collector	40 mA	15 V	320 mW	J, N
SN7448	high	2-kΩ pull-up	6.4 mA	5.5 V	265 mW	J, N
SN74LS47	low	open-collector	24 mA	15 V	35 mW	J, N
SN74LS48	high	2-kΩ pull-up	6 mA	5.5 V	125 mW	J, N
SN74LS49	high	open-collector	8 mA	5.5 V	40 mW	J, N

logic symbols†

†These symbols are in accordance with ANSI/IEEE Std 91-1984 and IEC Publication 617-12.
Pin numbers shown are for D, J, N, and W packages.

FIGURE 5-2 (*continued*)

SN5446A, '47A, '48, SN54LS47, 'LS48, 'LS49, SN7446A, '47A, '48, SN74LS47, 'LS48, 'LS49 BCD-TO-SEVEN-SEGMENT DECODERS/DRIVERS

description

The '46A, '47A, and 'LS47 feature active-low outputs designed for driving common-anode LEDs or incandescent indicators directly. The '48, 'LS48, and 'LS49 feature active-high outputs for driving lamp buffers or common-cathode LEDs. All of the circuits except 'LS49 have full ripple-blanking input/output controls and a lamp test input. The 'LS49 circuit incorporates a direct blanking input. Segment identification and resultant displays are shown below. Display patterns for BCD input counts above 9 are unique symbols to authenticate input conditions.

The '46A, '47A, '48, 'LS47, and 'LS48 circuits incorporate automatic leading and/or trailing-edge zero-blanking control ($\overline{\text{RBI}}$ and $\overline{\text{RBO}}$). Lamp test ($\overline{\text{LT}}$) of these types may be performed at any time when the $\overline{\text{BI}}/\overline{\text{RBO}}$ node is at a high level. All types (including the '49 and 'LS49) contain an overriding blanking input ($\overline{\text{BI}}$), which can be used to control the lamp intensity by pulsing or to inhibit the outputs. Inputs and outputs are entirely compatible for use with TTL logic outputs.

The SN54246/SN74246 and '247 and the SN54LS247/SN74LS247 and 'LS248 compose the 6 and the 9 with tails and were designed to offer the designer a choice between two indicator fonts.

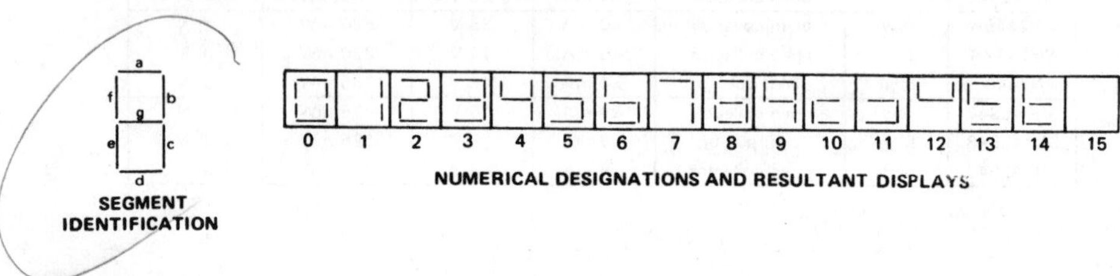

SEGMENT IDENTIFICATION

NUMERICAL DESIGNATIONS AND RESULTANT DISPLAYS

'46A, '47A, 'LS47 FUNCTION TABLE (T1)

DECIMAL OR FUNCTION	INPUTS						$\overline{\text{BI}}/\overline{\text{RBO}}$†	OUTPUTS							NOTE
	$\overline{\text{LT}}$	$\overline{\text{RBI}}$	D	C	B	A		a	b	c	d	e	f	g	
0	H	H	L	L	L	L	H	ON	ON	ON	ON	ON	ON	OFF	1
1	H	X	L	L	L	H	H	OFF	ON	ON	OFF	OFF	OFF	OFF	
2	H	X	L	L	H	L	H	ON	ON	OFF	ON	ON	OFF	ON	
3	H	X	L	L	H	H	H	ON	ON	ON	ON	OFF	OFF	ON	
4	H	X	L	H	L	L	H	OFF	ON	ON	OFF	OFF	ON	ON	
5	H	X	L	H	L	H	H	ON	OFF	ON	ON	OFF	ON	ON	
6	H	X	L	H	H	L	H	OFF	OFF	ON	ON	ON	ON	ON	
7	H	X	L	H	H	H	H	ON	ON	ON	OFF	OFF	OFF	OFF	
8	H	X	H	L	L	L	H	ON	ON	ON	ON	ON	ON	ON	
9	H	X	H	L	L	H	H	ON	ON	ON	OFF	OFF	ON	ON	
10	H	X	H	L	H	L	H	OFF	OFF	OFF	ON	ON	OFF	ON	
11	H	X	H	L	H	H	H	OFF	OFF	ON	ON	OFF	OFF	ON	
12	H	X	H	H	L	L	H	OFF	ON	OFF	OFF	OFF	ON	ON	
13	H	X	H	H	L	H	H	ON	OFF	OFF	ON	OFF	ON	ON	
14	H	X	H	H	H	L	H	OFF	OFF	OFF	ON	ON	ON	ON	
15	H	X	H	H	H	H	H	OFF	OFF	OFF	OFF	OFF	OFF	OFF	
BI	X	X	X	X	X	X	L	OFF	OFF	OFF	OFF	OFF	OFF	OFF	2
RBI	H	L	L	L	L	L	L	OFF	OFF	OFF	OFF	OFF	OFF	OFF	3
LT	L	X	X	X	X	X	H	ON	ON	ON	ON	ON	ON	ON	4

H = high level, L = low level, X = irrelevant

NOTES: 1. The blanking input ($\overline{\text{BI}}$) must be open or held at a high logic level when output functions 0 through 15 are desired. The ripple-blanking input ($\overline{\text{RBI}}$) must be open or high if blanking of a decimal zero is not desired.

2. When a low logic level is applied directly to the blanking input ($\overline{\text{BI}}$), all segment outputs are off regardless of the level of any other input.

3. When ripple-blanking input ($\overline{\text{RBI}}$) and inputs A, B, C, and D are at a low level with the lamp test input high, all segment outputs go off and the ripple-blanking output ($\overline{\text{RBO}}$) goes to a low level (response condition).

4. When the blanking input/ripple blanking output ($\overline{\text{BI}}/\overline{\text{RBO}}$) is open or held high and a low is applied to the lamp-test input, all segment outputs are on.

† $\overline{\text{BI}}/\overline{\text{RBO}}$ is wire AND logic serving as blanking input ($\overline{\text{BI}}$) and/or ripple-blanking output ($\overline{\text{RBO}}$).

FIGURE 5-2 ***(continued)***

SN54147, SN54148, SN54LS147, SN54LS148, SN74147, SN74148 (TIM9907), SN74LS147, SN74LS148 10-LINE TO 4-LINE AND 8-LINE TO 3-LINE PRIORITY ENCODERS

OCTOBER 1976 – REVISED MARCH 1988

'147, 'LS147

- **Encodes 10-Line Decimal to 4-Line BCD**
- **Applications Include:**

  Keyboard Encoding
  Range Selection: '148, 'LS148

- **Encodes 8 Data Lines to 3-Line Binary (Octal)**
- **Applications Include:**

  N-Bit Encoding
  Code Converters and Generators

SN54147, SN54LS147, SN54148, SN54LS148 . . . J OR W PACKAGE
SN74147, SN74148 . . . N PACKAGE
SN74LS147, SN74LS148 . . . D OR N PACKAGE
(TOP VIEW)

'147, 'LS147

Pin	Name	Pin	Name
1	4	16	VCC
2	5	15	NC
3	6	14	D
4	7	13	3
5	8	12	2
6	C	11	1
7	B	10	9
8	GND	9	A

'148, 'LS148

Pin	Name	Pin	Name
1	4	16	VCC
2	5	15	EO
3	6	14	GS
4	7	13	3
5	EI	12	2
6	A2	11	1
7	A1	10	0
8	GND	9	A0

TYPE	TYPICAL DATA DELAY	TYPICAL POWER DISSIPATION
'147	10 ns	225 mW
'148	10 ns	190 mW
'LS147	15 ns	60 mW
'LS148	15 ns	60 mW

SN54LS147, SN54LS148 . . . FK PACKAGE
(TOP VIEW)

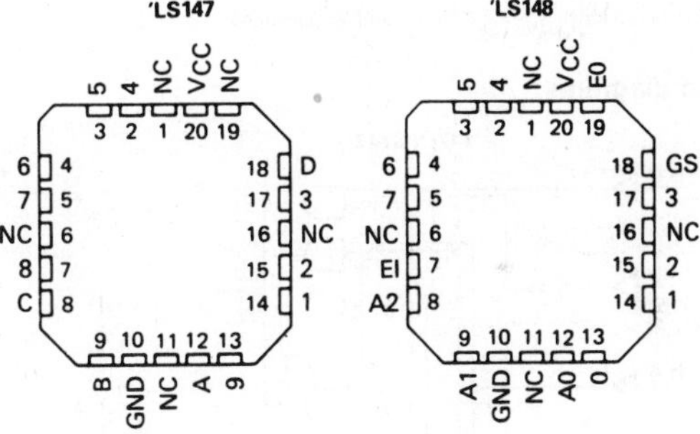

NC - No internal connection

description

These TTL encoders feature priority decoding of the inputs to ensure that only the highest-order data line is encoded. The '147 and 'LS147 encode nine data lines to four-line (8-4-2-1) BCD. The implied decimal zero condition requires no input condition as zero is encoded when all nine data lines are at a high logic level. The '148 and 'LS148 encode eight data lines to three-line (4-2-1) binary (octal). Cascading circuitry (enable input EI and enable output EO) has been provided to allow octal expansion without the need for external circuitry. For all types, data inputs and outputs are active at the low logic level. All inputs are buffered to represent one normalized Series 54/74 or 54LS/74LS load, respectively.

'147, 'LS147
FUNCTION TABLE

INPUTS									OUTPUTS			
1	2	3	4	5	6	7	8	9	D	C	B	A
H	H	H	H	H	H	H	H	H	H	H	H	H
X	X	X	X	X	X	X	X	L	L	H	H	L
X	X	X	X	X	X	X	L	H	L	H	H	H
X	X	X	X	X	X	L	H	H	H	L	L	L
X	X	X	X	X	L	H	H	H	H	L	L	H
X	X	X	X	L	H	H	H	H	H	L	H	L
X	X	X	L	H	H	H	H	H	H	L	H	H
X	X	L	H	H	H	H	H	H	H	H	L	L
X	L	H	H	H	H	H	H	H	H	H	L	H
L	H	H	H	H	H	H	H	H	H	H	H	L

H = high logic level, L = low logic level, X = irrelevant

'148, 'LS148
FUNCTION TABLE

INPUTS									OUTPUTS				
EI	0	1	2	3	4	5	6	7	A2	A1	A0	GS	EO
H	X	X	X	X	X	X	X	X	H	H	H	H	H
L	H	H	H	H	H	H	H	H	H	H	H	H	L
L	X	X	X	X	X	X	X	L	L	L	L	L	H
L	X	X	X	X	X	X	L	H	L	L	H	L	H
L	X	X	X	X	X	L	H	H	L	H	L	L	H
L	X	X	X	X	L	H	H	H	L	H	H	L	H
L	X	X	X	L	H	H	H	H	H	L	L	L	H
L	X	X	L	H	H	H	H	H	H	L	H	L	H
L	X	L	H	H	H	H	H	H	H	H	L	L	H
L	L	H	H	H	H	H	H	H	H	H	H	L	H

FIGURE 5-3 74147, 74148 Data Sheets (Courtesy Texas Instruments)

SN54147, SN54148, SN54LS147, SN54LS148, SN74147, SN74148 (TIM9907), SN74LS147, SN74LS148 10-LINE TO 4-LINE AND 8-LINE TO 3-LINE PRIORITY ENCODERS

logic symbols†

'147, 'LS147

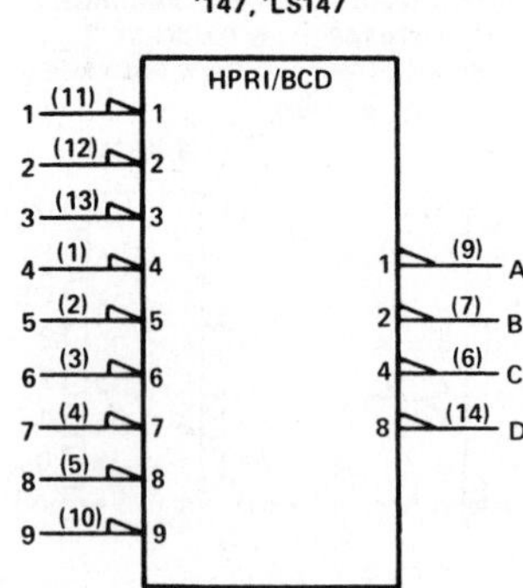

'148, 'LS148

HPRI/BIN
0 (10) 0/Z10 10
1 (11) 1/Z11 11
2 (12) 2/Z12 12
3 (13) 3/Z13 13
4 (1) 4/Z14 14
5 (2) 5/Z15 15
6 (3) 6/Z16 16
7 (4) 7/Z17 17
≥1
18 (15) EO
α (14) GS
1α (9) A0
2α (7) A1
4α (6) A2
V18
EI (5) ENα

†These symbols are in accordance with ANSI/IEEE Std. 91-1984 and IEC Publication 617-12.
Pin numbers shown are for D, J, N, and W packages.

logic diagrams

'147, 'LS147

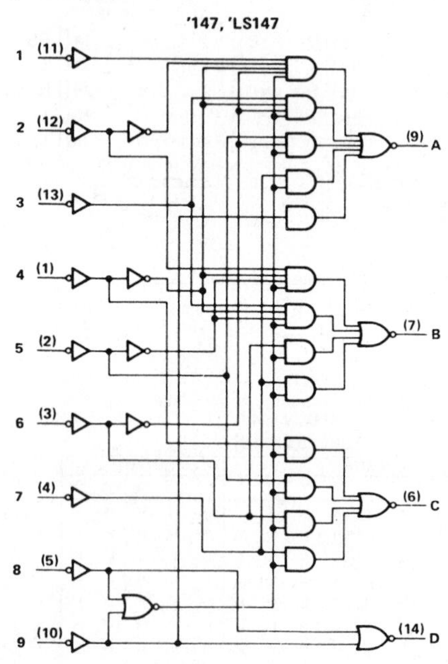

'148, 'LS148

0 (10)
1 (11)
2 (12)
3 (13)
4 (1)
5 (2)
6 (3)
7 (4)
EI (5)
(15) EO
(14) GS
(9) A0
(7) A1
(6) A2

Pin numbers shown are for D, J, N, and W packages.

FIGURE 5-3 (*continued*)

TYPES SN54184, SN54185A, SN74184, SN74185A BCD-TO-BINARY AND BINARY-TO-BCD CONVERTERS

FEBRUARY 1971 – REVISED DECEMBER 1972

SN54184, SN54185A . . . J OR W PACKAGE
SN74184, SN74185A . . . J OR N PACKAGE
(TOP VIEW)

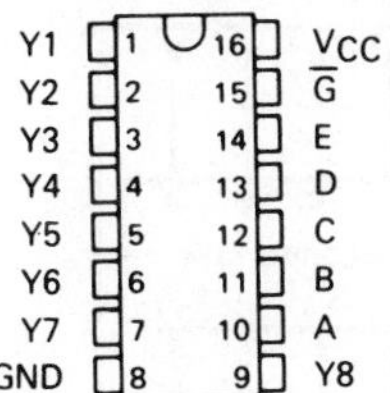

description

These monolithic converters are derived from the custom MSI 256-bit read-only memories SN5488 and SN7488. Emitter connections are made to provide direct read-out of converted codes at outputs Y8 through Y1 as shown in the function tables. These converters demonstrate the versatility of a read-only memory in that an unlimited number of reference tables or conversion tables may be built into a system using economical, customized read-only memories. Both of these converters comprehend that the least significant bits (LSB) of the binary and BCD codes are logically equal, and in each case the LSB bypasses the converter as illustrated in the typical applications. This means that a 6-bit converter is produced in each case. Both devices are cascadable to N bits.

TABLE I
SN54184, SN74184
PACKAGE COUNT AND DELAY TIMES
FOR BCD-TO-BINARY CONVERSION

INPUT	PACKAGES	TOTAL DELAY TIMES (ns)	
(DECADES)	REQUIRED	TYP	MAX
2	2	56	80
3	6	140	200
4	11	196	280
5	19	280	400
6	28	364	520

An overriding enable input is provided on each converter which, when taken high, inhibits the function, causing all outputs to go high. For this reason, and to minimize power consumption, unused outputs Y7 and Y8 of the '185A and all "don't care" conditions of the '184 are programmed high. The outputs are of the open-collector type.

The SN54184 and SN54185A are characterized for operation over the full military temperature range of −55°C to 125°C; the SN74184 and SN74185A are characterized for operation from 0°C to 70°C.

SN54184 and SN74184 BCD-to-binary converters

The 6-bit BCD-to-binary function of the SN54184 and SN74184 is analogous to the algorithm:

a. Shift BCD number right one bit and examine each decade. Subtract three from each 4-bit decade containing a binary value greater than seven.

b. Shift right, examine, and correct after each shift until the least significant decade contains a number smaller than eight and all other converted decades contain zeros.

In addition to BCD-to-binary conversion, the SN54184 and SN74184 are programmed to generate BCD 9's complement or BCD 10's complement. Again, in each case, one bit of the complement code is logically equal to one of the BCD bits; therefore, these complements can be produced on three lines. As outputs Y6, Y7, and Y8 are not required in the BCD-to-binary conversion, they are utilized to provide these complement codes as specified in the function table (following page, right) when the devices are connected as shown above the function table.

FIGURE 5-4 (a) 74184, 74185 Data Sheets (Courtesy Texas Instruments)

TYPES SN54184, SN74184
BCD-TO-BINARY AND BINARY-TO-BCD CONVERTERS

SN54184 and SN74184 BCD-to-binary converters (continued)

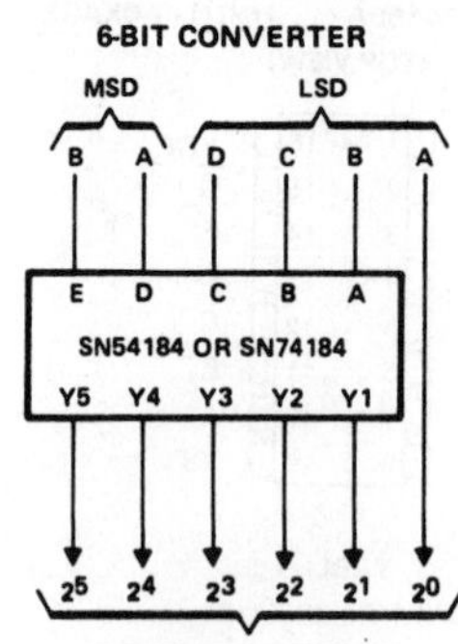

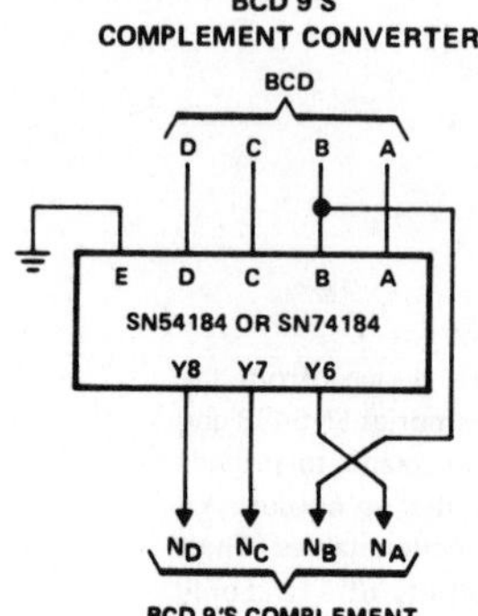

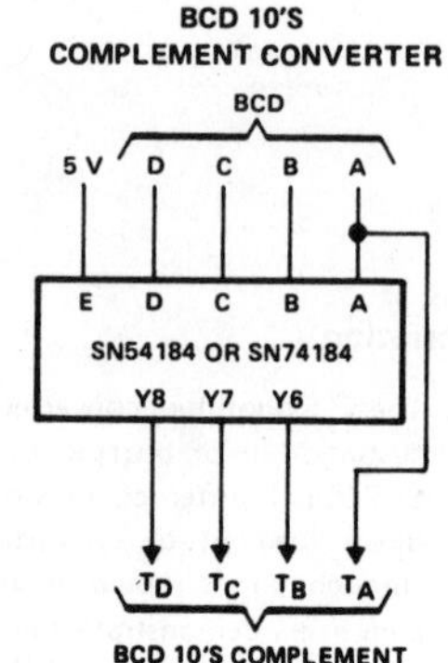

FUNCTION TABLE
BCD-TO-BINARY CONVERTER

BCD WORDS	INPUTS (See Note A)						OUTPUTS (See Note B)				
	E	D	C	B	A	$\overline{G}$	Y5	Y4	Y3	Y2	Y1
0-1	L	L	L	L	L	L	L	L	L	L	L
2-3	L	L	L	L	H	L	L	L	L	L	H
4-5	L	L	L	H	L	L	L	L	L	H	L
6-7	L	L	L	H	H	L	L	L	L	H	H
8-9	L	L	H	L	L	L	L	L	H	L	L
10-11	L	H	L	L	L	L	L	L	H	L	H
12-13	L	H	L	L	H	L	L	L	H	H	L
14-15	L	H	L	H	L	L	L	L	H	H	H
16-17	L	H	L	H	H	L	L	H	L	L	L
18-19	L	H	H	L	L	L	L	H	L	L	H
20-21	H	L	L	L	L	L	L	H	L	H	L
22-23	H	L	L	L	H	L	L	H	L	H	H
24-25	H	L	L	H	L	L	L	H	H	L	L
26-27	H	L	L	H	H	L	L	H	H	L	H
28-29	H	L	H	L	L	L	L	H	H	H	L
30-31	H	H	L	L	L	L	L	H	H	H	H
32-33	H	H	L	L	H	L	H	L	L	L	L
34-35	H	H	L	H	L	L	H	L	L	L	H
36-37	H	H	L	H	H	L	H	L	L	H	L
38-39	H	H	H	L	L	L	H	L	L	H	H
ANY	X	X	X	X	X	H	H	H	H	H	H

H = high level, L = low level, X = irrelevant

NOTES: A. Input conditions other than those shown produce highs at outputs Y1 through Y5.

B. Outputs Y6, Y7, and Y8 are not used for BCD-to-binary conversion.

FUNCTION TABLE
BCD 9'S OR BCD 10'S COMPLEMENT CONVERTER

BCD WORD	INPUTS (See Note C)						OUTPUTS (See Note D)		
	E†	D	C	B	A	$\overline{G}$	Y8	Y7	Y6
0	L	L	L	L	L	L	H	L	H
1	L	L	L	L	H	L	H	L	L
2	L	L	L	H	L	L	L	H	H
3	L	L	L	H	H	L	L	H	L
4	L	L	H	L	L	L	L	H	H
5	L	L	H	L	H	L	L	H	L
6	L	L	H	H	L	L	L	L	H
7	L	L	H	H	H	L	L	L	L
8	L	H	L	L	L	L	L	L	H
9	L	H	L	L	H	L	L	L	L
0	H	L	L	L	L	L	L	L	L
1	H	L	L	L	H	L	H	L	L
2	H	L	L	H	L	L	H	L	L
3	H	L	L	H	H	L	L	H	H
4	H	L	H	L	L	L	L	H	H
5	H	L	H	L	H	L	L	H	L
6	H	L	H	H	L	L	L	H	L
7	H	L	H	H	H	L	L	L	H
8	H	H	L	L	L	L	L	L	H
9	H	H	L	L	H	L	L	L	L
ANY	X	X	X	X	X	H	H	H	H

H = high level, L = low level, X = irrelevant

NOTES: C. Input conditions other than those shown produce highs at outputs Y6, Y7, and Y8.

D. Outputs Y1 through Y5 are not used for BCD 9's or BCD 10's complement conversion.

†When these devices are used as complement converters, input E is used as a mode control. With this input low, the BCD 9's complement is generated; when it is high, the BCD 10's complement is generated.

FIGURE 5-4 ***(continued)***

TYPES SN54185A, SN74185A
BCD-TO-BINARY AND BINARY-TO-BCD CONVERTERS

SN54185A and SN74185A binary-to-BCD converters

The function performed by these 6-bit binary-to-BCD converters is analogous to the algorithm:

a. Examine the three most significant bits. If the sum is greater than four, add three and shift left one bit.
b. Examine each BCD decade. If the sum is greater than four, add three and shift left one bit.
c. Repeat step b until the least-significant binary bit is in the least-significant BCD location.

6-BIT CONVERTER

6-BIT BINARY INPUT

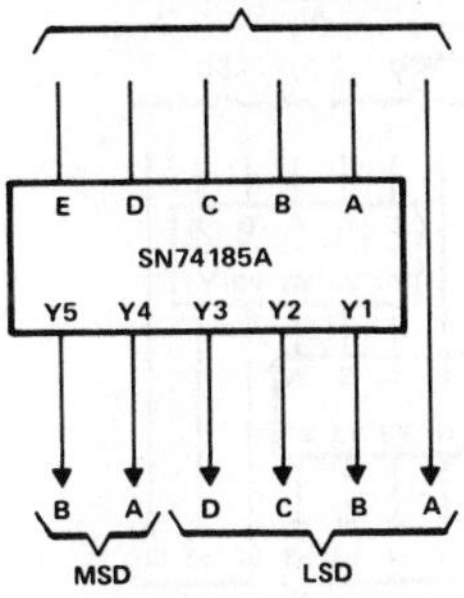

E D C B A
SN74185A
Y5 Y4 Y3 Y2 Y1

B A D C B A
MSD LSD

6-BIT BCD OUTPUT

TABLE II
SN54185A, SN74185A
PACKAGE COUNT AND DELAY TIMES FOR BINARY-TO-BCD CONVERSION

INPUT (BITS)	PACKAGES REQUIRED	TOTAL DELAY TIME (ns) TYP	MAX
4 to 6	1	25	40
7 or 8	3	50	80
9	4	75	120
10	6	100	160
11	7	125	200
12	8	125	200
13	10	150	240
14	12	175	280
15	14	175	280
16	16	200	320
17	19	225	360
18	21	225	360
19	24	250	400
20	27	275	440

FUNCTION TABLE

BINARY WORDS	INPUTS BINARY SELECT E	D	C	B	A	ENABLE $\overline{G}$	OUTPUTS Y8	Y7	Y6	Y5	Y4	Y3	Y2	Y1
0 - 1	L	L	L	L	L	L	H	H	L	L	L	L	L	L
2 - 3	L	L	L	L	H	L	H	H	L	L	L	L	L	H
4 - 5	L	L	L	H	L	L	H	H	L	L	L	L	H	L
6 - 7	L	L	L	H	H	L	H	H	L	L	L	L	H	H
8 - 9	L	L	H	L	L	L	H	H	L	L	L	H	L	L
10 - 11	L	L	H	L	H	L	H	H	L	L	H	L	L	L
12 - 13	L	L	H	H	L	L	H	H	L	L	H	L	L	H
14 - 15	L	L	H	H	H	L	H	H	L	L	H	L	H	L
16 - 17	L	H	L	L	L	L	H	H	L	L	H	L	H	H
18 - 19	L	H	L	L	H	L	H	H	L	L	H	H	L	L
20 - 21	L	H	L	H	L	L	H	H	L	H	L	L	L	L
22 - 23	L	H	L	H	H	L	H	H	L	H	L	L	L	H
24 - 25	L	H	H	L	L	L	H	H	L	H	L	L	H	L
26 - 27	L	H	H	L	H	L	H	H	L	H	L	L	H	H
28 - 29	L	H	H	H	L	L	H	H	L	H	L	H	L	L
30 - 31	L	H	H	H	H	L	H	H	L	H	H	L	L	L
32 - 33	H	L	L	L	L	L	H	H	L	H	H	L	L	H
34 - 35	H	L	L	L	H	L	H	H	L	H	H	L	H	L
36 - 37	H	L	L	H	L	L	H	H	L	H	H	L	H	H
38 - 39	H	L	L	H	H	L	H	H	L	H	H	H	L	L
40 - 41	H	L	H	L	L	L	H	H	H	L	L	L	L	L
42 - 43	H	L	H	L	H	L	H	H	H	L	L	L	L	H
44 - 45	H	L	H	H	L	L	H	H	H	L	L	L	H	L
46 - 47	H	L	H	H	H	L	H	H	H	L	L	L	H	H
48 - 49	H	H	L	L	L	L	H	H	H	L	L	H	L	L
50 - 51	H	H	L	L	H	L	H	H	H	L	H	L	L	L
52 - 53	H	H	L	H	L	L	H	H	H	L	H	L	L	H
54 - 55	H	H	L	H	H	L	H	H	H	L	H	L	H	L
56 - 57	H	H	H	L	L	L	H	H	H	L	H	L	H	H
58 - 59	H	H	H	L	H	L	H	H	H	L	H	H	L	L
60 - 61	H	H	H	H	L	L	H	H	H	H	L	L	L	L
62 - 63	H	H	H	H	H	L	H	H	H	H	L	L	L	H
ALL	X	X	X	X	X	H	H	H	H	H	H	H	H	H

H = high level, L = low level, X = irrelevant

FIGURE 5-4 ***(continued)***

TYPES SN54184, SN74184
BCD-TO-BINARY CONVERTERS

TYPICAL APPLICATION DATA
SN54184, SN74184

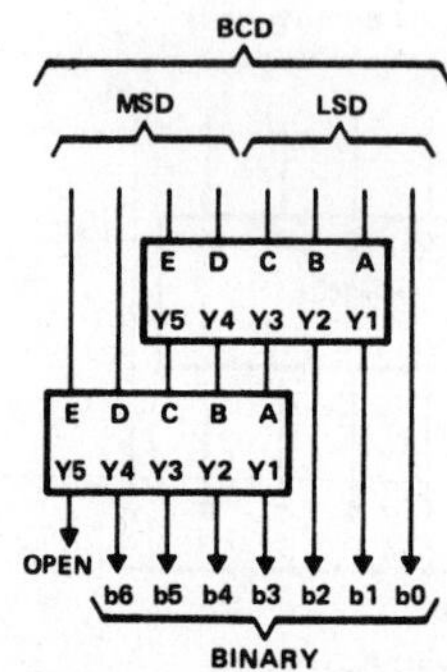

FIGURE 2—BCD-TO-BINARY CONVERTER FOR TWO BCD DECADES

MSD—most significant decade
LSD—least significant decade
Each rectangle represents an SN54184 or SN74184

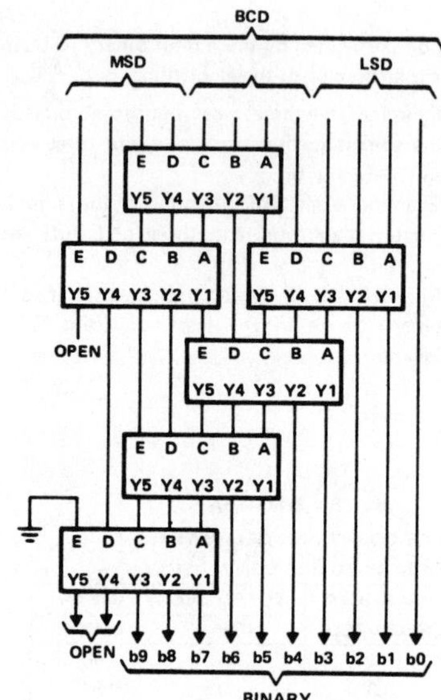

FIGURE 3—BCD-TO-BINARY CONVERTER FOR THREE BCD DECADES

FIGURE 5-4 *(continued)*

TYPICAL APPLICATION DATA
SN54184, SN74184

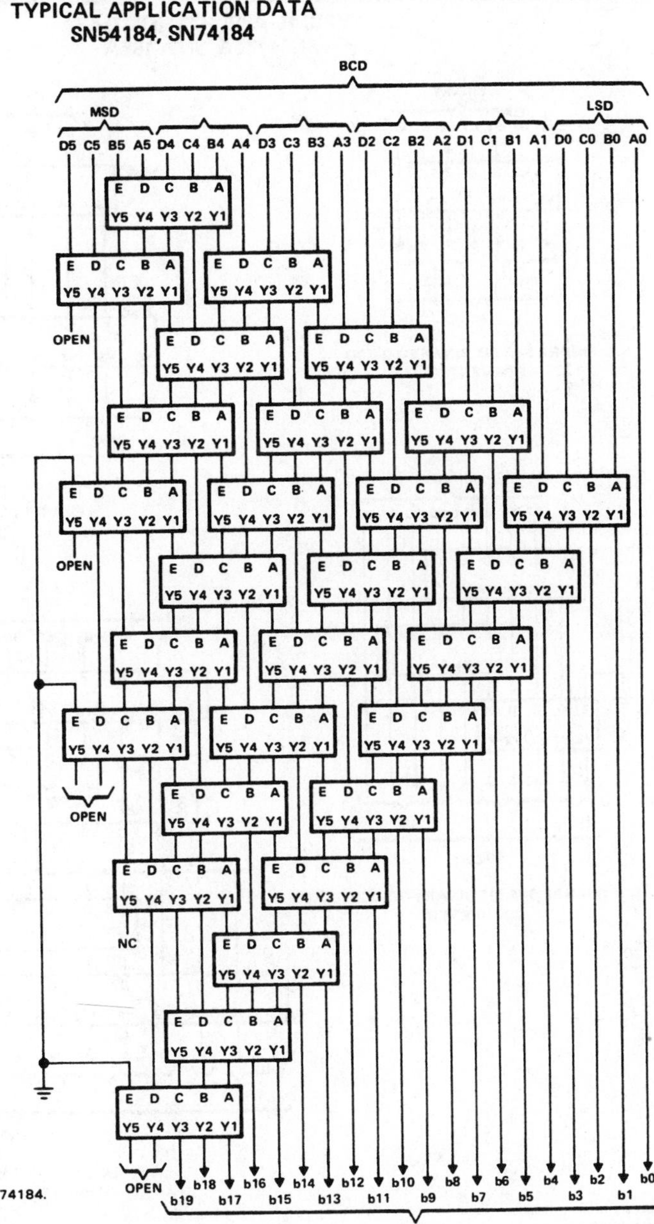

MSD—most significant decade
LSD—least significant decade
Each rectangle represents and SN54184 or SN74184.

FIGURE 4—BCD-TO-BINARY CONVERTER FOR SIX BCD DECADES

FIGURE 5-4 *(continued)*

TYPES SN54185A, SN74185A BINARY-TO-BCD CONVERTERS

TYPICAL APPLICATION DATA SN54185A, SN74185A

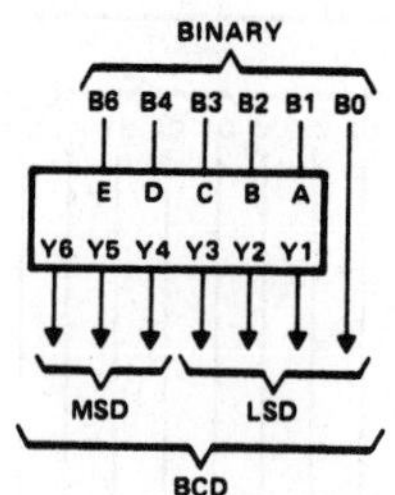

FIGURE 5—6-BIT BINARY-TO-BCD CONVERTER

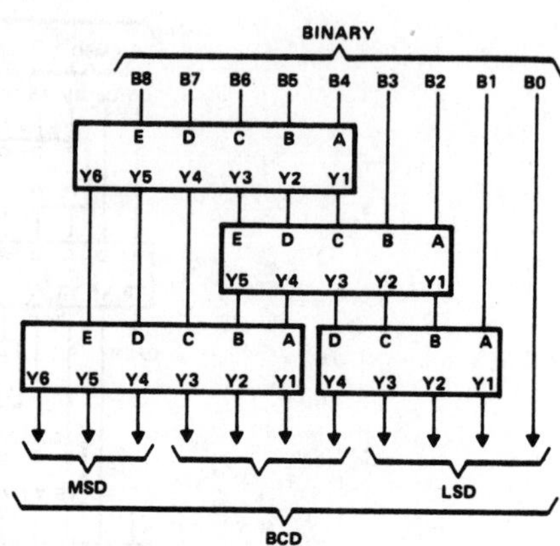

FIGURE 7—9-BIT BINARY-TO-BCD CONVERTER

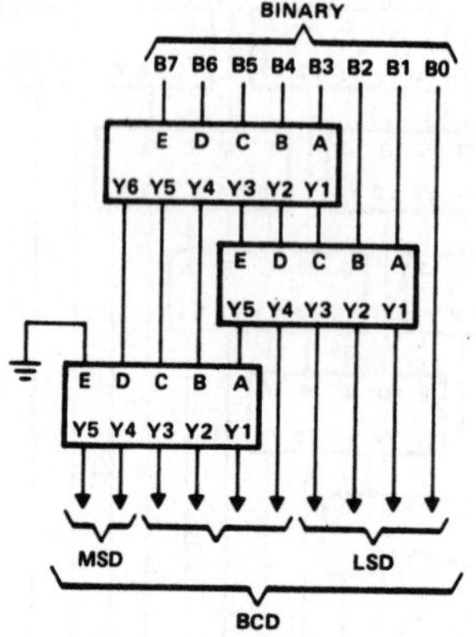

FIGURE 6—8-BIT BINARY-TO-BCD CONVERTER

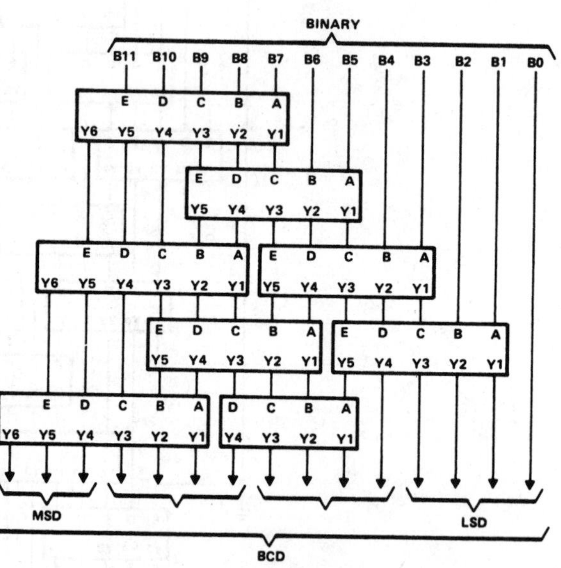

FIGURE 8—12-BIT BINARY-TO-BCD CONVERTER (SEE NOTE B)

MSD—Most significant decade
LSD—Least significant decade
NOTES: A. Each rectangle represents an SN54185A or an SN74185A.
B. All unused E inputs are grounded.

FIGURE 5-4 *(continued)*

TYPES SN54185A, SN74185A BINARY-TO-BCD CONVERTERS

TYPICAL APPLICATION DATA SN54185A, SN74185A

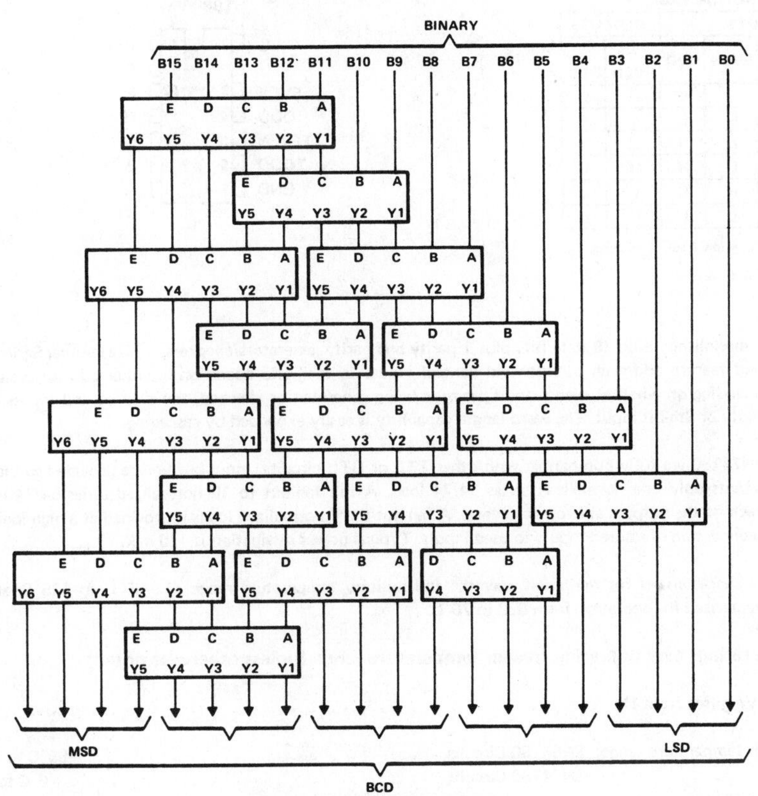

FIGURE 9—16 BIT BINARY-TO-BCD CONVERTER (SEE NOTE B)

MSD—most significant decade
LSD—least significant decade
NOTES: A. Each rectangle represents an SN54185A or SN74185A.
B. All unused E inputs are grounded.

FIGURE 5-4 ***(continued)***

SN54180, SN74180
9-BIT ODD/EVEN PARITY GENERATORS/CHECKERS

DECEMBER 1972—REVISED MARCH 1988

SN54180 . . . J OR W PACKAGE
SN74180 . . . N PACKAGE
(TOP VIEW)

G	1	14	V_{CC}
H	2	13	F
EVEN	3	12	E
ODD	4	11	D
ΣEVEN	5	10	C
ΣODD	6	9	B
GND	7	8	A

FUNCTION TABLE

INPUTS			OUTPUTS	
Σ OF H's AT A THRU H	EVEN	ODD	Σ EVEN	Σ ODD
EVEN	H	L	H	L
ODD	H	L	L	H
EVEN	L	H	L	H
ODD	L	H	H	L
X	H	H	L	L
X	L	L	H	H

H = high level, L = low level, X = irrelevant

description

These universal, monolithic, 9-bit (8 data bits plus 1 parity bit) parity generators/checkers, utilize familiar Series 54/74 TTL circuitry and feature odd/even outputs and control inputs to facilitate operation in either odd or even-parity applications. Depending on whether even or odd parity is being generated or checked, the even or odd inputs can be utilized as the parity or 9th-bit input. The word-length capability is easily expanded by cascading.

The SN54180/SN74180 are fully compatible with other TTL or DTL circuits. Input buffers are provided so that each data input represents only one normalized series 54/74 load. A full fan-out to 10 normalized series 54/74 loads is available from each of the outputs at a low logic level. A fan-out to 20 normalized loads is provided at a high logic level to facilitate the connection of unused inputs to used inputs. Typical power dissipation is 170 mW.

The SN54180 is characterized for operation over the full military temperature range of −55°C to 125°C; and the SN74180 is characterized for operation from 0°C to 70°C.

absolute maximum ratings over operating free-air temperature range (unless otherwise noted)

Supply voltage, V_{CC} (see Note 1) . . . . 7 V
Input voltage . . . . 5.5 V
Operating free-air temperature range: SN54180 Circuits . . . . −55°C to 125°C
SN74180 Circuits . . . . 0°C to 70°C
Storage temperature range . . . . −65°C to 150°C

NOTE 1: Voltage values are with respect to network ground terminal.

recommended operating conditions

	SN54180			SN74180			UNIT
	MIN	NOM	MAX	MIN	NOM	MAX	
Supply voltage, V_{CC}	4.5	5	5.5	4.75	5	5.25	V
High-level output current, I_{OH}			−800			−800	μA
Low-level output current, I_{OL}			16			16	mA
Operating free-air temperature, T_A	−55		125	0		70	°C

FIGURE 5-5 74180 Data Sheet (Courtesy Texas Instruments)

logic symbol†

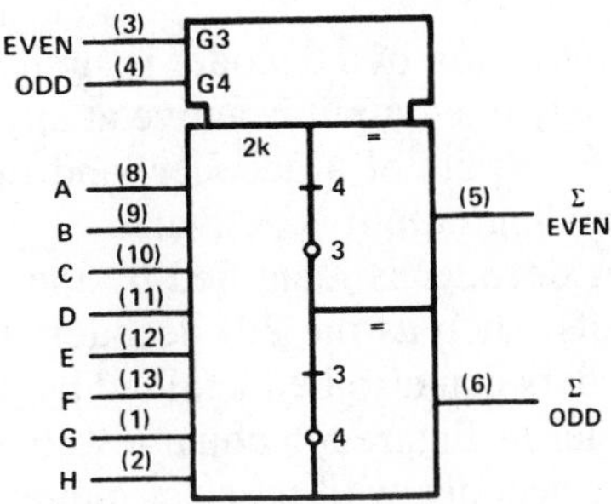

† This symbol is in accordance with ANSI/IEEE Std 91-1984 and IEC Publication 617-12.

logic diagram (positive logic)

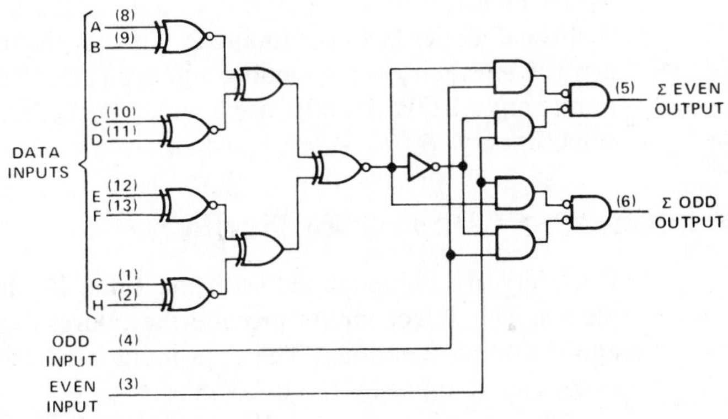

FIGURE 5-5 ***(continued)***

5-2 DECODERS

Decoders can detect a code and activate a single output to signal the presence of that code. The code, which is the address of the output to be activated, can be presented to the decoder as outputs from other logic circuits, such as addresses from a microprocessor, or from switches.

Decoders have many applications—the activated output can serve to alert a system that a specific input combination has occurred; the output can initiate another system in response to the decoded combination. Decoder outputs can be addressed with a specific input code in order to enable other circuitry. Decoders can be used as sophisticated address decoders to drive multiple devices such as memory chips in a microprocessor system.

5.2.1 Functional Description

The operation of a decoder is similar to the operation of a demultiplexer, in that only one output is active at any given time. However, no data is routed to the outputs of a decoder, and the address is "decoded" when the corresponding output is activated.

A decoder is identified by the number of select inputs to the decoded outputs, such as the 2:4 decoder shown as a block diagram in Figure 5-6. Decoders can also be identified by just the number of select inputs. The 2:4 decoder in Figure 5-6 could also be classified as a 2-bit decoder.

A decoder with n select inputs can address up to 2^n outputs. The operation of selecting or addressing the outputs is also referred to as **enabling** the outputs. The operation of the 2:4 decoder is specified in the function tables shown in Figure 5-7.

The function tables in Figure 5-7 define the operation of the decoder as nearly identical to the operation of a demultiplexer. The major difference is that the decoder has no data input. The outputs of an active-HIGH decoder are 1 when their corresponding address is on the select inputs. The outputs of an active-LOW decoder are 0 when their corresponding address is on the select inputs.

5.2.2 Integrated Circuit Specification

Decoders are implemented with the same IC that functions as a demultiplexer. The select inputs provide the address for both the demultiplexing and decoding functions. The data input used by the demultiplexer is used as an enable input by the decoder.

Many common decoders/demultiplexers available as standard transistor-transistor logic (TTL) MSI logic chips are listed in Tables 4-1 and 5-1.

In addition to those devices listed in Table 5-1, there are other decoders with output functions such as address latches, open-collector, or tristate outputs for special applications.

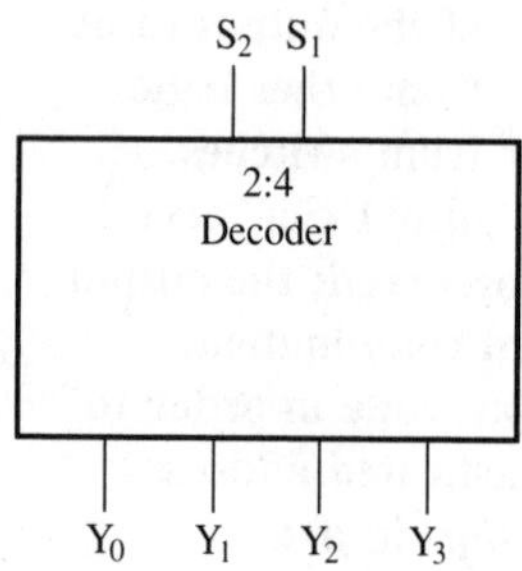

FIGURE 5-6 2:4 Decoder or 2-Bit Decoder

Active-HIGH Output

Address Inputs S_2	S_1	Decoded Outputs Y_0	Y_1	Y_2	Y_3
0	0	1	0	0	0
0	1	0	1	0	0
1	0	0	0	1	0
1	1	0	0	0	1

$Y_0 = \overline{S_2}\,\overline{S_1}$ $\quad Y_1 = \overline{S_2}\,S_1$

$Y_2 = S_2\,\overline{S_1}$ $\quad Y_3 = S_2\,S_1$

Active-LOW Output

Address Inputs S_2	S_1	Decoded Outputs Y_0	Y_1	Y_2	Y_3
0	0	0	1	1	1
0	1	1	0	1	1
1	0	1	1	0	1
1	1	1	1	1	0

$\overline{Y_0} = \overline{S_2}\,\overline{S_1}$ $\quad \overline{Y_1} = \overline{S_2}\,S_1$

$\overline{Y_2} = S_2\,\overline{S_1}$ $\quad \overline{Y_3} = S_2\,S_1$

FIGURE 5-7 2:4 Active-HIGH and Active-LOW Decoder Operation

5.2.3 Gate Equivalent Circuits

To have a thorough understanding of decoders, one should examine the equivalent logic circuits. A logic circuit can be constructed from the equations derived from the decoder operation specified in the function tables in Figure 5-7.

Each circuit is constructed by determining each output equation and forming the logic function. Figure 5-8 shows the gate equivalent circuits for active-HIGH and active-LOW decoders. These decoders have an enable input as well as address inputs since most IC decoders have at least one enable input.

The 74138, described in detail in Chapter 4 as a demultiplexer has a complicated decoder/demultiplexer circuit, as shown in the specification sheet in Chapter 4, Figure 4-24. It is now discussed in detail as a decoder.

The 74138 has three enable inputs: G_1, which is active-HIGH, and $\overline{G_{2A}}$ and $\overline{G_{2B}}$, which are active-LOW. These enable inputs are ANDed together

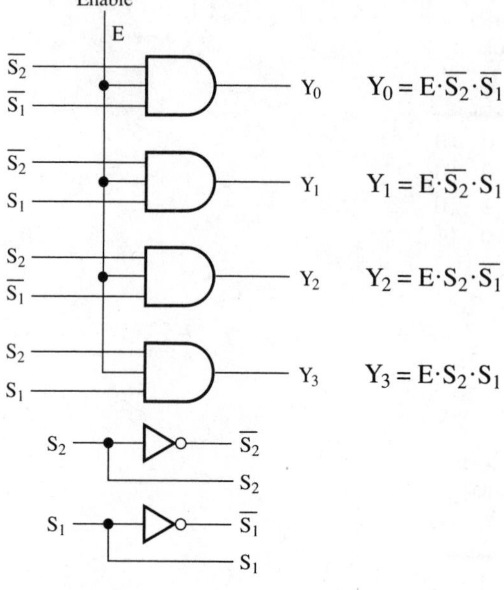

Active-LOW Decoder

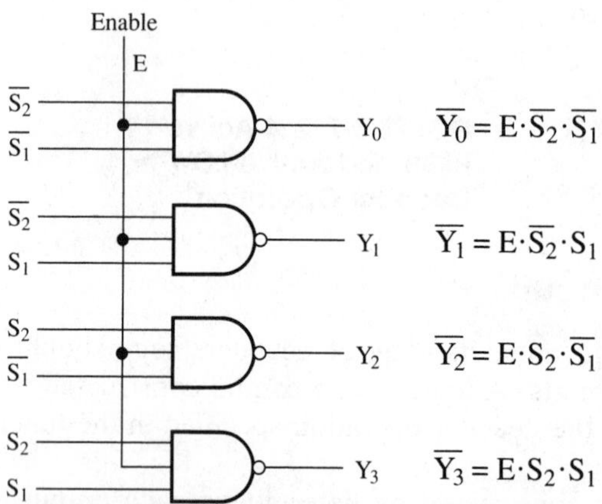

FIGURE 5-8 Active-HIGH and Active-LOW Decoder Circuits from Logic Gates

and the output is routed to each NAND gate that decodes the address on the select inputs.

The 74138 has three select inputs: C, B, and A. Note that C is the most significant bit of the select inputs. With three select inputs, eight outputs can be addressed for decoding. An array of **NAND gates**, rather than AND gates, is used to produce the **active-LOW outputs**, Y_0 through Y_7.

TABLE 5-2 74138 Decoding Operation

Enable Inputs			Select Inputs			"Decoded" (Activated) Output
G_1	$\overline{G_{2A}}$	$\overline{G_{2B}}$	C	B	A	
1	0	0	0	0	0	Y_0
1	0	0	0	0	1	Y_1
1	0	0	0	1	0	Y_2
1	0	0	0	1	1	Y_3
1	0	0	1	0	0	Y_4
1	0	0	1	0	1	Y_5
1	0	0	1	1	0	Y_6
1	0	0	1	1	1	Y_7

When the 74138 is used for decoding, all enable inputs must be tied to an appropriate logic level for the circuit to decode the input address. G_1 must be tied high, whereas $\overline{G_{2A}}$ and $\overline{G_{2B}}$ must be tied low. The enable inputs can be used to cascade several 74138s to increase the number of addresses that can be decoded. Table 5-2 describes the decoding operation of the 74138 decoder.

Section Self-Test

1. What is "address decoding?"
2. What is an active-LOW decoder?
3. How are some decoder circuits similar to demultiplexer circuits?

ANSWERS (Not necessarily in the same order as the questions)

- A decoder circuit can be used as a demultiplexer circuit if it has an enable input that can serve as the data input for the demultiplexer. The decoder functions similarly to a demultiplexer in that only one output is active at any one time.
- An output corresponding to a single address is activated to indicate that the address is on the select inputs of the decoder.
- The active state is a logic LOW.

5-3 DECODER APPLICATIONS

Decoders can detect a code and activate a single output to signal the presence of that code. The code, which is the same as the address of the output to be activated, can be presented to the decoder as outputs from other logic circuits, such as addresses from a microprocessor, or from switches.

Decoders have many applications: The activated outputs can serve to alert a system that a specific input combination, either good or bad, has occurred; initiate another system in response to the decoded combination; be addressed with a specific input code in order to enable other circuitry; and be used as sophisticated address decoders to drive multiple devices such as memory chips in a microprocessor system.

Decoder applications studied in this section are binary-to-octal address decoding, binary-to-hexadecimal address decoding, binary-to-decimal address decoding, and logic function generation.

5.3.1 Binary-to-Octal Address Decoding

Address decoding is the classic decoder application. One output is activated when its address is decoded in the select inputs of a decoder.

The 74138 is designed for binary to octal address decoding. The address is a binary number that is placed on the select inputs. The octal decoding refers to the eight outputs, one of which is activated for each address. The eight outputs can represent the eight unique characters in the octal number system. Any time a 3-bit binary input combination is decoded to produce eight individual output signals, binary to octal code conversion is performed.

■ EXAMPLE 5-1 Binary to Octal Conversion

Problem: Determine the binary input required to produce the specified random output sequence, using the 74138 for code conversion (see Figure 5-9). Output sequence: 7, 3, 0, 2, 1, 5, 4, 6.

Solution: The input combination must be the binary equivalent of the observed output since the 74138 is designed to perform binary to octal code conversion. The required input sequence is as follows:

Input Address			Output Activated
C	B	A	
1	1	1	Y_7
0	1	1	Y_3
0	0	0	Y_0
0	1	0	Y_2
0	0	1	Y_1
1	0	1	Y_5
1	0	0	Y_4
1	1	0	Y_6

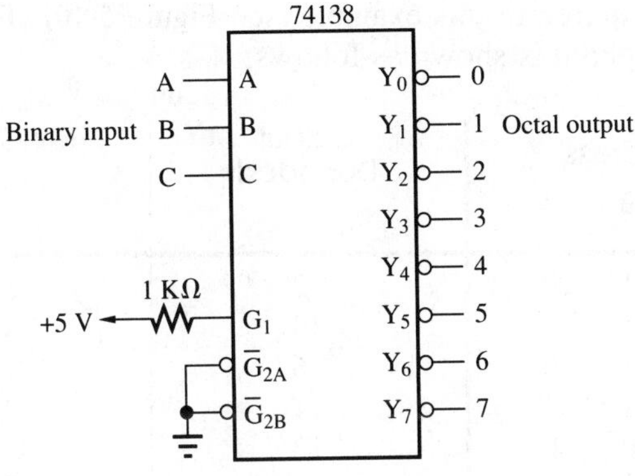

FIGURE 5-9 Example 5-1 Circuit ■

5.3.2 Binary to Hexadecimal Address Decoding

The 74154 is a 4:16 decoder, which is designed to perform binary-to-hexadecimal address decoding. A binary number is input on the four select inputs to activate one of 16 outputs.

The 16 individual outputs represent the 16 unique characters of the hexadecimal code. The outputs labeled 10 through 15 represent the hex characters A through F, respectively. Any time that a 4-bit binary number is converted to 1 of 16 unique signals, binary to hex code conversion is performed.

■ EXAMPLE 5-2 Binary to Hexadecimal Conversion

Problem: Specify the binary input sequence required to produce the specified output sequence using the 74154 for binary to hexadecimal code conversion. Output sequence: 2, A, 6, B, C, 8, F, 1, 7.

Solution: The binary equivalent of the output must be on the inputs of the 74154 in order to produce the desired output value. Not all 16 outputs of the hex code are required in this example (see Figure 5-10). The sequence of binary inputs required is shown as follows:

Input Address D	C	B	A	Output Decoded	Hex Code
0	0	1	0	2	2
1	0	1	0	10	A
0	1	1	0	6	6
1	0	1	1	11	B
1	1	0	0	12	C
1	0	0	0	8	8
1	1	1	1	15	F
0	0	0	1	1	1
0	1	1	1	7	7

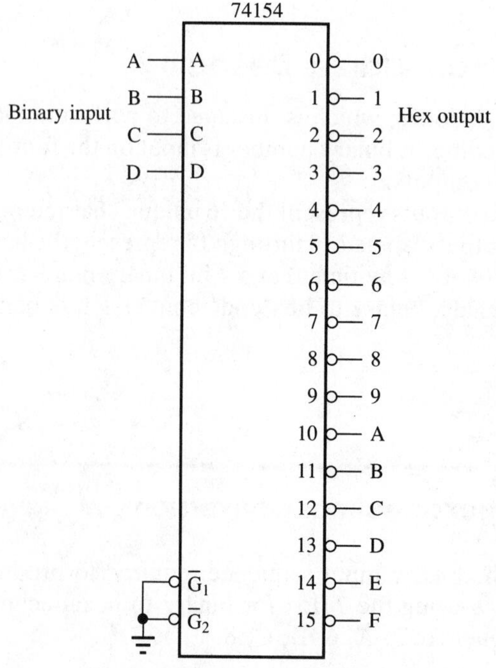

FIGURE 5-10 Example 5-2 Circuit

5.3.3 BCD to Decimal Address Decoding

BCD-to-decimal conversion is an important process that occurs frequently in digital applications. The 7442 is a 4:10 decoder that can be used as an 8421 BCD to decimal code converter. The data sheet for the 7442 IC is found in Figure 5-1.

The 7445, is also a BCD to decimal code converter. It is classified as a decoder/driver due to its higher current-carrying capabilities of the open-collector output stage of the device. The open-collector output is fully explained in Chapter 15.

The four select inputs on the 7442 and 7445 can be used to input only ten valid combinations. Therefore, the input code is BCD rather than binary. Ten outputs can be activated individually by a valid input code. They are active-LOW, and the inactive outputs remain at a logic HIGH level. If an invalid code is placed on the inputs, no output is activated.

Important applications of the BCD to decimal code converters include converting a binary input to a decimal value to activate ten different output displays.

It should be noted that the 7442 4:10 decoder cannot be used as a demultiplexer since it does not have an enable input. The decoders that also function as demultiplexers had at least one enable input so that the multiplexed data could be input and routed to the individual outputs.

5.3.4 Expanded Address Decoding

Decoders can be cascaded to expand the number of addresses that can be decoded. The enable inputs on the decoders are used for the most significant bits (MSBs) of the address when more than one decoder is cascaded together.

Without cascading, the 74138 can decode eight addresses, and the 74154 can decode 16 addresses, as shown in Figures 5-9 and 5-10, respectively. Both the 74138 and 74154 can be cascaded to decode additional addresses. Figures 5-11 and 5-12 are examples of decoder circuits cascaded for decoding up to 64 different addresses.

■ EXAMPLE 5-3 Address Decoding

Problem: Specify the range of addresses, in hex notation, that are decoded by each decoder in Figure 5-11.

Solution: There are five address bits that are decoded for a total hex address range of 00 to 1F. From most significant bit to least significant bit (LSB), the address bits are EDCBA. The most significant bit, E, is tied to the enable input $\overline{G_1}$ of the first 74154 1C, and $\overline{E}$ is tied to the $\overline{G_1}$ input of the second

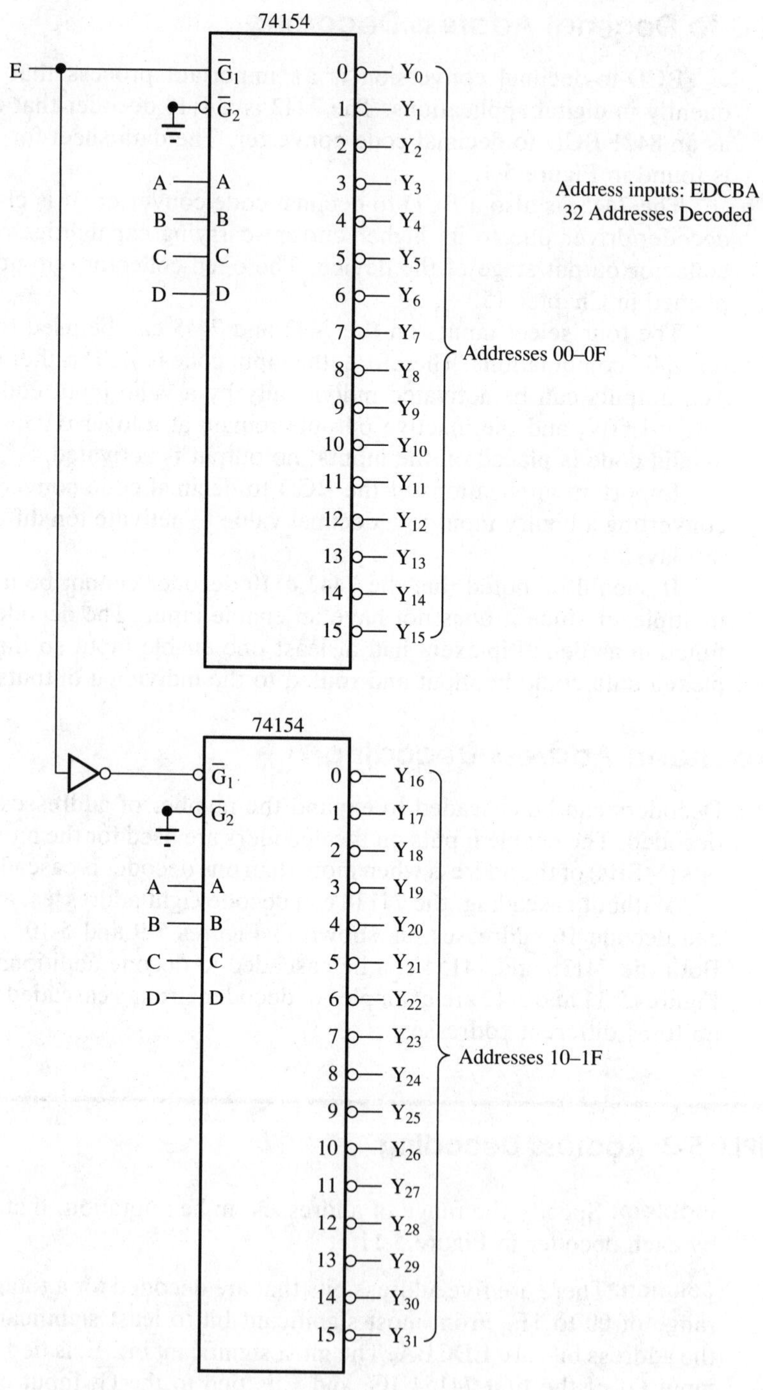

FIGURE 5-11 Decoding 32 Addresses

IC. The lower-order address bits, DCBA, are tied to the DCBA select inputs of each 74154 IC. The $\overline{G_1}$ input must be low to enable the IC, so that only one IC is enabled at a time. The first 16 hex addresses, 00 to 0F, are decoded by the first IC. The second 16 hex addresses, 10 to 1F, are decoded by the second IC. ■

■ EXAMPLE 5-4 Address Decoding

Problem: Specify the range of addresses, in hex notation, that are decoded by each decoder in Figure 5-12.

Solution: There are six address bits that are decoded for a total hex address range of 00 to 3F. From most significant bit to least significant bit, the address bits are FEDCBA. The most significant bits, F and E, are tied to the enable inputs $\overline{G_1}$ and $\overline{G_2}$ of each IC in their true or inverted form as required to enable one IC at a time for address decoding. The lower-order address bits, DCBA, are tied to the DCBA select inputs of each 74154 IC. The first 16 hex addresses, 00 to 0F, are decoded by the first IC; the second 16 hex addresses, 10 to 1F, by the second IC; the third 16 hex addresses, 20 to 2F, by the third IC; and the final 16 hex addresses, 30 to 3F, by the fourth IC. ■

5.3.5 Logic Function Generation

Decoders can be used to generate logic functions requiring several outputs by adding an output gate to the decoder IC in order to implement sum of products (SOP) logic functions. The internal decoder circuitry is an array of NAND gates if it is an active-LOW device, or AND gates if it is an active-HIGH device. This circuitry is identical to the second level of gates in SOP logic designs. By adding a NAND gate to active-LOW decoders, one can build a NAND-NAND circuit to implement an SOP equation. Similarly, an active-HIGH decoder requires an OR gate for the output level in order to complete the AND-OR circuit to implement an SOP equation.

In a similar manner, multiplexers are used to generate logic functions requiring only one output. However, decoders are better suited for multiple output applications than multiplexer logic function generators since they can provide multiple outputs from a single decoder IC by simply adding one output logic gate for each function needed. The SOP implementation of the function using the decoder does not require any simplification.

Several examples follow where the logic functions are implemented with a decoder.

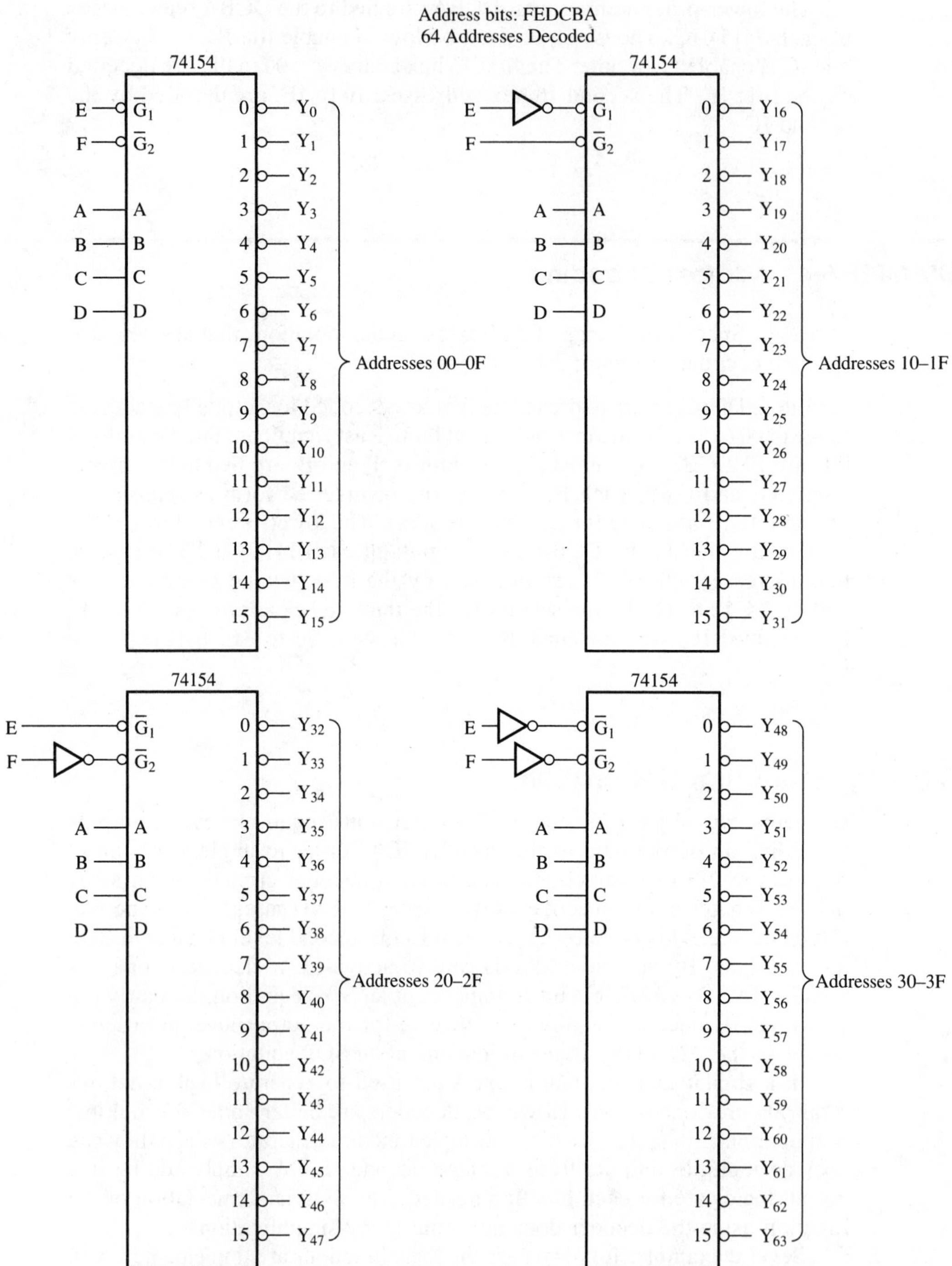

FIGURE 5-12 Decoding 64 Addresses

■ EXAMPLE 5-5 Two-Bit Multiplier

Problem: Design a multiplier circuit using the 74154 decoder and any additional circuitry that will multiply two 2-bit numbers and produce the product result.

Solution: Form a truth table of the necessary function and determine the unsimplified SOP equation required for each output bit. Recall that the 74154 is an active-LOW output decoder with an internal array of NAND gates. The SOP equations are formed with an additional NAND gate as the output level for each logic function. (See Figure 5-13.)

$$\begin{array}{r} A\ B \\ \times\ Y\ Z \\ \hline P_4\ P_3\ P_2\ P_1 \end{array}$$

■

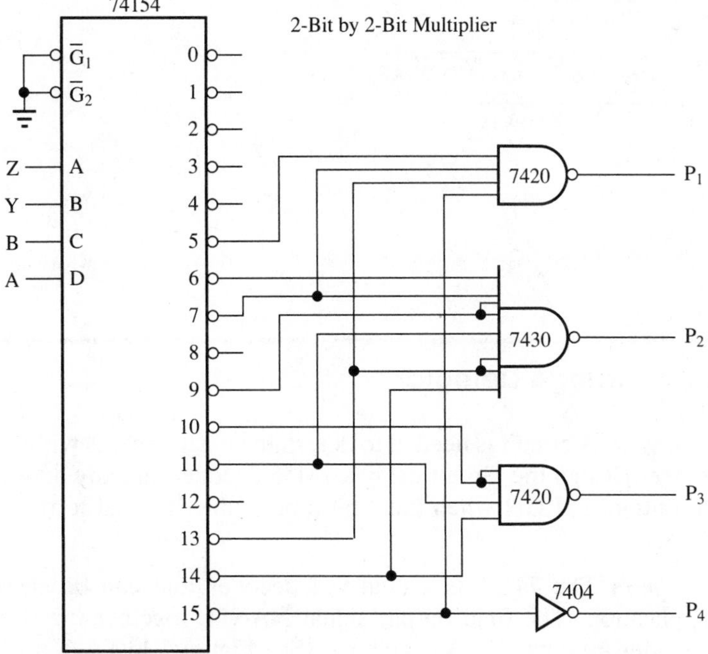

FIGURE 5-13 Example 5-5 Circuit

Two-Bit by Two-Bit Multiplier

A	B	Y	Z	P_4	P_3	P_2	P_1
0	0	0	0	0	0	0	0
0	0	0	1	0	0	0	0
0	0	1	0	0	0	0	0
0	0	1	1	0	0	0	0
0	1	0	0	0	0	0	0
0	1	0	1	0	0	0	1
0	1	1	0	0	0	1	0
0	1	1	1	0	0	1	1
1	0	0	0	0	0	0	0
1	0	0	1	0	0	1	0
1	0	1	0	0	1	0	0
1	0	1	1	0	1	1	0
1	1	0	0	0	0	0	0
1	1	0	1	0	0	1	1
1	1	1	0	0	1	1	0
1	1	1	1	1	0	0	1

$$P_4 = \overline{Y_{15}}$$

$$P_3 = \overline{Y_{10}\ Y_{11}\ Y_{14}}$$

$$P_2 = \overline{Y_6\ Y_7\ Y_9\ Y_{11}\ Y_{13}\ Y_{14}}$$

$$P_1 = \overline{Y_5\ Y_7\ Y_{13}\ Y_{15}}$$

EXAMPLE 5-6 Range Detector

Problem: A circuit is needed to determine if a number is within an acceptable range. Design the circuit using a 74155 decoder and any additional circuitry to output a HIGH when the 3-bit input value is equal to the values of 3, 4, or 5.

Solution: The 74155 is a dual 2:4 decoder that can be cascaded for this application. The final output signal NANDs together the three acceptable decoder outputs: Y_3, Y_4, and Y_5. (See Figure 5-14.)

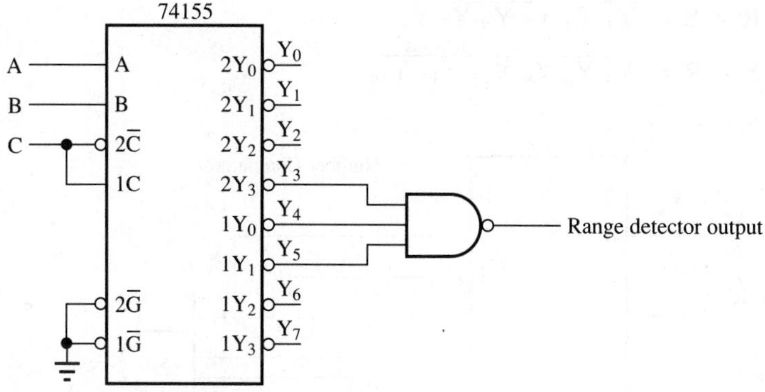

FIGURE 5-14 Example 5-6 Circuit

EXAMPLE 5-7 Number Comparator

Problem: Design a number comparator using the 74154 decoder and any additional logic gates that signals when one 2-bit binary number is less than the other.

Solution: The 74154 accepts four input bits to be decoded, so it can be used to determine if one number is less than the other. Label one number R and the other number S, and construct a truth table to determine which of the decoder outputs should be NANDed together to produce the comparator output. (See Figure 5-15.)

"R" D	C	"S" B	A	R < S	S < R
0	0	0	0	0	0
0	0	0	1	1	0
0	0	1	0	1	0
0	0	1	1	1	0
0	1	0	0	0	1
0	1	0	1	0	0
0	1	1	0	1	0
0	1	1	1	1	0
1	0	0	0	0	1
1	0	0	1	0	1
1	0	1	0	0	0
1	0	1	1	1	0
1	1	0	0	0	1
1	1	0	1	0	1
1	1	1	0	0	1
1	1	1	1	0	0

$$R < S = \overline{Y_1 Y_2 Y_3 Y_6 Y_7 Y_{11}}$$

$$S < R = \overline{Y_4 Y_8 Y_9 Y_{12} Y_{13} Y_{14}}$$

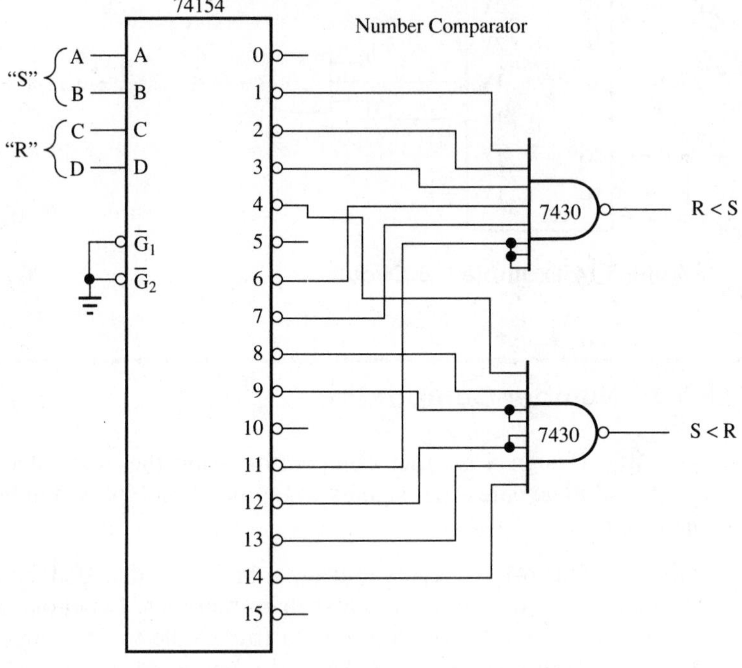

FIGURE 5-15 Example 5-7 Circuit

Section Self-Test

1. Cite three examples of decoder applications.
2. How are logic functions generated by a decoder?
3. How can decoders be cascaded to expand the number of addresses they decode?

ANSWERS (Not necessarily in the order of the questions)

- The decoder outputs represent all possible input variable combinations. Those combinations that are the SOP terms of the logic function are NANDed together to complete the SOP equation.
- Address decoding, display decoding, logic function generation
- To expand the number of addresses that can be decoded, multiple decoders can be cascaded by using the enable inputs as the inputs for the most significant address bits.

5-4 DISPLAY DECODER/DRIVERS

Display decoder/driver circuits are very important code conversion circuits. They convert an input binary code to an output combination appropriate to light specific light emitting diodes (LEDs) arranged in a display to form letters, numbers, and other symbols.

Figure 5-16 shows the arrangement of typical seven-segment LED displays. The diodes in the arrangement can be connected either **common-cathode**, as shown in Figure 5-16(a), or **common-anode**, as shown in Figure 5-16(b).

In the common-cathode display all the cathodes of the diodes are connected together, or are common. The cathodes are then connected to 0 volts or ground. The individual LED segments are lit by applying a positive voltage to the anode of the desired diode segment. The common-cathode display is an active-HIGH display since the logic HIGH level turns on the diode.

In the common-anode display the anodes of all the diodes are connected together and connected to V_{CC}, which is usually +5 volts. The individual LED segments are lit by applying 0 volts to the cathode of the desired diode segment. The common-anode display is an active-LOW display since the logic LOW level turns on the diode.

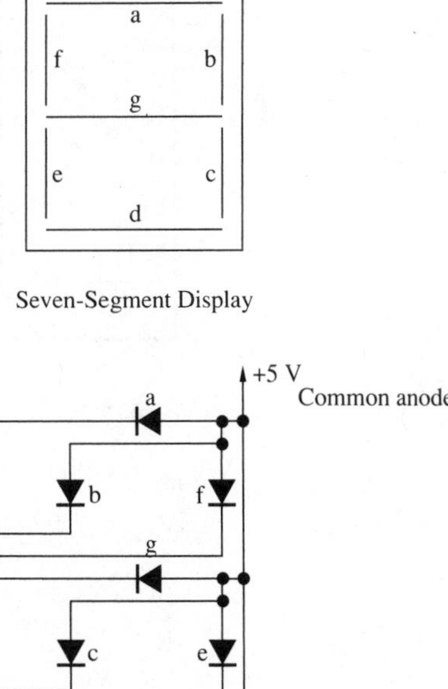

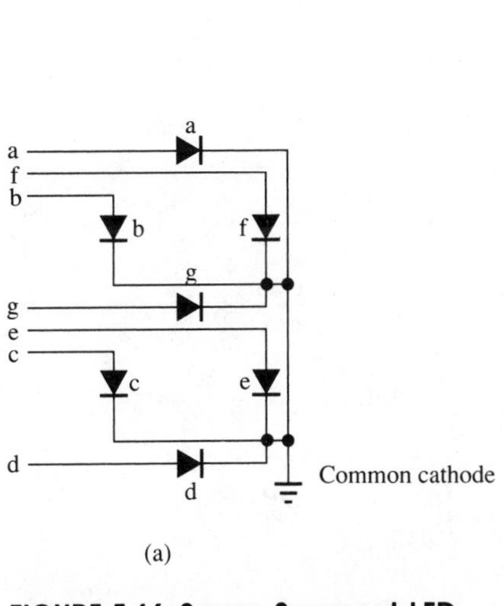

FIGURE 5-16 Seven-Segment LED Displays. (a) Common-Cathode Display; Common-Anode Display

The LED displays are used with current-limiting resistors in series with the output of the logic circuit to limit the current flow when the diodes are forward biased. A standard TTL gate with a logic-LOW output level can sink 16 mA of current; an open-collector output device, such as the 7447 decoder/driver, can sink 40 mA. A standard value for LED operation is with a current of approximately 10 mA. As a nominal value, 330 ohm resistors are used to limit the current to a safe value of approximately 10 mA through the LED.

EXAMPLE 5-8 Display Current Calculation

Problem: Calculate the current that flows for each segment of a common-anode display with 330 ohm current-limiting resistors connected between a 7447 display and the seven-segment display.

Solution: When the 7447 output is a logic-LOW, the LED is forward biased and lights. At this time, the supply voltage is equal to the voltage drop across the resistor plus the voltage drop across the LED. The current through the diode is equal to the current through the resistor. Current is the voltage divided by the resistance. The calculated value for I is 13 mA, as shown in Figure 5-17.

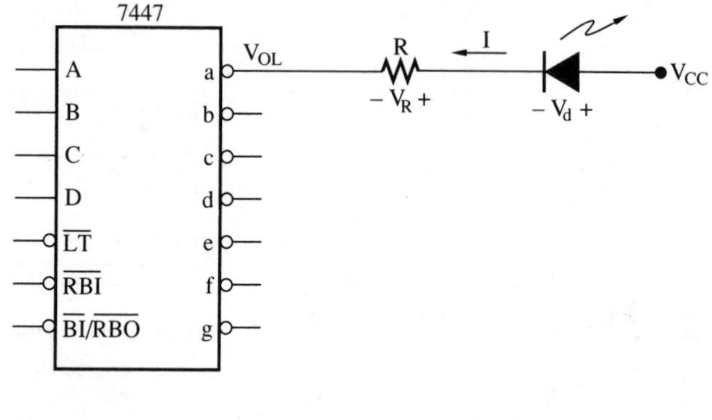

$V_{CC} = 5$ V

$V_{OL_{min}} = \text{GND}$

$V_d \sim 0.7$ V diode turn-on voltage

$V_R = V_{CC} - V_d$

$R = 330\ \Omega$

$I = \dfrac{V_R}{R} = 13$ mA

FIGURE 5-17 Example 5-8 Display Current Calculation

5.4.1 BCD to Seven-Segment Display Decoder/Drivers

Common seven-segment display decoder/drivers—the 7446, 7447, 7448, and 7449—are shown in Figure 5-2. The 7446 and 7447 circuits are designed to drive common-anode LED displays, as their outputs are active-LOW. The 7448 and 7449 circuits are designed to drive common-cathode LED displays, as their outputs are active-HIGH. In order for the 7449 to function properly, pull-up resistors are required on the output due to the open-collector output stage internal to the IC. A nominal value of 1K ohm is used to pull-up the open-collector output. (Chapter 15 has additional detailed information on open-collector devices.)

The variety of decoder/driver circuits allow the logic designer a selection on IC for specific display applications. The 7446 has the highest current and voltage ratings, with a maximum sink current of 40 mA and a maximum voltage of 30 volts. The 7447 is next with a 40 mA maximum sink current and a maximum voltage of 15 volts. The 7448 has the lowest current and voltage capabilities, with only a 6.4 mA sink current and 5.5 volts as its maximum ratings.

5.4.2 7447 Decoder/Driver Applications

The applications discussed in this section center on the use of the 7447 decoder/driver used in combination with a common-anode LED display, as shown in Figure 5-18. The special features of the 7447 and other display decoder/driver ICs increase their functionality, as well as increase their complexity. The features, all defined in the function table found in the data sheet for the 7447, are explained here in detail.

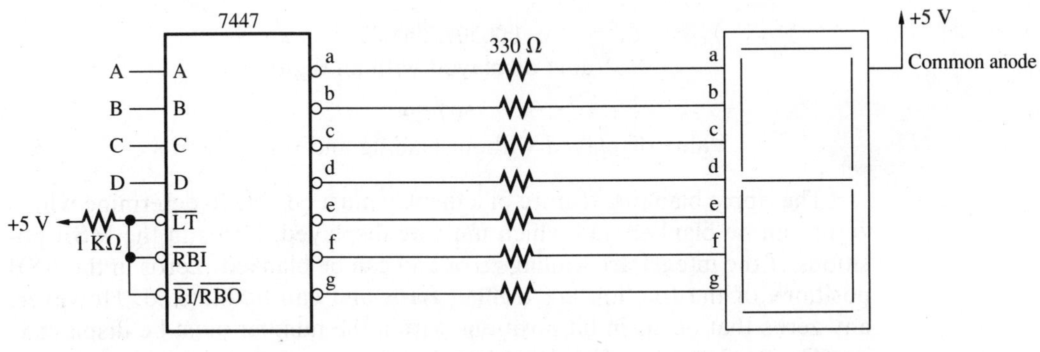

FIGURE 5-18 7447 Decoder/Driver Application Circuit

The four inputs for the BCD code allow 16 input combinations. **Invalid BCD codes display unique characters** to verify the input code, according to the table in the data sheet.

Segments of the LED display may be tested using the **lamp test** input. This input is active-LOW in order to test the lamps. During normal operation it is kept at a logic HIGH value.

The entire circuit can be blanked by using the **blanking input**. This is also an active-LOW input, so during normal operation when the input character is desired in the display, the blanking input is kept at a logic-HIGH value. One application of the blanking input is to prevent the display of the invalid BCD characters, if desired.

The **ripple blanking input**, used to blank unwanted leading or trailing zeros in multidigit displays, works in conjunction with the **ripple blanking output** to control the display depending on adjacent values. Its function will be explained in further detail later. The ripple blanking input is also an active-LOW input, so during normal operation and single-digit applications, it is kept at a logic HIGH level to display all values.

The application circuit of Figure 5-18 shows all inputs for normal operating conditions of the 7447 decoder/driver when all input values are to be displayed. The 330 ohm **current-limiting resistors** are placed in series between the IC outputs and the LED display inputs to prevent the segments from burning out.

The 7447 display decoder/driver is designed to be used with a common-anode LED display. The anode connection on the LED display is tied to a logic-HIGH value so that the low outputs from the IC forward bias the segments to light them for each character.

The **ripple blanking feature** is used in multidigit displays, such as in calculators. Most pocket calculators have up to 13 digits in their display. Without the ripple blanking feature, all values would be displayed as 13 digit numbers. Displays are easier to read if unnecessary leading or trailing zeros are not displayed.

000507.290000
Value displayed with all digits

507.29
Value displayed without leading and trailing zeros

The ripple blanking feature of a display must be able to determine which zeros can be blanked and which must be displayed. Zeros in the MSB positions of the integer are **leading zeros** and can be blanked. Zeros in the LSB positions of the fraction are **trailing zeros** and can be blanked. However, any zeros that occur in bit positions within the number must be displayed.

The 7447 display decoder/driver functions as follows for blanking unwanted leading zeros of integers or trailing zeros of fractions. The **ripple blanking input is tied to a logic-LOW for the digits farthest from the decimal**

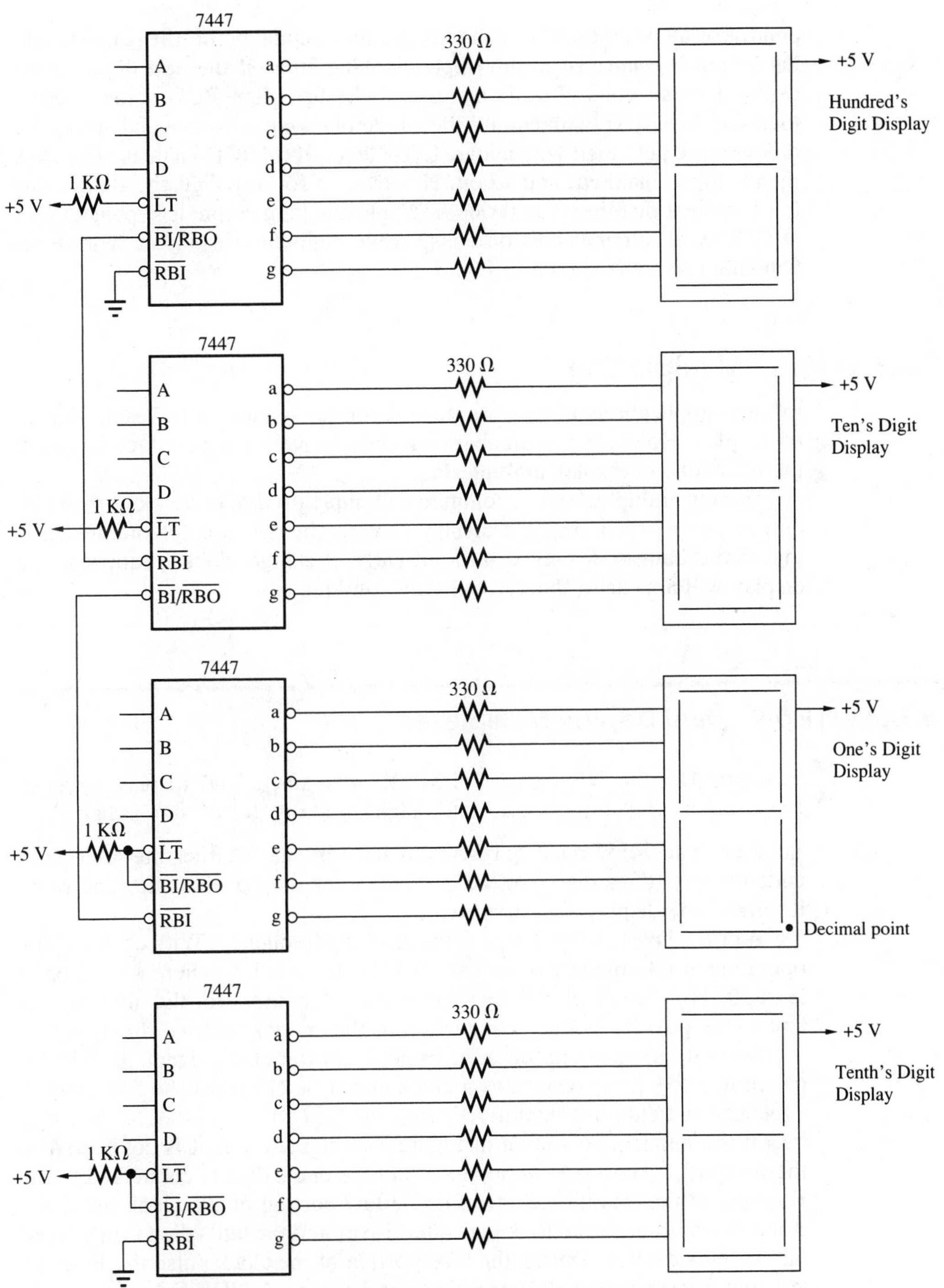

FIGURE 5-19 Ripple Blanking Application Circuit

the leading zeroes

point. For all other digits moving toward the decimal point, the **ripple blanking output is connected to the ripple blanking input of the next digit** closest to the decimal point. In this manner, if the first digit BCD value is 0000, then the display is blanked and the ripple blanking output signals this condition to the next digit with a logic LOW level. If its BCD value is also 0000, then it too is blanked, and so on. However, if for any digit the BCD value is a combination other than 0000, the ripple blanking output is kept at a logic-HIGH, so all other values on consecutive digits are displayed. The ripple blanking feature is shown in Figure 5-19.

5.4.3 Display Multiplexing

In most applications a separate decoder/driver is needed for each digit in the display. However, the number of decoder/drivers can be reduced through the technique of **display multiplexing**.

Display multiplexing is a common technique used to drive more than one output display from a single display driver. The principle of the design is that if the data is displayed intermittently at a high clock frequency, the display will appear to the eye to be on continuously.

■ EXAMPLE 5-9 Dual Display Multiplexer

Problem: Use the 74157 quad 2:1 MUX and a single 7447 display driver to drive two displays, one for a "ten's digit" and one for a "one's digit."

Solution: The 74157 quad 2:1 MUX is used to select either the 4-bit BCD code for the "ten's digit" or the BCD code for the "one's digit" and route it to the 7447 display decoder/driver.

A critical part of the design is the clocking frequency. With each display operating at a frequency of at least 100 Hz, the clock frequency must be at least 200 Hz. The clock will be used as the select input for the multiplexers and as the positive voltage connection to the anodes to drive the displays.

Several methods can be used to generate the clock signal. In this application a 555 timer generates a clock signal of 215 Hz. (The 555 timer is explained in detail in Chapter 7.)

In the application shown in Figure 5-20 the ten's digit is connected to the A inputs of the 74157 multiplexer and the one's digit is connected to the B inputs of the multiplexer. During the low portion of the clock pulse the A inputs are transmitted to the decoder/driver and the ten's digit is displayed on the ten's display. During the high portion of the clock pulse the B inputs are transmitted to the decoder/driver and the one's digit lights the one's display.

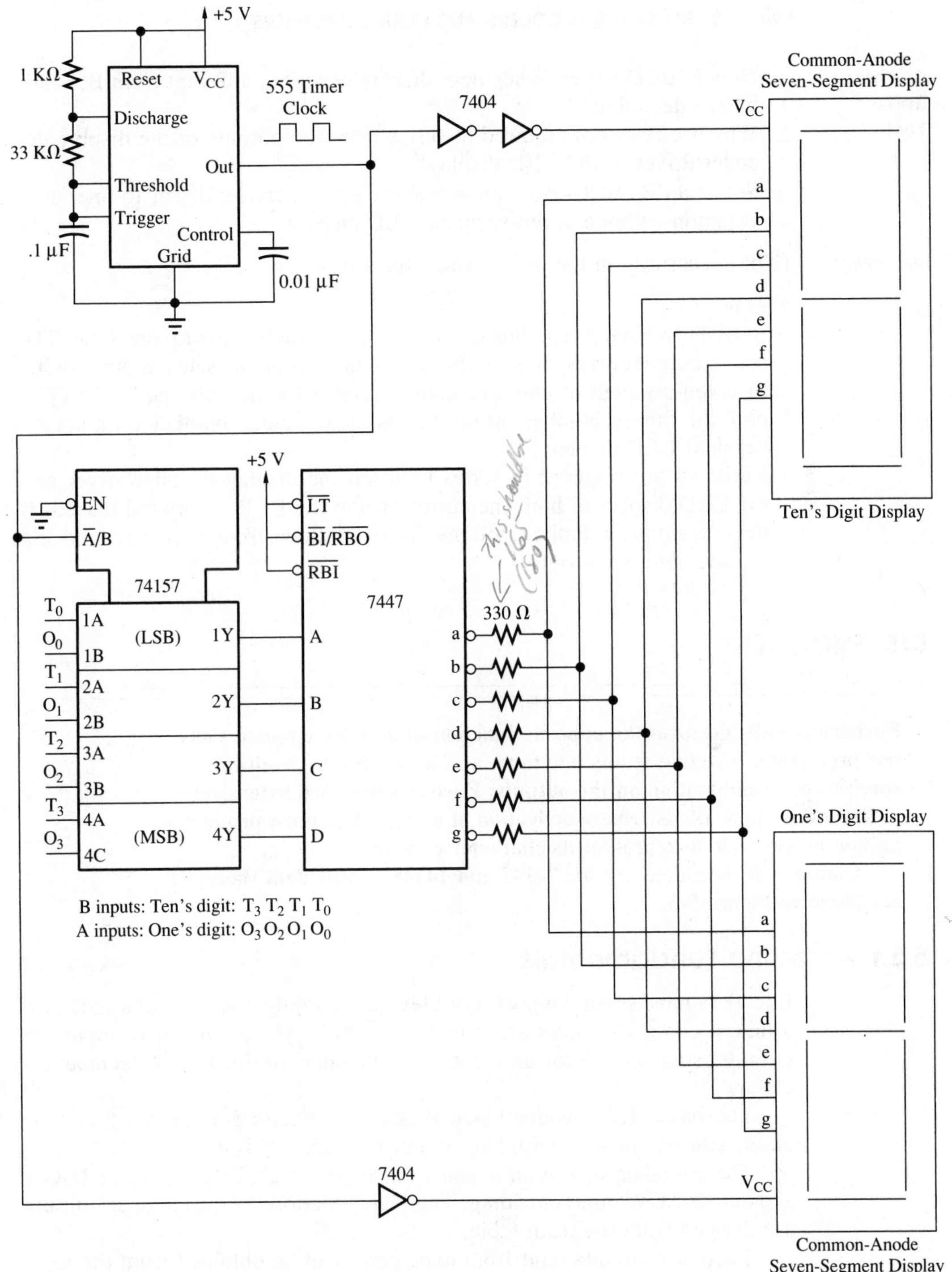

FIGURE 5-20 Example 5-9 Dual Display Multiplexing Application Circuit

Section Self-Test

1. How is BCD-to-seven segment display decoding different from BCD-to-binary decoding?
2. Why are resistors required in series from the outputs of the display decoder/driver to the LED display?
3. Select an IC BCD-to-seven-segment display decoder/driver to operate a common-cathode seven-segment LED display.

ANSWERS (Not necessarily in the order of the questions)

- 7448
- In BCD-to-binary decoding only one output is active at any one time. The active output corresponds to the binary address on the select inputs. BCD-to-seven-segment display decoding activates the outputs required to display the binary number on the inputs as a decimal number on a seven-segment LED display.
- Resistors are required in series between the display decoder/driver and the LED display to limit the current when the LED is forward biased. If the current is not limited, too much current flows from V_{CC} to ground and the segment burns out.

5-5 ENCODERS

Encoder circuits perform the opposite function of decoder circuits. Only one input value is active at any one time, and its activation produces a specific code combination on the outputs. Encoders are used extensively in keyboard applications, where activation of a single key must produce a unique binary code to represent its character or value.

Common IC encoders are the 74147 and 74148, whose data sheets are found in Figure 5-3.

5.5.1 Encoding Fundamentals

Encoders have several inputs, but they convert only one input at a time into a binary code. Encoders are usually specified by the number of inputs to outputs, such as 8:3 for an eight-input encoder, or 10:4 for a decimal encoder.

The basic 4:2 encoder block diagram in Figure 5-21 shows that four inputs can be encoded with two output bits since 2^2 is 4.

The encoding operation is shown in Figure 5-22 for both active-HIGH and active-LOW input encoding. The logic functions of the encoder outputs are derived from the truth table.

Encoding circuits built from logic gates can be obtained from the logic equations derived from the function table, as shown in Figure 5-23. Note that the I_0 input is not required in any encoder circuit. When no inputs are activated, the output is 0 0.

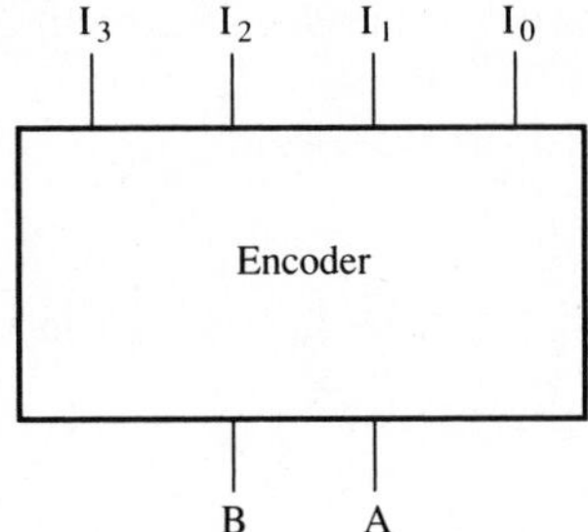

FIGURE 5-21 4:2 Encoder

Active-HIGH Inputs				Encoded Outputs	
I_0	I_1	I_2	I_3	B	A
1	0	0	0	0	0
0	1	0	0	0	1
0	0	1	0	1	0
0	0	0	1	1	1

$$B = \overline{I_0}\,\overline{I_1}\,I_2\,\overline{I_3} + \overline{I_0}\,\overline{I_1}\,\overline{I_2}\,I_3$$

$$A = \overline{I_0}\,I_1\,\overline{I_2}\,\overline{I_3} + \overline{I_0}\,\overline{I_1}\,\overline{I_2}\,I_3$$

Active-LOW Inputs				Encoded Outputs	
I_0	I_1	I_2	I_3	B	A
0	1	1	1	0	0
1	0	1	1	0	1
1	1	0	1	1	0
1	1	1	0	1	1

$$B = I_0\,I_1\,\overline{I_2}\,I_3 + I_0\,I_1\,I_2\,\overline{I_3}$$

$$A = I_0\,\overline{I_1}\,I_2\,I_3 + I_0\,I_1\,I_2\,\overline{I_3}$$

FIGURE 5-22 Active-HIGH and Active-LOW Encoding Operation

Active-HIGH Input Encoder

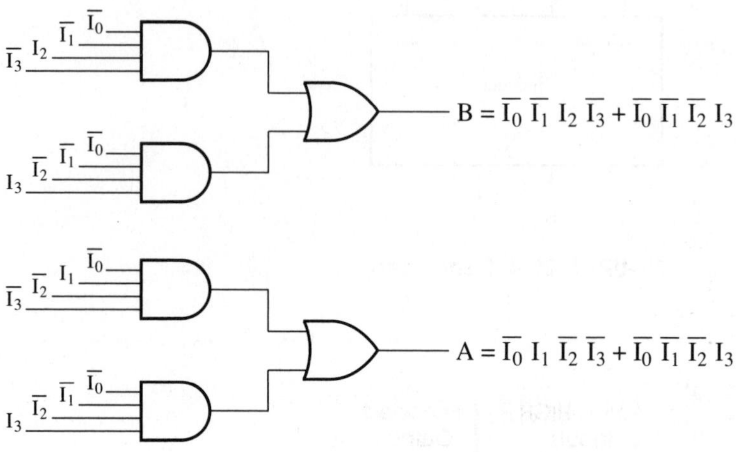

Active-LOW Input Encoder

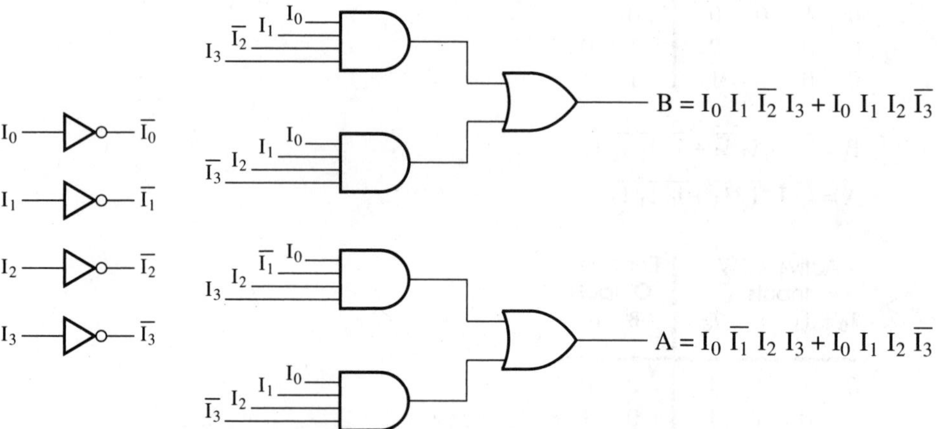

FIGURE 5-23 Encoders Built from Logic Gates

5.5.2 Priority Encoding

When more than one encoder input is pressed simultaneously, the circuits shown in Figure 5-23 encode 0 0. In many instances, such as keyboard encoding applications, it is common for a person to touch two keys accidentally. This would activate two inputs to the encoder simultaneously, and the value 0 0 would be the output.

The problem of multiple outputs is alleviated by **priority encoding**. **Priority encoding** is a technique used to encode the highest magnitude input and

Active-HIGH Inputs				Encoded Outputs	
I_0	I_1	I_2	I_3	B	A
1	0	0	0	0	0
X	1	0	0	0	1
X	X	1	0	1	0
X	X	X	1	1	1

$B = \overline{I_2}\, I_3 + \overline{I_3}$

$A = \overline{I_1}\, I_2\, I_3 + \overline{I_3}$

Active-LOW Inputs				Encoded Outputs	
I_0	I_1	I_2	I_3	B	A
0	1	1	1	0	0
X	0	1	1	0	1
X	X	0	1	1	0
X	X	X	0	1	1

$B = \overline{I_2}\, I_3 + \overline{I_3}$

$A = \overline{I_1}\, I_2\, I_3 + \overline{I_3}$

FIGURE 5-24 4:2 Priority Encoders

ignore lower magnitude inputs. The truth tables of Figure 5-22 are modified to indicate priority encoding, as shown in Figure 5-24.

5.5.3 Integrated Circuit Encoders

The 74147 and 74148 are two common IC encoders. The 74147 is a 10:4 priority encoder that performs the code conversion from **decimal to BCD**. The 74147 encoder has active-LOW inputs and active-LOW outputs. As an active-LOW BCD output, all number combinations have a logic HIGH where a logic LOW is expected, and vice versa. The outputs can be inverted to produce the true BCD combination.

The 74147 is a priority encoder, where the numbers of a greater magnitude have priority over those of a lesser magnitude. The priority characteristic is shown by the Xs in the function table on the data sheet, referring to "don't care" input states. When the input for the number 9 is activated, all other inputs are irrelevant since 9 has the highest priority, and the active-LOW BCD value for 9 is output. In order to display the BCD value for 1, only the 1 input can be active, and all others must be inactive. Zero has the lowest priority since all inputs must be inactive for the display to read an active-LOW BCD 0.

Although the 74147 is classified as a 10:4 encoder, the IC itself has only nine inputs for values 1 through 9. The zero input is assumed when no other keys are pressed. This is the condition of the first line of the function table for the 74147 as shown in its data sheet.

The 74148 is an 8:3 priority encoder performing the code conversion from octal to binary. It has eight inputs for values 0 through 7, and three outputs, A_2 A_1 A_0. Both the inputs and outputs on the 74148 are active-LOW. The binary combination on the outputs must be inverted in order to obtain the expected logic levels for the true binary code.

The Xs in the truth table for the 74148 encoder define the priority encoding operation. Input numbers of the larger magnitude have priority over smaller numbers, and their binary equivalent value is displayed on the output if more than one input is activated simultaneously.

In addition to the encoding inputs, the 74148 has an enable input, E_I. The enable must be tied to a logic-LOW for encoding. Because of the enable input, the 74148 encoder can easily be cascaded to expand the number of inputs to be encoded.

The 74148 has a strobe output, G_S, and an enable output, E_O, in addition to the active-LOW binary outputs. The strobe output is used to indicate if any of the inputs are activated.

The enable output, E_O, used to signal that no inputs are active when the encoder is enabled by E_I, is also used in cascading applications to enable additional encoders. Its function will be explained in more detail in Section 5.6.3 on "Hexadecimal to Binary Encoding."

■ EXAMPLE 5-10 Priority Encoding

Problem: Determine the output of the 74147 for the given inputs.

Encoder Inputs								
1	2	3	4	5	6	7	8	9
1	0	0	0	0	0	0	0	0
0	0	1	0	1	1	1	1	1
0	0	0	0	0	0	0	0	0
1	1	1	1	1	1	1	1	1
1	0	0	0	0	0	1	0	0

Solution: Refer to the function table for the 74147 in the data sheet of Figure 5-3. The 74147 is an active-LOW priority encoder; the 0's on the greatest magnitude encoder input determines the output code. The output from the 74147 is active-LOW, so the binary code appears in its one's complement form.

Encoder Inputs									Encoder Outputs			
1	2	3	4	5	6	7	8	9	D	C	B	C
1	0	0	0	0	0	0	0	0	0	1	1	0
0	0	1	0	1	1	1	1	1	1	0	1	1
0	0	0	0	0	0	0	0	0	0	1	1	0
1	1	1	1	1	1	1	1	1	1	1	1	1
1	0	0	0	0	0	1	0	0	0	1	1	0

■

Section Self-Test

1. How does encoding differ from decoding?
2. What is priority encoding and why is it used in encoder ICs?
3. What is active-LOW encoding?

ANSWERS (Not necessarily in the order of the questions)

- The input to be encoded is a logic LOW.
- Encoding circuits create the binary number that corresponds to a single input that is activated. Decoding activates a single output in response to a binary number on the inputs.
- Priority encoding ensures that if more than one input is activated, the input with the greater magnitude will be encoded. Otherwise an error will result at the output of the encoder.

5-6 ENCODER APPLICATIONS

The most common encoder applications are keypad encoders. Individual keys of a keyboard or keypad are pressed, and the keys must be encoded as a binary value in order to be processed by the system.

The applications studied in this section include decimal-to-binary keypad encoding, octal to binary encoding, and hexadecimal-to-binary encoding.

5.6.1 Decimal to Binary Keypad Encoding

The 74147 is a 10:4 priority encoder designed for decimal to binary encoding. Ten input combinations are accepted and the BCD values for the numbers

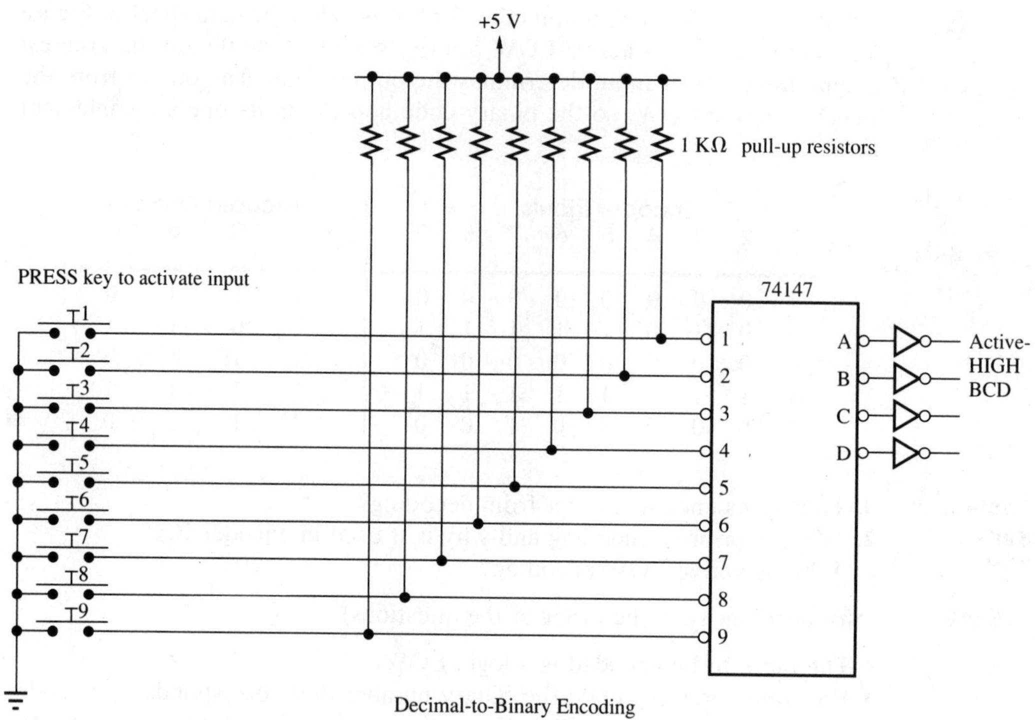

FIGURE 5-25 Keypad Encoder Application Circuit

bers 0 through 9 are produced at the outputs. The 74147 is commonly used to encode the binary equivalent of decimal numbers entered from a keypad.

The active-LOW inputs required for the encoder are easily accomplished by connecting the common terminal of the switch through a pull-up resistor to V_{CC}, and the other terminal of the switch to ground, as shown in Figure 5-25.

If the switch contacts are open, the pull-up resistor keeps the input to the IC at a logic HIGH level. As soon as a key is pressed to close a switch, the logic input is shorted to ground and the IC input is activated with a logic LOW level. The pull-up resistor connection for input switches is a reliable method for assuring that a specific logic level is input to the IC at all times to minimize errors caused by noise from unconnected inputs.

5.6.2 Octal-to-Binary Encoding

The 74148 is an 8:3 priority encoder that is well suited to perform octal-to-binary code conversion. The active-LOW inputs should be tied to V_{CC}

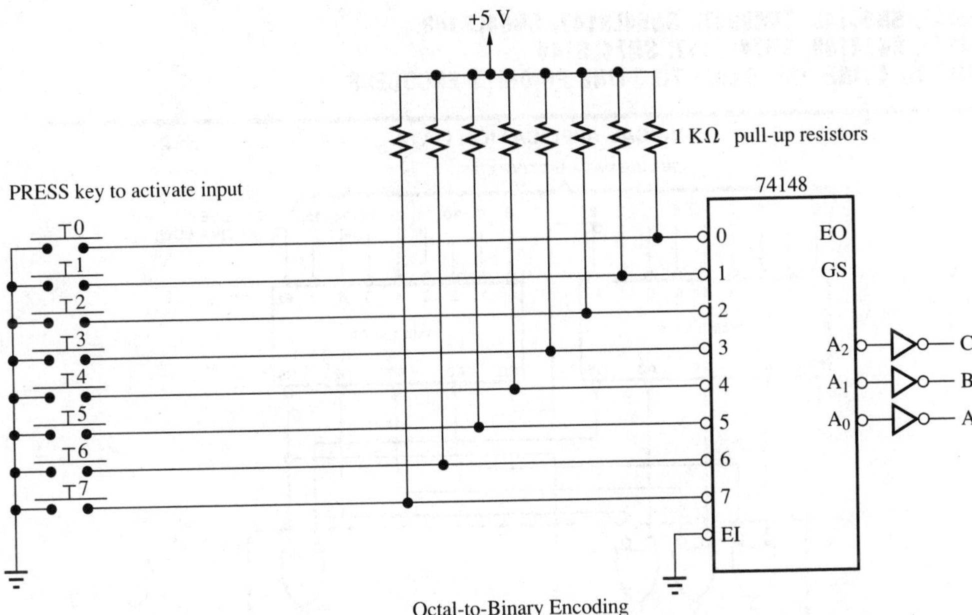

FIGURE 5-26 Octal-to-Binary Encoding Application Circuit

through pull-up resistors, and switches that activate the inputs should input a logic LOW when the switch contacts are closed. The active-LOW outputs must be inverted to read the binary code in its true form. Otherwise the encoder outputs the one's complement form of the binary result.

For octal-to-binary encoding, the 74148 must have its enable input, E_I, tied low. An application circuit for octal-to-binary encoding is shown in Figure 5-26.

5.6.3 Hexadecimal to Binary Encoding

The 74148 can be cascaded for hexadecimal-to-binary encoding applications. The enable input, E_I, and enable output, E_O, are designed for cascaded encoding applications. The strobe output, G_S, can be used as a priority indicator to signal that an encoding input has been activated.

The 74148 data sheet provides application circuits for cascaded operations, as shown in Figure 5-27. The circuit in the figure encodes 16 inputs to produce a binary output. The cascaded circuits require the addition of AND gates for the active-LOW outputs and NAND gates for the active-HIGH outputs.

SN54147, SN54148 (TIM9907), SN54LS147, SN54LS148, SN74147, SN74148, SN74LS147, SN74LS148 10-LINE TO 4-LINE AND 8-LINE TO 3-LINE PRIORITY ENCODERS

TYPICAL APPLICATION DATA

16-LINE DATA (ACTIVE LOW)

0 1 2 3 4 5 6 7 8 8 9 10 11 12 13 14 15 ENABLE (ACTIVE LOW)

'148/'LS148 '148/'LS148

'08/'LS08

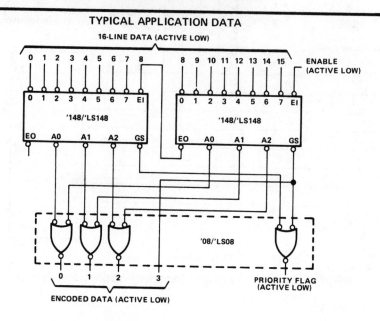

0 1 2 3 ENCODED DATA (ACTIVE LOW)

PRIORITY FLAG (ACTIVE LOW)

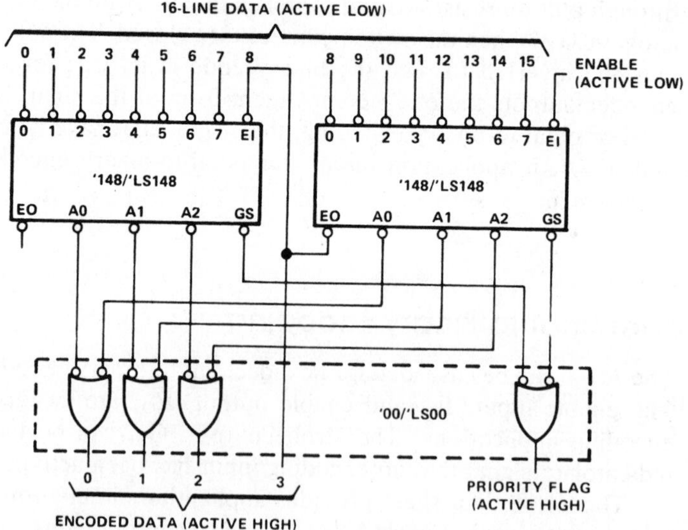

Since the '147/'LS147 and '148/'LS148 are combinational logic circuits, wrong addresses can appear during input transients. Moreover, for the '148/'LS148 a change from high to low at input EI can cause a transient low on the GS output when all inputs are high. This must be considered when strobing the outputs.

FIGURE 5-27 Hex-to-Binary Encoder Application Circuit (Courtesy Texas Instruments)

■ EXAMPLE 5-11 Decimal to Binary Encoding

Problem: Use the 74147 encoder and any additional logic gates to design a decimal to binary keypad encoder that has a priority output signal indicating that a keypad is pressed. The 0 keypad must activate the priority output signal, as well as the keypads for 1 through 9.

Decimal-to-Binary Keypad Encoder with a Priority Output Indicator

Keypad Inputs										Binary Output				Priority Indicator
0	1	2	3	4	5	6	7	8	9	D	C	B	A	P
0	1	1	1	1	1	1	1	1	1	0	0	0	0	1
X	0	1	1	1	1	1	1	1	1	0	0	0	1	1
X	X	0	1	1	1	1	1	1	1	0	0	1	0	1
X	X	X	0	1	1	1	1	1	1	0	0	1	1	1
X	X	X	X	0	1	1	1	1	1	0	1	0	0	1
X	X	X	X	X	0	1	1	1	1	0	1	0	1	1
X	X	X	X	X	X	0	1	1	1	0	1	1	0	1
X	X	X	X	X	X	X	0	1	1	0	1	1	1	1
X	X	X	X	X	X	X	X	0	1	1	0	0	0	1
X	X	X	X	X	X	X	X	X	0	1	0	0	1	1
1	1	1	1	1	1	1	1	1	1	0	0	0	0	0

Note: The 74147 outputs must be inverted to produce the specified binary code for DCBA.

$P = \overline{0 \cdot 1 \cdot 2 \cdot 3 \cdot 4 \cdot 5 \cdot 6 \cdot 7 \cdot 8 \cdot 9}$

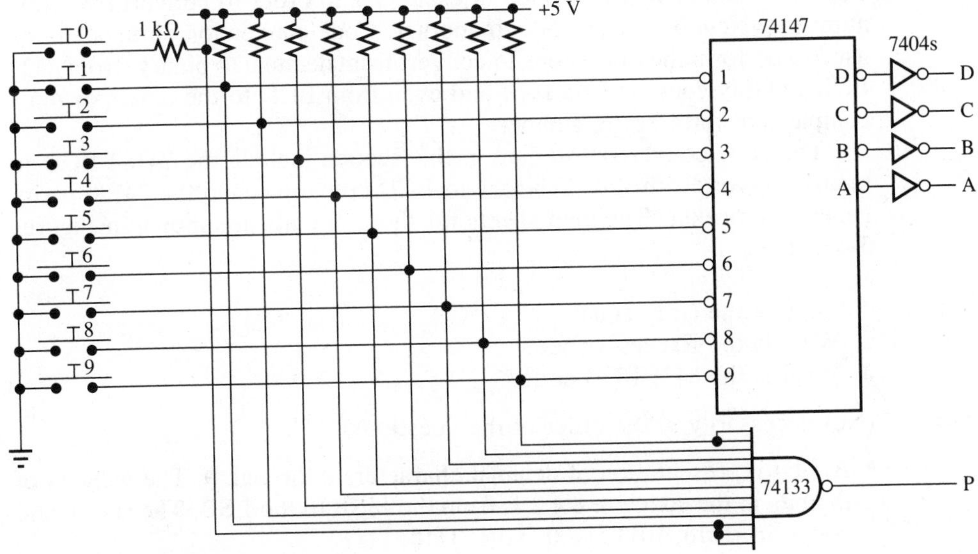

FIGURE 5-28 Example 5-11 Circuit

Solution: Create a function table for the problem and specify the necessary output. Derive the logic equation for the priority output signal, and implement that function with the needed logic gates. The function table and resulting circuit are shown in Figure 5-28. ■

SECTION SELF-TEST

1. What are three common encoding applications?
2. What is the purpose of the enable input, enable output, and strobe output on the 74148?
3. How should a keypad be wired to produce active-LOW inputs to the encoder?

ANSWERS (Not necessarily in the order of the questions)

- Keypad encoding, octal to binary encoding, and decimal to binary encoding
- Keypads should be wired with a pull-up resistor to V_{CC} at the common terminal to the encoder IC and the other terminal shorted to ground.
- The enable input, enable output, and strobe output are used when the 74148 is cascaded to expand its encoding capabilities.

5-7 CODE CONVERTERS

Code converter circuits are specially programmed logic circuits designed to perform a specific code conversion.

Code conversion was discussed in Chapter 2 in order to convert from one number system or binary code to another. Code conversion circuits can be used to perform the operations to convert from decimal to binary, from 8421 BCD to Gray code or Excess-3, and even from BCD to the nine's or ten's complement form of the number.

The code converters studied in this section include the 74184 BCD to binary converter, the 74185 binary to BCD converter, and the 74180 parity generator/checker. The data sheets for these circuits are shown in Figures 5-4 and 5-5.

Section Self-Test

1. What is the Gray code?
2. What is the Excess-3 code?
3. What is the 8421 BCD code?

ANSWERS (Not necessarily in the order of the questions)

- A 4-bit representation of decimal characters 0 through 9. The weights of the bits in the code are 8 4 2 1, from the MSB to the LSB. The six invalid codes are 1010, 1011, 1100, 1101, 1110, 1111.

- A 4-bit representation of decimal characters 0 through 9 in a self-complementing code. The six invalid codes are 0000, 0001, 0010, 1101, 1110, 1111.
- A binary code that allows only one bit to change between consecutive numbers

5-8 CODE CONVERTER APPLICATIONS

Complex code conversion applications that convert a multiple bit binary input to a different multiple bit binary output are performed by code converter circuits. Code converter circuits are manufactured to simplify the combinational logic circuit design for common code conversion applications.

The most common code conversion applications studied in this section include BCD to binary, binary to BCD, and BCD to nine's or ten's complement conversions.

5.8.1 BCD to Binary Conversion

BCD to binary code conversion is a complicated process for individual logic gate implementation, but it is simplified by using a specially programmed memory circuit to perform the conversion process. The 74184 is a **read-only memory**, or **ROM**, programmed to convert from **6-bit BCD to 6-bit binary**. A single 74184 IC can convert BCD values from 0 to 39 to their binary equivalent. The 74184 can be cascaded to perform BCD to binary code conversion for larger BCD input values.

To perform BCD to binary conversion, one must tie the enable input, $\overline{G}$, to a logic LOW. The BCD value is input in the E D C B A inputs, and the binary value is output in the Y_5 Y_4 Y_3 Y_2 and Y_1 outputs. It is important to note that the LSB of the BCD value and the binary value do not require any code conversion, and therefore they are not connected to the 74184.

In addition to programming for BCD-to-binary code conversion, the 74184 is also programmed to **convert a 4-bit BCD value to its nine's or ten's complement**. Nine's and ten's complements are useful for binary coded decimal arithmetic operations, such as those covered in Chapter 2.

When performing the BCD to complement conversion, one finds that the E input acts as a mode control rather than as an input for the BCD value. To obtain the nine's complement, the E input must be at a logic LOW level. To obtain the ten's complement, the E input must be at a logic HIGH level.

Figure 5-4 shows several application circuits for the 74184. These include applications for performing the conversions of 6-bit BCD to 6-bit binary, 8-bit BCD to 7-bit binary, 12-bit BCD to 10-bit binary, BCD to nine's complement, and BCD to ten's complement.

Special note should be made of open-collector outputs on the 74184. For proper operation, pull-up resistors are required in order to obtain a logic HIGH level at the output of the device. Figure 5-29 shows an application circuit with the necessary pull-up resistors at the outputs.

5.8.2 Binary to BCD Conversion

Binary to BCD conversion is complicated for logic gate implementation when binary values requiring over 5 bits must be converted to BCD. The 74185 is a **read-only-memory (ROM)** device designed to **convert 6-bit binary values to 6-bit BCD values.** A single 74185 IC can convert binary values of 0 through 63 to their BCD representation. Larger binary numbers are converted to BCD by cascading multiple 74185 ICs.

Figure 5-4 shows several application circuits for the 74185. The applications include the conversion of 6-bit binary to 6-bit BCD, 6-bit binary to 7-bit BCD, 8-bit binary to 10-bit BCD, 9-bit binary to 11-bit BCD, and 12-bit binary to 15-bit BCD.

Note that the least significant binary and BCD bits do not require code conversion. Therefore, the LSB of the number to be converted is not input into the 74185, but, rather, is routed directly to the BCD result.

The 74185 has open-collector outputs that require pull-up resistors in order to achieve a logic HIGH voltage level on the output. The enable input must be kept at a logic LOW level for the circuit to function as a code converter.

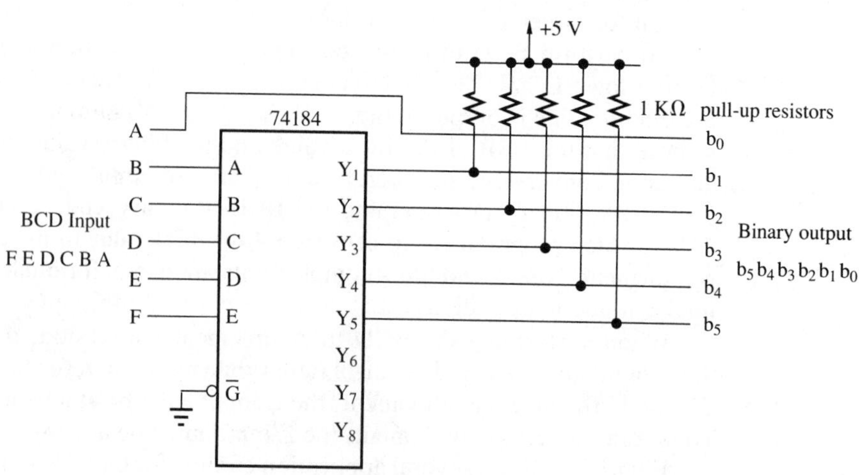

FIGURE 5-29 BCD-to-Binary Application Circuit

■ EXAMPLE 5-12 Binary to BCD Code Conversion

Problem: Design a circuit using the 74185 to perform binary to BCD code conversion for numbers up to $(99)_{10}$.

Solution: A single 74185 can convert binary numbers to BCD for values up to $(63)_{10}$. This limit is determined by the number of binary inputs on a single 74185. The five inputs can accommodate a 6-bit binary number. The maximum 6-bit binary number is $(63)_{10}$.

Two 74185s can be cascaded to perform the necessary conversion. A binary input for $(99)_{10}$ will require 7-bits. Figure 5-30 shows the circuit required for this application.

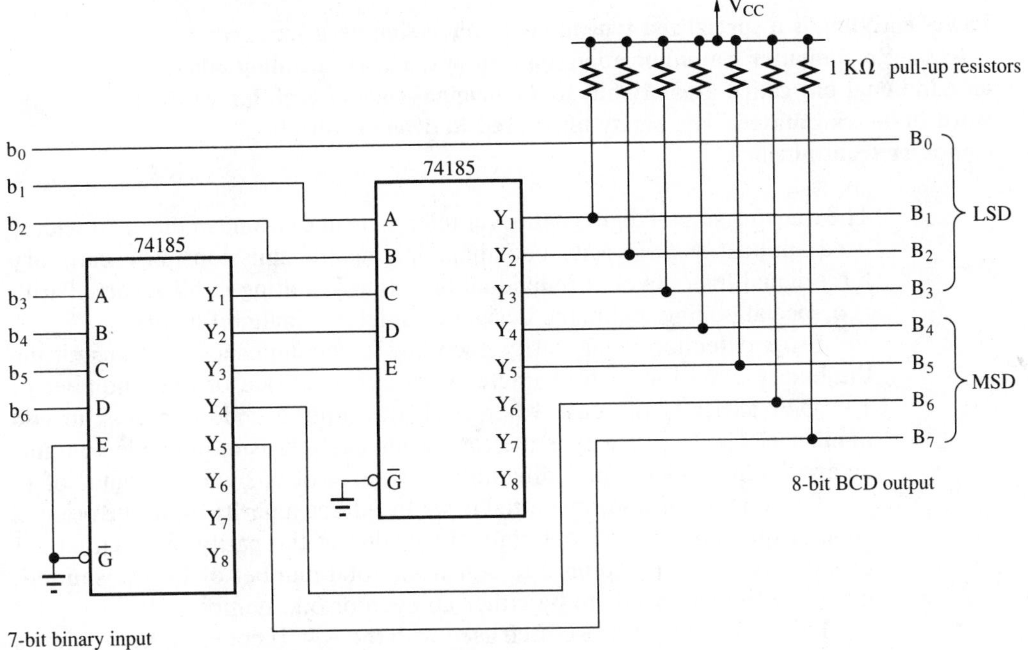

FIGURE 5-30 Example 5-12 Circuit ■

Section Self-Test

1. Why is binary to BCD and BCD to binary code conversion a complex process?
2. Why are pull-up resistors required when the IC has open-collector outputs?
3. What conversion processes does the 74184 perform?

ANSWERS (Not necessarily in the order of the questions)

- BCD to binary, BCD to nine's complement, and BCD to ten's complement
- The BCD code and the binary number system do not have the same weights on the bits that form the numbers in their codes.
- The IC has no internal connection to V_{CC} in its output stage. Therefore, to obtain a logic HIGH output, externally connected pull-up resistors are required.

5-9 PARITY ENCODING

Parity encoding is a specialized type of code conversion used for error detection in computer communication applications. Parity encoding adds an additional bit, called a parity bit, to the original code of each binary word to be transmitted. The parity bit is used to detect errors in computer transmissions.

The transmission of digital data over telephone lines is one of the most widely used applications of parity encoding. During transmission noise can vary the original logic level of individual bits, thus resulting in **bit errors**. Parity is a special coding technique designed to detect single bit errors.

Error detection using parity encoding is accomplished by transmitting the binary code for each character with either an odd or even number of 1's. **Odd parity** is the case when each transmitted code contains an **odd number of 1's. Even parity** is the case when each transmitted code contains an **even number of 1's**, including no occurrences of bits with the value of 1.

The number of 1's transmitted is set by adding a **parity bit** to the original code of the character, or data bits. The value of the parity bit is either a 1 or a 0, whichever is required to adjust the total number of 1's transmitted, including the parity bit, to be either an even or odd number.

Parity encoding is most often used with the ASCII code. Table 5-3 shows an example of 7-bit ASCII codes converted to even and odd parity for transmission by adding a parity bit in the most significant bit position.

In serial transmission the parity bit is transmitted after the data bits. This allows a circuit, called the **parity generator circuit**, to count the number of 1's in the data bits and to set the parity bit as a 1 or a 0 as required to form the correct parity encoding. When the transmitted bits are received, a circuit called the **parity checker circuit** counts the number of 1's received to determine if it is an odd or even number.

An error is signaled as having occurred during the transmission of a character if an incorrect number of 1's is detected by the parity checker circuitry. The circuitry cannot determine in which of the 7 bits the error

TABLE 5-3 Transmitted Codes: Odd and Even Parity

7-Bit ASCII Code	8-Bit Transmitted Codes			
	Even Parity		Odd Parity	
Data Bits	Parity Bit	Data Bits	Parity Bit	Data Bits
1010011	0	1010011	1	1010011
0000101	0	0000101	1	0000101
1000101	1	1000101	0	1000101
0010010	0	0010010	1	0010010
1001010	1	1001010	0	1001010
1000010	0	1000010	1	1000010
0000000	0	0000000	1	0000000

occurred, nor can it detect multiple bit errors that still result in the correct number of 1's transmitted for a character. An error that occurs in the parity also results in signaling an error.

5.9.1 Parity Generator/Checker Circuits

Parity generator and parity checker circuits must count the number of 1's in a character in order to generate or check the parity bit. The number of 1's transmitted in a character can be counted using Exclusive-OR gates, such as the circuit shown in Figure 5-31.

The circuit in Figure 5-31 is a parity generator, which analyzes the data bits and generates a parity bit for either even or odd parity, as controlled by the "set parity" bit. When the set parity bit is a 0, a parity bit is generated

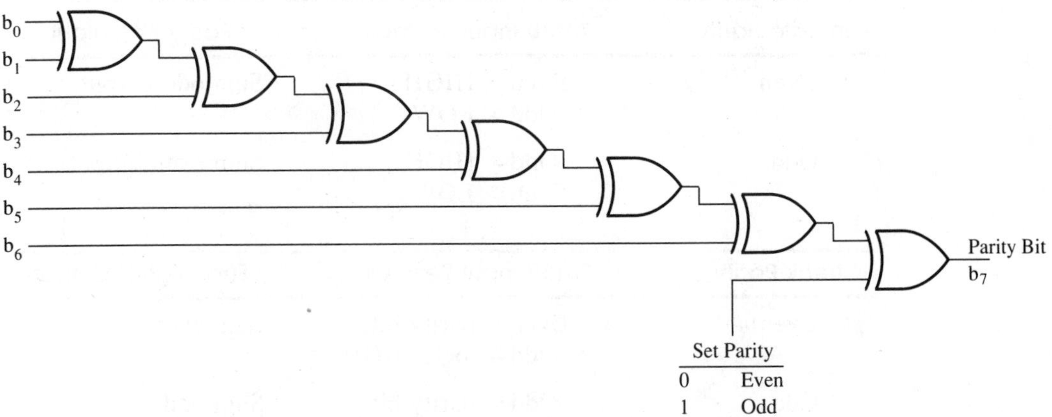

FIGURE 5-31 Exclusive-OR Parity Bit Generator

for even parity encoding. When the set parity bit is a 1, a parity bit is generated for odd parity encoding.

5.9.2 Integrated Circuit Parity Generator/Checker Circuits

Parity generator/checker circuits are available as single-chip MSI circuits. One parity generator/checker circuit is the 74180. The data sheet for the 74180 is shown in Figure 5-5.

The 74180 can be used to generate or check the parity for transmitted characters of eight data bits plus one parity bit, according to the function table given in the data sheet. The data inputs in the circuit are labeled A through H. The parity selection inputs are labeled "Even" and "Odd." The outputs, labeled "Sum Even" and "Sum Odd," are used to generate the parity bit and to signal an error in transmission.

The function table given in the data sheet is somewhat deceptive as to which inputs and outputs should be used in specific parity applications. In order to generate the parity bit for transmission, one sets the desired parity selection input to a logic HIGH and the other parity selection input to a logic LOW. The data bits of the character are input on the data inputs of the circuit, labeled A through H. The actual parity bit to be transmitted is obtained from the output labeled with the opposite parity type.

TABLE 5-4 74180 Parity Generate/Check Operation

Generate Parity	74180 Input Settings	Parity Bit Output
Even	Even = HIGH Odd = LOW	Sum odd output
Odd	Odd = HIGH Even = LOW	Sum even output

Check Parity	74180 Input Settings	Error Signal Output
Even	Even = parity bit Odd = logic HIGH	Sum even
Odd	Odd = parity bit Even = logic HIGH	Sum odd

To check the parity of a character received after transmission, the character data bits are input on the circuit inputs labeled A through H. The parity bit received is input to the desired parity selection input, whereas the other parity selection input is connected to a logic HIGH. An active-HIGH error signal is obtained from the output labeled with the desired parity as used for transmission. If an active-LOW error signal is required, then the parity output labeled with the opposite type as used for transmission should be used. The operation of the 74180 is summarized in Table 5-4.

Figure 5-32 shows circuits for even and odd parity generation and checking functions for computer transmission applications using the 74180 parity generator/checker IC.

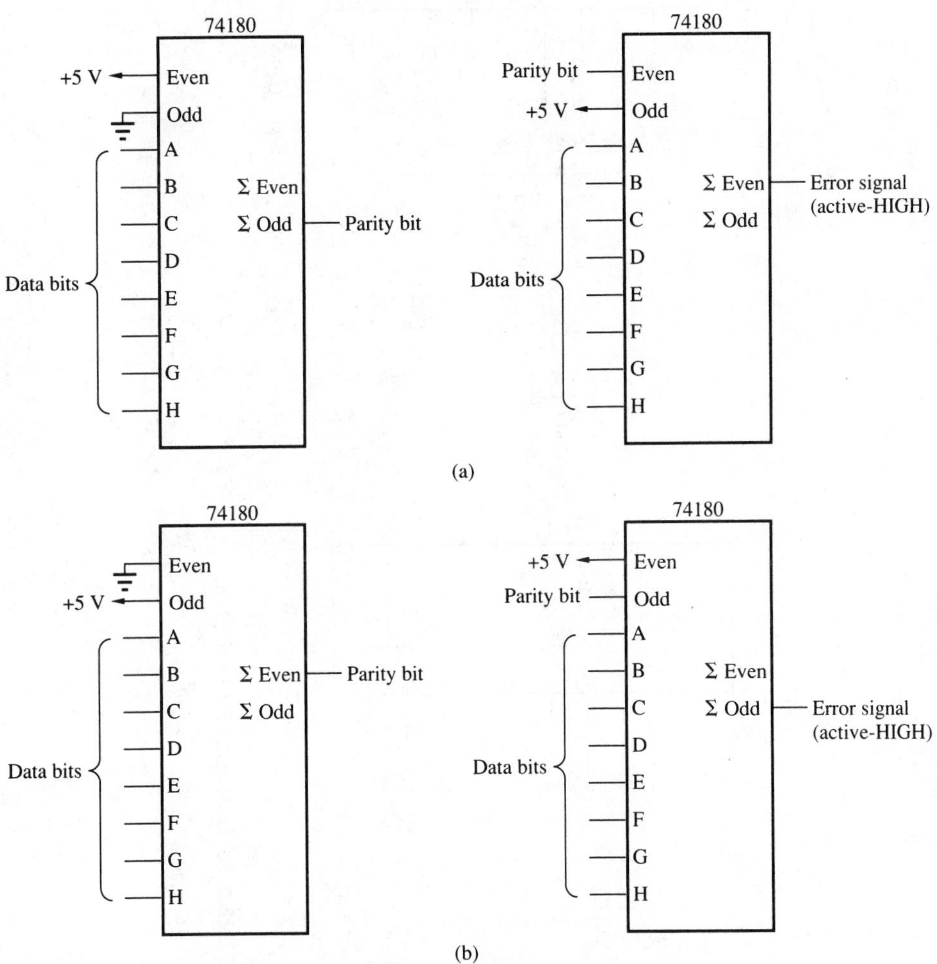

FIGURE 5-32 74180 Parity Transmission Circuits. (a) Even Parity Generator/Checker; (b) Odd Parity Generator/Checker

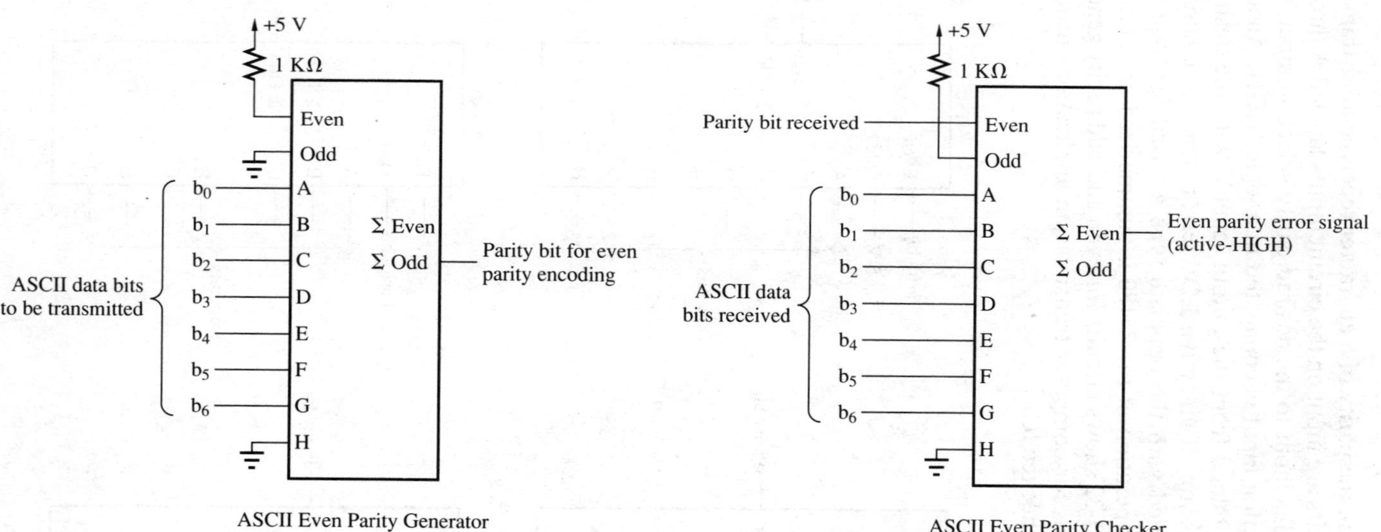

FIGURE 5-33 Example 5-13 Circuits

■ EXAMPLE 5-13 Parity Generator/Checker

Problem: Use the 74180 to generate and check even parity for a 7-bit ASCII code.

Solution: Refer to the circuits in Figure 5-32(a) for even parity generators/checkers. A separate 74180 will be used for parity generation and parity checking. The ASCII code has seven data bits that must be tied to the G F E D C B A inputs on the 74180s. The unused data bit, H, should be grounded. Figure 5-33 shows the circuits to perform this application. ■

Section Self-Test

1. In an odd parity system, what value is the parity bit if there are seven logic-HIGH data bits in the word to be transmitted?
2. In an even parity system, what value is the parity bit if there are six logic-HIGH data bits in the word to be transmitted?
3. What does it mean if an error is detected by checking parity?

ANSWERS (Not necessarily in the same order as the questions)

- An error occurred in either the data bits or the parity bit, and the word should be retransmitted.
- 0
- 0

5-10 TROUBLESHOOTING CODE CONVERSION CIRCUITS

Troubleshooting code conversion circuits requires careful analysis of the application, the circuit design, the observed circuit malfunction, the circuit wiring, and the input or output devices that require the code conversion operation. The mechanical operation of input switches, the electrical limits of displays, along with the complexities of addresses, active-HIGH, and active-LOW code conversion circuits can lead to lengthy troubleshooting sessions to determine the cause of a circuit fault.

Several troubleshooting examples are studied in this section to determine an appropriate procedure for correcting circuit faults in code conversion circuits.

■ EXAMPLE 5-14 The Minimum Resistor-Count Seven-Segment Display

Problem: To save on expenses, a fellow student proposed a new design for a seven-segment display circuit using a 7447 and a common-anode LED

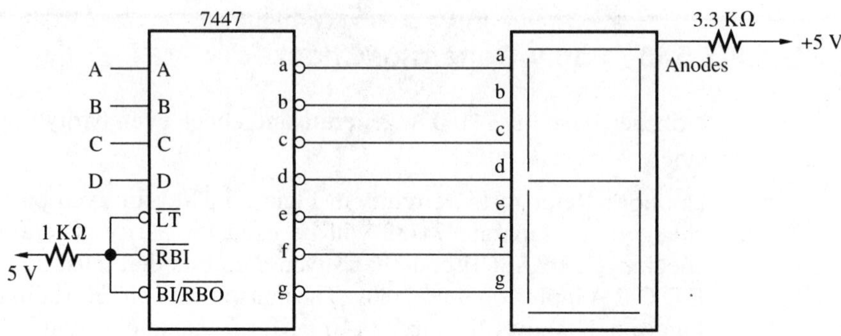

FIGURE 5-34 Example 5-14 Circuit with Circuit Faults

display. The design is shown in Figure 5-34. You are asked to review the design and determine if it is an improvement over the standard circuit shown in Figure 5-18.

Solution: You are quick to say that the circuit in Figure 5-34 is not an improvement over the standard circuit in Figure 5-18. The single resistor in the common anode of the seven-segment display cannot appropriately limit the current for each segment since the current varies depending on the number of segments to be lit. The equivalent electrical model for lighting the seven-segment display is shown in Figure 5-35. The total current in the circuit

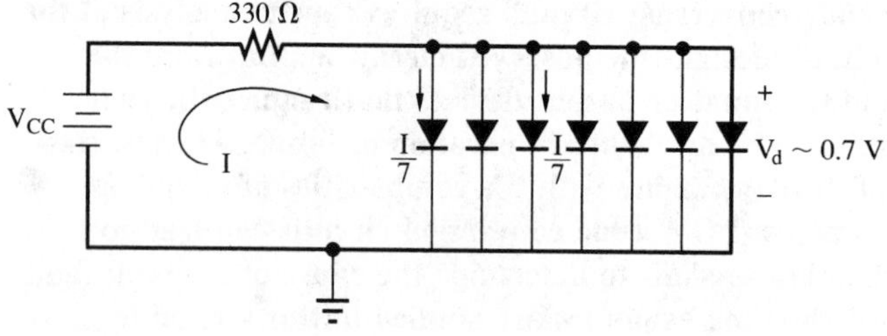

$$V_{CC} = IR + V$$

$$I = \frac{V_{CC} - V}{R} = \frac{5 - 0.7}{330} = 13 \text{ mA}$$

$$I = \frac{I}{7} = 1.86 \text{ mA}$$

FIGURE 5-35 Electrical Model of the Circuit in Figure 5-34

is 13 mA. When only one segment is lit, the current through that segment is the full 13 mA. However, when seven segments are lit, the current through each segment is 1.86 mA. With the circuit in Figure 5-34, the intensity of each segment will vary with the number of segments that are lit. This is not a reliable circuit and therefore should not be used. ■

■ EXAMPLE 5-15 Minimum Priority Encoder

Problem: A student builds an octal to binary encoder using the 74148 IC. He tests if it is working by activating only one switch at a time. Believing that it works, he takes the circuit to the professor to be verified and to receive credit for the lab project. When the professor tries to operate the encoder, the priority encoding does not operate according to the function table for the 74148. In fact, the student's circuit operates with minimum priority, as shown in the table. The professor will not give the student credit for the circuit, and recommends that he analyze it. Assist in the analysis and propose the necessary action to correct the circuit.

Solution: The student forgot that the 74148 has active-LOW outputs. Rather than adding inverters to convert the outputs to the expected binary value, he changed the input switches. With its current operation, the circuit input switches are connected in reverse order to the inputs of the encoder. In other words, switch 0 is actually connected to the encoder input 7. To correct the problem, the student must connect the switches properly and add inverters at the outputs of the 74148.

Student's Minimum Priority Encoder

Switch Inputs								Encoder Output		
0	1	2	3	4	5	6	7	C	B	A
0	X	X	X	X	X	X	X	0	0	0
1	0	X	X	X	X	X	X	0	0	1
1	1	0	X	X	X	X	X	0	1	0
1	1	1	0	X	X	X	X	0	1	1
1	1	1	1	0	X	X	X	1	0	0
1	1	1	1	1	0	X	X	1	0	1
1	1	1	1	1	1	0	1	1	1	0
1	1	1	1	1	1	1	0	1	1	1

■

■ EXAMPLE 5-16 Simplified Encoder

Problem: A student builds a simplified encoder based on the encoder truth tables in Figure 5-22. The simplified encoder circuits are shown in Figure 5-36. Analyze the encoders in the figure and determine if they are reliable.

Solution: You carefully analyze the circuits and find that they are not reliable encoders. They do not perform like the truth tables in Figure 5-22 if more than one input is activated at the same time. You recommend that the circuit should not be used.

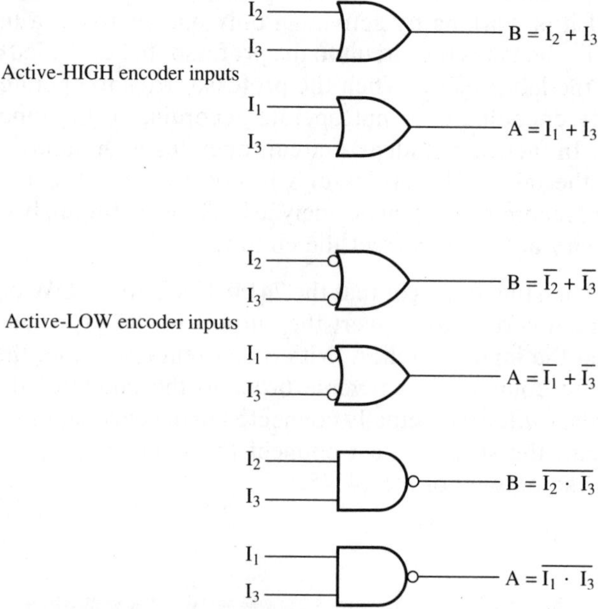

FIGURE 5-36 Example 5-15 Simplified Encoder Circuits for Troubleshooting

■

■ EXAMPLE 5-17 "Return to Sender" Lost Address Decoder

Problem: A student uses a 74138 to design a circuit to decode eight addresses. However, several of the addresses are lost and never decoded. The circuit incorrectly operates according to the table given. You step in to determine the cause of the lost addresses.

Decoder Inputs						Decoder Outputs							
G_1	$\overline{G}_{2A}$	$\overline{G}_{2B}$	C	B	A	Y_0	Y_1	Y_2	Y_3	Y_4	Y_5	Y_6	Y_7
1	0	0	0	0	0	1	1	0	1	1	1	1	1
1	0	0	0	0	1	1	1	0	1	1	1	1	1
1	0	0	0	1	0	1	1	0	1	1	1	1	1
1	0	0	0	1	1	1	1	0	1	1	1	1	1
1	0	0	1	0	0	1	1	0	1	1	1	1	1
1	0	0	1	0	1	1	1	1	1	1	1	1	0
1	0	0	1	1	0	1	1	0	1	1	1	1	1
1	0	0	1	1	1	1	1	1	1	1	1	1	0

Solution: A close examination of the table reveals some interesting patterns. The circuit is decoding, so the problem does not appear to be related to the enable inputs. The circuit seems to be stuck with the address 010 for all but two of the combinations, and then it decodes the address 111. Therefore, further analysis is needed to scrutinize the theoretical address inputs with those that the circuit is apparently receiving and decoding.

Theoretical Addresses			Observed Addresses		
C	B	A	C	B	A
0	0	0	0	1	0
0	0	1	0	1	0
0	1	0	0	1	0
0	1	1	0	1	0
1	0	0	0	1	0
1	0	1	1	1	1
1	1	0	0	1	0
1	1	1	1	1	1

By inspecting the table of the theoretical addresses versus observed addresses, one sees clearly that the B address input is either shorted to V_{CC} or left floating. The A and C address inputs are always equal to each other, and the result for both is 0 if either A or C in the theoretical address is a 0. The suspicion is that the A and C inputs are shorted together at the IC, even though they are operated from two switches. That is why a 0 is input to the decoder if either switch is low. Only when both the A and C switches are high is a 1 entered into the decoder. (See Figure 5-37.)

After completing the thorough analysis, one uses a logic probe to verify the findings. Indeed, B is left unconnected and C and A are shorted at the 74138 decoder. The problems are corrected, and now all the addresses have been located by the decoder!

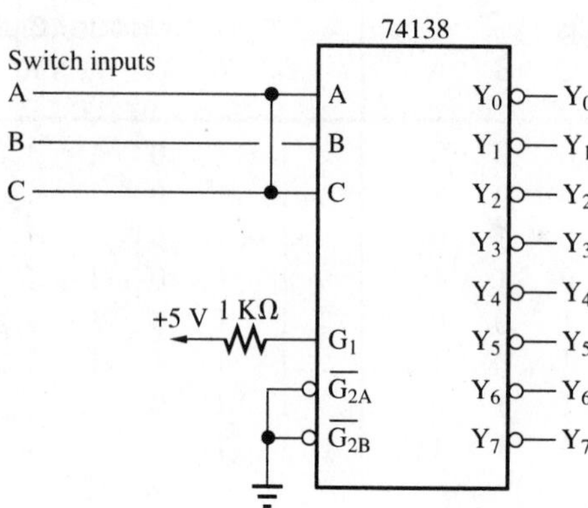

FIGURE 5-37 Example 5-16 Circuit with Wiring Errors

■

Section Self-Test

Determine if the following statements are true or false:

1. The individual current-limiting resistors for each segment of a seven-segment display can be replaced by one resistor.
2. The inputs on a 8:3 priority encoder with active-LOW outputs can be reversed in order to eliminate the need for inverters at the outputs.
3. All addresses will be decoded by a decoder even if the select inputs are not properly connected.

ANSWERS • False • False • False

SUMMARY

The analysis, application, and design of decoders, encoders, and code converters were studied in this chapter. The applications centered on keyboard encoding, display decoding, address decoding, memory address selection, function generation, error detection, and display multiplexing. The code conversion applications described focused primarily on input and output logic applications, especially for interfacing with mechanical devices such as keyboards or switches on the input and with display devices such as LEDs on the output.

ANALYSIS

Decoders, encoders, and code converters were analyzed, both as circuits built from logic gates and as MSI ICs. Decoders activate a single output that corresponds to an address. Encoders produce the binary code for a single input. Code converters perform complex code conversion operations, such as BCD-to-binary and binary-to-BCD code conversions.

Decoder circuits driving LED displays were analyzed to determine the amount of current flowing when the LEDs are lit. Current-limiting resistors are required to limit the current to a safe level so that the LED display is not damaged.

Cascaded decoders were studied to determine how to expand the number of addresses a system can decode. The enable inputs on the decoders can be used by the most significant address inputs for expanded address decoding.

Encoders and priority encoding circuits were analyzed. Encoders can also be cascaded through the use of enable inputs to expand the number of switch outputs that can be encoded.

APPLICATION

Address decoding, display decoding, keypad encoding, display multiplexing, and logic function generation were the key applications studied in this chapter. Several application circuits were given to illustrate the examples, and several examples expanded the operation of the basic application circuits.

DESIGN

Decoder, encoder, and code converter circuits were designed based on an application specification. A truth table for each application is developed in order to derive the necessary logic functions for the design. Whenever possible, available decoder, encoder, and code converter ICs were used in the designs.

TROUBLESHOOTING

Decoder, encoder, and display circuits were used in troubleshooting examples to analyze the cause of incorrect circuit operation and to correct the error. Troubleshooting must encompass the operation of the electronics, the wiring, and the input/output devices in question.

In computational applications, code conversion can take place via hardware with circuits as described in this chapter, or via software in microprocessors. The selection of hardware versus software code conversion depends on a complete examination of the application requirements. In many situations a hardware solution can provide a faster code conversion than a software solution can.

Code conversion ICs have reduced the logic design complexity and will continue to be used in standard applications. However, some of these circuits will be replaced in large-scale applications by programmable logic devices (PLDs) that will allow a greater degree of flexibility in programming the specific code conversion while still only requiring a single IC. PLDs and their application in logic design are covered in detail in Chapter 12.

PROBLEMS

5-1 Code Conversion Circuits—Analysis Problem

1. Make a table of the performance characteristics of TTL code conversion circuits listed in Table 5-1. The table should include the:
   a. number of inputs
   b. number of outputs
   c. type of output (open-collector?)
   d. propagation delay for the code conversion

5.2 Decoder—Analysis Problems

*2. Examine the data sheet for the 74154 decoder/demultiplexer.
   a. What is the maximum delay to decode the select inputs?
   b. If the final logic level were a 7420 NAND gate, what will be the total maximum delay to implement a logic function using the 74154 and the 7420?
   c. What will be the maximum delay for a two-level circuit of solely 7420 NAND gates?

3. Examine the data sheets for the 74139 and the 74155 decoders/demultiplexers. What is the primary difference between these two ICs relative to their decoding operation.

5-3 Decoder Applications—Application and Design Problems

*4. Use the 74138 to design a decoder system to decode 32 addresses.

5. Use the 74138 to design a decoder system to decode 64 addresses.

6. Use the 74154 to design a decoder system to decode 128 addresses.

7. How many 74138 decoders are required to decode hex addresses 00 through 3F?

8. How many 74154 decoders are required to decode hex addresses 00 through FF?

9. Decode the binary values of 3, 6, 9, 12, and 15 using the necessary number of:
   (a) 74138 decoders (b) 74154 decoders

*10. Design a controlled decoder that will decode the values 3, 6, 9, 12, and 15 when the control line, A, is HIGH, and that will decode the values 2, 4, 6, 8, 10, 12 when the control line, A, is LOW. Use the 74154 decoders and any additional circuitry.

---

* *See* Answers to Selected Problems.

11. Design a multiplier that will multiply a 3-bit number times a 2-bit number and produce the correct results. Use 75154 decoders and any additional logic gates to complete the design.

*12. Design a logic circuit to subtract two 2-bit binary numbers and output the resulting number. Use the 74154 decoder and any additional logic gates for the design.

13. Design the decoder circuitry to decode hex addresses 00 to 3F, using the necessary number of 74138 decoders and any additional circuitry as required.

14. For the circuitry designed for Problem 5-13, show which outputs correspond to the following hex addresses: 05, 0F, 15, 2B, 3D.

*15. Use a 74154 decoder and any additional logic gates to implement three logic functions simultaneously. The functions are the following:
a. $\overline{A}\,B\,C + A\,D + B\,C\,D + \overline{C}\,D = L$
b. $(A + B + \overline{D})(C + A)(B + D) = K$
c. $A\,\overline{B}\,\overline{C} + A\,\overline{B}\,C + \overline{A}\,\overline{B}\,C = M$

16. An application requires ten decoded outputs according to the following function table:

Select Inputs				Decoded Outputs									
D	C	B	A	0	1	2	3	4	5	6	7	8	9
0	0	0	0	0	1	1	1	1	1	1	1	1	1
0	0	0	1	1	0	1	1	1	1	1	1	1	1
0	0	1	0	1	1	0	1	1	1	1	1	1	1
0	0	1	1	1	1	1	0	1	1	1	1	1	1
0	1	0	0	1	1	1	1	0	1	1	1	1	1
1	0	0	0	1	1	1	1	1	0	1	1	1	1
1	0	0	1	1	1	1	1	1	1	0	1	1	1
1	0	1	0	1	1	1	1	1	1	1	0	1	1
1	0	1	1	1	1	1	1	1	1	1	1	0	1
1	1	0	0	1	1	1	1	1	1	1	1	1	0

a. Design a decoder circuit from basic logic gates for this application.
b. Design a decoder circuit using 74138 ICs for this application.

17. Modify the 7442 BCD-to-decimal decoder to add an active-LOW enable input. If the input is at a logic-HIGH level, all outputs should remain at a logic-HIGH level.

5-4 Display Decoder Drivers—Application and Design Problems

18. Design a display multiplexer to drive four seven-segment output displays from one display driver.

*19. Design a BCD to seven-segment display that displays the character "E" when an invalid 4-bit code is entered by adding additional logic circuitry as needed to the 7447 display decoder/driver.

20. Design an alphabetic to seven-segment display decoder/driver for a common-anode display using basic logic gates, according to the following function table:

Input Code				Display
1	0	1	0	A
1	0	1	1	B
1	1	0	0	C
1	1	0	1	D
1	1	1	0	E
1	1	1	1	F

21. Modify the 7447 display decoder/driver to perform hexadecimal to seven-segment display code conversion. This requires that the characters A, B, C, D, E, and F be displayed instead of the characters originally programmed by the IC.

22. Design an alphabetic to seven-segment display decoder/driver for a common-cathode display to display the first 16 letters of the alphabet, corresponding to input combinations 0000 through 1111.

23. Enhanced LED displays have 14 segments. Design a hex to 14-segment display decoder/driver for a common-cathode display to function as shown in Figure 5-38.

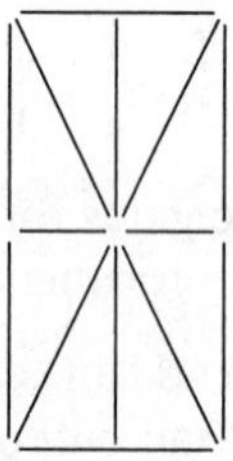

Input Code				Display
0	0	0	0	0
0	0	0	1	1
0	0	1	0	2
0	0	1	1	3
0	1	0	0	4
0	1	0	1	5
0	1	1	0	6
0	1	1	1	7
1	0	0	0	8
1	0	0	1	9
1	0	1	0	A
1	0	1	1	B
1	1	0	0	C
1	1	0	1	D
1	1	1	0	E
1	1	1	1	F

LED Segment Pattern

FIGURE 5-38 Problem 5-23 Display

5-5 Encoders—Analysis Problems

*24. Examine the data sheet for the 74147 priority encoder.
   a. What is the maximum propagation delay from any input to any output?
   b. What is the maximum propagation delay for a 74LS147 from any input to any output?

25. Examine the data sheet for the 74148 priority encoder.
   a. What is the maximum propagation delay from input 1 to the A_2, A_1, A_0 outputs?
   b. What is the maximum propagation delay from input 0 to the E_O output?
   c. What is the maximum propagation delay from input 0 to the G_S output?
   d. What warning is given at the bottom of the data sheet page showing the application circuits?

5-6 Encoder Applications—Application and Design Problems

26. Modify the 74147 decimal to BCD encoder to provide an enable input, enable output, and strobe output for cascading purposes. These signals should function as those on the 74148 encoder.

27. Design a 16-line data encoder using the 74148 ICs and any additional logic gates for active-HIGH encoded data.

5-7 Code Converters—Analysis Problems

*28. Examine the data sheet for the 74184 code converter.
   a. What is the maximum delay time to convert BCD values up to 99 to their binary equivalent?
   b. What is the maximum delay time required to convert BCD values up to 9999 to their binary equivalent?
   c. What is the maximum BCD value that requires six BCD digits?
   d. How many 74184 code converters are required to convert BCD numbers up to 9999 to their binary equivalent.

29. Examine the data sheet for the 74185 code converter.
   a. What is the maximum delay time to convert binary values up to 99 to their BCD equivalent?
   b. What is the maximum delay time required to convert binary values up to 9999 to their BCD equivalent?
   c. What is the maximum binary value that requires 20 input bits?
   d. How many 74185 code converters are required to convert binary numbers up to 9999 to their BCD equivalent.

5-8 Code Converter Applications—Application and Design Problems

30. Design a code converter using basic logic gates to convert from binary to BCD for values 0 through 15.

31. Expand the design of Problem 5-30 to design a code converter to convert from binary to BCD for values 0 through 31.

32. Design a decimal to Gray code converter from basic logic gates.

33. Design a Gray to decimal code converter from basic logic gates.

*34. Similar to the application circuit in Figure 5-32, show the application circuit for BCD-to-nine's and ten's complement conversion using the 74184. Include all enable and resistor connections required for proper operation, and define the mode setting for each complement.

35. Show the application circuit for converting binary values of 0 through 255 to BCD using the 74185. Include all enable and resistor connections required for proper operation.

36. The BCD values from Problem 5-35 must be displayed on common-cathode seven-segment LED displays. Select the display decoder/drivers, and show the complete circuit required to display binary values 0 through 255.

5-9 Parity Encoding

*37. Refer to the ASCII code table in Chapter 2, Table 2-8. Determine the data code for each character of ''Digital Logic'' and encode each character for even parity transmission using the 74180. Show in a table the original and transmitted codes, and draw the circuit required for parity generation and transmission of these codes.

38. Design a parity checker circuit using only Exclusive-OR gates that will output an error signal if the transmitted bits are not of the proper parity.

5-10 Troubleshooting Code Conversion Circuits

*39. Determine the output of the circuit in Example 5-1 if the A and B inputs are shorted together but still connected to their input switches.

40. Determine the output of the circuit in Example 5-2 if the C input is left unconnected.

*41. Determine the output of the circuit in Example 5-2 if the D and B inputs are shorted to ground.

42. Determine the output of the circuit in Figure 5-14 if the address inputs on the second IC are connected in the reverse order as they are connected to the first IC.

43. Determine the output of a common-cathode display used with a 7447 decoder/driver for binary inputs 0000 through 1111. Assume that the lamp test, ripple blanking input, and blanking input are tied to a logic HIGH.

44. Determine the output of a common-anode display that has been used once before without the current-limiting resistors in series between a 7447 and the display.

45. Determine the output from the 74148 encoder if keypads 0 through 7 are connected in reverse order to inputs 7 through 0, respectively.

*46. Determine the output from the circuit in Figure 5-29 if the $\overline{G}$ input is left unconnected.

Chapter 6

Arithmetic Circuits

Upon completing and mastering the material in this chapter, you should be able to perform the following tasks in the areas of analysis, application, and design of arithmetic circuits:

ANALYSIS

1. Define the logic function for half-adders and full adders in a truth table.
2. Analyze half-adder and full-adder circuits built from logic gates.
3. Analyze arithmetic circuits such as adders, multipliers, arithmetic logic units, and comparators.

APPLICATION

4. Apply arithmetic circuits such as adders, comparators, multipliers, and arithmetic logic units in digital systems.
5. Perform binary subtraction using adder circuits.
6. Perform signed arithmetic with one's and two's complement arithmetic circuits.
7. Detect and correct overflow conditions in arithmetic operations.
8. Perform multiplication with adders and multipliers.

DESIGN

9. Design multifunction arithmetic circuits.
10. Design adders, multipliers, comparators, and other arithmetic circuits from basic logic gates.

TROUBLESHOOTING

11. Analyze incorrect arithmetic circuit operation to determine the fault.
12. Correct the cause of incorrect circuit operation and test the circuit for proper operation.

Arithmetic circuits are a class of combinational logic circuits that perform arithmetic and logic processes. The operation and application of arithmetic circuits are the subject of this chapter. The chapter begins with addition and builds on it as the fundamental arithmetic operation by which the other operations are performed. A thorough understanding of all arithmetic operations described in detail in Chapter 2 is necessary in order to apply the information in this chapter to logic design applications.

Arithmetic circuits available as SSI and MSI circuits include a variety of adders, multipliers, comparators, and multifunction arithmetic/logic units. Subtraction and division are performed through addition processes. Multiplication can be performed by addition, but IC multiplier circuits are available as well. The arithmetic logic ICs covered in this chapter are listed in Table 6-1, and the data sheets for these circuits are in Figures 6-1 through 6-5.

TABLE 6-1 Arithmetic Logic Integrated Circuits

74283	Four-bit adder
7486	Quad 2-input Exclusive-OR gates
74135	Quad Exclusive-OR/NOR gates
74284 and 74285	4 × 4 multiplier
7485	Four-bit comparator
74682	Six-bit comparator
74181	Four-bit ALU function generator

SN54283, SN54LS283, SN54S283, SN74283, SN74LS283, SN74S283
4-BIT BINARY FULL ADDERS WITH FAST CARRY

OCTOBER 1976 – REVISED MARCH 1988

- Full-Carry Look-Ahead Across the Four Bits
- Systems Achieve Partial Look-Ahead Performance with the Economy of Ripple Carry
- Supply Voltage and Ground on Corner Pins to Simplify P-C Board Layout

TYPICAL ADD TIMES

TYPE	TWO 8-BIT WORDS	TWO 16-BIT WORDS	TYPICAL POWER DISSIPATION PER ADDER
'283	23ns	43ns	310 mW
'LS283	25ns	45ns	95 mW
'S283	15ns	30ns	510 mW

SN54283, SN54LS283 . . . J OR W PACKAGE
SN54S283 . . . J PACKAGE
SN74283 . . . N PACKAGE
SN74LS283, SN74S283 . . . D OR N PACKAGE
(TOP VIEW)

Signal	Pin	Pin	Signal
Σ2	1	16	VCC
B2	2	15	B3
A2	3	14	A3
Σ1	4	13	Σ3
A1	5	12	A4
B1	6	11	B4
C0	7	10	Σ4
GND	8	9	C4

SN54LS283, SN54S283 . . . FK PACKAGE
(TOP VIEW)

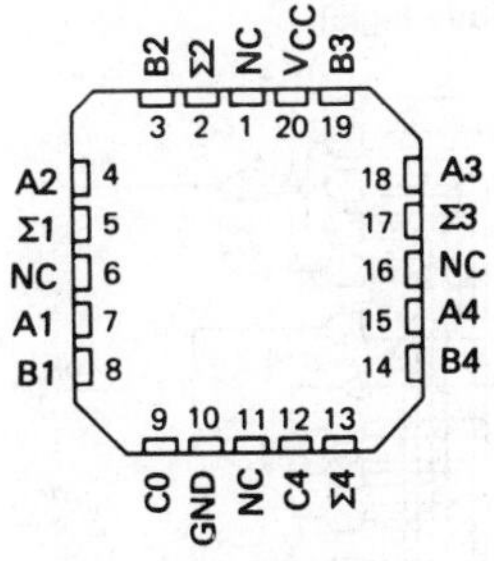

NC - No internal connection

description

The '283 and 'LS283 adders are electrically and functionally identical to the '83A and 'LS83A, respectively; only the arrangement of the terminals has been changed. The 'S283 high performance versions are also functionally identical.

These improved full adders perform the addition of two 4-bit binary words. The sum (Σ) outputs are provided for each bit and the resultant carry (C4) is obtained from the fourth bit. These adders feature full internal look-ahead across all four bits generating the carry term in ten nanoseconds, typically, for the '283 and 'LS283, and 7.5 nanoseconds for the 'S283. This capability provides the system designer with partial look-ahead performance at the economy and reduced package count of a ripple-carry implementation.

The adder logic, including the carry, is implemented in its true form. End around carry can be accomplished without the need for logic or level inversion.

Series 54, Series 54LS, and Series 54S circuits are characterized for operation over the full temperature range of −55°C to 125°C. Series 74, Series 74LS, and Series 74S circuits are characterized for 0°C to 70°C operation.

FUNCTION TABLE

INPUT				OUTPUT WHEN C0 = L / WHEN C2 = L			OUTPUT WHEN C0 = H / WHEN C2 = H		
A1 / A3	B1 / B3	A2 / A4	B2 / B4	Σ1 / Σ3	Σ2 / Σ4	C2 / C4	Σ1 / Σ3	Σ2 / Σ4	C2 / C4
L	L	L	L	L	L	L	H	L	L
H	L	L	L	H	L	L	L	H	L
L	H	L	L	H	L	L	L	H	L
H	H	L	L	L	H	L	H	H	L
L	L	H	L	L	H	L	H	H	L
H	L	H	L	H	H	L	L	L	H
L	H	H	L	H	H	L	L	L	H
H	H	H	L	L	L	H	H	L	H
L	L	L	H	L	H	L	H	H	L
H	L	L	H	H	H	L	L	L	H
L	H	L	H	H	H	L	L	L	H
H	H	L	H	L	L	H	H	L	H
L	L	H	H	L	L	H	H	L	H
H	L	H	H	H	L	H	L	H	H
L	H	H	H	H	L	H	L	H	H
H	H	H	H	L	H	H	H	H	H

H = high level, L = low level

NOTE: Input conditions at A1, B1, A2, B2, and C0 are used to determine outputs Σ1 and Σ2 and the value of the internal carry C2. The values at C2, A3, B3, A4, and B4 are then used to determine outputs Σ3, Σ4, and C4.

FIGURE 6-1 74283 4-Bit Adder Data Sheets. (Courtesy of Texas Instruments.)

SN54283, SN54LS283, SN54S283, SN74283, SN74LS283, SN74S283 4-BIT BINARY FULL ADDERS WITH FAST CARRY

logic symbol†

†This symbol is in accordance with ANSI/IEEE Std. 91-1984 and IEC Publication 617-12.
Pin numbers shown are for D, J, N, and W packages.

logic diagram (positive logic)

Pin numbers shown are for D, J, N, and W packages.

schematics of inputs and outputs

'283

'LS283

'S283

absolute maximum ratings over operating free-air temperature range (unless otherwise noted)

Supply voltage, V_{CC} (see Note 1)	7V
Input voltage: '283, 'S283	5.5V
'LS283	7V
Interemitter voltage (see Note 2)	5.5V
Operating free-air temperature range: SN54283, SN54LS283, SN54S283	−55°C to 125°C
SN74283, SN74LS283, SN74S283	0°C to 70°C
Storage temperature range	−65°C to 150°C

NOTES: 1. Voltage values, except interemitter voltage, are with respect to network ground terminal.
2. This is the voltage between two emitters of a multiple-emitter transistor. This rating applies for the '283 and 'S283 only between the following pairs: A1 and B1, A2 and B2, A3 and B3, A4 and B4.

FIGURE 6-1 (*continued*)

SN54284, SN54285, SN74284, SN74285
4-BIT BY 4-BIT PARALLEL BINARY MULTIPLIERS

MAY 1972 — REVISED MARCH 1988

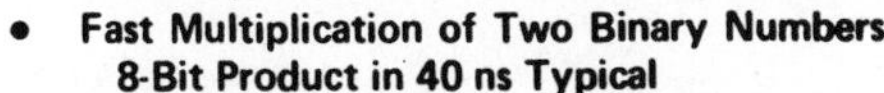

- **Fast Multiplication of Two Binary Numbers**
  8-Bit Product in 40 ns Typical
- **Expandable for N-Bit-by-n-Bit Applications:**
  16-Bit Product in 70 ns Typical
  32-Bit Product in 103 ns Typical
- **Fully Compatible with Most TTL Circuits**
- **Diode-Clamped Inputs Simplify System Design**

description

These high-speed TTL circuits are designed to be used in high-performance parallel multiplication applications. When connected as shown in Figure A, these circuits perform the positive-logic multiplication of two 4-bit binary words. The eight-bit binary product is generated with typically only 40 nanoseconds delay.

This basic four-by-four multiplier can be utilized as a fundamental building block for implementing larger multipliers. For example, the four-by-four building blocks can be connected as shown in Figure B to generate submultiple partial products. These results can then be summed in a Wallace tree, and, as illustrated, will produce a 16-bit product for the two eight-bit words typically in 70 nanoseconds. SN54H183/SN74H183 carry-save adders and SN54S181/SN74S181 arithmetic logic units with the SN54S182/SN74S182 look-ahead generator are used to achieve this high performance. The scheme is expandable for implementing N × M bit multipliers.

The SN54284 and SN54285 are characterized for operation over the full military temperature range of −55°C to 125°C; the SN74284 and SN74285 are characterized for operation from 0°C to 70°C.

SN54284 . . . J OR W PACKAGE
SN74284 . . . N PACKAGE
(TOP VIEW)

Signal	Pin	Pin	Signal
2C	1	16	V_{CC}
2B	2	15	2D
2A	3	14	$\overline{GA}$
1D	4	13	$\overline{GB}$
1A	5	12	Y4
1B	6	11	Y5
1C	7	10	Y6
GND	8	9	Y7

SN54285 . . . J OR W PACKAGE
SN74285 . . . N PACKAGE
(TOP VIEW)

Signal	Pin	Pin	Signal
2C	1	16	V_{CC}
2B	2	15	2D
2A	3	14	$\overline{GA}$
1D	4	13	$\overline{GB}$
1A	5	12	Y0
1B	6	11	Y1
1C	7	10	Y2
GND	8	9	Y3

logic symbols†

'284

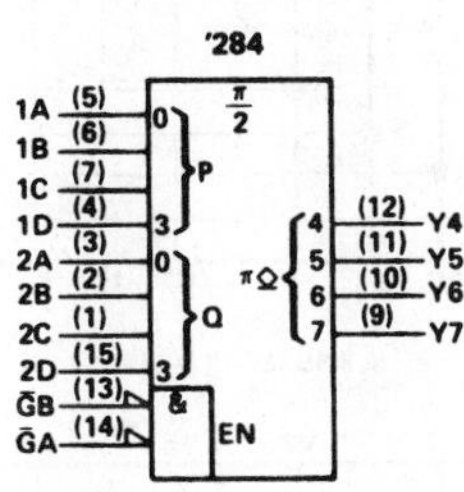

'285

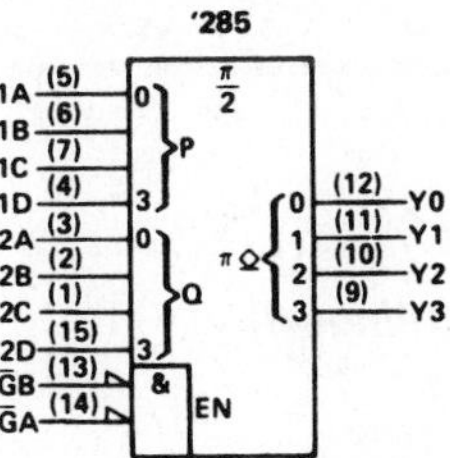

†These symbols are in accordance with ANSI/IEEE Std. 91-1984 and IEC Publication 617-12.

FIGURE 6-2 74284 and 74285 4 × 4 Multiplier Data Sheet. (Courtesy of Texas Instruments.)

SN54284, SN54285, SN74284, SN74285
4-BIT BY 4-BIT PARALLEL BINARY MULTIPLIERS

schematics

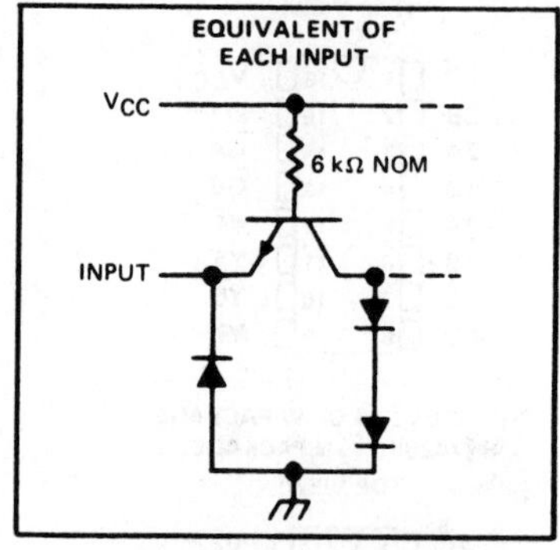

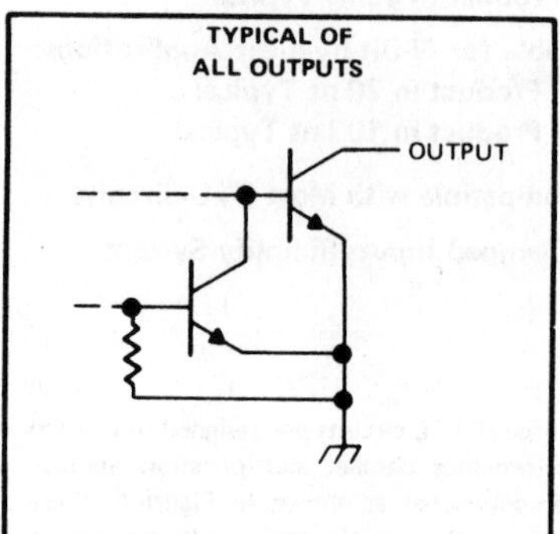

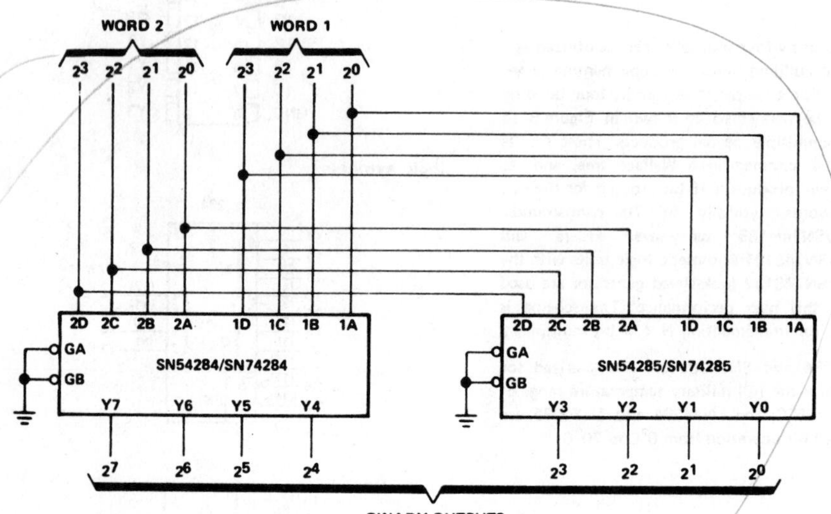

FIGURE A–4 X 4 MULTIPLIER

FIGURE 6-2 (*continued*)

SN5485, SN54LS85, SN54S85 SN7485, SN74LS85, SN74S85 4-BIT MAGNITUDE COMPARATORS

MARCH 1974 – REVISED MARCH 1988

TYPE	TYPICAL POWER DISSIPATION	TYPICAL DELAY (4-BIT WORDS)
'85	275 mW	23 ns
'LS85	52 mW	24 ns
'S85	365 mW	11 ns

description

These four-bit magnitude comparators perform comparison of straight binary and straight BCD (8-4-2-1) codes. Three fully decoded decisions about two 4-bit words (A, B) are made and are externally available at three outputs. These devices are fully expandable to any number of bits without external gates. Words of greater length may be compared by connecting comparators in cascade. The A > B, A < B, and A = B outputs of a stage handling less-significant bits are connected to the corresponding A > B, A < B, and A = B inputs of the next stage handling more-significant bits. The stage handling the least-significant bits must have a high-level voltage applied to the A = B input. The cascading paths of the '85, 'LS85, and 'S85 are implemented with only a two-gate-level delay to reduce overall comparison times for long words. An alternate method of cascading which further reduces the comparison time is shown in the typical application data.

SN5485, SN54LS85, SN54S85 . . . J OR W PACKAGE
SN7485 . . . N PACKAGE
SN74LS85, SN74S85 . . . D OR N PACKAGE
(TOP VIEW)

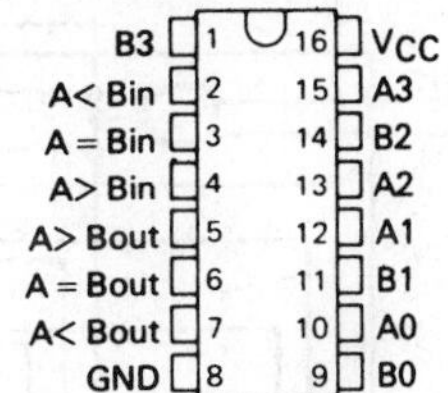

SN54LS85, SN54S85 . . . FK PACKAGE
(TOP VIEW)

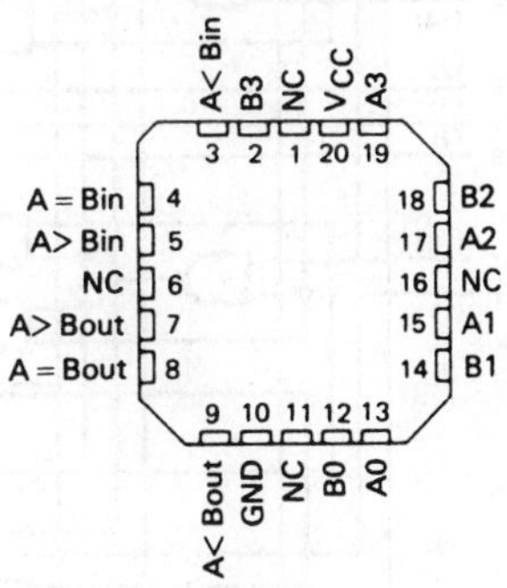

NC - No internal connection

FUNCTION TABLE

COMPARING INPUTS				CASCADING INPUTS			OUTPUTS		
A3, B3	A2, B2	A1, B1	A0, B0	A > B	A < B	A = B	A > B	A < B	A = B
A3 > B3	X	X	X	X	X	X	H	L	L
A3 < B3	X	X	X	X	X	X	L	H	L
A3 = B3	A2 > B2	X	X	X	X	X	H	L	L
A3 = B3	A2 < B2	X	X	X	X	X	L	H	L
A3 = B2	A2 = B2	A1 > B1	X	X	X	X	H	L	L
A3 = B3	A2 = B2	A1 < B1	X	X	X	X	L	H	L
A2 = B3	A2 = B2	A1 = B1	A0 > B0	X	X	X	H	L	L
A3 = B3	A2 = B2	A1 = B1	A0 < B0	X	X	X	L	H	L
A3 = B3	A2 = B2	A1 = B1	A0 = B0	H	L	L	H	L	L
A3 = B3	A2 = B2	A1 = B1	A0 = B0	L	H	L	L	H	L
A3 = B3	A2 = B2	A1 = B1	A0 = B0	X	X	H	L	L	H
A3 = B3	A2 = B2	A1 = B1	A0 = B0	H	H	L	L	L	L
A3 = B3	A2 = B2	A1 = B1	A0 = B0	L	L	L	H	H	L

FIGURE 6-3 7485 4-Bit Comparator Data Sheets. (Courtesy of Texas Instruments.)

SN5485, SN54LS85, SN54S85, SN7485, SN74LS85, SN74S85 4-BIT MAGNITUDE COMPARATORS

logic diagrams (positive logic)

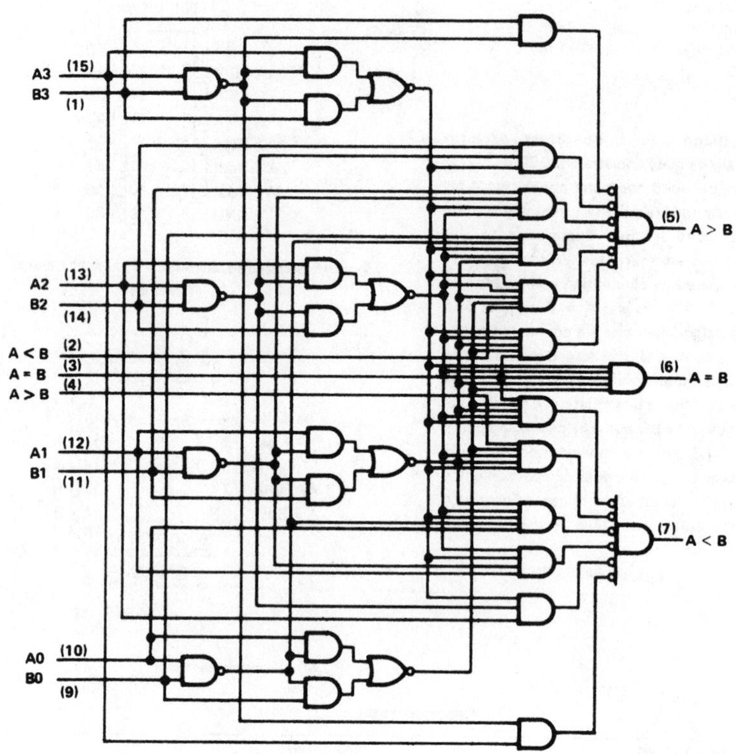

logic symbol†

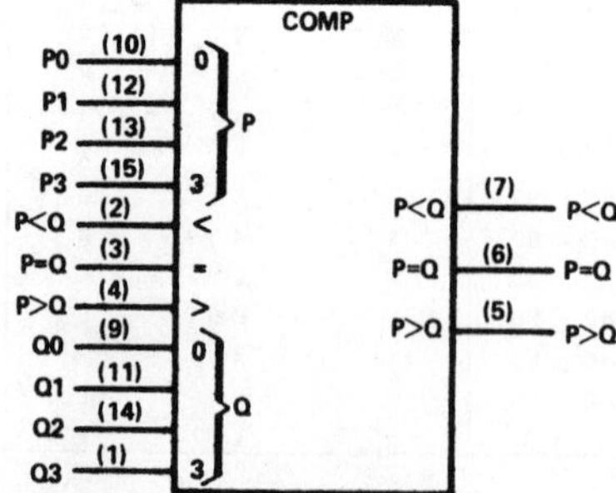

†This symbol is in accordancae with ANSI/IEEE Std 91-1984 and IEC Publication 617-12.
Pin numbers shown are for D, J, N, and W packages.

FIGURE 6-3 (*continued*)

SN54LS682, SN54LS684, SN54LS685, SN54LS687, SN54LS688, SN74LS682, SN74LS684 THRU SN74LS688 8-BIT MAGNITUDE/IDENTITY COMPARATORS

D2617, JANUARY 1981 – REVISED MARCH 1988

- Compares Two-8-Bit Words
- Choice of Totem-Pole or Open-Collector Outputs
- Hysteresis at P and Q Inputs
- 'LS682 has 20-kΩ Pullup Resistors on the Q Inputs
- SN74LS686 and 'LS687 . . . JT and NT 24-Pin, 300-Mil Packages

TYPE	P = Q	P > Q	OUTPUT ENABLE	OUTPUT CONFIGURATION	20-kΩ PULLUP
'LS682	yes	yes	no	totem-pole	yes
'LS684	yes	yes	no	totem-pole	no
'LS685	yes	yes	no	open-collector	no
SN74LS686	yes	yes	yes	totem-pole	no
'LS687	yes	yes	yes	open-collector	no
'LS688	yes	no	yes	totem-pole	no

SN54LS682, SN54LS684, SN54LS685 . . . J PACKAGE
SN74LS682, SN74LS684, SN74LS685 . . . DW OR N PACKAGE
(TOP VIEW)

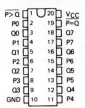

Pin	Name	Pin	Name
1	P>Q	20	VCC
2	P0	19	P=Q
3	Q0	18	Q7
4	P1	17	P7
5	Q1	16	Q6
6	P2	15	P6
7	Q2	14	Q5
8	P3	13	P5
9	Q3	12	Q4
10	GND	11	P4

SN54LS682, SN54LS684, SN54LS685 . . . FK PACKAGE
(TOP VIEW)

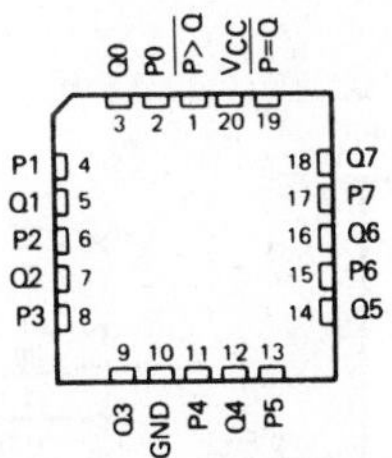

SN54LS687 . . . JT PACKAGE
SN74LS686, SN74LS687 . . . DW OR NT PACKAGE
(TOP VIEW)

Pin	Name	Pin	Name
1	P>Q	24	VCC
2	G1	23	G2
3	P0	22	P=Q
4	Q0	21	Q7
5	P1	20	P7
6	Q1	19	NC
7	NC	18	Q6
8	P2	17	P6
9	Q2	16	Q5
10	P3	15	P5
11	Q3	14	Q4
12	GND	13	P4

SN54LS688 . . . J PACKAGE
SN74LS688 . . . DW OR N PACKAGE
(TOP VIEW)

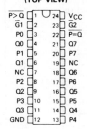

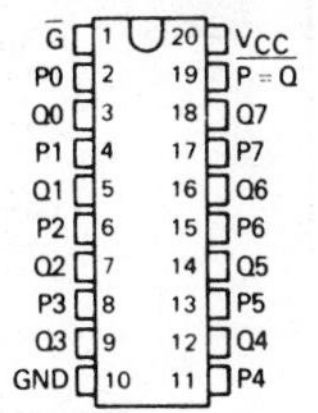

SN54LS687 . . . FK PACKAGE
(TOP VIEW)

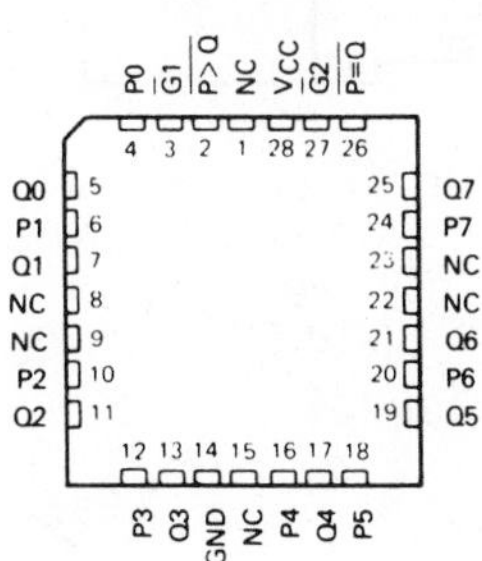

NC – No internal connection

SN54LS688 . . . FK PACKAGE
(TOP VIEW)

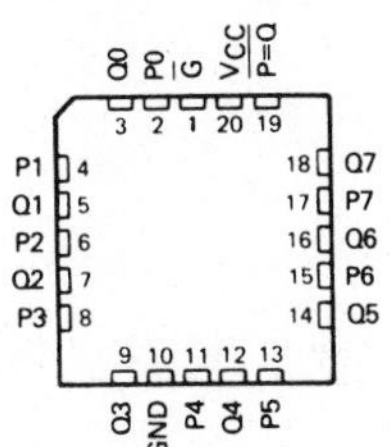

FIGURE 6-4 74682 6-Bit Comparator Data Sheets. (Courtesy of Texas Instruments.)

SN54LS682, SN54LS684, SN54LS685, SN54LS687, SN54LS688
SN74LS682, SN74LS684 THRU SN74LS688
8-BIT MAGNITUDE/IDENTITY COMPARATORS

description

These magnitude comparators perform comparisons of two eight-bit binary or BCD words. All types provide $\overline{P = Q}$ outputs and all except 'LS688 provide $\overline{P > Q}$ outputs as well. The 'LS682, 'LS684, 'LS686, and 'LS688 have totem-pole outputs, while the 'LS685 and 'LS687 have open-collector outputs. The 'LS682 features 20-kΩ pullup termination resistors on the Q inputs for analog or switch data.

FUNCTION TABLE

INPUTS			OUTPUTS	
DATA	ENABLES		$\overline{P=Q}$	$\overline{P>Q}$
P, Q	$\overline{G}$, $\overline{G1}$	$\overline{G2}$		
P=Q	L	X	L	H
P>Q	X	L	H	L
P<Q	X	X	H	H
P=Q	H	X	H	H
P>Q	X	H	H	H
X	H	H	H	H

NOTES: 1. The last three lines of the function table applies only to the devices having enable inputs, i.e., 'LS686 thru 'LS688.

2. The $\overline{P<Q}$ function can be generated by applying the $\overline{P=Q}$ and $\overline{P>Q}$ outputs to a 2-input NAND gate.

3. For 'LS686 and 'LS687, $\overline{G}1$ enables $\overline{P=Q}$ and $\overline{G}2$ enables $\overline{P>Q}$.

logic symbols†

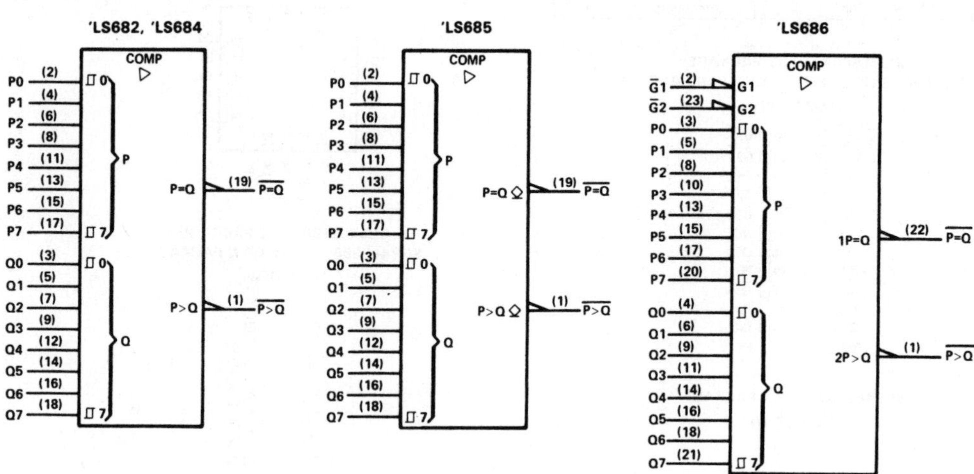

†These symbols are in accordance with ANSI/IEEE Std 91-1984 and IEC Publication 617-12.
Pin numbers shown are for DW, J, JT, N, and NT packages.

FIGURE 6-4 (*continued*)

SN54LS181, SN54S181, SN74LS181, SN74S181
ARITHMETIC LOGIC UNITS/FUNCTION GENERATORS

DECEMBER 1972—REVISED MARCH 1988

- **Full Look-Ahead for High-Speed Operations on Long Words**
- **Input Clamping Diodes Minimize Transmission-Line Effects**
- **Darlington Outputs Reduce Turn-Off Time**
- **Arithmetic Operating Modes:**
  - Addition
  - Subtraction
  - Shift Operand A One Position
  - Magnitude Comparison
  - Plus Twelve Other Arithmetic Operations
- **Logic Function Modes:**
  - Exclusive-OR
  - Comparator
  - AND, NAND, OR, NOR
  - Plus Ten Other Logic Operations

SN54LS181, SN54S181 . . . J OR W PACKAGE
SN74LS181, SN74S181 . . . DW OR N PACKAGE
(TOP VIEW)

Signal	Pin	Pin	Signal
$\overline{B0}$	1	24	V_{CC}
$\overline{A0}$	2	23	$\overline{A1}$
S3	3	22	$\overline{B1}$
S2	4	21	$\overline{A2}$
S1	5	20	$\overline{B2}$
S0	6	19	$\overline{A3}$
C_n	7	18	$\overline{B3}$
M	8	17	$\overline{G}$
$\overline{F0}$	9	16	C_{n+4}
$\overline{F1}$	10	15	$\overline{P}$
$\overline{F2}$	11	14	A = B
GND	12	13	$\overline{F3}$

SN54LS181, SN54S181 . . . FK PACKAGE
(TOP VIEW)

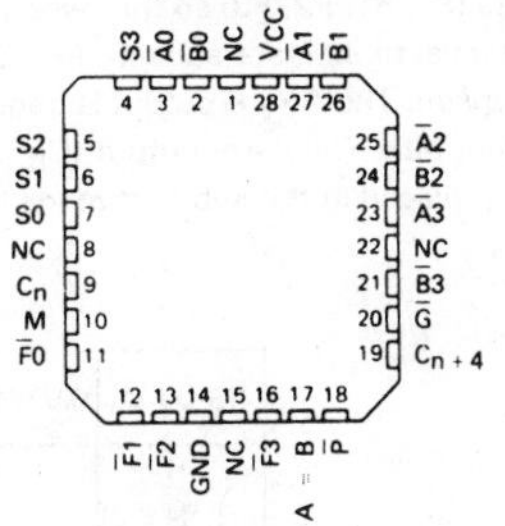

NC - No internal connection

TYPICAL ADDITION TIMES

NUMBER OF BITS	ADDITION TIMES		PACKAGE COUNT		CARRY METHOD BETWEEN ALUs
	USING 'LS181 AND 'S182	USING 'S181 AND 'S182	ARITHMETIC/ LOGIC UNITS	LOOK-AHEAD CARRY GENERATORS	
1 to 4	24 ns	11 ns	1		NONE
5 to 8	40 ns	18 ns	2		RIPPLE
9 to 16	44 ns	19 ns	3 or 4	1	FULL LOOK-AHEAD
17 to 64	68 ns	28 ns	5 to 16	2 to 5	FULL LOOK-AHEAD

description

The 'LS181 and 'S181 are arithmetic logic units (ALU)/function generators that have a complexity of 75 equivalent gates on a monolithic chip. These circuits perform 16 binary arithmetic operations on two 4-bit words as shown in Tables 1 and 2. These operations are selected by the four function-select lines (S0, S1, S2, S3) and include addition, subtraction, decrement, and straight transfer. When performing arithmetic manipulations, the internal carries must be enabled by applying a low-level voltage to the mode control input (M). A full carry look-ahead scheme is made available in these devices for fast, simultaneous carry generation by means of two cascade-outputs (pins 15 and 17) for the four bits in the package. When used in conjunction with the SN54S182 or SN74S182 full carry look-ahead circuits, high-speed arithmetic operations can be performed. The typical addition times shown above illustrate the little additional time required for addition of longer words when full carry look-ahead is employed. The method of cascading 'S182 circuits with these ALUs to provide multi-level full carry look-ahead is illustrated under typical applications data for the 'S182.

If high speed is not of importance, a ripple-carry input (C_n) and a ripple-carry output (C_{n+4}) are available. However, the ripple-carry delay has also been minimized so that arithmetic manipulations for small word lengths can be performed without external circuitry.

FIGURE 6-5 74181 Arithmetic Logic Unit Data Sheets. (Courtesy of Texas Instruments.)

SN54LS181, SN54S181
SN74LS181, SN74S181
ARITHMETIC LOGIC UNITS/FUNCTION GENERATORS

description (continued)

The 'LS181 and 'S181 will accommodate active-high data if the pin designations are interpreted as follows:

PIN NUMBER	2	1	23	22	21	20	19	18	9	10	11	13	7	16	15	17
Active-low data (Table 1)	$\overline{A}_0$	$\overline{B}_0$	$\overline{A}_1$	$\overline{B}_1$	$\overline{A}_2$	$\overline{B}_2$	$\overline{A}_3$	$\overline{B}_3$	$\overline{F}_0$	$\overline{F}_1$	$\overline{F}_2$	$\overline{F}_3$	C_n	C_{n+4}	$\overline{P}$	$\overline{G}$
Active-high data (Table 2)	A_0	B_0	A_1	B_1	A_2	B_2	A_3	B_3	F_0	F_1	F_2	F_3	$\overline{C}_n$	$\overline{C}_{n+4}$	X	Y

Subtraction is accomplished by 1's complement addition where the 1's complement of the subtrahend is generated internally. The resultant output is A–B–1, which requires an end-around or forced carry to provide A–B.

The 'LS181 or 'S181 can also be utilized as a comparator. The A = B output is internally decoded from the function outputs (F0, F1, F2, F3) so that when two words of equal magnitude are applied at the A and B inputs, it will assume a high level to indicate equality (A = B). The ALU must be in the subtract mode with C_n = H when performing this comparison. The A = B output is open-collector so that it can be wire-AND connected to give a comparison for more than four bits. The carry output (C_{n+4}) can also be used to supply relative magnitude information. Again, the ALU must be placed in the subtract mode by placing the function select inputs S3, S2, S1, S0 at L, H, H, L, respectively.

INPUT C_n	OUTPUT C_{n+4}	ACTIVE-LOW DATA (FIGURE 1)	ACTIVE-HIGH DATA (FIGURE 2)
H	H	$A \geq B$	$A \leq B$
H	L	$A < B$	$A > B$
L	H	$A > B$	$A < B$
L	L	$A \leq B$	$A \geq B$

These circuits have been designed to not only incorporate all of the designer's requirements for arithmetic operations, but also to provide 16 possible functions of two Boolean variables without the use of external circuitry. These logic functions are selected by use of the four function-select inputs (S0, S1, S2, S3) with the mode-control input (M) at a high level to disable the internal carry. The 16 logic functions are detailed in Tables 1 and 2 and include exclusive-OR, NAND, AND, NOR, and OR functions.

Series 54, 54LS, and 54S devices are characterized for operation over the full military temperature range of −55 °C to 125 °C; Series 74LS and 74S devices are characterized for operation from 0 °C to 70 °C.

signal designations

In both Figures 1 and 2, the polarity indicators (⊾) indicate that the associated input or output is active-low with respect to the function shown inside the symbol, and the symbols are the same in both figures. The signal designations in Figure 1 agree with the indicated internal functions based on active-low data, and are for use with the logic functions and arithmetic operations shown in Table 1. The signal designations have been changed in Figure 2 to accommodate the logic functions and arithmetic operations for the active-high data given in Table 2. The 'LS181 and 'S181, together with the 'S182, can be used with the signal designation of either Figure 1 or Figure 2.

FIGURE 6-5 *(continued)*

SN54LS181, SN54S181, SN74LS181, SN74S181 ARITHMETIC LOGIC UNITS/FUNCTION GENERATORS

logic symbols† and signal designations (active-low data)

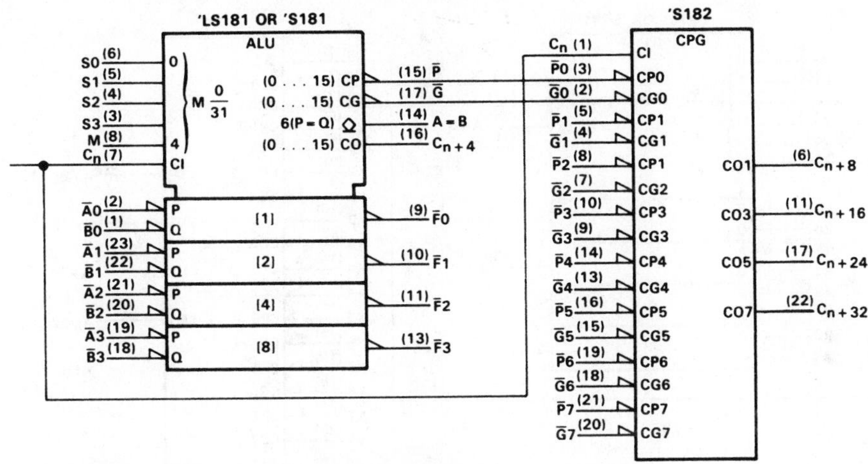

†These symbols are in accordance with ANSI/IEEE Std. 91-1984 and IEC Publication 617-12.
Pin numbers shown are for dual-in-line and "small outline" packages.

FIGURE 1 (USE WITH TABLE 1)

TABLE 1

SELECTION				ACTIVE-LOW DATA		
				M = H	M = L; ARITHMETIC OPERATIONS	
S3	S2	S1	S0	LOGIC FUNCTIONS	Cn = L (no carry)	Cn = H (with carry)
L	L	L	L	$F = \overline{A}$	F = A MINUS 1	F = A
L	L	L	H	$F = \overline{AB}$	F = AB MINUS 1	F = AB
L	L	H	L	$F = \overline{A} + B$	F = $A\overline{B}$ MINUS 1	F = $A\overline{B}$
L	L	H	H	F = 1	F = MINUS 1 (2's COMP)	F = ZERO
L	H	L	L	$F = \overline{A + B}$	F = A PLUS $(A + \overline{B})$	F = A PLUS $(A + \overline{B})$ PLUS 1
L	H	L	H	$F = \overline{B}$	F = AB PLUS $(A + \overline{B})$	F = AB PLUS $(A + \overline{B})$ PLUS 1
L	H	H	L	$F = \overline{A \oplus B}$	F = A MINUS B MINUS 1	F = A MINUS B
L	H	H	H	$F = A + \overline{B}$	$F = A + \overline{B}$	F = $(A + \overline{B})$ PLUS 1
H	L	L	L	$F = \overline{A}B$	F = A PLUS (A + B)	F = A PLUS (A + B) PLUS 1
H	L	L	H	$F = A \oplus B$	F = A PLUS B	F = A PLUS B PLUS 1
H	L	H	L	F = B	F = $A\overline{B}$ PLUS (A + B)	F = $A\overline{B}$ PLUS (A + B) PLUS 1
H	L	H	H	F = A + B	F = (A + B)	F = (A + B) PLUS 1
H	H	L	L	F = 0	F = A PLUS A‡	F = A PLUS A PLUS 1
H	H	L	H	$F = A\overline{B}$	F = AB PLUS A	F = AB PLUS A PLUS 1
H	H	H	L	F = AB	F = $A\overline{B}$ PLUS A	F = $A\overline{B}$ PLUS A PLUS 1
H	H	H	H	F = A	F = A	F = A PLUS 1

‡Each bit is shifted to the next more significant position.

FIGURE 6-5 (*continued*)

SN54LS181, SN54S181, SN74LS181, SN74S181 ARITHMETIC LOGIC UNITS/FUNCTIONS GENERATORS

logic symbols† and signal designations (active-high data)

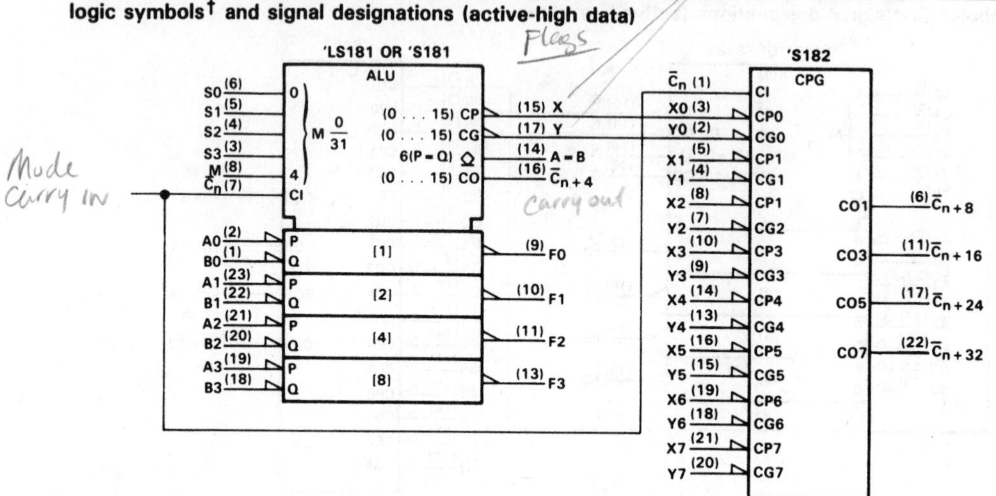

†These symbols are in accordance with ANSI/IEEE Std. 91-1984 and IEC Publication 617-12. Pin numbers shown are for dual-in-line and "small outline" packages.

FIGURE 2 (USE WITH TABLE 2)

TABLE 2

SELECTION				ACTIVE-HIGH DATA		
				M = H	M = L; ARITHMETIC OPERATIONS	
S3	S2	S1	S0	LOGIC FUNCTIONS	$\overline{C}_n$ = H (no carry)	$\overline{C}_n$ = L (with carry)
L	L	L	L	F = $\overline{A}$	F = A	F = A PLUS 1
L	L	L	H	F = $\overline{A + B}$	F = A + B	F = (A + B) PLUS 1
L	L	H	L	F = $\overline{A}$B	F = A + $\overline{B}$	F = (A + $\overline{B}$) PLUS 1
L	L	H	H	F = 0	F = MINUS 1 (2's COMPL)	F = ZERO
L	H	L	L	F = $\overline{AB}$	F = A PLUS A$\overline{B}$	F = A PLUS A$\overline{B}$ PLUS 1
L	H	L	H	F = $\overline{B}$	F = (A + B) PLUS A$\overline{B}$	F = (A + B) PLUS A$\overline{B}$ PLUS 1
L	H	H	L	F = A ⊕ B	F = A MINUS B MINUS 1	F = A MINUS B
L	H	H	H	F = A$\overline{B}$	F = A$\overline{B}$ MINUS 1	F = A$\overline{B}$
H	L	L	L	F = $\overline{A}$ + B	F = A PLUS AB	F = A PLUS AB PLUS 1
H	L	L	H	F = $\overline{A \oplus B}$	F = A PLUS B	F = A PLUS B PLUS 1
H	L	H	L	F = B	F = (A + $\overline{B}$) PLUS AB	F = (A + $\overline{B}$) PLUS AB PLUS 1
H	L	H	H	F = AB	F = AB MINUS 1	F = AB
H	H	L	L	F = 1	F = A PLUS A†	F = A PLUS A PLUS 1
H	H	L	H	F = A + $\overline{B}$	F = (A + B) PLUS A	F = (A + B) PLUS A PLUS 1
H	H	H	L	F = A + B	F = (A + $\overline{B}$) PLUS A	F = (A + $\overline{B}$) PLUS A PLUS 1
H	H	H	H	F = A	F = A MINUS 1	F = A

† Each bit is shifted to the next more significant position.

FIGURE 6-5 (*continued*)

6-1 BINARY ADDITION

Binary addition is the basic arithmetic function by which other arithmetic operations are performed. The basic rules of binary addition, found in Chapter 2, Section 2.4.1, should be reviewed and thoroughly understood before beginning this chapter.

Binary addition follows these basic rules:

0 + 0 = 0

0 + 1 = 1

1 + 0 = 1

1 + 1 = 1 0

1 + 1 + 1 = 1 1

A carry-out was generated when two or more 1's were added together. Four of the preceding rules involve adding 2-bits. This is referred to as the half-adder operation. The fifth rule involves adding 3-bits, which is referred to as the full-adder operation. The full-adder and half-adder circuits can be designed from basic logic gates and combined to form binary adders.

6.1.1 Half-Adder

Binary addition circuits are classified as half-adders or full-adders. A **half-adder adds 2 bits** and generates two outputs: **a sum and a carry-out.** Table 6-2 is the truth table for a half-adder.

The logic circuits required for the carry and the sum outputs can be determined by examining the outputs of the truth table and solving the sum

TABLE 6-2 Half-Adder

B	A	B + A = Carry-Out	Sum
0	0	0	0
0	1	0	1
1	0	0	1
1	1	1	0

of products (SOP) equations. The SOP expressions for the half-adder are shown in Equations 6-1 and 6-2.

Eq. 6-1 Carry-out $= B\,A$

Eq. 6-2 Sum $= \overline{B}\,A + B\,\overline{A} = B \oplus A$

The logic circuit for the half-adder is shown in Figure 6-6(a), whereas the logic block representation of the half-adder is shown in Figure 6-6(b).

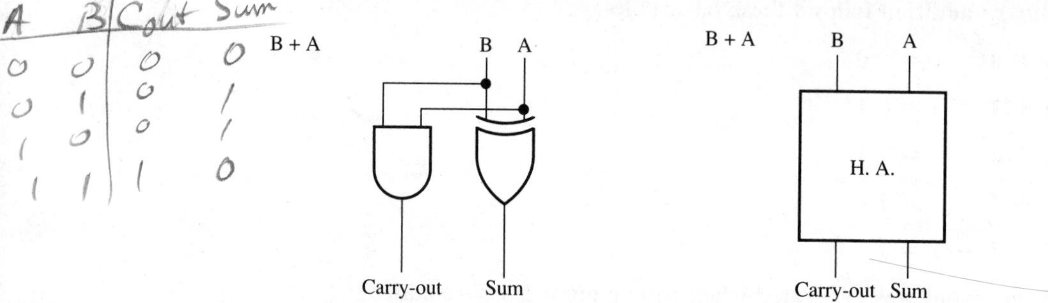

FIGURE 6-6 (a) Half-Adder Circuit; (b) Half-Adder Logic Symbol

6.1.2 Full-Adder

In order to add a series of bits, we need to add the carry-out of a previous addition operation to the next group of bits. One way to accomplish this is

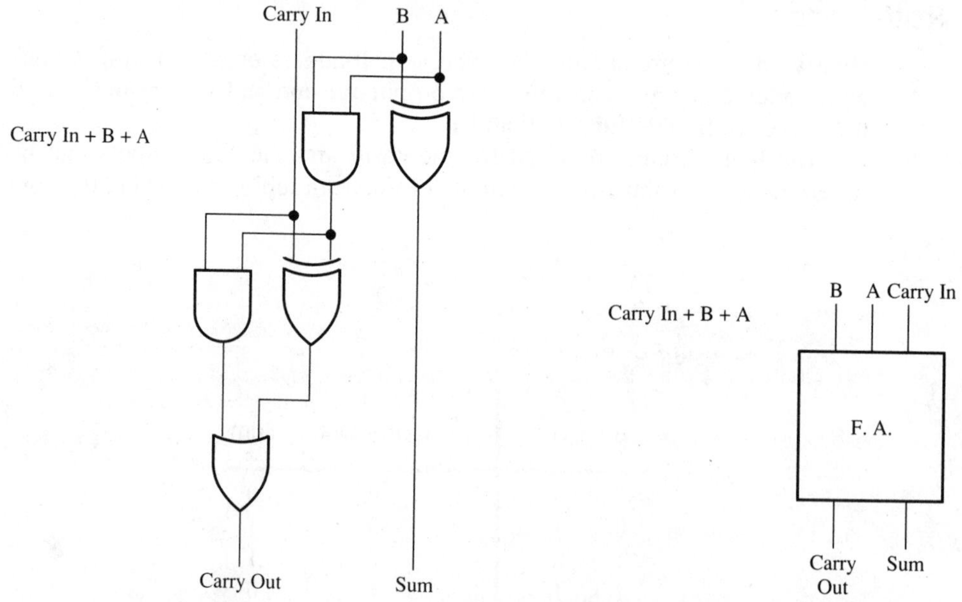

FIGURE 6-7 (a) Full-Adder Circuit; (b) Full-Adder Logic Symbol

to cascade two half-adder circuits, as shown in Figure 6-7(a). The resulting circuit is a full-adder. The **full-adder adds 3 bits.** The **third bit is a carry-in from a previous addition,** as shown in the logic block symbol for the full-adder in Figure 6-7(b).

The logic circuit for the full-adder can be obtained from a truth table by deriving the SOP equations for the 3-bit addition process. Table 6-3 shows the truth table for a full-adder. The logic equations for the full-adder are shown in Equations 6-3 and 6-4.

TABLE 6-3 Full Adder

Carry-In	B	A	C_{in} + B + A = Carry-Out	Sum
0	0	0	0	0
0	0	1	0	1
0	1	0	0	1
0	1	1	1	0
1	0	0	0	1
1	0	1	1	0
1	1	0	1	0
1	1	1	1	1

Eq. 6-3 Carry-out $= \overline{C}_{in}\,B\,A + C_{in}\,\overline{B}\,A + C_{in}\,B\,\overline{A} + C_{in}\,B\,A$

$$= A\,B(\overline{C}_{in} + C_{in}) + C_{in}(\overline{B}\,A + B\,\overline{A})$$

$$= A\,B + C_{in}(A \oplus B)$$

Eq. 6-4 Sum $= \overline{C}_{in}\,\overline{B}\,A + \overline{C}_{in}\,B\,\overline{A} + C_{in}\,\overline{B}\,\overline{A} + C_{in}\,B\,A$

$$= C_{in}(B \oplus A) + C_{in}(\overline{B \oplus A})$$

$$= C_{in} \oplus (B \oplus A)$$

The sum is denoted by the Greek letter sigma, Σ. The carry-out is often labeled C_{out}, or with a subscript indicating the output from the highest bit operation, such as C_4. The carry-in is commonly labeled C_{in}, or with a subscript indicating the input to the lowest bit operation, such as C_0.

The Exclusive-OR operation (XOR) is used extensively in addition and other arithmetic operations, so it is often classified in the data books as an arithmetic circuit. Two Exclusive-OR integrated circuits (ICs), the 7486 and the 74135, are useful in various arithmetic applications.

The addition process of adding multiple bits is accomplished by cascading the full-adder and half-adder logic blocks. An adder circuit that adds two 4-bit numbers is shown in Figure 6-8. The least significant bit (LSB) requires only a half-adder since there is no carry into this bit position.

$$\begin{array}{r} A_4\ A_3\ A_2\ A_1 \\ +\ B_4\ B_3\ B_2\ B_1 \\ \hline C_{out\,4}\ \Sigma_4\ \Sigma_3\ \Sigma_2\ \Sigma_1 \end{array}$$

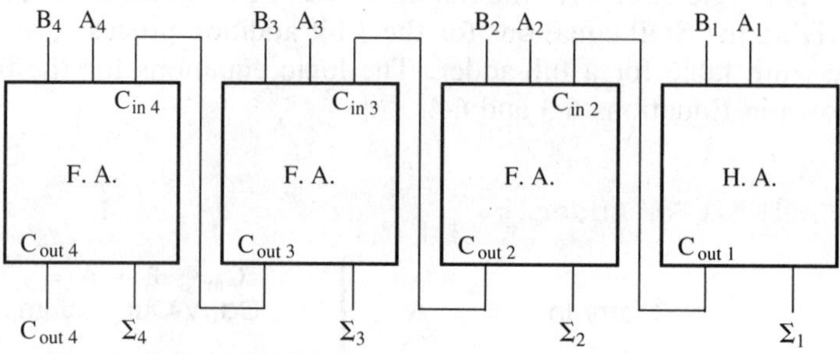

FIGURE 6-8 Four-Bit Ripple-Carry Parallel Adder

The operation shown in Figure 6-8 is referred to as **parallel addition** since all the bits of the numbers are added simultaneously. This parallel adder has a **ripple-carry** because the carry-out of the LSB stage is added as the carry-in to the next stage, and so on, propagating or ''rippling'' through all the stages of the adder.

6.1.3 Look-Ahead Carry

The ripple-carry through several full-adders is a straightforward operation, which is identical to the carry operation when addition is performed by hand. However, ripple addition is a slow process for large number binary addition. To speed up the addition process, we can obtain an equation for the final carry-out of the addition as a combination of the inputs, and a separate logic circuit can be built to eliminate the ripple-carry. This technique is referred to as **look-ahead-carry.**

The look-ahead-carry circuitry can be derived by analyzing which input combinations result in a carry-out at each full-adder stage. At any stage a **carry-out will occur if both bits being added are 1, or if either bit is a 1 and a carry-in is present from a previous stage.** This situation was first described in Equation 6-3, the carry-out for a full adder. The relationship can be written for any bit, n, as shown in Equation 6-5.

Eq. 6-5 $$\text{Carry-out}_n = A_n\, B_n + (A_n \oplus B_n)\text{Carry-in}_n$$

In the look-ahead-carry design the term $(A_n\, B_n)$ is the **carry-generate** and the term $(A_n \oplus B_n)$ is the **carry-propagate.** The logic equation for the look-ahead-carry can be written using these labels for each stage. The carry-out expression for each addition stage is shown in Equation 6-6.

Eq. 6-6

$$\text{Carry-out}_n = \text{Carry-generate}_n + (\text{Carry-propagate}_n)(\text{Carry-in}_n)$$

$$\text{Carry-out}_n = \text{Carry-generate}_n + (\text{Carry-propagate}_n)(\text{Carry-out}_{n-1})$$

The look-ahead-carry circuitry for the 4-bit adder can be obtained by deriving the equation for the carry-out and carry-in at each individual stage as a function of the inputs, as shown in Equations 6-7 through 6-10.

Eq. 6-7

$$\begin{aligned}\text{Carry-out}_1 &= A_1 B_1 + (A_1 \oplus B_1)\,\text{Carry-in}_1 \\ &= \text{Carry-in}_2\end{aligned}$$

Eq. 6-8

$$\begin{aligned}\text{Carry-out}_2 &= A_2 B_2 + (A_2 \oplus B_2)\text{Carry-in}_2 \\ &= A_2 B_2 + (A_2 \oplus B_2)[A_1 B_1 + (A_1 \oplus B_1)\text{Carry-in}_1] \\ &= A_2 B_2 + (A_2 \oplus B_2)A_1 B_1 + (A_1 \oplus B_1)(A_2 \oplus B_2)\text{Carry-in}_1 \\ &= \text{Carry-in}_3\end{aligned}$$

Eq. 6-9

$$\begin{aligned}\text{Carry-out}_3 &= A_3 B_3 + (A_3 \oplus B_3)\text{Carry-in}_3 \\ &= A_3 B_3 + (A_3 \oplus B_3)[A_2 B_2 + (A_2 \oplus B_2)A_1 B_1 \\ &\quad + (A_1 \oplus B_1)(A_2 \oplus B_2)\text{Carry-in}_1] \\ &= A_3 B_3 + (A_3 \oplus B_3)A_2 B_2 + (A_3 \oplus B_3)(A_2 \oplus B_2)A_1 B_1 \\ &\quad + (A_3 \oplus B_3)(A_2 \oplus B_2)(A_1 \oplus B_1)\text{Carry-in}_1 \\ &= \text{Carry-in}_4\end{aligned}$$

Eq. 6-10

$$\begin{aligned}\text{Carry-out}_4 &= A_4 B_4 + (A_4 \oplus B_4)\text{Carry-in}_4 \\ &= A_4 B_4 + (A_4 \oplus B_4)[A_3 B_3 + (A_3 \oplus B_3)A_2 B_2 \\ &\quad + (A_3 \oplus B_3)(A_2 \oplus B_2)A_1 B_1 \\ &\quad + (A_3 \oplus B_3)(A_2 \oplus B_2)(A_1 \oplus B_1)\text{Carry-in}_1] \\ &= A_4 B_4 + (A_4 \oplus B_4)A_3 B_3 + (A_4 \oplus B_4)(A_3 \oplus B_3)A_2 B_2 \\ &\quad + (A_4 \oplus B_4)(A_3 \oplus B_3)(A_2 \oplus B_2)A_1 B_1 \\ &\quad + (A_4 \oplus B_4)(A_3 \oplus B_3)(A_2 \oplus B_2)(A_1 \oplus B_1)\text{Carry-in}_1\end{aligned}$$

A 4-bit full-adder with look-ahead-carry circuitry requires the circuits for Equations 6-7 through 6-10 to form the carry-in function for each full-adder stage and the final carry-out stage. The carry-out of the full-adder is not used since it is a ripple-carry process.

The block diagram of the look-ahead-carry circuit for the 4-bit full-adder is shown in Figure 6-9. All carry-out terms are functions of the inputs.

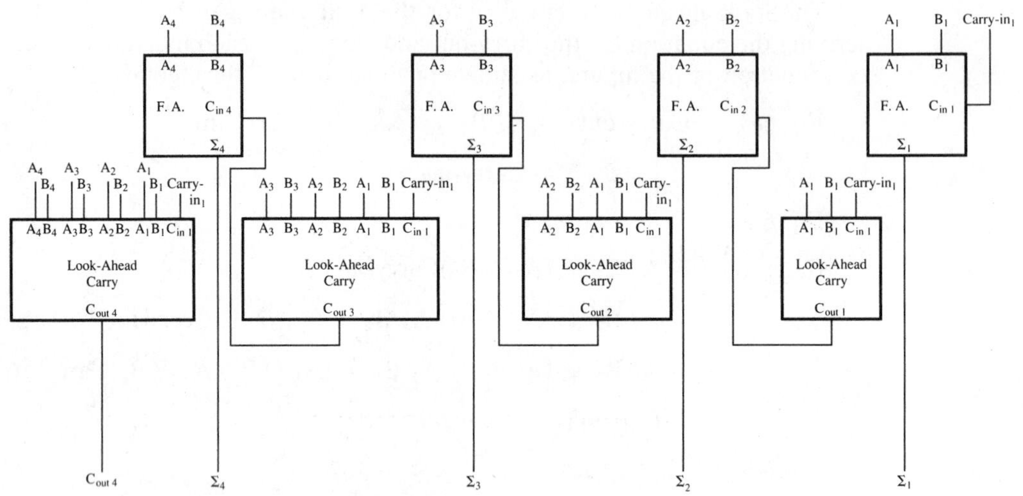

FIGURE 6-9 Four-Bit Look-Ahead-Carry Parallel Adder

6.1.4 Integrated Circuit Adders

Special function medium scale integration (MSI) ICs are available to perform arithmetic functions, eliminating the need to build half-adders, full-adders, and look-ahead-carry circuits. The operation and internal logic circuitry is based on the binary addition operations previously discussed. Most of the ICs available perform arithmetic operations on 4-bit values and can be cascaded for computing larger values. Some 8- and 16-bit circuits are also available.

The 74283 **4-bit full-adder** performs a parallel addition on two 4-bit values. The data sheet for the 74283 is found in Figure 6-1. It is designed with look-ahead-carry circuitry to speed the addition.

The adder consists of four full-adder sections, allowing a carry-in to the LSB stage. This feature simplifies cascaded configurations and subtraction operations.

The 74283 is a versatile circuit. The logic symbol for the 74283 is shown in Figure 6-10. Application circuits for 4- and 8-bit addition operations are shown in Figures 6-11 and 6-12, respectively. The 74283 adder will be used in numerous arithmetic operations throughout this chapter.

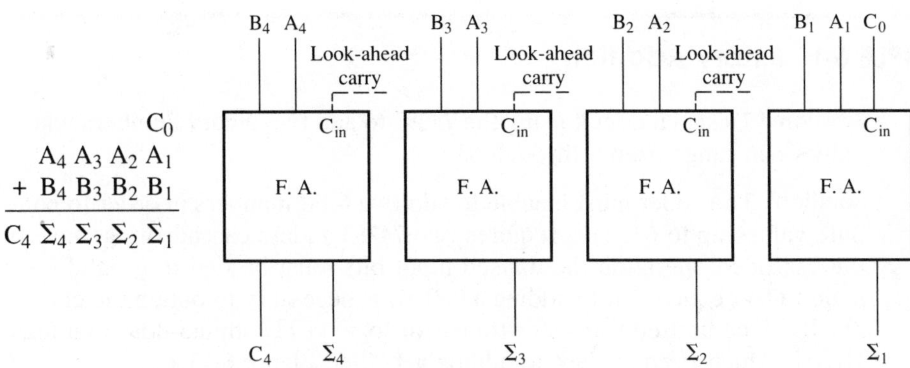

FIGURE 6-10 74283 Adder Logic Block Symbol

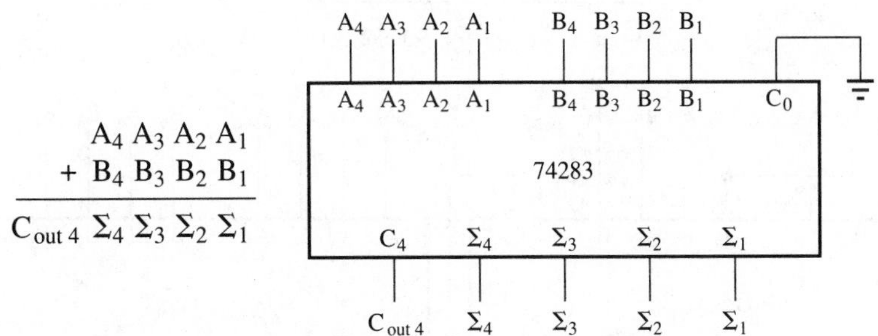

FIGURE 6-11 74283 4-Bit Addition Application Circuit

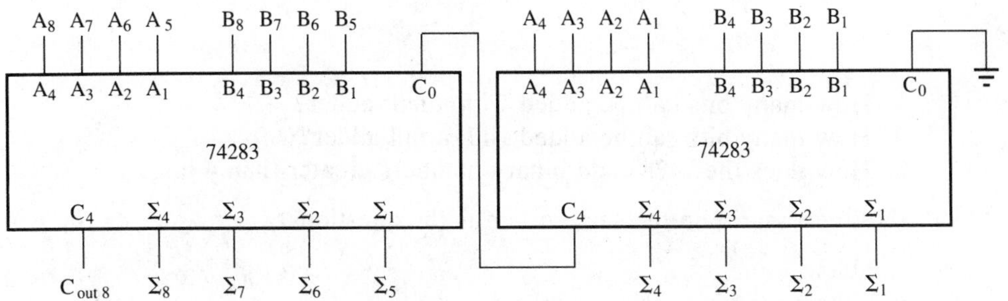

FIGURE 6-12 74283 8-Bit Addition Application Circuit

■ EXAMPLE 6-1 Binary Addition

Problem: Design a circuit using the 74283 to add two binary numbers whose values can range from 0 through 63.

Solution: The adder must be able to add two 6-bit numbers in order to compute values up to 63. This requires two 74283 adders cascaded together. In the cascaded operation the unused input bits must be tied to ground for a logic LOW, equivalent to adding a 0. This is necessary to obtain the correct results since unused transistor-transistor logic (TTL) inputs float to a logic HIGH, which is equivalent to adding a 1. (See Figure 6-13.) ■

$$\begin{array}{r} 0\ 0\ A_6\ A_5\ A_4\ A_3\ A_2\ A_1 \\ +\ 0\ 0\ B_6\ B_5\ B_4\ B_3\ B_2\ B_1 \\ \hline C_{out\,6}\ \Sigma_6\ \Sigma_5\ \Sigma_4\ \Sigma_3\ \Sigma_2\ \Sigma_1 \end{array}$$

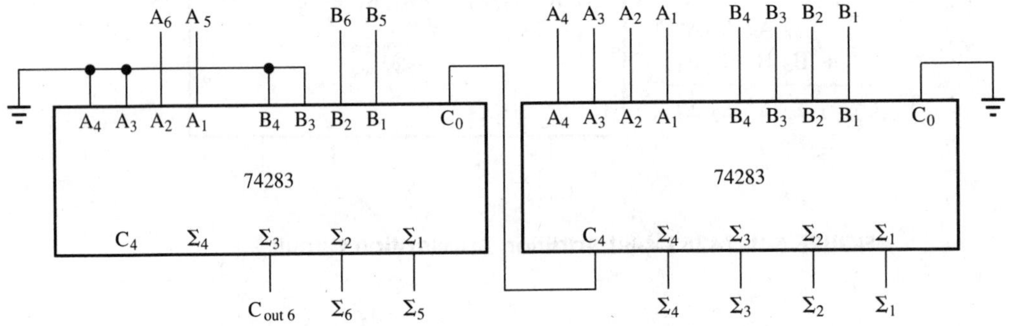

FIGURE 6-13 Example 6-1 Circuit ■

Section Self-Test

1. How many bits can be added with a half-adder?
2. How many bits can be added with a full-adder?
3. How does the 74283 add binary numbers greater than 4 bits?

ANSWERS (Not necessarily in the same order as the questions)

- 2 bits
- 3 bits
- Several 74283 ICs can be cascaded by connecting the C_4 from one adder to the C_0 of the next adder.

6-2 BINARY SUBTRACTION

Binary subtraction can be accomplished through addition by converting the subtraction operation to a negative number representation and adding the complement of the value. The rules for representing negative binary numbers and one's and two's complement subtraction were covered in Chapter 2, Sections 2.4.5 and 2.4.6. They should be reviewed and thoroughly understood before beginning this section on subtraction circuits.

6.2.1 Signed Number Arithmetic

Chapter 2 covered the one's and two's complement representation of signed binary numbers. Recall that the most significant bit (MSB) in the number representation is reserved for the sign bit. A 0 in the MSB position indicates a positive number. A 1 in the MSB position indicates a negative number.

A subtraction operation can be changed to addition by changing the sign of the number and adding. Thus, it is important to differentiate between positive and negative values.

In the one's and two's complement representation positive numbers are written in their true form and the sign bit is a 0, while negative numbers are written in their complement form and the sign bit is a 1. The one's complement is formed by inverting all bits. The two's complement is formed by inverting all bits and then adding 1 to obtain the final result. Digital logic and microprocessor systems rely extensively on the one's and two's complements to represent negative numbers and perform arithmetic operations.

■ EXAMPLE 6-2 One's and Two's Complements

Problem: Represent the following values as 8-bit numbers in their one's and two's complement form.

DECIMAL NUMBERS

$+14$

-14

$+25$

-25

Solution: Obtain the binary equivalent of the positive number. Form the one's complement by inverting each bit. Form the two's complement by adding 1 to the one's complement form.

VALUE	ONE'S COMPLEMENT	TWO'S COMPLEMENT
+14	00001110	00001110
−14	11110001	11110010
+25	00011001	00011001
−25	11100110	11100111

■

The circuitry to convert a value to the one's complement form is an array of inverters. One inverter is required for each bit of the number, including the sign bit. To form the two's complement, first form the one's complement and then add a 1 at the LSB position. Figure 6-14 shows examples of the circuitry to form the one's and two's complements for 4-bit values.

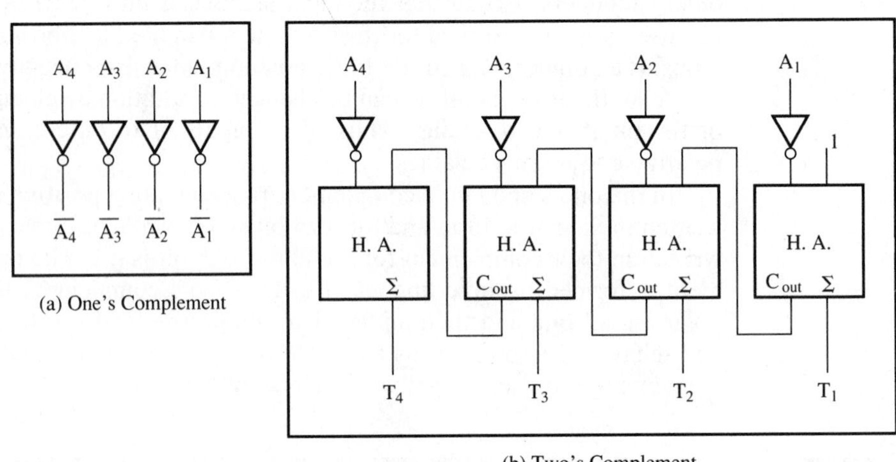

FIGURE 6-14 One's and Two's Complement Circuitry

Special ICs exist that can be used to build circuitry that either complements the bits of a number or leaves them in their true form. This is useful when both addition and subtraction operations might have to be performed by the same circuit.

The 7487 true/complement unit or the 7486 Exclusive-OR IC can be used to form the one's complement of a value, or to leave it in its true form. The applications circuits for the true/complement operation for 4 bit numbers are shown in Figure 6-15.

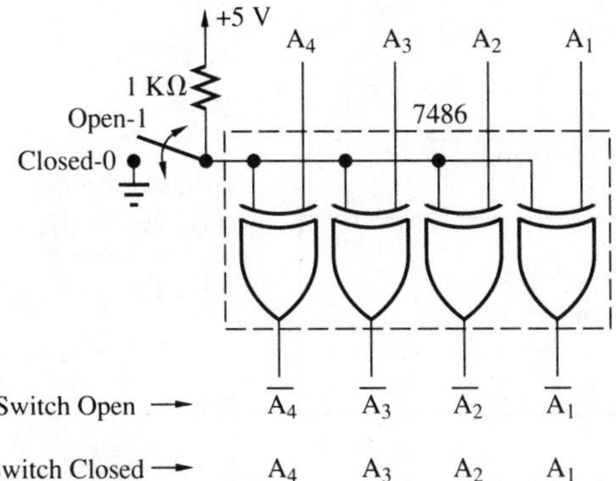

FIGURE 6-15 True/Complement Circuit

Adders can be used to form the two's complement of a value in arithmetic operations. The 74283 will be used in the following sections in applications requiring the one's and two's complement method for subtraction.

6.2.2 One's Complement Method

The rules for the one's complement method for subtraction are given in Table 2-12. To summarize the procedures, perform the subtraction by representing the **subtrahend** (the value to be subtracted) in its one's complement form and then adding. If a carry-out occurs, the subtrahend must be added back to the LSB by an end-around-carry. The complete subtraction process requires two addition operations.

One example of a circuit that performs the one's complement subtraction is shown in Figure 6-16, using the 74283. The circuit performs the operation, A − B, on two 4-bit numbers. The A inputs are used for the **minuend,** and the B inputs are used for the **subtrahend.** The inverters on the B inputs form the one's complement, and the end-around-carry is performed by routing C_4 to C_0.

Although the one's complement is easy to form, it is often inconvenient to perform the end-around-carry. This is especially true in circuits used for both addition and subtraction operations, as will be covered in Section 6.2.4. The two's complement subtraction procedure does not require an end-around-carry and can be conveniently implemented with the IC adders available.

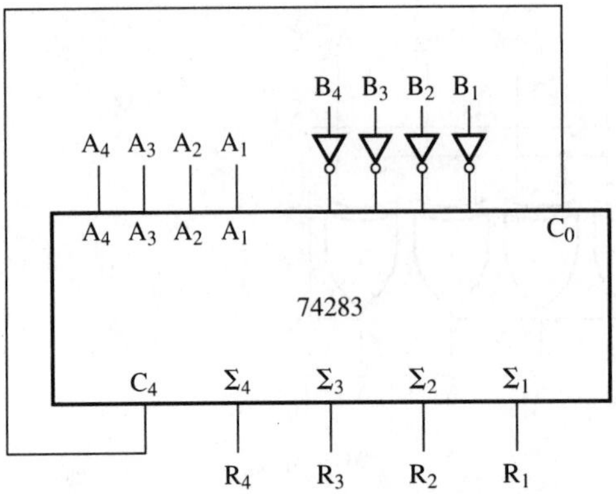

$$\begin{array}{r} A_4\,A_3\,A_2\,A_1 \\ -\;B_4\,B_3\,B_2\,B_1 \\ \hline R_4\,R_3\,R_2\,R_1 \end{array}$$

FIGURE 6-16 One's Complement Subtraction Circuit

6.2.3 Two's Complement Method

The two's complement method can be used for addition and subtraction, according to the rules given in Table 2-12. When performing subtraction using the two's complement method, represent positive values in their true form and negative values in their two's complement form. The subtraction operation is accomplished by complementing the subtrahend and adding. If a carry-out of the sign bit occurs, it is dropped; no end-around-carry is performed.

■ EXAMPLE 6-3 Hexadecimal Two's Complement Subtraction

Problem: Subtract AD_{16} from 57_{16} using two's complement subtraction.

$57_{16} - AD_{16} = ?$

Solution: Perform the subtraction in binary and convert the final result back to hex. Take the two's complement of the subtrahend, AD_{16}, and add it to the true form of the minuend, 57_{16}.

True form of 57_{16} = $(0101\ 0111)_2$

True form of AD_{16} = $(1010\ 1100)_2$

Two's complement of AD_{16} = $(0101\ 0100)_2$

$$\begin{array}{rl} 0101\ 0111 & \quad 57_{16} \\ +0101\ 0100 & - AD_{16} \\ \hline 1010\ 1011 & = AB_{16} \end{array}$$

■

The two's complement method of subtraction is in general easier to implement in logic circuit designs since it does not require an end-around-carry. One example of a circuit that performs two's complement subtraction is shown in Figure 6-17. In this circuit the 74283 adder is used for the operation A − B. The A inputs are reserved for the minuend, and the B inputs are reserved for the subtrahend. The two's complement is formed by the inverters on the B inputs and the logic-HIGH input to C_0. The C_4 output is not used since any carry-out that occurs is dropped.

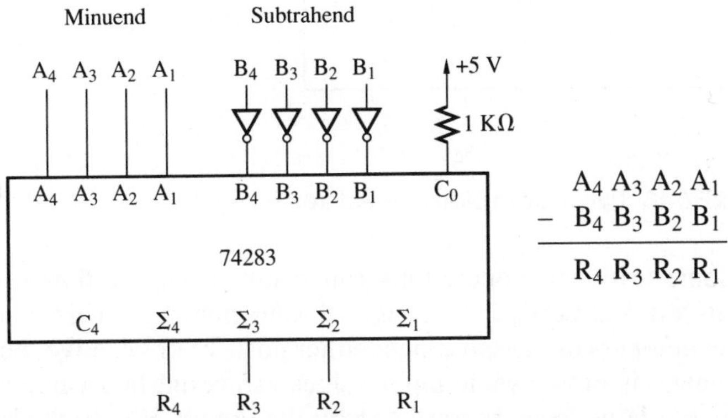

FIGURE 6-17 Two's Complement Subtraction Circuit

6.2.4 Adder/Subtracter Circuits

The one's and two's complement circuits shown in Figures 6-16 and 6-17, respectively, can be used only for subtraction operations due to the inverters on the B inputs. Circuits that must perform both addition and subtraction operations require the ability to add values in their original form, as well as to complement values for the subtraction.

The circuit can have the capability of adding and subtracting by using Exclusive-OR gates or a true/complementing circuit such as those shown in Figure 6-15. A two's complement adder/subtracter circuit can be designed using either of these circuits in place of the inverters in the circuit of Figure 6-17. The resulting 4-bit adder/subtracter circuit is shown in Figure 6-18.

6.2.5 Overflow Detection Circuitry

The values that can be input into arithmetic circuits are limited by the number of bits the circuit is designed to handle. The 4-bit adder/subtracter circuit of Figure 6-18 can only accept values between +7 and −7 since the MSB is used for the sign bit. The result is also limited to values between +7 and −7.

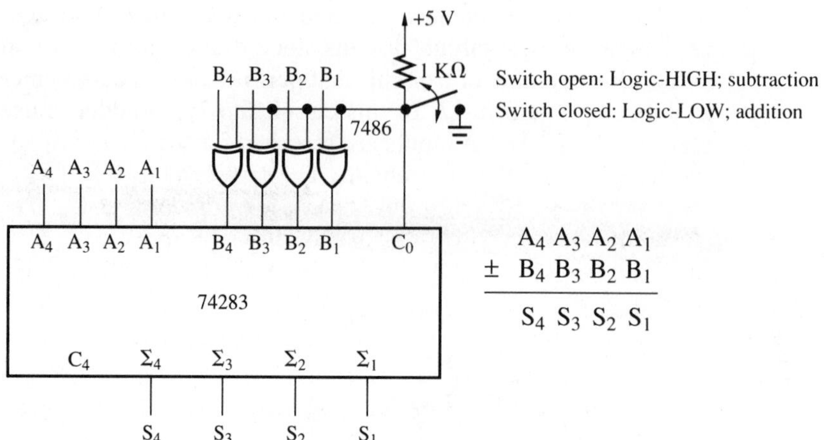

FIGURE 6-18 Two's Complement Adder/Subtracter

Some arithmetic operations can result in an **overflow condition if the output result is beyond the range of valid numbers.** This can occur when adding numbers of the same sign, either positive or negative, because certain combinations of allowable input values can result in a value at the outputs that is too large to be represented by the output bits available. Several examples of overflow are shown in Chapter 2. One such problem is Example 2-50.

Overflow detection circuitry can be added to the adder/subtracter circuits to signal when an output result is invalid because overflow has occurred. As discussed in Chapter 2, overflow can only occur when two values of the same sign are added. The condition of overflow exists when two values of the same sign are added but the result is of the opposite sign. The statement of this situation can be described in a truth table or directly in a logic equation. The logic equation for the overflow condition for the 4-bit adder/subtracter circuit is shown in Equation 6-11.

Eq. 6-11 $\quad \text{Overflow} = A_4B_4\overline{S}_4 + \overline{A}_4\,\overline{B}_4\,S_4$

The circuit indicating overflow is a simple SOP implementation of the expression, as shown in Figure 6-19.

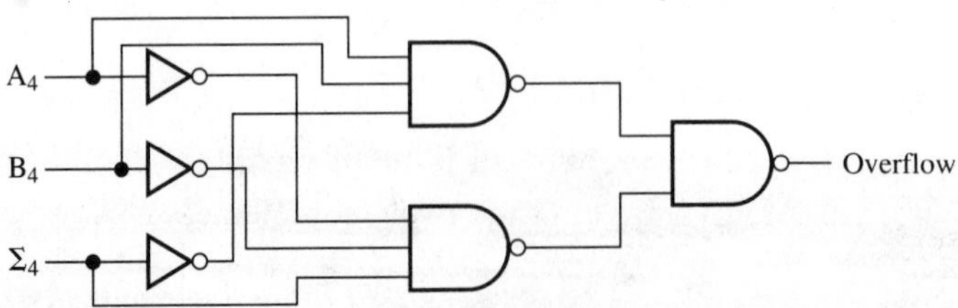

FIGURE 6-19 Overflow Detection Circuitry

To eliminate the occurrence of an overflow condition, one must design arithmetic circuits that can process additional bits.

EXAMPLE 6-4 Adder/Subtracter

Problem: Design an adder/subtracter that can compute values between the range of +63 and −63 and never result in an overflow condition, using the 74283, the 7486, and any additional circuitry.

Solution: The range of results that must be accommodated so that overflow does not occur is $(\pm 63) \times 2$, or +126 to −126. The result requires a total of 8-bits, including the sign bit. The input values will require only 7 bits, including the sign bit. (See Figure 6-20.)

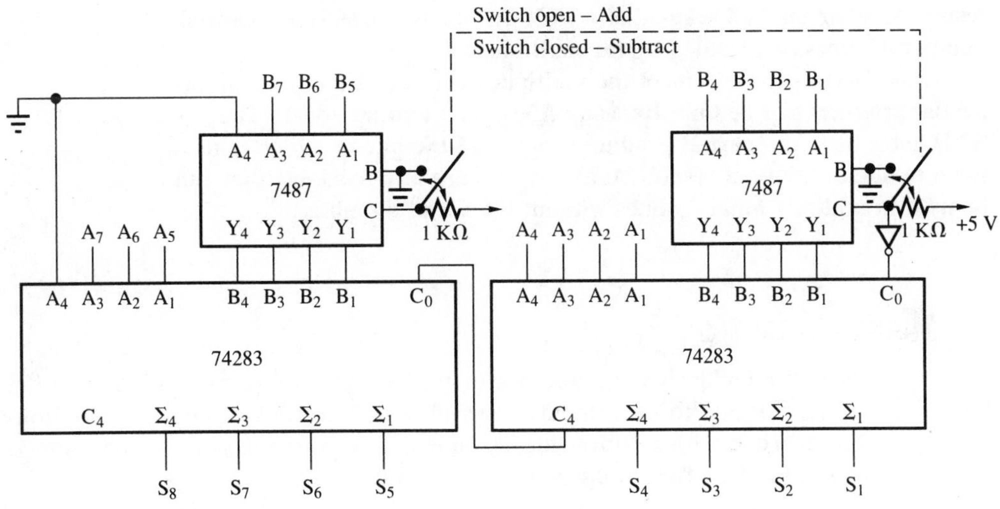

$$
\begin{array}{r}
0\ A_7\ A_6\ A_5\ A_4\ A_3\ A_2\ A_1 \\
\pm\ 0\ B_7\ B_6\ B_5\ B_4\ B_3\ B_2\ B_1 \\
\hline
S_8\ S_7\ S_6\ S_5\ S_4\ S_3\ S_2\ S_1
\end{array}
$$

FIGURE 6-20 Example 6-4 Circuit

Section Self-Test

1. What are the advantages of the one's complement method of signed number addition?
2. What are the advantages of the two's complement method of signed number addition?
3. Is overflow the same as the "carry-out" that can occur in one's and two's complement addition?

ANSWERS (Not necessarily in the order of the questions)

- No
- No end-around-carry is required.
- The complement is formed using only inverters.

6-3 MULTIPLICATION

Binary multiplication, described in Chapter 2, follows the same rules as decimal multiplication. The multiplication process can be accomplished by several methods. One method, which is similar to multiplying by hand, forms partial products and then adds them to obtain the final result. Another method sequentially adds the value to itself the required number of times as specified by the multiplier.

Logic circuits that perform the multiplication operation as a sum of partial products can be built by using AND gates and an adder. The AND gates form the partial product terms, and the binary adder sums them to obtain the final result. Multiplier ICs are also available that can be used to multiply binary values without the use of an adder.

6.3.1 Multiplier Design

In multiplier design the number of bits in each value as well as the total number of bits to be computed are important considerations. The multiplication process for a 3-bit value, A, times a 2-bit value, B, can be represented as a **sum of partial products,** as shown in Equation 6-12.

Eq. 6-12

$$\begin{array}{ccccc} & & A_3 & A_2 & A_1 \\ & & \times & B_2 & B_1 \\ \hline & & A_3B_1 & A_2B_1 & A_1B_1 \\ & A_3B_2 & A_2B_2 & A_1B_2 & \\ \hline P_5 & P_4 & P_3 & P_2 & P_1 \end{array}$$

It is assumed in multiplication operations that the values are represented in their true form. The sign of the result can be determined by comparing the signs of the input values. If the signs are the same, then the result is positive; if the signs are different, then the result is negative.

By specifying the sign conditions in a truth table for multiplying two values, we can see that the resulting sign bit is an Exclusive-OR operation of the sign bits of the input values.

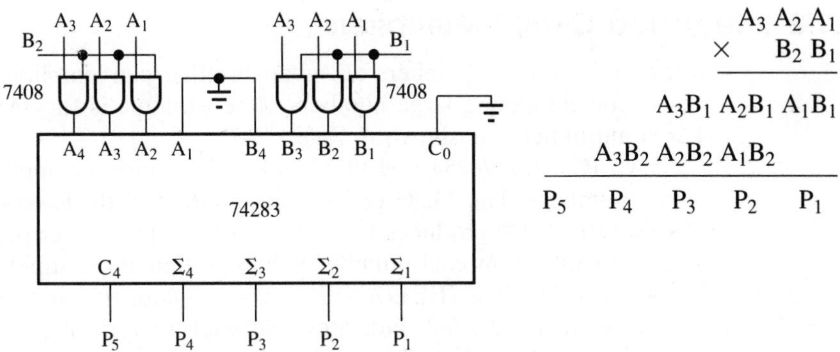

FIGURE 6-21 Three-Bit by Two-Bit Multiplier

Input Sign A_m	B_m	Output Sign P_m	
0	0	0	positive
0	1	1	negative
1	0	1	negative
1	1	0	positive

The 3-bit by 2-bit multiplier can be designed using AND gates and the 74283 adder, with separate Exclusive-OR circuitry to interpret the sign of the results if required. This multiplier circuit is shown in Figure 6-21. The multiplier can process values ranging in magnitude from 0 to 7 for the multiplicand and 0 to 3 for the multiplier. The results will range from 0 to 21.

Six AND operations are required to form the six partial products. The outputs of the AND gates are input to the adder at the required bit positions, as shown in the circuit. Any unused inputs to the adder must be tied low to prevent them from floating high and adding a 1 to the partial product results.

All five outputs from the adder are required to allow a sufficient number of output bits to prevent overflow from occurring. The sign bits of the values cannot be input to the adder because they are not involved in an addition process. If the sign of the result is required, it must be obtained through the separate Exclusive-OR circuitry.

Multipliers can be designed to handle large values by increasing the number of AND gates and adders so that more partial products can be added. For multiplying large values, such as a two 4-bit values, the operation becomes slow since it requires 16 partial products and 4 sequential additions. One option available for multiplying large binary numbers is to use IC multipliers.

6.3.2 Integrated Circuit Multipliers

Integrated circuit multipliers are available that can simplify the multiplier design for computing large numbers. One example is the 74284 and 74285 4 × 4 multipliers, as shown in Figure 6-2.

Two ICs, the 74284 and the 74285, are required to multiply two 4-bit binary numbers. The **74285** produces the output of the **lower-order product bits,** and the **74284** produces the output of the **higher-order product bits.** All four input bits from each number being multiplied are input into both the 74284 and 74285. The IEEE/ANSI logic symbol for the circuits, given in the data sheet in Figure 6-2, indicates that each individual circuit is a "half-multiplier" and specifies the weight of the product output bits.

Multiplication of larger numbers requires a very complex circuit design, with interfacing the multiplier circuits to additional circuitry such as adders, arithmetic logic units, and carry-look-ahead generators. Examples of large multiplier circuits are given in the data sheets in most data books.

The 74284 and 74285 ICs are designed with open-collector outputs, requiring pull-up resistors on the outputs to obtain a logic-HIGH value. An applications circuit for the 4 × 4 multiplier is shown in Figure 6-22.

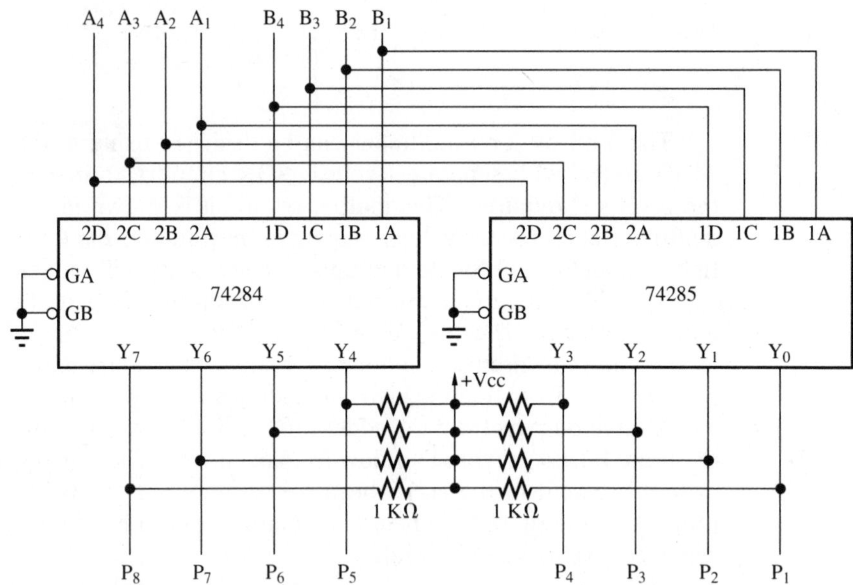

$$\begin{array}{r} A_4\ A_3\ A_2\ A_1 \\ \times\ B_4\ B_3\ B_2\ B_1 \\ \hline P_8\ P_7\ P_6\ P_5\ P_4\ P_3\ P_2\ P_1 \end{array}$$

FIGURE 6-22 Four-Bit by Four-Bit Multiplier

■ EXAMPLE 6-5 Binary Multiplier

Problem: Design a binary multiplier to perform a 3-bit by 2-bit multiplication using the 74284 and 74285 multiplier ICs.

Solution: The multiplication operation can be represented by the following equation:

$$
\begin{array}{ccccc}
 & & A_3 & A_2 & A_1 \\
 & & \times & B_2 & B_1 \\
\hline
 & & A_3B_1 & A_2B_1 & A_1B_1 \\
 & A_3B_2 & A_2B_2 & A_1B_2 & \\
\hline
P_5 & P_4 & P_3 & P_2 & P_1
\end{array}
$$

The 74284 and 74285 have inputs for two 4-bit binary numbers. Leading 0's must be placed in the MSB positions of the A and B number in this application. The circuit is shown in Figure 6-23.

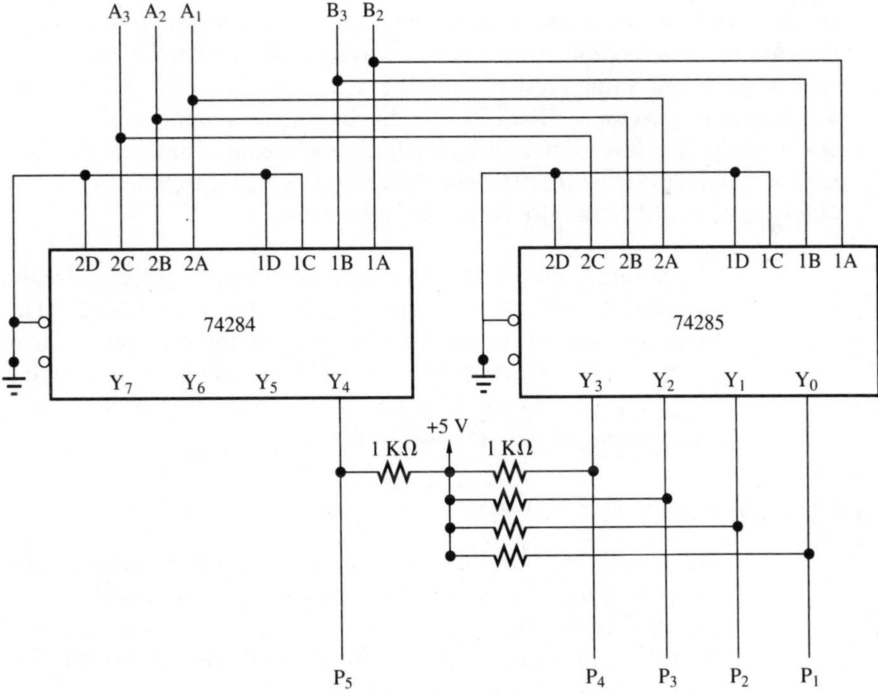

FIGURE 6-23 Example 6-5 Circuit ■

Section Self-Test

1. How does a circuit constructed of an adder IC, such as the 74283, and AND gates perform multiplication?
2. Can a multiplier be built using only adder ICs and no AND gates?
3. What is the purpose of multiplier chips?

ANSWERS (Not necessarily in the same order as the questions)

- They simplify the multiplication process, especially in the case of multiplying large binary numbers.
- The AND gates form the partial products of the multiplication operation. The partial products are then added to form the final result.
- Yes. A number can be multiplied by adding it to itself several times.

6-4 COMPARATORS

Comparators are logic circuits that determine if input values are less than, greater than, or equal to each other. Comparators are used in numerous applications, many of which are arithmetic operations. They can be used to evaluate input values from many processes to determine if they are in an acceptable range; to verify relationships between values, such as when one value must remain above or below the other value; and as magnitude detectors to indicate invalid conditions. Comparators are one of the digital blocks of analog-to-digital conversion. They can also be used in combination with arithmetic operations to signal overflow or other conditions that require corrective measures.

Comparators are relatively simple combinational logic circuits that can be specified in a truth table and designed from logic gates. The comparator examines two values and usually has up to three outputs. The most common IC comparators available evaluate 4-bit numbers, although 8- and 16-bit comparators exist as well. The IC comparators can be cascaded to accept binary input values as large as required.

6.4.1 Comparator Operations

Comparator circuits determine the relationship between input values by comparing the bits to determine if the values are equal to, greater than, or less than each other. The process is simple since the bits can only take on the values of 0 and 1. The Exclusive-NOR gate is the simplest comparator to indicate equivalency between 2-bits.

Comparators can be designed and built from logic gates by evaluating like bit positions, or by means of a truth table. An example of a comparator designed with a truth table is in Chapter 3 in Problem 3-117. In this problem two 2-bit values are compared to determine their relationship to each other.

The SOP or POS (product of sums) equations are derived and simplified, and the circuit is constructed from the simplified logic expression.

Comparators can also be designed through a logical evaluation sequence, beginning with the MSB position of each number and moving toward the LSB position. To determine if the numbers are equal to each other, each equivalent bit weight must have the same value in its respective position. The logic equation, A "equal to" B, to compare two 4-bit numbers is shown in Equation 6-13.

Eq. 6-13: A "equal to" B

$$A = B: \quad (\overline{A_4 \oplus B_4})(\overline{A_3 \oplus B_3})(\overline{A_2 \oplus B_2})(\overline{A_1 \oplus B_1})$$

To test if one number is greater than another, first evaluate the MSB positions. If the bits are not equal, the number with the 1 in the MSB position is the greatest. If the MSBs are equal, then the next bit must be evaluated, and whichever one has the largest bit value at that position is the number of greatest magnitude. This process continues, if necessary, to the LSB position. The logic statement, A "greater than" B, to compare two 4-bit values is shown in Equation 6-14.

Eq. 6-14: A "greater than" B

$$A > B: \quad A_4\overline{B}_4 + (\overline{A_4 \oplus B_4})(A_3\overline{B}_3) + (\overline{A_4 \oplus B_4})(\overline{A_3 \oplus B_3})(A_2\overline{B}_2) + (\overline{A_4 \oplus B_4})(\overline{A_3 \oplus B_3})(\overline{A_2 \oplus B_2})(A_1\overline{B}_1)$$

The logic statement to evaluate if A is less than B can be obtained from the equations to determine if A is greater than B by switching all A's for B's, and vice versa. The logic statement, A "less than" B, to compare two 4-bit values is shown in Equation 6-15.

Eq. 6-15: A "less than" B

$$A < B: \quad \overline{A}_4B_4 + (\overline{A_4 \oplus B_4})(\overline{A}_3B_3) + (\overline{A_4 \oplus B_4})(\overline{A_3 \oplus B_3})(\overline{A}_2B_2) + (\overline{A_4 \oplus B_4})(\overline{A_3 \oplus B_3})(\overline{A_2 \oplus B_2})(\overline{A}_1B_1)$$

The circuit for a 4-bit comparator that tests for A "equal to" B, A "greater than" B, and A "less than" B is shown in Figure 6-24.

The outputs from a comparator of "equal to," "greater than," or "less than" can be input to logic gates to obtain additional logical comparisons, such as "not equal to," "greater than or equal to," and "less than or equal to," as shown in Equations 6-16 through 6-18.

Eq. 6-16: A "not equal to" B

$$A \neq B = \overline{A = B} = (A > B) \quad \text{or} \quad (A < B)$$

Eq. 6-17: A "greater than or equal to" B

$$A \geq B = \overline{A < B} = (A > B) \quad \text{or} \quad (A = B)$$

$$\begin{array}{r} A_3\ A_2\ A_1 \\ \times \quad B_2\ B_1 \\ \hline P_5\ P_4\ P_3\ P_2\ P_1 \end{array}$$

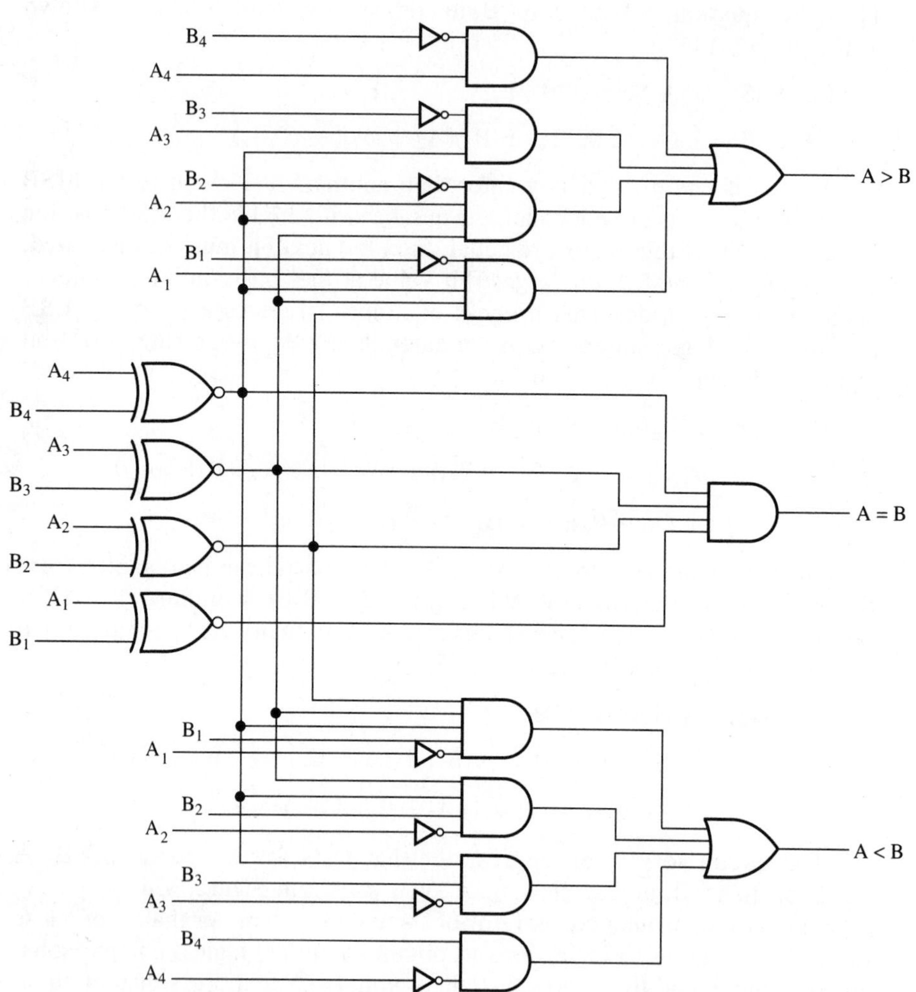

FIGURE 6-24 Four-Bit Comparator

Equation 6-18: A "less than or equal to" B

$$A \leq B = \overline{A > B} = (A < B) \quad \text{or} \quad (A = B)$$

These comparison results are shown in their logic gate form in Figure 6-25.

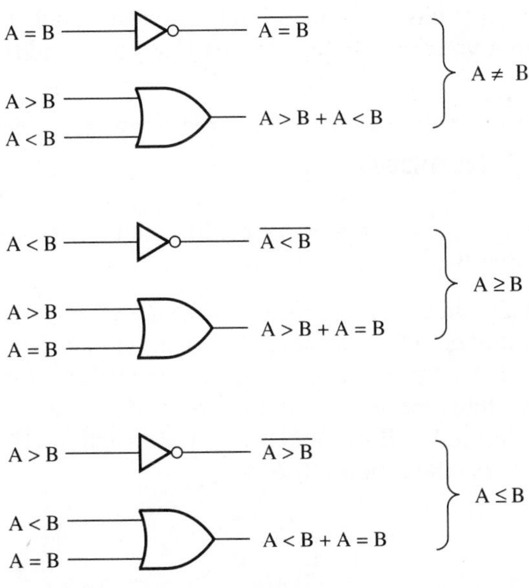

FIGURE 6-25 Comparator Output Combinations

6.4.2 Integrated Circuit Comparators

Comparators are conveniently available as MSI ICs. The 7485, shown in Figure 6-3, is designed to compare two 4-bit numbers. The 74682, shown in Figure 6-4, is designed to compare two 8-bit numbers.

The 7485 has three outputs available, all operating in an active-HIGH mode. The outputs are A = B, A < B, and A > B. These can be combined with logic gates as shown in Figure 6-25 to obtain additional comparison results.

The comparator has cascade control inputs for designs requiring the comparison of values greater than 4-bits. These inputs must be set as directed by the data sheet for proper operation in both single-IC and cascaded-IC designs.

The 74682 is one of several 6-bit comparators available. The features of the 74682 are that it has totem-pole outputs and 20K ohm pull-up termination resistors on one set of inputs for analog or switch data. This comparator only provides the active-LOW comparison outputs of "not equal to" and "not greater than." These outputs can be combined with logic gates to obtain additional comparison values as needed, as seen by the function table in the data sheet in Figure 6-4.

Comparator applications can require that one variable input value be compared to a fixed number hard-wired to the second set of inputs, or they can require that two variable input values be compared to each other. Comparator applications that have boundary limits between which an input value must remain require two comparators to verify that both conditions are met.

EXAMPLE 6-6 Valid BCD Numbers

Problem: Design a comparator circuit to test for valid binary coded decimal (BCD) numbers using the 7485 comparator.

Solution: Valid BCD numbers range from 0 through 9. Any value less than 10 is a valid BCD number. The 7485 could be used to input the BCD number to be verified on the A inputs and the binary value $(1010)_2$ on the B inputs. The cascade inputs must be set as follows: $A < B_{in} = 0$, $A > B_{in} = 0$, $A = B_{in} = 1$. The output $A < B_{out}$ could be used as an active-HIGH indicator of valid BCD numbers. (See Figure 6-26.)

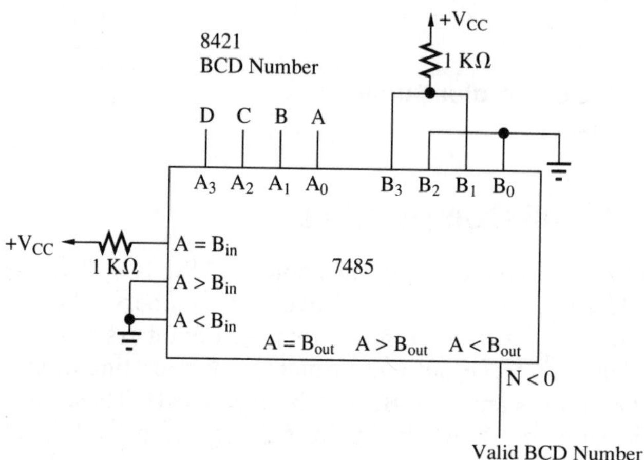

FIGURE 6-26 Example 6-6 Circuit

EXAMPLE 6-7 Valid Excess-3 Numbers

Problem: Design a comparator circuit to test for valid Excess-3 numbers, using the 7485 comparator and any additional logic gates.

Solution: Excess-3 numbers range from the binary values of 0011 to 1100. This is equivalent to saying that they range from 3 through 12. The two limits to this problem require that two comparators be used to verify the relationship, $3 \leq N \leq 12$. This is equivalent to the active-HIGH logic statement:

$$(N \geq 3) \quad \text{AND} \quad (N \leq 12) = \overline{(N < 3)} \quad \text{AND} \quad \overline{(N > 12)}$$

By applying DeMorgan's Theorem to the AND equation, we can form an equivalent NOR equation that requires only one additional logic gate for the design, in addition to the two comparators. (See Figure 6-27)

$$\overline{(N < 3)} \quad \text{AND} \quad \overline{(N > 12)} = (N < 3) \quad \text{NOR} \quad (N > 12)$$

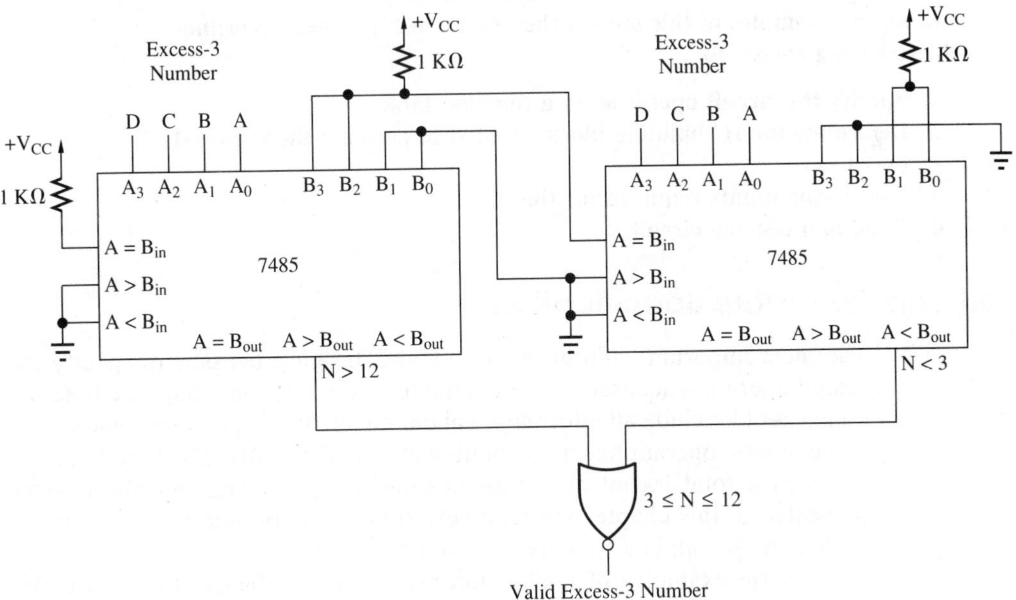

FIGURE 6-27 Example 6-7 Circuit

■

Section Self-Test

1. What is the purpose of the input controls labeled $A = B_{in}$, $A > B_{in}$, and $A < B_{in}$ on the 7485 IC?
2. When using the 74682 8-bit comparator, how can the output function for "$P < Q$" be obtained?
3. How can comparator circuits be used to form a range detector?

ANSWERS

(Not necessarily in the same order as the questions)

- The enable inputs should be tied LOW and the comparator outputs should be ANDed together.
- Two comparators are required to check the bounds of the range.
- The input controls are for cascading several of the chips to enlarge the size of the binary numbers that can be compared.

6-5 MULTIFUNCTION CIRCUIT DESIGN

The arithmetic circuits described in this chapter can be used as building blocks in many multifunction circuit designs. Although the function of the circuits may seem complicated, the design can be accomplished systematically to simplify the process.

Since the addition operation can be used to perform all other arithmetic operations, the 74283 4-bit adder will form the basis of many of the multifunction circuit design examples. The designs can be expanded or varied using other circuits in similar ways.

In all the examples of this section the designs will proceed according to the following rules:

1. **Specify the circuit operation in a function table.**
2. **Determine the IC building blocks needed to perform the required operations.**
3. **Specify the inputs required for the ICs.**
4. **Build and test the circuit.**

6.5.1 Function Table Specification

The most important step in the systematic design process is to specify the circuit operation accurately and completely in a function table. The function table should include all information about enable inputs, control inputs, data value inputs, operations on the input values, and outputs. The function table provides a total layout of the application problem. Although the designs presented in this chapter are relatively simple, the principles of systematic design can be applied to more complex problems.

Several examples of application problems specified in function tables follow. The designs will be completed in Sections 6.5.2 and 6.5.3 when the circuit equations are derived from function tables.

■ EXAMPLE 6-8 Controlled Adder Application: Function Table

Problem: Design an adder that is controlled by two control inputs, N and M. The inputs are used to specify what value is to be added to a 4-bit input number, I. If the control inputs are 0 0, do not change the input value. If the control inputs are 0 1, then add the number 2. If the control inputs are 1 0, then add the number 3. If the control inputs are 1 1, then add the number 5.

Solution: The application requirements are entered into the function table, as shown in Table 6-4.

TABLE 6-4 Controlled Adder—Function Table

Control Inputs		Operation	74283 Adder Inputs		
N	M		$A_4\ A_3\ A_2\ A_1$	$B_4\ B_3\ B_2\ B_1$	C_0
0	0	I + 0	$I_4\ I_3\ I_2\ I_1$	0 0 0 0	0
0	1	I + 2	$I_4\ I_3\ I_2\ I_1$	0 0 1 0	0
1	0	I + 3	$I_4\ I_3\ I_2\ I_1$	0 0 1 1	0
1	1	I + 5	$I_4\ I_3\ I_2\ I_1$	0 1 0 1	0

■

■ EXAMPLE 6-9 Arithmetic Processor: Function Table

Problem: Design an arithmetic processor circuit that will add two input values, subtract them, or increment each individually. The processor only functions when the enable input is HIGH. If the enable input is LOW, the output is 0. The four processes require two control inputs and four data inputs for each value, along with an active-HIGH enable for the circuit.

Solution: The application requirements are entered into a function table, as shown in Table 6-5.

TABLE 6-5 Arithmetic Processor—Function Table

Control Inputs			Operation	74283 Adder Inputs		
E	X	Y		$A_4\ A_3\ A_2\ A_1$	$B_4\ B_3\ B_2\ B_1$	C_0
1	0	0	A + B	$A_4\ A_3\ A_2\ A_1$	$B_4\ B_3\ B_2\ B_1$	0
1	0	1	A − B	$A_4\ A_3\ A_2\ A_1$	$\overline{B_4}\ \overline{B_3}\ \overline{B_2}\ \overline{B_1}$	1
1	1	0	A + 1	$A_4\ A_3\ A_2\ A_1$	0 0 0 0	1
1	1	1	B + 1	0 0 0 0	$B_4\ B_3\ B_2\ B_1$	1
0	X	X	Output 0	X X X X	X X X X	X

■

■ EXAMPLE 6-10 Difference Circuit: Function Table

Problem: Design a difference circuit that will always subtract the smaller of two 4-bit binary numbers from the larger number.

Solution: The application requirements are entered into a function table, as shown in Tables 6-6 and 6-7.

TABLE 6-6 Difference Circuit—Function Table—Comparator

	7485 Comparator Inputs	
Use Output	$A_3\ A_2\ A_1\ A_0$	$B_3\ B_2\ B_1\ B_0$
$A > B_{out}$	$A_4\ A_3\ A_2\ A_1$	$B_4\ B_3\ B_2\ B_1$

TABLE 6-7 Difference Circuit—Function Table—Adder

Control Input	Operation	74283 Adder Inputs		
$A > B_{out}$		$A_4\ A_3\ A_2\ A_1$	$B_4\ B_3\ B_2\ B_1$	C_0
0	B − A	$\overline{A_4}\ \overline{A_3}\ \overline{A_2}\ \overline{A_1}$	$B_4\ B_3\ B_2\ B_1$	1
1	A − B	$A_4\ A_3\ A_2\ A_1$	$\overline{B_4}\ \overline{B_3}\ \overline{B_2}\ \overline{B_1}$	1

Recall

$$A \leq B = \overline{A > B}$$

Use a comparator for the $A > B$ output as the control input to the adder. When $A > B_{out}$ is a 0, the adder then performs the operation B − A. When $A > B_{out}$ is a 1, the adder then performs A − B. ■

6.5.2 Input Logic Equations

After the problem has been specified in a function table, the logic equations for the inputs to the ICs can be determined. Data values are arbitrary values that will be input from other processes or from switches. Control inputs and enable inputs will be set by switch settings, or in some cases by other circuits.

The input equations must be functions of the data, control, and enable inputs. The input equations to the ICs are obtained by reading down the required input column and deriving an SOP or POS equation that will provide the necessary logic operations.

The equations for the function tables set up in Section 6.5.1 will be derived in the next examples.

■ EXAMPLE 6-11 Controlled Adder Application: Logic Equations

Problem: Derive logic equations from the function table developed in Example 6-8 for the controlled adder application.

Controlled Adder—Function Table

Control Inputs		Operation	74283 Adder Inputs								
N	M		A_4	A_3	A_2	A_1	B_4	B_3	B_2	B_1	C_0
0	0	I + 0	I_4	I_3	I_2	I_1	0	0	0	0	0
0	1	I + 2	I_4	I_3	I_2	I_1	0	0	1	0	0
1	0	I + 3	I_4	I_3	I_2	I_1	0	0	1	1	0
1	1	I + 5	I_4	I_3	I_2	I_1	0	1	0	1	0

Solution: Examining the required inputs into the adder, it can be seen the A inputs always require one of the input number bits, as specified by the function table. The B inputs vary from a logic HIGH to a logic LOW, depending on the function required. The C_0 input is always low. The A and C_0 inputs are constants, as specified below. The B_4 input is also a constant. The B_3, B_2, and B_1 inputs are the result of logic functions formed with the N and M control inputs.

CONTROLLED ADDER EQUATIONS

$A_4 = I_4$ $\quad B_4 = 0$ $\quad C_0 = 0$

$A_3 = I_3$ $\quad B_3 = N\,M$

$A_2 = I_2$ $\quad B_2 = N \oplus M$

$A_1 = I_1$ $\quad B_1 = N$ ■

■ EXAMPLE 6-12 Arithmetic Processor: Logic Equations

Problem: Derive logic equations from the function table developed in Example 6-9 for the arithmetic processor.

Arithmetic Processor Function Table

Control Inputs	Operation	74283 Adder Inputs		
E X Y		A_4 A_3 A_2 A_1	B_4 B_3 B_2 B_1	C_0
1 0 0	A + B	A_4 A_3 A_2 A_1	B_4 B_3 B_2 B_1	0
1 0 1	A − B	A_4 A_3 A_2 A_1	$\overline{B_4}$ $\overline{B_3}$ $\overline{B_2}$ $\overline{B_1}$	1
1 1 0	A + 1	A_4 A_3 A_2 A_1	0 0 0 0	1
1 1 1	B + 1	0 0 0 0	B_4 B_3 B_2 B_1	1
0 X X	Output 0	X X X X	X X X X	X

Solution: The circuit is "inactive" if the enable input is a logic LOW. This can be accomplished by ANDing E with the individual outputs of the 74283 adder. Therefore, if E is LOW, the outputs of the adder are LOW; if E is HIGH, the AND gate passes the result of the adder to the output of the circuit.

The A inputs to the 74283 are the result of NANDing the X and Y inputs and then ANDing this result with the respective A number bit. The B inputs are more complicated, but they are still a combination of basic logic functions. One way to derive the required function is to specify the SOP equation. The equation for each B input is derived as

$$B_n = \overline{X}\,\overline{Y}\,B_n + \overline{X}\,Y\,\overline{B_n} + X\,Y\,B_n$$

$$= (\overline{X}\,\overline{Y} + X\,Y)B_n + \overline{X}\,Y\,\overline{B_n}$$

$$= (\overline{X \oplus Y})B_n + \overline{X}\,Y\,\overline{B_n}$$

The equation for the C_0 input is the result of ORing the X and Y control inputs.

ARITHMETIC PROCESSOR EQUATIONS

Outputs: $S_4 = \text{Sum}_4\, E$

$S_3 = \text{Sum}_3\, E$

$S_2 = \text{Sum}_2\, E$

$S_1 = \text{Sum}_1\, E$

Inputs:

$$A_4 = A_4(\overline{XY}) \qquad B_4 = B_4(\overline{X \oplus Y}) + \overline{B}_4\overline{X}Y$$

$$A_3 = A_3(\overline{XY}) \qquad B_3 = B_3(\overline{X \oplus Y}) + \overline{B}_3\overline{X}Y$$

$$A_2 = A_2(\overline{XY}) \qquad B_2 = B_2(\overline{X \oplus Y}) + \overline{B}_2\overline{X}Y$$

$$A_1 = A_1(\overline{XY}) \qquad B_1 = B_1(\overline{X \oplus Y}) + \overline{B}_1\overline{X}Y$$

$$C_0 = X + Y$$

■

■ EXAMPLE 6-13 Difference Circuit: Logic Equations

Problem: Derive the logic equations from the function tables developed in Example 6-10 for the difference circuit.

Difference Circuit Function Table—Comparator

	7485 Comparator Inputs	
Use Output	$A_3\ A_2\ A_1\ A_0$	$B_3\ B_2\ B_1\ B_0$
$A > B_{out}$	$A_4\ A_3\ A_2\ A_1$	$B_4\ B_3\ B_2\ B_1$

Solution: Comparator Inputs: Input A number bits to the comparator A inputs. Input B number bits to the comparator B inputs. Set the comparator input control for standard operation, with $A = B_{in}$ tied HIGH, $A > B_{in}$ tied LOW, and $A < B_{in}$ tied LOW. Use the comparator output $A > B_{out}$ as the control input to the 74283 adder to control the arithmetic operation performed, and call the control input D as it goes to the 74283 adder.

Difference Circuit Function Table—Adder

Control Input	Operation	74283 Adder Inputs		
$D = A > B_{out}$		$A_4\ A_3\ A_2\ A_1$	$B_4\ B_3\ B_2\ B_1$	C_0
0	B − A	$\overline{A}_4\ \overline{A}_3\ \overline{A}_2\ \overline{A}_1$	$B_4\ B_3\ B_2\ B_1$	1
1	A − B	$A_4\ A_3\ A_2\ A_1$	$\overline{B}_4\ \overline{B}_3\ \overline{B}_2\ \overline{B}_1$	1

Solution: Adder Inputs: Recall that when the comparator output $A > B_{out}$ is LOW, it is signaling that the B input number is greater than or equal to the A input number. This is the condition for the adder to subtract A from

B since A is in fact less than or equal to B. When the comparator output $A > B_{out}$ is HIGH, it is signaling that the A input number is greater than the B input number. This is the condition for the adder to subtract B from A since A is the larger number.

The input functions to the adder are formed by specifying the logic operation as a function of the D control input and the respective A or B number bit. The C_0 input is always tied HIGH.

DIFFERENCE CIRCUIT EQUATIONS

Adder Inputs:

$$A_4 = \overline{A_4}\overline{D} + A_4D = \overline{A_4 \oplus D} \qquad C_0 = 1$$

$$A_3 = \overline{A_3}\overline{D} + A_3D = \overline{A_3 \oplus D}$$

$$A_2 = \overline{A_2}\overline{D} + A_2D = \overline{A_2 \oplus D}$$

$$A_1 = \overline{A_1}\overline{D} + A_1D = \overline{A_1 \oplus D}$$

$$B_4 = B_4\overline{D} + \overline{B_4}D = B_4 \oplus D$$

$$B_3 = B_3\overline{D} + \overline{B_3}D = B_3 \oplus D$$

$$B_2 = B_2\overline{D} + \overline{B_2}D = B_2 \oplus D$$

$$B_1 = B_1\overline{D} + \overline{B_1}D = B_1 \oplus D$$

(*Note:* D is $A > B_{out}$ from the 7485 comparator.) ■

6.5.3 Circuit Implementation

The final step in the systematic design process is to build and test the circuit. Each equation is used to design the individual inputs into the adder circuit, and any other circuits as required by the specific design. The circuit design and layout should be organized so that inputs and logic block functions are not confused and wired incorrectly. A sensible circuit layout often eliminates, or at least simplifies, any later troubleshooting.

The following examples complete the design problems by specifying the ICs required and showing the application circuit as designed.

■ EXAMPLE 6-14 Controlled Adder: Logic Circuit

Problem: Design the logic circuit based on the equations that were derived in Example 6-11 for the controlled adder.

Solution: See Figure 6-28.

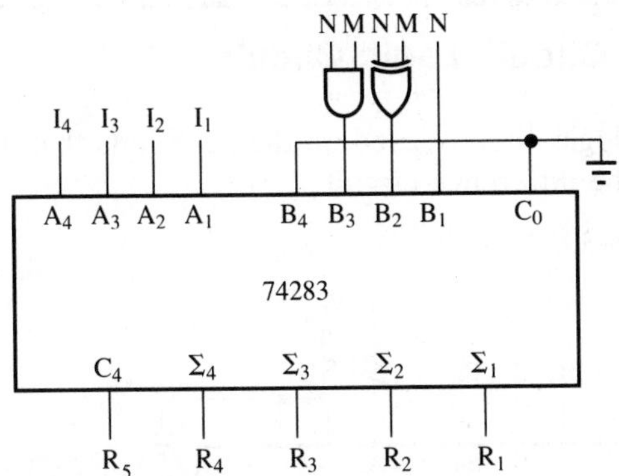

Controls		Operation
N	M	
0	0	I + 0
0	1	I + 2
1	0	I + 3
1	1	I + 5

FIGURE 6-28 Controlled Adder Circuit

EXAMPLE 6-15 Arithmetic Processor: Logic Circuit

Problem: Design the logic circuit based on the equations that were derived in Example 6-12 for the arithmetic processor.

Solution: See Figure 6-29.

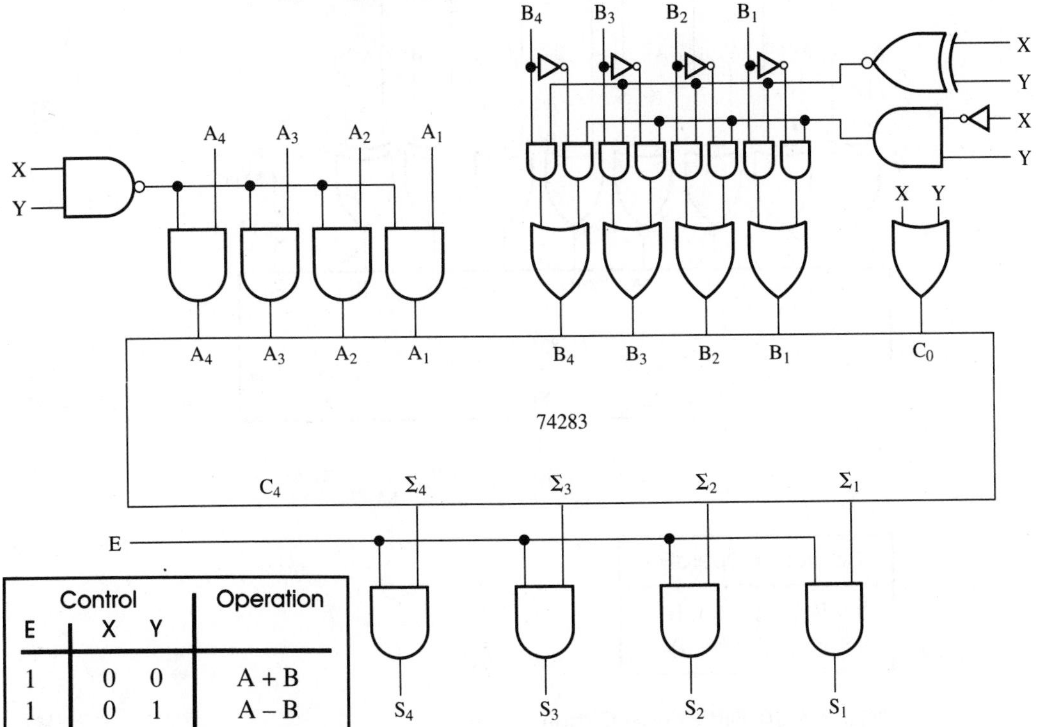

Control			Operation
E	X	Y	
1	0	0	A + B
1	0	1	A − B
1	1	0	A + 1
1	1	1	B + 1
0	X	X	Output zero

FIGURE 6-29 Arithmetic Processor Circuit

■ EXAMPLE 6-16 Difference Circuit: Logic Circuit

Problem: Design the logic circuit based on the equations that were derived in Example 6-13 for the difference circuit.

Solution: See Figure 6-30.

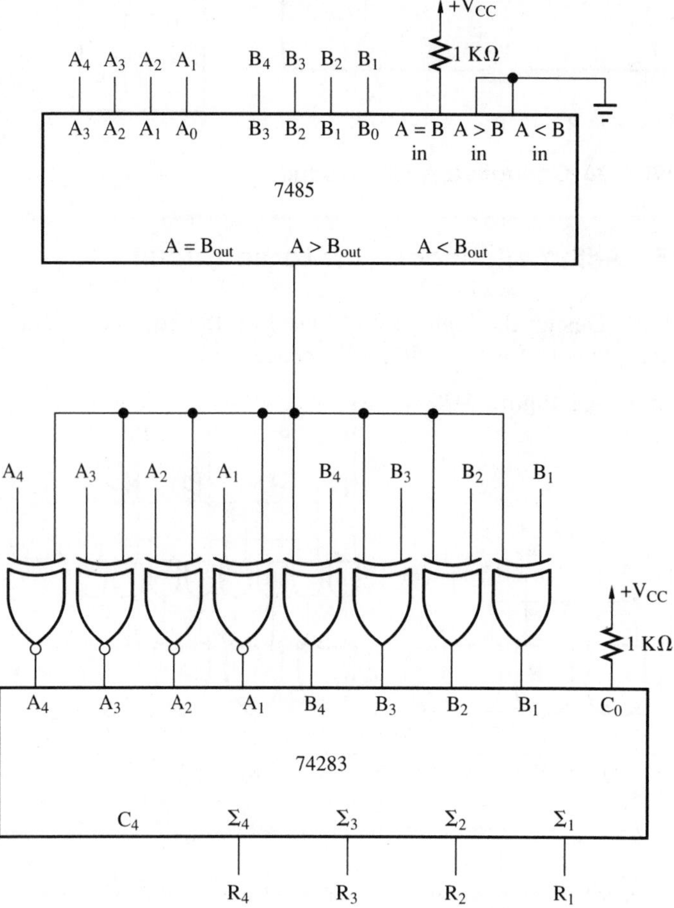

Control	Operation
$A > B_{out}$	$A - B$
$A \leq B_{out}$	$B - A$

FIGURE 6-30 Difference Circuit ■

Section Self-Test

1. What are the steps to follow when designing a multifunction logic circuit?

ANSWERS

- Specify the circuit operation in a function table.
- Determine the IC building blocks needed to perform the required operations.
- Specify the inputs required for the ICs.
- Build and test the circuit.

6-6 ARITHMETIC LOGIC UNITS

The multifunction circuit design offered a great deal of flexibility for applications circuits. Some of the standardized arithmetic and logic functions are available in specially programmed MSI ICs, referred to as arithmetic/logic units, or ALUs. These ICs are used primarily in more complicated arithmetic applications, either involving operations on large numbers or requiring that many operations be performed, and are a part of the internal circuitry of microprocessor ICs.

6.6.1 Integrated Circuit Specification

The data sheet for the 74181, shown in Figure 6-5, provides detailed information about the operation of the circuit. The ALU is far more complex than any of the arithmetic circuits used thus far. The circuit is able to perform 16 logic operations and 16 arithmetic operations on two 4-bit input values, or words as they are referred to in the data sheet. Four select or control inputs plus a mode control input are used to select the desired operation out of the 32 different logic or arithmetic functions.

The 74181 can operate with either active-LOW or active-HIGH data. Separate circuit configurations and function tables are specified, depending on which type of data is to be used.

The logic operations are performed by the 74181 as four separate two-input logic functions. For instance, the F = AB function on the two 4-bit input values is actually four AND operations of the bits of the values as shown:

$$F = AB \quad \text{performed as} \quad F = A_0B_0$$

$$F = A_1B_1$$

$$F = A_2B_2$$

$$F = A_3B_3$$

The mode control of the 74181 must be set to a logic-HIGH level in order to perform the logic functions so that each bit weight is operated on independently of the other bits. In other words, there is no carry operation from one bit to the next as is required for arithmetic operations.

The standard logic functions are all available, such as NAND, NOR, AND, OR, XNOR, XOR, and NOT. Also available are many logic functions that are not classified as basic gate operations, such as $F = \overline{A} + B$, $F = A + \overline{B}$, $F = \overline{A}B$, $F = A\overline{B}$, and others.

The arithmetic operations performed by the 74181 include addition and subtraction, increment (the addition of 1), decrement (the subtraction of 1), and many combinations of these operations. The operations vary depending on whether or not the carry-in to the LSB, C_n, is active.

The arithmetic operations are performed using the one's complement method, and an end-around-carry from C_{n+4} back to C_n must be connected to obtain the correct results.

Comparator operations are also available, but they require external circuitry. An A = B output is provided on the 74181. It is an open-collector output, requiring a pull-up resistor to obtain a logic-HIGH output. The comparator results of greater than and less than require the analysis of the carry-in and carry-out with additional logic gates, as specified in a table in the data sheet. To perform comparator operations, one must set the 74181 in the subtract mode by the control inputs with the carry-in at a logic-HIGH level.

6.6.2 Arithmetic Logic Unit Applications

Although the ALU such as the 74181 may seem like a one-stop answer to all logic problems, it poses several drawbacks from other available circuits. The first problem is its complexity. Proper operation depends on thoroughly understanding and programming the IC by means of control inputs. The programming of control inputs varies depending on whether active-HIGH or active-LOW data is being accepted. The select inputs, the mode control, and the carry-in inputs must be connected to the specified logic levels for the type of data being operated on in order to obtain the correct results.

The 74181 can be cascaded for operations on input values larger than 4 bits. Additional circuitry such as the 74182 look-ahead-carry generator is required for acceptable performance when the binary words exceed 9 bits each. There is no internal look-ahead-carry circuitry in the 74181 ALU. The carry-out, C_{n+4}, and the carry-in, C_n, are generated by ripple-carry operations.

The speed parameters for the circuit must be carefully evaluated. In some applications, the 74181 is slower than the 74283 or traditional logic gates.

The 74181 ALU can serve in some applications to reduce the number of ICs in the total application design. If speed and power are not critical concerns, then the 74181 could be used beneficially in logic applications requiring the operation of a large variety of functions.

Circuit design applications using the 74181 proceed by the same steps as outlined in Section 6.5. The application must be specified in a function table, the input equations to the IC must be derived, and the circuit must be built and tested.

■ EXAMPLE 6-17 Arithmetic Processor Design for an Arithmetic Logic Unit

Problem: To compare the application of the 74181 with a multifunction adder design, repeat the design for the arithmetic processor application described in Example 6-9. Design a logic circuit that uses the 74181 ALU.

Solution: A function table must be completed to determine the inputs required for the ALU to perform the required operations. The operations for determining the inputs logic equations and designing the circuit are identical to the processes shown in Examples 6-9, 6-12, and 6-15. (See Figure 6-31.)

Arithmetic Processor—Function Table

Control Inputs			Operation	74181 ALU Inputs													
E	X	Y		A_3	A_2	A_1	A_0	B_3	B_2	B_1	B_0	$\overline{C}_n$	M	S_3	S_2	S_1	S_0
0	0	0	A + B	A_4	A_3	A_2	A_1	B_4	B_3	B_2	B_1	1	0	1	0	0	1
0	0	1	A − B	A_4	A_3	A_2	A_1	B_4	B_3	B_2	B_1	0	0	0	1	1	0
0	1	0	A + 1	A_4	A_3	A_2	A_1	B_4	B_3	B_2	B_1	0	0	0	0	0	0
0	1	1	B + 1	0	0	0	0	B_4	B_3	B_2	B_1	0	0	0	0	0	1
1	X	X	Output 0	X	X	X	X	X	X	X	X	X	X	X	X	X	X

ARITHMETIC PROCESSOR EQUATIONS

Outputs: $S_4 = F_3\,\overline{E}$

$S_3 = F_2\,\overline{E}$

$S_2 = F_1\,\overline{E}$

$S_1 = F_0\,\overline{E}$

Inputs:

$$A_3 = A_4(\overline{XY}) \qquad B_3 = B_4$$
$$A_2 = A_3(\overline{XY}) \qquad B_2 = B_3$$
$$A_1 = A_2(\overline{XY}) \qquad B_1 = B_2$$
$$A_0 = A_1(\overline{XY}) \qquad B_0 = B_1$$
$$C_n = \overline{X + Y} \qquad M = 0$$
$$S_3 = \overline{X + Y}$$
$$S_2 = \overline{X}\,Y$$
$$S_1 = \overline{X}\,Y$$
$$S_0 = \overline{X \oplus Y}$$

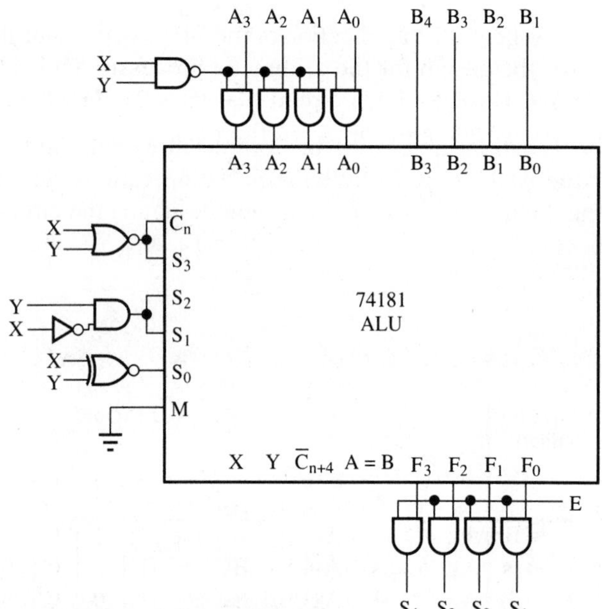

Control			Operation
E	X	Y	
1	0	0	A + B
1	0	1	A – B
1	1	0	A + 1
1	1	1	B + 1
0	X	X	Output zero

FIGURE 6-31 Arithmetic Processor Circuit

Section Self-Test

1. State three logic functions that the 74181 ALU can perform that are not basic logic gates.
2. State three arithmetic functions that the 74181 ALU can perform.
3. Cite one advantage and one disadvantage of using the ALU in logic designs.

ANSWERS (Not necessarily in the order of the questions)

- A minus B; A plus A plus 1; A minus 1
- A + B; A + B; A B
- Many functions are available; the circuit is very complex and relatively slow.

(*Note:* Many other correct answers are also possible.)

6-7 TROUBLESHOOTING ARITHMETIC CIRCUITS

Troubleshooting arithmetic circuits requires careful analysis of the operation to be performed and the circuit requirements. In several of the circuits described in this chapter special control inputs, or carry inputs, were required for correct operation. In other circuits open-collector outputs required external pull-up resistors. A few circuits required additional ICs for proper operation, such as the two-chip multiplier and the look-ahead-carry IC required by the ALU. Several examples of troubleshooting arithmetic circuits are illustrated in this section.

■ EXAMPLE 6-18 The Kaput Comparator

Problem: A 6-bit comparator is designed using two 7485s to compare two 6-bit binary numbers, A and B, and to indicate if the numbers are equal to each other, if A is greater than B, or if B is greater than A. You have already been troubleshooting the circuit to verify that the ground and power are connected, that the correct IC is being used. Furthermore, you borrowed the IC from a friend who just completed a problem correctly, so you know that the IC is working. The circuit, as wired, is shown in Figure 6-32. Locate the wiring errors and correct the schematic.

Solution: Several input bits are out of order. The lower-order bits, B_3 B_2 B_1 B_0 and A_3 A_2 A_1 A_0, must be input to the comparator where the cascade inputs are tied to ground and V_{CC}. The remaining bits, B_4 B_5 and A_4 A_5, are to be connected to the B_0 B_1 and A_0 A_1 inputs on the second comparator, respectively. The comparator outputs from the first comparator are to be

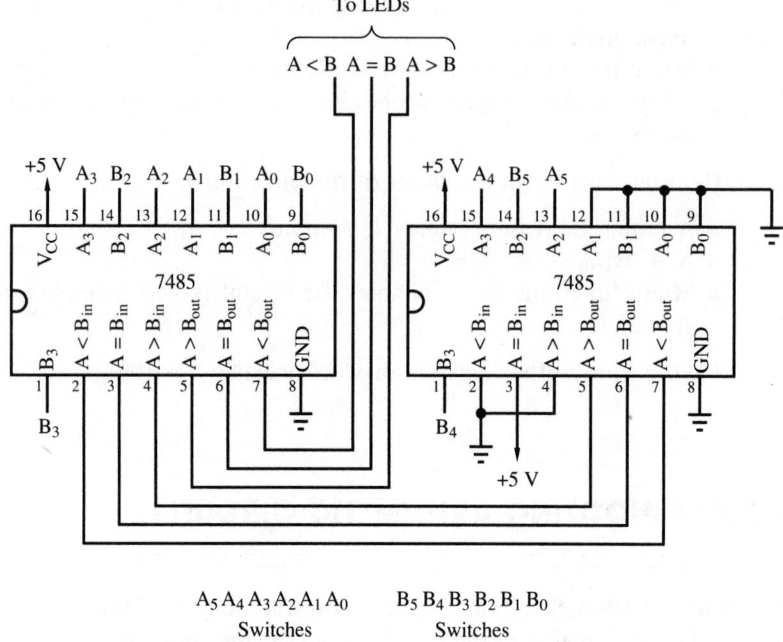

FIGURE 6-32 Example 6-17 Circuit with Wiring Errors

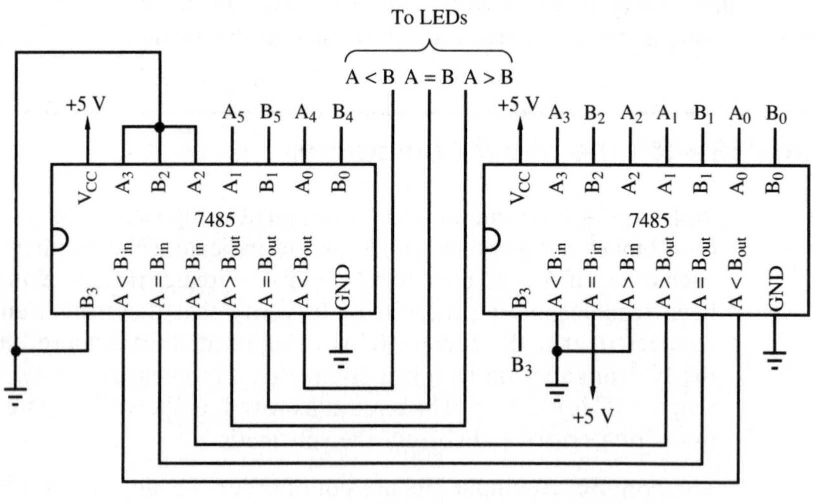

FIGURE 6-33 Example 6-17 Correctly Wired Circuit

connected to the cascade inputs of the second comparator, which was done correctly. Any unused A or B inputs are to be tied LOW. The correctly wired logic circuit is shown in Figure 6-33. ■

■ EXAMPLE 6-19 The Odd Number Adder

Problem: An adder application circuit is to accept a 4-bit input number, I, and to add either 2, 4, 6, or 8 to it based on the control inputs, M and N. The function table for the proper operation of the adder is shown in Figure 6-34. The circuit was designed and built using the 74283 IC. When tested, the adder unfortunately adds 3, 5, 7, or 9 to the input value. How would you correct this circuit malfunction?

Function Table

M	N	Operation	74283 Inputs A_4	A_3	A_2	A_1	B_4	B_3	B_2	B_1
0	0	I + 2	I_3	I_2	I_1	I_0	0	0	1	0
0	1	I + 4	I_3	I_2	I_1	I_0	0	1	0	0
1	0	I + 6	I_3	I_2	I_1	I_0	0	1	1	0
1	1	I + 8	I_3	I_2	I_1	I_0	1	0	0	0

FIGURE 6-34 Example 6-18 Function Table

Solution: **(a)** Design a subtracter circuit for the outputs.
(b) Check the C_0 input to make sure it is tied LOW.
(c) Check the B_1 input to make sure it is tied LOW.

(b) or (c) is the preferred solution. ■

Section Self-Test

1. List three key troubleshooting strategies that should be used when trying to determine the cause of error in arithmetic circuits.

ANSWERS

- Check any "unused" inputs to make sure that they are tied to a logic-LOW.
- Check the control inputs to make sure that they are tied to their appropriate level for the desired operation.
- Check the order of input bits to make sure that they are in the proper order for the weight of the bit.

SUMMARY

Arithmetic operations can be performed by special arithmetic ICs. Arithmetic ICs are available for addition, multiplication, true/complement, comparator functions, and multifunction arithmetic and logic operations. Addition operations form the basis for all other arithmetic functions, and IC adders are used to perform many multifunction arithmetic operations.

Comparator operations, closely related to arithmetic operations, are available using special purpose ICs. The comparator operations are often used in conjunction with arithmetic operations in many applications.

The arithmetic circuits can be hardware-programmed by control inputs to provide flexible operations for more complex applications. The hardware-programmed arithmetic circuits can be used instead of microprocessor circuits, where software is used to control the circuit functions. Applications requiring high speed and reliability may be best suited for hardware circuit designs. The application requirements must be fully evaluated to select the best solution to the problem.

This chapter studied the analysis, application, and design of numerous arithmetic circuits.

ANALYSIS

Adders formed the basis of the study of arithmetic circuits, as all arithmetic operations can be performed through addition. Half-adders and full-adders were analyzed to determine their function. IC adders, in particular, the 74283, were studied as stand-alone ICs and integrated into digital application circuits.

In addition to adders, other arithmetic circuits such as multipliers, comparators, true/complement circuits, and arithmetic logic units were analyzed in the context of several applications.

APPLICATION

The major arithmetic applications studied in this chapter included cascaded adders, adder/subtracter circuits, multipliers, range detectors, threshold detectors, and multifunction arithmetic circuits. Special emphasis was placed on signed number arithmetic circuits and the analysis of the computational limits of the circuits.

DESIGN

Extensive digital design examples were carried out based on a systematic method for developing a logic circuit from an application specification. The design applications in the chapter required the use of several logic circuits and arithmetic circuits. The methods used are applicable to a wide range of digital logic design problems.

TROUBLESHOOTING

Troubleshooting arithmetic circuits relies heavily on the analysis of the arithmetic operation to be performed and the requirements of the ICs. Special attention must be given to unused inputs, control inputs, open-collector outputs, and cascading configurations.

PROBLEMS

6-1 Binary Addition—Analysis and Application Problems

*1. What range of values can be added with the 8-bit adder?

2. How can the 8-bit adder circuit of Figure 6-12 be expanded using any additional logic gates for a 9-bit addition?

6-2 Binary Subtraction—Analysis and Application Problems

3. Convert the 9-bit adder circuit of Problem 6-2 to a 9-bit adder/subtracter circuit.

4. What range of values can be added and subtracted using the circuit of Problem 6-3 without overflow occurring?

*5. Add the necessary circuitry to detect if an overflow condition occurs in the circuitry of Problem 6-3.

6. The following waveforms are input to an adder/subtracter circuit similar to the one shown in Figure 6-18. The addition or subtraction operation is determined by a **mode control, M,** rather than by a switch. When the mode control is LOW, the circuit adds; when the mode control is HIGH, the circuit subtracts. Determine the circuit output waveforms.

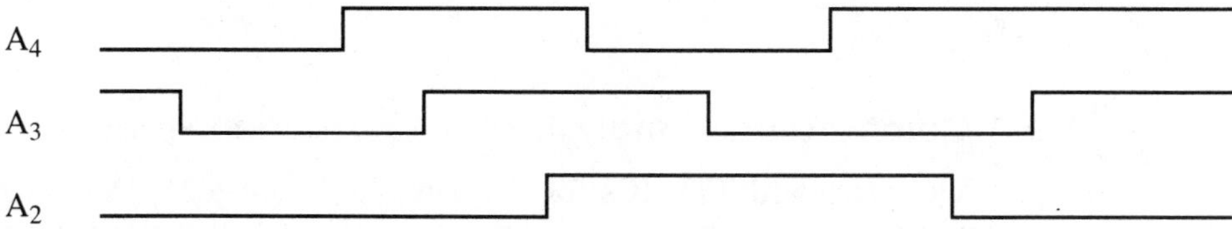

* *See* Answers to Selected Problems.

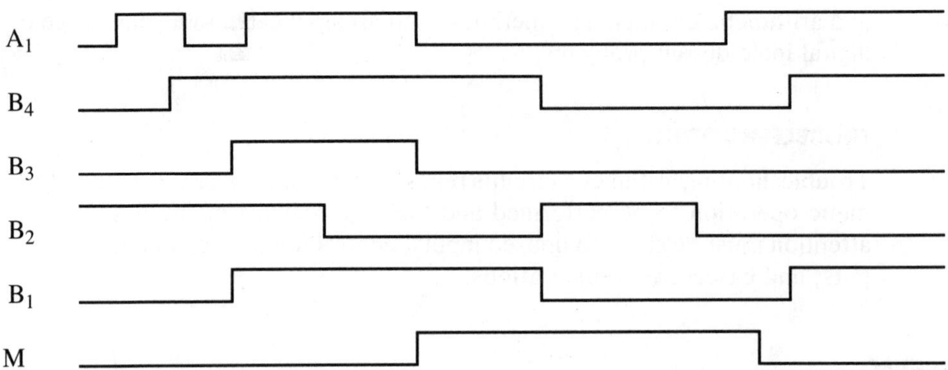

7. Did overflow occur during the operation of the circuit for the given waveforms in Problem 6-6? If so, indicate which sections of the output waveforms have "invalid" results.

6-3 Multiplication—Analysis and Application Problems

8. Compare the multiplier circuits in Figure 6-21 and 6-23. How many ICs are required by each circuit, and what is the maximum propagation delay from any input to any output on the circuit?
9. The multiplier circuit of Figure 6-21 is used to multiply signed numbers. The "A" number can be within the range of +7 to −7. The "B" number can be within the range of +3 to −3. Add the required logic circuitry to the given circuit to do the following:
   a. Determine the sign of the result.
   b. Convert negative results to their two's complement form, and keep positive results in their true form.

*10. A 4-bit by 4-bit multiplier is shown in Figure 6-22. If such a multiplier was built using only 74283 adders and 7408 AND gates, specify how many chips of each type would be necessary to complete the design.

11. What range of values can be multiplied by the circuit shown in Figure 6-22?

6-4 Comparators—Analysis and Application Problems

12. Select standard TTL ICs for the gates in Figure 6-24. Determine the maximum propagation delay from any input to any output for the circuits shown in Figure 6-24.

*13. Determine the maximum propagation delay from any input to any output on the 7485 comparator.

6-5 Multifunction Circuit Design—Design Problems

14. Design a circuit to convert BCD values to the Excess-3 code, using the 74283 adder.

15. Values entered from two octal key pads must be added, and the resulting value displayed on seven-segment displays. Design a circuit using the 74148 encoders, 74283 adders, 7447 display drivers, common-anode displays, and any additional circuitry for this application.

16. Design a circuit to convert Excess-3 code to the 8421 BCD code using the 74283 adder.

*17. Design a comparator using the 7485 to compare two numbers ranging in magnitude from 0 through 200. Show all connections required.

18. Design a BCD adder using the 74283, the 7485, and any additional logic gates to add two BCD digits. The design should include the necessary correction circuitry to obtain valid BCD results.

19. Design a BCD adder using the 74283, 74185, the 7485, and any additional logic gates or ICs to add two BCD numbers ranging from 0 through 9.

20. Design a BCD ten's complement subtractor using the 74283, 74184, and any additional logic gates or ICs to subtract two BCD numbers ranging from 0 through 9.

21. Design a multifunction processor using the 74283 and any additional logic gates to perform the following operations on two 4-bit binary numbers:

Enable Inputs	Control Inputs		Operation
G	J	K	
0	0	0	Output A
0	0	1	Output B
0	1	0	Complement A ($\overline{A_4}\ \overline{A_3}\ \overline{A_2}\ \overline{A_1}$)
0	1	1	Complement B ($\overline{B_4}\ \overline{B_3}\ \overline{B_2}\ \overline{B_1}$)
1	X	X	Output 1 1 1 1

22. Design a multifunction processor using the 74283 and any additional logic gates to perform the following operation on a 4-bit binary value:

Enable Inputs	Control Inputs		Operation
G	M	N	
0	0	0	Form the BCD equivalent
0	0	1	Form the Excess-3 equivalent
0	1	X	Keep in the binary format
1	X	X	Output 0 0 0 0

6-6 Arithmetic Logic Units—Design

*23. Design a circuit for the function specified in Problem 6-21 using the 74181 ALU.

6-7 Troubleshooting Arithmetic Circuits—Troubleshooting Problems

24. Determine the output equation of the circuit in Figure 6-13 if the C_0 inputs were left unconnected.

25. Determine the output equation of the circuit in Figure 6-21 if the AND gates were connected to B_4 B_3 and B_2 while B_1 was grounded.

*26. Determine the output of the circuit in Figure 6-22 if there were no pull-up resistors at the outputs.

27. Determine the output of the circuit in Figure 6-26 if the cascade inputs were left unconnected on the 7485.

Part 4

SEQUENTIAL LOGIC

Chapter 7

Monostable and Astable Circuits

Upon completing and mastering the material in this chapter, you should be able to perform the following functions in the areas of analysis, application, and design of monostable and astable circuits:

ANALYSIS

1. Construct present state-next state tables for sequential circuit analysis.
2. Analyze digital circuits with feedback.
3. Perform sequential waveform analysis.
4. Understand the importance of propagation delay in sequential analysis.
5. Analyze astable multivibrators.
6. Analyze monostable multivibrators.
7. Analyze 555 IC timer circuits.
8. Troubleshoot astable and monostable circuits.
9. Analyze Schmitt trigger circuits.
10. Understand hysteresis in digital circuits.
11. Graph and analyze input and output voltage transfer characteristics.

APPLICATION

12. Use astable circuits in clock generation applications.
13. Use monostable circuits in one-shot applications.
14. Utilize Schmitt trigger circuits in pulse shaping, threshold detection, and noise elimination circuit applications.

DESIGN

15. Design a variety of astable and monostable circuits using the 555 timer IC.
16. Design oscillator and one-shot circuits for a given application.
17. Design with Schmitt trigger ICs.

7-1 SEQUENTIAL LOGIC

The logic circuits and devices analyzed and designed thus far have been combinational logic circuits. Another important classification of logic circuits are sequential circuits. Sequential circuit outputs depend on the sequence of inputs applied. They are analyzed with respect to time, as compared to combinational circuits that are analyzed based only on the logic levels presently input to the circuit under analysis.

Sequential logic has many applications. Counters, shift registers, memory, and timing circuits are all based on the principles of sequential logic.

Astable and monostable circuits, which are some of the simplest types of sequential circuits, are an ideal introduction to some of the key concepts of sequential logic. Astable and monostable circuits are used for many of the timing and clock circuits necessary for digital circuit operation.

7.1.1 Sequential Logic States

Sequential circuits are circuits whose output values depend on the sequence of inputs applied with respect to time. Sequential circuit outputs are described in terms of logic conditions, also known as states. A **logic state** is the logic value of a gate or circuit output. One important difference in the analysis of combinational logic and sequential logic is that sequential logic outputs depend on the state of a circuit with respect to time. This time element is denoted by the terms previous, present, and next.

The **present state** is the present time logic state of the output of a circuit. The **previous state** is the logic state of a circuit one time period prior to the present state. The **next state** is the logic state of a circuit one time period after the present state. The time periods are determined by the frequency of the timing waveform input to the circuit.

For sequential logic, the timing waveform takes on additional significance and is referred to as the **timing clock,** or simply the **clock.** The operation of the device or circuit depends on the clock rising and falling edges and the frequency of the clock.

■ EXAMPLE 7-1 Sequential Logic

Problem: Logic circuit X changes its state each time the clock input changes from a LOW to a HIGH, as shown by the timing waveform in Figure 7-1.

Determine the present, previous, and next state logic values of the circuit if:

(a) Clock pulse 4 is the present state.
(b) Clock pulse 1 is the present state.

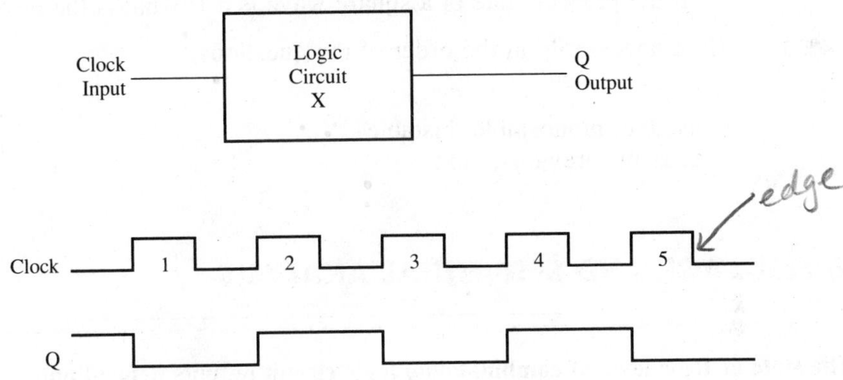

FIGURE 7-1 Logic State Circuit

Solution:

(a)	Present state	1
	Previous state	0
	Next state	0
(b)	Present state	0
	Previous state	1
	Next state	1

■

A logic circuit whose output remains in its present logic state until some input changes is described as being in a **stable state.** Logic circuits may also have **unstable states,** which are outputs that will change logic states after a given amount of time, even if the inputs remain unchanged.

7.1.2 Sequential Circuit Classification

Clock timing and output states are important in the analysis and design of sequential circuits. In addition, the number of stable output states a device has is used to classify the sequential circuit.

Astable circuits are sequential circuits that have no stable states. **Monostable circuits** are sequential circuits that have one stable state. Important astable and monostable circuits for sequential logic applications are discussed in this chapter.

Bistable circuits are sequential circuits that have two stable output states,

a 0 and a 1. The two major types of bistable devices are the latch and the flip-flop. These devices are described in detail in Chapters 8 and 9.

Section Self-Test

1. List the three types of sequential circuits.
2. List the three types of logic states.
3. If the present state of a square wave is a 1, what is the next state?

ANSWERS (Not necessarily in the order of the questions)

- 0
- astable, monostable, bistable
- present, previous, next

7-2 FEEDBACK AND SEQUENTIAL ANALYSIS

The state or logic level of combinational logic circuit outputs depend only on the present inputs to the circuit, whereas sequential circuit outputs depend on the sequence of inputs to the circuit. The inputs are sequenced in most sequential circuits by connecting one or more of the outputs of the circuit to the inputs of the circuit. This is known as feedback. The truth table for a sequential circuit is known as a present input-present state-next state table.

7.2.1 Digital Feedback

Feedback is the process of connecting the output of a device or circuit into the input of the same device or circuit. Thus, the output is "fed back" into the input. Feedback may involve one or more of the outputs, or one or more of the inputs. Both analog and digital circuits can employ feedback. Feedback is especially important in the operation of many digital sequential ICs and circuits.

With feedback employed, the logic state of the circuit is now time-dependent. For this reason, it is necessary to define previous, present, and next states to completely describe and analyze sequential operation.

Feedback can be illustrated with any of the basic logic gates. Figure 7-2 shows an OR gate with feedback. Since the logic gate does not operate

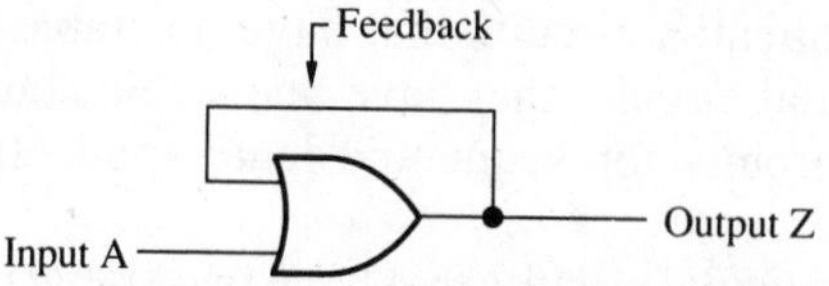

FIGURE 7-2 Basic Sequential Circuit; OR Gate with Feedback

instantaneously (it has a finite delay time), the output Z and the connected input to the OR gate may not be the same logic value, depending on the time at which the analysis is taking place. With only the combinational truth table for an OR gate, it is not possible to determine the final output states for the circuit. In order to analyze sequential circuits, additional tools are needed.

7.2.2 Present Input-Present State-Next State Table

A **present input-present state-next state table** is a truth table used to analyze sequential circuits as shown in Table 7-1. The output of a sequential circuit depends on the present inputs as well as on the present state of the output. With this information, can be predicted the next state of the output.

TABLE 7-1 Present Input–Present State–Next State Table

Present Inputs		Present State	Next State
J	K	Q_n	Q_{n+1}
0	0	0	0
0	0	1	1
0	1	0	0
0	1	1	0
1	0	0	1
1	0	1	1
1	1	0	1
1	1	1	0

To construct a present input-present state-next state table, list all the input variable combinations and a variable for each output. Then use conventional truth tables and sequential circuit analysis to determine the next state columns, one for each present state column. It is traditional to denote the present state with the variable Q(n) and the next state with the variable Q(n + 1).

For some sequential analysis, it is often convenient to condense the present input-present state-next state table into a **present state-next state table.** Either form of the table will be used as appropriate for a given sequential application. These two tables are also commonly called **state tables.**

7.2.3 Sequential State Table Analysis

Analyze the sequential circuit and state table for the OR gate with the feedback shown in Figure 7-2. First, note that the next state output, Q(n + 1), is the same as that of a combinational logic OR gate truth table output. Next, notice that since feedback is present, the input column Q and the present state column Q(n) must be the same.

Performing the sequential analysis, when A = 1 and Q = 0, we find that the output will initially be a 0 (present state), but the output will change to a logic 1 (next state) due to the feedback in accordance with the operation of an OR gate. All four states reach a final state that is stable, but when A = 1 and Q(n) = 0 (row 3 of the state table), the condition is temporarily an unstable state since an OR gate output of 0 when 0 and 1 are input violates the OR gate's truth table. The present input-present state-next state table for the OR gate shows that an unstable present state changes to a stable next state. This may not always occur, as some sequential circuits have states that are always unstable.

7.2.4 Sequential Waveform Clocks and Triggering

Waveforms are a very important way to illustrate the operation of sequential circuits. Since sequential circuits are time dependent, most waveform analysis is done in reference to a **timing clock**, simply referred to as the **clock**, as illustrated in Example 7-1.

Synchronous digital devices rely on a clock input to control when the device recognizes the signals placed on the data inputs and responds accordingly. Synchronous logic can also be called clocked logic.

A device that responds to a particular type of timing occurrence such as the change of a clock waveform or a voltage level is referred to as a **triggered device.** There are several types of triggering. **Edge triggered** devices respond to the timing edges of a clock. **Positive** or **leading edge triggered** devices are allowed to change state when the clock input signal changes from a LOW to a HIGH. **Negative** or **trailing edge triggered** devices are allowed to change state when the clock input signal changes from a HIGH to a LOW. Edge triggering will be discussed during the analysis of monostable multivibrators.

■ EXAMPLE 7-2 Sequential Logic Waveforms

Problem:

(a) A sequential device has an initial output of 0 and changes state on the leading edge of the input clock. Draw the resulting output waveform.

(b) A sequential device has an initial output of 0 and changes state on the trailing edge of the input clock. Draw the resulting output waveform.

Solution: Figure 7-3 illustrates the device output waveforms for a leading edge and trailing edge triggered device. Note that the only time the output changes state is when it is on the trigger edge.

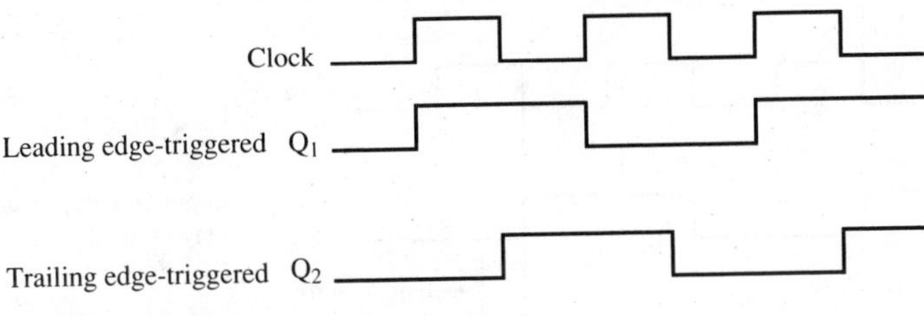

FIGURE 7-3 Device triggering ■

Voltage level triggered devices respond to voltage levels. Latches and the 555 timer IC are voltage level triggered. Many oscilloscopes are triggered based on a voltage setting.

7.2.5 Propagation Delay

One important parameter to consider when analyzing sequential circuits is propagation delay. **Propagation delay** is the time it takes the output of a device to respond to a change at the inputs of the device. In specification data sheets two propagation delay times are usually listed. They are t_{PHL}, propagation delay time, HIGH-to-LOW level output, and t_{PLH}, propagation delay time, LOW-to-HIGH **level output.**

Waveforms can be drawn with or without showing the propagation delay of a device. If the actual propagation delay is needed for a circuit, it is important to show the delay times. For many circuits, however, delay times are often ignored to determine the basic logic operation of a circuit.

■ EXAMPLE 7-3 Propagation Delay in Sequential Circuits

Problem: A device has a t_{PHL} = 20 ns and t_{PLH} = 25 ns. The device initially has a LOW output. If the input to the device is always a logic 1, the device changes logic state on the leading edge of each clock input into the device. Show the output waveform for the device for the first four clock pulses with and without the propagation delay. The clock frequency is f = 10 MHz.

Solution: First, determine the period of the clock: T = 1/f = 1/10 MHz = 100 ns. Then draw the propagation delays for the LOW-to-HIGH output pulse transition, and the HIGH-to-LOW output pulse transition, as shown in Figure 7-4.

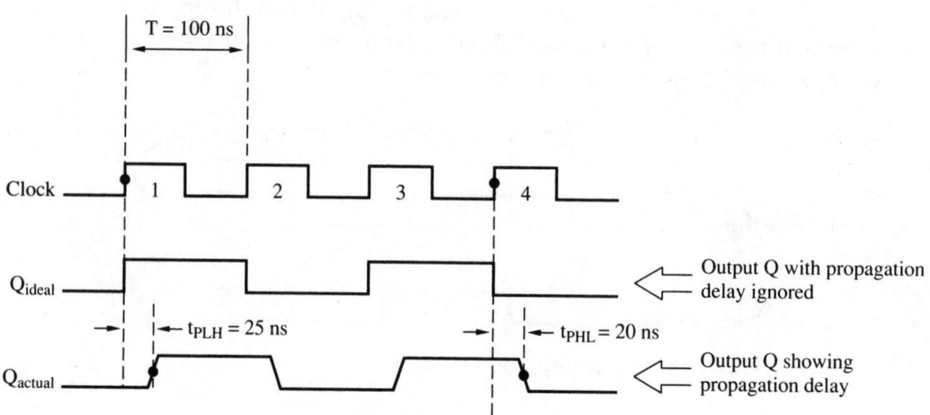

FIGURE 7-4 Output waveform for Example 7-3

EXAMPLE 7-4 Propagation Delay

Problem:

(a) Find the propagation delays for a standard 2-input NAND gate, a 74HC00, and a 74HCT00. For the CMOS devices, assume V_{CC} = 4.5 volts and a temperature of 25°C.

(b) If the output of the 7400 was tied to one of its inputs, how long would it take for a change in the NAND gate state to occur due to feedback?

Solution: Refer to the TTL and CMOS data books for the NAND gates, and look at the AC switching characteristics, under t_{PHL} and t_{PLH}. (See Table 7-2.)

TABLE 7-2 Propagation Delay Parameters

Device	Parameter	Typical (ns)	Maximum (ns)
7400	t_{PHL}	7	15
	t_{PLH}	11	22
74HC00	t_{PHL}	9	18
	t_{PLH}	9	18
74HCT00	t_{PHL}	10	19
	t_{PLH}	10	19

Section Self-Test

1. A positive triggered device has a clock input that changes from a HIGH to a LOW. Will the device trigger?
2. Device A has a propagation delay of 10 ns. Device B has a propagation delay of 15 ns. Is device A faster than device B?
3. A device that changes its state when it is triggered has a present state of 1. If the device is triggered, is the next state 1?

ANSWERS (Not necessarily in the order of the questions)

• No • No • Yes

7-3 MONOSTABLE MULTIVIBRATORS

Monostable multivibrators, or one-shots, are sequential devices that have one stable state. They are used in a variety of applications where one pulse of a specific pulse width is needed.

A **monostable multivibrator** is a logic device that has one stable state and one unstable state. It is also known as a **one-shot** device, as it outputs one pulse for every valid input signal. The typical monostable multivibrator has one input, the **trigger input,** which may be positive or negative edge triggered, depending on the type of monostable device.

If a timing transition is input into the trigger of the monostable, the multivibrator will output one pulse of a specific time duration. The time duration of the pulse, the **pulse width,** is the time that the one-shot is in its unstable state and depends on the operational characteristics of the individual device. Often an external resistor and capacitor are used to control the pulse width, which is determined by the RC time constant of the resistor and capacitor. Monostable multivibrators normally have both an active HIGH output, Q, and an active LOW output, $\overline{Q}$. The one-shot produces a HIGH pulse when triggered at the Q output and a LOW pulse at the $\overline{Q}$ output. Figure 7-5 shows the standard and IEEE/ANSI logic symbols for a monostable multivibrator.

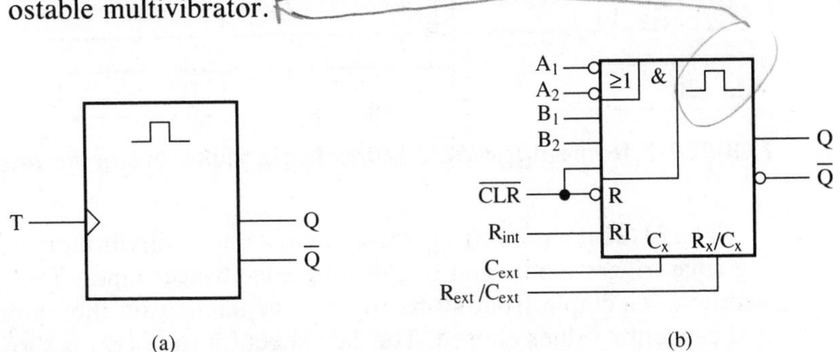

FIGURE 7-5 Monostable Multivibrator (One Shot) Logic Symbols. (a) Standard Logic Symbol; (b) IEEE/ANSI Standard 91 Logic Symbol

A typical output for a monostable multivibrator is shown in Figure 7-6. Analysis of the output indicates that this device is leading edge triggered since the output Q begins to change on the leading edge of the trigger input T. The output pulse width, t_W, will be the same value, even if the input pulse T varies, as shown in Figure 7-6(b). The output pulse width is controlled strictly by the values of the timing capacitor and resistor selected for the given pulse width. Types of triggering will be considered in the next sections.

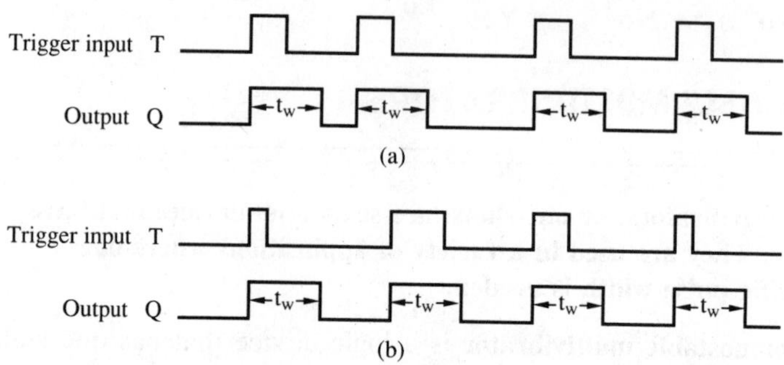

FIGURE 7-6 Monostable Multivibrator Waveforms. (a) Leading Edge-Triggered, Constant Trigger Pulse Width; (b) Leading Edge-Triggered, Variable Trigger Pulse Width

7.3.1 Nonretriggerable Monostable Multivibrators

One type of monostable multivibrator is the **nonretriggerable multivibrator.** This device will not respond to any additional trigger inputs if the device has already been triggered to its unstable state, as shown in Figure 7-7.

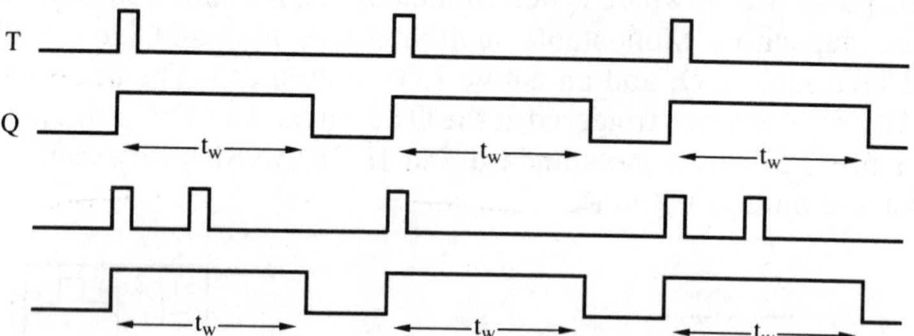

FIGURE 7-7 Nonretriggerable Monostable Multivibrator Waveforms

The 74121 is a nonretriggerable monostable multivibrators with two trailing edge trigger inputs and one leading edge trigger input. The output pulse width is selectable from 40 ns to 25 s, depending on the external resistor and capacitor values chosen. The data sheet for the 74121 is shown in Figure 7-8.

The 74221, 74LS221, and 74HC221 are dual nonretriggerable monostable multivibrators. The 74221 and 74LS221 are electrically compatible with the

SN54121, SN74121 MONOSTABLE MULTIVIBRATORS WITH SCHMITT-TRIGGER INPUTS

MAY 1983 – REVISED MARCH 1988

- Programmable Output Pulse Width
  With R_{int} . . . 35 ns Typ
  With R_{ext}/C_{ext} . . . 40 ns to 28 Seconds
- Internal Compensation for Virtual Temperature Independence
- Jitter-Free Operation up to 90% Duty Cycle
- Inhibit Capability

SN54121 . . . J OR W PACKAGE
SN74121 . . . N PACKAGE
(TOP VIEW)

Pin	Name	Pin	Name
1	$\overline{Q}$	14	V_{CC}
2	NC	13	NC
3	A1	12	NC
4	A2	11	R_{ext}/C_{ext}
5	B	10	C_{ext}
6	Q	9	R_{int}
7	GND	8	NC

NC - No internal connection.

FUNCTION TABLE

INPUTS			OUTPUTS	
A1	A2	B	Q	$\overline{Q}$
L	X	H	L	H
X	L	H	L†	H†
X	X	L	L†	H†
H	H	X	L†	H†
H	↓	H	⊓	⊔
↓	H	H	⊓	⊔
↓	↓	H	⊓	⊔
L	X	↑	⊓	⊔
X	L	↑	⊓	⊔

logic symbol‡

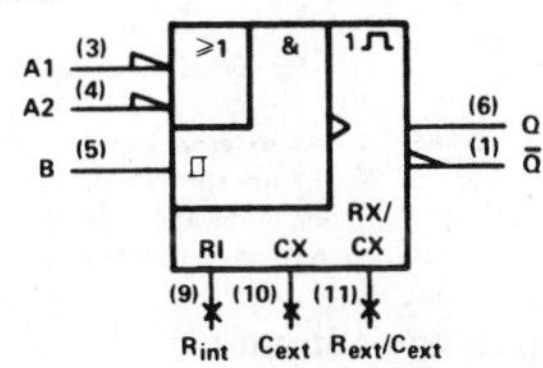

‡This symbol is in accordance with ANSI/IEEE Std 91-1984 and IEC Publication 617-12.

For explanation of function table symbols, see page

† These lines of the function table assume that the indicated steady-state conditions at the A and B inputs have been setup long enough to complete any pulse started before the setup.

description

These multivibrators feature dual negative-transition-triggered inputs and a single positive-transition-triggered input which can be used as an inhibit input. Complementary output pulses are provided.

Pulse triggering occurs at a particular voltage level and is not directly related to the transition time of the input pulse. Schmitt-trigger input circuitry (TTL hysteresis) for the B input allows jitter-free triggering from inputs with transition rates as slow as 1 volt/second, providing the circuit with an excellent noise immunity of typically 1.2 volts. A high immunity to V_{CC} noise of typically 1.5 volts is also provided by internal latching circuitry.

Once fired, the outputs are independent of further transitions of the inputs and are a function only of the timing components. Input pulses may be of any duration relative to the output pulse. Output pulse length may be varied from 40 nanoseconds to 28 seconds by choosing appropriate timing components. With no external timing components (i.e., R_{int} connected to V_{CC}, C_{ext} and R_{ext}/C_{ext} open), an output pulse of typically 30 or 35 nanoseconds is achieved which may be used as a d-c triggered reset signal. Output rise and fall times are TTL compatible and independent of pulse length.

Pulse width stability is achieved through internal compensation and is virtually independent of V_{CC} and temperature. In most applications, pulse stability will only be limited by the accuracy of external timing components.

Jitter-free operation is maintained over the full temperature and V_{CC} ranges for more than six decades of timing capacitance (10 pF to 10 μF) and more than one decade of timing resistance (2 kΩ to 30 kΩ for the SN54121 and 2 kΩ to 40 kΩ for the SN74121). Throughout these ranges, pulse width is defined by the relationship $t_{w(out)} = C_{ext}R_T \ln 2 \approx 0.7\, C_{ext}R_T$. In circuits where pulse cutoff is not critical, timing capacitance up to 1000 μF and timing resistance as low as 1.4 kΩ may be used. Also, the range of jitter-free output pulse widths is extended if V_{CC} is held to 5 volts and free-air temperature is 25°C. Duty cycles as high as 90% are achieved when using maximum recommended $R_{T'}$. Higher duty cycles are available if a certain amount of pulse-width jitter is allowed.

FIGURE 7-8 74121 Data Sheet. (Courtesy of Texas Instruments)

SN54121, SN74121
MONOSTABLE MULTIVIBRATORS
WITH SCHMITT-TRIGGER INPUTS

logic diagram (positive logic)

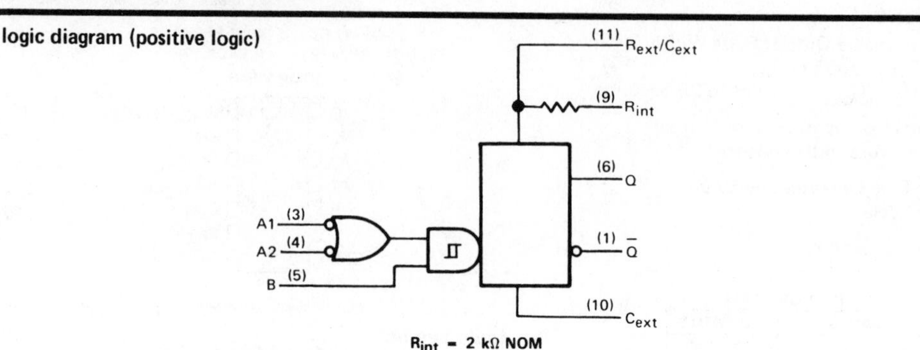

Pin numbers shown on logic notation are for J or N packages.

NOTES: 1. An external capacitor may be connected between C_{ext} (positive) and R_{ext}/C_{ext}.
2. To use the internal timing resistor, connect R_{int} to V_{CC}. For improved pulse width accuracy and repeatability, connect an external resistor between R_{ext}/C_{ext} and V_{CC} with R_{int} open-circuited.

schematics of inputs and outputs

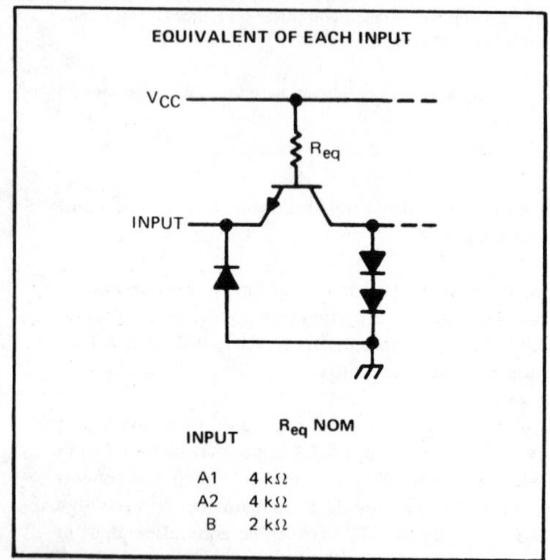

INPUT	R_{eq} NOM
A1	4 kΩ
A2	4 kΩ
B	2 kΩ

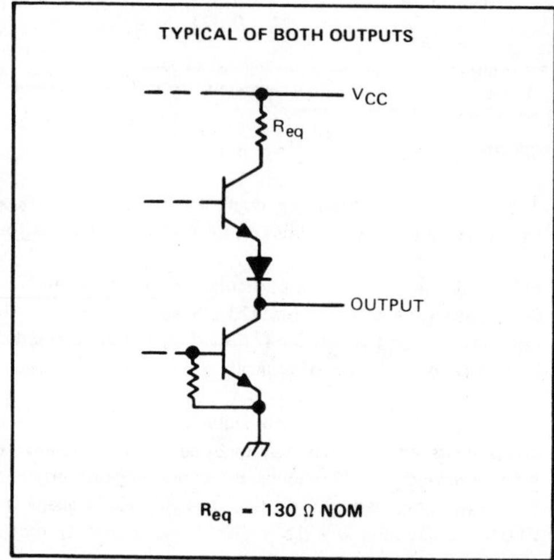

FIGURE 7-8 (*continued*)

74121, except that there are two devices per IC. The 74HC221 is a CMOS version of the 74221.

For all the preceding ICs, the pulse width is determined by application of Equation 7-1.

Eq. 7-1
$$t_w = \ln 2(C_{ext})(R_{ext})$$
$$\approx 0.7(C_{ext})(R_{ext})$$

■ EXAMPLE 7-5 74121 Pulse Width

Problem: Determine the pulse width for a 74121 if

$C_{ext} = 1\ \mu F, \qquad R_{ext} = 10K\ \Omega$

Solution

$$t_w = 0.7(C_{ext})(R_{ext})$$
$$= 0.7(1 \times 10^{-6})(10 \times 10^3)$$
$$= 0.007\ s = 7\ ms$$

■

■ EXAMPLE 7-6 74121 RC Component Selection

Problem: Select component values for use with a 74121 to produce a 500 ns pulse.

Solution: Since there are fewer standard capacitor values than resistor values, first select a capacitor value. Note, however, that there are limits to the values of the resistors and capacitors recommended by the data sheets that will provide good output pulses. The data book recommends a capacitor within the range of 10 pF to 10 μF and a resistor within the range of 2 to 40K ohms for jitter-free output. Choose a standard capacitor value (1000 pF, e.g.) and solve the equation for R. Then check to see if R is within the allowed range of resistor values. If not, choose a new capacitor value and recalculate.

$$500 \times 10^{-9}\ s = 0.7(1000 \times 10^{-12})(R_{ext})$$

$$R_{ext} = 7.1K\ \Omega \qquad \text{(within allowable range of R)}$$

■

It is important to note that the 74121 is capable of producing a pulse of up to 25 seconds duration. A timing capacitor can be selected as large as 1000 μF. Long pulse duration 74121 circuits have slow rise and fall times, and cannot be used in applications requiring fast rise and fall times.

7.3.2 The Retriggerable Monostable Multivibrator

Another type of monostable multivibrator is the **retriggerable monostable multivibrator,** or **retriggerable one-shot.** This type of one-shot will retrigger if an active trigger is input during the time of an output pulse from a previous trigger. Thus, if the retriggerable one-shot is triggered at an interval less than the output pulse width, t_w, the output will stay in the unstable (pulsed) state. This has the effect of extending the pulse for longer than the time, t_w.

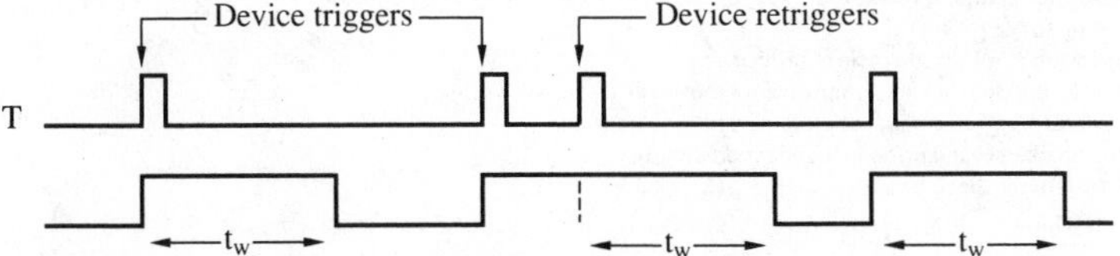

FIGURE 7-9 Retriggerable Monostable Multivibrator Waveforms

SN54122, SN54123, SN54130, SN54LS122, SN54LS123, SN74122, SN74123, SN74130, SN74LS122, SN74LS123 RETRIGGERABLE MONOSTABLE MULTIVIBRATORS

DECEMBER 1983 – REVISED MARCH 1988

- **D-C Triggered from Active-High or Active-Low Gated Logic Inputs**
- **Retriggerable for Very Long Output Pulses, Up to 100% Duty Cycle**
- **Overriding Clear Terminates Output Pulse**
- **'122 and 'LS122 Have Internal Timing Resistors**

description

These d-c triggered multivibrators feature output pulse-duration control by three methods. The basic pulse time is programmed by selection of external resistance and capacitance values (see typical application data). The '122 and 'LS122 have internal timing resistors that allow the circuits to be used with only an external capacitor, if so desired. Once triggered, the basic pulse duration may be extended by retriggering the gated low-level-active (A) or high-level-active (B) inputs, or be reduced by use of the overriding clear. Figure 1 illustrates pulse control by retriggering and early clear.

The 'LS122 and 'LS123 are provided enough Schmitt hysteresis to ensure jitter-free triggering from the B input with transition rates as slow as 0.1 millivolt per nanosecond.

The R_{int} in nominall 10 kΩ for '122 and 'LS122.

SN54123, SN54130, SN54LS123 . . . J OR W PACKAGE
SN74123, SN74130 . . . N PACKAGE
SN74LS123 . . . D OR N PACKAGE
(TOP VIEW) (SEE NOTES 1 THRU 4)

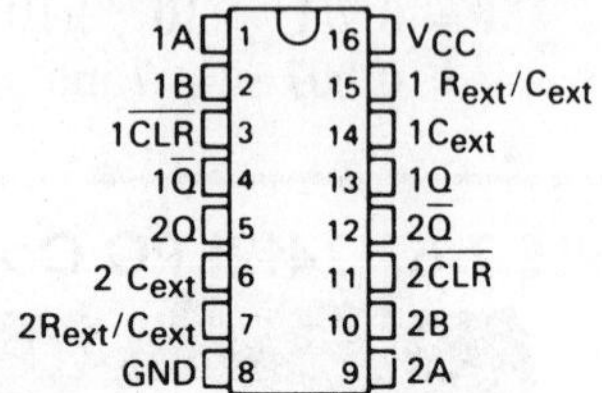

SN54LS122 . . . FK PACKAGE
(TOP VIEW) (SEE NOTES 1 THRU 4)

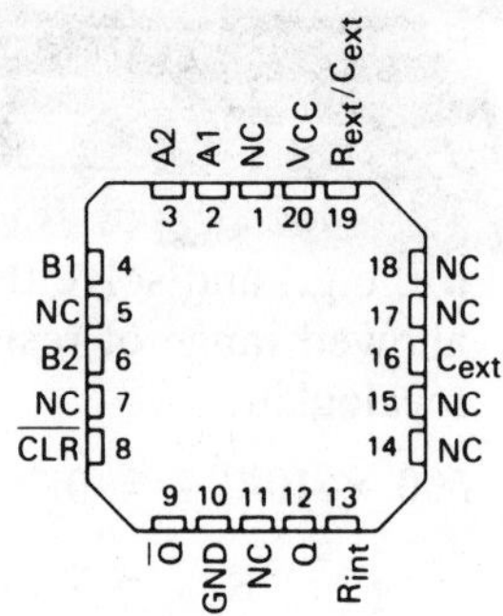

SN54122, SN54LS122 . . . J OR W PACKAGE
SN74122 . . . N PACKAGE
SN74LS122 . . . D OR N PACKAGE
(TOP VIEW) (SEE NOTES 1 THRU 4)

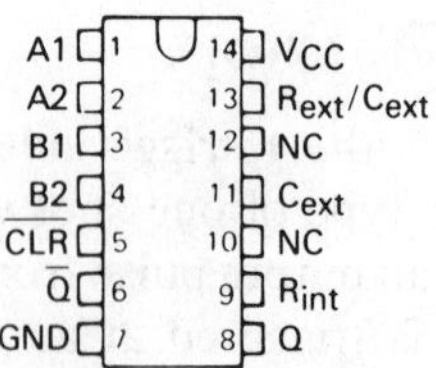

SN54LS123 . . . FK PACKAGE
(TOP VIEW) (SEE NOTES 1 THRU 4)

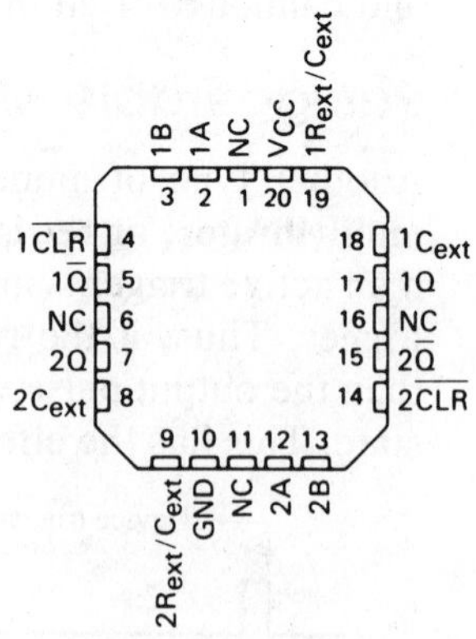

NC - No internal connection

NOTES:
1. An external timing capacitor may be connected between C_{ext} and Re_{xt}/C_{ext} (positive).
2. To use the internal timing resistor of '122 or 'LS122, connect R_{int} to V_{CC}.
3. For improved pulse duration accuracy and repeatability, connect an external resistor between R_{ext}/Ce_{xt} and V_{CC} with R_{int} open-circuited.
4. To obtain variable pulse durations, connect an external variable resistance between R_{int} or R_{ext}/C_{ext} and V_{CC}.

FIGURE 7-10 74122 Data Sheet. (Courtesy of Texas Instruments)

The retriggerable monostable multivibrator will return to its stable (non-pulsed) state exactly one pulse width, t_w, from the *last* trigger pulse input. Figure 7-9 illustrates the various waveforms possible with a retriggerable one-shot.

The 74122 and 74LS122 are retriggerable monostable multivibrators. There are four trigger inputs, A_1, A_2, B_1, and B_2, with either A_1 or A_2 acting as an active LOW trigger, and B_1 or B_2 acting as an active HIGH trigger. In addition, an active low clear input, $\overline{CLR}$, can be used to override the output and produce an output of shorter duration than t_w. As with the non-retriggerable one-shot ICs, the pulse width is controlled by the connection of the appropriate valued timing resistor and capacitor. The external timing resistor can range from 5 KΩ to 50 KΩ for the 74122, and from 5 KΩ to 260 KΩ for the 74LS122. The data sheet for the 74122 is shown in Figure 7-10.

SN54122, SN54123, SN54130, SN54LS122, SN54LS123,
SN74122, SN74123, SN74130, SN74LS122, SN74LS123
RETRIGGERABLE MONOSTABLE MULTIVIBRATORS

description (continued)

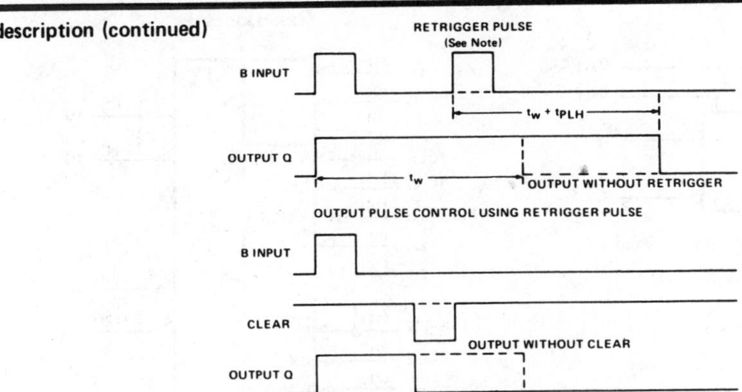

NOTE: Retrigger pulses starting before 0.22 C_{ext} (in picofrads) nanoseconds after the initial trigger pulse will be ignored and the output duration will remain unchanged.

FIGURE 1–TYPICAL INPUT/OUTPUT PULSES

'122, 'LS122
FUNCTION TABLE

INPUTS					OUTPUTS	
CLEAR	A1	A2	B1	B2	Q	$\overline{Q}$
L	X	X	X	X	L	H
X	H	H	X	X	L†	H†
X	X	X	L	X	L†	H†
X	X	X	X	L	L†	H†
H	L	X	↑	H	⎍	⊔
H	L	X	H	↑	⎍	⊔
H	X	L	↑	H	⎍	⊔
H	X	L	H	↑	⎍	⊔
H	H	↓	H	H	⎍	⊔
H	↓	↓	H	H	⎍	⊔
H	↓	H	H	H	⎍	⊔
↑	L	X	H	H	⎍	⊔
↑	X	L	H	H	⎍	⊔

'123, '130, 'LS123
FUNCTION TABLE

INPUTS			OUTPUTS	
CLEAR	A	B	Q	$\overline{Q}$
L	X	X	L	H
X	H	X	L†	H†
X	X	L	L†	H†
H	L	↑	⎍	⊔
H	↓	H	⎍	⊔
↑	L	H	⎍	⊔

See explanation of function tables on page

† These lines of the functional tables assume that the indicated steady-state conditons at the A and B inputs have been set up long enough to complete any pulse started before the set up.

FIGURE 7-10 (*continued*)

SN54122, SN54123, SN54130, SN54LS122, SN54LS123, SN74122, SN74123, SN74130, SN74LS122, SN74LS123 RETRIGGERABLE MONOSTABLE MULTIVIBRATORS

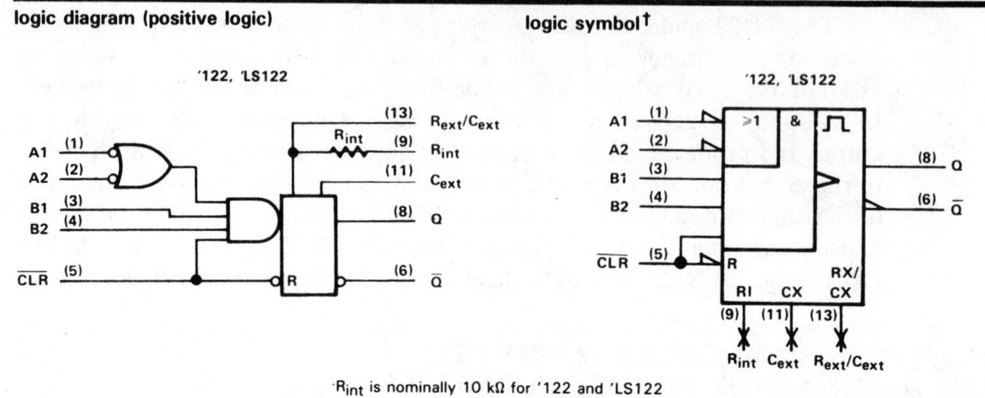

ˈRint is nominally 10 kΩ for '122 and 'LS122

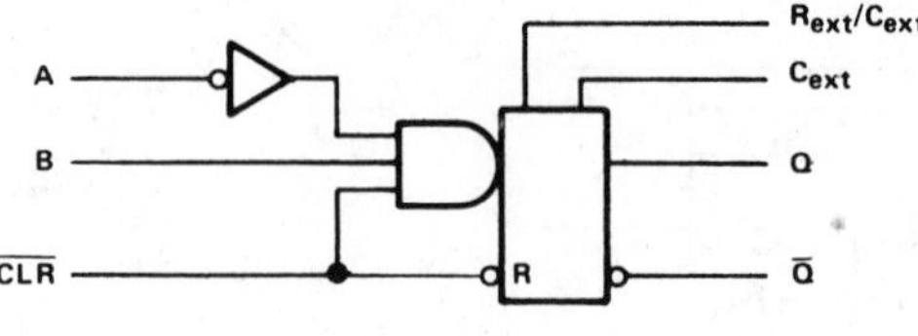

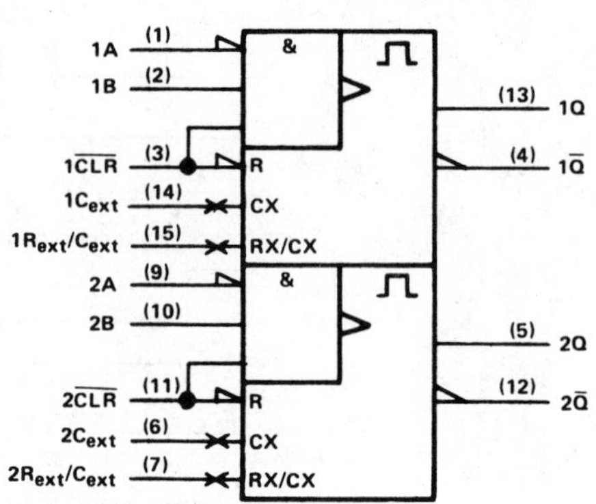

Pin numbers shown are for D, J, N, and W packages.

†These symbols are in accordance with ANSI/IEEE Std 91-1984 and IEC Publication 617-12.

FIGURE 7-10 (*continued*)

The '122 and 'LS122 have an internal timing resistor that allows these devices to be used only with the addition of an external timing capacitor. The internal resistance, R_{int}, is 10K ohms for the '122 and 'LS122 and 20K ohms for the 'L122. The retriggerable monostable multivibrators are also available in dual ICs for the same logic subfamilies as the '122 and the 74123 family of ICs.

The nominal pulse width, t_w, for all the retriggerable monostable multivibrators, can be calculated by using the equations and graphs for the appropriate applications and ICs. Several equations apply, depending on the size of the timing capacitor and the internal device constant, K. Always refer to the manufacturer's data sheets for the correct equations to use.

■ EXAMPLE 7-7 74122 One-Shot

Problem:

(a) Calculate the nominal pulse width for a 74122 if C_{ext} is 2200 pF and no external timing resistor is used.
(b) Repeat part (a), but this time use an external 20K ohm resistor.
(c) Draw the circuit for part (b), showing all pin connections.
(d) Which is more accurate, using R_{int} or R_{ext}? Why?

Solution:

(a) Using the information from the Texas Instruments data sheet for a 74122, the appropriate equation to use if the C_{ext} is greater than 1000 pF is

Eq. 7-2 $$t_w = K(R_T)(C_{ext})\left[1 + \frac{0.7}{R_T}\right]$$

R_T is the internal or external timing resistor, in K ohms; C_{ext} is the timing capacitor, in pF; and t_w is the pulse width, in ns. The timing constant, K, for a 74122 is 0.32. R_T in this example is the internal resistance, which is 20K ohms for a 74L122. Solving for the pulse width, we obtain

$$t_w = 0.32(20)(2200)\left[1 + \frac{0.7}{20}\right]$$

$$= 14{,}573 \text{ ns or } 14.57\ \mu\text{s}$$

(b) The answer is the same, 14.57 μs; only an external resistor is used.
(c) See Figure 7-11 for the circuit.

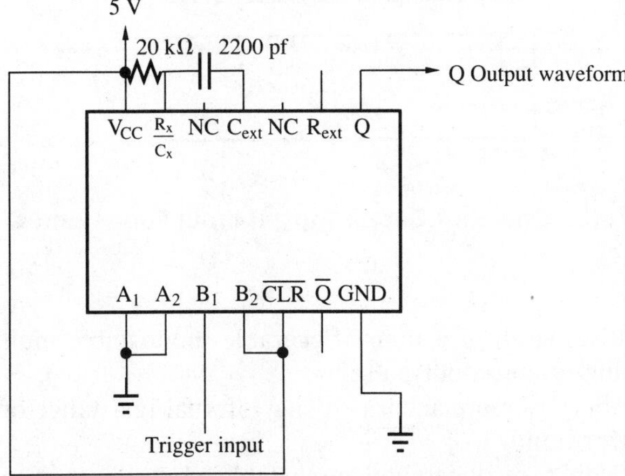

FIGURE 7-11 74122 Retriggerable One-Shot Circuit

(d) Since there is no accurate way to determine the exact value of the internal resistance, it is more accurate to use a known measured external resistance. ■

■ EXAMPLE 7-8 74122 One-Shot Waveforms

Problem: A 74122 is wired to produce an output pulse of 20 ms.

(a) Draw the pulses necessary to produce a periodic 20 ms pulse output.
(b) Draw the pulses necessary to produce a 60 ms output pulse.
(c) Draw the pulses necessary to produce a 10 ms output pulse without using the clear feature.

Solution: See Figure 7-12 for the waveforms. ■

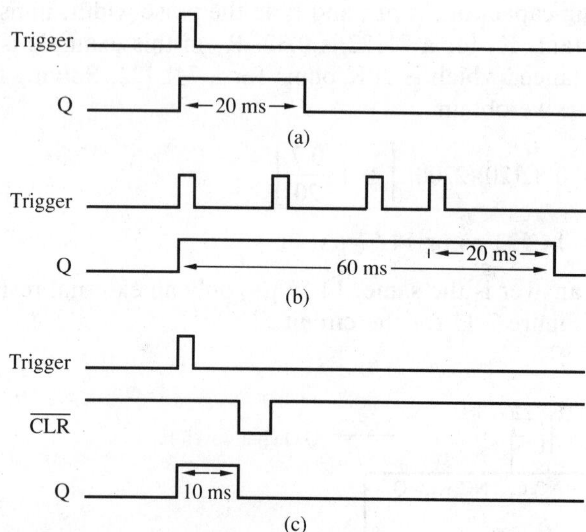

FIGURE 7-12 74122 One-Shot Circuit Trigger Input Pulses and Q Outputs ■

Section Self-Test

1. Can the pulse width of a nonretriggerable monostable multivibrator be extended during an output pulse?
2. Are multivibrators more accurate using internal resistance or an external resistance for timing?
3. How long can a retriggerable monostable multivibrator be kept in its unstable state?

ANSWERS (Not necessarily in the order of the questions)

- no
- external
- As long as a new trigger pulse occurs before the output pulse is completed

7-4 ASTABLE MULTIVIBRATORS

An astable multivibrator, or oscillator, is a logic device that does not have any stable states. The astable multivibrator switches between a HIGH and LOW logic state.

One of the most common uses for an astable multivibrator is as the oscillator or clock of a logic circuit. Instead of using some external device such as a waveform function generator to provide timing signals, an astable multivibrator can be designed to provide a circuit timing clock.

An **astable multivibrator** is a logic device that automatically switches between a LOW and HIGH logic state. The automatic switching of a device between two states is known as **oscillation,** and the astable multivibrator is also called an **oscillator.** Since the astable multivibrator does not stay in a stable state, it has zero stable states. If an astable multivibrator automatically oscillates when power is applied, it is known as a **free-running oscillator.** If there is an enable feature that is part of the oscillator, it is referred to as a **gated oscillator.**

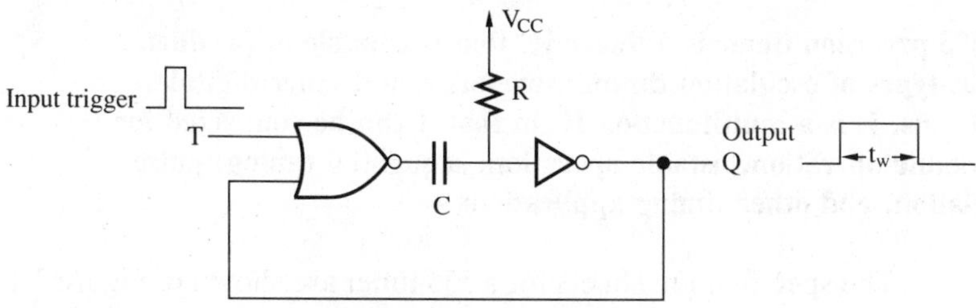

FIGURE 7-13 Free-Running Astable Multivibrator

Monostable

Figure 7-13 shows a simple circuit that can be used to construct a free-running astable multivibrator. The values of the resistors and capacitors are chosen to produce RC time constants that allow the inverters to oscillate automatically between two output voltages. This type of circuit is seldom used today in actual digital circuits due to the availability of ICs and timers for generating timing signals. One such IC is the 555 timer, which will be discussed in Section 7-5.

A useful multivibrator IC is the CMOS 4047B multifunction monostable/astable multivibrator. This IC is a gatable astable multivibrator that can be configured to operate as a positive or negative edge-triggered retriggerable monostable multivibrator, or as an oscillator with a 50% duty cycle. This IC has many applications, including frequency division and multiplication, timing, and time-delay circuits.

The 4047B can operate with a supply voltage from 3V to 18V. The supply voltage significantly affects the timing parameters of rise time, fall time, and propagation delay. Refer to a CMOS data book for complete specifications.

Section Self-Test

1. How many stable states does an oscillator have?
2. How many stable states does a retriggerable monostable multivibrator have?
3. What are the switching states for an astable multivibrator?

ANSWERS

(Not necessarily in the order of the questions)

• 1, 0 • 0 • 1

7-5 THE 555 TIMER

The 555 precision timer is a linear IC that is capable of producing various types of oscillation timing waveforms and other digital waveforms. It is a multifunction IC in that it can be connected for monostable operation, astable operation, sequential timing, pulse modulation, and other timing applications.

The specification sheets for a 555 timer are shown in Figure 7-14. The CMOS version of the 555 time is known as the TLC555 timer. Its data sheets are shown in Figure 7-15. The CMOS version is recommended for new designs, and it is functionally identical to the bipolar version of the 555 timer.

Some of the notable features of the IC include a wide range of timing periods that the IC can be used to produce, adjustable duty cycle, and TTL compatible outputs capable of sourcing up to 200 mA of current. In addition, the 555 supply voltage can be set from 5 volts to 15 volts. The input V_{CC} voltage can vary anywhere from a nominal voltage value of 5 to 15 volts. The wide range of allowed supply voltage lets the 555 be used in both TTL and CMOS designs.

SE555, SE555C, SA555, NE555 PRECISION TIMERS

D1669, SEPTEMBER 1973—REVISED OCTOBER 1988

- **Timing from Microseconds to Hours**
- **Astable or Monostable Operation**
- **Adjustable Duty Cycle**
- **TTL-Compatible Output Can Sink or Source Up to 200 mA**
- **Functionally Interchangeable with the Signetics SE555, SE555C, SA555, NE555; Have Same Pinout**

SE555C FROM TI IS NOT RECOMMENDED FOR NEW DESIGNS

description

These devices are monolithic timing circuits capable of producing accurate time delays or oscillation. In the time-delay or monostable mode of operation, the timed interval is controlled by a single external resistor and capacitor network. In the astable mode of operation, the frequency and duty cycle may be independently controlled with two external resistors and a single external capacitor.

The threshold and trigger levels are normally two-thirds and one-third, respectively, of V_{CC}. These levels can be altered by use of the control voltage terminal. When the trigger input falls below the trigger level, the flip-flop is set and the output goes high. If the trigger input is above the trigger level and the threshold input is above the threshold level, the flip-flop is reset and the output is low. The reset input can override all other inputs and can be used to initiate a new timing cycle. When the reset input goes low, the flip-flop is reset and the output goes low. Whenever the output is low, a low-impedance path is provided between the discharge terminal and ground.

The output circuit is capable of sinking or sourcing current up to 200 mA. Operation is specified for supplies of 5 to 15 V. With a 5-V supply, output levels are compatible with TTL inputs.

The SE555 and SE555C are characterized for operation over the full military range of −55 °C to 125 °C. The SA555 is characterized for operation from −40 °C to 85 °C, and the NE555 is characterized for operation from 0 °C to 70 °C.

SE555, SE555C . . . JG PACKAGE
SA555, NE555 . . . D, JG, OR P PACKAGE
(TOP VIEW)

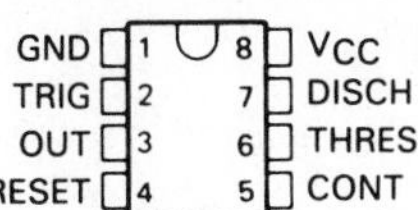

SE555, SE555C . . . FK PACKAGE
(TOP VIEW)

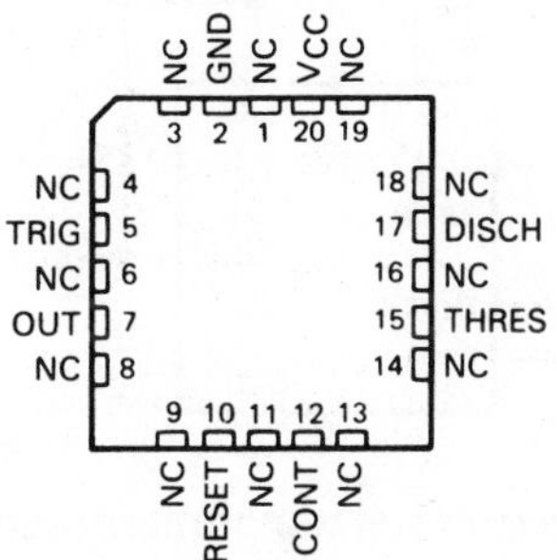

NC—No internal connection

functional block diagram

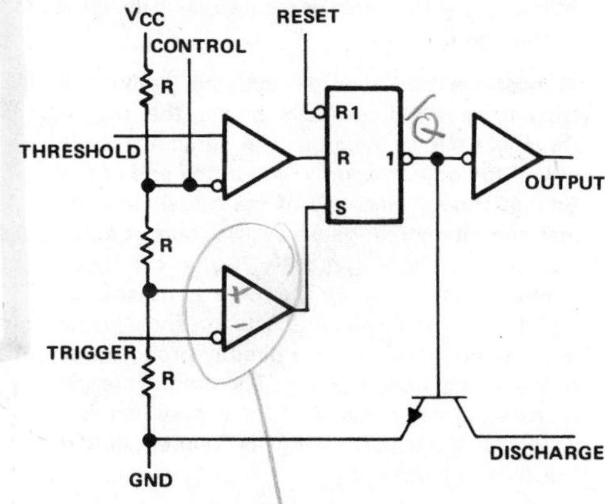

Reset can override Trigger, which can override Threshold.

FIGURE 7-14 SE 555 Timer Specifications. (Courtesy of Texas Instruments)

SE555, SE555C, SA555, NE555 PRECISION TIMERS

TYPICAL APPLICATION DATA

monostable operation

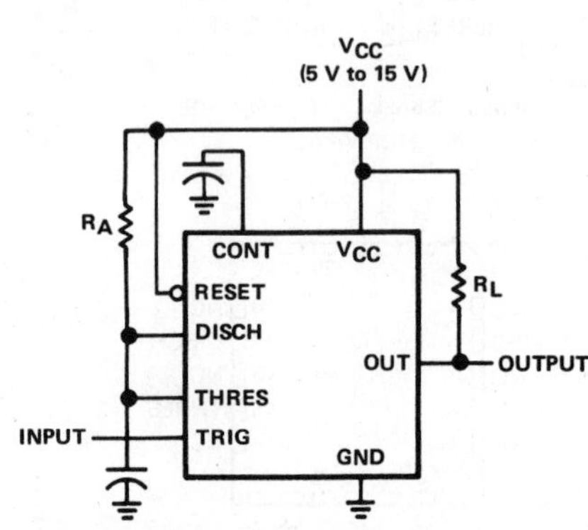

FIGURE 9. CIRCUIT FOR MONOSTABLE OPERATION

RA = 9.1 kΩ
CL = 0.01 μF
RL = 1 kΩ
See Figure 9

INPUT VOLTAGE

OUTPUT VOLTAGE

CAPACITOR VOLTAGE

Voltage—2 V/div

Time—0.1 ms/div

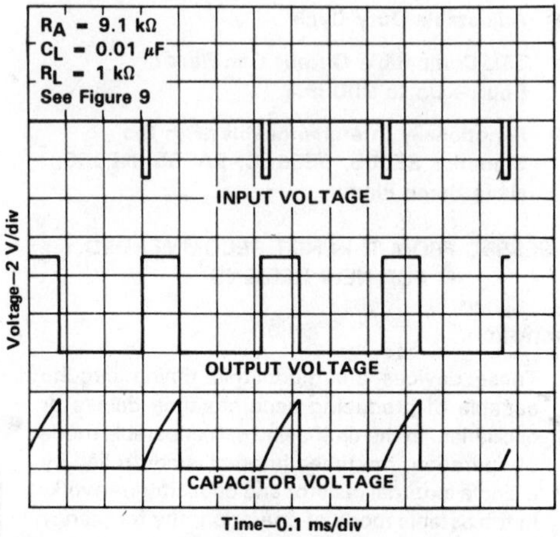

FIGURE 10. TYPICAL MONOSTABLE WAVEFORMS

For monostable operation, any of these timers may be connected as shown in Figure 9. If the output is low, application of a negative-going pulse to the trigger input sets the flip-flop ($\overline{Q}$ goes low), drives the output high, and turns off Q1. Capacitor C is then charged through R_A until the voltage across the capacitor reaches the threshold voltage of the threshold input. If the trigger input has returned to a high level, the output of the threshold comparator will reset the flip-flop ($\overline{Q}$ goes high), drive the output low, and discharge C through Q1.

Monostable operation is initiated when the trigger input voltage falls below the trigger threshold. Once initiated, the sequence ends only if the trigger input is high at the end of the timing interval. Because of the threshold level and saturation voltage of Q1, the output pulse duration is approximately $t_w = 1.1\ R_A C$. Figure 11 is a plot of the time constant for various values of R_A and C. The threshold levels and charge rates are both directly proportional to the supply voltage, V_{CC}. The timing interval is therefore independent of the supply voltage, so long as the supply voltage is constant during the time interval.

Applying a negative-going trigger pulse simultaneously to the reset and trigger terminals during the timing interval discharges C and re-initiates the cycle, commencing on the positive edge of the reset pulse. The output is held low as long as the reset pulse is low. To prevent false triggering, when the reset input is not used, it should be connected to V_{CC}.

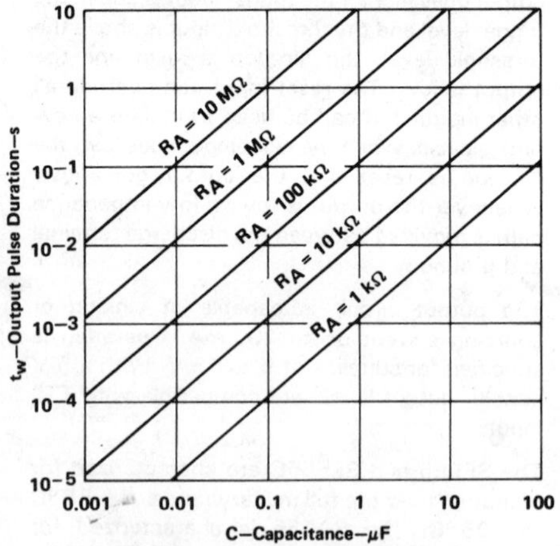

FIGURE 11. OUTPUT PULSE DURATION vs CAPACITANCE

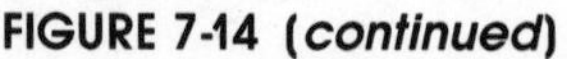

FIGURE 7-14 (*continued*)

Standard caps: μF 1, 2.2, 3.3, 4.7, etc...

TYPICAL APPLICATION DATA

astable operation

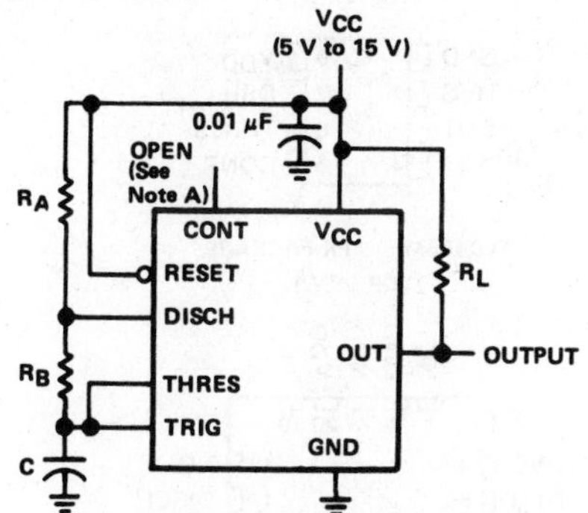

NOTE A: Decoupling the control voltage input to ground with a capacitor may improve operation. This should be evaluated for individual applications.

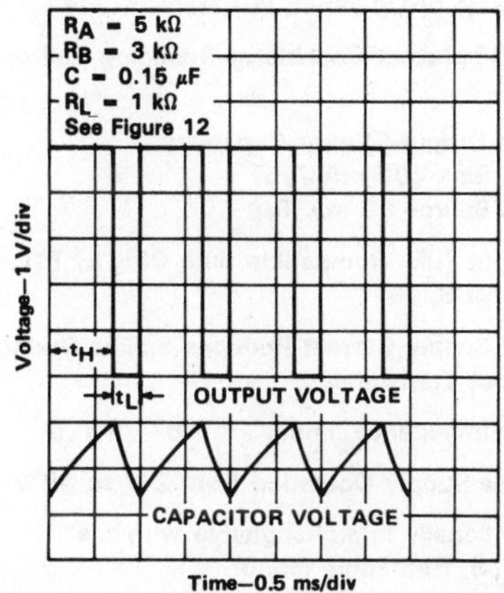

FIGURE 12. CIRCUIT FOR ASTABLE OPERATION

FIGURE 13. TYPICAL ASTABLE WAVEFORMS

As shown in Figure 12, adding a second resistor, R_B, to the circuit of Figure 9 and connecting the trigger input to the threshold input causes the timer to self-trigger and run as a multivibrator. The capacitor C will charge through R_A and R_B and then discharge through R_B only. The duty cycle may be controlled, therefore, by the values of R_A and R_B.

This astable connection results in capacitor C charging and discharging between the threshold-voltage level ($\approx 0.67 \cdot V_{CC}$) and the trigger-voltage level ($\approx 0.33 \cdot V_{CC}$). As in the monostable circuit, charge and discharge times (and therefore the frequency and duty cycle) are independent of the supply voltage.

Figure 13 shows typical waveforms generated during astable operation. The output high-level duration t_H and low-level duration t_L may be calculated as follows:

$$t_H = 0.693\,(R_A + R_B)\,C$$

$$t_L = 0.693\,(R_B)\,C$$

Other useful relationships are shown below.

$$\text{period} = t_H + t_L = 0.693\,(R_A + 2R_B)\,C$$

$$\text{frequency} \approx \frac{1.44}{(R_A + 2R_B)\,C}$$

$$\text{Output driver duty cycle} = \frac{t_L}{t_H + t_L} = \frac{R_B}{R_A + 2R_B}$$

$$\text{Output waveform duty cycle} = \frac{t_H}{t_H + t_L} = 1 - \frac{R_B}{R_A + 2R_B}$$

$$\text{Low-to-high ratio} = \frac{t_L}{t_H} = \frac{R_B}{R_A + R_B}$$

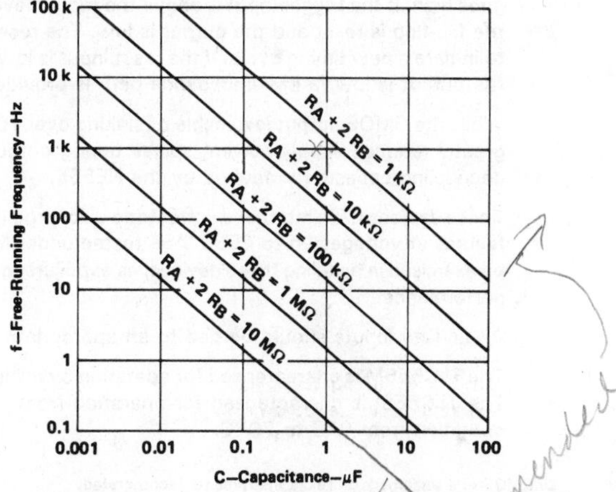

FIGURE 14. FREE-RUNNING FREQUENCY

not recommended

FIGURE 7-14 (*continued*)

TLC555M, TLC555I, TLC555C LinCMOS™ TIMERS

D2784, SEPTEMBER 1983—REVISED OCTOBER 1988

- **Very Low Power Consumption . . . 1 mW Typ at V_{DD} = 5 V**
- **Capable of Operation in Astable Mode**
- **CMOS Output Capable of Swinging Rail to Rail**
- **High Output-Current Capability . . . Sink 100 mA Typ . . . Source 10 mA Typ**
- **Output Fully Compatible with CMOS, TTL, and MOS**
- **Low Supply Current Reduces Spikes During Output Transitions**
- **High-Impedance Inputs . . . 10^{12} Ω Typ**
- **Single-Supply Operation from 2 V to 18 V**
- **Functionally Interchangeable with the NE555; Has Same Pinout**

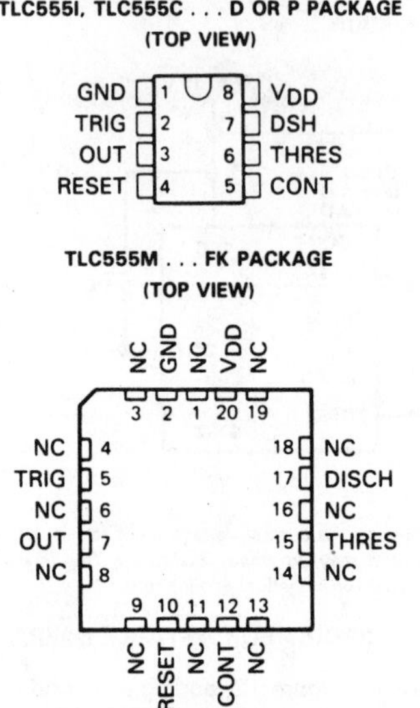

description

The TLC555 is a monolithic timing circuit fabricated using TI's LinCMOS™ process, which provides full compatibility with CMOS, TTL, and MOS logic and operation at frequencies up to 2 MHz. Accurate time delays and oscillations are possible with smaller, less-expensive timing capacitors than the NE555 because of the high input impedance. Power consumption is low across the full range of power supply voltage.

Like the NE555, the TLC555 has a trigger level approximately one-third of the supply voltage and a threshold level approximately two-thirds of the supply voltage. These levels can be altered by use of the control voltage terminal. When the trigger input falls below the trigger level, the flip-flop is set and the output goes high. If the trigger input is above the trigger level and the threshold input is above the threshold level, the flip-flop is reset and the output is low. The reset input can override all other inputs and can be used to initiate a new timing cycle. If the reset input is low, the flip-flop is reset and the output is low. Whenever the output is low, a low-impedance path is provided between the discharge terminal and ground.

While the CMOS output is capable of sinking over 100 mA and sourcing over 10 mA, the TLC555 exhibits greatly reduced supply-current spikes during output transitions. This minimizes the need for the large decoupling capacitors required by the NE555.

These devices have internal electrostatic discharge (ESD) protection circuits that will prevent catastrophic failures at voltages up to 2000 V as tested under MIL-STD-883C, Method 3015. However, care should be exercised in handling these devices, as exposure to ESD may result in degradation of the device parametric performance.

All unused inputs should be tied to an appropriate logic level to prevent false triggering.

The TLC555M is characterized for operation over the full military temperature range of −55°C to 125°C. The TLC555I is characterized for operation from −40°C to 85°C. The TLC555C is characterized for operation from 0°C to 70°C.

FIGURE 7-15 TLC555 Timer Specifications. (Courtesy of Texas Instruments)

TLC555M, TLC555I, TLC555C LinCMOS™ TIMERS

AVAILABLE OPTIONS

T_A RANGE	V_{CC} RANGE	PACKAGE			
		SMALL OUTLINE (D)	CHIP CARRIER (FK)	CERAMIC DIP (JG)	PLASTIC DIP (P)
0°C to 70°C	2 V to 18 V	TLC555CD			TLC555CP
−40°C to 85°C	3 V to 18 V	TLC555ID			TLC555IP
−55°C to 125°C	5 V to 18 V		TLC555MFK	TLC555MJG	

The D package is available taped and reeled. Add the suffix R to the device type (e.g., TLC555CDR).

FUNCTION TABLE

RESET VOLTAGE†	TRIGGER VOLTAGE†	THRESHOLD VOLTAGE†	OUTPUT	DISCHARGE SWITCH
<MIN	Irrelevant	Irrelevant	Low	On
>MAX	<MIN	Irrelevant	High	Off
>MAX	>MAX	>MAX	Low	On
>MAX	>MAX	<MIN	As previously established	

†For conditions shown as MIN or MAX, use the appropriate value specified under electrical characteristics.

functional block diagram

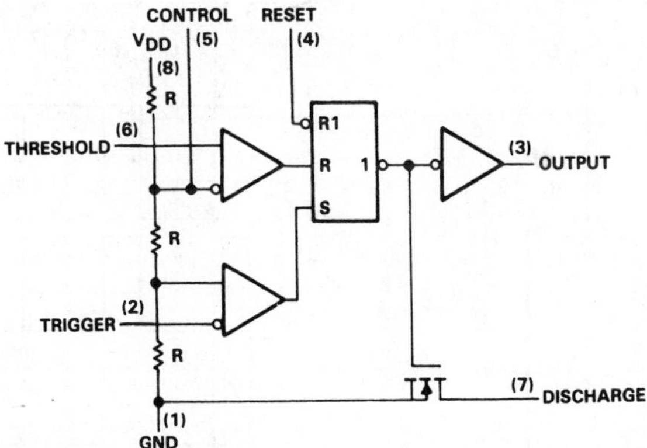

Pin numbers are for all packages except FK.
Reset can override Trigger, which can override Threshold.

FIGURE 7-15 *(continued)*

TLC555M, TLC555I, TLC555C
LinCMOS™ TIMERS

TYPICAL APPLICATION DATA

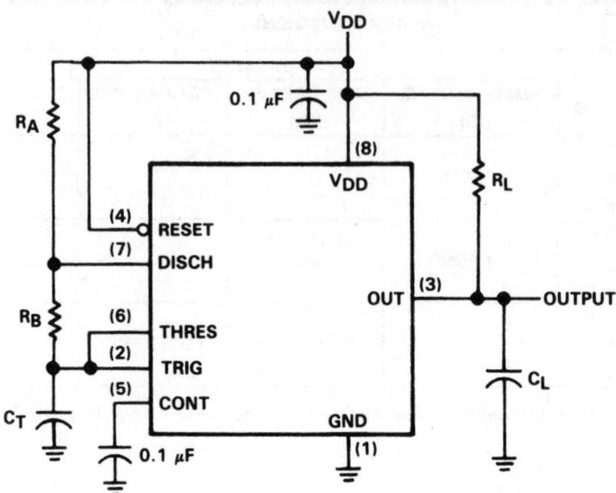

FIGURE 7-15 *(continued)*

7.5.1 Monostable 555 Timer Operation

One mode of operation for the 555 timer is to provide a monostable multivibrator output. This is also known as the **delay mode** of operation.

Figure 7-16 shows a 555 timer wired to operate in the monostable mode. A timing capacitor, C, and a timing resistor, R_A, control the pulse width of

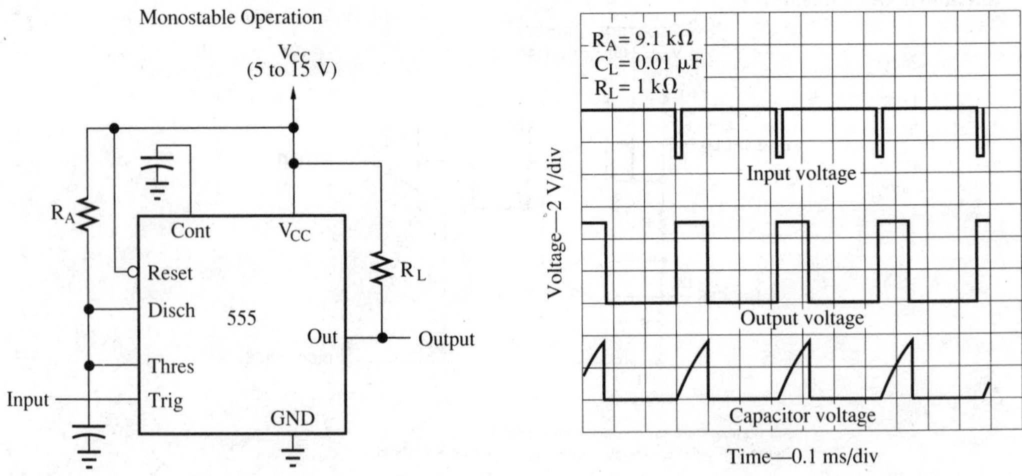

FIGURE 7-16 555 Circuit and Typical Waveforms for Monostable Operation

the monostable output waveform. The pulse width of the waveform can be calculated by using Equation 7-3.

Eq. 7-3 $$t_w = (1.1)(R_A)(C)$$

The timing resistor is connected from V_{CC} to the discharge and threshold pins, and the timing capacitor is connected from ground to the discharge and threshold pins. The active LOW reset pin is connected to V_{CC} to disable the reset function. If a LOW voltage is placed on the reset pin, the output immediately goes LOW. The control pin is disabled by connecting a coupling capacitor from the control pin to ground. The coupling capacitor is typically 0.01 μF.

Timing for the 555 output waveforms is accomplished by controlling the inputs to two important timing pins, the trigger and threshold. The 555 timer has a **trigger voltage.** When the trigger pin input voltage is lower than the trigger voltage, monostable operation is initiated. The 555 timer also has a **threshold voltage.** When the voltage level on the threshold pin reaches the threshold voltage, the output will return to its stable state; that is, the monostable pulse will terminate. In the normal mode of operation the trigger and threshold voltages are as shown in Equations 7-4 and 7-5.

Eq. 7-4 $$\text{Trigger voltage} = \frac{1}{3} V_{CC}$$

Eq. 7-5 $$\text{Threshold voltage} = \frac{2}{3} V_{CC}$$

Figure 7-16 also shows typical monostable waveforms. Notice that the output waveform begins when the trigger voltage is reached, and that the output pulse terminates when the timing capacitor is charged to the threshold voltage.

■ EXAMPLE 7-9 555 Timer—One-Shot Applications

Problem:

(a) Find the pulse width for a 555 timer in monostable operation if R_A = 10K ohms, and C = 0.1 μF.
(b) If V_{CC} = 5 volts, find the threshold and trigger voltages.
(c) If V_{CC} = 15 volts, find the threshold and trigger voltages.
(d) For part (a), draw the input and output waveforms and the voltage across the timing capacitor, and indicate the threshold, trigger, and output voltages, and the output pulse width. Use V_{CC} = 5.0 volts.

Solution:

(a) $t_w = (1.1)(R_A)(C)$

$= 1.1(10{,}000)(0.1 \times 10^{-6})$

$= 0.0001 \text{ s} = 100\ \mu\text{s}$

(b) $\text{Trigger voltage} = \frac{1}{3} V_{CC}$

$= \frac{1}{3}(5.0) = 1.67 \text{ V}$

$\text{Threshold voltage} = \frac{2}{3} V_{CC}$

$= \frac{2}{3}(5.0) = 3.33 \text{ V}$

(c) $V_{trigger} = 5.0 \text{ V}$

$V_{threshold} = 10.0 \text{ V}$

(d) See Figure 7-17.

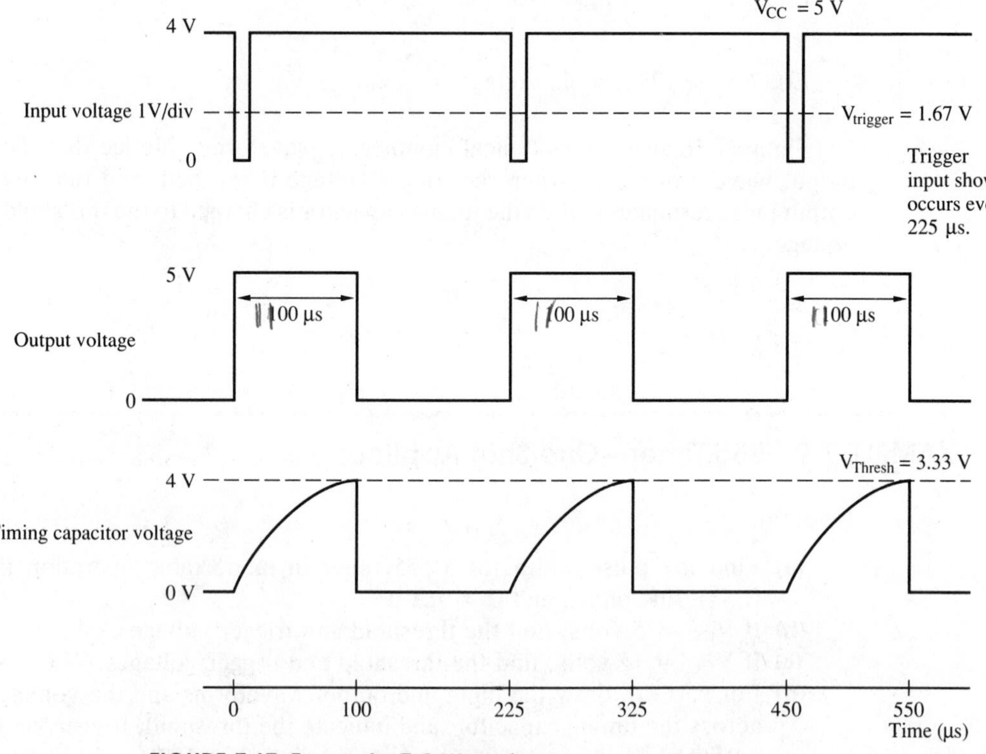

FIGURE 7-17 Example 7-9 Waveforms ■

7.5.2 Astable 555 Timer Operation

Another mode of operation for the 555 timer is to operate as an astable multivibrator. This is also known as the **self-trigger mode** of operation.

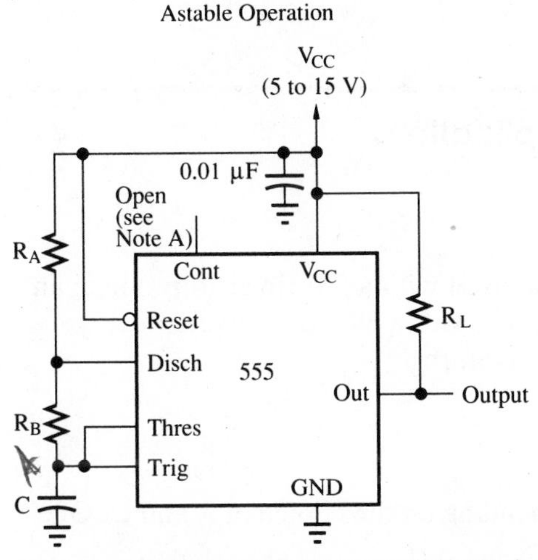

Note A: Decoupling the control voltage input to ground with a capacitor may improve operation. This should be evaluated for individual applications.

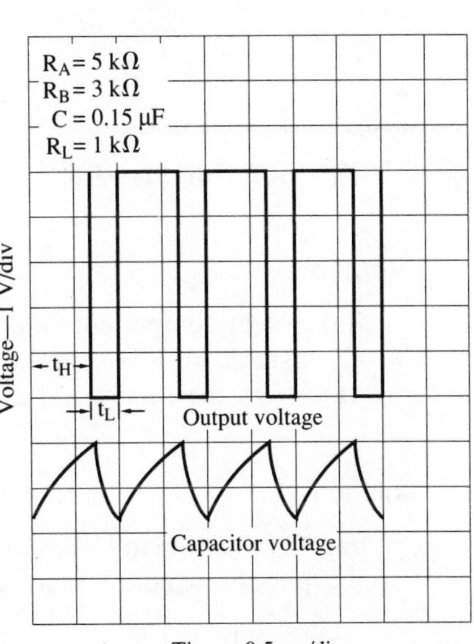

FIGURE 7-18 555 Circuit and Typical Waveforms for Astable Operation

Figure 7-18 shows the 555 circuit for astable operation. It is similar to the monostable circuit of Figure 7-16 but has an additional timing resistor, R_B, and the threshold is now connected to the trigger instead of to the discharge pin. These changes will cause the 555 timer to self-trigger and run as an astable multivibrator, producing the oscillating output waveform as shown in Figure 7-18.

The threshold and trigger voltages are the same as for the monostable circuit, 2/3 V_{CC} and 1/3 V_{CC}, respectively. The duty cycle of the output waveform is determined by the ratio of R_A and R_B, as shown in Equation 7-6.

Eq. 7-6 $$\text{Astable duty cycle} = 1 - \frac{R_B}{R_A + 2R_B}$$

Other useful equations for calculating parameters for the astable mode of operation are shown in Equations 7-7 through 7-10.

Eq. 7-7 $$\text{Output HIGH} = t_H = 0.693(R_A + R_B)C$$

Eq. 7-8 $$\text{Output LOW} = t_L = 0.693(R_B)C$$

Eq. 7-9 $$\text{Output frequency} = f = \frac{1.44}{(R_A + 2R_B)C}$$

Eq. 7-10 $$\text{Output period} = t_H + t_L = \frac{1}{f}$$

■ EXAMPLE 7-10 555 Timer—Astable Applications

Problem:

(a) Select component values to be used with a 555 timer to produce an astable 10 KHz output frequency with a 80% duty cycle.
(b) Draw the theoretical output waveform.

Solution:

(a) There are many solutions, depending on the choice of R and C. One possible solution is as follows:

$$T = \frac{1}{f} = \frac{1}{10}\,\text{KHz} = 0.1\ \text{ms}$$

Let

$$C = 0.001\ \mu\text{F}$$

Then

$$t_L = 0.693\ R_B C$$

$$= 20\%\ \text{of}\ 0.1\ \text{ms} = 0.2(0.1) = 0.02\ \text{ms}$$

$$t_H = T - t_L = 0.1\ \text{ms} - 0.02\ \text{ms} = 0.08\ \text{ms}$$

$$R_B = \frac{0.02 \times 10^{-3}}{(0.001 \times 10^{-6})(0.693)}$$

$$= 28{,}860\ \text{ohms} = 28.9\text{K ohms}$$

$$R_A = \left(\frac{t_H}{0.693\ C}\right) - R_B$$

$$= \frac{0.08 \times 10^{-3}}{0.693(0.001 \times 10^{-6})} - 28{,}860$$

$$= 86{,}580\ \text{ohms} = 86.6\text{K ohms}$$

(b) See Figure 7-19.

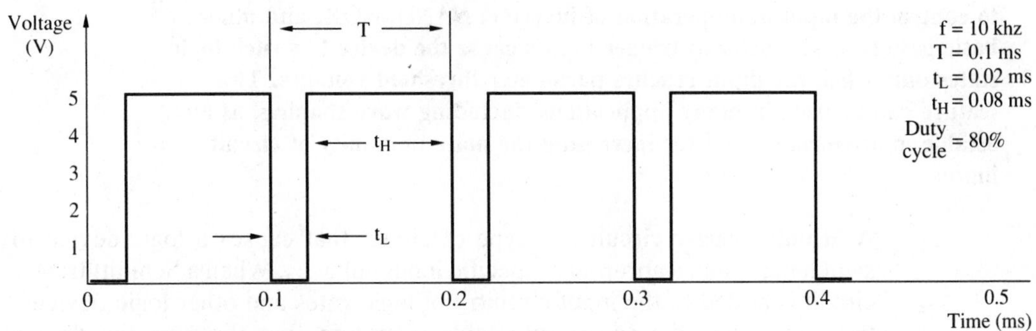

FIGURE 7-19 555 Astable Waveform

It is important to note that there are several parametric limitations associated with using the 555 timer, including maximum frequency of operation, minimum and maximum pulse widths, and associated minimum and maximum values for timing resistors and capacitors. The rise and fall times, for example, are much slower than those encountered in typical digital circuits. The 555 ICs have rise and fall times of several hundred nanoseconds. In addition, the 555 is susceptible to frequency variations as a result of operating temperature changes.

Also, note that the amount of capacitive and resistive load placed on the output pin can affect the output waveform timing parameters. Be sure to check the output waveforms with and without the intended load connected to ensure that the waveform predicted by the equations has not changed significantly due to loading. Consult a linear data book for complete 555 specifications before using this IC in digital circuitry.

Section Self-Test

1. If a 555 timer is operated with V_{CC} = 12 volts, what are the threshold and trigger voltages?
2. What two types of output waveforms can be produced with a 555 IC?
3. List four critical operational parameters to consider when using a 555 timer.

ANSWERS

- $V_{trigger}$ = 4 volts $V_{threshold}$ = 8 volts
- monostable pulses or oscillator waveforms
- temperature of operation, output loading, required output rise-and-fall times, supply voltage

7-6 SCHMITT TRIGGER DEVICES

A Schmitt trigger device is a special type of bistable logic device that has two threshold transition voltages. Schmitt trigger circuits are often used

to control the input and operation of inverter, NAND, NOR, and other basic gate ICs. The Schmitt trigger inputs cause the device to switch logic states only when the input reaches parameter threshold voltages. This feature can be used in many applications, including wave shaping, as an astable multivibrator, and for increasing the noise immunity of circuit inputs.

A **Schmitt trigger** circuit is a type of circuit that causes a logic device to switch logic states abruptly at specific input voltages. When a Schmitt trigger circuit is added to the input circuitry of logic gates and other logic devices, the device has the same truth table operation, but the way the device switches from a HIGH to a LOW or a LOW to a HIGH has been changed. The graphical representation of the output voltage versus the input voltage is known as the **switching characteristic** or **transfer characteristic.**

Schmitt trigger devices are bistable. The Schmitt trigger operation is denoted by the addition of a ''square loop'' symbol, also known as a **hysteresis symbol,** inside the standard device logic symbol. For devices that have specific inputs that are Schmitt trigger, the input is marked with the hysteresis symbol. Figure 7-20 shows the logic symbols for several Schmitt trigger logic gates and a monostable multivibrator with a Schmitt trigger input.

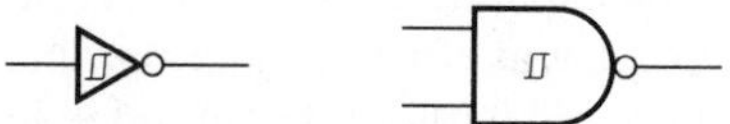

FIGURE 7-20 Schmitt Trigger Symbols

7.6.1 Schmitt Trigger Operation and Hysteresis

A Schmitt trigger has two stable states. It will stay in its present state until a voltage is input that reaches one of its state switching voltages, known as **threshold voltages.** When the threshold voltage is reached, the device will switch states. The more positive threshold voltage is known as the **positive threshold voltage, V_{t+},** whereas the more negative threshold voltage is known as the **negative threshold voltage, V_{t-}.**

Figure 7-21(a) illustrates the input and output waveforms to a Schmitt trigger buffer. Figure 7-21(b) illustrates the input and output waveforms for a Schmitt trigger inverter.

A 7414 is a hex Schmitt trigger inverter IC. The threshold voltages for this device are shown in Table 7-3. If the inverter's present state output is LOW, the Schmitt trigger inverter output will stay LOW until the input is reduced to V_{t-}, and the device will switch and produce a HIGH output.

If the inverter output is HIGH, when the input to the inverter reaches V_{t+}, the device will switch and produce a LOW output.

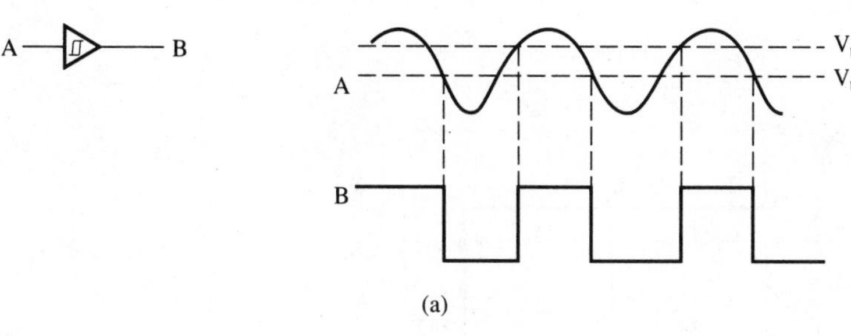

(a)

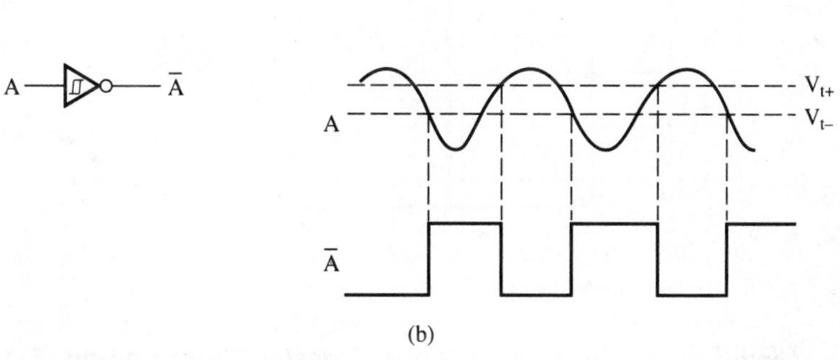

(b)

FIGURE 7-21 Schmitt Trigger Buffer and Inverter. (a) Schmitt Trigger Buffer; (b) Schmitt Trigger Inverter

Figure 7-22 shows the voltage transfer characteristic for the 7414. Notice the "square loop" transfer characteristic. This is where the Schmitt trigger logic symbol originates.

The **hysteresis** for a Schmitt trigger device is the difference in voltage between V_{t+} and V_{t-}. The minimum, typical, and maximum hysteresis values for a 7414 are shown in Table 7-3 and indicated in Figure 7-21.

Some of the other TTL Schmitt trigger logic ICs are the 7413 dual 4-input NAND, the 74132 quad 2-input NAND, 74LS18 dual NAND, 74LS19 hex NAND, and 74LS24 quad 2-input NAND. Some of the CMOS Schmitt trigger logic ICs are the 4093B quad 2-input NAND, and the 40106B hex inverter.

TABLE 7-3 7414 Schmitt Trigger Threshold Voltages

	Minimum (V)	Typical (V)	Maximum (V)
V_{t+}	1.5	1.7	2.0
V_{t-}	0.6	0.9	1.1
Hysteresis	0.4	0.8	1.4

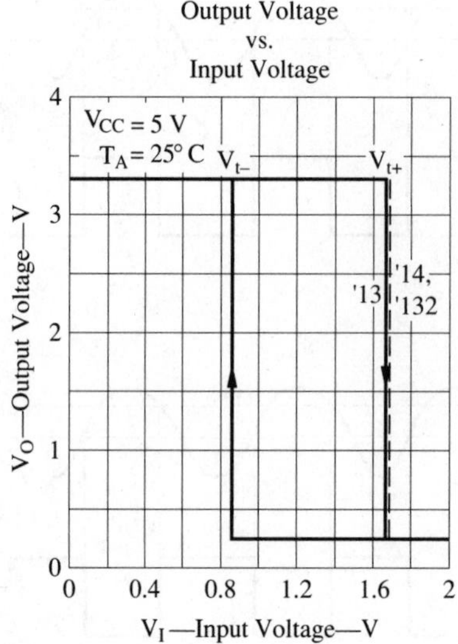

FIGURE 7-22 7414 Schmitt Trigger Transfer Characteristic

■ EXAMPLE 7-11 Schmitt Trigger Waveforms

Problem: A 1 KHz sine wave from 0 to 5 volts is input into an 7414 inverter. Draw the output waveform in relation to the input waveform.

Solution: See Figure 7-23.

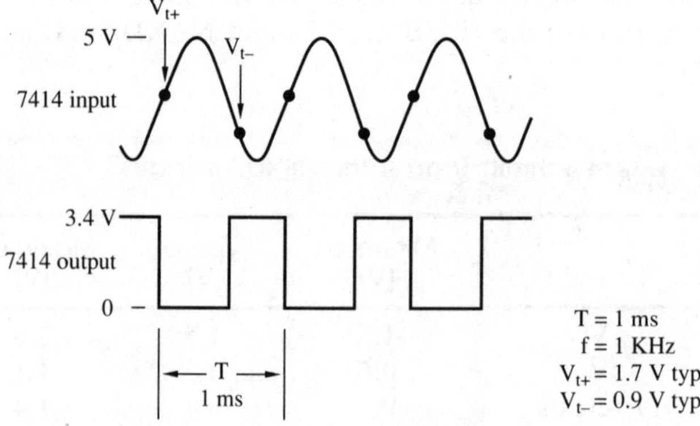

FIGURE 7-23 7414 Schmitt Trigger Output Waveform ■

7.6.2 Astable and Monostable Schmitt Trigger Circuits

The hysteresis action of the Schmitt trigger allows these devices to be used as astable and monostable multivibrator circuits. Figure 7-24 shows a 7414 as an astable multivibrator or oscillator circuit.

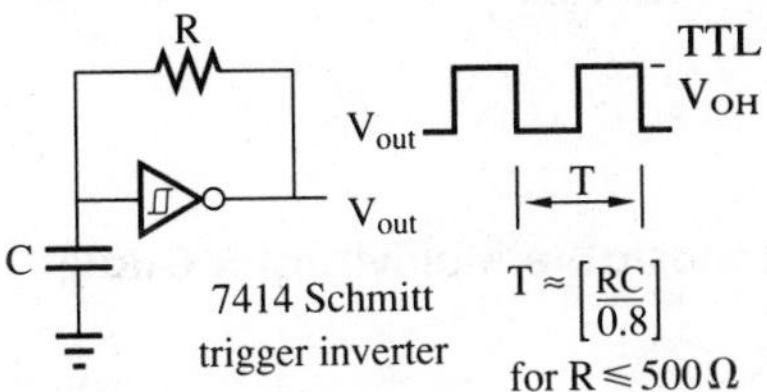

FIGURE 7-24 7414 Astable Multivibrator Circuit

The output frequency for a 7414 and 74LS14 are given by Equation 7-11.

Eq. 7-11 $$f = \frac{0.8}{RC} \quad (R < 500\ \Omega)$$

If the resistance value is greater than 500 ohms, the circuit may not oscillate.

■ EXAMPLE 7-12 7414 Schmitt Trigger Astable Applications

Problem: Calculate the output frequency for a 74LS14 astable multivibrator circuit if R = 330 ohms, and C = 0.1 μF.

Solution: The calculations are as follows:

$$f = \frac{0.8}{RC}$$

$$= \frac{0.8}{330(0.1 \times 10^{-6})} = 24.2\text{ KHz}$$

Figure 7-25 shows a 4093B CMOS NAND gate wired as a monostable multivibrator. The pulse width, t_w, is given by Equation 7-12.

Eq. 7-12 $$t_w = RC \ln\left(\frac{V_{DD}}{V_{DD} - V_{t+}}\right)$$ with 50 KΩ < R < 1 MΩ and 100 pF < C < 1 μF

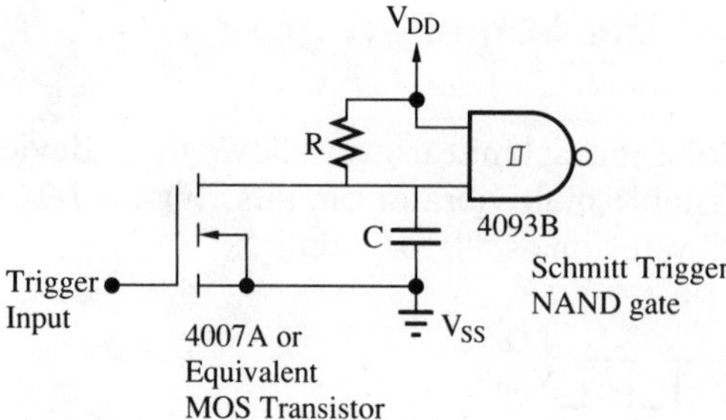

FIGURE 7-25 4093B CMOS Monostable Multivibrator Circuit

EXAMPLE 7-13 4093 Schmitt Trigger Monostable Applications

Problem: Calculate the monostable pulse width for a 4093B NAND gate with R = 100K ohms and C = 0.001 μF. Use V_{DD} = 10 volts and V_{t+} = 5.9 volts.

Solution: The calculations are as follows:

$$t_w = RC \ln\left(\frac{V_{DD}}{V_{DD} - V_{t+}}\right)$$

$$= (100 \times 10^3)(0.001 \times 10^{-6}) \ln \frac{10}{(10^{-5.9})}$$

$$= 89\ \mu s$$

7.6.3 Schmitt Trigger Applications

In addition to monostable and astable circuit applications, Schmitt trigger devices can be used for many applications, including pulse shaping, threshold detection, and noise elimination, as well as to prevent oscillation due to slow input signals.

EXAMPLE 7-14 Pulse Shaping

Problem: A digital signal has been distorted due to transmission line effects. Use a Schmitt trigger device to reshape the digital waveform.

Solution: A Schmitt trigger device removes signal distortion, as shown in Figure 7-26.

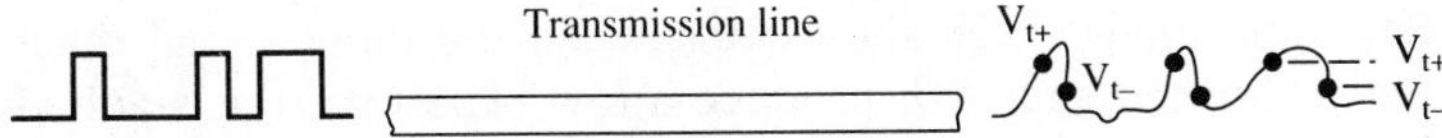

Solution: Put the output of the transmission line into a Schmitt trigger inverter; then invert, or use a Schmitt trigger buffer.

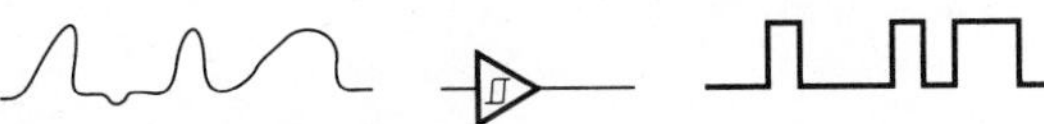

FIGURE 7-26 Pulse Shaping Circuit ■

■ EXAMPLE 7-15 Oscillation Elimination

Problem: A signal with a very slow rise and fall time is input into a standard inverter, which can result in oscillations on the output. How can a Schmitt trigger inverter be used to eliminate the oscillations?

Solution: Figure 7-27 shows an input waveform with a slow transition that would cause an oscillation in a standard logic circuit. The Schmitt trigger device eliminates the oscillation.

The slow transistor pulse is inverted to a digital waveform, where the pulse width, t_W, is the time period from the input waveform V_{t+} to V_{t-}.

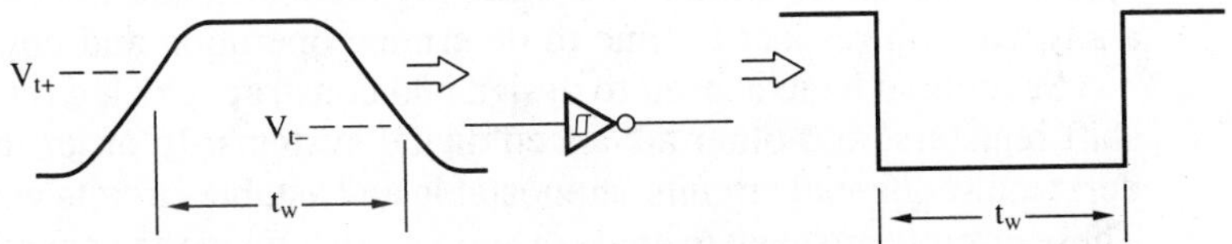

FIGURE 7-27 Slow Input Transition Oscillation Elimination Circuit ■

■ EXAMPLE 7-16 Threshold Detection

Problem: A circuit is needed to detect when an input signal reaches +5 volts. Use a Schmitt trigger device to detect the presence of an input of 5 volts or greater.

Solution: Figure 7-28 shows that when the input signal reaches +5 volts, the Schmitt trigger will produce a low. The inverter is added to indicate a HIGH when the input is ≥5 volts.

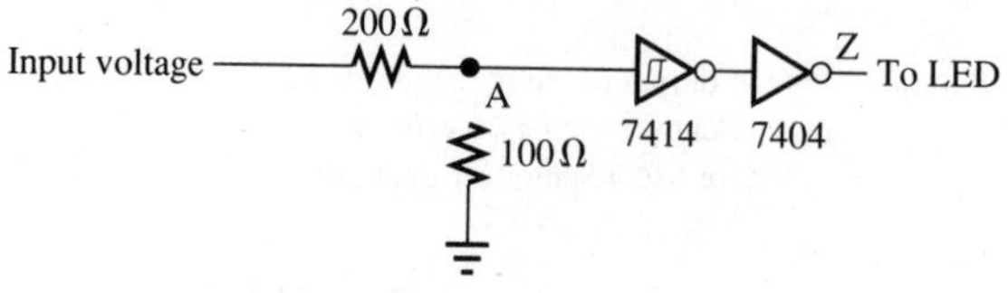

Input voltage — 200 Ω — A — 100 Ω — 7414 — 7404 — Z — To LED

The voltage *divider* provides for approximately 1.66 V at input A when the input is 5 V. Z will be a logic HIGH at the V_{t+} of the 7414.

FIGURE 7-28 Threshold Detection Circuit

Section Self-Test

1. A Schmitt trigger device has a $V_{t+} = 1.6$ volts, and a $V_{t-} = 0.4$ volts. What is the hysteresis?
2. Is it better for a device to have a large or small hysteresis?
3. A Schmitt trigger inverter has 3 volts as an input. What is the output state?

ANSWERS

- 1.2 volts
- Small
- LOW

SUMMARY

Sequential logic circuits have outputs that depend on the sequence of inputs applied. Sequential circuits often employ feedback, and the circuits must be analyzed with respect to time to determine operation and output states.

Sequential logic is used to design and construct clock circuits, counters, shift registers, and other advanced digital systems. In order to begin to understand sequential circuits, monostable and astable circuits were examined. These circuits are easy to analyze and very useful in the generation of timing signals.

ANALYSIS

Sequential logic is analyzed by using a special type of truth table known as a present input-present state-next state table. Sequential analysis involves circuits using feedback, and state table analysis is a useful tool in determining circuit operation. Circuits are further analyzed with input and output waveform analysis.

Several basic types of sequential circuits are the monostable and astable multivibrators and Schmitt trigger circuits. The analysis of these devices involved calculating the pulse width for the one-shot and the frequency of the oscillator.

Schmitt trigger circuit analysis involves identifying the positive and negative threshold voltages and constructing a transfer characteristic of the input and output voltages.

APPLICATION

Monostable multivibrators are used to generate specific pulse duration waveform pulses. One application is the conversion of a series of nonuniform pulses into a waveform with uniform pulse widths. Another application would be to use the one-shot as an event counter. The one-shot would produce one pulse for every input trigger. This output pulse could be used as the input to a counter or memory circuit.

Astable multivibrators, commonly called oscillator circuits, are used to generate clock waveforms. The clock frequency can be controlled to produce various types of timing clocks for different applications.

Schmitt trigger devices are used to provide a rapid switch in logic states. This is useful in the elimination of noise, conversion of a sine, ramp, or triangle waveform into a pulse waveform, oscillation prevention, and voltage threshold detection.

DESIGN

There are several monostable and astable multivibrator ICs available. They can be used to design all the applications described previously. The 555 IC timer is a very useful IC that can be used to design both monostable and astable circuits. Schmitt trigger ICs are available for each of the basic logic gates for designs that require fast output state transitions.

PROBLEMS

7.1 Sequential Logic—Analysis Problems

*1. Define the following terms:
   a. previous state
   b. present state
   c. next state

2. Define the following terms:
   a. stable state
   b. unstable state
   c. oscillation

* *See* Answers to Selected Problems.

3. Define the following terms:
   a. monostable
   b. astable
   c. bistable

7-2 Feedback and Sequential Analysis—Analysis Problems

4. Construct a present input-present state-next state table for the circuit shown in Figure 7-29.

FIGURE 7-29 Problem 7-4 Circuit

*5. a. Draw a present input-present state-next state table for the circuit in Figure 7-30.

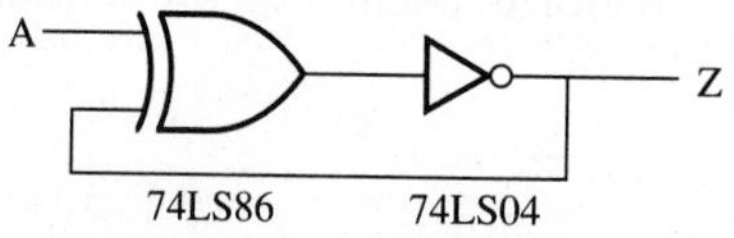

FIGURE 7-30 Problem 7-5 Circuit

b. Which states are stable?
c. Which states are unstable?

6. From the waveforms given for the circuit shown in Figure 7-31, draw a present state-next state table.

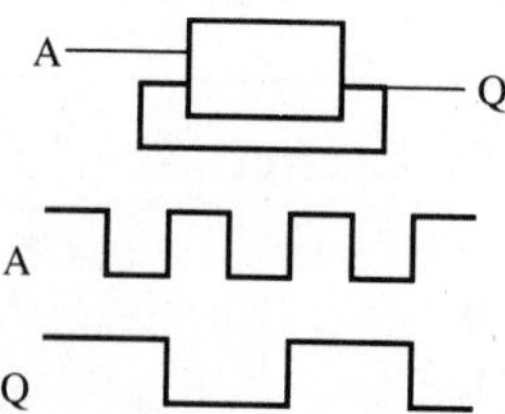

FIGURE 7-31 Problem 7-6 Circuit

*7. What is the typical and maximum propagation delay for the circuit shown in Figure 7-30, from input A to output Z for Schottky TTL gates?

---

* *See* Answers to Selected Problems.

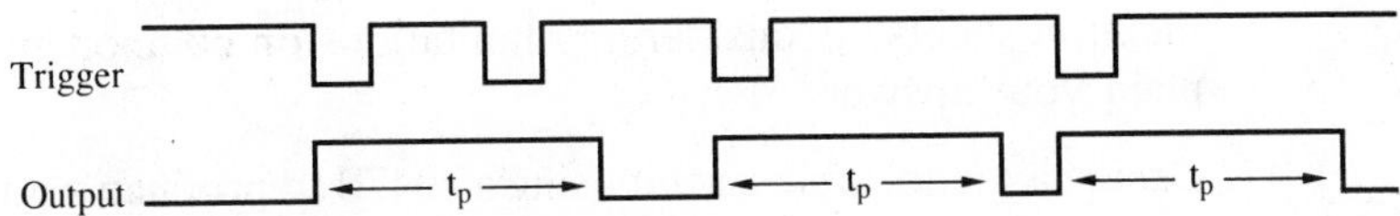

FIGURE 7-32 Problem 7-7 Circuit

8. Find the typical and maximum t_{PLH} and t_{PHL} for a 7400.
9. Repeat Problem 8 for a 74LS00.
10. Repeat Problem 8 for a 7413.
*11. Repeat Problem 8 for a 74132.

7-3 Monostable Multivibrators—Analysis and Application Problems

12. a. For the waveforms shown in Figure 7-32, determine if the multivibrator is monostable or astable. Explain your decision.
    b. Is the multivibrator retriggerable? Why or why not?
13. A 74121 is used to produce a monostable output waveform pulse, t_p = 1.0 s. Find *two* combinations of C_{ext} and R_{ext} that will produce a 1 second pulse.
14. Select a multivibrator that can be used to produce the waveform shown in Figure 7-33. Draw your final circuit, showing all necessary waveforms, component values, and schematic pin numbers.

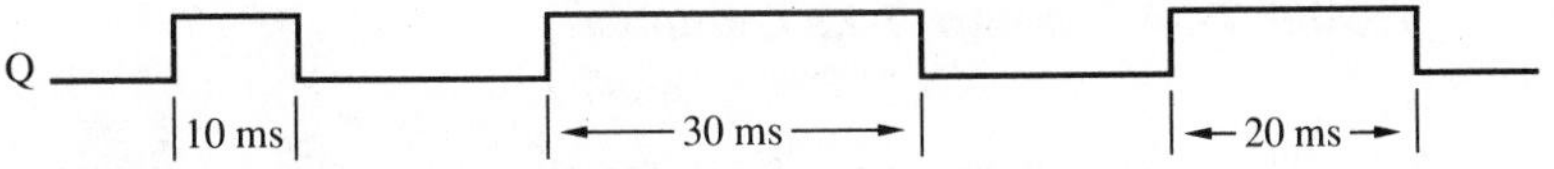

FIGURE 7-33 Problem 7-14 Waveform

*15. A 74LS122 is used with a timing capacitor of 100 nF. Find the typical t_p if no external timing resistor is used.
16. Repeat Problem 15, and find the typical t_p if a 5K ohm external timing resistor is used.
17. Examine the answers and circuitry of Problem 15. Will these component values produce a good quality output waveform according to the specification sheets? (Consider any limitations on component values.) Explain your answer.
18. Examine the answer and circuitry of Problem 16. Will these component values produce a good quality output waveform according to the spec-

ification sheets? (Consider any limitations on component values.) Explain your answer.

19. Design a monostable circuit using a 4047B to produce a μs pulse width.

7-4 Astable Multivibrators—Analysis and Design Problems

20. Analyze the circuit of Figure 7-13 and explain its operation.

*21. Design a circuit using a 4047B to produce an active HIGH timing clock with a 50% duty cycle and a 30 μs period.

22. Design a circuit using a 4047B to produce an oscillator with a 50% duty cycle and a 250 ns period.

7-5 The 555 Timer—Analysis and Design Problems

23. Draw the output waveforms for the circuit shown in Figure 7-34.

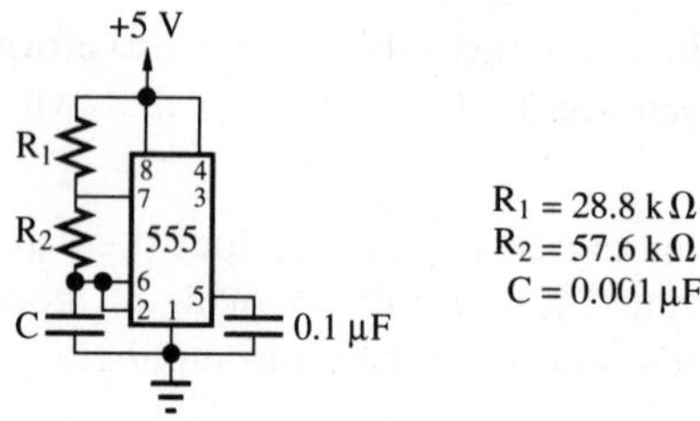

FIGURE 7-34 Problem 7-23 Circuit

24. Draw the output waveform for the circuit shown in Figure 7-35.

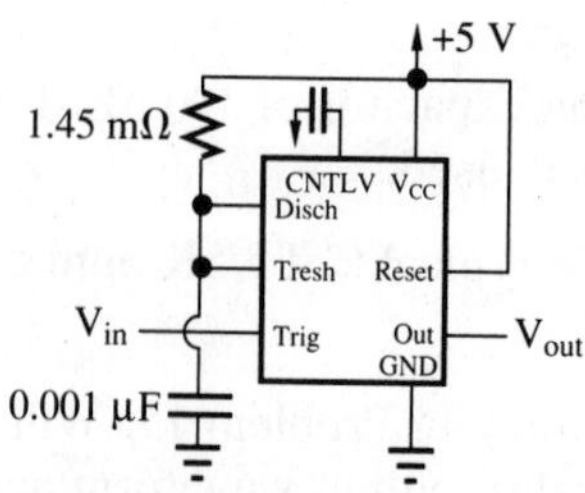

FIGURE 7-35 Problem 7-24 Circuit

25. Design a 555 timer circuit to produce a one-shot output pulse of 10 μs.

26. Modify the design of Problem 25 to produce an output pulse of 100 μs.

*27. Modify the design of Problem 25 to produce an output pulse of 1000 μs.

28. Examine the answers and circuit components for the designs of Problems 25 through 27. What is the relationship between component values and period for a 555 timer IC circuit design?

29. A 555 timer in astable mode has an output frequency of 4 KHz and a 60% duty cycle. Find valid specification values for R_A, R_B, and C.

30. Modify the design of Problem 29 to produce a 4 KHz frequency and 20% duty cycle.

*31. Modify the design of Problem 29 to produce a 4 KHz frequency and 90% duty cycle.

32. Examine the answers and circuit components for the designs in Problems 29 through 31. (a) What is the relationship between component values and duty cycle for an astable 555 circuit? (b) Is there a limitation on the smallest duty cycle possible? Explain.

33. A 555 timer in astable operation has the following component values:

    $R_A = 2.2\text{K}\ \Omega$ $R_B = 10\text{K}\ \Omega$ $C = 2200$ pF

    Find the following:

    a. t_H b. t_L c. Duty cycle d. f e. T

34. Repeat Problem 18 for $R_A = 20\text{K}\ \Omega$, $R_B = 10\text{K}\ \Omega$, and $C = 20\ \mu\text{F}$

35. A 555 timer in the monostable mode has $R_A = 100\text{K}\ \Omega$ and $C = 0.01\ \mu\text{F}$. Find t_p.

36. Repeat Problem 35 for $R_A = 500\text{K}\ \Omega$ and $C = 0.1\ \mu\text{F}$.

*37. If $V_{CC} = 10$ V for a 555 timer in a monostable mode, find:
    a. $V_{trigger}$ b. $V_{threshold}$

38. List four parametric limitations to consider when designing with a 555 timer.

39. Design a frequency divider circuit to produce an output waveform of 1 KHz using a 555 timer.

7-6 Schmitt Trigger Devices—Analysis and Design Problems

*40. Graph the nominal specification transfer characteristic for a 74LS19.

41. Graph the worst case specification transfer characteristic for a 74LS19.

42. Explain how a Schmitt trigger device operates. Include in your explanation a definition of the term *hysteresis*.

*43. Graph the transfer characteristic for a Schmitt trigger buffer, with $V_{t-} = 1.0$ V and $V_{t+} = 3.0$ V. Label all critical values.

44. Graph the transfer characteristic for a Schmitt trigger inverter, with $V_{t-} = 1.0$ V and $V_{t+} = 3.0$ V. Label all critical values.

45. List four uses for a Schmitt trigger device.

46. A Schmitt trigger buffer has $V_{t+} = 1.9$ V and a 1 V hysteresis. If $V_{OH} = 4$ V, $V_{OL} = 0.2$ V, $V_{IH} = 2.4$ V, and $V_{IL} = 0.8$ V, graph the complete transfer characteristic for this device.

47. Repeat Problem 46 for a Schmitt trigger inverter.

*48. An astable Schmitt trigger (7414) multivibrator circuit has R = 330 Ωs and C = 0.1 μF. Find the output frequency.

49. a. Repeat Problem 48 for C = 0.001 μF.
    b. What is the relationship between capacitor size and frequency for a Schmitt trigger multivibrator circuit?

50. What is the minimum, typical, and maximum hysteresis for a 4093B at $V_{DD} = 5$ V, and 25°C?

*51. For a 4093B monostable circuit, R = 500 Ω, C = 1 μF, and $V_{DD} =$ 10 V. Use the typical specification value for V_{t+} and find the output pulse, t_p.

52. Repeat problem 51 at $V_{DD} = 5.0$ V.

53. Design a Schmitt trigger circuit to detect an input voltage >7 V. Draw and label your completed circuit.

54. Design a circuit that will convert a 60 Hz and 120 V sine wave (typical U.S. AC electricity) into a 60 Hz 0 to 5 V, 50% duty cycle square wave. (*Hint:* Show a step down transformer that first converts the 120 V AC into the appropriate amplitude AC for conversion to a square wave.)

Chapter 8

Bistable Logic Circuits: Latches

Upon completing and mastering the material in this chapter, you should be able to define and understand latches in the areas of analysis, application, and design:

ANALYSIS

1. Understand D latch operation.
2. Understand S-R and $\bar{S}$-$\bar{R}$ latch operation.
3. Analyze sequential cross-coupled feedback circuits.
4. Understand voltage level-triggering.
5. Understand the difference between a latch and a flip-flop.

APPLICATION

6. Apply latches as delay elements.
7. Apply latches as temporary storage devices.
8. Use latches in display applications.

DESIGN

9. Design latch circuits for the preceding applications.
10. Utilize data book information to select latch ICs suited to a particular design.

8-1 LATCHING CONCEPTS

A latch is a basic digital storage device that is capable of storing one bit of information. The storage feature of the latch is very useful in digital circuits. The primary purpose of a latch is to temporarily store a logic level. Latches are used to store small amounts of data temporarily as compared to semiconductor memories which are used for long-term storage and the storage of large amounts of data.

8.1.1 Latches for Temporary Data Storage

A **latch** is a bistable multivibrator that can store one bit of data. A one bit latch can store either a binary one or zero state, and therefore is known as a **bistable memory element**. Latches employ feedback to operate. In combinational logic, if the inputs are removed, the outputs will become invalid. A latch takes advantage of sequential feedback to store binary data and produce valid output logic levels even after removal of the inputs.

Latches are often combined into groups of 4, 8, 16, or 32 in order to temporarily store a nibble, byte, or word of data. Latches are often used in microprocessor-based designs.

There are several reasons that temporary storage is needed. One problem encountered in digital circuits is variable propagation delays. Digital circuits can experience hazards and logic errors if the inputs to a circuit arrive at different times. Latches can be used to store the inputs to a time critical circuit, and then these stored inputs can be clocked simultaneously into the next circuit for error-free operation. This is illustrated in Figure 8-1.

Another use for temporary storage is the use of signal lines for more than one type of signal. For example, a signal line can be used to carry address information and data, so long as the addresses and data are latched onto the signal line at different times. This multiple signal line usage is called

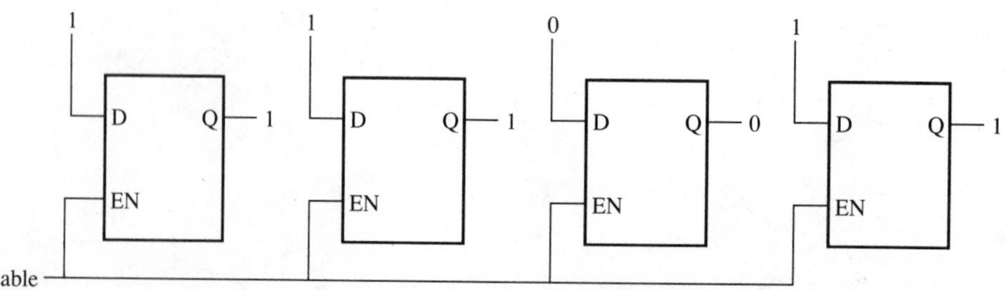

FIGURE 8-1 Temporary Storage Using Latches. [The binary data 1101 (hexadecimal D) is input into four 1 bit latches. The data will remain in the latches until new data is input, even if the inputs are removed.]

multiplexing. Multiplexing is very common in microprocessor circuits, and digital latches are employed to demultiplex digital information.

Digital communication technology also uses latches to convert a serial data bit stream into a parallel format. For example, serial data can be latched into a byte by sequentially storing 8 bits into eight latches. The output from the latches can then be simultaneously clocked for parallel output, which is more compatible with many memory and microprocessor systems.

8.1.2 Asynchronous and Synchronous Latches

There are several latch modes of operation. If the latch is **asynchronous**, data will be stored as soon as the input or inputs attain a valid voltage level. Asynchronous latches operate independently of any type of clock or timing, with the output becoming valid as governed by the propagation delay of the latch circuit. Thus, the only difference between an asynchronous latch and a truth table equivalent combinational circuit is that the output will remain valid on the latch even *after the inputs are removed.* Figure 8-2 shows the operation of an asynchronous latch.

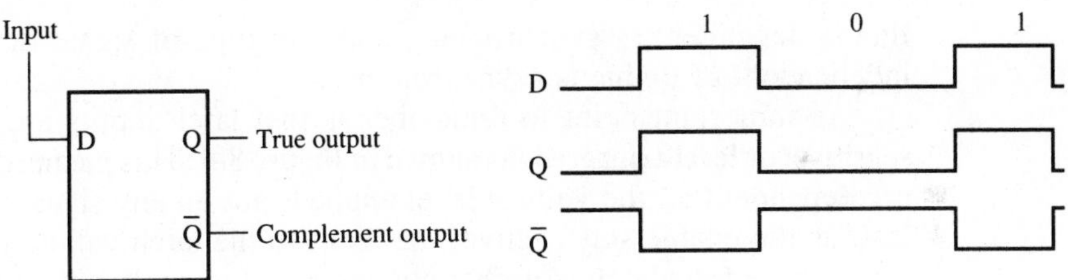

Non-gated D Latch Truth Table

D	Q	$\overline{Q}$
0	0	1
1	1	0

FIGURE 8-2 Asynchronous D Latch Operation

A **gated latch** has some additional control circuitry and an enable input. This type of latch will not operate unless the enable is active. First, the input is placed on the latch. If the enable input is not activated, no storage or change occurs on the output of the latch. Once the enable is active, the latch stores new data and places that data on the output line. Figure 8-3 shows the operation of a gated latch. A gated latch is **synchronous**, in that the operation of the latch is now dependent on the application of another input, the **enable**, often abbreviated **EN**. Thus, any type of signal or input that is

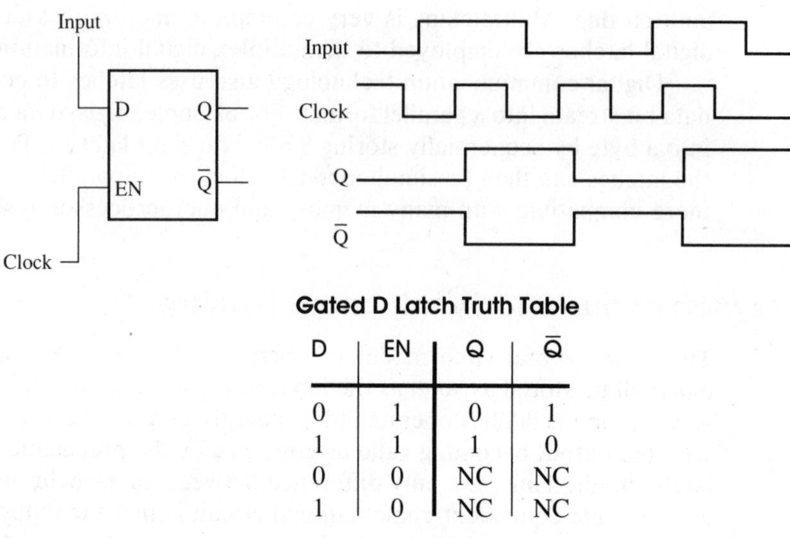

Gated D Latch Truth Table

D	EN	Q	$\overline{Q}$
0	1	0	1
1	1	1	0
0	0	NC	NC
1	0	NC	NC

NC = no change in output

FIGURE 8-3 Synchronous D Latch Operation

timing dependent is synchronous, and any type of signal or input that is independent of timing is asynchronous.

An important point to remember is that latch inputs are voltage **level sensitive**, or **level-triggered**, as shown in Figure 8-4. This means that the inputs are dependent on the voltage level applied, not on any signal transition. As long as the enable stays active, the input to the latch will be transferred to the output of the latch. Another common way to explain the function of the latch is that the output will **follow** the input as long as the enable is active. The action of the output following the input with the device enabled is also known as **transparent** operation.

Flip-flops are bistable storage devices that operate based on the transition of a signal. The operation of a device dependent on a signal transition is known as **edge-triggering**. The various forms of triggering will be discussed with flip-flop devices in Chapter 9.

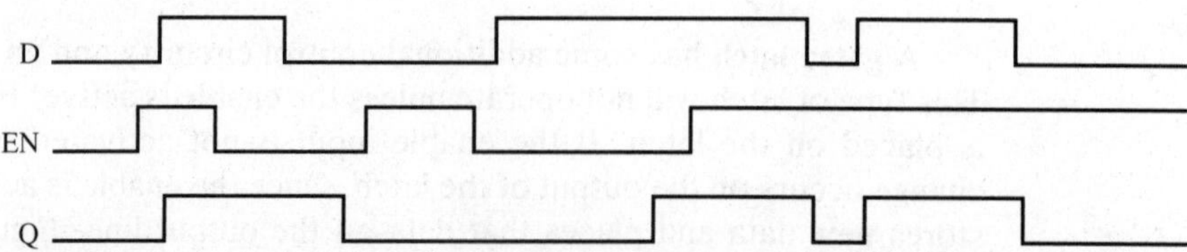

FIGURE 8-4 Voltage Level Triggering. (When the enable input is a logic HIGH, the output follows the input. When the clock is a logic LOW, the output does not change.)

Section Self-Test

1. What is the difference between a latch and a flip-flop?
2. What is the main use of a latch?
3. What is an asynchronous input?

ANSWERS

- A latch is level-triggered and a flip-flop is edge-triggered.
- Latches are mainly used for temporary data storage.
- Asynchronous inputs operate independently of any timing clock.

8-2 D LATCHES

The D latch, also known as the delay latch, is the easiest latch to understand from a functional viewpoint. It is the simplest form of memory, and each D latch can store or retain one binary bit of information.

8.2.1 Delay Latch

The basic **delay latch**, or **D latch** has one input commonly labeled "D," and one output, commonly labeled "Q." This latch is asynchronous in its operation since there is no clock or enable input to control the function of the latch. The asynchronous or nongated D latch is shown in Figure 8-2. The D latch is bistable, since it can store two values, a logic 1 or a logic 0 (HIGH or LOW).

The asynchronous D latch is no longer commonly available in IC form. It was used as a propagation delay element, thus giving the D latch its name of delay latch.

One application for a D latch is to add a timing delay to one part of a digital circuit that is faster than another part of the circuit due to an imbalance in propagation delays. If, for example, one part of a circuit has three levels of logic and another part has five levels of logic, a D latch can be added to the three-level circuit to give the overall circuit a time delay equal to five levels of logic. The D latch equalizes the propagation delay and prevents logic glitches or hazards. Since a gated D latch can be used as a delay element as well as a controllable storage device, the nongated D latch is no longer produced. In addition, ICs such as the 74LS31 are specifically designed to be accurate propagation **delay elements**.

8.2.2 Gated D Latch

Although it is possible to construct a D latch with only the data input, commercial D latches also have an enable input to control the operation of the device. D latches with an enable input are known as **gated D latches**. The gated D latch has two inputs: a data input, "D," and an enable input, "EN."

The D latch has one true output, labeled, "Q," and may also have a complement output, labeled "$\overline{Q}$."

Whenever the enable is active, the logic level placed on the input D will be transferred to the output Q. Another way of stating this operation is that the output Q will **follow** the input D whenever the enable is active. If the input D is removed, the output Q will remain in its present state.

The D latch **stores** the input value, and the latch is said to have **memory**. When the output of a latch is a logic HIGH, the latch is **set**; and when the output is a logic LOW, the latch is **cleared** or **reset**. The gated D latch and the corresponding timing waveforms and truth table are shown in Figure 8-3.

■ EXAMPLE 8-1 D Latch Operation

Problem: Determine the output Q for the following circuit for a gated D latch with the input waveforms shown in Figure 8-5. (Assume the output Q is initially LOW.)

Solution: See the output waveform in Figure 8-5.

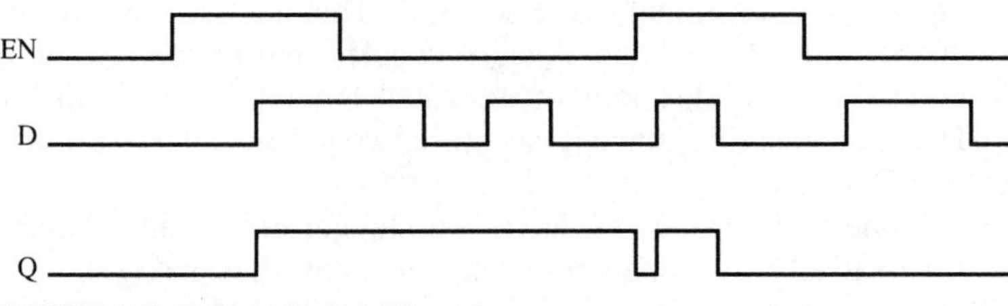

FIGURE 8-5 Example 8-1 Waveforms ■

■ EXAMPLE 8-2 D Latch Operation

Problem: A gated D latch is always enabled. Draw the output Q and its inverse for the input D as shown in Figure 8-6. (Q is initially HIGH.)

Solution: See the output waveform in Figure 8-6.

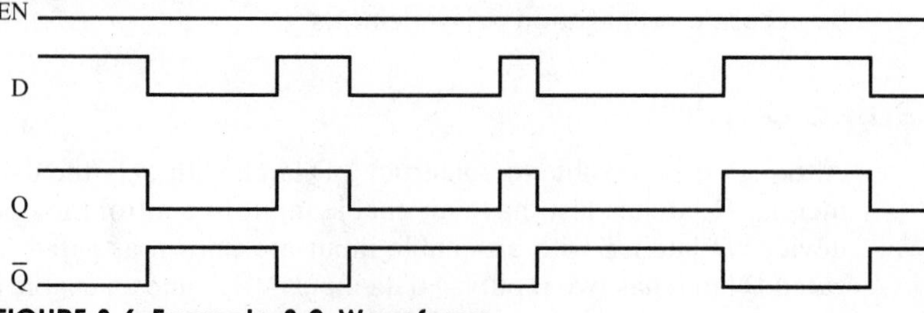

FIGURE 8-6 Example 8-2 Waveforms ■

Section Self-Test

Determine if the following statements are true or false:

1. A nongated D latch operation is the same as that of a gated D latch with the enable always HIGH.
2. A gated latch has Q = 1 and EN = 0. If D = 0, then the latch changes state such that Q = 0.
3. A gated latch has Q = 1 and EN = 1. If the EN input changes to 0, then Q changes to 0.

ANSWERS (Not necessarily in the order of the questions)

• True • False • True

8-3 S-R AND $\overline{S}$-$\overline{R}$ LATCHES

S-R and $\overline{S}$-$\overline{R}$ latches are bistable devices, each of which is capable of storing 1 bit of data. These types of latches can be built with two basic logic gates utilizing feedback.

8.3.1 S-R Latch

Another common type of latch is the **S-R** or **Set-Reset latch**. The S-R latch has two inputs, S and R, one true output, Q, and one complementary output, $\overline{Q}$. The S-R latch is easily constructed by using two NOR gates, with the $\overline{Q}$ output NORed with the R input, and the Q output NORed with the S input. Thus, the output is fed back to the input, which is known electronically as **feedback**.

Also note that the output of one of the NOR gates is connected to the

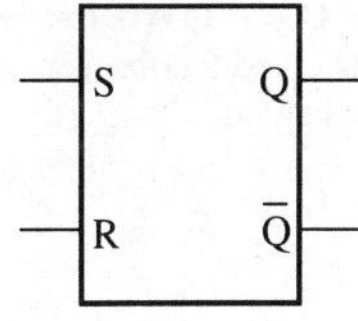

S	R	Q	$\overline{Q}$	Operation
0	0	Q_0	$\overline{Q}_0$	Hold (no change)
0	1	0	1	Reset
1	0	1	0	Set
1	1	?	?	Unstable

?: The outputs for the S = 1, R = 1 input condition will either oscillate or reach some invalid TTL voltage, e.g., 2.0 volts.

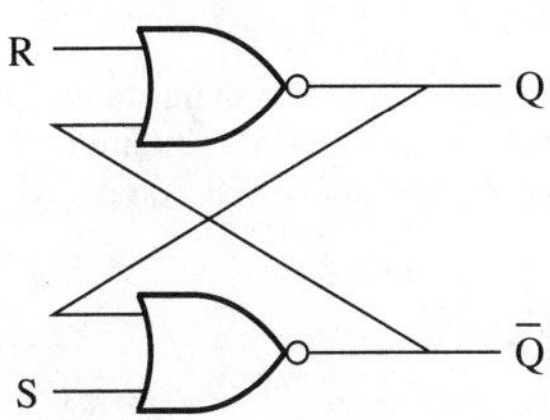

FIGURE 8-7 S-R Latch

input of the other NOR gate. This crossing of the outputs is known as **cross-coupling**. In total, this simple circuit is said to employ **cross-coupled feedback**. The block diagram, truth table, and cross-coupled NOR circuit are shown in Figure 8-7.

The truth table in Figure 8-7 indicates that the S-R latch can be set (Q = 1) or reset (Q = 0), as with the gated D latch. In addition, two additional output conditions are possible. If logic LOWs are applied to both the S and R input, there is no change in the output. The no change condition is known as the **hold** latch operation. If logic HIGHs are applied to both the S and R

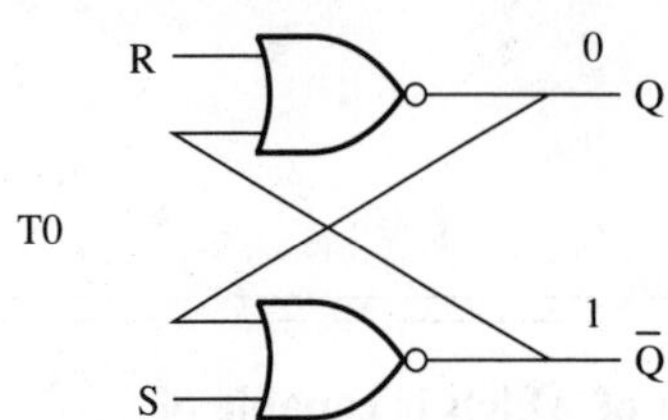
T0
R
S
0
Q
1
$\overline{Q}$
Initial condition: Q = 0
$\overline{Q}$ = 1
Apply the appropriate inputs, to set the latch:
R = 0 S = 1 and analyze.

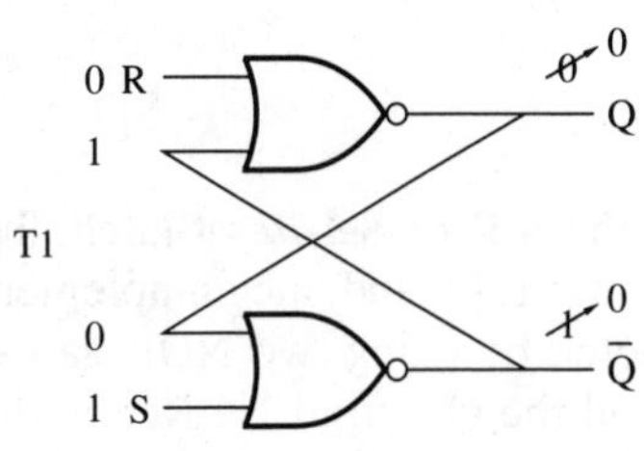
T1
0 R
1
0
1 S
0
Q
0
$\overline{Q}$
For a small time period (1 gate delay) the outputs Q and $\overline{Q}$ are both LOW. This is an unstable condition that the feedback will correct.

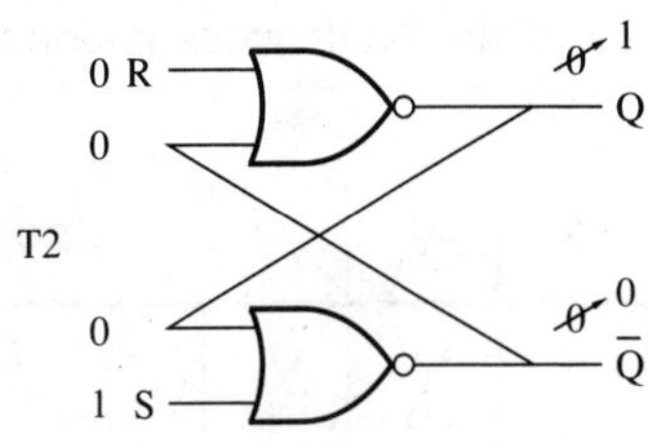
T2
0 R
0
0
1 S
1
Q
0
$\overline{Q}$
The outputs Q and $\overline{Q}$ have changed to a stable condition Q = 1, $\overline{Q}$ = 0, but the feedback changed the outputs, and feedback gate analysis must be performed again.

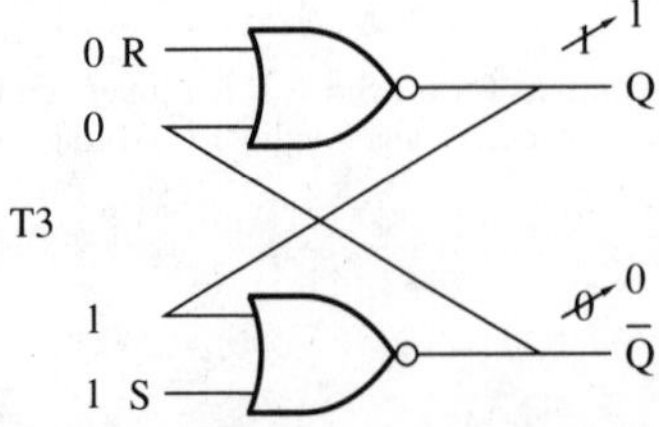
T3
0 R
0
1
1 S
1
Q
0
$\overline{Q}$
The outputs Q and $\overline{Q}$ remain stable, Q = 1, $\overline{Q}$ = 0, in the correct truth table set condition. Since the outputs did not change, analysis is complete.

FIGURE 8-8 S-R Latch Set Operation

input, the final output cannot be determined and is an **invalid** condition for the S-R latch to be in. Careful analysis of the latch indicates that the invalid condition will cause the latch output to oscillate between the 0 and 1 state. Data book truth tables indicate that the S-R latch should not have HIGH logic levels on both S and R. It is the responsibility of the logic circuit designer to ensure that this condition does not occur.

The cross-coupled NOR circuit is a good example of sequential logic since the output logic state depends on what point in time the circuit is analyzed. The truth table for an S-R latch shows the final **steady state** output. The output for an S-R latch may in fact change its logic state as a result of the feedback until the steady state output condition is established. This is illustrated in the examination of the set mode of operation of the S-R latch as shown in Figure 8-8.

Figure 8-8 illustrates the primary steps to undertake when analyzing sequential logic devices and circuits. As mentioned earlier, sequential circuits have time dependent logic states. As discussed in Chapter 7, a **present input-present state-next state table** can be utilized to aid in sequential analysis. Figure 8-9 illustrates a present input-present state-next state table for the S-R latch.

Present Input		Present State	Next State	State
S	R	Q_n	Q_{n+1}	Comment
0	0	0	0	Hold
0	0	1	1	Hold
0	1	0	0	Reset
0	1	1	0	Reset
1	0	0	1	Set
1	0	1	1	Set
1	1	0	Oscillating	Invalid
1	1	1	Oscillating	Invalid

FIGURE 8-9 S-R Latch Present Input-Present State-Next State Table

■ EXAMPLE 8-3 S-R Latch Operation

Problem: An S-R latch is initially set. If S = 1 and R = 0, find Q.

Solution: Using the S-R latch truth table, when S = 1 and R = 0, the latch is in the set mode. Since the latch is initially set, the latch output will remain HIGH. ■

■ EXAMPLE 8-4 S-R Latch Operation

Problem: Given the waveforms of Figure 8-10 as inputs into an S-R latch that is initially cleared, find the output Q.

Solution: Refer to the output waveforms shown in Figure 8-10.

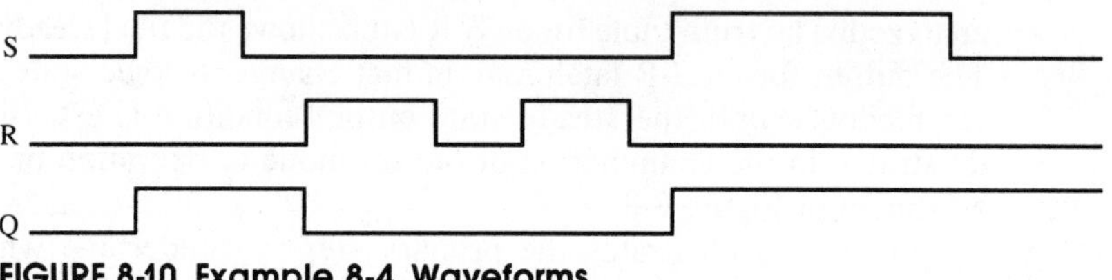

FIGURE 8-10 Example 8-4 Waveforms ■

8.3.2 $\overline{S}$-$\overline{R}$ Latch

Another type of set-reset latch is the $\overline{S}$-$\overline{R}$ latch. This latch has the same possible output conditions as the S-R latch, but inputs opposite to those of the S-R latch are used to produce the latch states. Thus, this latch is often referred to as an S-R latch with active-LOW inputs. The $\overline{S}$-$\overline{R}$ latch can be built from two cross-coupled NAND gates. Figure 8-11 shows the $\overline{S}$-$\overline{R}$ latch block diagram, truth table, and cross-coupled NAND circuit used to construct the latch. In addition to the change in gate type between the S-R and $\overline{S}$-$\overline{R}$ cross-

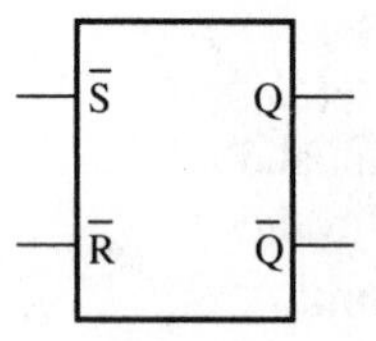

$\overline{S}$	$\overline{R}$	Q	$\overline{Q}$	State Comment
1	1	Q_0	$\overline{Q}_0$	Hold (no change)
1	0	0	1	Reset
0	1	1	0	Set
0	0	?	?	Unstable

?: The outputs for the $\overline{S} = 0$, $\overline{R} = 0$ input condition will either oscillate or reach some invalid TTL voltage, e.g., 2.0 volts.

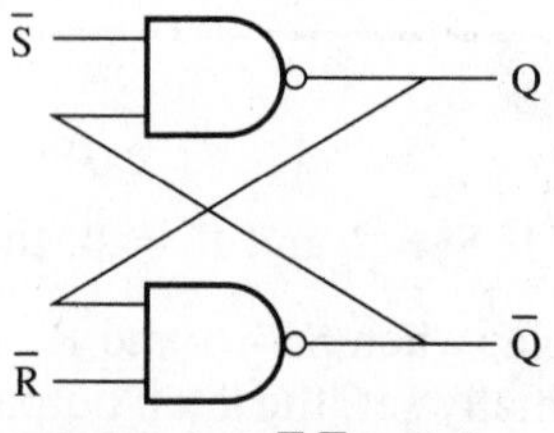

FIGURE 8-11 $\overline{S}$-$\overline{R}$ Latch

coupled latch circuits, it is important to note the input and output labeling. The S-R inputs and the Q and $\overline{Q}$ outputs are *not* identical for the two circuits.

■ EXAMPLE 8-5 Active-LOW $\overline{S}$-$\overline{R}$ Latch Operation

Problem: An $\overline{S}$-$\overline{R}$ latch has a HIGH input into $\overline{S}$ and a LOW input into $\overline{R}$. What is the output Q?

Solution: Referring to the $\overline{S}$-$\overline{R}$ truth table, the output Q will be HIGH. ■

8.3.3 Gated S-R Latch

The S-R and $\overline{S}$-$\overline{R}$ latches discussed previously were asynchronous latches since the operation of the latch did not depend on any type of timing input. Both types of S-R latches can be made synchronous by adding an enable circuit, similar to the enable circuit of a gated D latch. S-R latches with an enable input are referred to as **gated S-R latches**. A gated S-R and a gated $\overline{S}$-$\overline{R}$ latch circuit are shown in Figure 8-12, along with corresponding truth tables.

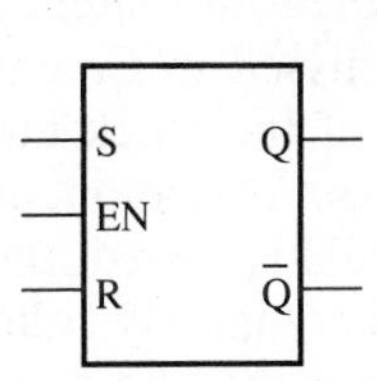

EN	S	R	Q	$\overline{Q}$	Operation
1	0	0	Q_0	$\overline{Q_0}$	Hold
1	0	1	0	1	Reset
1	1	0	1	0	Set
1	1	1	?	?	Unstable
0	x	x	Q_0	$\overline{Q_0}$	Disabled

x = don't care

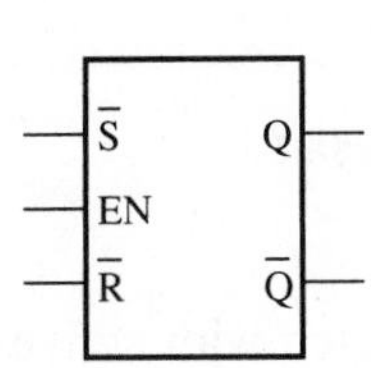

EN	$\overline{S}$	$\overline{R}$	Q	$\overline{Q}$	Operation
1	1	1	Q_0	$\overline{Q_0}$	Hold
1	1	0	0	1	Reset
1	0	1	1	0	Set
1	0	0	?	?	Unstable
0	x	x	Q_0	$\overline{Q_0}$	Disabled

x = don't care

FIGURE 8-12 Gated S-R Latches

■ EXAMPLE 8-6

Problem: A gated S-R latch has inputs as shown in Figure 8-13. Q is initially 0. Find Q.

Solution: Refer to the output waveforms in Figure 8-13.

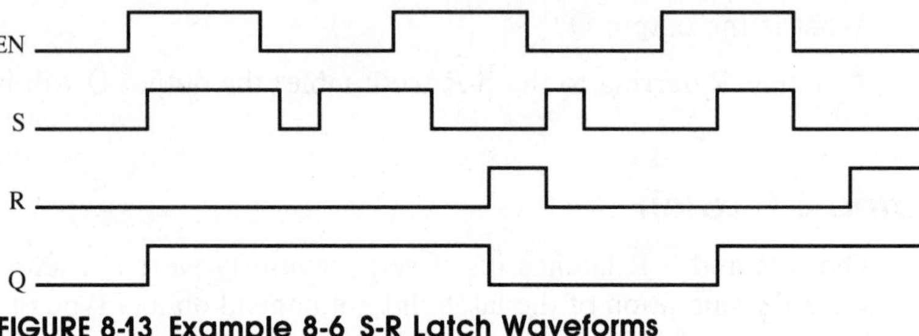

FIGURE 8-13 Example 8-6 S-R Latch Waveforms ■

8.3.4 Asynchronous Latch Inputs; Preset and Clear

Commercially available latches are synchronous in operation. The clock input provides digital circuit designer control over the operation of the latch.

Another useful feature that has been designed into latches, as well as other synchronous ICs such as flip-flops (discussed in Chapter 9), is the ability to set or reset the device independent of the clock input. When a LOW is stored, this is referred to as a **clear** or **reset** operation, and this input is commonly called the **clear** input. When a HIGH is stored, this is referred to as a **set** or **preset** operation, and this input is commonly called the **preset** input. Depending on the IC, the preset and clear may be active HIGH or active LOW. Most latch ICs have only a clear feature, whereas flip-flops and other ICs, such as counters and shift registers, will have both a preset and clear function. Figure 8-14 shows the data sheets for the 74116, a dual 4-bit latch with clear.

■ EXAMPLE 8-7 S-R Latch with Asynchronous Preset and Clear Inputs

Problem: Determine the output Q for an S-R latch with active-LOW PRESET and active-LOW clear inputs for the input waveforms given in Figure 8-15.

SN54116, SN74116
DUAL 4-BIT LATCHES WITH CLEAR

DECEMBER 1972—REVISED MARCH 1988

- Two Independent 4-Bit Latches in a Single Package
- Separate Clear Inputs Provide One-Step Clearing Operation
- Dual Gated Enable Inputs Simplify Cascading Register Implementations
- Compatible for Use with TTL Circuits
- Input Clamping Diodes Simplify System Design

SN54116 . . . J OR W PACKAGE
SN74116 . . . N PACKAGE
(TOP VIEW)

Signal	Pin	Pin	Signal
$1\overline{CLR}$	1	24	V_{CC}
$1\overline{C}1$	2	23	2Q4
$1\overline{C}2$	3	22	2D4
1D1	4	21	2Q3
1Q1	5	20	2D3
1D2	6	19	2Q2
1Q2	7	18	2D2
1D3	8	17	2Q1
1Q3	9	16	2D1
1D4	10	15	$2\overline{C}2$
1Q4	11	14	$2\overline{C}1$
GND	12	13	$2\overline{CLR}$

description

These monolithic TTL circuits utlize D-type bistables to implement two independent four-bit latches in a single package. Each four-bit latch has an independent asynchronous clear input and a gated two-input enable circuit. When both enable inputs are low, the output levels will follow the data input levels. When either or both of the enable inputs are taken high, the outputs remain at the last levels setup at the inputs prior to the low-to-high-level transition at the enable input(s). After this, the data inputs are locked out.

The clear input is overriding and when taken low will reset all four outputs low regardless of the levels of the enable inputs.

The SN54116 is characterized for operation over the full military temperature range of −55°C to 125°C; the SN74116 is characterized for operation from 0°C to 70°C.

FUNCTION TABLE
(EACH LATCH)

INPUTS				OUTPUT
$\overline{CLEAR}$	ENABLE $\overline{C1}$	ENABLE $\overline{C2}$	DATA	Q
H	L	L	L	L
H	L	L	H	H
H	X	H	X	Q_0
H	H	X	X	Q_0
L	X	X	X	L

H = high level, L = low level, X = irrelevant
Q_0 = the level of Q before these input conditions were established.

logic symbol†

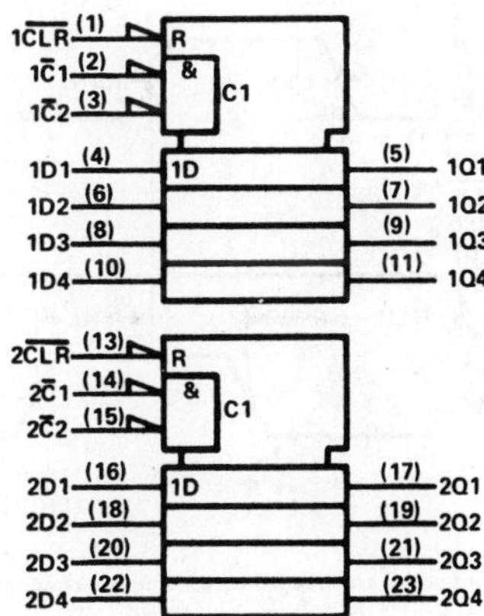

†This symbol is in accordance with ANSI/IEEE Std. 91-1984 and IEC Publication 617-12.

FIGURE 8-14 74116 with Asynchronous Clear (Courtesy of Texas Instruments.)

SN54116, SN74116
DUAL 4-BIT LATCHES WITH CLEAR

PARAMETER MEASUREMENT INFORMATION

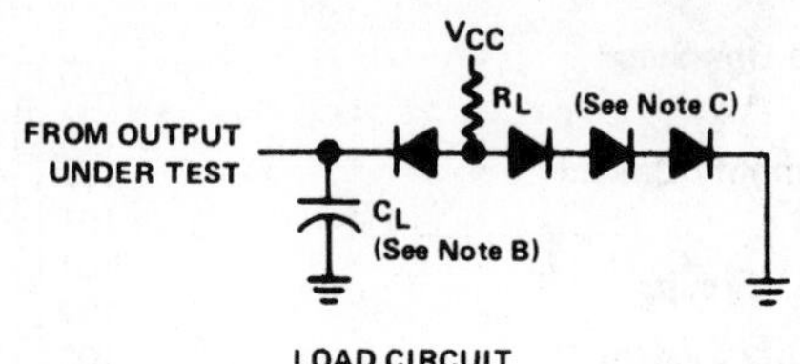

LOAD CIRCUIT

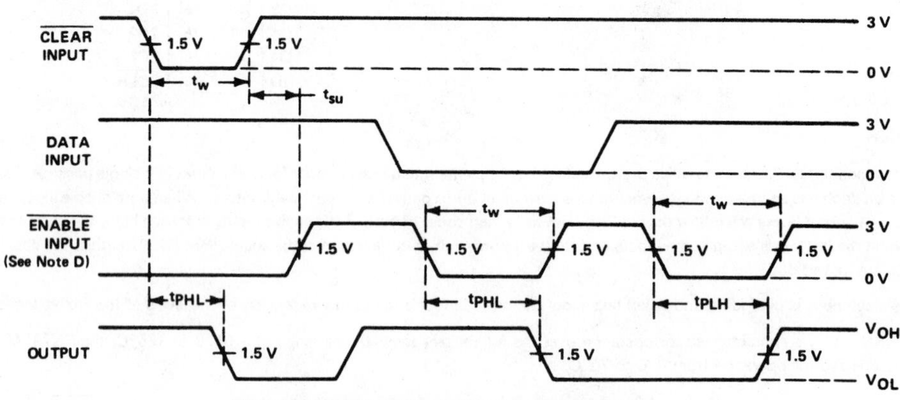

SWITCHING TIMES FROM CLEAR AND ENABLE INPUTS

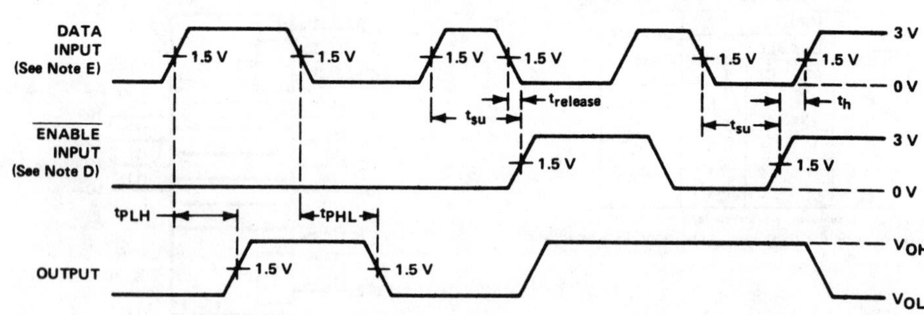

SWITCHING TIMES FROM DATA INPUTS

NOTES: A. Input pulses are supplied by generators having the following characteristics: $t_r \leqslant 10$ ns, $t_f \leqslant 10$ ns, PRR = 1 MHz, duty cycle $\leqslant$ 50%, $Z_{out} \approx 50\Omega$.

B. C_L includes probe and jig capacitance.

C. All diodes are 1N3064 or equivalent.

D. The other enable input is low.

E. Clear input is high.

FIGURE 8-14 ***(continued)***

Solution: Refer to the output waveforms shown in Figure 8-15.

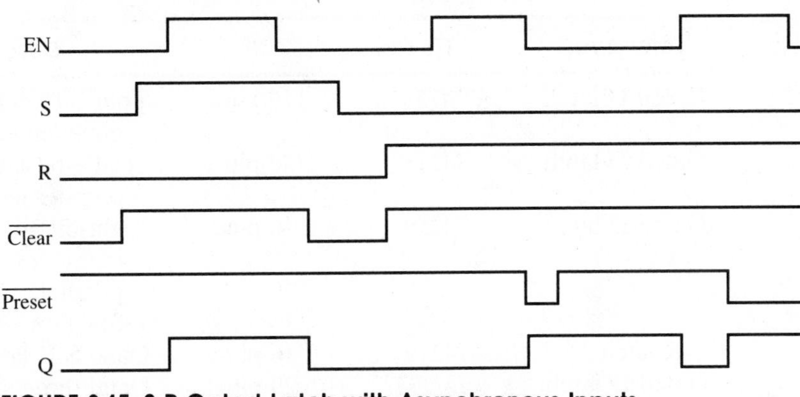

FIGURE 8-15 S-R Gated Latch with Asynchronous Inputs ■

Section Self-Test

Determine if the following statements are true or false:

1. S = 0, R = 0 is the invalid input for an S-R latch.
2. If a gated $\overline{S}$-$\overline{R}$ latch has S = 0, R = 1, and EN = 0, the latch will be set.
3. An asynchronous input will override the EN, S, and R inputs for an S-R latch.

ANSWERS (Not necessarily in the same order as the questions)

• False • True • False

8-4 INTEGRATED CIRCUIT LATCHES

A variety of D and S-R latches are available in IC form. The most widely available IC latch is the D latch. Latch ICs are used in many types of digital circuits, including memory and microprocessor circuits.

8.4.1 TTL IC Latches

There are over 40 different TTL IC latches currently available. Table 8-1 lists several of the TTL IC latches available.

Several of the D latches are available only in certain TTL subfamilies, such as Schottky (S), low-power Schottky (LS), or advanced low-power

TABLE 8-1 TTL Latch ICs

Latch Type	TTL No.	DIP	Description
Gated D latch	7475	16-pin	Four-bit latch, true and complement outputs
Gated D latch	74116	24-pin	Dual 4-bit latch, true outputs with clear input
Gated D latch	74259	16-pin	Eight-bit addressable true outputs, clear input, parallel output, DMUX function
$\overline{S}$-$\overline{R}$ latch	74279	16-pin	Quad $\overline{S}$-$\overline{R}$ latch
Gated D latch	74LS373	20-pin	Octal three-state transparent latch true outputs, active-LOW enable
Gated D latch	74LS375	16-pin	Same electrically and functionally as 7475, but with different pin assignments

TABLE 8-2 CMOS Latch ICs

Latch Type	CMOS No.	DIP	Description
Gated D latch	74HC75 74HCT75	16-pin	Four-bit latch, true and complement outputs
Gated D latch	74HC77 74HCT77	14-pin	Four-bit latch, true outputs
Gated D latch	74HC259 74HCT259	16-pin	Eight-bit addressable true outputs, clear input, parallel output, DMUX function
Gated D latch	74HC373 74HCT373	20-pin	Eight-bit latch, true outputs with tristate
Gated D latch	74HC573 74HCT573	20-pin	Eight-bit latch, complement outputs with tristate

Schottky (ALS). The 8-bit or **octal** latch is the most common size available, but 9-bit (74ALS992) and 10-bit (74ALS994) latches are also available. The additional one or two bits above the standard byte are used for parity and other error-checking digital circuitry.

Latches are also available with tristate outputs (74LS373) and open-collector outputs (74LS605) for special interfacing and storage applications.

8.4.2 CMOS IC Latches

Table 8-2 lists available CMOS latch ICs.

8.4.3 Latch Integrated Circuit Parameters

The data specifications for the 74LS75 4-bit bistable D latch is shown in Figure 8-16. It is common for manufacturers to show the internal logic diagram, and many data sheets will also show the actual bipolar transistor circuits used in the design.

The 74LS75 has four D latches, with true and complement outputs. Two of the latches are gated by the enable input 1C, 2C, and the other two latches are gated by the enable input 3C, 4C. Thus, two latches are enabled at a time.

The important timing parameters are the **setup time, t_{SU}**, the **hold time, t_H**, and the **enabling pulse width, t_W**. The setup time is the amount of time that the inputs to a device must be stable (at a valid logic level) before the device is enabled. The hold time is the amount of time that the inputs to a device must be stable (at a valid logic level) after the device has completed its operation. The enabling pulse width is the amount of time the enabling pulse must be active for the device to be properly enabled. These critical timing parameters are illustrated in the timing diagram in Figure 8-17. The other voltage, current, and timing parameters are like those of other TTL ICs, and are not unique to latches.

■ EXAMPLE 8-8 Latch Application

Problem: A digital circuit is needed to latch 8 bits of data from another circuit.

a. Determine the clock pulse needed to latch 8 bits of binary data using two 74LS75 ICs.

SN5475, SN5477, SN54LS75, SN54LS77, SN7475, SN74LS75 4-BIT BISTABLE LATCHES

MARCH 1974 – REVISED MARCH 1988

FUNCTION TABLE
(each latch)

INPUTS		OUTPUTS	
D	C	Q	$\overline{Q}$
L	H	L	H
H	H	H	L
X	L	Q_0	$\overline{Q}_0$

H = high level, L = low level, X = irrelevant
Q_0 = the level of Q before the high-to-low transition of G

SN5475, SN54LS75 . . . J OR W PACKAGE
SN7475 . . . N PACKAGE
SN74LS75 . . . D OR N PACKAGE
(TOP VIEW)

Signal	Pin	Pin	Signal
1$\overline{Q}$	1	16	1Q
1D	2	15	2Q
2D	3	14	2$\overline{Q}$
3C, 4C	4	13	1C, 2C
V_{CC}	5	12	GND
3D	6	11	3$\overline{Q}$
4D	7	10	3Q
4$\overline{Q}$	8	9	4Q

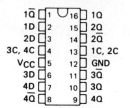

SN5477, SN54LS77 . . . W PACKAGE
(TOP VIEW)

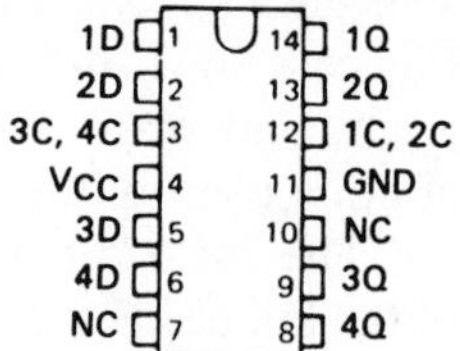

NC - No internal connection

description

These latches are ideally suited for use as temporary storage for binary information between processing units and input/output or indicator units. Information present at a data (D) input is transferred to the Q output when the enable (C) is high and the Q output will follow the data input as long as the enable remains high. When the enable goes low, the information (that was present at the data input at the time the transition occurred) is retained at the Q output until the enable is permitted to go high.

The '75 and 'LS75 feature complementary Q and $\overline{Q}$ outputs from a 4-bit latch, and are available in various 16-pin packages. For higher component density applications, the '77 and 'LS77 4-bit latches are available in 14-pin flat packages.

These circuits are completely compatible with all popular TTL families. All inputs are diode-clamped to minimize transmission-line effects and simplify system design. Series 54 and 54LS devices are characterized for operation over the full military temperature range of −55°C to 125°C; Series 74, and 74LS devices are characterized for operation from 0°C to 70°C.

logic symbols†

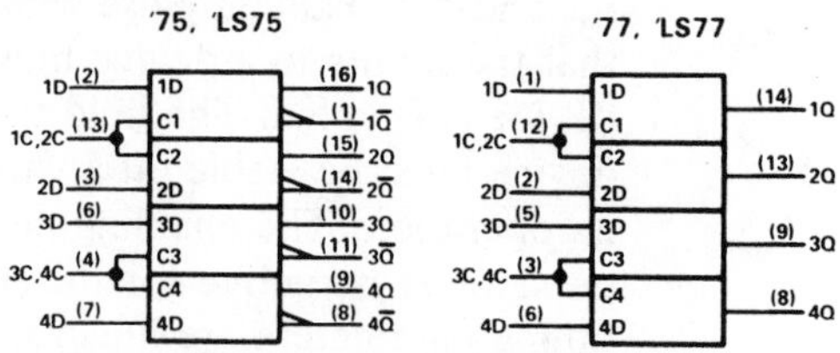

†These symbols are in accordance with ANSI/IEEE Std 91-1984 and IEC Publication 617-12.

absolute maximum ratings over operating free-air temperature range (unless otherwise noted)

Supply voltage, V_{CC} (See Note 1)	7 V
Input voltage: '75, '77	5.5 V
'LS75, 'LS77	7 V
Interemitter voltage (see Note 2)	5.5 V
Operating free-air temperature range: SN54'	−55°C to 125°C
SN74'	0° C to 70°C
Storage temperature range	−65°C to 150°C

NOTES: 1. Voltage values are with respect to network ground terminal.
2. This is the voltage between two emitters of a multiple-emitter input transistor and is not applicable to the 'LS75 and 'LS77.

FIGURE 8-16 74LS75 Four-Bit Latch Specifications (Courtesy of Texas Instruments.)

SN5475, SN5477, SN54LS75, SN54LS77, SN7475, SN74LS75 4-BIT BISTABLE LATCHES

PARAMETER MEASUREMENT INFORMATION

switching characteristics†

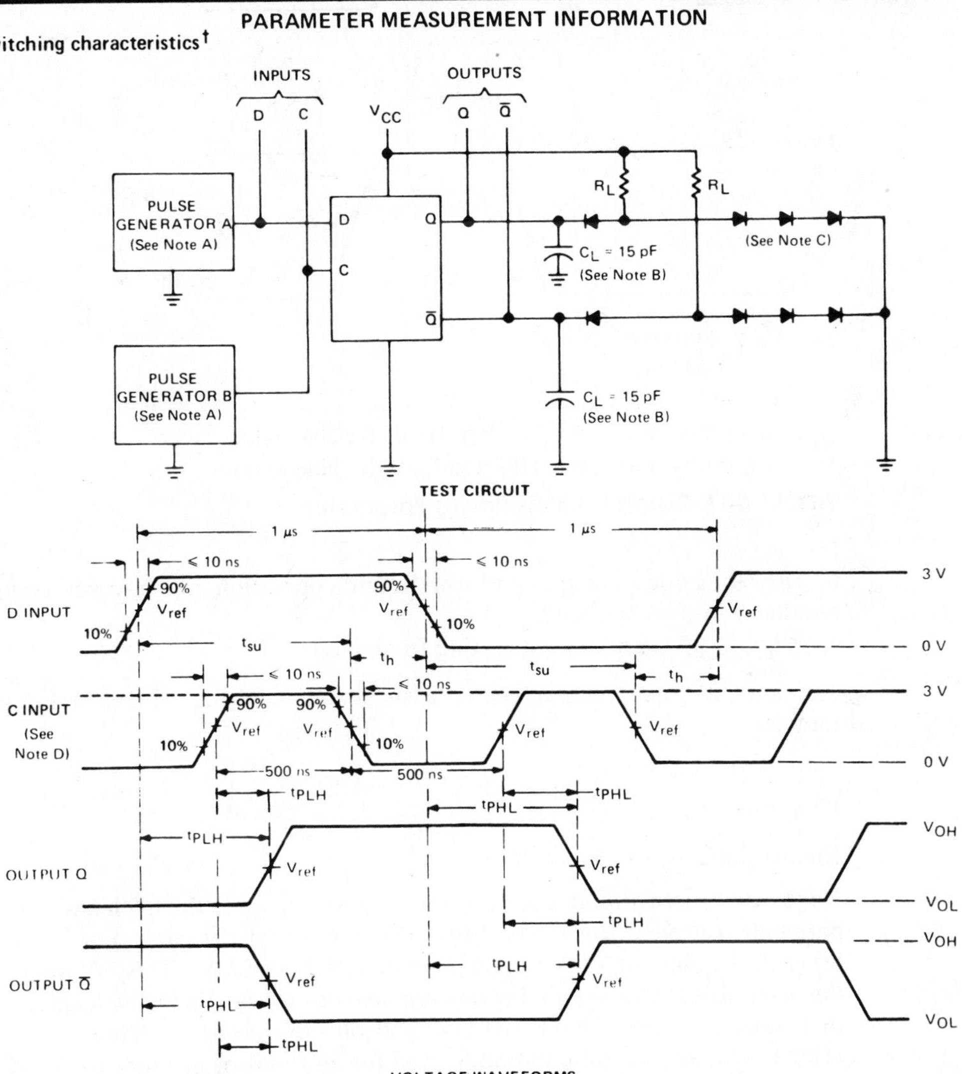

†Complementary Q outputs are on the '75 and 'LS75 only.

NOTES: A. The pulse generators have the following characteristics: $Z_{out} \approx 50\ \Omega$; for pulse generator A, PRR ≤ 500 kHz; for pulse generator B, PRR ≤ 1 MHz. Positions of D and C input pulses are varied with respect to each other to verify setup times.

B. C_L includes probe and jig capacitance.

C. All diodes are 1N3064 or equivalent.

D. When measuring propagation delay times from the D input, the corresponding C input must be held high.

E. For '75 and '77, V_{ref} = 1.5 V; for 'LS75 and 'LS77, V_{ref} = 1.3 V.

FIGURE 8-16 (*continued*)

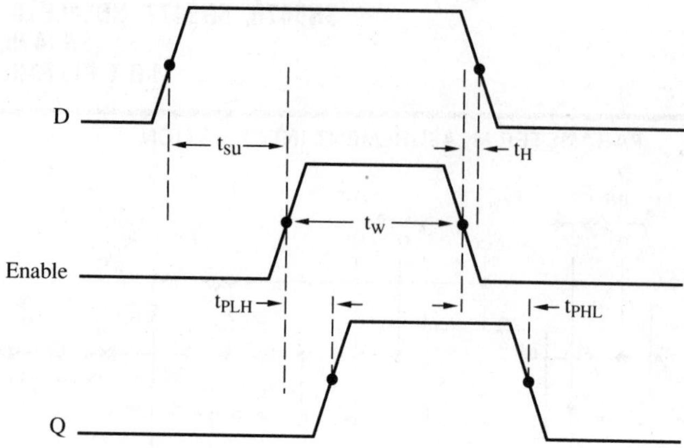

t_{su} = setup time
t_H = hold time
t_w = pulse width (Enable)
t_{PLH} = propagation delay LOW to HIGH (Enable to Q)
t_{PHL} = propagation delay HIGH to LOW (Enable to Q)

FIGURE 8-17 Gated D Latch Timing Parameters

b. How long does it take to perform the latch operation, and how soon could another 8 bits be latched?
c. What is the maximum operating frequency?

Solution: (a) First, refer to the data sheets and find the critical timing parameters:

Setup time: $t_{SU} = 20$ ns

Hold time: $t_H = 5$ ns

Enable pulse width: $t_W = 20$ ns

Next, construct a timing diagram, showing the inputs to the latch and timing parameters needed to construct the enable input for the latch. For this and other timing diagrams, the inputs may be HIGH or LOW. This is shown on the same waveform in a timing diagram as two overlapping waveforms, one that switches from HIGH to LOW and one that switches from LOW to HIGH. This shorthand notation is used for all types of memory timing diagrams. The timing diagram is shown in Figure 8-18. (b) The fastest that the device can be clocked is the combination of the minimum data setup time, the minimum enable pulse width, and the minimum hold time. The time it takes to complete one device operation (in this case, latch 1 bit) is known as the **cycle time**. For the 74LS75,

$$t_{cycle} = t_{SU} + t_w + t_H$$

$$t_{cycle(min)} = 20 \text{ ns} + 20 \text{ ns} + 5 \text{ ns} = 45 \text{ ns}$$

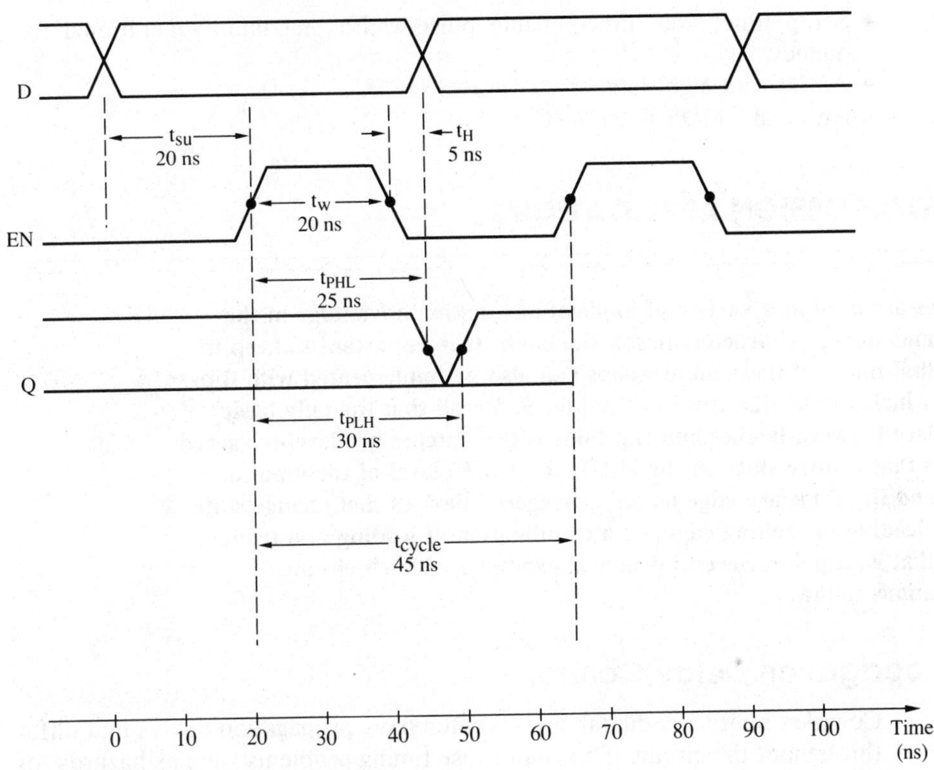

FIGURE 8-18 74LS75 Timing Diagram

(c) The maximum operating frequency, f_{max}, is the reciprocal of the minimum cycle time. In this example, $f_{max} = \frac{1}{45}$ ns $= 22.2$ MHz.

Some IC manufacturers list the maximum operating frequency, but this IC manufacturer did not. It is therefore important to be able to perform these calculations as a digital circuit designer. ■

IC manufacturers typically integrate the latch function into other MSI logic devices, such as shift registers, decoders, demultiplexers, encoders, and multiplexers. The 74HC237, for example, is a 3-to-8 decoder with address latches. The three address inputs are controlled by a latch enable input, $\overline{LE}$. Data that is input to the address lines is latched when $\overline{LE}$ is at a logic-LOW. This eliminates the need for an additional IC to latch the address lines before they are input to the decoder.

Section Self-Test

1. What are four critical latch timing parameters?
2. What is an octal latch IC?
3. What is a 74HCT373?

ANSWERS

- Setup time, hold time, enable pulse width, maximum operational frequency
- An IC with eight latches
- An octal CMOS D latch IC

8-5 LATCH DESIGN APPLICATIONS

Latches are used in a variety of applications, taking advantage of the delay and storage characteristics of the latch. It is important to keep in mind that many of these applications can also be implemented with flip-flops, which will be discussed in Chapter 9. Recall that the only basic difference between latches and flip-flops is that latches are level-triggered devices that change state on the HIGH (or LOW) level of the input or clock and flip-flops are edge or pulse-triggered devices that change state on the leading or trailing edge, or a combination of leading and trailing edge, that is, a pulse. Several practical examples of latch circuit applications follow.

8.5.1 Propagation Delay Control

Complex multilevel digital circuits often have propagation delays that differ throughout the circuit. This may cause timing problems such as hazards, or it may make examining multiple bits at the same time difficult. In addition, it is often useful to be able to control when a signal or binary data propagates through a circuit.

Several design choices are available. Individual gates can be added to a circuit to add small incremental propagation delays, or special programmable delay ICs can be used. A nongated latch can add a fixed amount of delay, dependent on the propagation delay of the latch itself, or a gated latch can be used as a programmable delay by customizing the enable input.

■ EXAMPLE 8-9 Time Delay Application Design

Problem: A digital circuit designer wants to add a propagation delay of approximately 300 ns to 1 bit of a circuit and .5 μs of delay to another bit of a circuit. In addition, the 300 ns bit needs to be inverted. Design a CMOS delay circuit to accomplish this.

Solution: A 74HC75 4-bit D latch can be used to construct the delay circuit and bit inversion since both true and complement outputs are available.

Using the specification data at 25°C we find that the enable pulse width minimum is 16 ns, the minimum setup time is 12 ns, and the minimum hold time is 3 ns. For the 74HC75, input 1C, 2C is the active-HIGH enable that controls latches 1 and 2, and input 3C, 4C is the active-HIGH enable that controls latches 3 and 4. Use latch data input 1D and enable input 1C, 2C for the 300 ns delay, with $1\overline{Q}$ as the output, and use latch data input 3D and enable input 3C, 4C for the .5 μs delay. The waveforms are shown in Figure 8-19.

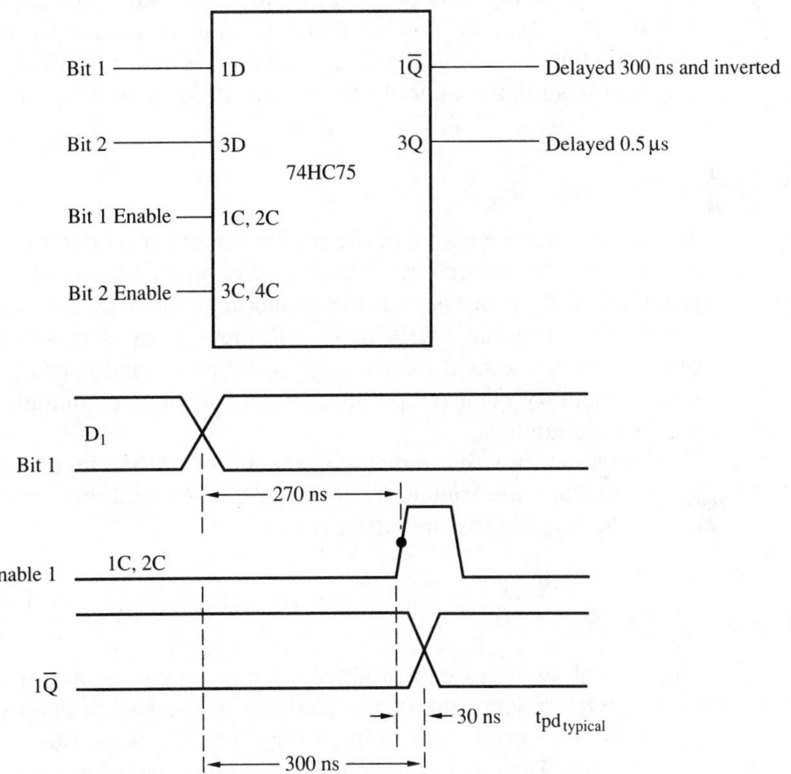

Waveforms for the 0.5 μs delay would be the same, but with 0.5 μs from data in to the 3Q output.

FIGURE 8-19 Latch Propagation Control ■

The previous example illustrates a time delay. If a smaller delay is needed, a nonclocked circuit can be constructed by always enabling the latch enable input and using the inherent propagation delay of the latch. A 7475 would produce a typical delay of 15 ns when always enabled.

■ EXAMPLE 8-10 Time Delay Analysis

Problem: How much delay would a standard TTL 5477 provide if the four latches were wired together serially with all the latches always enabled?

Solution: Each latch has an average typical propagation delay of 15 ns and an average maximum propagation delay of 28 ns from input D to output Q. Thus, the delay provided by the four D latches in series could range from a typical value of 60 ns (4 × 15 ns) to a maximum of 112 ns (4 × 28 ns). The design would be much simpler to implement due to its forced asynchronous operation, but the delay variation is over 90%. This type of circuit is good for adding a noncritical amount of delay to a circuit. ■

8.5.2 Temporary Storage

Temporary storage is one of the primary uses for a latch in digital circuitry. Address bits or other binary codes often must be stored until needed by circuitry. Microprocessors are complex logic devices that sequentially process digital information. While a microprocessor is processing one set of binary codes, the next binary code to be processed is often stored in temporary memory. The temporary memory devices commonly used in these designs are latches.

Individual bits that indicate the result of arithmetic or logic operations, known as **flags**, are frequently stored in latches until the microprocessor can check the flag for the operation result.

8.5.3 Switch Debounce

Mechanical switches can produce what is known as a voltage **bounce** due to the physical vibration of the contacts of the switch upon closure. These vibrations can produce a voltage logic bounce for up to several hundred milliseconds. Digital circuitry, which switches in nanoseconds, is susceptible to the logic bounce and may cause a circuit to change state unintentionally.

Figure 8-20 illustrates an $\overline{S}$-$\overline{R}$ latch used to eliminate the effects of switch bounce. This type of circuit is known as a **switch debounce** circuit. Examination of the NAND gate cross-coupled latch debounce circuit illustrates that when the switch is open, the $\overline{S}$ and $\overline{R}$ inputs are held HIGH with pull-up resistors. This is the hold state of the latch, and no transition of the output will take place. When the switch is in either of the other positions, the latch is either set or reset on the first logic transition caused by the switch and any additional bounce does not change the output Q since the latch is held in the set or reset mode. If the pull-up resistors were not used, the latch

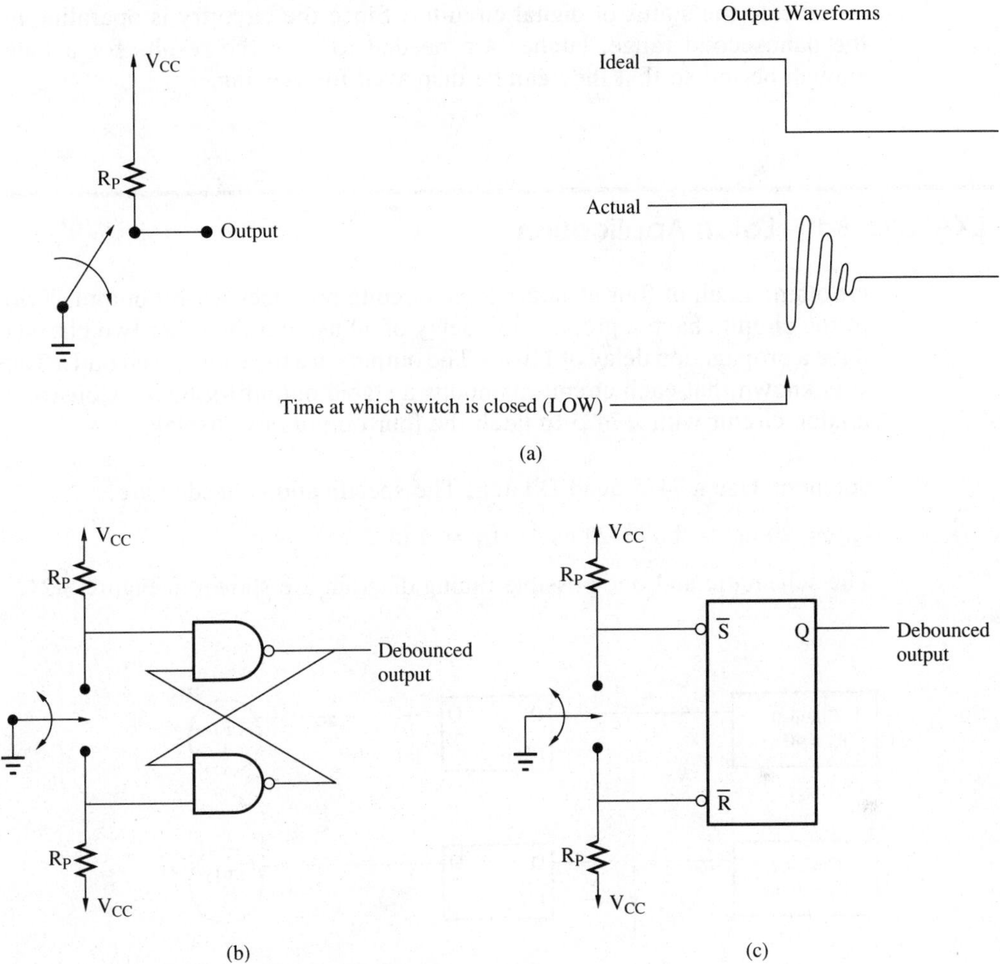

FIGURE 8-20 Switch Contact Debounce

would not reliably eliminate contact bounce since the inputs would only float to a HIGH voltage that was around 2.4 volts, making the gates susceptible to contact noise. The pull-up resistors ensure that the inputs are held to a strong 5 volt logic HIGH, vastly improving noise immunity and totally eliminating contact bounce.

8.5.4 Display Control

Another useful application of a latch is to store the results of several circuits for the purpose of display. LEDs or some other type of display can be used to indicate the status of digital circuitry. Since the circuitry is operating in the nanosecond range, latches are needed to save the results for a long enough period so that they can be displayed for viewing.

■ EXAMPLE 8-11 Latch Application

Problem: Each of four separate logic circuits produces a 1-bit output. Two of the circuits have a propagation delay of 40 ns, and the other two circuits have a propagation delay of 120 ns. The outputs are to be displayed on LEDs. It is known that each circuit maintains a stable output for 60 ns. Construct a latch circuit with a 7475 to latch the four outputs for display.

Solution: Use a 7475 quad D latch. The specifications needed are:

$t_{SU} = 20$ ns $\quad t_W = 20$ ns $\quad t_H = 5$ ns

The schematic and one possible timing diagram are shown in Figure 8-21.

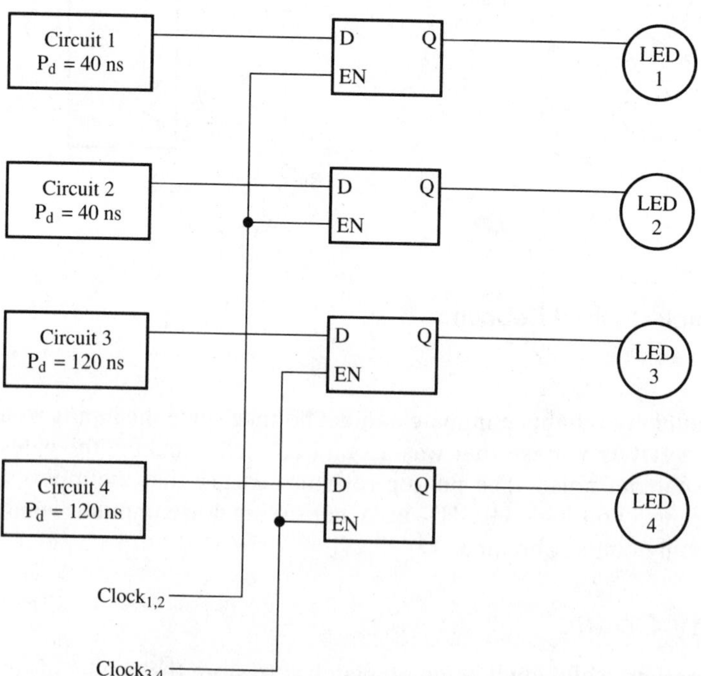

FIGURE 8-21 Output Delay Control Timing Diagram and Schematic

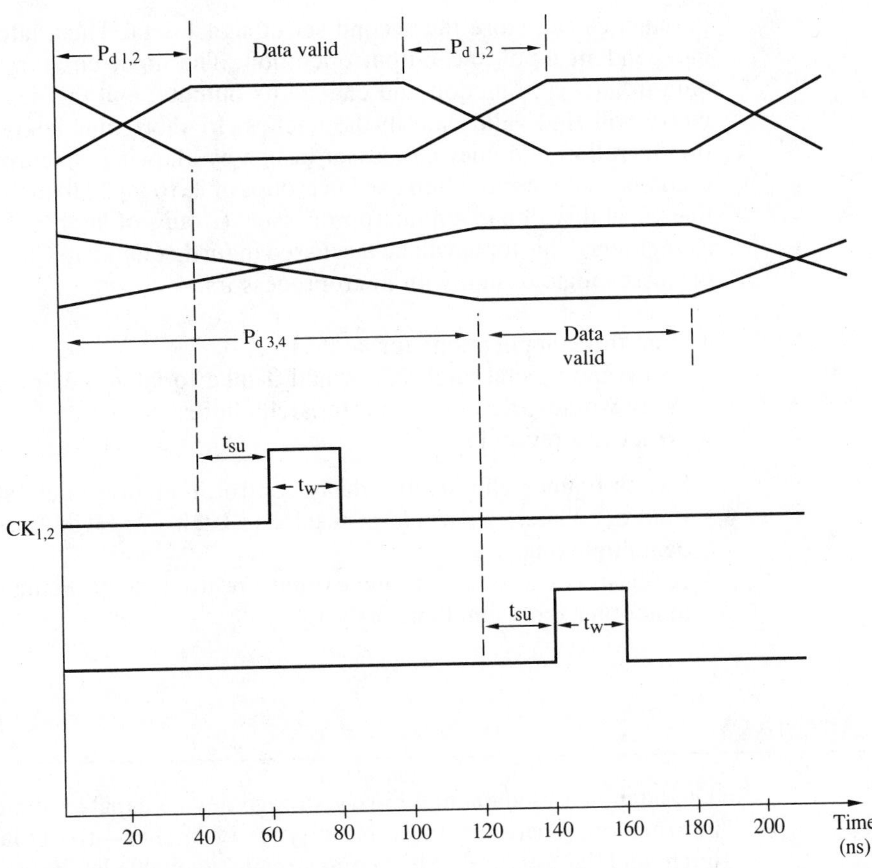

8.5.5 Demultiplexing

Microprocessors, LSI memory devices, and other LSI and VLSI logic devices often have input or output pins that are used for more than one signal. The use of a device pin for more than one signal is known as **multiplexing**. Multiplexing reduces the number of pins that an IC needs, which is often important, since there are standards for the number of pins an IC can have.

Several available microprocessors use pins for both address inputs and data outputs. It is common to use latches to store the address information on the multiplexed pins so that the microprocessor can use the pins for data output but still be able to find the address information now stored in latches. This is called **demultiplexing** the addresses. Latches are used to temporarily store the first set of signals, and the digital circuitry that needs this first set of signals will find valid signal data in the latches (due to the storage). Then the latches can store the second set of signal data. Thus, latches allow for independent input and output operation. The input circuitry can store its data in latches, function and change its outputs, and the next stage of circuitry will find valid data in the latches. In short, this latching speeds up the operation of a microprocessor design by allowing concurrent digital operations. Latches are often used in groups of 8, 16, or 32 to match the address line capability of a given microprocessor. Groups of latches are also known as **registers**. This topic will be discussed in further detail in Chapter 14, which discusses logic design with microprocessors.

Section Self-Test

1. List three applications for latches.
2. How many octal latch ICs would it take to latch a 32-bit address line? Why would a designer want to latch address lines?
3. What is a register?

ANSWERS

- Switch bounce elimination, delay control, temporary data storage
- Four octal latch ICs would be needed to latch a 32-bit address; for address demultiplexing
- A register is a group of latches that are used to store small amounts of temporary data simultaneously

SUMMARY

The latch is a fundamental binary storage device capable of storing 1 bit of information. There are three basic types of latches—the D latch, the S-R latch, and the $\overline{S}$-$\overline{R}$ latch. Most commercially available latches are gated, with an enable input to allow for synchronous operation.

ANALYSIS

Latches are voltage level-triggered devices. A gated latch has an enable input that may be active-HIGH or active-LOW. When the latch is enabled, the latch output will change according to the inputs. For a D latch, when the latch is enabled, the output Q will follow the input D.

Chapter 9 discusses flip-flops, which are transition or edge-triggered devices. There are flip-flops that have the same functional operation as their latch counterparts, the only difference being the method of triggering. Because of this, the terms *latch* and *flip-flop* are mistakenly interchanged in many digital texts and references.

Several important timing parameters are associated with latches and flip-flops, including setup time, hold time, propagation delay, and operating frequency.

APPLICATION AND DESIGN

Latches are used extensively in digital logic, especially in the area of microprocessor and memory design. The most common applications for latch ICs are for temporary data storage (memory), programmable delay, switch bounce elimination, and address line demultiplexing. Latches can also be utilized in a variety of display applications.

PROBLEMS

8-1 Latching Concepts—Analysis Problems

1. a. Explain the difference between device level-triggering and edge-triggering.
   b. What is the difference between a latch and a flip-flop?
2. a. Draw the standard device symbol for a synchronous and asynchronous D latch.
   b. Draw the IEEE/ANSI device symbol for a synchronous and asynchronous D latch.
3. Explain the transparent mode of latch operation.

8-2 D Latches—Analysis Problems

4. Given the waveforms shown in Figure 8-22 for a D latch with an initial LOW output ($Q_0 = 0$), find the output Q if the latch is:
   (a) synchronous (b) asynchronous

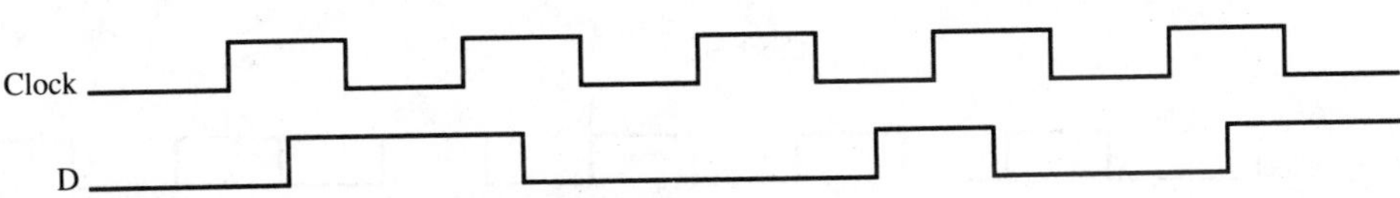

FIGURE 8-22 Problem 8-4 Waveforms

5. Compare the parameters for a 7475 and a 74HCT75. Find the minimum, maximum, and typical values for each parameter as they apply:
   (a) P_{DLH} (b) P_{DHL} (c) t_W (d) t_H (e) t_{su}
   (f) I_{CC} (g) t_{PLH}(D to Q) (h) t_{PHL}(D to Q)

*6. Determine the output Q for the latch and waveforms shown in Figure 8-23. $Q_0 = 1$.

---

* *See* Answers to Selected Problems.

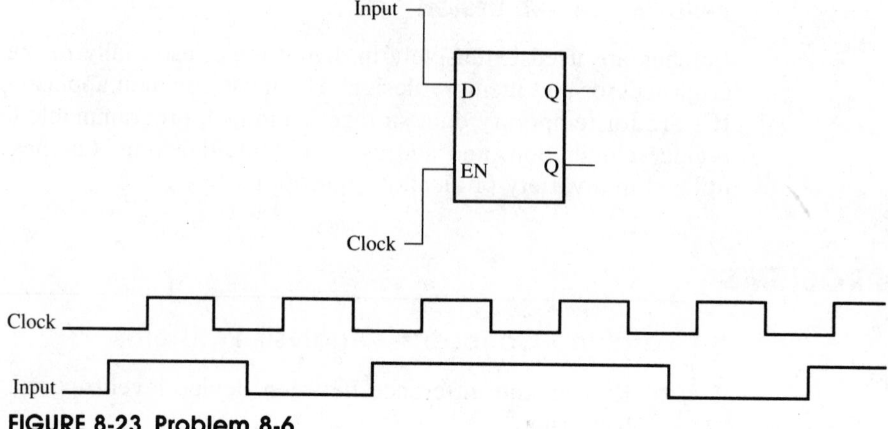

FIGURE 8-23 Problem 8-6

7. Determine the output Q for the latch and waveforms shown in Figure 8-24.

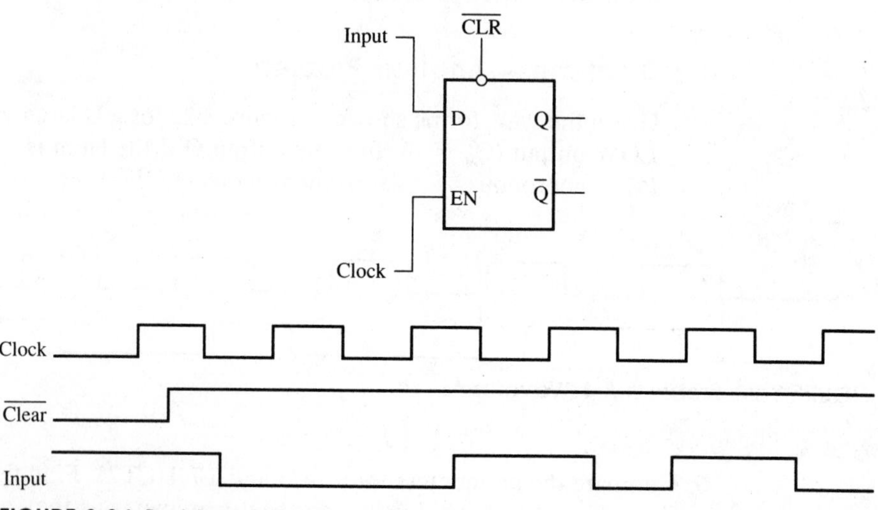

FIGURE 8-24 Problem 8-7

8-3 S-R and $\overline{S}$-$\overline{R}$ Latches—Analysis Problems

8. A gated S-R latch is initially set. Find Q and $\overline{Q}$ given the waveform in Figure 8-25.

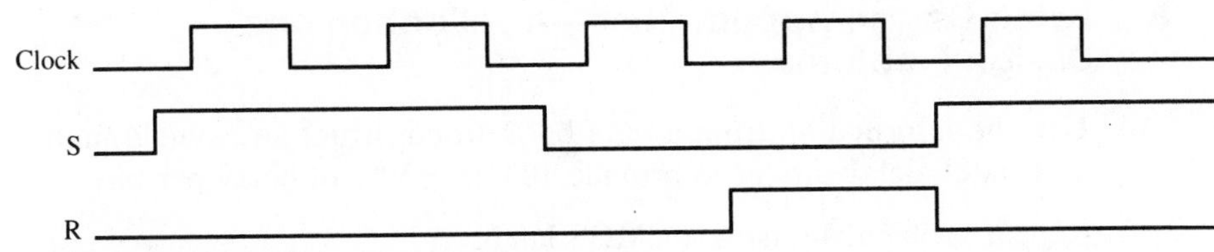

FIGURE 8-25 Problem 8-8 Waveforms

9. For a gated $\overline{S}$-$\overline{R}$ latch, the output Q is shown in Figure 8-26. Determine the inputs $\overline{S}$ and $\overline{R}$ needed to produce Q.

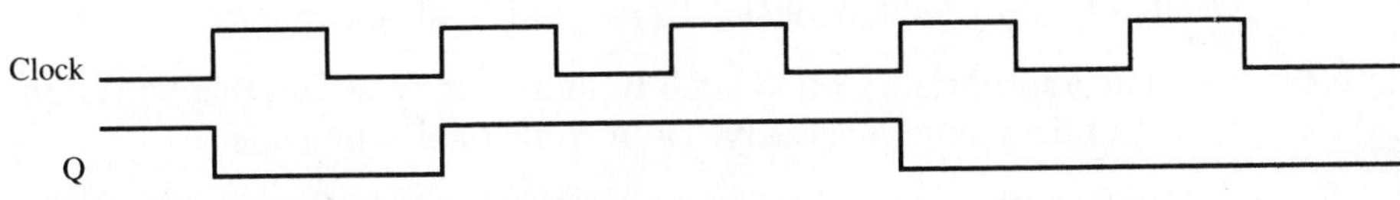

FIGURE 8-26 Problem 8-9 Waveform

10. For a gated S-R latch, the output $\overline{Q}$ is shown. Determine the inputs S and R needed to produce $\overline{Q}$, as shown in Figure 8-27.

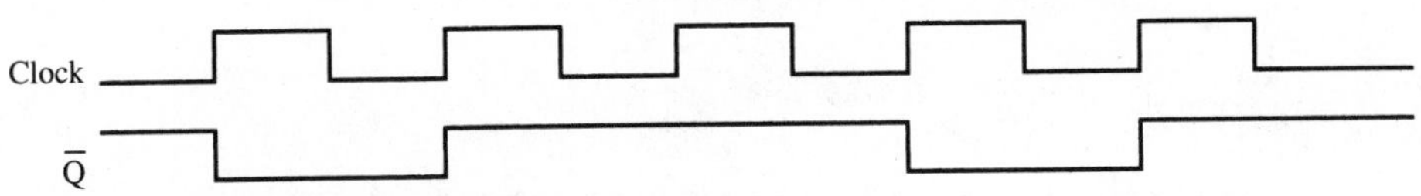

FIGURE 8-27 Problem 8-10 Waveform

11. Using the logic gate circuit for a gated $\overline{S}$-$\overline{R}$ latch, show why a LOW placed on both inputs produces an unstable (invalid) output. Analyze at least four changes in the output Q.

8-4 IC Latches—Analysis Problems

*12. a. Draw the internal logic circuitry for one latch of a 74LS75 IC as shown in the data book.
b. Use the function table in the data book to analyze all possible input combinations. Draw a truth table that shows the outputs of each gate in the latch circuit.

13. Use the typical timing parameters for a 74LS75, and draw the input D and output Q waveforms. Show t_{PLH}, t_{PHL}, t_{SU}, and t_H.

8-5 Latch Design Applications—Application and Design Problems

14. Use the information from a data book to construct an asynchronous TTL latch delay circuit to provide 100 ns ±30% of delay per bit.

15. Repeat Problem 14 using a CMOS latch.

*16. Use the information from a data book to construct a synchronous TTL latch delay circuit to provide 100 ns ±15% of delay per bit. Assume the input data is valid for a time interval greater than the 100 ns delay.

17. Repeat Problem 16 using a CMOS latch.

18. Select an appropriate TTL latch IC and design a circuit that will latch 32 bits of data simultaneously. Draw your final schematic.

19. Select an appropriate CMOS latch IC and design a circuit that will latch 32 bits of data simultaneously. Draw your final schematic.

20. a. Calculate the power dissipation for the circuit designed in Problems 18 and 19.
    b. How many times more power does the TTL design require than the CMOS design?

21. Design a 4-bit latch circuit that will latch a 4-bit input everytime a pushbutton is pressed. This is an example of a basic sampling circuit. (*Hint:* use a one-shot as an enable.)

TABLE 8-3

	Latch 1	Latch 2	Latch 3	Latch 4
Initial	0	0	0	1
After 1 s	0	0	1	0
After 2 s	0	1	0	0
After 3 s	1	0	0	0

Troubleshooting Problems

*22. A 74LS75 has two latches operating correctly and two latches that always have a LOW output. The two latches that are not functional are latches 3 and 4. What could be one of the problems with the IC wiring or pin connections causing the difficulty.

23. a. A 74116 has outputs that sometimes appear to be "stuck" at a LOW logic output. However, sometimes the latches function correctly. The device has an active-LOW clear that is unconnected. Could this cause the problem? Explain.
    b. How would you fix the problem?

*24. A student decides to set the function generator output at 100 KHz to produce a square wave as input to a D latch. The student wants to observe the Q output of the latch on the oscilloscope, but he only sees "noise," and the scope will not trigger. All the latch wiring and power is checked and found to be correct. The latch is also enabled.

The student then takes a switch that operates from 0 to 5 volts as the D input, and the latch also works correctly. He also checks the function generator output on the scope, and it is generating a square wave at 100 KHz. Why doesn't the latch work with the function generator input? (*Hint:* Something hasn't been checked pertaining to the function generator output.)

Chapter 9

Flip-Flops

Upon completing and mastering the material in this chapter, you should be able to perform the following functions in the areas of analysis, application, and design of flip-flop devices:

ANALYSIS

1. Analyze D, S-R, $\overline{S}$-$\overline{R}$, and J-K flip-flops.
2. Differentiate between flip-flop and latch operation.
3. Understand master-slave flip-flop operation.
4. Interpret flip-flop data book timing parameters.
5. Troubleshoot flip-flop devices.

APPLICATION AND DESIGN

6. Select appropriate flip-flop ICs for an application.
7. Use flip-flops for temporary data storage.
8. Design frequency divider circuits.
9. Understand how flip-flops are applied as the basic digital block of counter circuits.

This chapter introduces the operation, analysis, and application of D, J-K, and S-R flip-flops. A flip-flop is a synchronous edge-triggered bistable memory element. A one bit flip-flop can store one bit of data, either a binary one or a binary zero. A flip-flop is synchronous since its output is timing dependent.

Flip-flops are widely used in digital logic design. They are the basic logic element of most sequential logic circuits, making use of their memory capability. Digital counters and shift registers rely on the operation and storage characteristics of the flip-flop.

9-1 FLIP-FLOP OPERATION

Flip-flops are bistable storage devices. Each flip-flop is capable of storing 1 bit of data. Flip-flops differ from latches in the method of triggering employed in the operation of the device. Several different types of triggering are used for the various types of flip-flop ICs available. Flip-flops have timing dependent synchronous inputs and timing independent asynchronous inputs.

9.1.1 Flip-Flop Triggering

A flip-flop changes its output state based on its data inputs and the **transition of the clock input**. Devices that change state based on the transition of an input timing waveform are known as **edge-triggered** devices. The timing input waveform is commonly referred to as the **clock**, abbreviated **CLK**.

Recall from Chapter 8 that a latch, also a bistable memory element, is **level-triggered**. Thus, the major difference between a latch and a flip-flop is the method of triggering. A latch is level-triggered based on the input voltage on the EN (enable) input. A flip-flop is edge-triggered based on the timing input waveform transition from a LOW to a HIGH, or HIGH to a LOW.

9.1.2 Types of Edge-Triggering

Synchronous digital devices rely on a timing input, the clock, to control when the device recognizes the signals placed on the data inputs and responds accordingly. One way of characterizing flip-flops is according to the type of edge-triggering used to operate the device. There are three basic types of edge-triggering employed to control the function of a flip-flop. The type of edge-triggering is denoted on the flip-flop symbol, as shown for J-K flip-flops (discussed later) in Figure 9-1.

Leading edge-triggered flip-flops, also known as **positive edge-triggered** flip-flops, respond to the present input or inputs when the clock signal to the device makes a transition from a logic LOW to a logic HIGH.

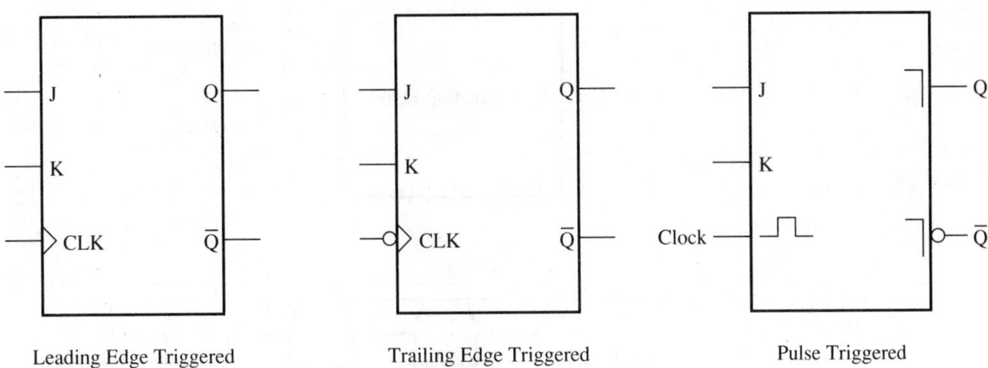

FIGURE 9-1 Edge-Triggered Clock Indicator Symbols

Trailing edge-triggered flip-flops, also known as **negative edge-triggered** flip-flops, respond to the present input or inputs when the clock signal to the device makes a transition from a logic HIGH to a logic LOW.

Pulse-triggered flip-flops, also known as **master-slave** flip-flops, respond to the present input or inputs when the clock signal to the device makes a pulse transition from a logic LOW to a logic HIGH, and back to a logic LOW.

The type of device triggering for a given device can also be indicated in a truth table. If a device is leading edge-triggered, the truth table for the operation of the device will have an upward arrow placed in the CLK column of the table. If a device is trailing edge-triggered, the CLK column will have a downward arrow. If the device triggering is pulse-triggered, a small pulse will be shown in the CLK column. Sample truth tables for each type triggering are also shown in Figure 9-1.

Leading, trailing, and pulse-triggered flip-flop operation is illustrated in Figure 9-2 for a flip-flop that changes state (toggles) at each clock trigger. Note that the output Q for the trailing edge- and pulse-triggered flip-flops are the same. Unless the flip-flop input changes during the active (HIGH) clock, the trailing edge and master-slave flip-flop outputs will be identical. Cases when this is not true will be discussed in the section on master-slave flip-flops.

9.1.3 Clock Synchronization

Synchronous operation is the control of the time that devices can change their output state through the use of an input clock signal. Any pulse waveform used to control timing in a digital circuit is referred to as the circuit clock.

Multiple devices can be connected to the same clock. If all of the devices are of the same trigger type, leading edge, for example, the devices will

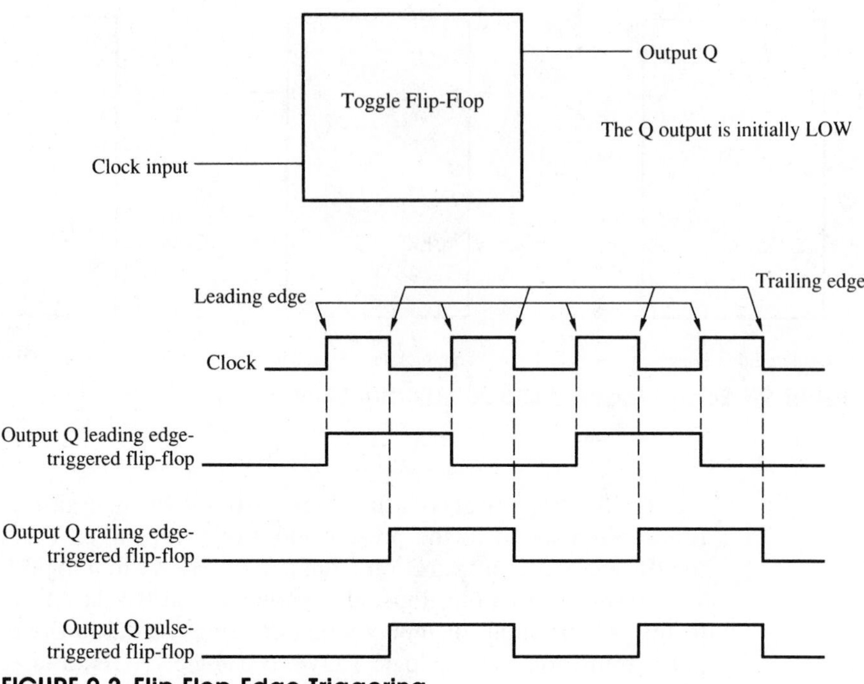

FIGURE 9-2 Flip-Flop Edge-Triggering

change state in a manner that can be reliably predicted. This predictable state transition forms the basis of all sequential circuit analysis needed to predict circuit operation. Synchronized circuits are also easier to troubleshoot than asynchronous circuits since the state transitions occur only at specific points in time.

9.1.4 Asynchronous Inputs

IC flip-flops often have inputs that can force the output of the flip-flop to a desired state independent of the clock and data inputs. These inputs are **asynchronous**. An active-LOW **preset**, $\overline{\textbf{PRE}}$, forces the output to a HIGH. An active-LOW **clear**, $\overline{\textbf{CLR}}$, forces the output to a LOW. If a $\overline{\text{CLR}}$ input is applied to a flip-flop, the flip-flop output will immediately become 0, independent of the other data and clock inputs. A $\overline{\text{PRE}}$ immediately forces the flip-flop output to 1.

Most flip-flop preset and clear inputs are active-LOW, but some special purpose devices may have active-HIGH preset and clear inputs. Always check the data book specification truth table for the device in use to determine the triggering and asynchronous input operation.

Section Self-Test

1. An upward arrow indicates leading edge-triggering.
2. If a $\overline{PRE}$ input on a flip-flop is HIGH, the flip-flop output will be forced to a HIGH.
3. Pulse-triggered flip-flops are also called master-slave flip-flops.

ANSWERS • False • True • True

9-2 D FLIP-FLOP

D flip-flops are widely used in digital logic designs. A D flip-flop stores one bit of information clocked into the flip-flop.

9.2.1 D Flip-Flop Operation

A **D flip-flop**, also known as a **delay** or **data flip-flop**, has one data input, D, a clock input, and a true output, Q. Some D flip-flops also have a complement output, $\overline{Q}$. The standard and IEEE symbol for a D flip-flop are shown in Figure 9-3.

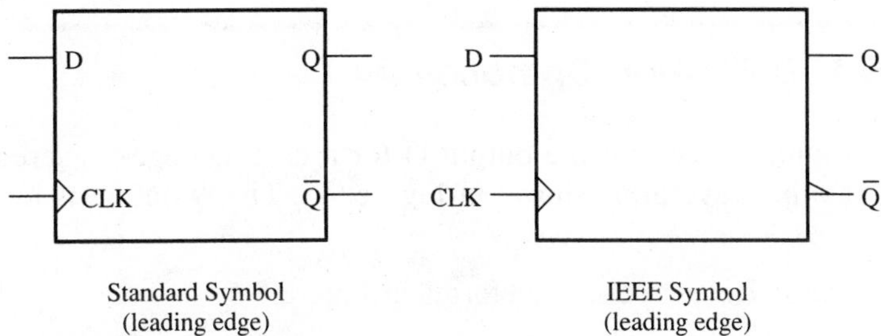

FIGURE 9-3 D Flip-Flop Symbols

D flip-flops have the ability to store 1 bit of data. The data bit that is placed on the D input is stored in the flip-flop when the clock trigger occurs. The data stored in the flip-flop will be present at the Q output. Thus, the output Q equals the value of the data stored in the D flip-flop. If the logic level on the D input changes, the flip-flop value will change to the logic level on the input D at the clock trigger. Figure 9-4 illustrates the operation of a leading edge-triggered D flip-flop. Note that the only time the output Q can change state is on the leading edge of the clock pulse. Most of the standard D flip-flops are leading edge-triggered.

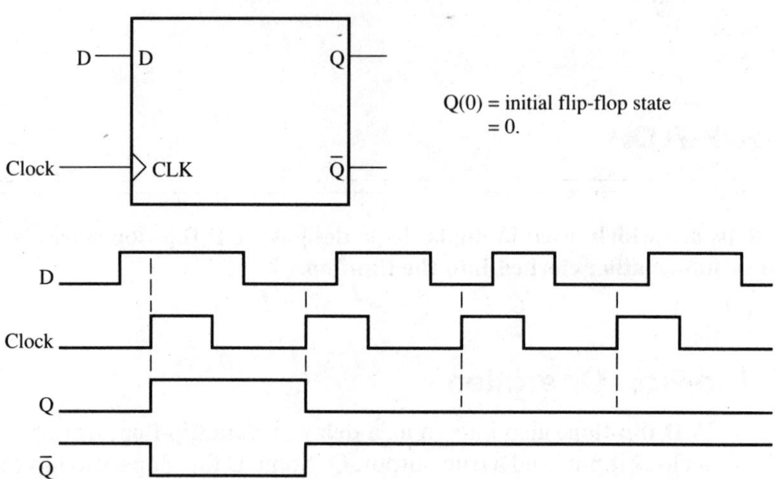

FIGURE 9-4 Leading Edge-Triggered D Flip-Flop

■ EXAMPLE 9-1 D Flip-Flop Operation

Problem: Determine the output Q for a leading edge-triggered D flip-flop, given the waveforms shown in Figure 9-5. The Q output is initially LOW.

Solution: Refer to the waveforms in Figure 9-5.

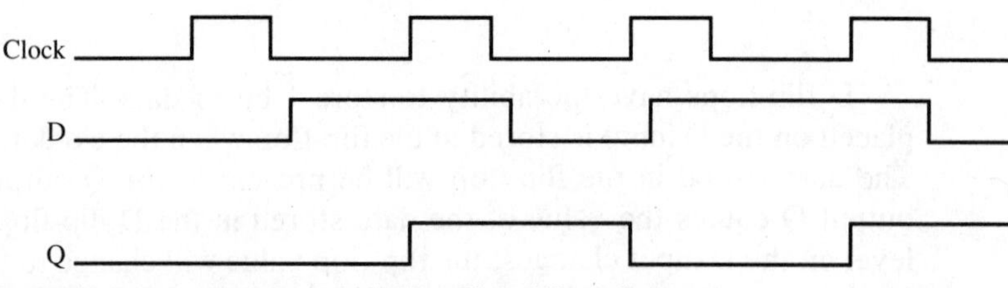

FIGURE 9-5 Example 9-1 D Flip-Flop Waveforms ■

9.2.2 D Flip-Flop Integrated Circuits

D flip-flops are available in ICs in several different types of configurations. These include dual, 4, 6, 8, 9, and 10 flip-flop ICs, and D flip-flops with asynchronous preset and clear inputs. Some D flip-flops are available with tristate outputs for bus applications. (Tristate outputs are explained in Chapter 15.)

Table 9-1 lists the D flip-flop ICs available and their respective features. The type indicates the IC number that may be available in several TTL or CMOS subfamilies of logic. The only difference between several of the ICs listed in the table is the availability of an **output enable (OE)** instead of a clear input.

TABLE 9-1 D Flip-Flop Integrated Circuits

Number	Flip-Flop Type	Outputs	Features
'74	Dual D	$\overline{Q}$, Q	Preset, Clear
'174	Hex D	Q	Clear
'171/'175	Quad D	$\overline{Q}$, Q	Clear
'273	Octal D	Q	Clear
'374/'377	Octal D	Q	Output enable
'378	Hex D	Q	Output enable
'379	Quad D	$\overline{Q}$, Q	Output enable

■ EXAMPLE 9-2 Flip-Flop Application

Problem: Construct a one IC digital TTL flip-flop circuit that can store a byte of data on the leading edge of a timing clock with an asynchronous clear input.

Solution: Refer to Table 9-1 or a TTL data book to select an appropriate octal latch with a clear function. One appropriate IC is the 74LS273. The circuit is shown in Figure 9-6.

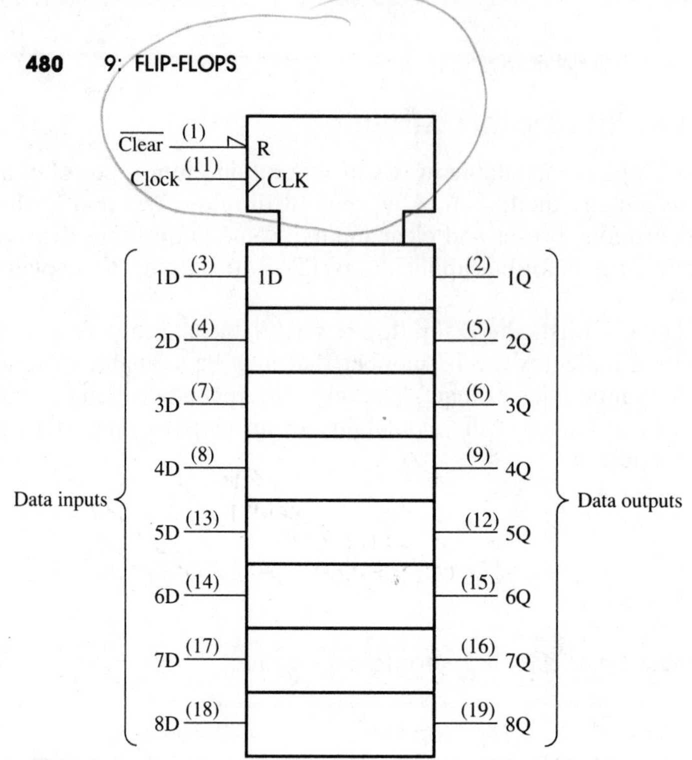

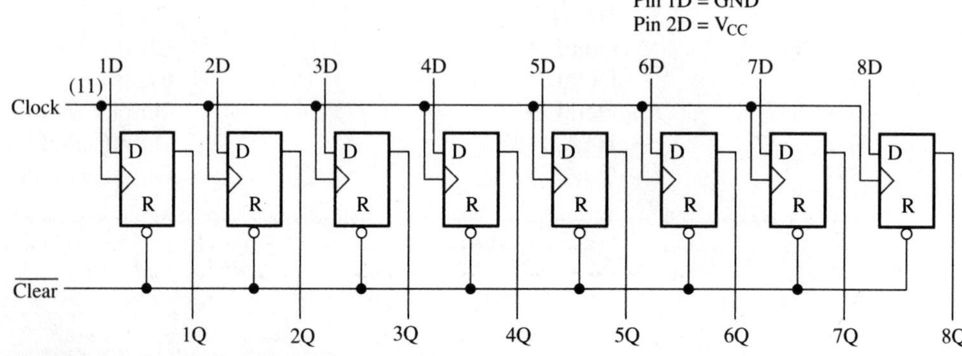

FIGURE 9-6 74LS273 Flip-Flop Circuit ■

Section Self-Test

1. Eight bits of data can be stored with a 74174.
2. Most of the TTL D latches commercially available are negative edge-triggered.
3. A D flip-flop will store data even if the data input and clock signals are removed.

ANSWERS (Not necessarily in the order of the questions)

- False • True • False

9-3 S-R AND $\overline{S}$-$\overline{R}$ FLIP-FLOPS

S-R flip-flops have three stable states and one unstable or invalid state. Their use in discrete logic designs has been replaced by the J-K flip-flop, but it is important to understand the operation of the S-R flip-flop, as some integrated circuit logic will use an S-R flip-flop as a functional block within a larger logic system.

9.3.1 S-R Flip-Flop Operation

An **S-R flip-flop**, also known as a **set-reset flip-flop**, has two state control inputs, S and R, one clock input, a true output, Q, and a complement output $\overline{Q}$. If the S-R flip-flop has active-LOW inputs, it is known as an $\overline{S}$-$\overline{R}$ flip-flop. The symbols and truth tables for S-R and $\overline{S}$-$\overline{R}$ flip-flops are shown in Figure 9-7.

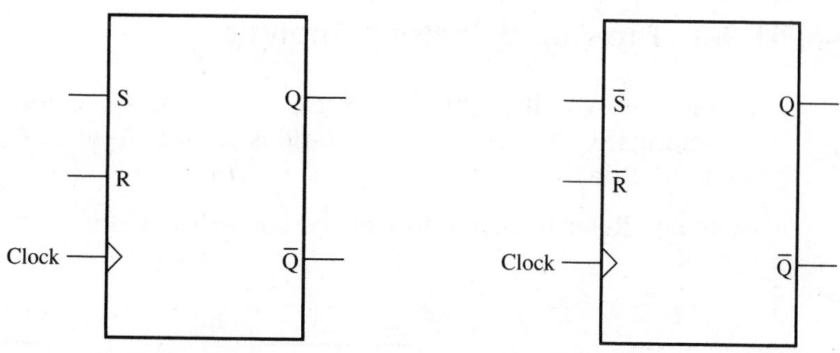

S	R	Clock	Q	Operation
0	0	X	Q_0	Hold
0	1	↑	0	Clear
1	0	↑	1	Set
1	1	↑	?	Unstable

$\overline{S}$	$\overline{R}$	Clock	Q	Operation
0	0	↑	?	Unstable
0	1	↑	1	Set
1	0	↑	0	Clear
1	1	X	Q_0	Hold

Q_0 = initial state of Q
↑ = leading edge-triggered clock
? = indeterminate
X = don't care

FIGURE 9-7 S-R and $\overline{S}$-$\overline{R}$ Flip-Flops

The **hold** operation for a flip-flop means that whatever the output of the flip-flop is in the present state, when the clock triggers the flip-flop next state output will be the same. Thus, there is no change in the output for this input condition when the device is triggered.

The **clear** operation, also known as the **reset**, means that the output of the flip-flop will change to 0—be cleared—when the clock triggers. The **set** operation for a flip-flop indicates that the output will change to 1—be set—when the clock triggers.

In addition to the hold, clear, and set operations, the S-R flip-flops have an **unstable** or **invalid state**. The invalid state results in an invalid flip-flop operation if both S-R inputs are HIGH (LOW for an active-LOW S-R). Thus, the invalid condition must be avoided by the logic designer when using S-R flip-flops. The S-R unstable state of the S-R flip-flop is explained in detail in Section 8.3. Due to the existence of an invalid state, the S-R flip-flop is seldom commercially available as an individual flip-flop IC. An S-R flip-flop can be leading edge, trailing edge, or pulse-triggered.

■ EXAMPLE 9-3 Flip-Flop Waveform Analysis

Problem: Given the input waveforms in Figure 9-8, determine the output waveforms, Q, for each of the flip-flops shown. Assume $Q_0 = 0$. Identify each flip-flop.

Solution: Refer to Figure 9-8 for the output waveforms.

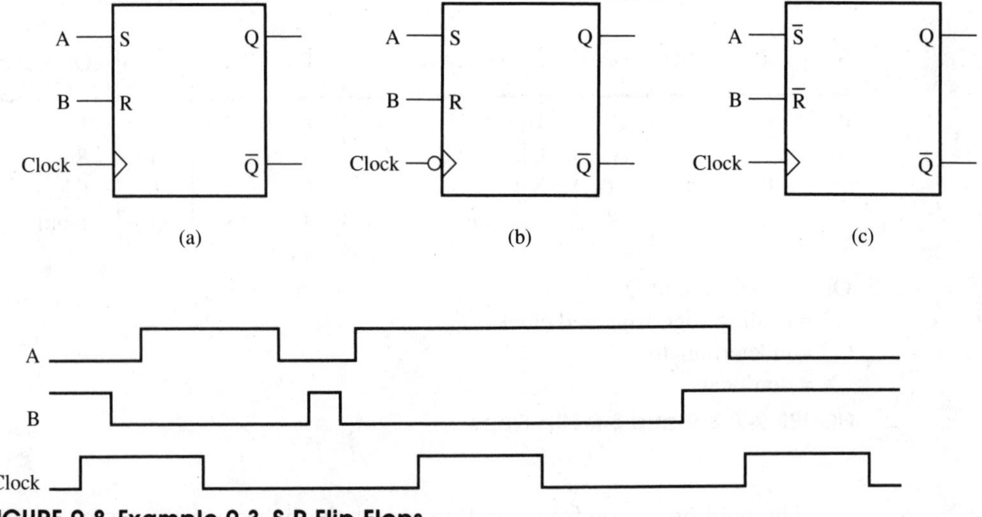

FIGURE 9-8 Example 9-3 S-R Flip-Flops

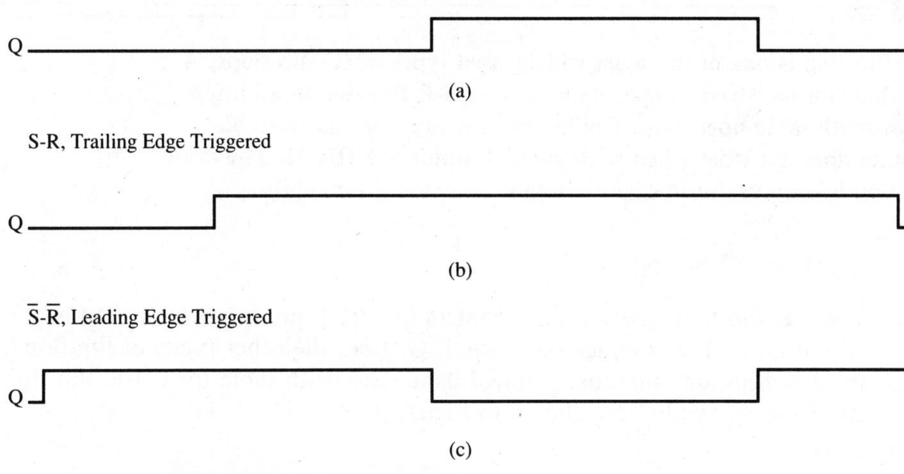

FIGURE 9-8 (*continued*) ■

9.3.2 S-R Flip-Flop Wired as a D Flip-Flop

An S-R flip-flop can be wired to operate as a D flip-flop by the addition of an inverter between the S and R inputs of the S-R flip-flop. This configuration is shown in Figure 9-9.

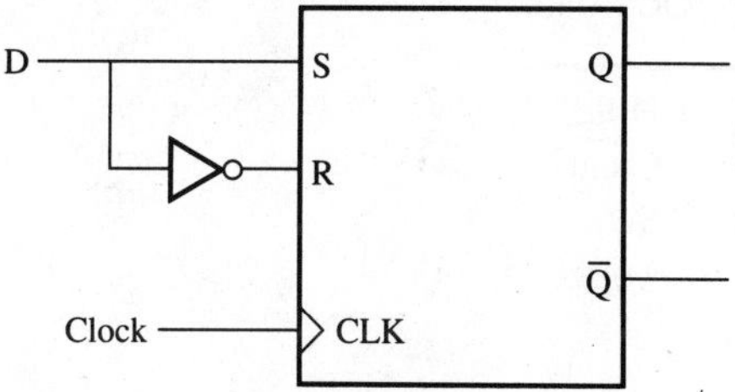

FIGURE 9-9 D Flip-Flop Using an S-R Flip-Flop

Section Self-Test

1. An S-R flip-flop has S = 0, R = 1. What is Q?
2. An S-R flip-flop has S = 1, R = 0. What is Q?
3. An $\overline{S}$-$\overline{R}$ flip-flop has S = 1, R = 0. What is Q?

ANSWERS (Not necessarily in the order of the questions)

• 1 • 0 • 0

9-4 J-K FLIP-FLOPS

The J-K flip-flop is one of the most widely used types of IC flip-flops. A J-K flip-flop can be wired to operate as a D or S-R flip-flop in addition to its own truth table operation. Unlike the S-R flip-flop, an unstable output state does not exist when both control inputs are HIGH. Thus, the J-K flip-flop is very useful in digital design.

9.4.1 J-K Flip-Flop Operation

The **J-K flip-flop** has two state control inputs, J and K, a clock, and a true output Q, with a complement output, $\overline{Q}$. Like the other types of flip-flops, the J-K flip-flop can store 1 bit of data. The truth table for a J-K flip-flop and its logic symbol are shown in Figure 9-10.

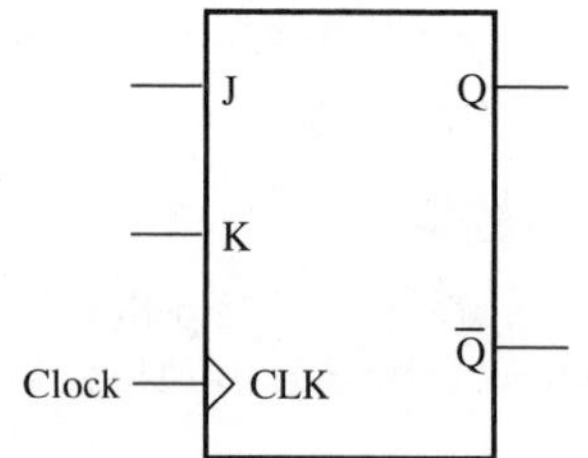

J	K	Clock	Q	Operation
0	0	↑	Q_0	Hold
0	1	↑	0	Clear
1	0	↑	1	Set
1	1	↑	$\overline{Q_0}$	Toggle

FIGURE 9-10 J-K Flip-Flop

Note that in addition to the hold, clear, and set operations, the J-K flip-flop has another operation referred to as the **toggle**. If the control inputs J and K are both HIGH, the J-K flip-flop will change state at each clock trigger. Thus, it changes or toggles between 0 and 1 at each clock trigger.

J-K flip-flops are available as leading or trailing edge-triggered devices. The 74LS76, shown in Figure 9-11, is a dual trailing edge-triggered J-K flip-flop. The 74LS76 has asynchronous preset and clear inputs for each flip-flop.

Most pulse-triggered devices (master-slave) are J-K devices. Before discussing the operation of the master-slave J-K flip-flop, it is necessary to examine the important timing parameters of flip-flops.

SN5476, SN54LS76A, SN7476, SN74LS76A DUAL J-K FLIP-FLOPS WITH PRESET AND CLEAR

DECEMBER 1983—REVISED MARCH 1988

- **Package Options Include Plastic and Ceramic DIPs and Ceramic Flat Packages**
- **Dependable Texas Instruments Quality and Reliability**

description

The '76 contains two independent J-K flip-flops with individual J-K, clock, preset, and clear inputs. The '76 is a positive-edge-triggered flip-flop. J-K input is loaded into the master while the clock is high and transferred to the slave on the high-to-low transition. For these devices the J and K inputs must be stable while the clock is high.

The 'LS76A contain two independent negative-edge-triggered flip-flops. The J and K inputs must be stable one setup time prior to the high-to-low clock transition for predicatble operation. The preset and clear are asynchronous active low inputs. When low they override the clock and data inputs forcing the outputs to the steady state levels as shown in the function table.

The SN5476 and the SN54LS76A are characterized for operation over the full military temperature range of −55°C to 125°C. The SN7476 and the SN74LS76A are characterized for operation from 0°C to 70°C.

SN5476, SN54LS76A . . . J PACKAGE
SN7476 . . . N PACKAGE
SN74LS76A . . . D OR N PACKAGE
(TOP VIEW)

Signal	Pin	Pin	Signal
1CLK	1	16	1K
1 $\overline{PRE}$	2	15	1Q
1 $\overline{CLR}$	3	14	1$\overline{Q}$
1 J	4	13	GND
V_{CC}	5	12	2K
2CLK	6	11	2Q
2 $\overline{PRE}$	7	10	2$\overline{Q}$
2 $\overline{CLR}$	8	9	2J

'76
FUNCTION TABLE

INPUTS					OUTPUTS	
$\overline{PRE}$	$\overline{CLR}$	CLK	J	K	Q	$\overline{Q}$
L	H	X	X	X	H	L
H	L	X	X	X	L	H
L	L	X	X	X	H†	H†
H	H	⎍	L	L	Q_0	$\overline{Q}_0$
H	H	⎍	H	L	H	L
H	H	⎍	L	H	L	H
H	H	⎍	H	H	TOGGLE	

'LS76A
FUNCTION TABLE

INPUTS					OUTPUTS	
$\overline{PRE}$	$\overline{CLR}$	CLK	J	K	Q	$\overline{Q}$
L	H	X	X	X	H	L
H	L	X	X	X	L	H
L	L	X	X	X	H†	H†
H	H	↓	L	L	Q_0	$\overline{Q}_0$
H	H	↓	H	L	H	L
H	H	↓	L	H	L	H
H	H	↓	H	H	TOGGLE	
H	H	H	X	X	Q_0	$\overline{Q}_0$

† This configuration is nonstable; that is, it will not persist when either preset or clear returns to its inactive (high) level.

FIGURE 9-11 74LS76 J-K Flip-Flop Integrated Circuit (Courtesy of Texas Instruments.)

SN5476, SN54LS76A, SN7476, SN74LS76A DUAL J-K FLIP-FLOPS WITH PRESET AND CLEAR

logic diagrams (positive logic) (continued)

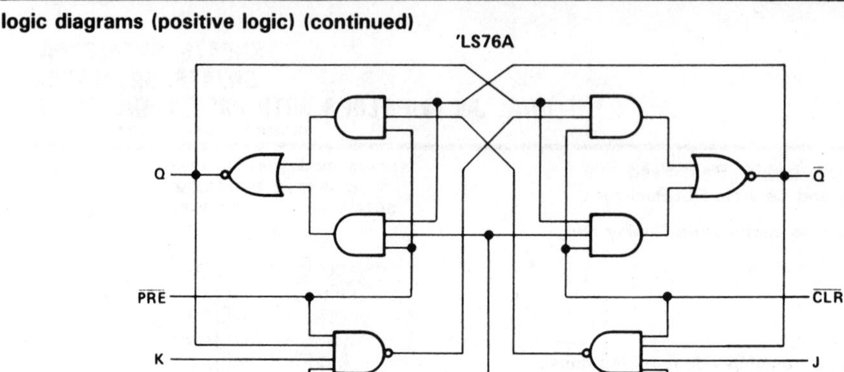

logic symbols†

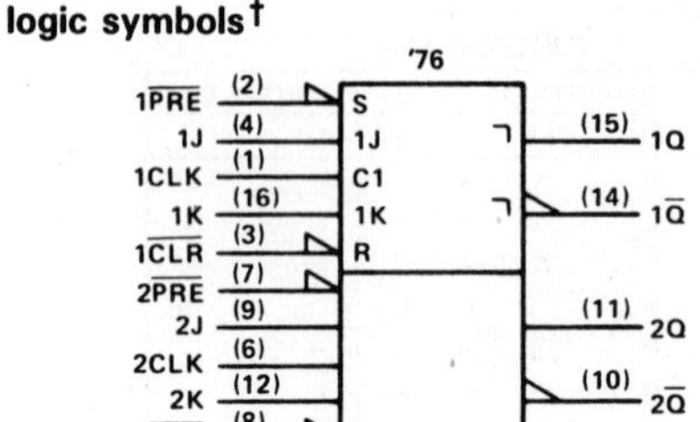

'LS76A

$1\overline{PRE}$ (2), 1J (4), 1CLK (1), 1K (16), $1\overline{CLR}$ (3), $2\overline{PRE}$ (7), 2J (9), 2CLK (6), 2K (12), $2\overline{CLR}$ (8); S, 1J, >C1, 1K, R; (15) 1Q, (14) $1\overline{Q}$, (11) 2Q, (10) $2\overline{Q}$

†These symbols are in accordance with ANSI/IEEE Std 91-1984 and IEC Publication 617-12.

schematics of inputs and outputs

'76

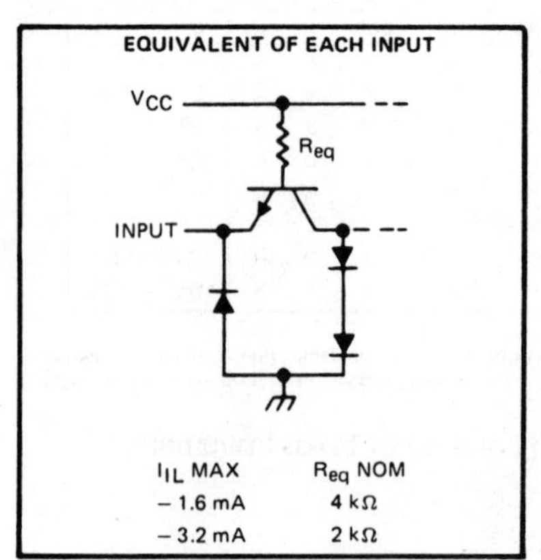

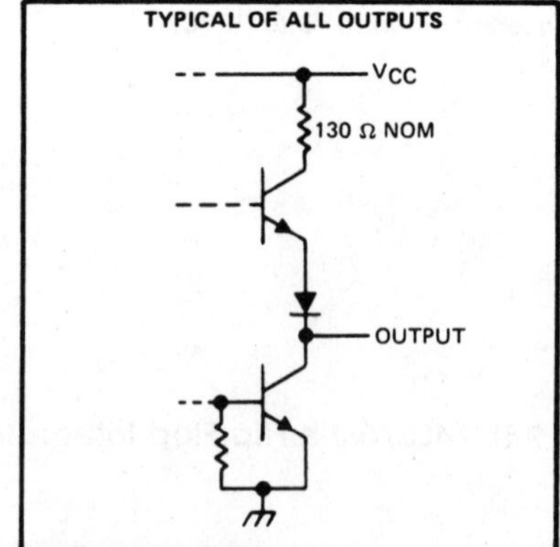

FIGURE 9-11 *(continued)*

SN5476, SN54LS76A, SN7476, SN74LS76A DUAL J-K FLIP-FLOPS WITH PRESET AND CLEAR

schematics of inputs and outputs (continued)

'LS76A

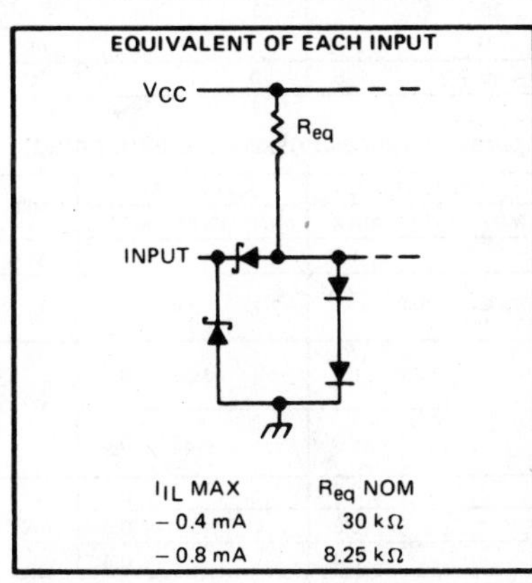

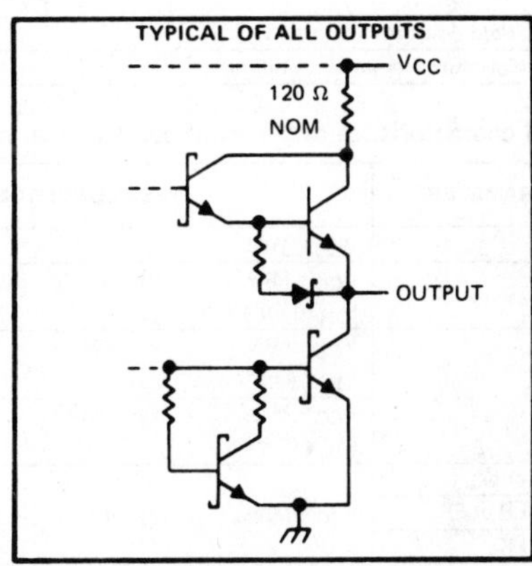

absolute maximum ratings over operating free-air temperature range (unless otherwise noted)

Supply voltage, V_{CC} (see Note 1)	7 V
Input voltage: '76	5.5 V
'LS76A	7 V
Operating free-air temperature range: SN54'	−55°C to 125°C
SN74'	0°C to 70°C
Storage temperature range	−65°C to 150°C

NOTE 1: Voltage values are with respect to network ground terminal.

FIGURE 9-11 (*continued*)

SN54LS76A, SN74LS76A
DUAL J-K FLIP-FLOPS WITH PRESET AND CLEAR

recommended operating conditions

			SN54LS76A			SN74LS76A			UNIT
			MIN	NOM	MAX	MIN	NOM	MAX	
V_{CC}	Supply voltage		4.5	5	5.5	4.75	5	5.75	V
V_{IH}	High-level input voltage		2			2			V
V_{IL}	Low-level input voltage				0.7			0.8	V
I_{OH}	High-level output current				– 0.4			– 0.4	mA
I_{OL}	Low-level output current				4			8	mA
f_{clock}	Clock frequency		0		30	0		30	MHz
t_w	Pulse duration	CLK high	20			20			ns
		$\overline{\text{PRE}}$ or $\overline{\text{CLR}}$ low	25			25			
t_{su}	Setup time before CLK↓	data high or low	20			20			ns
		$\overline{\text{CLR}}$ inactive	20			20			
		$\overline{\text{PRE}}$ inactive	25			25			
t_h	Hold time-data after CLK↓		0			0			ns
T_A	Operating free-air temperature		– 55		125	0		70	°C

electrical characteristics over recommended operating free-air temperature range (unless otherwise noted)

PARAMETER		TEST CONDITIONS†	SN54LS76A			SN74LS76A			UNIT
			MIN	TYP‡	MAX	MIN	TYP‡	MAX	
V_{IK}		V_{CC} = MIN, I_I = – 18 mA			– 1.5			– 1.5	V
V_{OH}		V_{CC} = MIN, V_{IH} = 2 V, V_{IL} = MAX, I_{OH} = – 0.4 mA	2.5	3.4		2.7	3.4		V
V_{OL}		V_{CC} = MIN, V_{IL} = MAX, V_{IH} = 2 V, I_{OL} = 4 mA		0.25	0.4		0.25	0.4	V
		V_{CC} = MIN, V_{IL} = MAX, V_{IH} = 2 V, I_{OL} = 8 mA					0.35	0.5	
I_I	J or K	V_{CC} = MAX, V_I = 7 V			0.1			0.1	mA
	$\overline{\text{CLR}}$ or $\overline{\text{PRE}}$				0.3			0.3	
	CLK				0.4			0.4	
I_{IH}	J or K	V_{CC} = MAX, V_I = 2.7 V			20			20	μA
	$\overline{\text{CLR}}$ or $\overline{\text{PRE}}$				60			60	
	CLK				80			80	
I_{IL}	J or K	V_{CC} = MAX, V_I = 0.4 V			– 0.4			– 0.4	mA
	All other				– 0.8			– 0.8	
I_{OS}§		V_{CC} = MAX, See Note 4	– 20		– 100	– 20		– 100	mA
I_{CC} (Total)		V_{CC} = MAX, See Note 2		4	6		4	6	mA

† For conditions shown as MIN or MAX, use the appropriate value specified under recommended operating conditions.
‡ All typical values are at V_{CC} = 5 V, T_A = 25°C.
§ Not more than one output should be shorted at a time, and the duration of the short circuit should not exceed one second.
NOTE 2: With all outputs open, I_{CC} is measured with the Q and $\overline{Q}$ outputs high in turn. At the time of measurement, the clock input is grounded.
NOTE 4: For certain devices where state commutation can be caused by shorting an output to ground, an equivalent test may be performed with V_O = 2.25 V and 2.125 V for the 54 family and the 74 family, respectively, with the minimum and maximum limits reduced to one half of their stated values.

switching characteristics, V_{CC} = 5 V, T_A = 25°C (see note 3)

PARAMETER	FROM (INPUT)	TO (OUTPUT)	TEST CONDITIONS	MIN	TYP	MAX	UNIT
f_{max}			R_L = 2 kΩ, C_L = 15 pF	30	45		MHz
t_{PLH}	$\overline{\text{PRE}}$, $\overline{\text{CLR}}$ or CLK	Q or $\overline{Q}$			15	20	ns
t_{PHL}					15	20	ns

NOTE 3: Load circuits and voltage waveforms are shown in Section 1.

FIGURE 9-11 ***(continued)***

■ EXAMPLE 9-4 J-K Flip-Flop Analysis

Problem: Determine the output, Q, for a leading edge-triggered J-K flip-flop, given the input waveforms shown in Figure 9-12. Assume that the flip-flop is initially set.

Solution: Refer to the waveforms in Figure 9-12.

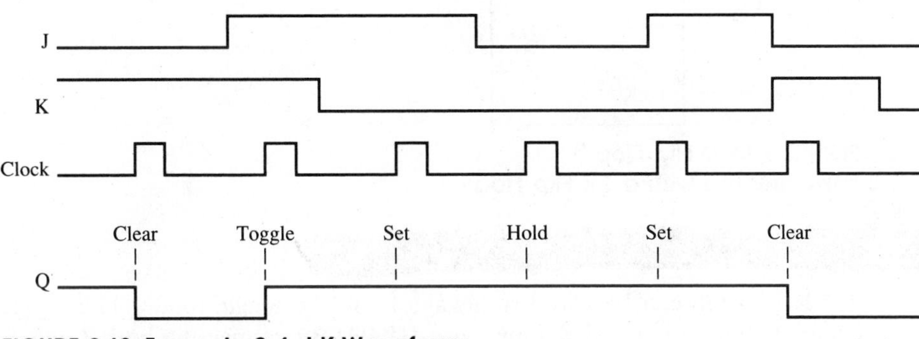

FIGURE 9-12 Example 9-4 J-K Waveforms ■

■ EXAMPLE 9-5 J-K Flip-Flop Analysis

Problem: Repeat Example 9-4 for a trailing edge-triggered J-K flip-flop.

Solution: Refer to the waveform in Figure 9-13.

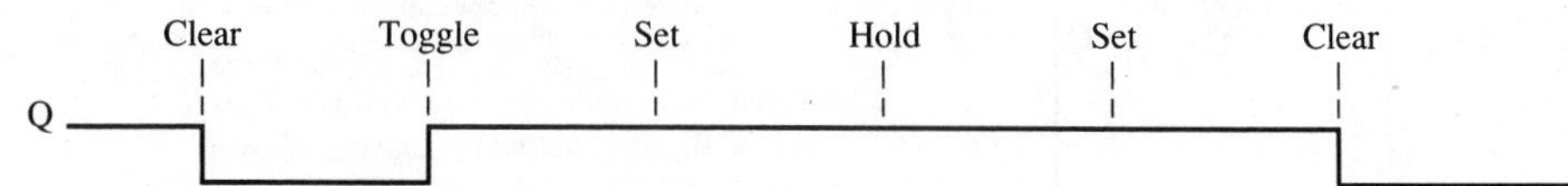

FIGURE 9-13 Example 9-5 J-K Waveform ■

In the previous examples the only difference in the outputs is a time delay due to the flip-flop in one example that is leading edge-triggered and the flip-flop in the other example that is trailing edge-triggered. This, however, is unique to these examples since the values of J and K do not change while the clock pulse is HIGH. This will not always be the case. Always be sure to check the values of J and K at the triggering clock edge to determine the state of the output Q.

9.4.2 J-K Flip-Flop Wired as a D Flip-Flop

A J-K flip-flop can be wired to operate as a D flip-flop by using the J input as the D input and inputting the complement of D into the K input. The implementation of a D flip-flop using a J-K flip-flop is shown in Figure 9-14.

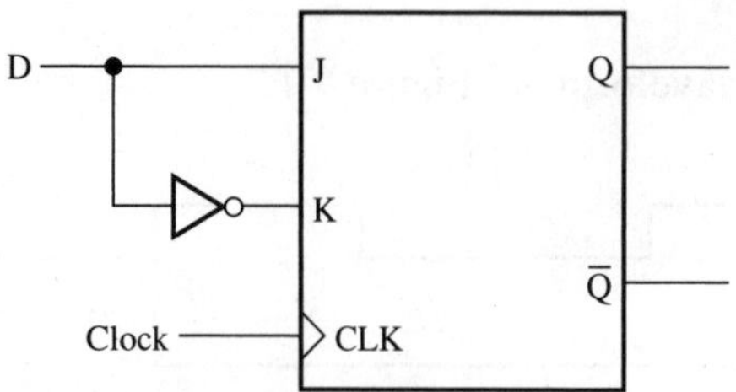

FIGURE 9-14 D Flip-Flop Implemented with a J-K Flip-Flop

9.4.3 J-K Flip-Flop Wired for Toggle Operation

A J-K flip-flop can be wired to always be in the toggle mode. The toggle occurs when both J and K inputs are HIGH. By connecting both J and K inputs to a logic HIGH, as shown in Figure 9-15, the flip-flop will toggle its output state at every clock trigger.

One important property of a flip-flop in toggle mode is that the output frequency is one half the input clock frequency. Examine the waveforms of Figure 9-15 to verify this. The property of flip-flop frequency division will be used extensively in later flip-flop applications such as counter circuits.

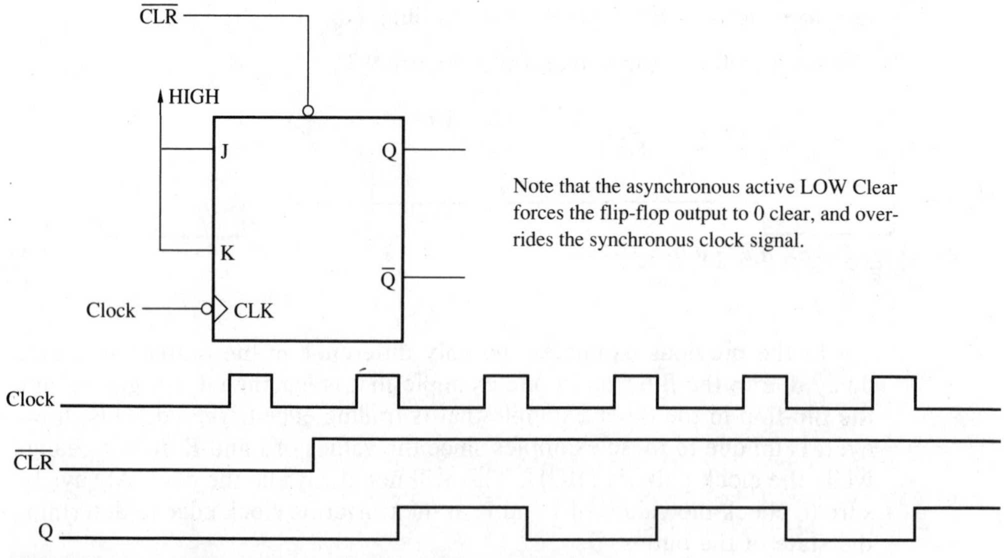

FIGURE 9-15 J-K Flip-Flop in Constant Toggle Mode

■ EXAMPLE 9-6 Toggle Flip-Flop Analysis

Problem: A J-K flip-flop is wired as a toggle flip-flop. The frequency of the input clock is 20 KHz.
a. What is the output frequency at the Q output?
b. What is the output frequency at the $\overline{Q}$ output?

Solution: (a) Since the output of a flip-flop in the toggle mode divides the frequency by 2. The output frequency is equal to 10 KHz.
(b) The frequency at the complement output will also be 10 KHz. ■

Section Self-Test

1. A J-K flip-flop is in the toggle mode. If the present state of the output is 1, the next state will also be 1.
2. For a J-K flip-flop, if J = 0 and K = 1, Q = 1.
3. For a J-K flip-flop, if J = 1 and K = 0, Q = 1.

ANSWERS (Not necessarily in the order of the questions)

• False • False • True

9-5 FLIP-FLOP TIMING PARAMETERS

Up to this point flip-flop operation has been examined as a function of the flip-flop truth table and waveform analysis. The control inputs at the trigger point (leading edge or trailing edge) determine the next state of the flip-flop output.

The examples so far have purposely avoided the case when the control inputs are switching at or near the trigger timing edge. What happens if J and K, for example, are switching logic levels when a clock trigger is applied? Analysis of the flip-flop timing parameters will provide the answer to this question, along with providing the background necessary to understand the operation of a master-slave (pulse-triggered) flip-flop. IC timing parameters are listed in the AC characteristics section of data books.

9.5.1 Propagation Delay

Propagation delay for a flip-flop is the amount of time it takes for the output of the flip-flop to change its state from a clock trigger or asynchronous set or reset. It is defined from the 50% point of the input pulse to the 50% point of the output pulse, as shown in Figure 9-16.

Propagation delay is specified as $\mathbf{t_{PHL}}$—the propagation time from a HIGH to a LOW—and as $\mathbf{t_{PLH}}$—the propagation time from a LOW to a HIGH.

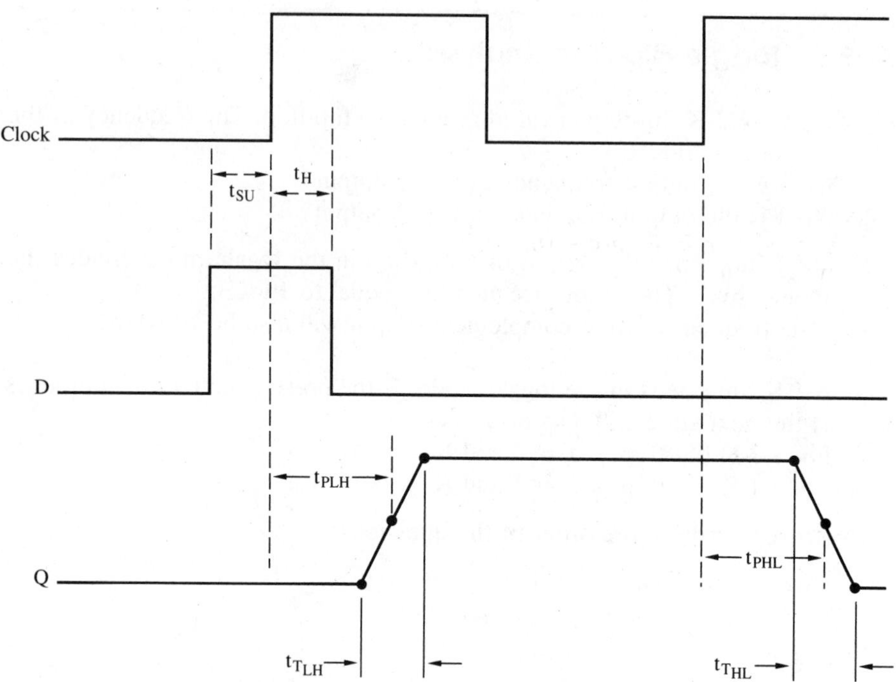

FIGURE 9-16 Flip-Flop Timing Parameters

9.5.2 Output Transition Time

The **output transition time** is defined as the rise time or fall time of the output. The t_{TLH} is the 10% to 90% time, or LOW to HIGH transition time. The t_{THL} is the 90% to 10% time, or HIGH to LOW transition time. Output transition time is shown in Figure 9-16.

9.5.3 Setup Time

The **setup time** is defined as the interval immediately preceding the active transition of the clock pulse during which the control or data inputs must be stable (at a valid logic level). Its parameter symbol is $\mathbf{t_{SU}}$.

The t_{SU} is the parameter that answers the previously posed question concerning input transitions at or near the clock trigger. If, for example, the set up time for a negative edge-triggered J-K flip-flop is 5 ns, the J and K inputs must be stable 5 ns or more before the trailing edge of the clock is applied to the flip-flop clock input. If the J and K inputs are still in transition, the operation of the flip-flop will be unreliable and may not follow the truth table for a J-K flip-flop. The t_{SU} is also shown in Figure 9-16.

The smaller the setup time parameter is for a flip-flop, the better the device will be. Some flip-flops have negative values for t_{SU}, indicating that inputs can be valid the specified number of nanoseconds after the application of the clock trigger.

9.5.4 Hold Time

The **hold time** is the amount of time that the control or data inputs must be stable after the clock trigger occurs. The $\mathbf{t_H}$ is the parameter symbol for hold time, as shown in Figure 9-16.

The smaller the hold time is, the better the flip-flop from a design standpoint. As with setup time, some of the better flip-flops have zero or negative hold times.

9.5.5 Removal Time

Removal time, $\mathbf{t_{rem}}$, is the time between the end of an overriding asynchronous input, such as clear or reset, and the earliest allowable beginning of a synchronous clock input.

■ EXAMPLE 9-7 Flip-Flop Data Sheet Analysis

Problem: Use a TTL data book, and determine the following parameters for a 74LS114:

(a) setup time (b) hold time
(c) removal time (d) propagation delay
(e) output transition time

Solution: (a) t_{SU} (data to CLK) = 20 ns
(b) t_H = 0 ns (data input can change on the clock edge)
(c) Since removal time is not listed in the specifications, the manufacturer should be contacted to determine this parameter value.

(d) $t_{PLH(max)}$ = 20 ns $t_{PHL(max)}$ = 20 ns

(e) The notes refer to the parameter measurement section of the data book. In this section the rise and fall times are dependent on the subfamily that is used. For a low-power Schottky (LS), t_r = 1.5 ns and t_f = 2.6 ns. ■

9.5.6 Operating Frequency

The **operating frequency** of a flip-flop is defined as the frequency of the clock input to the flip-flop. The maximum operating frequency, $\mathbf{f_{max}}$, is the maximum input clock frequency that will cause the outputs to change state from the 10% and 90% levels in accordance with the device function table.

Often f_{max} is listed in the AC parametric table. This number is usually based on a 50% duty cycle input clock waveform. If f_{max} is not listed, an approximate maximum frequency of operation can be found by taking the reciprocal of the worst case average propagation delay time, $(t_{PHL} + t_{PLH})/2$. If the calculated f_{max} is larger than the listed f_{max}, always use the lower value for f_{max}.

■ EXAMPLE 9-8 Flip-Flop Speed Analysis

Problem: A 74HCT73 is a TTL compatible CMOS negative edge-triggered JK flip-flop. Given that the maximum $t_{PHL} = 38$ ns and that the maximum $t_{PLH} = 36$ ns, calculate the maximum clock pulse frequency, f_{max}.

Solution:

$$t_{PDavg(max)} = \frac{38 \text{ ns} + 36 \text{ ns}}{2} = 37 \text{ ns}$$

$$f_{max} = \frac{1}{37 \text{ ns}} = 27 \text{ MHz}$$

Examination of the AC characteristics lists an $f_{max(min)}$ of 27 MHz. The results correspond. ■

■ EXAMPLE 9-9 Flip-Flop Speed Analysis

Problem: Determine the maximum operation frequency for a 74LS114.

Solution: The maximum operating frequency, $f_{max(min)}$, is listed for this device.

$f_{max} = 30$ MHz ■

9.5.7 Static and Dynamic Timing

It is often difficult when learning to analyze flip-flops and other sequential circuits to understand the importance of timing analysis in actual circuits. "On paper" analysis is done using **static timing** and ideal or near ideal waveforms.

In static timing analysis a flip-flop output will go to the logic state determined by the control inputs just before the clock trigger occurs. Actual circuit operation involves **dynamic timing** and nonideal waveforms. With dynamic timing, each of the timing parameters must be examined to ensure that control and data inputs are not changing in violation of the parameter specifications. The timing parameters become increasingly important as the frequency of operation increases toward f_{max}. J and K, for example, may be changing state millions of times per second (MHz).

The point to remember is that in actual circuit operation timing parameters become very significant, and troubleshooting tools such as oscilloscopes and logic analyzers are needed to examine the timing parameters discussed.

In synchronous flip-flop circuits a common clock will be input into each flip-flop clock input, as shown in Figure 9-17. As long as the flip-flop propagation delay of the drive flip-flop is longer than the hold time of the receive flip-flop, the circuit will operate as predicted by the flip-flop truth table and static timing analysis. In multiple device circuits this also assumes that all synchronous devices are triggered synchronously by a common clock input. If this is not the case, timing skew can occur.

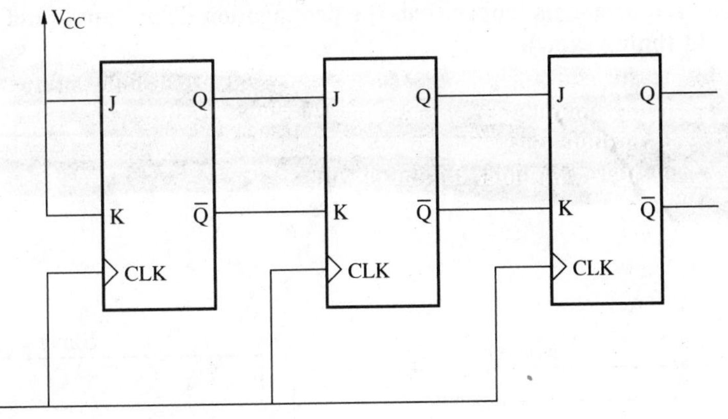

FIGURE 9-17 Synchronous Flip-Flop Circuit

9.5.8 Timing Skew

Timing skew is a timing problem in synchronous circuits that occurs when a clock signal common to several devices arrives at the clock inputs to the devices at different times. The easiest way to avoid timing skew is to ensure that clock signal arrives to all synchronized devices at the same time. This means that any delay, such as an extra gate, not common to all devices should be avoided. If for some reason unequal clock delays cannot be avoided, a careful timing analysis must be performed to ensure proper flip-flop and circuit operation.

Section Self-Test

1. Unequal propagation delays from a common clock to flip-flops in synchronous operation can result in timing skew.
2. The minimum value of f_{max} is used to determine the maximum operating frequency of a device.

3. The minimum value of propagation delay is used to determine the guaranteed device propagation delay.

ANSWERS (Not necessarily in the order of the questions)

• False • True • True

9-6 MASTER-SLAVE FLIP-FLOPS (pulse triggered flip flops)

Improvements in semiconductor processing technology has resulted in edge-triggered flip-flops with hold times of zero or less. Before these flip-flop parametric improvements, pulse-triggered or master-slave flip-flops were used to prevent timing problems associated with flip-flops that had hold time requirements longer than the propagation delay times (and thus avoid timing skew).

Today master-slave flip-flops are seldom used. Most logic subfamilies no longer have available any type of master-slave flip-flop. Some J-K master-slave flip-flops are still manufactured, and master-slave flip-flops may be encountered in older digital circuits, so their operation will be discussed.

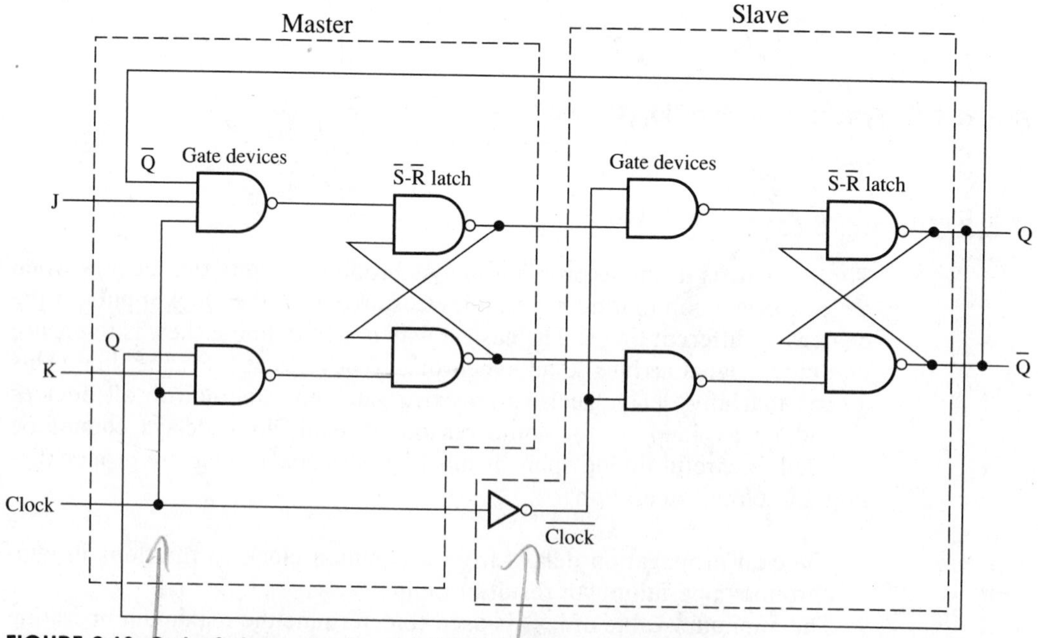

FIGURE 9-18 Gate Schematic for a J-K Master-Slave Flip-Flop

upstroke of clock

downstroke

9.6.1 Master-Slave J-K Operation

A **master-slave** or **pulse-triggered** J-K flip-flop is two $\overline{S}$-$\overline{R}$ gated latches. Recall from Chapter 8 that a $\overline{S}$-$\overline{R}$ latch can be constructed with two cross-coupled NAND gates. The first gated $\overline{S}$-$\overline{R}$ latch is referred to as the **master**. The master responds to the J-K inputs on the leading edge of the clock pulse. This is referred to as data clocked into the master.

The second gated $\overline{S}$-$\overline{R}$ latch is called the **slave**. On the trailing edge of the clock pulse the output of the master is transferred to the slave device, resulting in the final J-K output, Q.

A logic gate schematic for a J-K master-slave flip-flop is shown in Figure 9-18. Note that internally, the clock for the slave section is the inverted clock input into the master. This results in the pulsed clock operation of the master-slave flip-flop.

■ **EXAMPLE 9-10 Master-Slave Flip-Flop Analysis**

Problem: Determine the output Q for the master-slave J-K flip-flop waveforms in Figure 9-19.

Solution: Refer to the waveforms in Figure 9-19.

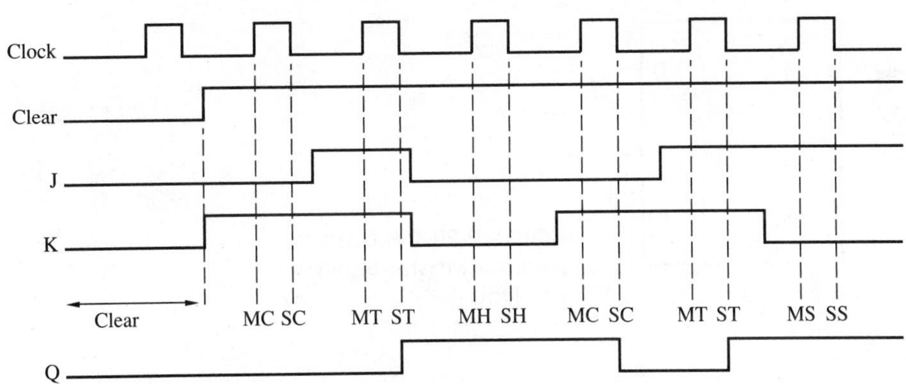

The abbreviations above Q correspond to the internal operation of the master-slave flip-flop, as follows:

MC = master clears	MC = master clears
SC = slave clears	SC = slave clears
MT = master toggles	MT = master toggles
ST = slave toggles	ST = slave toggles
MH = master holds	MS = master sets
SH = slave holds	SS = slave sets

FIGURE 9-19 J-K Master-Slave Flip-Flop Waveforms ■

Note that the master-slave flip-flop only changes its state on the trailing edge of the clock. Internally, however, the master responds to the leading edge of the clock.

The J-K master-slave flip-flop eliminates the need for J and K to remain stable once the clock input goes LOW. This eliminates the need for a hold time. That is, the J and K inputs can change at the same time the clock goes LOW. Today's negative edge-triggered devices (with small or zero hold time) allow this as well, eliminating the need for a master-slave flip-flop.

A major limitation of the master-slave flip-flop is that the J and K inputs can affect the flip-flop at any time while the clock input is at a logic HIGH. For a normal master-slave flip-flop, the inputs must not be changed while the clock is HIGH.

9.6.2 Master-Slave Data Lockout

To prevent the master-slave flip-flop from changing state while the clock is HIGH, **data lockout** is used. Master-slave data lockout flip-flops prevent any changes in J and K from affecting the flip-flop operation, even if J and K are changed while the clock is HIGH. A dynamic clock indicator is added to the clock input of the master-slave flip-flop symbol to indicate data lockout, as shown in Figure 9-20.

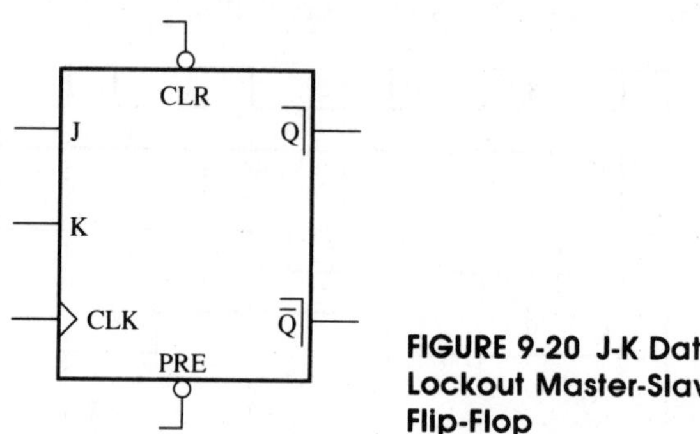

FIGURE 9-20 J-K Data Lockout Master-Slave Flip-Flop

The 74111 is a dual J-K master-slave flip-flop with data lockout. The master is enabled on the leading edge of the trigger pulse. After waiting 30 ns, changes in the J and K inputs will not affect the state of the master, even if the clock is HIGH.

Section Self-Test

1. If the inputs to a master-slave flip-flop are changed while the clock is HIGH, the flip-flop output may change.
2. Master-slave flip-flops are seldom used today due to improvements in flip-flop timing parameters.
3. A J-K master-slave flip-flop output will be the same as that of a positive edge-triggered J-K flip-flop.

ANSWERS (Not necessarily in the order of the questions)

• True • False • True

9-7 J-K FLIP-FLOP INTEGRATED CIRCUITS

A large number of different types of J-K flip-flops are available in IC form. J-K and D flip-flops comprise the majority of IC flip-flops commercially available. A brief summary of the various types of J-K flip-flops that are available follows.

9.7.1 J-K Flip-Flop IC Features

In addition to the previously discussed features of asynchronous clear and preset, some J-K flip-flops also have gated inputs that allow for multiple J and K inputs to be logically combined. The J-K flip-flop ICs commonly available, along with their features, are listed in Table 9-2.

TABLE 9-2 J-K Flip-Flop Integrated Circuits

Integrated Circuit No.	Number of Flip-Flops	Clock Trigger	Have a Preset?	Have a Clear?	Other Features
7470	1	Leading*	Yes	Yes	AND gated J and K
74H71	1	Pulse‡	Yes	No	AND/OR gated J and K
7473	2	Pulse‡	No	Yes	
74LS73	2	Trailing†	No	Yes	
7476	2	Pulse‡	Yes	Yes	
74LS76	2	Trailing†	Yes	Yes	
74LS107	2	Pulse‡	No	Yes	
74LS109	2	Leading*	Yes	Yes	K input inverted
74111	2	Pulse‡	Yes	Yes	Data lockout
74LS114	2	Trailing†	Yes	Yes	Common $\overline{CLR}$, $\overline{PRE}$, CLK
74276	4	Trailing†	Yes	Yes	Common $\overline{CLR}$, $\overline{PRE}$, CLK K input inverted
74376	4	Leading*	No	Yes	Common $\overline{CLR}$ and CLK K input inverted

* Leading edge-triggered is the same as positive clocked.
† Trailing edge-triggered is the same as negative clocked.
‡ Pulse-triggered is the same as master-slave clocked.

It is important to note that unlike most other types of SSI and MSI ICs, flip-flop ICs may not have the same function between logic subfamilies. This may also mean that the ICs may not be pin compatible.

A 7473, for example, is a dual J-K master-slave flip-flop IC, and a 74LS73 is a dual J-K trailing edge flip-flop IC. Be sure to examine carefully the data sheets for the *specific* flip-flop IC selected.

Section Self-Test

1. Find a TTL J-K flip-flop IC that is negative triggered, with four flip-flops in the IC.
2. Find all TTL J-K flip-flop ICs that have preset inputs and are leading edge triggered.
3. Find TTL J-K flip-flops that are trailing edge-triggered with two flip-flops and a clear input in the IC.

ANSWERS

- 74276
- 7470, 74LS109
- 74LS73, 74LS76, 74114, 74276

9-8 FLIP-FLOP APPLICATIONS

Flip-flops are the basic building block of many different types of digital circuits. Once the operation of the different types of flip-flops is understood, flip-flops can then be used to design a variety of sequential digital circuits. The next two sections introduce a few basic flip-flop applications. Additional flip-flop applications and design techniques are covered in detail in subsequent chapters.

9.8.1 Data Storage

Since the flip-flop is a basic storage element capable of storing one bit of information, data storage is a common flip-flop application. Latches are used to store data on the occurrence of a voltage level trigger, and flip-flops are used to store data on the occurrence of an edge trigger.

Figure 9-21 shows an 8 bit parallel data storage circuit utilizing D flip-flops. Flip-flops combined into a synchronously clocked circuit for data storage are often called **data registers**, or simply **registers**. One special type of register, called a **shift register**, will be discussed in detail in Chapter 11.

9.8.2 Counter Circuits

Flip-flops can be combined into circuits that produce binary counts of any length and any type of sequence. This is such an important application of flip-flops that the next chapter is devoted to the application and design of counter circuits.

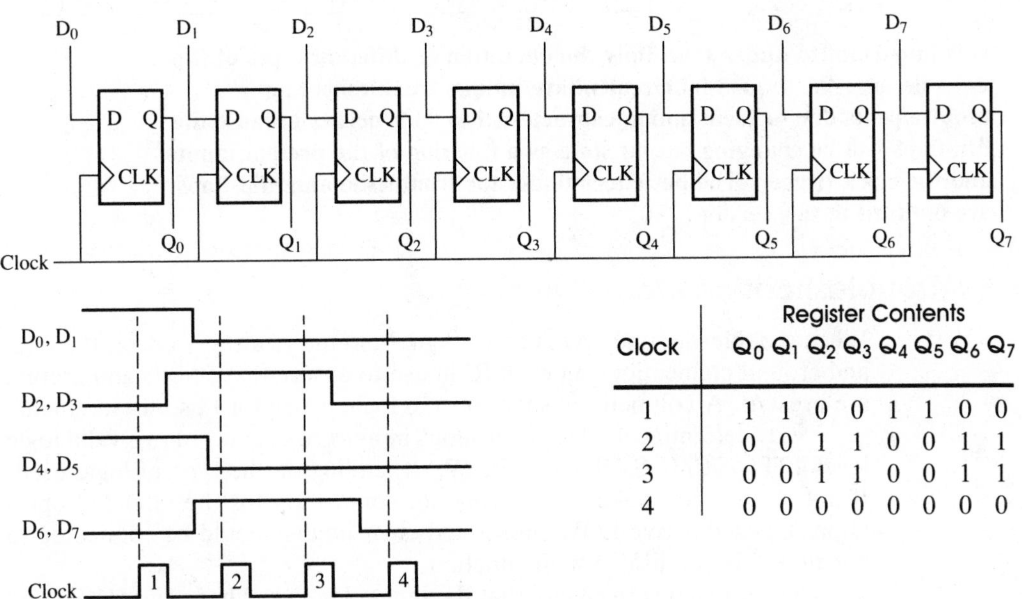

Clock	Register Contents Q_0	Q_1	Q_2	Q_3	Q_4	Q_5	Q_6	Q_7
1	1	1	0	0	1	1	0	0
2	0	0	1	1	0	0	1	1
3	0	0	1	1	0	0	1	1
4	0	0	0	0	0	0	0	0

FIGURE 9-21 Eight-Bit Flip-Flop Data Register

9.8.3 Timing Circuits and Frequency Division

An important application of flip-flops that is closely related to counters is clock timing. Synchronous circuits often require several different clocks at different frequencies to control synchronous circuit operation. A common example is a wristwatch.

Most wristwatches today use a quartz crystal oscillating at a high frequency as the reference input clock. The input frequency is frequency divided with flip-flop counter circuits to produce the timing clocks for seconds, minutes, and hours. Design procedures for timing and frequency division are discussed in Chapter 10.

Section Self-Test

1. If a 2 KHz clock is input into a J-K flip-flop in the toggle mode, what is the frequency at the output Q?
2. List four applications for flip-flops.
3. What is a register?

ANSWERS

- The output would be 1 KHz.
- Data storage, frequency division, timing circuits, counters.
- A register is a synchronously clocked group of flip-flops or latches used for temporary data storage.

9-9 TROUBLESHOOTING FLIP-FLOPS

It is important to understand fully the operation of different types of flip-flops because the sequential circuits have unique troubleshooting requirements due to their timing characteristics. This occurs because the flip-flops will be changing output state as a function of the present inputs and the clock trigger. The basic techniques for troubleshooting flip-flops are outlined in this section.

9.9.1 Troubleshooting Procedures

When troubleshooting any type of digital circuitry, always check the V_{CC} and ground connections on each IC in use to ensure that 5 volts and ground are present. A voltmeter is superior to a logic probe for this measurement.

Next, determine if all asynchronous inputs are connected to a valid logic level TTL or CMOS HIGH or LOW, depending on the type of logic used. If not connected, make the appropriate connection for the intended operation. Unused active-LOW preset and clear inputs should be connected to a logic HIGH to disable their function.

The next step is to ensure that the input clock used has valid HIGH and LOW logic levels. For TTL, the clock waveform should be a square wave for pulse wave with a HIGH of 5 volts and a LOW of 0 volts. The clock waveform must have a DC offset of 0 volts. If a DC offset voltage is present, the input clock may appear correct on the oscilloscope if AC coupling is used to display the signal on the oscilloscope, but the actual clock signal will have invalid logic LOW and HIGH voltage levels.

After the power supply and input connections are verified correct, the flip-flop operation can be analyzed and compared to its truth table. Check each flip-flop condition with input combination logic switches and a light emitted diodes (LED) on the outputs to verify correct operation. If any of the input and output combinations are incorrect, the flip-flop may be defective.

■ EXAMPLE 9-11 J-K Flip-Flop Troubleshooting

Problem: Document a procedure for checking a J-K flip-flop for correct truth table operation after power and other inputs have been checked.

Solution:

1. Determine the output state.
2. Input 0 on J and 0 on K. Manually clock the input and verify that the output holds.

3. Input 1 on J and 0 on K. Manually clock the input and verify that the output sets.
4. Input 0 on J and 1 on K. Manually clock the input to verify that the output clears.
5. Input 1 on J and 1 on K. Manually clock the input to verify that the output toggles.

If the device operates correctly manually but not when the timing inputs are applied, this indicates a problem with the input clock or some other timing parameter violation. Check the data book timing parameters to ensure that none of the timing specifications are being violated. An oscilloscope is necessary for timing and waveform troubleshooting. ■

Section Self-Test

1. List three types of wiring errors that could cause a flip-flop to operate improperly.
2. What troubleshooting tools are needed for manual flip-flop troubleshooting?
3. How do you determine if the input clock is TTL compatible?

ANSWERS

- Floating asynchronous inputs, no ground connection on the flip-flop IC, clock input to the wrong pin.
- For manual troubleshooting, a voltmeter, 0- and 5-volt switch inputs, and an LED are used. Logic probes do not provide enough voltage information.
- Set a ground reference on the oscilloscope. Set the oscilloscope for DC coupling. Input the clock waveform into the oscilloscope and adjust it for a 0-volt DC offset and a LOW (0 volt) and a HIGH (5 volts) for a TTL input with operating margin.

SUMMARY

ANALYSIS AND TROUBLESHOOTING

The flip-flop is the basic clock edge-triggered digital storage element. Each flip-flop is capable of storing 1 bit of binary data, either 0 or 1, due to its bistable operation.

One way to characterize flip-flops is by the method of clock triggering employed. Positive edge-triggered flip-flops change state on the leading edge of the input clock pulse. Negative edge-triggered flip-flops change state on the trailing edge of the input clock pulse. Master-slave flip-flops change state on the trailing edge of the input pulse, but only after an entire clock pulse since the master triggers on the leading edge of the clock. Master-slave flip-flops are seldom used today due to improvements in the timing parameters of edge-triggered flip-flops.

The three basic types of flip-flops available are the D, S-R, and J-K. Each flip-flop has its own unique operation as indicated by its truth table.

When a flip-flop output is changed to a LOW, the flip-flop operation is known as a clear or reset operation. These terms are interchangeable. When a flip-flop output is changed to a one, the flip-flop is set. The S-R and J-K flip-flops are available in ICs with complemented inputs.

Timing parameters are very important in synchronous circuits. The designer must ensure that the operation of the circuit does not violate the flip-flop timing parameters of maximum frequency of operation, data setup, and data hold times. Propagation delay must be carefully considered to avoid timing problems such as clock skew. Also, flip-flops with asynchronous inputs must have the asynchronous inputs connected to a TTL logic level. They cannot be left floating or unconnected.

Good troubleshooting techniques are necessary to analyze sequential circuits efficiently. The flip-flop operation is checked against the appropriate truth table for each nonoperational flip-flop in a flip-flop circuit.

APPLICATION AND DESIGN

Data books are a valuable source of flip-flop IC information. The designer must be cautious in selecting flip-flop ICs, as identical IC numbers may have different pin configurations and functions across subfamilies. A 7473 and a 74LS73, for example, are not the same type of flip-flop.

There are numerous flip-flop applications, including data storage and transfer, timing, timing and clock circuits, clock edge detection, and frequency division. Two other important flip-flop applications, counter circuits and shift registers, are discussed in detail with design procedures in Chapters 10 and 11.

PROBLEMS

9-1 Flip-Flop Operation—Analysis Problems

1. Define the following:
   a. flip-flop
   b. trailing edge-triggered
   c. positive edge-triggered
   d. negative edge-triggered
   e. leading edge-triggered
   f. pulse-triggered
   g. master-slave
   h. clock synchronization
   i. asynchronous inputs

* *See* Answers to Selected Problems.

9-2 D Flip-Flop—Analysis and Design Problems

2. a. List three applications for a D flip-flop.
   b. Draw the standard and IEEE symbol for a positive edge-triggered D flip-flop with active LOW asynchronous clear and set inputs.
3. Review the data sheet for a '74 flip-flop.
   a. List all available compatible TTL and CMOS subfamilies.
   b. Make a chart comparing the maximum propagation delay from the clock to the Q output for each subfamily in part (a).
4. Repeat Problem 3 for a '273 flip-flop.
5. Find Q for a positive edge-triggered D flip-flop, given the waveforms shown in Figure 9-22. Assume $Q_0 = 0$.

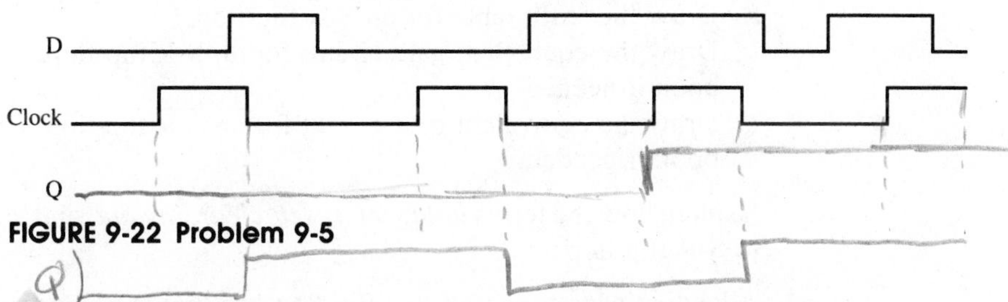

FIGURE 9-22 Problem 9-5

6. Repeat Problem 5 for a negative edge-triggered D flip-flop.

*7. Find Q for a D leading edge-triggered flip-flop, given the waveforms shown in Figure 9-23.

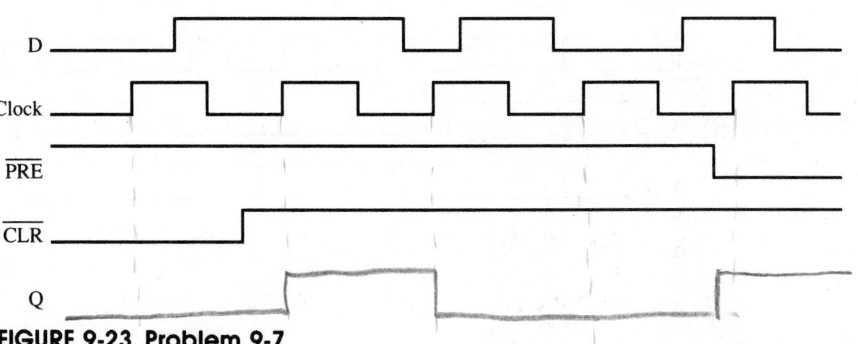

FIGURE 9-23 Problem 9-7

*8. Repeat Problem 7 for a trailing edge-triggered D flip-flop.

9. a. Design a D flip-flop circuit that will store 8 bits of data from eight different inputs.
   b. Consult a data book to determine which flip-flop IC or ICs are needed to store all 8 bits of data within 20 ns after the inputs are valid.

c. Draw the schematic for the circuit.
d. You are told that the inputs change every 100 ns, ±10 ns. Determine the clock input needed to control the circuit to ensure that previous inputs are stored until the new input timing window. (*Hint:* The circuit must be disabled 20 ns after the *last* input is valid, and must be enabled when the *first* new input is valid; then repeat.)

10. Explain the difference between a clock input and an ouput enable input on a flip-flop. (See a '378, for example.)

9-3 S-R and $\overline{S}$-$\overline{R}$ Flip-Flops—Analysis and Design Problems

11. a. Draw the truth table for an S-R flip-flop.
    b. Draw the truth table for an $\overline{S}$-$\overline{R}$ flip-flop.
    c. Draw the equivalent gate circuit for an S-R flip-flop. Consult a data book if needed.
    d. Draw the equivalent gate circuit for an $\overline{S}$-$\overline{R}$ flip-flop. Consult a data book if needed.

12. Explain how the terms *hold, set, reset, clear, invalid,* and *unstable* relate to S-R flip-flops.

13. A leading edge-triggered S-R flip-flop has inputs as shown in Figure 9-24. Determine Q and $\overline{Q}$.

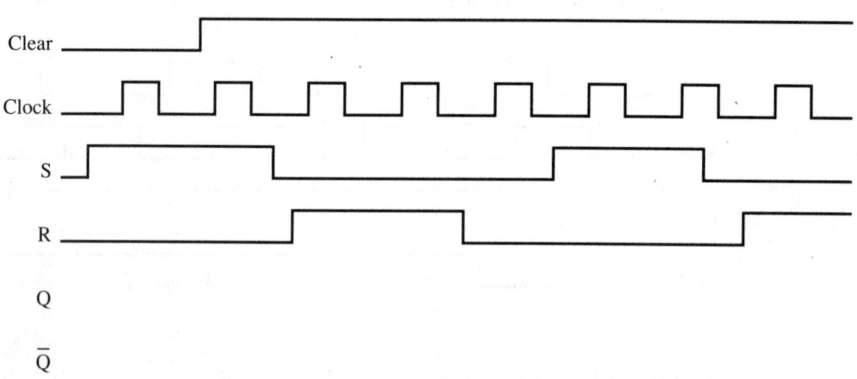

FIGURE 9-24 Problem 9-13

14. Repeat Problem 13 for a trailing edge-triggered S-R flip-flop.

*15. Given the waveforms shown in Figure 9-25, determine Q for a positive edge-triggered $\overline{S}$-$\overline{R}$ flip-flop. A is input into $\overline{S}$ and B is input into $\overline{R}$. $Q_0 = 1$.

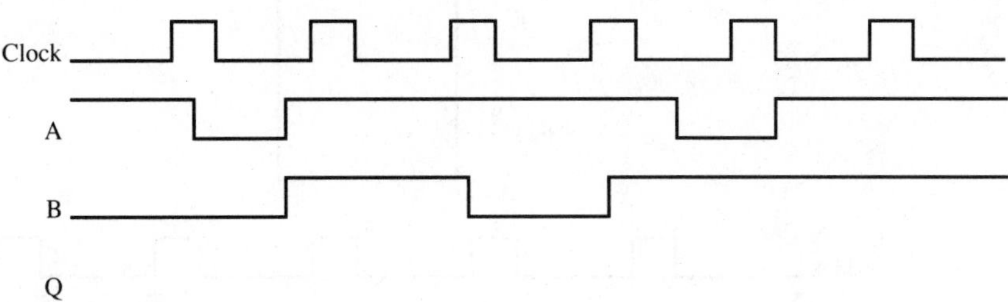

FIGURE 9-25 Problem 9-15

16. a. Explain how adding an inverter between the S and R inputs of an S-R flip-flop results in a D flip-flop operation.
    b. What happens if an inverter is placed between the inputs of an $\overline{S}$-$\overline{R}$ flip-flop? Does it also become a D flip-flop? Explain. Use waveforms as needed.

9-4 J-K Flip-Flop—Analysis and Design Problems

* 17. A leading edge-triggered J-K flip-flop is initially set. Given the waveforms shown in Figure 9-26, find Q.

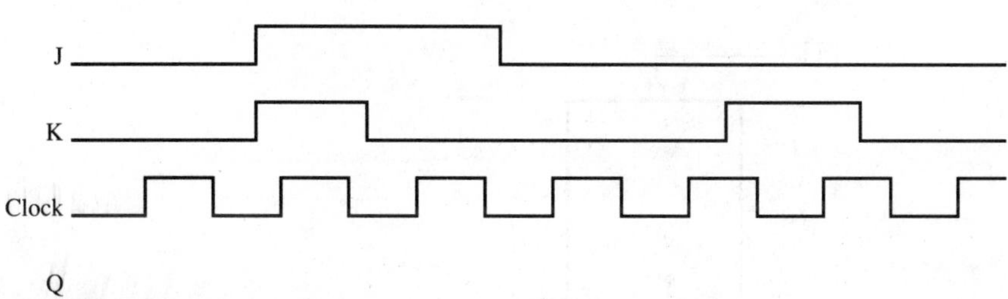

FIGURE 9-26 Problem 9-17

*18. Repeat Problem 17 for a trailing edge-triggered J-K flip-flop.

*19. Repeat Problem 17, if the flip-flop is initially reset.

20. Given the flip-flop and waveforms shown in Figure 9-27, determine Q and $\overline{Q}$.

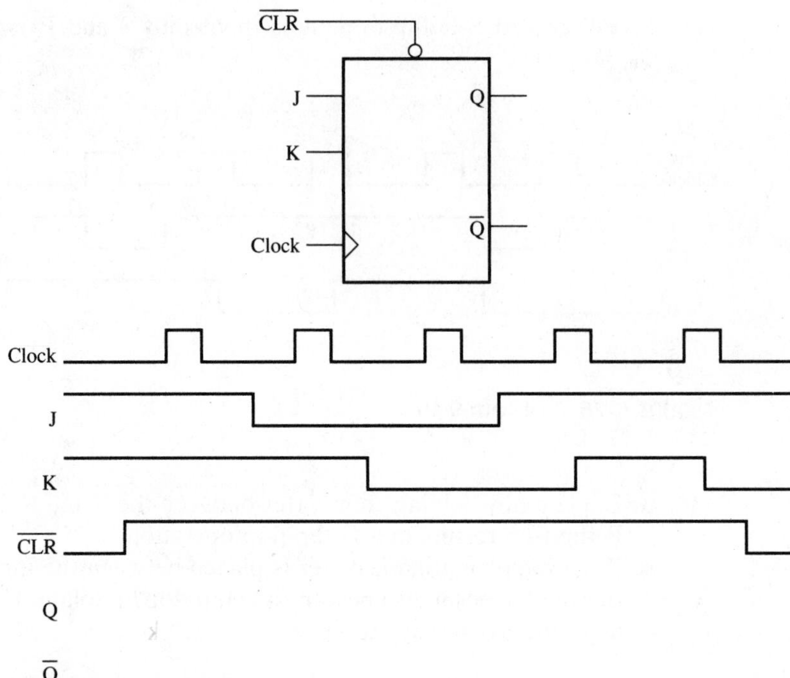

FIGURE 9-27 Problem 9-20

21. Use the waveforms of Problem 20 to determine output Q for the flip-flop shown in Figure 9-28.

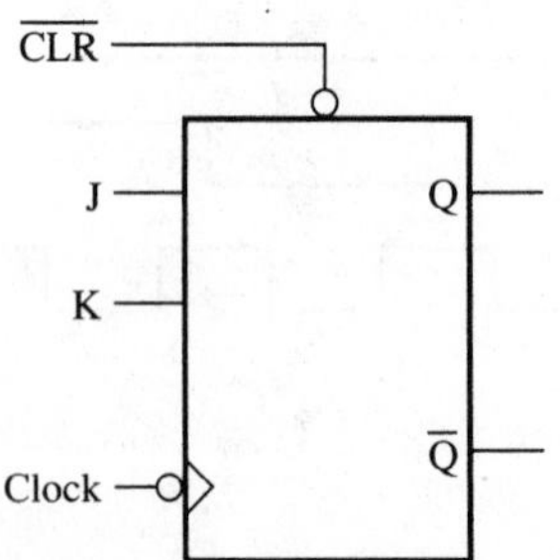

FIGURE 9-28 Problem 9-21

22. a. Design a circuit using J-K flip-flops to store 4 bits of data synchronously on the leading edge of a clock pulse.
    b. Use a data book to choose an appropriate CMOS J-K flip-flop, and draw a schematic for the circuit.

c. What CMOS device would you use for a negative edge-triggered design?

*23. a. Design a flip-flop toggle circuit, and show four input clocks of operation.
b. If the input clock is at 10 KHz, what is the output frequency?
c. What is the fastest a 74LS73 can toggle? Explain using timing parameters.

9-5 Flip-Flop Timing Parameters—Analysis Problems

24. Define the following:
(a) t_{PHL} (b) t_{PLH} (c) t_H (d) t_{SU} (e) t_{rem}

25. Explain the difference between dynamic and static timing.

26. a. What is timing skew?
b. Give an example of timing skew.
c. List two problems caused by timing skew.
d. Describe two ways to prevent timing skew.

27. A leading edge-triggered D flip-flop with asynchronous clear has the following timing parameters:
$t_{PHL} = 10$ ns $t_{PLH} = 15$ ns $t_H = 10$ ns $t_{SU} = 5$ ns
$t_{rem} = 10$ ns
Draw the timing waveforms.

28. a. Calculate the average maximum propagation delay for a 74LS76, clock to Q.
b. Calculate the average typical propagation delay for a 74LS76, clock to Q.

29. Find the maximum propagation delay, clock to Q, for a 74HCT76.
a. at $V_{CC} = 4.5$ V and 25°C.
b. at $V_{CC} = 4.5$ V and 120°C.
c. at $V_{CC} = 6.0$ V and 25°C.

*30. Repeat Problem 29 for a 74HC76.

9-6 and 9-7 Master-Slave Flip-Flops and J-K Flip-Flop ICs—Analysis Problems

31. Repeat Problem 20 for a J-K master-slave flip-flop.

*32. A master-slave J-K flip-flop has waveforms as shown in Figure 9-29. $Q_0 = 1$. Find the waveform for Q.

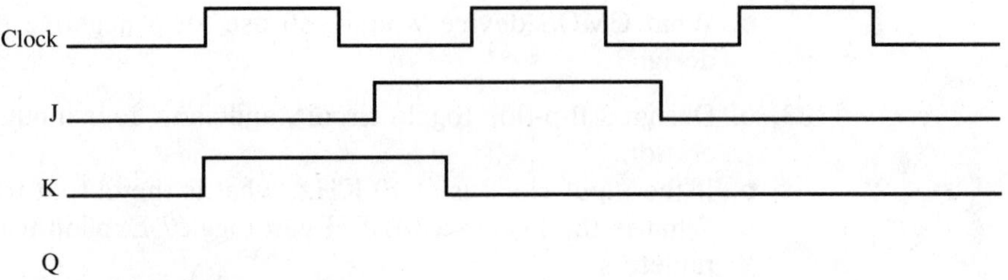

FIGURE 9-29 Problem 9-34

33. Find Q for the flip-flop shown in Figure 9-30.

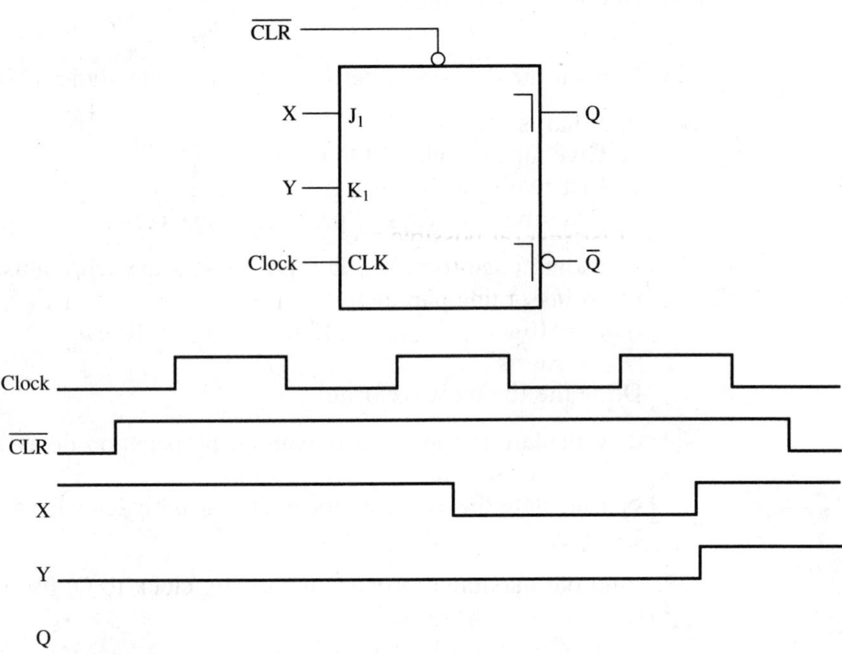

FIGURE 9-30 Problem 9-35

34. a. Examine a TTL data book and find the D flip-flop with the shortest propagation delay.
    b. Examine a TTL data book and find the J-K flip-flop with the shortest propagation delay.
35. Repeat Problem 34 for HC and HCT CMOS flip-flops.
36. a. Explain what happens if inputs to a master-slave flip-flop are changed during the active part (HIGH) of the clock.
    b. Why are master-slave flip-flops no longer selected for digital designs?

37. What is a data lockout flip-flop? Explain its use.

9-8 Flip-Flop Applications—Application Problems

*38. List five specific flip-flop applications.

*39. a. Construct a toggle flip-flop circuit using one flip-flop.
b. If a 100 KHz clock is input, what is the frequency of the output, Q?
c. What is the duty cycle of the output Q?
d. Take the Q output of the circuit in part (a) and input it as the clock of another toggle flip-flop. What is the output frequency and duty cycle of the second flip-flop Q output?

9-9 Troubleshooting Flip-Flops—Troubleshooting Problems

40. A student inputs a 1 KHz clock waveform into a 74LS113 and expects to see 500 Hz at the Q output on the oscilloscope. Instead, the student gets a straight line on the scope.
a. List several possible problems with the circuit.
b. List the troubleshooting methods and steps you would recommend to find out what is wrong with the flip-flop circuit.

41. A student has a flip-flop circuit that seems to operate correctly only when the laboratory instructor is not around. The student also notices, however, that when troubleshooting, the circuit seems to work when a finger is touching some of the pins of the flip-flop IC. What do you think the problem could be? How would you find the problem with the circuit?

42. A student with a D flip-flop only gets a HIGH out of the Q output. The output is HIGH, even if the D input is LOW, and the flip-flop is clocked. V_{CC} and ground on the 74LS74 IC are connected properly. What could the problem be?

43. A student wires one of the flip-flops in a 74109 IC to operate in the toggle mode. The student places a HIGH on both data inputs, and the device always stays HIGH. What is one possible problem with the circuit?

Part 5

ADVANCED SEQUENTIAL LOGIC DESIGN

Chapter 10

Counter Circuits

Upon completing and mastering this chapter, you should be able to perform the following operations in the areas of analysis, application, and design of counter circuits:

ANALYSIS

1. Analyze synchronous and asynchronous counters to determine their repetitive count sequence.
2. Classify synchronous and asynchronous counters, specifying the number of stages in the counter, the count modulus, the frequency division performed by the counter, and the trigger edge that forces the counter to a new count in the sequence.
3. Analyze the operation of counter ICs cascaded together.
4. Analyze the performance of counter circuits to determine the speed of the circuit.
5. Analyze ring counter circuits, including the Johnson counter, the twisted ring counter, the modified twisted ring counter, and the maximum length ring counter.
6. Specify the differences in performance between synchronous and asynchronous counters.
7. Determine the states where glitches will occur in asynchronous counters.
8. Analyze the 74193 and 7490 counters.
9. Troubleshoot counter circuits that are operating incorrectly.
10. Diagnose the cause of incorrectly operating counter circuits and correct the situation so that the counter functions properly.

APPLICATION

11. Determine the criteria for selecting IC counters for specific applications.
12. Specify applications that are appropriate for synchronous counters.
13. Specify applications that are appropriate for asynchronous counters.
14. Decode any count state generated by a synchronous or asynchronous counter.
15. Specify applications that are appropriate for ring counters.
16. Decode any count state generated by a ring counter.
17. Perform frequency division applications using synchronous or asynchronous counters.
18. Cascade IC counters to obtain the necessary frequency division in an application.

DESIGN

19. Design asynchronous counters that count binary numbers up or down.
20. Design synchronous counters that count binary numbers up or down.
21. Design synchronous counters that count any specified binary count sequence.
22. Design self-starting and self-correcting synchronous counters.
23. Design bidirectional counters that count up or down according to an input that controls the direction of the count.
24. Design binary up and down counters using IC counters.
25. Design a time clock that displays A.M. and P.M. times and that can be reset to any hour and minute.

The fundamentals of sequential logic circuits in Chapters 7 through 9 emphasized the need for logic devices with memory capabilities and timing control. The study of basic sequential logic devices focused on the operational characteristics of latches, flip-flops, one-shots, and timers.

The study of advanced sequential logic design focuses on the use of sequential logic circuits in counter and shift register applications. Chapter 10 examines the analysis and design of digital logic counters using flip-flops and IC counter circuits. Chapter 11 examines shift registers designed with flip-flops and specialized shift register integrated circuits (ICs). At the completion of these chapters students should be able to analyze and design counter and shift register circuits for numerous logic applications.

10-1 DIGITAL COUNTER APPLICATIONS

A digital counter is a device that generates binary numbers in a specified count sequence. The counter progresses through the specified sequence of numbers when triggered by an incoming clock waveform, and it advances from one number to the next only on a clock pulse. The counter cycles through the same sequence of numbers continuously so long as there is an incoming clock pulse.

The binary number sequence generated by the digital counter can be used in logic systems to count up or down, to generate truth table input variable sequences for logic circuits, to cycle through addresses of memories in microprocessor applications, to generate waveforms of specific patterns and frequencies, and to activate other logic circuits in a complex process.

Two common types of counters are **decade counters** and **binary counters**. A decade counter counts a sequence of ten numbers, ranging from 0 to 9. The counter generates four output bits whose logic levels correspond to the number in the count sequence. Figure 10-1 shows the output waveforms of a decade counter.

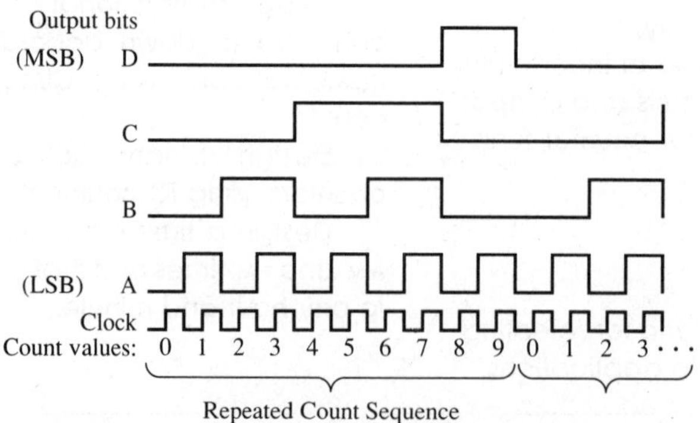

FIGURE 10-1 Decade Counter Output Waveforms

A binary counter counts a sequence of binary numbers. A binary counter with four output bits counts 2^4 or 16 numbers in its sequence, ranging from 0 to 15. Figure 10-2 shows the output waveforms of a 4-bit binary counter.

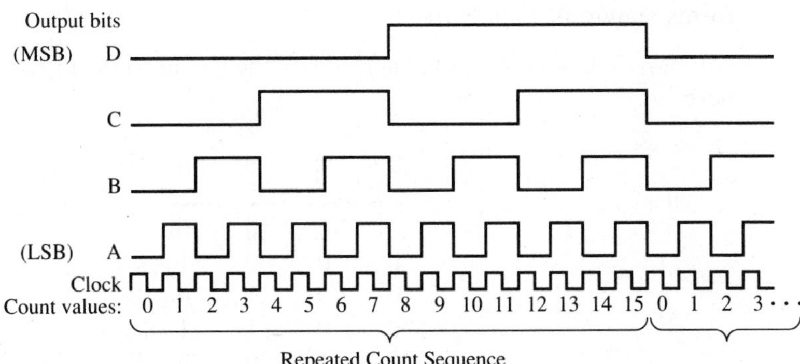

FIGURE 10-2 Binary Counter Output Waveforms

■ EXAMPLE 10-1 Decade Counter

Problem: Determine the 4-bit decade counter output that corresponds to the waveforms shown in Figure 10-1. Determine the time required for the counter to generate the entire count sequence if the input clock has a period of 1 ms.

Solution: The count sequence generated by the decade counter whose waveforms are shown in Figure 10-1 is listed here:

D	C	B	A
0	0	0	0
0	0	0	1
0	0	1	0
0	0	1	1
0	1	0	0
0	1	0	1
0	1	1	0
0	1	1	1
1	0	0	0
1	0	0	1

The time necessary to generate the decade count sequence is 10 ms if the input clock has a 1 ms period. ■

■ EXAMPLE 10-2 Four-Bit Binary Counter

Problem: Determine the 4 bit output that corresponds to the output waveforms shown in Figure 10-2.

Solution: The 4-bit output generated by the waveforms in Figure 10-2 is listed here.

D	C	B	A
0	0	0	0
0	0	0	1
0	0	1	0
0	0	1	1
0	1	0	0
0	1	0	1
0	1	1	0
0	1	1	1
1	0	0	0
1	0	0	1
1	0	1	0
1	0	1	1
1	1	0	0
1	1	0	1
1	1	1	0
1	1	1	1

■

■ EXAMPLE 10-3 Four-Bit Binary Counter Timing

Problem: Determine the period and frequency of each output waveform shown in Figure 10-2 if the input clock has a period of 1 ms.

Solution: A output:

Period = 2 ms, frequency = 500 Hz

B output:

Period = 4 ms, frequency = 250 Hz

C output:

Period = 8 ms, frequency = 125 Hz

D output:

Period = 16 ms, frequency = 62.5 Hz

■

Section Self-Test

1. What is a decade counter?
2. What is a binary counter?
3. What relationship is there between the frequency output from each bit of a binary counter?

ANSWERS (Not necessarily in the order of the questions)

- The frequency of the least significant bit is one half the clock frequency. The frequency of each bit is one half the frequency of the previous output.
- Counts binary numbers in a sequence, either up or down. For a binary counter with n bits, there are 2^n count values in the sequence.
- Counts a sequence of ten values.

10-2 COUNTER CLASSIFICATION

Digital logic counters can be classified according to their operational characteristics. The key characteristics that must be determined through analyzing the counter circuit are the count modulus, counter stages, output bits, frequency division, asynchronous operation, synchronous operation, and trigger characteristics, as described in Sections 10.2.1 through 10.2.6.

10.2.1 Count Modulus

The **count modulus** is the total number of **states** or values generated by the counter as it progresses through its specified sequence. The modulus, or **MOD**, is one of the most important characteristics to specify when classifying a counter since it identifies the number of values in the count sequence and determines the frequency division capabilities of the counter. **Decade counters** always have a **modulus of 10** and are sometimes referred to as **MOD-10 counters**. **Binary counters** of n bits have a **modulus of 2^n**.

Figures 10-1 and 10-2 show that the modulus of a counter can be determined by a waveform generated by the counter. A count modulus can also be designated by a **state transition diagram**. The states of a counter are the output numbers generated by the counter. A state transition diagram shows the progression of the number generated from one clock pulse to the next. The total number of states in the diagram is the modulus of the counter. Figure 10-3 shows the state transition diagrams for the decade counter and binary counter whose waveforms were shown in Figures 10-1 and 10-2.

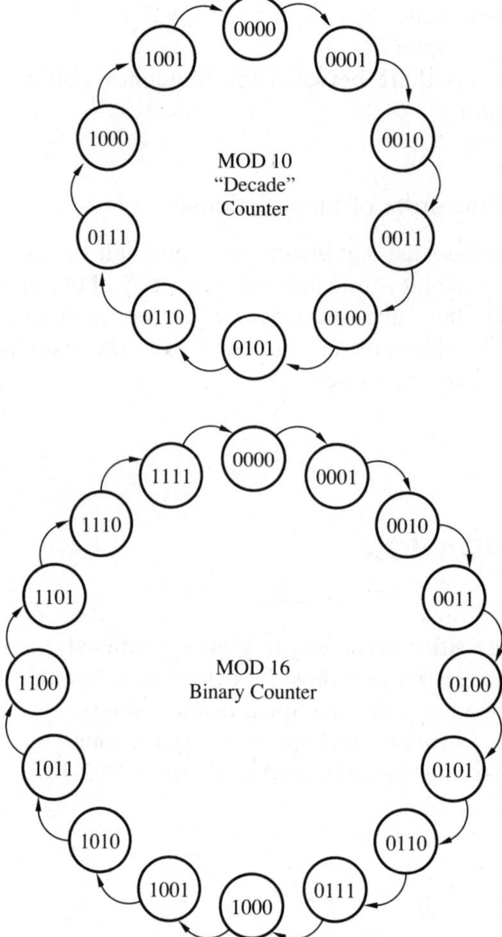

FIGURE 10-3 Counter State Transition Diagrams

10.2.2 Counter Stages or Bits

The number of **output bits** of a counter is equal to the flip-flop **stages** of the counter. A MOD-2^n counter requires n stages or flip-flops in order to produce a count sequence of the desired length. The first stage of a counter is the **least significant bit (LSB)**. The last stage of a counter is the **most significant bit (MSB)**.

10.2.3 Frequency Division

Digital counters function as frequency dividers since they *divide the input control clock frequency by the modulus of the counter*. As shown in Example

10-2 for binary counters that count up or down in a counting sequence, the clock frequency is divided by 2 at the output of each stage of the counter.

The output waveform produced at the most significant output stage has a frequency of 1/modulus of the counter. Therefore, a ''MOD-16'' counter can also be referred to as a ''divide-by-16'' counter. The waveform in Figures 10-1 and 10-2 demonstrate these frequency division characteristics.

Frequency division is an important property that is required when designing digital clock circuits or other applications needing several frequencies that are integer factors of the original clock signal. Counters serve the significant function of producing output waveforms that are synchronous with the incoming clock but are divided by a factor of 2 at each stage of the counter.

10.2.4 Asynchronous Counters

Asynchronous counters are also referred to as **ripple counters**. The incoming clock waveform is routed into the first stage of the counter, which generates the LSB of the numbers in the count sequence. The output of the LSB stage serves as the clock input to the next stage. Each stage of an asynchronous counter obtains its clock signal from the output of the prior stage, which results in the clock signal rippling through all the flip-flops of the counter. A 4-bit asynchronous counter is shown in Figure 10-4.

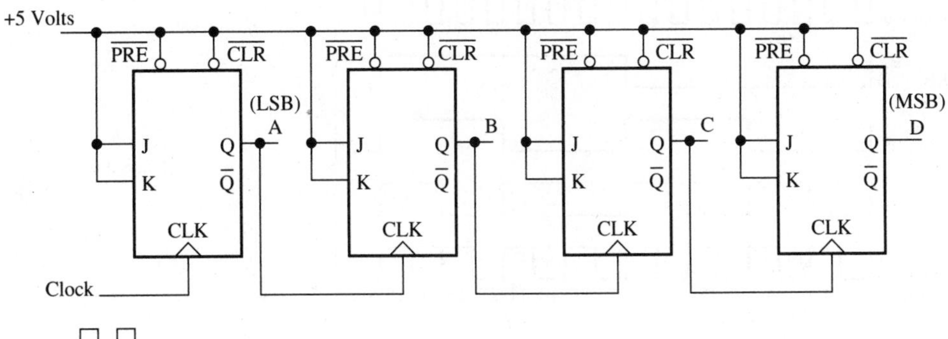

FIGURE 10-4 Four-Bit Asychronous Counter

10.2.5 Synchronous Counters

Synchronous counters are constructed with one common clock signal as the input to all the flip-flops simultaneously. The clock does not ripple through the counter stages. Synchronous counters are also referred to as **parallel counters** due to the parallel manner that the clock is fed to all the counter stages. Figure 10-5 shows the basic configuration of a 4-bit synchronous counter.

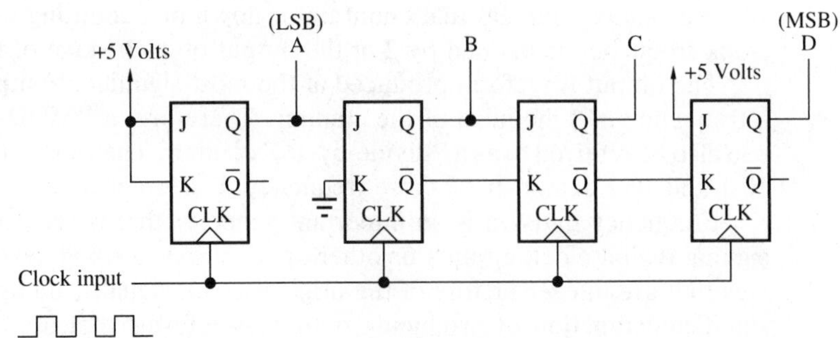

FIGURE 10-5 Four-Bit Synchronous Counter

10.2.6 Counter Triggering

A counter is classified as a **positive edge-triggered** or **negative edge-triggered** device, depending on the trigger characteristic of the flip-flop circuits that form the counter. It is important to know the triggering of the counter because the count states only change on the triggering edge of the incoming clock. Figure 10-6 compares the output waveforms for a positive edge-triggered and negative edge-triggered 4-bit binary counter. Notice the timing shift relative to the incoming clock pulse.

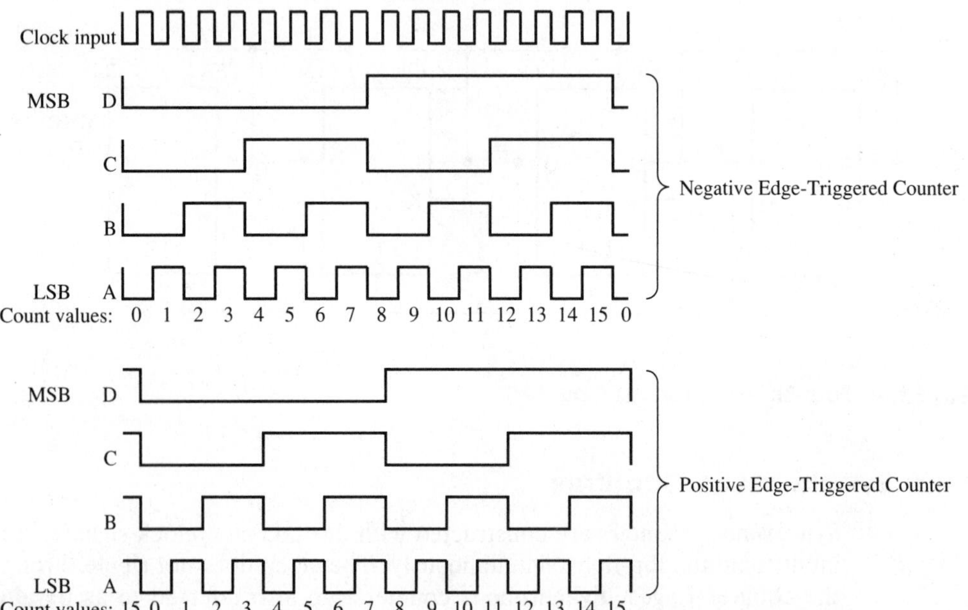

FIGURE 10-6 Negative Edge-Triggered versus Positive Edge-Triggered Counter Waveforms

■ EXAMPLE 10-4 Decade Counter Classification

Problem: Classify as completely as possible the counter circuit that generated the waveforms shown in Figure 10-1.

Solution: It cannot be determined from these waveforms whether or not the counter is a synchronous or asynchronous counter. However, all other aspects of the counter can be determined: It is a MOD-10 4-bit decade counter that has a frequency division of 10 and counts a sequence of binary coded decimal (BCD) values from 0 to 9 triggered on the positive edge of the input clock. ■

■ EXAMPLE 10-5 Binary Counter Classification

Problem: Classify the 4-bit binary counter circuit that generated the waveforms in Figure 10-2.

Solution: As stated in Example 10-3, the waveforms shown cannot positively identify the counter circuit as synchronous or asynchronous. However, all other characteristics can be classified. The binary counter is a 4-bit MOD-16 positive edge-triggered counter circuit. The A output stage has a frequency of one half the original clock signal; each stage divides the frequency of the previous stage by one half; and the final output, D, has a frequency of $\frac{1}{16}$ the original clock frequency. ■

Section Self-Test

1. What is the count modulus?
2. Must the states in the count modulus be in counting order?
3. Where does the greatest frequency division take place, at the LSB or MSB output of a counter?

ANSWERS (Not necessarily in the order of the questions)

- No
- MSB
- The number of count states that are in the repetitive count pattern

10-3 COUNTER ANALYSIS

Counter analysis is the procedure used to determine the operation of a counter circuit and to classify the operation. The counter circuit must be analyzed to determine the modulus, the "divide-by" factor of the

counter, the number of stages, whether it is asynchronous or synchronous, the triggering of the flip-flops, whether it is an up or down counter, and the count sequence of the counter.

A counter circuit should be analyzed following these seven steps:

1. *Observe the counter system clock.* If it is common to all flip-flop stages, the counter is **synchronous**. If it is not common to all flip-flop stages, the counter is **asynchronous**.
2. *Determine the number of stages of the counter* by counting the flip-flops or outputs.
3. *Observe the type of flip-flops used in the counter circuit,* noting their triggering and operation. Most asynchronous counters are built from toggle flip-flops.
4. For asynchronous counters built with toggle flip-flops, *determine the operation of the counter through* ***waveform analysis****.*
5. *Determine the* ***output waveforms*** *from the clock stages relative to the input clock waveform.* For toggle flip-flops, the output signal changes from HIGH to LOW continuously on the clock trigger point.
6. *Determine the modulus of the counter.*
7. *Construct a state transition diagram to describe the counter operation.*

■ EXAMPLE 10-6 Two-Bit Binary Counter Analysis

Problem: Analyze the 2-bit counter shown in Figure 10-7.

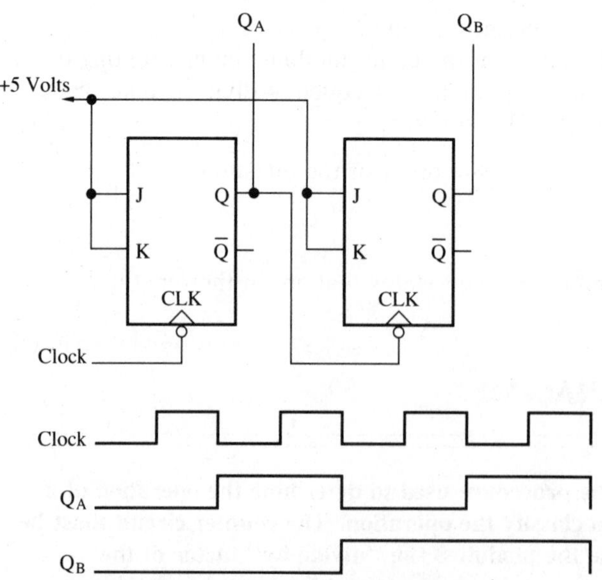

FIGURE 10-7 Example 10-6 Two-Bit Binary Counter Analysis

Solution: The counter in Figure 10-7 has two flip-flops and two output bits, therefore it is a **two stage** counter. The input clock does not trigger both flip-flops, and thus it is an asynchronous counter circuit. The Q_A output is used as the clock to the second stage of the flip-flop. The J-K flip-flops have the J and K inputs tied high, so they are considered **toggle** flip-flops. The flip-flops are shown as **negative edge-triggered** devices. The waveforms are analyzed to determine the count sequence. The initial state of Q_A and Q_B is assumed to be a logic-LOW. The waveforms are drawn so that the Q_A output triggers on the negative edge of the input clock and the Q_B output triggers on the negative edge of the Q_A output.

From the waveforms it can be seen that Q_A is the LSB of the count sequence, and its frequency is one half the input clock frequency. The Q_B output is the MSB of the count sequence, and its frequency is one quarter the input clock frequency. The count sequence can be determined from the waveform. The sequence is listed here.

Q_B	Q_A
0	0
0	1
1	0
1	1

From the count sequence it is determined that the counter is a MOD-4 binary up counter. ■

More complex examples of the analysis of synchronous and asynchronous counters are shown in Sections 10.5.1 and 10.6.1.

Section Self-Test

1. What is the difference between an asynchronous and synchronous counter?
2. What is the maximum modulus of a 3-bit counter?
3. What is a positive edge-triggered counter?

ANSWERS (Not necessarily in the order of the questions)

- 8
- In a synchronous counter the same input clock controls all the flip-flops in the counter circuit. In an asynchronous counter the input clock only controls the LSB stage. The other flip-flops obtain their clock signal from the output of prior flip-flop stages.
- The counter output changes value on the positive edge of the input clock.

10-4 COUNT STATE DECODING

Counter applications often require decoding the output count states produced by a counter. Counter decoding can be used to shorten a count

sequence, to enable other logic circuits when a specific count state is reached, or to display the count state as a decimal number.

Decoding a count state means that a signal is activated for only one count state. The concept of decoding was first studied in Chapter 5. Simple active-HIGH decoding can be accomplished with an AND gate, whereas active-LOW decoding requires the use of a NAND gate.

Count states are decoded by forming a "minterm" of the variables that represent the desired count sequence. For example, in order to decode the output state 1101, the output variables $Q_D Q_C \overline{Q}_B Q_A$ are ANDed together. The output from the AND gate is high only when the input logic levels represent the value 13. Replacing the AND gate with a NAND gate would result in an active-LOW output signal for the decoded count state of 1101.

If numerous count states have to be decoded, then a digital IC decoder such as the 74LS138 or 74LS154 should be used to simplify the circuitry. When the count states have to be decoded and displayed, a display decoder/driver such as the 74LS47 can be used with a light emitted diode (LED) display.

■ EXAMPLE 10-7 Count State Decoding

Problem: In the case of the binary counter that generated the waveforms shown in Figure 10-2, determine the terms required for active-LOW decoding of states 1, 3, 9, 13, and 15.

Solution: The output values of the states to be decoded are listed here, along with the minterm required for active-LOW decoding of each state:

Count State	D C B A	Decoding Minterm
1	0 0 0 1	$\overline{\overline{D}\ \overline{C}\ \overline{B}\ A}$
3	0 0 1 1	$\overline{\overline{D}\ \overline{C}\ B\ A}$
9	1 0 0 1	$\overline{D\ \overline{C}\ \overline{B}\ A}$
13	1 1 0 1	$\overline{D\ C\ \overline{B}\ A}$
15	1 1 1 1	$\overline{D\ C\ B\ A}$

■

Section Self-Test

1. What is meant by "decoding" a count state?
2. When should NAND gates be used for count state decoding?
3. When should an IC decoder, such as the 74138 or 74154 be used for count state decoding?

ANSWERS (Not necessarily in the order of the questions)

- For active-LOW decoding

- When several count states must be decoded, an IC decoder can decode numerous count states with a single IC. Individual logic gates, such as NANDs or ANDs, require one gate and inverters for each decoded state, resulting in the use of several ICs.
- The occurrence of a single count state activates a logic circuit to produce an output signal.

10-5 ASYNCHRONOUS COUNTER CIRCUITS

Asynchronous counters do not have a common clock that controls all the flip-flop stages. The control clock is input into the first stage, or the LSB stage of the counter. The clock for each subsequent stage is obtained from the output from the prior flip-flop stage.

Toggle flip-flops are used almost exclusively in the design of asynchronous counters. With the toggle flip-flop, the output state toggles between a logic HIGH and a logic LOW on each clock pulse. The external clock that controls the flip-flop output state is input into the LSB stage. Either the true or inverted output from the flip-flop can serve as the output bit value to form the count state or as the clock to the next stage in the counter circuit.

For any given asynchronous counter circuit, the count direction for counting serially up or down is dependent on the triggering of the flip-flops. An asynchronous counter designed for positive edge-triggered flip-flops will not generate the desired count sequence if negative edge-triggered flip-flops are substituted in the circuit design. Analyzing waveforms into and out of the flip-flops is crucial to obtaining a properly functioning circuit.

Asynchronous counters often experience many timing and glitch problems due to the cumulative propagation delays resulting from the clock ripple action through the flip-flop stages. The effects of the delays worsen with increased counter size and limit the input clock rate.

The design procedures for asynchronous serial counters are relatively simple. Techniques for analyzing the operation and designing asynchronous counters are the subject of Sections 10.5.1 and 10.5.2.

10.5.1 Asynchronous Counter Analysis

Asynchronous counter analysis is carried out according to the procedures specified in Section 10.3. A detailed procedure to follow for analyzing asynchronous counters is demonstrated in Examples 10-8 and 10-9.

■ EXAMPLE 10-8 Asynchronous Counter Analysis

Problem: Analyze the operation of the counter in Figure 10-4.

Solution: By observing the circuit in Figure 10-4, it can be seen that it is a 4-bit positive edge-triggered asynchronous counter.

Begin the waveform analysis by drawing an input clock waveform. Assume a 50% duty cycle unless otherwise known. Then graph the output waveforms from each flip-flop stage of the counter. Note that only the LSB stage is triggered by the input clock; all other stages are triggered by an output from the previous stage. The waveforms are shown in Figure 10-8.

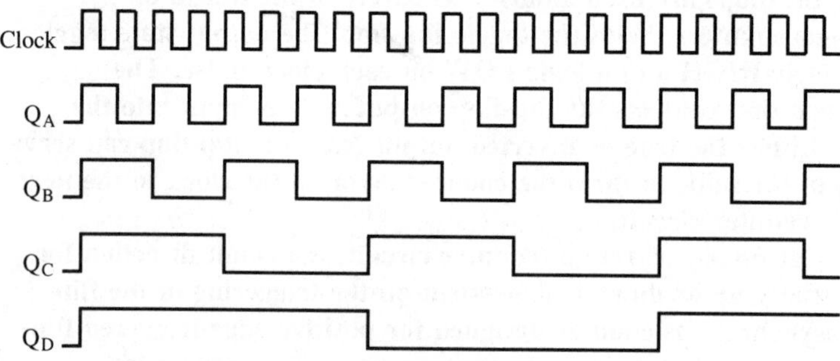

FIGURE 10-8 Example 10-8 Waveforms

The state transition diagram, derived from the waveforms, is shown in Figure 10-9.

The counter classification is completed by summarizing the characteristics displayed in the state transition diagram:

- MOD 16
- Divide by 16
- Asynchronous
- Four-bit
- Positive edge triggered
- Binary down counter

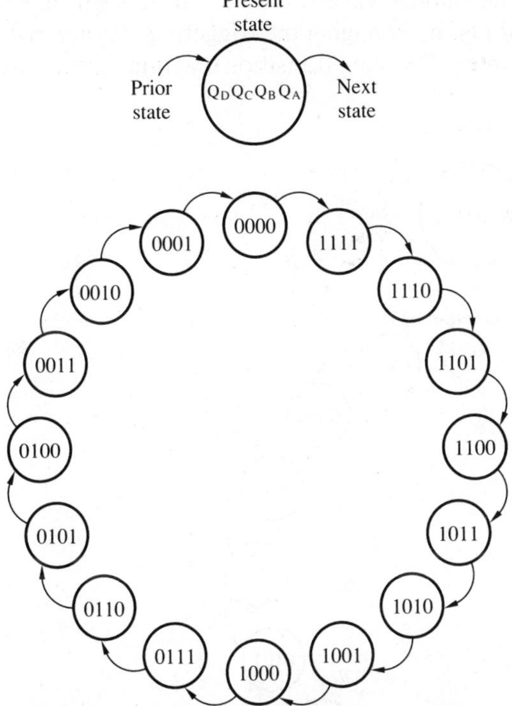

FIGURE 10-9 Example 10-8 State Transition Diagram

EXAMPLE 10-9 Asynchronous Counter Analysis

Problem: For the counter circuit shown in Figure 10-4, replace positive edge-triggered flip-flops with negative edge-triggered flip-flops and analyze the operation of the circuit.

Solution: The output waveforms are graphed in Figure 10-10 to determine the operation of the counter.

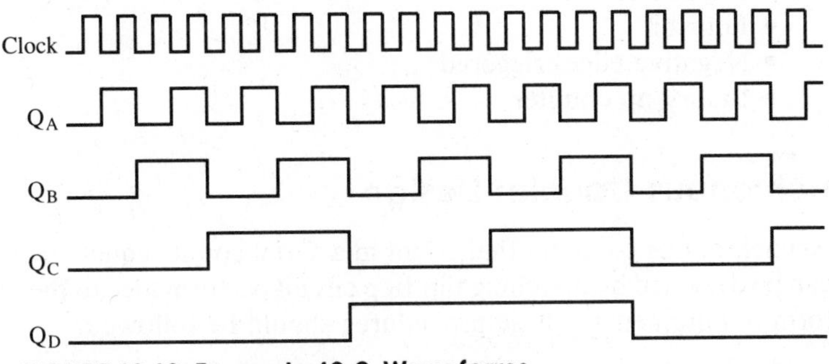

FIGURE 10-10 Example 10-9 Waveforms

By observing the output waveforms, it can be seen that the count direction has changed just by changing the triggering characteristic of the flip-flop forming the counter. The state transition diagram for this circuit is shown in Figure 10-11.

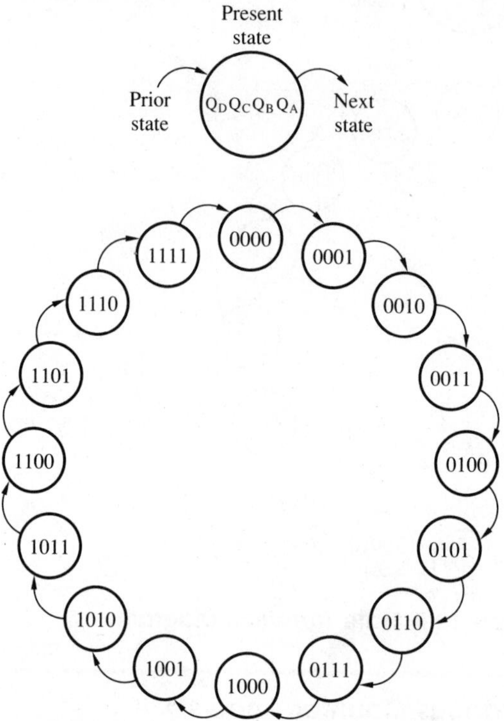

FIGURE 10-11 Example 10-9 State Transition Diagram

The counter classification is summarized here:

- MOD 16
- Divide by 16
- Asynchronous
- Four-bit
- Negative edge-triggered
- Binary up counter ■

10.5.2 Asynchronous Counter Design

Asynchronous counters that count in a serial count sequence of up or down can be designed by matching flip-flop circuit performance to the output waveform requirements. These procedures should be followed:

1. *Specify the operational requirements of the counter,* including the number of *stages, modulus,* and *trigger characteristics.*

2. *Graph the required output waveforms.*
3. *Determine the necessary output to use as the clock input to the following stage.* Either the true or complemented output could serve as the clock signal.
4. *Verify the design through analysis and testing.*

■ EXAMPLE 10-10 Asynchronous Counter Design

Problem: Design a 4-bit, MOD-16, asynchronous binary up counter using positive edge-triggered toggle flip-flops.

Solution: By observing the output waveforms for a binary up counter, such as those shown in Figure 10-8, it can be seen that the proper count sequence for a 4-bit binary up counter could be achieved by using the inverted outputs from the flip-flops stages of the counter. Therefore, the counter circuit uses the inverted outputs to produce the output count states, while the true outputs provide the clock signal to the next stage of the counter. The desired counter output waveforms are shown in Figure 10-12, and the counter circuit is shown in Figure 10-13.

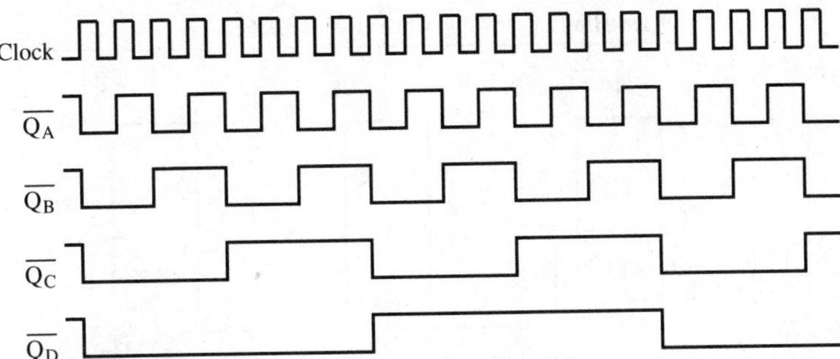

FIGURE 10-12 Example 10-10 Waveforms

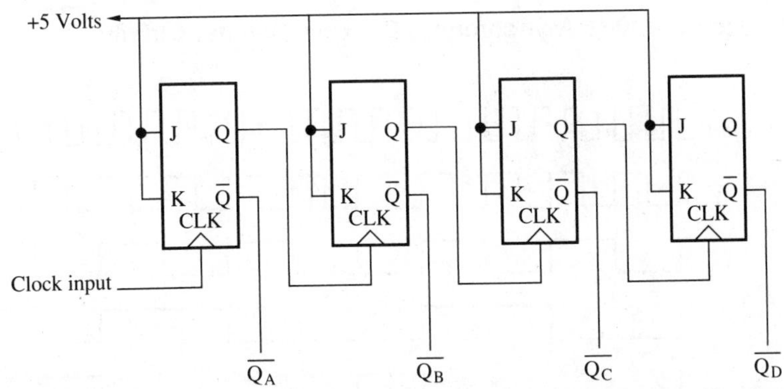

FIGURE 10-13 Example 10-10 Asynchronous Four-Bit Binary Up Counter ■

■ EXAMPLE 10-11 Counter Decoding

Problem: Design a MOD-10 asynchronous counter by shortening the count sequence of the counter circuit designed in Example 10-10. (*Hint:* Use the active-LOW asynchronous clear input on the flip-flops to reset the counter to zero.)

Solution: A decade or MOD-10 counter can be designed that counts only from 0 to 9. The MOD-16 counter of Example 10-10 can be redesigned to produce a MOD-10 count sequence by adding a decoding circuit. The decoding circuit resets the counter back to zero after the ten count states so that it only counts 0 to 9 repetitively.

The counter will produce the output 1 0 1 0 as its eleventh count state, but this state is not desired. Therefore, decode the output state 1 0 1 0 and reset the counter back to zero using the asynchronous clear inputs to the flip-flops. Decoding the state 1 0 1 0 and clearing the counter to 0 0 0 0 results in a glitch in one of the waveforms. This glitch serves as the clear signal to reset the flip-flops. Figure 10-14 shows the modified counter circuit and Figure 10-15 shows the resulting output waveforms.

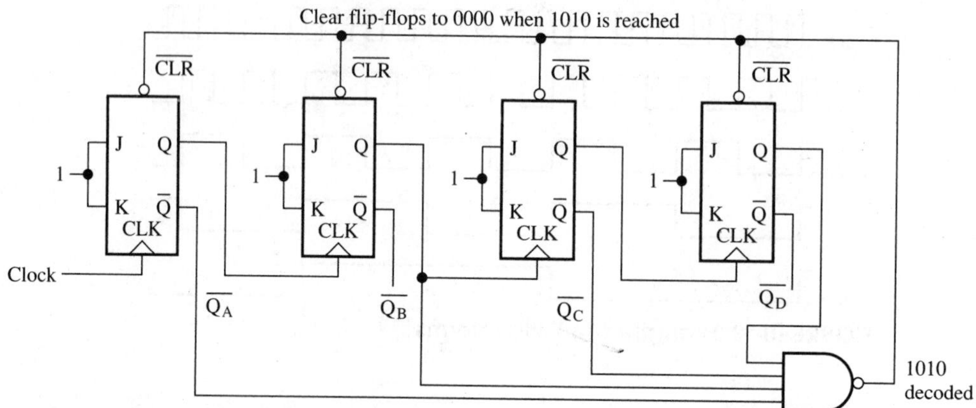

FIGURE 10-14 Example 10-11 Asynchronous Decade Counter Circuit

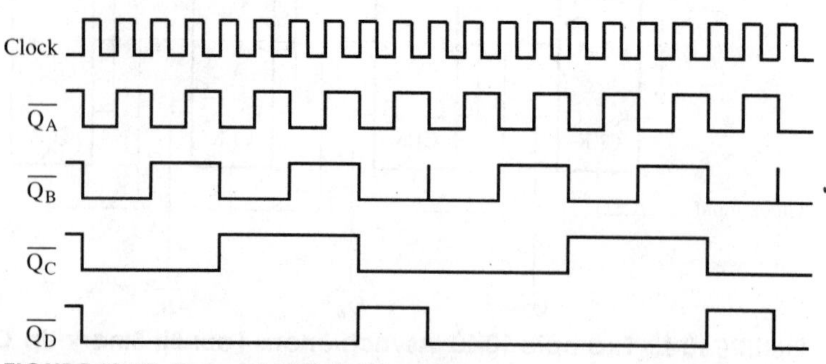

FIGURE 10-15 Example 10-11 Waveforms

■

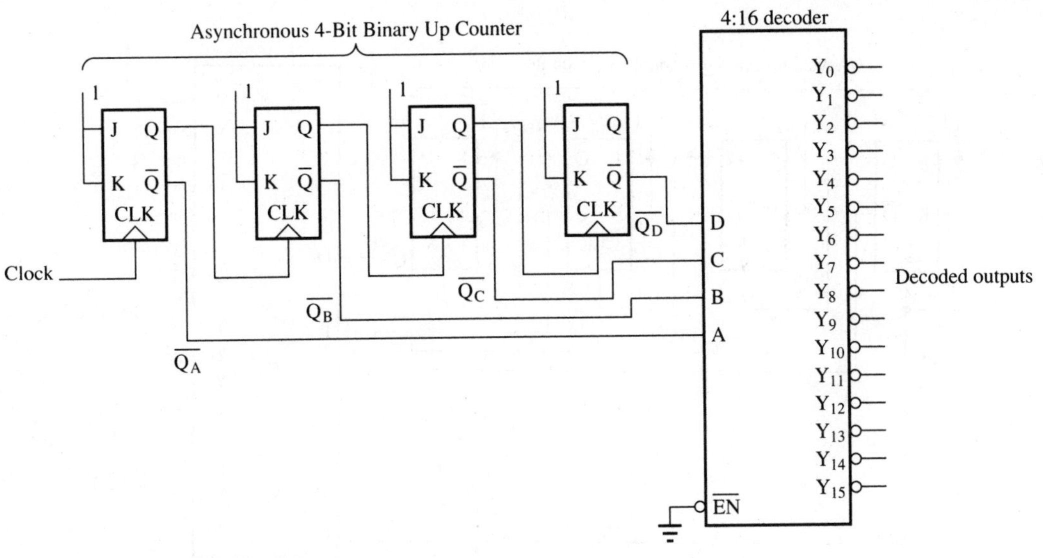

Clock
$\overline{Q_A}$
$\overline{Q_B}$
$\overline{Q_C}$
$\overline{Q_D}$
Counter outputs
Y_0
Y_1
Y_2
Y_3
Y_4
Y_5
Y_6
Y_7
Y_8
Y_9
Y_{10}
Y_{11}
Y_{12}
Y_{13}
Y_{14}
Y_{15}
Decoder outputs

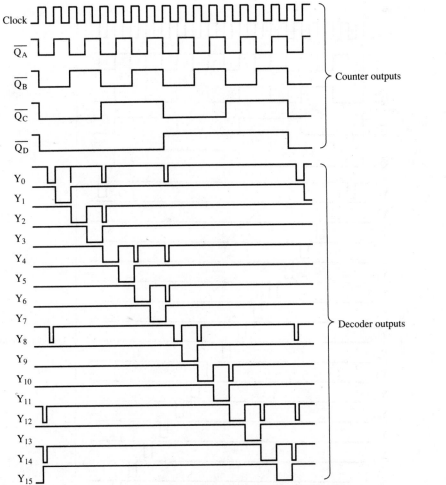

FIGURE 10-16 Asynchronous Counter with Decoded Output Glitches

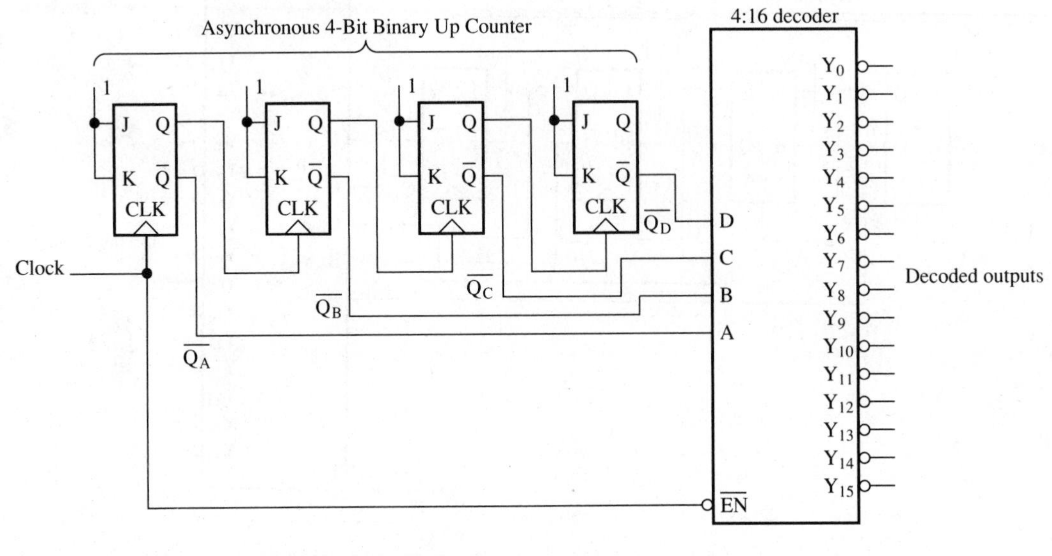

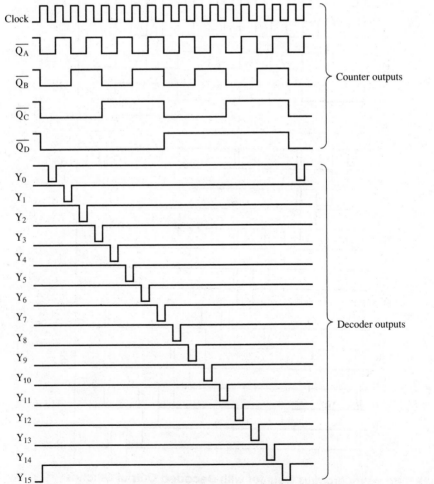

Clock
$\overline{Q_A}$
$\overline{Q_B}$
$\overline{Q_C}$
$\overline{Q_D}$
Counter outputs
Y_0 Y_1 Y_2 Y_3 Y_4 Y_5 Y_6 Y_7 Y_8 Y_9 Y_{10} Y_{11} Y_{12} Y_{13} Y_{14} Y_{15}
Decoder outputs

FIGURE 10-17 Asynchronous Counter with No Decoded Output Glitches

10.5.3 Asynchronous Counter Timing

The ripple configuration of the clock in an asynchronous counter results in glitches and timing delays in the output waveform due to propagation delays at each flip-flop stage. The timing delay worsens as the signal passes through each flip-flop stage.

The results of the propagation delays with the asynchronous clock configuration can best be seen at the output of a binary decoder connected to the asynchronous counter. Figure 10-16 shows the circuit and resulting timing diagram at the output of the decoder.

One method of eliminating glitches in the decoder output is to enable the decoder with the clock signal so that the decoder output is only active while the clock pulse is LOW. This would give the counter outputs an opportunity to settle to their final and correct count state prior to being decoded. Figure 10-17 shows the improved counter circuit and output waveforms without glitches.

Section Self-Test

1. Why do asynchronous counters have glitches in their decoded outputs?
2. What output states are decoded to produce the glitches and which output state produces the most glitches?
3. How can glitches be eliminated in the decoded output?

ANSWERS (Not necessarily in the order of the questions)

- Glitches result when more than one bit must change from one count state to another. The stages of the counter do not change simultaneously since they are not triggered by a common clock.
- Eliminate glitches by enabling the decoder when the clock is LOW for a positive edge-triggered asynchronous counter. Eliminate the glitches by enabling the decoder when the clock is HIGH for a negative edge-triggered asynchronous counter.
- Glitches result when the even-numbered states occur inadvertently. The most common state that produces output glitches is when all bits of the counter are LOW.

10-6 SYNCHRONOUS COUNTERS

Synchronous digital counters have a common clock signal that controls all flip-flop stages. Since a common clock controls all flip-flops simultaneously, there are no cumulative delays that result when a clock signal must ripple through the stages, as in the case of asynchronous counters.

Synchronous counters can count up and down, and can be designed to produce special purpose count sequences of nonconsecutive numbers.

The count sequence produced by a synchronous counter is not dependent on the trigger characteristics of the flip-flops that comprise the count stages. The count sequence is achieved by applying the required logic function into the flip-flops.

10.6.1 Synchronous Counter Analysis

Synchronous counters can be analyzed by using a procedure similar to the analysis of asynchronous counters to classify fully or define the counter operation.

Analyze a synchronous counter circuit by proceeding through the following steps:

1. *Verify that the counter system clock is common to all flip-flop stages and that the circuit is in fact a synchronous counter.*
2. *Determine the number of stages of the counter* by counting the flip-flops or outputs.
3. *Determine the type of flip-flops and the input logic function for each stage.* For reference, recall the present state-present input-next state table for each flip-flop.
4. *Construct a present input-present state-next state table for the counter circuit to determine the inputs to the flip-flops and the resulting outputs.*
5. *Analyze the counter using the present input-present state-next state table to determine the complete count sequence.* Continue the analysis until the count sequence begins to repeat.
6. *Determine the modulus of the counter.*
7. *Construct a state transition diagram to describe the counter operation.*
8. *Graph the output waveforms produced by the counter.*

The key to the synchronous counter analysis is the present state-present input-next state table that serves as a truth table description of the counter operation as it progresses with each clock pulse. To complete this table properly, we need to define correctly the flip-flops of each stage by their own present input-present state-next state table.

Thorough examples of synchronous counter analysis are illustrated in Examples 10–12 and 10–13.

■ EXAMPLE 10-12 Synchronous Counter Analysis

Problem: Analyze the counter circuit shown in Figure 10-18.

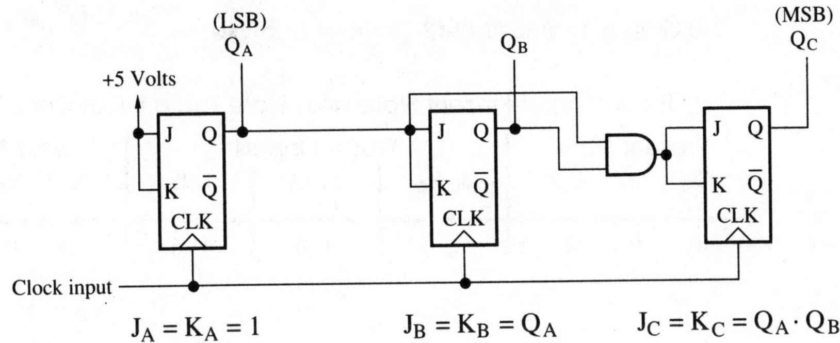

FIGURE 10-18 Example 10-12 Synchronous Counter

Solution: The circuit in Figure 10-18 is a three-stage synchronous counter since a common clock signal controls all four J-K flip-flop stages of the counter. The J-K flip-flop operation is defined in Table 10-1.
The present input-present state-next table describing the counter operation is constructed with the initial present state of the flip-flops assumed to be a logic-LOW. The J and K inputs can be specified according to their logic equations:

Present states $Q_C, Q_B, Q_A = 0, 0, 0$

Present inputs $J_C = K_C = Q_A Q_B$

$J_B = K_B = Q_A$

$J_A = K_A = 1$

TABLE 10-1 J-K Flip-Flop Operation

Present Inputs J	Present Inputs K	Present State Q_N	Next State Q_{N+1}
0	0	0	0 Hold
0	0	1	1
0	1	0	0 Reset (clear)
0	1	1	0
1	0	0	1 Set
1	0	1	1
1	1	0	1 Toggle
1	1	1	0

TABLE 10-2 Example 10-12 Counter Analysis

Present Input-Present State-Next State Table Initial Conditions

Present State			Present Inputs			Next State		
Q_C	Q_B	Q_A	$J_C K_C$	$J_B K_B$	$J_A K_A$	Q_C	Q_B	Q_A
0	0	0	0 0	0 0	1 1	0	0	1

The first entries in the present input-present state-next state table are shown in Table 10-2. The next output state is determined by the present inputs and present state of each flip-flop. Given the initial input conditions, the Q_A output will toggle and the Q_B and Q_C outputs will remain unchanged. The resulting 0, 0, 1 output state is recorded in the table as the next state.

The analysis continues for all possible count states that can be generated by a 3-bit counter. The next count state is determined by each present state and the present inputs. The analysis of each present state and the resulting next state is shown in Table 10-3.

The counter sequence resulting from the analysis is defined in the state transition diagram shown in Figure 10-19, and the waveforms resulting from this circuit are shown in Figure 10-20. Each output changes on the positive edge of the input clock. Note that the glitches occurring with the asynchronous counter do not occur with the synchronous counter.

TABLE 10-3 Example 10-12 Counter Analysis

Present Input-Present State-Next State Table Completed

Present State			Present Inputs			Next State		
Q_C	Q_B	Q_A	$J_C K_C$	$J_B K_B$	$J_A K_A$	Q_C	Q_B	Q_A
0	0	0	0 0	0 0	1 1	0	0	1
0	0	1	0 0	1 1	1 1	0	1	0
0	1	0	0 0	0 0	1 1	0	1	1
0	1	1	1 1	1 1	1 1	1	0	0
1	0	0	0 0	0 0	1 1	1	0	1
1	0	1	0 0	1 1	1 1	1	1	0
1	1	0	0 0	0 0	1 1	1	1	1
1	1	1	1 1	1 1	1 1	0	0	0

The counter classification is summarized as follows:

- MOD 8
- Divide by 8
- Three-bit
- Synchronous
- Binary up counter

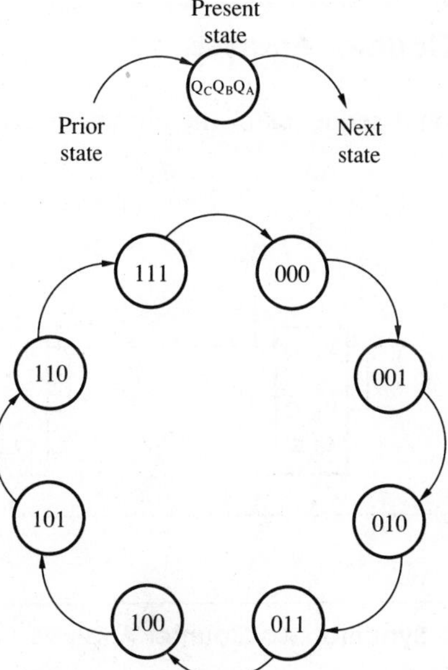

FIGURE 10-19 Example 10-12 State Transition Diagram

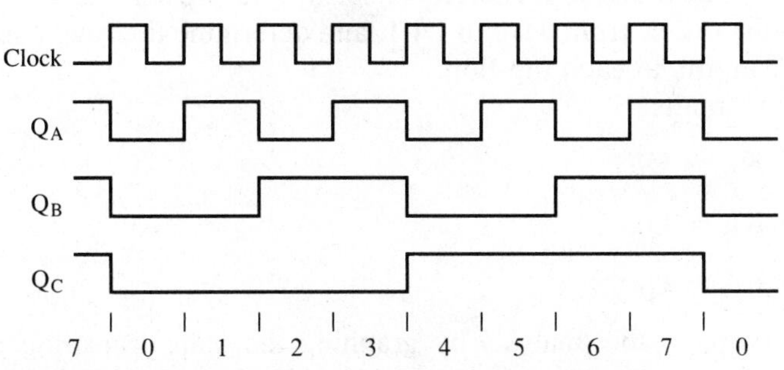

FIGURE 10-20 Example 10-12 Output Waveforms

■

Synchronous counters can produce a count sequence that is not in counting order. Digital security locks might need a counter that generates a random sequence of numbers to serve as a password that must be matched by an appropriate input. Other applications that can use a nonserial count feature are ones where the counter output is decoded to enable certain circuits within a digital system. An example of such a counter is featured in Example 10-13.

■ EXAMPLE 10-13 Synchronous Counter Analysis

Problem: Determine the count sequence of the circuit shown in Figure 10-21.

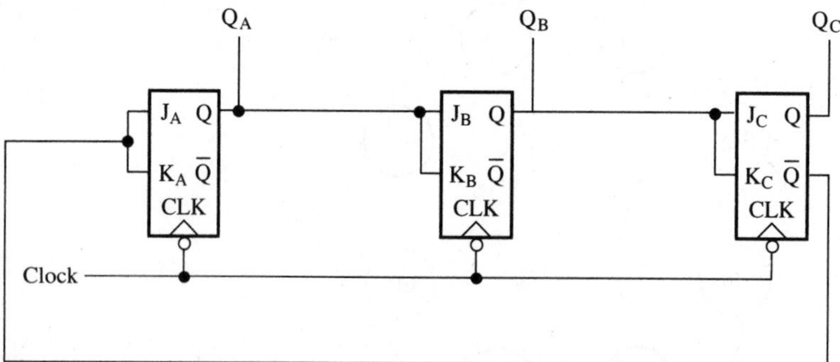

FIGURE 10-21 Example 10-13 Synchronous Counter Analysis

Solution: Analyze the counter by completing a present input-present state-next state table to determine the operation of the counter for all possible output states. The counter is a 3-bit counter. All 2^3 count states must be analyzed in the table. Therefore, set up the present states on the table in counting order, from 0 0 0 to 1 1 1, and determine their next state as a result of the inputs to each flip-flop.
Present inputs:

$$J_A = K_A = Q_C$$

$$J_B = K_B = Q_A$$

$$J_C = K_C = Q_B$$

Complete the analysis by graphing the state transition diagram. The present input-present state-next state table is shown in Table 10-4. The state transition diagram is shown in Figure 10-22.

TABLE 10-4 Example 10-13 Counter Analysis

Present State-Present Inputs-Next State Table

Present State			Present Inputs						Next State		
Q_C	Q_B	Q_A	J_C	K_C	J_B	K_B	J_A	K_A	Q_C	Q_B	Q_A
0	0	0	0	0	0	0	1	1	0	0	1
0	0	1	0	0	1	1	1	1	0	1	0
0	1	0	1	1	0	0	1	1	1	1	1
0	1	1	1	1	1	1	1	1	1	0	0
1	0	0	0	0	0	0	0	0	1	0	0
1	0	1	0	0	1	1	0	0	1	1	1
1	1	0	1	1	0	0	0	0	0	1	0
1	1	1	1	1	1	1	0	0	0	0	1

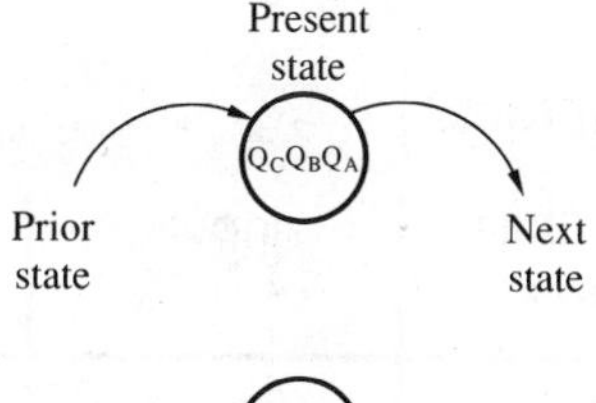

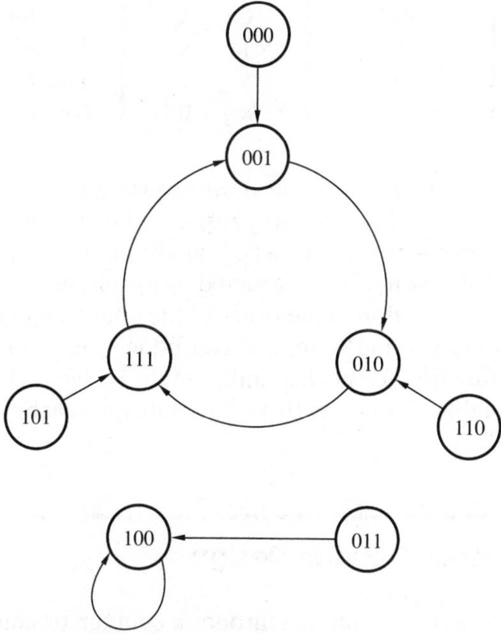

FIGURE 10-22 Example 10-13 State Transition Diagram

From the state transition shown in Figure 10-22, it can be seen that this is a MOD-3 counter that has a "lockout loop." A lockout loop, usually an undesirable situation for most applications, is a repetitive count sequence that is not part of the intended modulus of the counter. In this example the lockout loop can cause the counter to remain in the 1, 0, 0 state forever once it gets into that state. If this state is not desirable in a digital system, the counter should be redesigned to be **self-starting** so that all possible states lead to the count sequence. ■

10.6.2 Synchronous Counter Design

Synchronous counter design follows a systematic procedure to specify the count sequence required and to determine the input logic functions to obtain the desired count sequence. The flip-flop **excitation table** describes the input conditions that produce the output state from each individual J-K flip-flop. The excitation table for J-K flip-flops is shown in Table 10-5.

TABLE 10-5 J-K Excitation Table

Present State Q_N	Next State Q_{N+1}	Inputs J	Inputs K	Condition
0	0	0	x	No change, reset
0	1	1	x	Toggle, set
1	0	x	1	Toggle, reset
1	1	x	0	No change, set

With synchronous counters, *the next output state from each flip-flop is determined by the present state and the present inputs* applied to that stage. The J-K excitation table forms the basis of synchronous counter design. An excitation table for the counter is constructed by specifying the present state and next state for each flip-flop in the order of the count sequence. For each transition, the necessary J and K inputs to produce the required sequence are listed. A logic function for each J and K input is then derived from the counter excitation table. Example 10-14 illustrates a synchronous counter design.

■ EXAMPLE 10-14 Synchronous Counter Design

Problem: Design a MOD-5, 3-bit synchronous counter to count in the following sequence: 2, 3, 5, 1, 7. The counter must be self-starting, with the count states of 0, 4, and 6 leading directly to 2.

Solution: Follow these procedures:

1. *Create a state transition diagram.*
2. *Create a counter excitation table* by listing the present state and next state sequence.
3. *Expand the table* by adding the J and K input states for each flip-flop.
4. *Determine the logic functions for the J and K inputs as a function of the present states.*
5. *Analyze the counter to verify the design.*
6. *Construct and test the counter.*

The state transition diagram for the counter is shown in Figure 10-23.

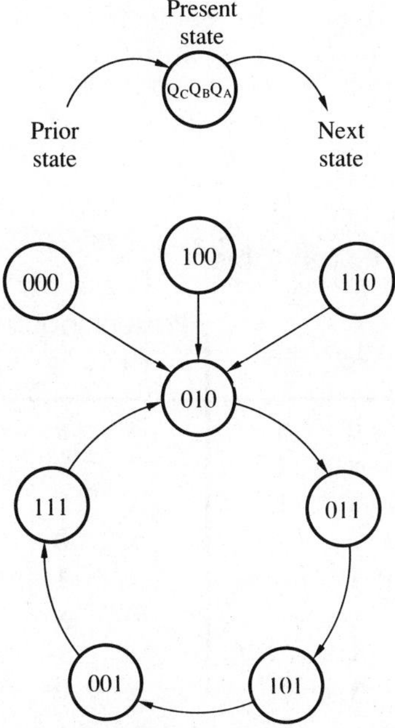

FIGURE 10-23 Example 10-14 State Transition Diagram

The present state-next state table is constructed, as shown in Table 10-6.
The present state-next state table is expanded by adding the required J and K inputs to obtain the desired state transitions on each clock pulse. The expanded table is the counter excitation table, as shown in Table 10-7.

To determine the logic function required at each J and K input, K-maps can be used to simplify the logic equations as functions of the present states of Q_C, Q_B, and Q_A. Note that the present states listed in the excitation table,

TABLE 10-6 Present State-Next State Table for Example 10-14 Synchronous Counter Design

Present State			Next State		
Q_C	Q_B	Q_A	Q_C	Q_B	Q_A
0	0	0	0	1	0
1	0	0	0	1	0
1	1	0	0	1	0
0	1	0	0	1	1
0	1	1	1	0	1
1	0	1	0	0	1
0	0	1	1	1	1
1	1	1	0	1	0

TABLE 10-7 Example of 10-14 Counter Excitation Table

Present State			Next State			Present Inputs					
Q_C	Q_B	Q_A	Q_C	Q_B	Q_A	J_C	K_C	J_B	K_B	J_A	K_A
0	0	0	0	1	0	0	x	1	x	0	x
1	0	0	0	1	0	x	1	1	x	0	x
1	1	0	0	1	0	x	1	x	0	0	x
0	1	0	0	1	1	0	x	x	0	1	x
0	1	1	1	0	1	1	x	x	1	x	0
1	0	1	0	0	1	x	1	0	x	x	0
0	0	1	1	1	1	1	x	1	x	x	0
1	1	1	0	1	0	x	1	x	0	x	1

Table 10-7, do not follow counting order, so be careful when filling in the K-maps. The K-maps and resulting logic functions for the J and K inputs are shown in Figure 10-24.

The resulting circuit to produce the required count sequence is shown in Figure 10-25.

The counter design should be analyzed to verify if it is correct, using the steps followed in Example 10-13. Finally, the counter circuit should be built and tested in the laboratory. ■

$Q_C Q_B$ \ Q_A	0	1
0 0	0	1
0 1	0	1
1 1	x	x
1 0	x	x

$J_C = Q_A$ $K_C = 1$ by inspection of table

(a)

$Q_C Q_B$ \ Q_A	0	1
0 0	1	1
0 1	x	x
1 1	x	x
1 0	1	0

$Q_C Q_B$ \ Q_A	0	1
0 0	x	x
0 1	0	1
1 1	0	0
1 0	x	x

$J_B = \overline{Q_C Q_A}$ $K_B = \overline{Q_C} Q_A$

(b)

$Q_C Q_B$ \ Q_A	0	1
0 0	0	x
0 1	1	x
1 1	0	x
1 0	0	x

$Q_C Q_B$ \ Q_A	0	1
0 0	x	0
0 1	x	0
1 1	x	1
1 0	x	0

$J_A = \overline{Q_C} Q_B$ $K_A = Q_C Q_B$

(c)

FIGURE 10-24 Example 10-14 (a) J_C and K_C Inputs; (b) J_B and K_B Inputs; (c) J_A and K_A Inputs

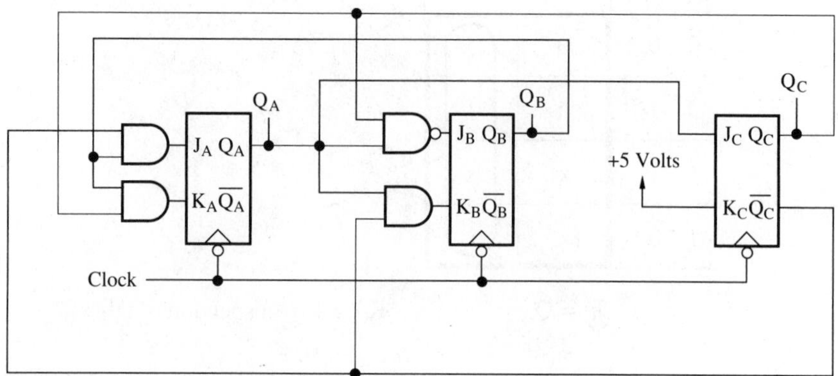

FIGURE 10-25 Example 10-14 Synchronous Counter

The synchronous counter design in Example 10-14 can be built with fewer additional logic gates required for the J and K inputs if the design requirements are slightly modified. Example 10-15 illustrates the modified synchronous counter circuit.

■ EXAMPLE 10-15 Synchronous Counter Design Modification

Problem: Design a MOD-5, 3-bit synchronous counter to count in the following sequence: 2, 3, 5, 1, 7. To modify the design and minimize the additional gates required for the J and K inputs, route the unused states to their next natural count state. In other words, route 0 to 1, 4 to 5, and 6 to 7.

Solution: The state transition diagram for the synchronous counter is shown in Figure 10-26.

Design the synchronous counter by defining the present states, next states, and the necessary J and K inputs in an excitation table. Determine the J and K inputs from the excitation table.
The excitation table is shown in Table 10-8, and the K-maps for the J and K inputs and the resulting synchronous counter circuit are shown in Figure 10-27 and Figure 10-28, respectively. ■

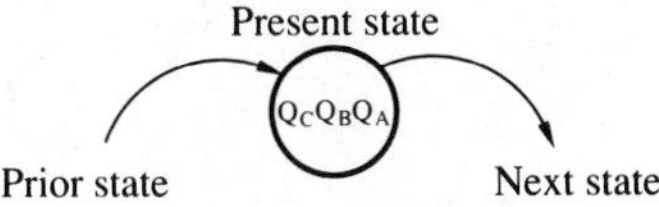

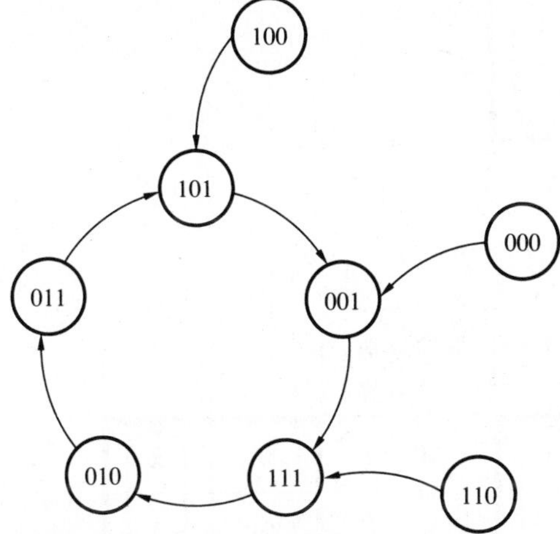

FIGURE 10-26 Example 10-15 State Transition Diagram

TABLE 10-8 Example 10-15 Counter Excitation Table

Present State			Next State			Present Inputs					
Q_C	Q_B	Q_A	Q_C	Q_B	Q_A	J_C	K_C	J_B	K_B	J_A	K_A
0	0	0	0	0	1	0	x	0	x	1	x
1	0	0	1	0	1	x	0	0	x	1	x
1	1	0	1	1	1	x	0	x	0	1	x
0	1	0	0	1	1	0	x	x	0	1	x
0	1	1	1	0	1	1	x	x	1	x	0
1	0	1	0	0	1	x	1	0	x	x	0
0	0	1	1	1	1	1	x	1	x	x	0
1	1	1	0	1	0	x	1	x	0	x	1

$Q_C Q_B$ \ Q_A	0	1
0 0	0	1
0 1	0	1
1 1	0	1
1 0	0	1

$J_C = K_C = Q_A$

(a)

$Q_C Q_B$ \ Q_A	0	1
0 0	0	1
0 1	x	x
1 1	x	x
1 0	0	0

$J_B = \overline{Q}_C Q_A$

$Q_C Q_B$ \ Q_A	0	1
0 0	x	x
0 1	0	1
1 1	0	0
1 0	x	x

$K_B = \overline{Q}_C Q_A$

(b)

$Q_C Q_B$ \ Q_A	0	1
0 0	1	x
0 1	1	x
1 1	1	x
1 0	1	x

$J_A = 1$

$Q_C Q_B$ \ Q_A	0	1
0 0	x	0
0 1	x	0
1 1	x	1
1 0	x	0

$K_A = Q_C Q_B$

(c)

FIGURE 10-27 Example 10-15 K-Maps (a) J_C and K_C Inputs; (b) J_B and K_B Inputs; (c) J_A and K_A Inputs

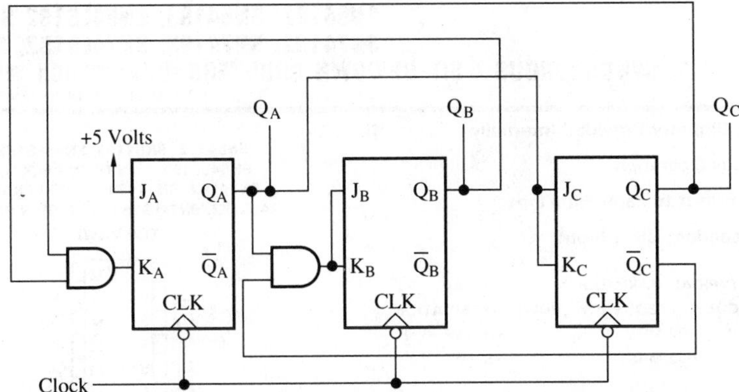

FIGURE 10-28 Example 10-15 Synchronous Counter

Section Self-Test

1. A synchronous counter has a common clock input to all flip-flop stages.
2. A synchronous counter of n flip-flop stages always has a modulus of 2^n.
3. A synchronous counter must count binary numbers in sequence, either up or down.

ANSWERS (Not necessarily in the order of the questions)

- True • False • False

10-7 INTEGRATED CIRCUIT COUNTERS

Integrated circuit counters are available for counter applications that require serial up or down count sequences. The IC counters available are 4-bit binary or decade counters that can be cascaded together for applications requiring more than four output stages. The IC counters have asynchronous inputs that allow the flexibility of presetting the counter to an initial start value other than zero or resetting the counter back to zero at any instant of time. The 74LS193 and 74LS90 are two IC counters that are used in examples throughout this chapter.

10.7.1 The 74LS193 Four-Bit Binary Counter

The 74LS193 is a 4-bit synchronous, positive edge-triggered, binary counter capable of counting up or down. It has two asynchronous inputs for presetting and clearing the counter. The manufacturer's data sheets for the 74LS193 are shown in Figure 10-29.

SN54192, SN54193, SN54LS192 SN54LS193, SN74192, SN74193, SN74LS192, SN74LS193 SYNCHRONOUS 4-BIT UP/DOWN COUNTERS (DUAL CLOCK WITH CLEAR)

DECEMBER 1972—REVISED MARCH 1988

- **Cascading Circuitry Provided Internally**
- **Synchronous Operation**
- **Individual Preset to Each Flip-Flop**
- **Fully Independent Clear Input**

TYPES	TYPICAL MAXIMUM COUNT FREQUENCY	TYPICAL POWER DISSIPATION
'192,'193	32 MHz	325 mW
'LS192,'LS193	32 MHz	95 mW

SN54192, SN54193, SN54LS192, SN54LS193 . . . J OR W PACKAGE
SN74192, SN74193 . . . N PACKAGE
SN74LS192, SN74LS193 . . . D OR N PACKAGE
(TOP VIEW)

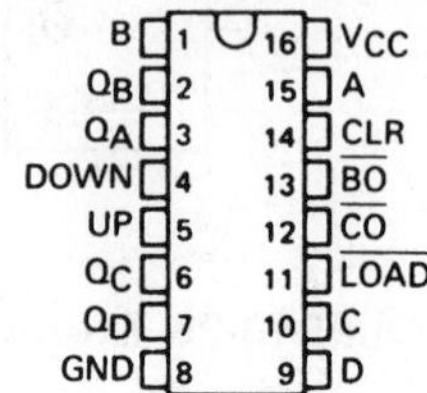

SN54LS192, SN54LS193 . . . FK PACKAGE
(TOP VIEW)

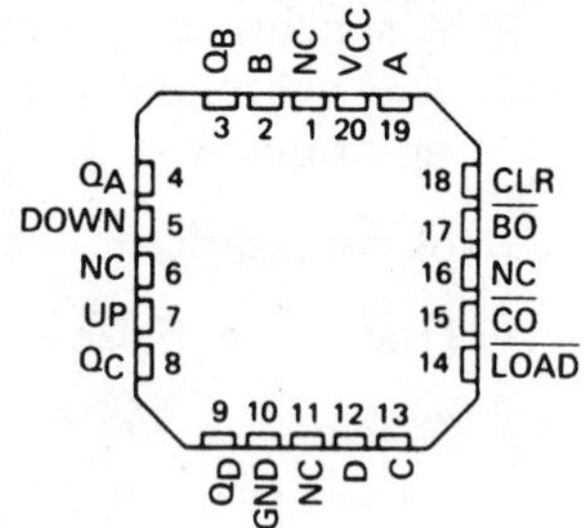

NC - No internal connection

description

These monolithic circuits are synchronous reversible (up/down) counters having a complexity of 55 equivalent gates. The '192 and 'LS192 circuits are BCD counters and the '193 and 'LS193 are 4-bit binary counters. Synchronous operation is provided by having all flip-flops clocked simultaneously so that the outputs change coincidently with each other when so instructed by the steering logic. This mode of operation eliminates the output counting spikes which are normally associated with asynchronous (ripple-clock) counters.

The outputs of the four master-slave flip-flops are triggered by a low-to-high-level transition of either count (clock) input. The direction of counting is determined by which count input is pulsed while the other count input is high.

All four counters are fully programmable; that is, each output may be preset to either level by entering the desired data at the data inputs while the load input is low. The output will change to agree with the data inputs independently of the count pulses. This feature allows the counters to be used as modulo-N dividers by simply modifying the count length with the preset inputs.

A clear input has been provided which forces all outputs to the low level when a high level is applied. The clear function is independent of the count and load inputs. The clear, count, and load inputs are buffered to lower the drive requirements. This reduces the number of clock drivers, etc., required for long words.

These counters were designed to be cascaded without the need for external circuitry. Both borrow and carry outputs are available to cascade both the up- and down-counting functions. The borrow output produces a pulse equal in width to the count-down input when the counter underflows. Similarly, the carry output produces a pulse equal in width to the count-up input when an overflow condition exists. The counters can then be easily cascaded by feeding the borrow and carry outputs to the count-down and count-up inputs respectively of the succeeding counter.

absolute maximum ratings over operating free-air temperature range (unless otherwise noted)

	SN54'	SN54LS'	SN74'	SN74LS'	UNIT
Supply voltage, V_{CC} (see Note 1)	7	7	7	7	V
Input voltage	5.5	7	5.5	7	V
Operating free-air temperature range	−55 to 125		0 to 70		°C
Storage temperature range	−65 to 150		−65 to 150		°C

NOTE 1: Voltage values are with respect to network ground terminal.

FIGURE 10-29 74LS193 Manufacturer's Data Sheets (Courtesy of Texas Instruments)

SN54192, SN54193, SN54LS192, SN54LS193
SN74192, SN74193, SN74LS192, SN74LS193
SYNCHRONOUS 4-BIT UP/DOWN COUNTERS (DUAL CLOCK WITH CLEAR)

logic symbols†

'192

CTRDIV 10
CLR (14) CT = 0
UP (5) 2+
G1
DOWN (4) 1−
G2
$\overline{\text{LOAD}}$ (11) C3
$\overline{1}$CT = 9 (12) $\overline{\text{CO}}$
$\overline{2}$CT = 0 (13) $\overline{\text{BO}}$
A (15) 3D [1] (3) Q_A
B (1) [2] (2) Q_B
C (10) [4] (6) Q_C
D (9) [8] (7) Q_D

'193

CTRDIV 16
CLR (14) CT = 0
UP (5) 2+
G1
DOWN (4) 1−
G2
$\overline{\text{LOAD}}$ (11) C3
$\overline{1}$CT = 15 (12) $\overline{\text{CO}}$
$\overline{2}$CT = 0 (13) $\overline{\text{BO}}$
A (15) 3D [1] (3) Q_A
B (1) [2] (2) Q_B
C (10) [4] (6) Q_C
D (9) [8] (7) Q_D

†These symbols are in accordance with ANSI/IEEE Std. 91-1984 and IEC Publication 617-12.
Pin numbers shown are for D, J, N, and W packages.

schematics of inputs and outputs

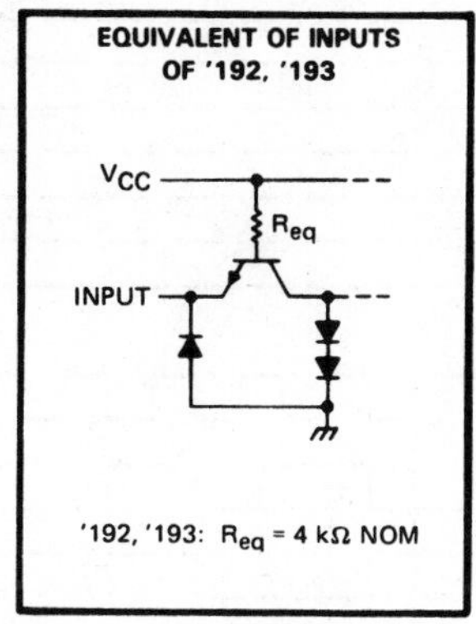

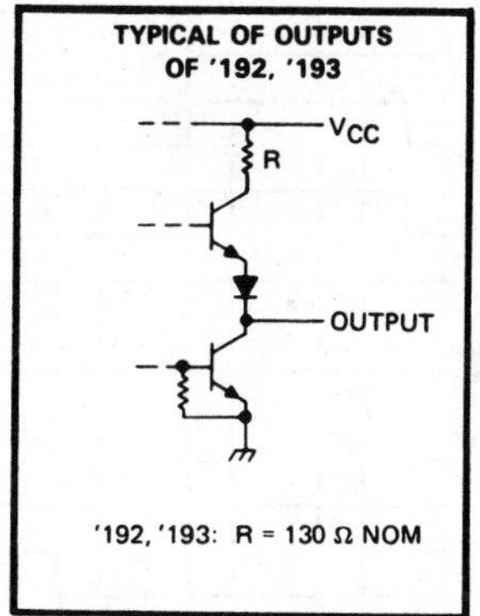

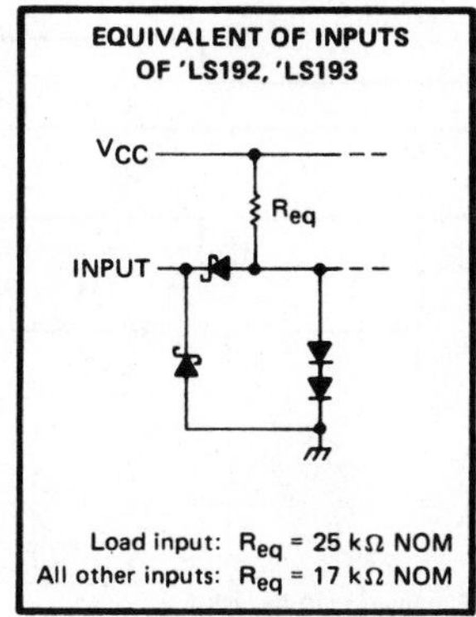

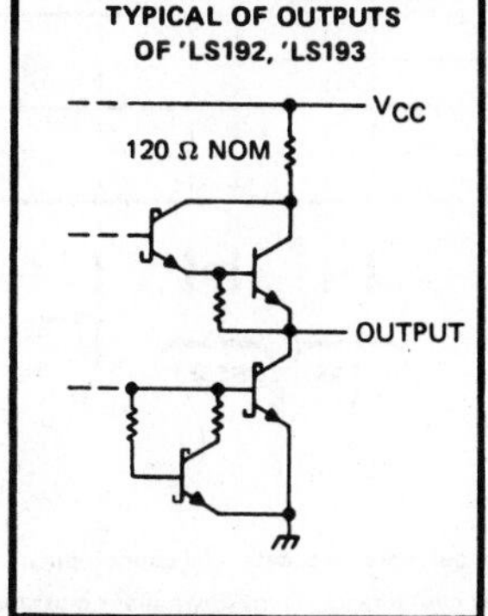

FIGURE 10-29 (*continued*)

SN54193, SN54LS193, SN74193, SN74LS193
SYNCHRONOUS 4-BIT UP/DOWN COUNTERS (DUAL CLOCK WITH CLEAR)

'193, 'LS193 BINARY COUNTERS

typical clear, load, and count sequences

Illustrated below is the following sequence:

1. Clear outputs to zero.
2. Load (preset) to binary thirteen.
3. Count up to fourteen, fifteen, carry, zero, one, and two.
4. Count down to one, zero, borrow, fifteen, fourteen, and thirteen.

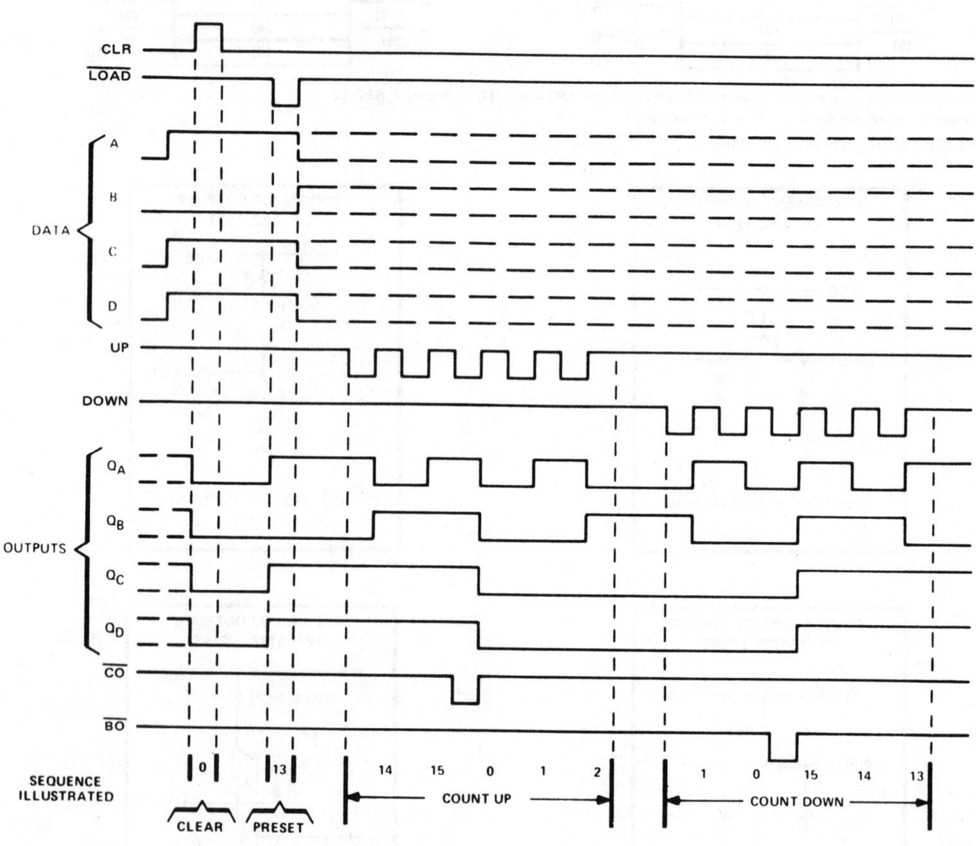

NOTES: A. Clear overrides load, data, and count inputs.

B. When counting up, count-down input must be high; when counting down, count-up input must be high.

FIGURE 10-30 74LS193 Count Sequence Waveforms (Courtesy of Texas Instruments)

The 74193 is a **programmable counter** to allow either up or down counting and complete control over the count modulus through the use of the asynchronous inputs. Two separate clock inputs are used to control up or down counting.

The counter has a maximum MOD-16 count sequence that can be shortened to any modulus less than 16 by using the asynchronous control inputs. The **clear input** resets all count stages back to zero. The **preset input** sets the counter stages to any 4-bit binary number loaded on the **parallel inputs** of the 74LS193.

The counter can be easily cascaded while counting up or down through the **carry output** and **borrow output** to lengthen the modulus and to provide additional counter output stages. The 74LS193 waveforms shown in Figure 10-30 illustrate the operation of the asynchronous inputs and cascade outputs.

An example of using the asynchronous inputs on the 74LS193 is shown in Example 10-16.

■ EXAMPLE 10-16 The 74LS193 Programmable Counter

Problem: Design a MOD-4 counter that produces the count sequence: 0, 1, 13, 14.

Solution: The count sequence is an up count that skips states 2 through 12 and 15. This count sequence can be achieved by forcing the counter to **load** the value 13 instead of the value 2, and by **clearing** the counter after the count state 14, as shown in Table 10-9.
Note that the counts 0 0 1 0 and 1 1 1 1 do not appear as output states. They are very narrow "spikes" in the output that are decoded by additional logic gates to load and clear the 74LS193 counter through the asynchronous load and clear inputs.

TABLE 10-9 Example 10-16 Count Sequence

Count Outputs				Count Operations
Q_D	Q_C	Q_B	Q_A	
0	0	0	0	Up counting
0	0	0	1	
0	*0*	*1*	*0*	*Decode 0 0 1 0 and load 1 1 0 1*
1	1	0	1	
1	1	1	0	
1	*1*	*1*	*1*	*Decode 1 1 1 1 and clear*

The asynchronous clear input on the 74193 is an active-HIGH logic input. Therefore, the output count states that represent the value 1 1 1 1 can be decoded with an AND gate, and the AND gate is input into the clear input. The asynchronous load input is an active-LOW logic input. The output count state 0 0 1 0 should be decoded with a NAND gate, and the output of the NAND gate is input to the load control. The parallel load inputs of the counter should be tied to the constant logic levels of 1 1 0 1 to load the value of 13 when dictated by the NAND gate decoder. The final circuit for Example 10-16 is shown in Figure 10-31. The state transition diagram, also shown in Figure 10-31, indicates how all possible states will reach the count sequence. ■

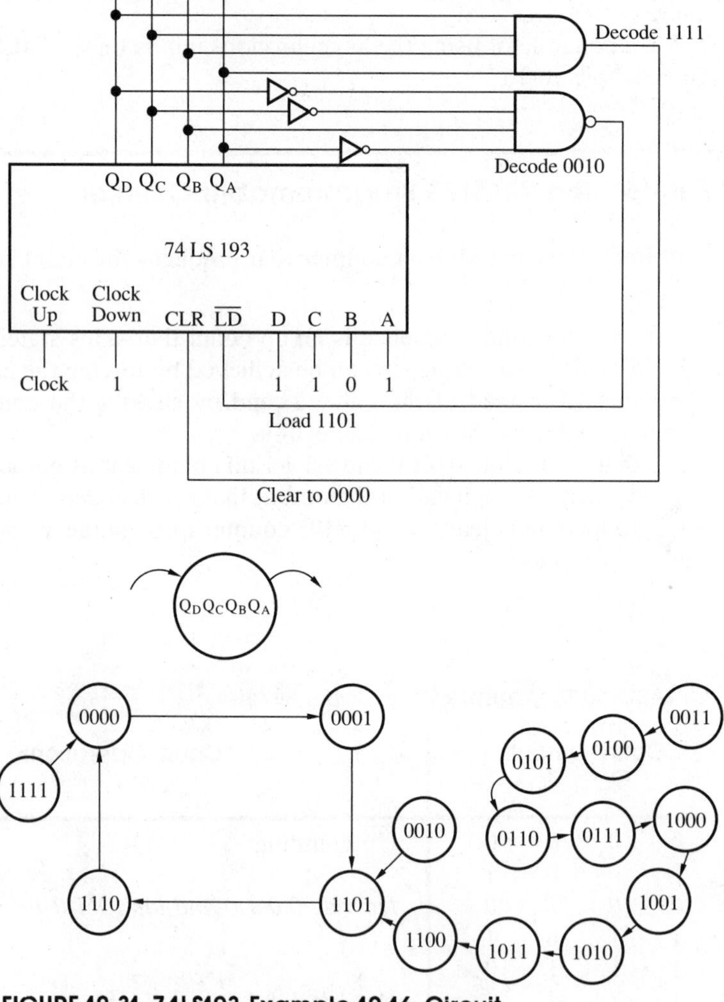

FIGURE 10-31 74LS193 Example 10-16 Circuit

10.7.2 The 74LS90 Decade Counter

The 74LS90 is a 4-bit asynchronous, negative edge-triggered decade counter with asynchronous clear and preset inputs for programmable counter applications. The manufacturer's data sheets for the 74LS90 is shown in Figure 10-32.

The 74LS90 counts only in an ascending sequence. The IC actually consists of two separate counters that can be configured for three different modes of operation. The two internal counters are a MOD-2 counter and a MOD-5 counter, providing a total of four output stages.

- **Mode 1.** The MOD-2 and MOD-5 counters operate separately with individual clock inputs. The MOD-2 counter toggles from a logic HIGH to a logic LOW state on each clock pulse. The MOD-5 counter produces a 3-bit count sequence from 0 to 4. Figure 10-33 shows the 74LS90 in this configuration, along with the resulting waveforms and state transition diagrams.

- **Mode 2.** The MOD-2 counter operates as the LSB of a 4-bit decade counter producing a BCD count sequence. The control clock is input into the clock A input, and the Q_A output is input to clock B to form the cascaded connection. This MOD-2 to MOD-5 cascaded counter configuration produces a 4-bit BCD count sequence of 0 to 9. Figure 10-34 shows the 74LS90 connected in this configuration and the output waveforms.

- **Mode 3.** The MOD-2 counter operates as the MSB of a 4-bit decade counter. The control clock is input into clock B and the Q_D output is input into clock A. This is referred to as the **biquinary counter** since it produces two five-state count sequences: In the first five sequences of 0 to 4 the most significant output, Q_A, is a logic LOW; in the last five sequences of 0 to 4 the most significant output, Q_A, is a logic HIGH. The resulting set of output waveforms are with the Q_A output having a 50% duty cycle, while the three lower order outputs, Q_D, Q_C, and Q_B, cycle through the 3-bit sequence of 0 to 4. Figure 10-35 shows the 74LS90 in the biquinary configuration with the output waveforms.

The 74LS90 can be reset to zero or preset to 9 through the asynchronous clear inputs. Example 10-17 illustrates the use of the control and preset inputs on the 74LS90 to modify the modulus of the count sequence.

TYPES SN5490A, SN5492A, SN5493A, SN54L90, SN54L93, SN54LS90, SN54LS92, SN54LS93, SN7490A, SN7492A, SN7493A, SN74LS90, SN74LS92, SN74LS93 DECADE, DIVIDE-BY-TWELVE, AND BINARY COUNTERS

MARCH 1974 – REVISED DECEMBER 1983

'90A, 'L90, 'LS90 . . . DECADE COUNTERS

'92A, 'LS92 . . . DIVIDE-BY-TWELVE COUNTERS

'93A, 'L93, 'LS93 . . . 4-BIT BINARY COUNTERS

TYPES	TYPICAL POWER DISSIPATION
'90A	145 mW
'L90	20 mW
'LS90	45 mW
'92A, '93A	130 mW
'LS92, 'LS93	45 mW
'L93	16 mW

description

Each of these monolithic counters contains four master-slave flip-flops and additional gating to provide a divide-by-two counter and a three-stage binary counter for which the count cycle length is divide-by-five for the '90A, 'L90, and 'LS90, divide-by-six for the '92A and 'LS92, and divide-by-eight for the '93A, 'L93, and 'LS93.

All of these counters have a gated zero reset and the '90A, 'L90, and 'LS90 also have gated set-to-nine inputs for use in BCD nine's complement applications.

To use their maximum count length (decade, divide-by-twelve, or four-bit binary) of these counters, the CKB input is connected to the Q_A output. The input count pulses are applied to CKA input and the outputs are as described in the appropriate function table. A symmetrical divide-by-ten count can be obtained from the '90A, 'L90, or 'LS90 counters by connecting the Q_D output to the CKA input and applying the input count to the CKB input which gives a divide-by-ten square wave at output Q_A.

SN5490A, SN54LS90 . . . J OR W PACKAGE
SN54L90 . . . J PACKAGE
SN7490A . . . J OR N PACKAGE
SN74LS90 . . . D, J OR N PACKAGE
(TOP VIEW)

Pin	Name	Pin	Name
1	CKB	14	CKA
2	R0(1)	13	NC
3	R0(2)	12	Q_A
4	NC	11	Q_D
5	V_{CC}	10	GND
6	R9(1)	9	Q_B
7	R9(2)	8	Q_C

SN5492A, SN54LS92 . . . J OR W PACKAGE
SN7492A . . . J OR N PACKAGE
SN74LS92 . . . D, J OR N PACKAGE
(TOP VIEW)

Pin	Name	Pin	Name
1	CKB	14	CKA
2	NC	13	NC
3	NC	12	Q_A
4	NC	11	Q_B
5	V_{CC}	10	GND
6	R0(1)	9	Q_C
7	R0(2)	8	Q_D

SN5493A, SN54LS93 . . . J OR W PACKAGE
SN7493A . . . J OR N PACKAGE
SN74LS93 . . . D, J OR N PACKAGE
(TOP VIEW)

Pin	Name	Pin	Name
1	CKB	14	CKA
2	R0(1)	13	NC
3	R0(2)	12	Q_A
4	NC	11	Q_D
5	V_{CC}	10	GND
6	NC	9	Q_B
7	NC	8	Q_C

SN54L93 . . . J PACKAGE
(TOP VIEW)

Pin	Name	Pin	Name
1	R0(1)	14	CKA
2	R0(2)	13	Q_A
3	NC	12	Q_D
4	V_{CC}	11	GND
5	NC	10	Q_C
6	NC	9	Q_B
7	NC	8	CKB

NC - No internal connection

For new chip carrier design, use 'LS290, 'LS292, and 'LS293.

FIGURE 10-32 74LS90 Manufacturer's Data Sheets (Courtesy of Texas Instruments)

TYPES SN5490A, '92A, '93A, SN54L90, 'L93, SN54LS90, 'LS92, 'LS93, SN7490A, '92A, '93A, SN74LS90, 'LS92, 'LS93 DECADE, DIVIDE-BY-TWELVE, AND BINARY COUNTERS

'90A, 'L90, 'LS90
BCD COUNT SEQUENCE
(See Note A)

COUNT	OUTPUT			
	Q_D	Q_C	Q_B	Q_A
0	L	L	L	L
1	L	L	L	H
2	L	L	H	L
3	L	L	H	H
4	L	H	L	L
5	L	H	L	H
6	L	H	H	L
7	L	H	H	H
8	H	L	L	L
9	H	L	L	H

'90A, 'L90, 'LS90
BI-QUINARY (5-2)
(See Note B)

COUNT	OUTPUT			
	Q_A	Q_D	Q_C	Q_B
0	L	L	L	L
1	L	L	L	H
2	L	L	H	L
3	L	L	H	H
4	L	H	L	L
5	H	L	L	L
6	H	L	L	H
7	H	L	H	L
8	H	L	H	H
9	H	H	L	L

'92A, 'LS92
COUNT SEQUENCE
(See Note C)

COUNT	OUTPUT			
	Q_D	Q_C	Q_B	Q_A
0	L	L	L	L
1	L	L	L	H
2	L	L	H	L
3	L	L	H	H
4	L	H	L	L
5	L	H	L	H
6	H	L	L	L
7	H	L	L	H
8	H	L	H	L
9	H	L	H	H
10	H	H	L	L
11	H	H	L	H

'90A, 'L90, 'LS90
RESET/COUNT FUNCTION TABLE

RESET INPUTS				OUTPUT			
$R_{0(1)}$	$R_{0(2)}$	$R_{9(1)}$	$R_{9(2)}$	Q_D	Q_C	Q_B	Q_A
H	H	L	X	L	L	L	L
H	H	X	L	L	L	L	L
X	X	H	H	H	L	L	H
X	L	X	L	COUNT			
L	X	L	X	COUNT			
L	X	X	L	COUNT			
X	L	L	X	COUNT			

'93A, 'L93, 'LS93
COUNT SEQUENCE
(See Note C)

COUNT	OUTPUT			
	Q_D	Q_C	Q_B	Q_A
0	L	L	L	L
1	L	L	L	H
2	L	L	H	L
3	L	L	H	H
4	L	H	L	L
5	L	H	L	H
6	L	H	H	L
7	L	H	H	H
8	H	L	L	L
9	H	L	L	H
10	H	L	H	L
11	H	L	H	H
12	H	H	L	L
13	H	H	L	H
14	H	H	H	L
15	H	H	H	H

'92A, 'LS92, '93A, 'L93, 'LS93
RESET/COUNT FUNCTION TABLE

RESET INPUTS		OUTPUT			
$R_{0(1)}$	$R_{0(2)}$	Q_D	Q_C	Q_B	Q_A
H	H	L	L	L	L
L	X	COUNT			
X	L	COUNT			

NOTES:
A. Output Q_A is connected to input CKB for BCD count.
B. Output Q_D is connected to input CKA for bi-quinary count.
C. Output Q_A is connected to input CKB.
D. H = high level, L = low level, X = irrelevant

FIGURE 10-32 (*continued*)

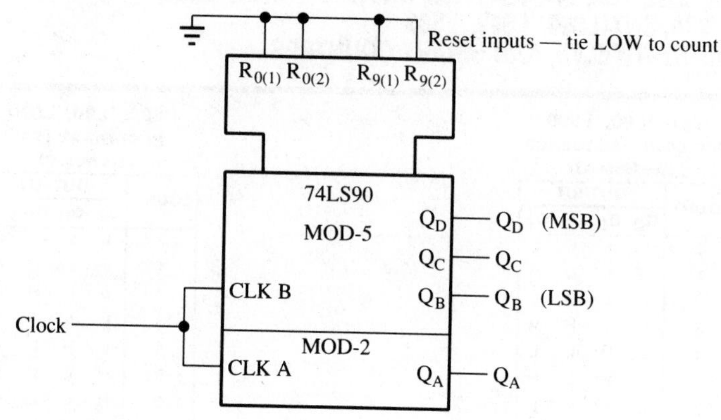

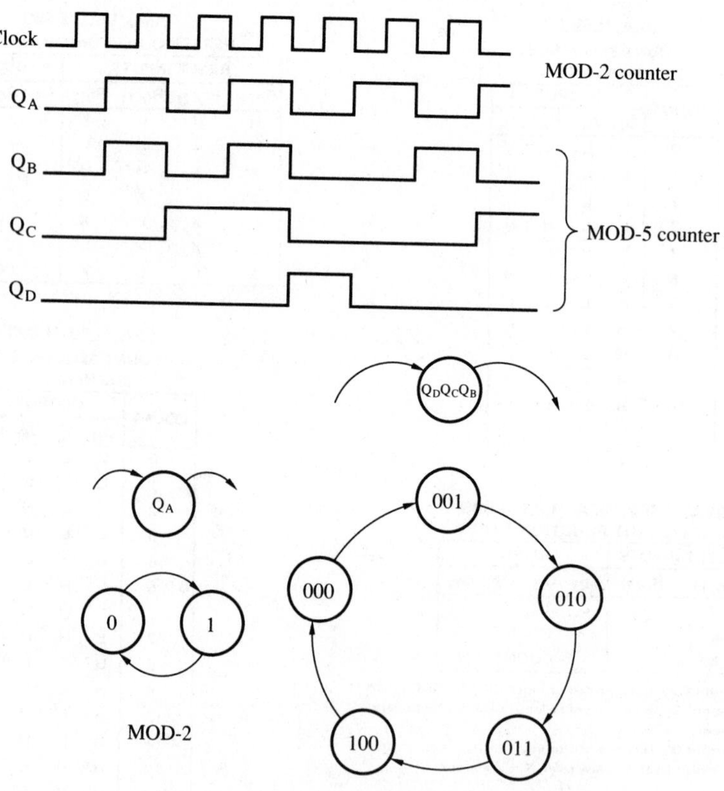

FIGURE 10-33 74LS90 MOD-2 and MOD-5 Counters

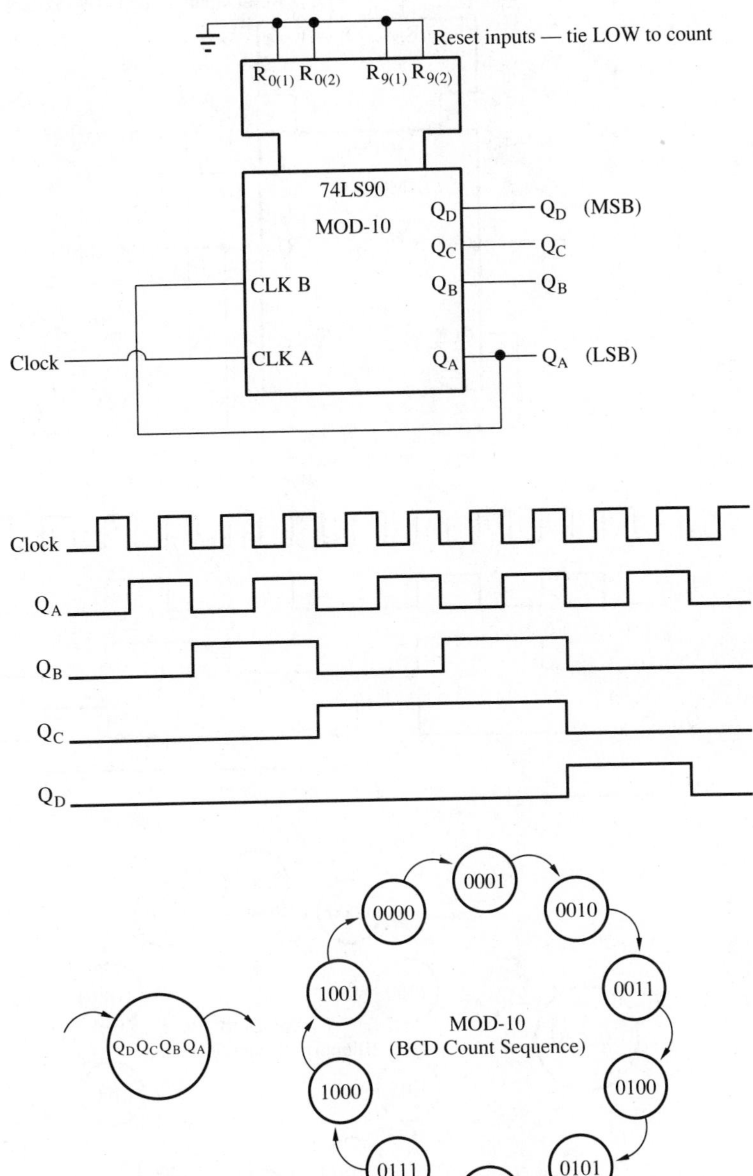

FIGURE 10-34 74LS90 Decade Binary Code Decimal Counter

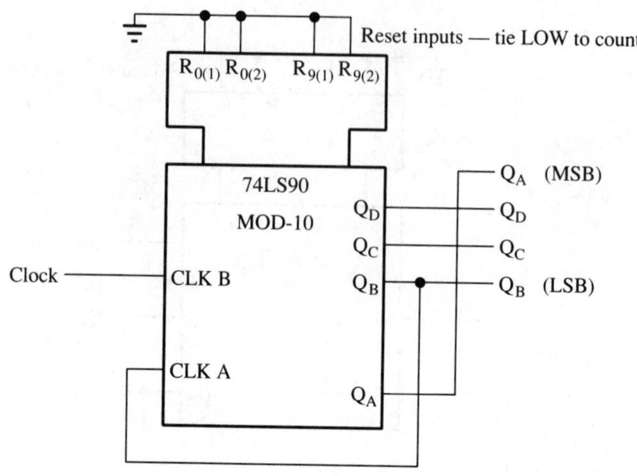

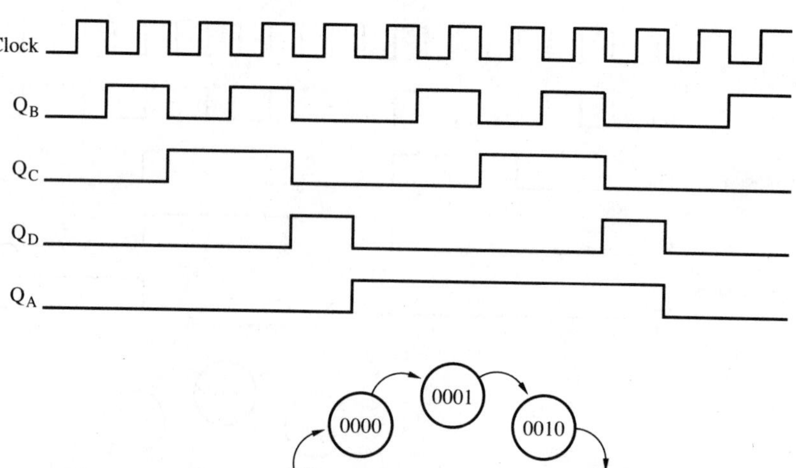

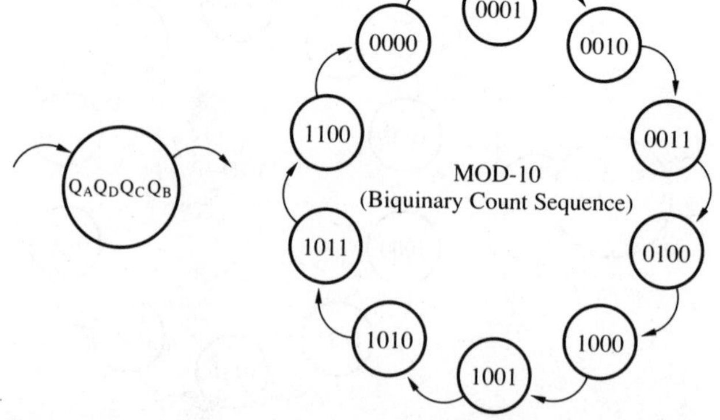

FIGURE 10-35 74LS90 Biquinary Decade Counter

■ EXAMPLE 10-17 The 74LS90 Counter Application

Problem: Design a MOD-6 BCD counter using the 74LS90.

Solution: The 74LS90 can only count up and can only be reset to zero or preset to 9. To design a MOD-6 BCD counter, the 74LS90 must be configured with Q_A as the LSB (mode 2), and the seventh count state, 0 1 1 0, must be decoded to reset the counter to 0 0 0 0. The count sequence and the 74LS90 operation is shown in Table 10-10.

TABLE 10-10 74LS90 MOD-6 BCD Counter Operation

Counter Outputs Q_D	Q_C	Q_B	Q_A	Counter Operation
0	0	0	0	Up counting
0	0	0	1	
0	0	1	0	
0	0	1	1	
0	1	0	0	
0	1	0	1	
0	*1*	*1*	*0*	*Decode 0110 and reset*

Note that the 0 1 1 0 output state is seen only as a spike in the output waveforms. As soon as the 0 1 1 0 state is reached, it is decoded using additional logic gates and the counter resets to 0 0 0 0. The circuit configuration to perform this count sequence is shown in Figure 10-36.

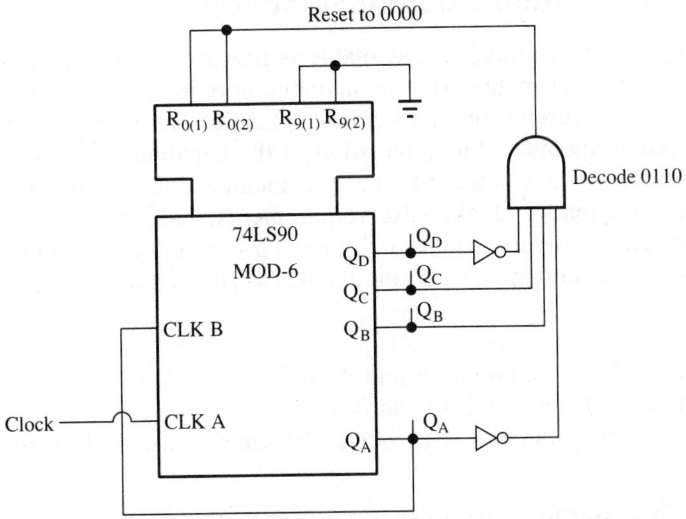

FIGURE 10-36 74LS90 Example 10-17 Counter Circuit

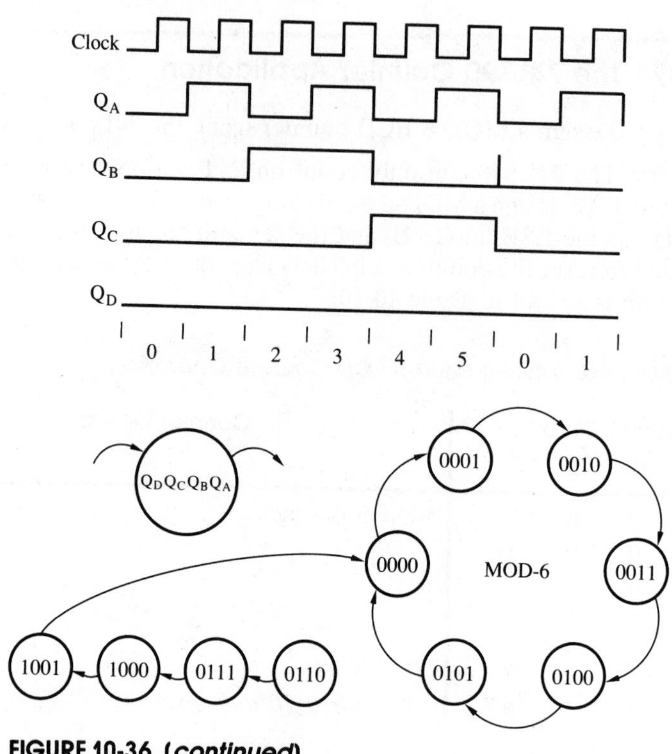

FIGURE 10-36 *(continued)*

■

10.7.3 Integrated Circuit Counter Selection

Numerous IC counters are available as transistor-transistor logic (TTL) and complementary metal-oxide semiconductor (CMOS) logic devices. Selection of a counter circuit for a particular application should be based on matching the requirements of the application to the capabilities of the counter. Key parameters that should be checked include counter modulus, maximum clock frequency, clock pulse requirements, cascade inputs and outputs, count enable inputs, and asynchronous preset and clear inputs. Table 10-11 lists several common TTL counter ICs available today.

Section Self-Test

1. The 74193 can count up and down.
2. The 7490 can count up and down.
3. The 7490 biquinary sequence is the same as the BCD sequence.

ANSWERS (Not necessarily in the order of the questions)

• False • False • True

TABLE 10-11 Integrated Circuit Counters

Synchronous Counters				
74LS160	Decade	Up	Asynch., clear	32 MHz
74LS161	Binary	Up	Asynch., clear	32 MHz
74LS162	Decade	Up	Synch., clear	32 MHz
74LS163	Binary	Up	Synch., clear	32 MHz
74LS190	Decade	Up/Down	Asynch., load	25 MHz
74LS191	Binary	Up/Down	Asynch., load	25 MHz
74LS192	Decade	Up/Down	Load/Clear	32 MHz
74LS193	Binary	Up/Down	Load/Clear	32 MHz

Asynchronous Counters				
74LS90	Decade	Up	Load 9 or 0	32 MHz
74LS92	MOD 12	Up	Clear	32 MHz
74LS93	Binary	Up	Clear	32 MHz
74196	Decade	Up	Load/Clear	50 MHz
74LS196	Decade	Up	Load/Clear	30 MHz
74S196	Decade	Up	Load/Clear	100 MHz
74S197	Binary	Up	Load/Clear	100 MHz
74LS390	Decade (equivalent to dual 74LS90)			25 MHz
74LS393	Binary (equivalent to dual 74LS93)			25 MHz

10-8 CASCADED COUNTERS

Counter circuits can be cascaded to increase both the modulus of the count sequence and the frequency division. Large counter applications requiring several stages of cascaded counters include digital time clocks, frequency dividers, and synchronization circuits.

The simplest example of cascaded counter stages is an asynchronous counter. The individual toggle flip-flop stages of an asynchronous counter are MOD-2 counters. MOD-2 counters are cascaded by routing the output of one stage into the clock input of the next stage. With each cascaded stage, the modulus of the counter increases. The final modulus of the counter is equal to the modulus of the individual stages multiplied together. Thus, a 4-bit asynchronous counter has a modulus of $2 \times 2 \times 2 \times 2 = 16$. The output frequency from the final stage is equal to the input frequency divided by the modulus. A simplified block diagram of the cascaded counter stages is shown in Figure 10-37. The input clock frequency is divided by 2 at each stage.

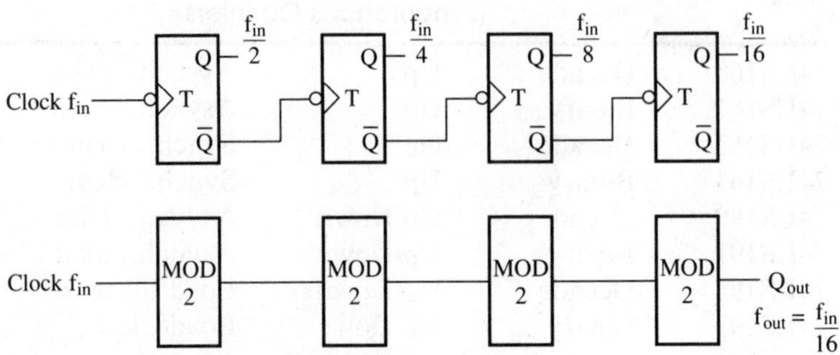

FIGURE 10-37 Cascaded MOD-2 Counters

The 74LS90 IC counter is an example of a counter circuit that requires cascading in order to obtain a decade counter. The decade counter is formed by cascading a MOD-2 counter with a MOD-5 counter. The final modulus is 2 × 5, or 10.

Several 74LS90 counters could be cascaded together to obtain MOD-10, MOD-100, and MOD-1000 counters. The most significant output bit, Q_D, is used as the cascaded clock input to the next stage, Figure 10-38 shows a simplified block diagram of MOD-10 counters cascaded together.

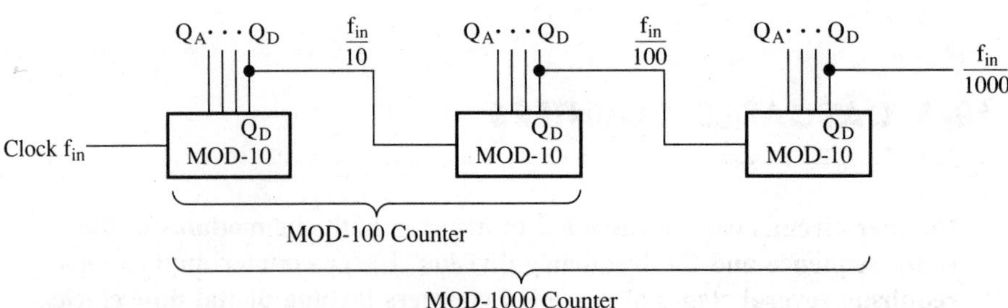

FIGURE 10-38 Cascaded MOD-10 Counters

Synchronous counters can be cascaded by maintaining a common clock signal to all count stages and by routing a **ripple carry output** from one stage to a **count enable input** in the next counter stage. Synchronous counters such as the 74LS160, 74LS161, 74LS162, and 74LS163 have ripple carry outputs and count enable inputs to ensure synchronous operation through all the cascaded count stages. An example of synchronous counter cascading using the ripple carry out and count enable is shown in Figure 10-39.

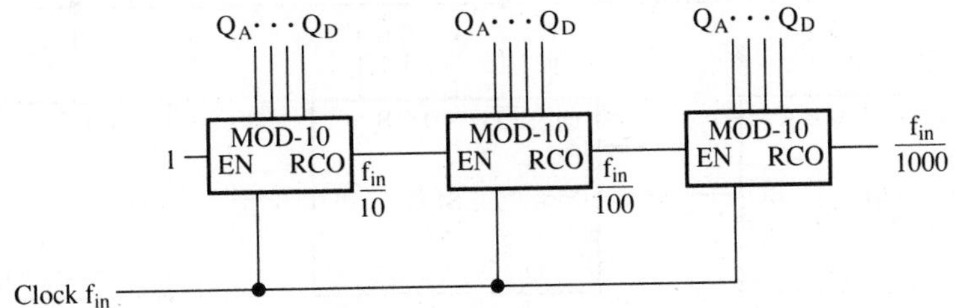

FIGURE 10-39 Synchronous Counter Cascading

The modulus of the cascaded counter is not limited to a multiple of the full modulus of the counters in the cascaded circuit. It can be fine-tuned to be any integer value by presetting or clearing the count stages as required. By presetting the count stages, we find that the final modulus obtained from the cascaded circuit is equal to the maximum modulus minus the initial state.

Eq. 10-1 Counter Modulus

Desired modulus = maximum modulus − initial state

EXAMPLE 10-18 Cascaded Counter

Problem: Design a divide-by-365 counter using 74LS193 counters.

Solution: Three 74LS193 counters are needed for the design. The maximum modulus of three cascaded 74LS193 counters is:

$$16 \times 16 \times 16 = 4096$$

The desired modulus is 365. To determine the initial state required to preset the counters to obtain a MOD-365 counter, subtract the desired modulus from the maximum modulus:

$$4096 - 365 = 3731$$

The 74LS193 counters generate 4-bit binary numbers; each counter can be considered a hexadecimal counter. The initial setting, $(3731)_{10}$ should be converted to its hexadecimal equivalent. (Recall the procedure of repetitive division by 16 in Chapter 2.)

$$(3731)_{10} = (E93)_H = (1\,1\,1\,0 \quad 1\,0\,0\,1 \quad 0\,0\,1\,1)_2$$

The initial setting for the most significant counter stage is 1 1 1 0. The next stage is preset to 1 0 0 1. The least significant counter stage is set to 0 0 1 1. The MOD-365 circuit is shown in Figure 10-40.

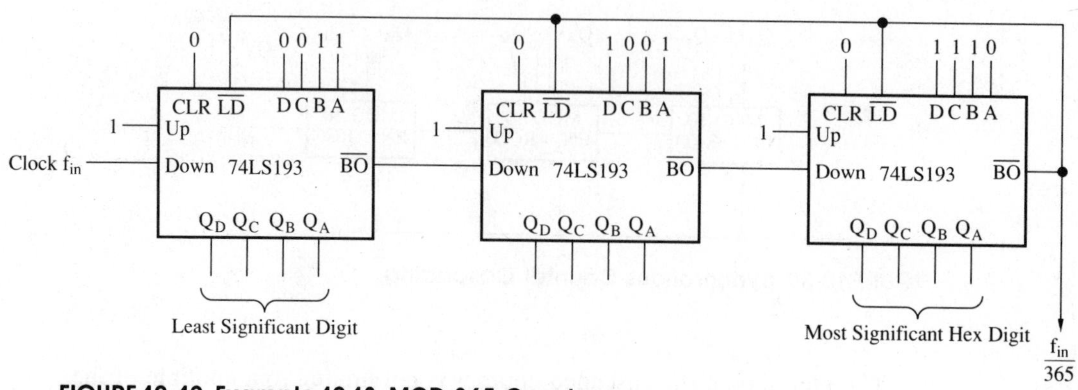

FIGURE 10-40 Example 10-18 MOD-365 Counter ■

■ EXAMPLE 10-19 Digital Time Clock

Problem: Design a digital time clock that displays the hours, minutes, and AM/PM, and that can be set to the proper time of day. The clock should run off a 6 MHz quartz crystal oscillator.

Solution: The functional block diagram for a digital time clock is shown in Figure 10-41.

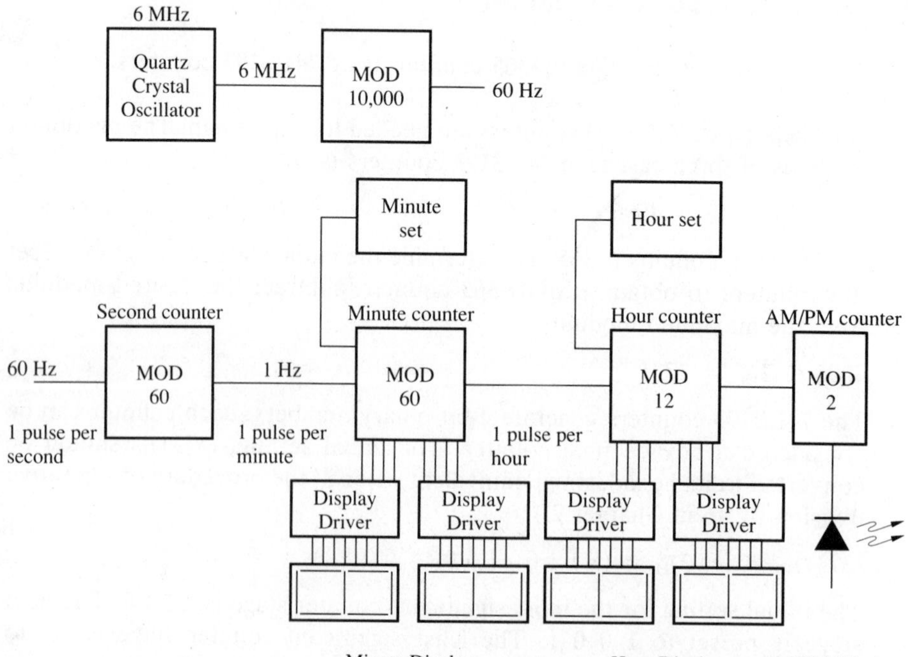

FIGURE 10-41 Example 10-19 Digital Time Clock—Functional Block Diagram

The circuitry required includes a MOD-10000 counter to obtain a 60 Hz signal, two MOD-60 counters to drive the seconds and minutes counters, and a MOD-12 counter and a MOD-2 counter to count the hours. The ICs are selected to simplify the design and to meet operational requirements. The circuits selected and their function are noted in Table 10-12.

TABLE 10-12 Example 10-19 Digital Time Clock Components

2—74LS390 MOD-10000 counter
1—74LS57 MOD-60 seconds counter
1—74LS390 MOD-60 minutes counter
1—74LS92 MOD-12 hour counter
1—74LS83 Adder for hour display
1—74LS76A MOD-2 AM/PM counter
1—74LS297 S-R latch debounce circuitry
3—push-button switches for manual clock setting
4—74LS47 minute and hour display drivers
1—74LS32, 1-74LS02, 2-74LS08—logic gates
4—common anode seven-segment LED* displays
1—LED AM/PM indicator
1—6 MHz quartz crystal oscillator

* Light emitting diode.

The digital time clock circuitry is shown in Figures 10-42 and 10-43.

Design Notes

- **MOD-10000 Counter.** Cascade two 74LS390s to build a four-stage MOD-10000 counter. The output pulse frequency is 60 Hz.
- **MOD-60 "Seconds" Counter.** This block functions only as a frequency divider since the seconds will not be displayed on the final time clock. Use the 74LS57 to perform the divide-by-60 operation.
- **Time Reset Inputs.** Debounce circuitry is required to prevent stray pulses from occurring. Three push buttons can be used as inputs for the time reset control circuitry. The normal or resting position of the switches should be "set" to produce a logic HIGH output from the S-R latch. When the time is to be reset, the "time set" push button is held in the "reset" position while the "min set" or the "hour set" button is pulsed to increment the appropriate counter circuit.

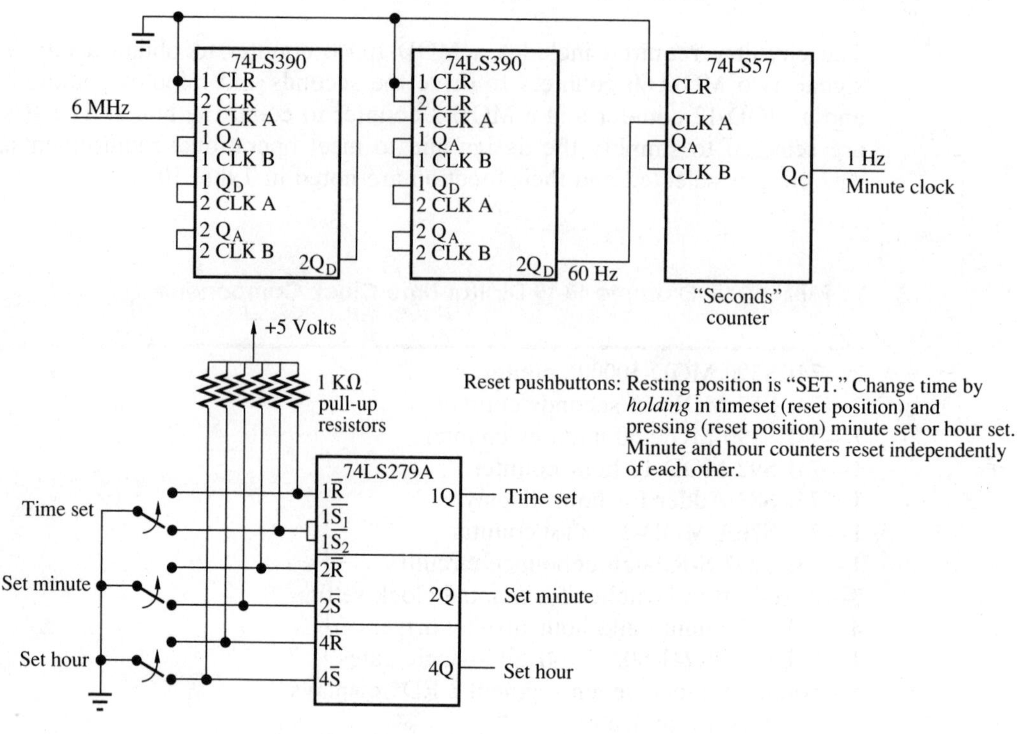

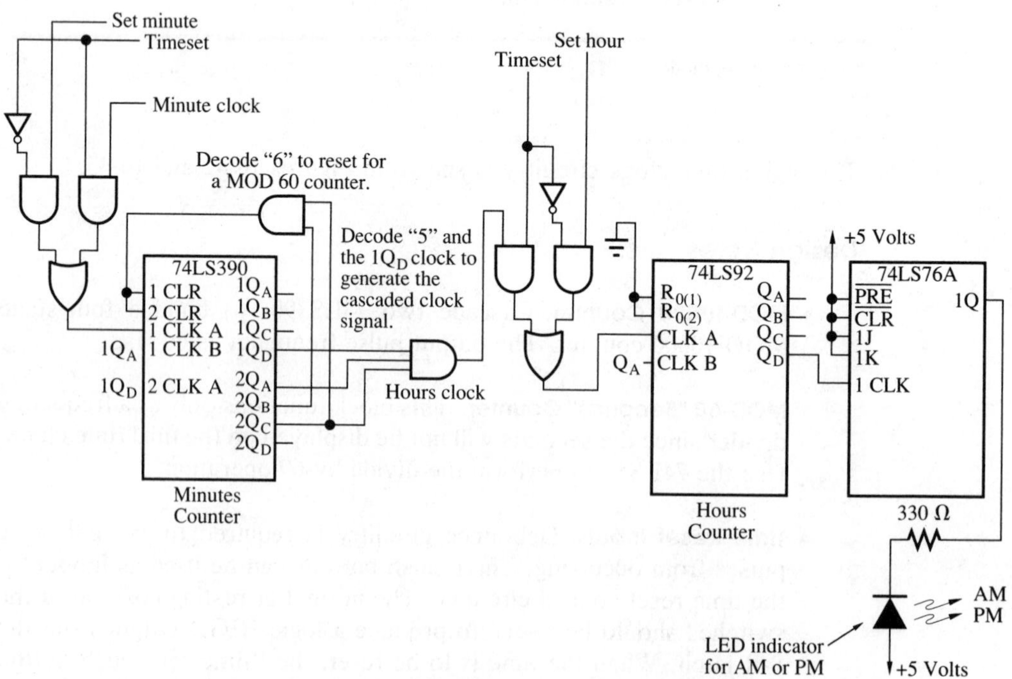

FIGURE 10-42 Example 10-19 Digital Time Clock Counter Circuitry

FIGURE 10-43 Example 10-19 Digital Time Clock Display Circuitry

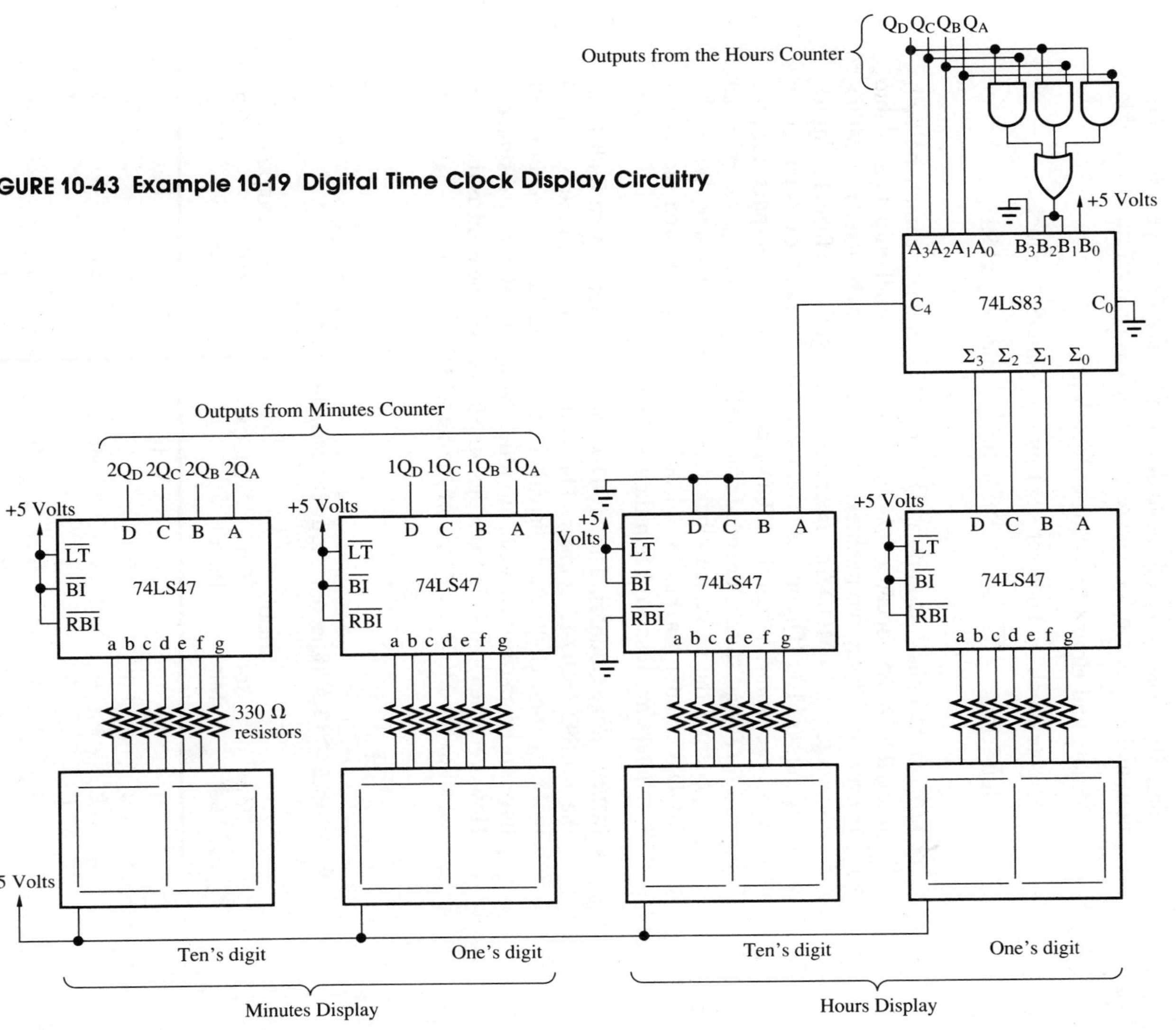

- **Minute Clock and Hour Clock Logic Circuitry.** Logic circuitry is required to control the time reset operations and clocking functions. Table 10-13 shows a truth table defining the required operation of the hour and minute clocks. The resulting logic is read off the truth table.

  Minute and Hour Clock Logic Equations:

  $$\text{Minute clock} = \overline{\text{Time-set}} \cdot \text{Set-min} + \text{Time-Set} \cdot \text{clock}$$

  $$\text{Hour clock} = \overline{\text{Time-set}} \cdot \text{Set-hour} + \text{Time-Set} \cdot \text{clock}$$

- **MOD-60 "Minutes" Counters.** This MOD-60 counter cannot be built using the 74LS57 because it is necessary to have all outputs available in order to display the minutes. The 74LS390 can be used as a MOD-10 counter and a MOD-6 counter cascaded together to form the MOD-60 counter. The $1Q_D$ output from the MOD-10 counter is input to the MOD-6 counter. When the MOD-6 counter (the 2Q outputs) reaches "0 1 0 1," that state is decoded and ANDed with the $1Q_D$ clock signal to generate the cascaded clock for the "hours" counter. When the MOD-6 counter reaches "0 1 1 0," both the MOD-10 and the MOD-6 counters are reset to begin their sequence again.
- **MOD-12 Hour Counter.** The MOD-12 hour counter can be built from the 74LS92 MOD-12 counter. This counter, however, counts from 0 to 11. A time clock must display 1 through 12, so a correction will have to be performed with an adder before the hour is displayed. However, the Q_D output from the 74LS92 can still be used as the clock signal to the MOD-2 counter of the next stage.

TABLE 10-13 Minute and Hour Clock Operation

Inputs				Outputs	
Time Set	Set Min	Set Hour	Clock	Minute Clock	Hour Clock
0	0	0	0	0	0
0	0	0	1	0	0
0	0	1	0	0	1
0	0	1	1	0	1
0	1	0	0	1	0
0	1	0	1	1	0
0	1	1	0	1	1
0	1	1	1	1	1
1	X	X	0	0	0
1	X	X	1	1	1

- **MOD-2 AM/PM Counter.** The MOD-12 and MOD-2 cascaded counters actually form a MOD-24 hour counter. But it is usually preferred to display time as two 12-hour cycles, one for AM and one for PM. The 74LS76A is used as a toggle flip-flop. Its output, Q, can be routed to a single LED to indicate AM or PM.

- **"Minutes" Display Circuitry.** The 10 outputs from the 74LS390 minutes counter are decoded with a 74LS47 as the one's digit. The 2Q outputs from the minutes counter are decoded with a separate 74LS47 as the ten's digit of the minute's display. Common anode seven-segment LED displays are used with 330 Ohm current-limiting resistors.

- **"Hours" Display Circuitry.** The hours display circuitry requires considerable correction circuitry to display properly the one's and ten's hour digits. Table 10–14 shows a truth table defining the required one's and ten's output with the corresponding output produced from the 74LS92.

  A 74LS83 adder can be used to provide the needed correction. When the output from the MOD-12 counter is less than 9, the binary value 0 0 0 1 must be added. When the output from the MOD-12 counter is equal to or greater than 9, the binary value 0 1 1 1 must be added. The carry-out from the 74LS83 adder can serve as the ten's output digit. In the circuitry shown in Figure 10-39 the outputs from the 74LS92 are the A inputs of the adder. The B_3 and C_0 inputs are tied to a logic LOW. The B_1 input is tied to a logic HIGH. The B_2 and B_3

TABLE 10-14 Hours Display Operation

Inputs 74LS92				Outputs	
Q_D	Q_C	Q_B	Q_A	Ones Digit	Tens Digit
0	0	0	0	0 0 0 1	0 0 0 0
0	0	0	1	0 0 1 0	0 0 0 0
0	0	1	0	0 0 1 1	0 0 0 0
0	0	1	1	0 1 0 0	0 0 0 0
0	1	0	0	0 1 0 1	0 0 0 0
0	1	0	1	0 1 1 0	0 0 0 0
0	1	1	0	0 1 1 1	0 0 0 0
0	1	1	1	1 0 0 0	0 0 0 0
1	0	0	0	1 0 0 1	0 0 0 0
1	0	0	1	0 0 0 0	0 0 0 1
1	0	1	0	0 0 0 1	0 0 0 1
1	0	1	1	0 0 1 0	0 0 0 1

inputs are equal to each other, controlled by the following logic function:

$$B_2 = B_3 = D_C + D_B + D_A$$

Two 74LS47 decoders are used to drive two common anode displays for the one's and ten's hours digits. ■

Section Self-Test

1. What is the total modulus of a counter system consisting of a MOD-2, a MOD-4, a MOD-10, and a MOD-16 counter cascaded together?
2. A MOD-100 counter must be implemented with a MOD-256 counter IC that can be preset to any state and can count up or down. What should be the preset state in order to obtain a MOD-100 counter when the IC is counting down?
3. A master clock has a frequency of 1 MHz. An output clock frequency of 62.5 Hz is required in an application. What modulus counter is required to perform the frequency division?

ANSWERS (Not necessarily in the order of the questions)

• 156 • 16,000 • 1280

10-9 RING COUNTERS

Ring counters are a special class of synchronous counter circuits designed from cascaded D flip-flops. Ring counters produce bit patterns that shift through all counter stages. A feedback path between the last stage and the first stage determines the bit pattern that is shifted through the ring counter. Ring counters are also called shift register counters because their design requires a shift register circuit of cascaded D flip-flops. Shift register circuits are covered in Chapter 11.

The purpose of ring counters is to simplify the decoding process required to identify unique count states. Ring counters are used in synchronization circuits, especially time division-multiplexing applications, that require trigger pulses to enable a series of outputs in a given time sequence. Ring counters can also be seen in display circuits where lights ripple on and off in a cyclical pattern.

Ring counters have important characteristics that distinguish them from binary counters. These characteristics are summarized in Table 10-15.

There are four basic types of ring counters, identified by unique count sequences, modulus, and circuit configuration. These ring counters are defined and analyzed in Sections 10.9.1 through 10.9.4.

TABLE 10-15 Ring Counter Characteristics

- Synchronous
- D flip-flop stages (or J-K flip-flops configured as D flip-flops)
- Cyclical output bit pattern
- Modulus is *less than* 2^n for an n-stage ring counter
- Feedback path from the last stage to the first stage determines the count sequence

10.9.1 Basic Ring Counter

The **basic ring counter** cycles a single logic-HIGH output pulse through the stages of the counter. The modulus of a basic ring counter is equal to the number of stages; an n-bit ring counter is a MOD-n counter. Each output state is identified by the unique position of the logic-HIGH pulse in the count sequence. Therefore, no additional decoding circuitry is required. A basic 4-bit ring counter sequence is given in Table 10-16. Figure 10-44 shows a 4-bit ring counter circuit and the output waveforms.

10.9.2 Twisted Ring Counter

The **twisted ring counter** is also known as a **switch tail counter**, **Johnson counter**, or **moebus counter**. The twisted ring counter generates a count sequence where only one output changes between consecutive count states. This pattern prevents output glitches from arising. The count sequences can be decoded with just 2 bits from each count state, no matter how many stages are in the counter.

The modulus of an n-bit twisted ring counter is 2n. The increased capability of the counter, over the basic ring counter, requires increased complexity in encoding the output states.

TABLE 10-16 Four-Bit Ring Counter

Q_D	Q_C	Q_B	Q_A	Decoded Output
1	0	0	0	$Q_D = C_0$
0	1	0	0	$Q_C = C_1$
0	0	1	0	$Q_B = C_2$
0	0	0	1	$Q_A = C_3$

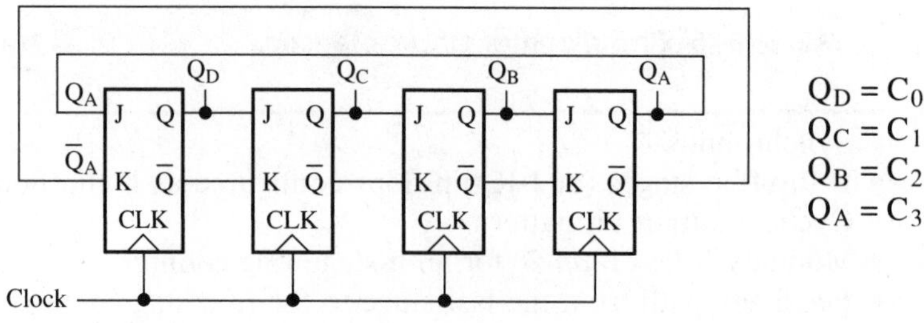

No decoding logic required

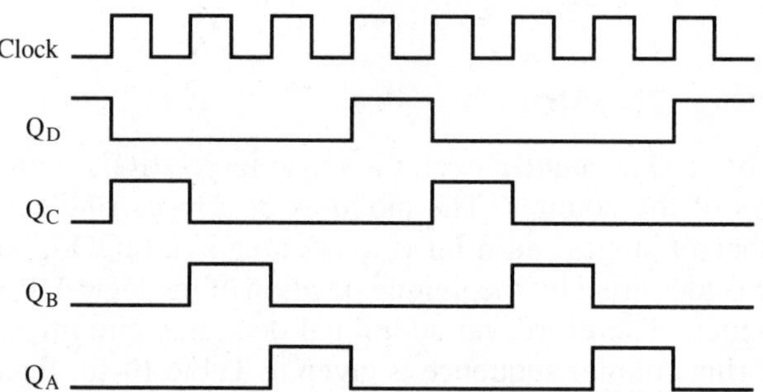

FIGURE 10-44 Four-Bit Ring Counter Circuit and Waveforms

Table 10-17 shows a 4-bit twisted ring counter and the decoded output logic functions. Figure 10-45 shows the 4-bit twisted ring counter circuit with decoding logic.

10.9.3 Modified Twisted Ring Counter

The modified twisted ring counter is very similar to the twisted ring counter. It has one less output state in its count sequence. The modulus of an n-bit

TABLE 10-17 Four-Bit Twisted Ring Counter

Q_D	Q_C	Q_B	Q_A	Decoded Outputs
0	0	0	0	$\overline{Q}_D\overline{Q}_A = C_0$
1	0	0	0	$Q_D\overline{Q}_C = C_1$
1	1	0	0	$Q_C\overline{Q}_B = C_2$
1	1	1	0	$Q_B\overline{Q}_A = C_3$
1	1	1	1	$Q_DQ_A = C_4$
0	1	1	1	$\overline{Q}_DQ_C = C_5$
0	0	1	1	$\overline{Q}_CQ_B = C_6$
0	0	0	1	$\overline{Q}_BQ_A = C_7$

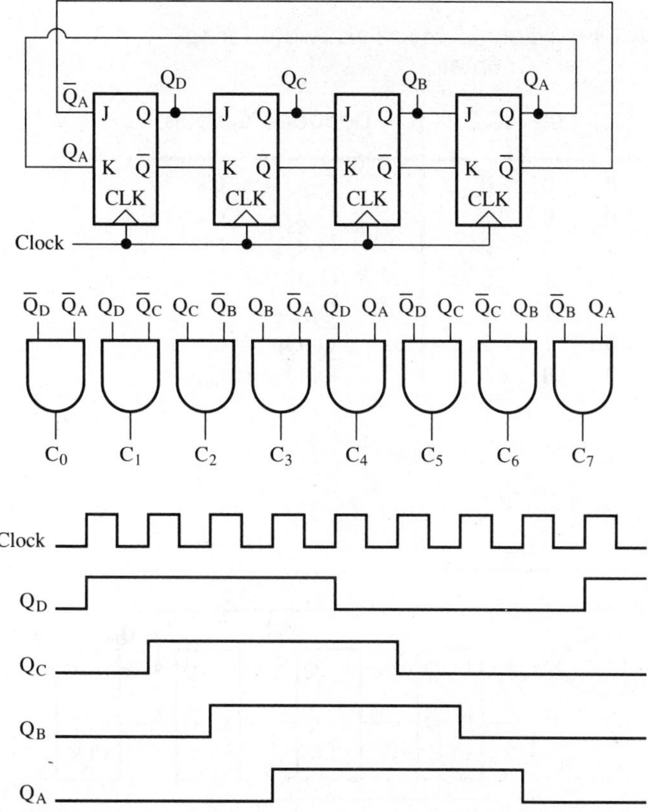

FIGURE 10-45 Four-Bit Twisted Ring Counter Circuit and Waveforms

modified twisted ring counter is 2n − 1. The count sequence for a modified twisted ring counter is shown in Table 10-18. Notice that there is no state where all the outputs are at a logic HIGH level. Figure 10-46 shows a 4-bit modified twisted ring counter circuit and waveforms.

10.9.4 Maximum Length Ring Counter

The basic ring counter, twisted ring counter, and modified twisted ring counters have been easy to implement, but they have been inefficient due to their short count sequence for the stages in the counter. For example, a MOD-10 decade ring counter requires ten stages. A MOD-10 twisted ring counter requires five stages plus ten decoding gates.

An n-stage **maximum length ring counter** has a modulus of $2^n - 1$. Although this modulus is greater than the other ring counters, the decoding circuitry required is much more complex. Each count state must be decoded with a four-input AND or four-input NAND gate. Table 10-19 shows the

TABLE 10-18 Four-Bit Modified Twisted Ring Counter

Q_D	Q_C	Q_B	Q_A	Decoded Outputs
0	0	0	0	$\overline{Q}_D\overline{Q}_A = C_0$
1	0	0	0	$Q_D\overline{Q}_C = C_1$
1	1	0	0	$Q_C\overline{Q}_B = C_2$
1	1	1	0	$Q_B\overline{Q}_A = C_3$
0	1	1	1	$\overline{Q}_D Q_C = C_4$
0	0	1	1	$\overline{Q}_C Q_B = C_5$
0	0	0	1	$\overline{Q}_B Q_A = C_6$

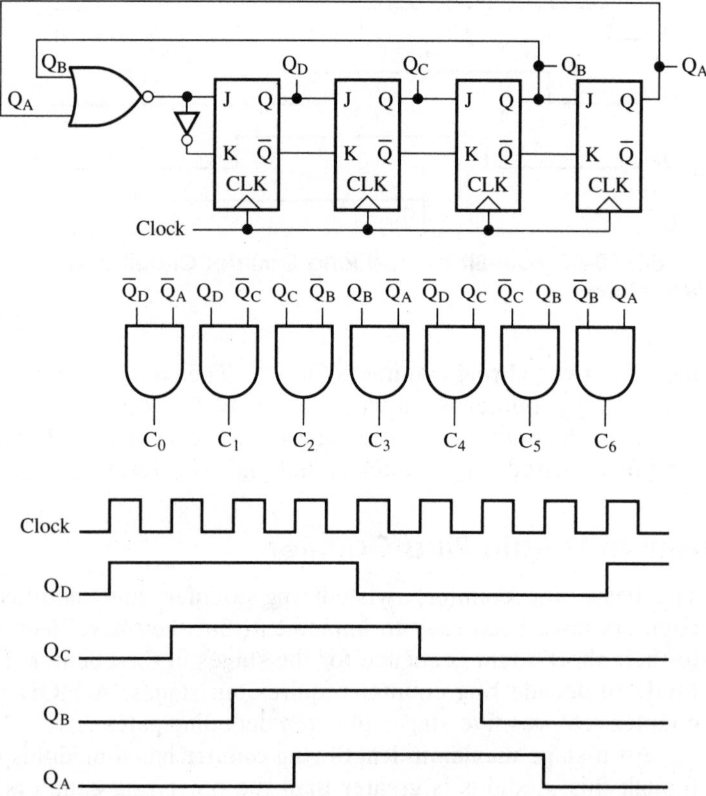

FIGURE 10-46 Four-Bit Modified Twisted Ring Counter Circuit and Waveforms

TABLE 10-19 Four-Bit Maximum Length Ring Counter

Q_D	Q_C	Q_B	Q_A	Count State
1	0	0	0	C_0
0	1	0	0	C_1
0	0	1	0	C_2
1	0	0	1	C_3
1	1	0	0	C_4
0	1	1	0	C_5
1	0	1	1	C_6
0	1	0	1	C_7
1	0	1	0	C_8
1	1	0	1	C_9
1	1	1	0	C_{10}
1	1	1	1	C_{11}
0	1	1	1	C_{12}
0	0	1	1	C_{13}
0	0	0	1	C_{14}
1	0	0	0	C_{15}

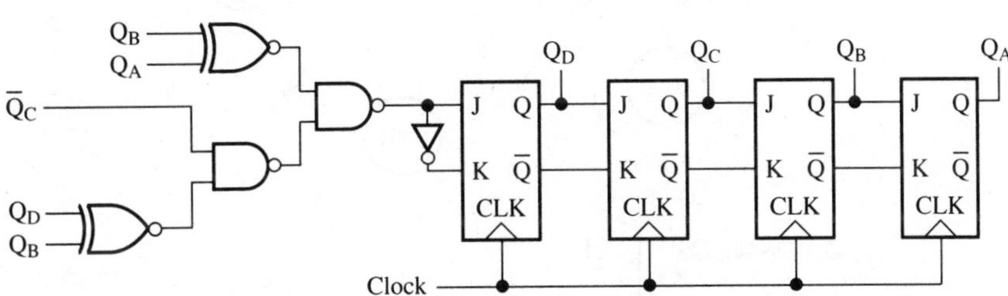

$Q_D Q_C Q_B Q_A$

See Table 10-19 for decoder inputs.

C_0 C_1 C_2 C_3 C_4 C_5 C_6 C_7 C_8 C_9 C_{10} C_{11} C_{12} C_{13} C_{14}

FIGURE 10-47 Maximum Length Ring Counter

count sequence for a 4-bit maximum length ring counter. Figure 10-47 shows a 4-bit maximum length ring counter circuit.

■ EXAMPLE 10-20 Ring Counter Analysis

Problem: Analyze the 4-bit ring counter shown in Figure 10-44. Closely examine the 0 0 0 0 state to determine how to set the ring counter if this state occurs.

Solution: Construct a table with the present state and the feedback. Analyze the **essential states** of the ring counter that produce the output shown in Table 10-16. The 0 0 0 0 state must be decoded and one of the D flip-flops set to a logic-HIGH in order to create the ring counter sequence. The result is shown in Figure 10-48.

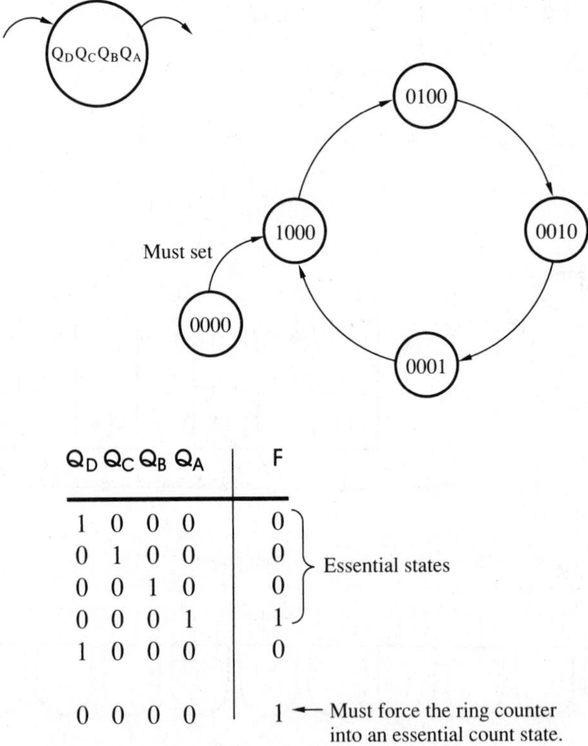

Q_D	Q_C	Q_B	Q_A	F	
1	0	0	0	0	Essential states
0	1	0	0	0	
0	0	1	0	0	
0	0	0	1	1	
1	0	0	0	0	
0	0	0	0	1	← Must force the ring counter into an essential count state.

FIGURE 10-48 Example 10-20 Ring Counter Analysis ■

Section Self-Test

1. Which n-bit ring counter has a modulus of n?
2. Which n-bit ring counter has a modulus of 2n?
3. Which n-bit ring counter has a modulus of 2n − 1?

ANSWERS (Not necessarily in the order of the questions)

- Modified twisted ring counter
- Twisted ring counter
- Ring counter

10-10 RING COUNTER DESIGN

Ring counters are designed by specifying the feedback logic required to generate the desired count sequence. All the logic levels input into the first stage are shifted through the remaining stages of the counter.

The desired count states in a ring counter are the essential states. All other states that are not in the count sequences are nonessential states. Ring counters should be designed so that they do not get caught in a loop outside the essential states. This can be accomplished by presetting the D flip-flops to a count state with the asynchronous preset or clear controls, or it can be accomplished by determining a sequence so that nonessential states reach the desired sequence.

■ EXAMPLE 10-21 Ring Counter Design

Problem: Design a 4-bit basic ring counter that can be set with the asynchronous controls on the D flip-flops to begin counting in the 1 0 0 0 state.

Solution: The feedback to the first state of the ring counter must be defined, as shown in Table 10-20. It can be seen from the table that the feedback

TABLE 10-20 Four-Bit Ring Counter Design

Q_D	Q_C	Q_B	Q_A	Feedback
1	0	0	0	0
0	1	0	0	0
0	0	1	0	0
0	0	0	1	1

required into the Q_D flip-flop stage is equal to the output from the Q_A flip-flop. To begin counting in the 1 0 0 0 count state, the Q_D flip-flop must be preset and the remaining stages must be cleared. Figure 10-49 shows the ring counter circuit.

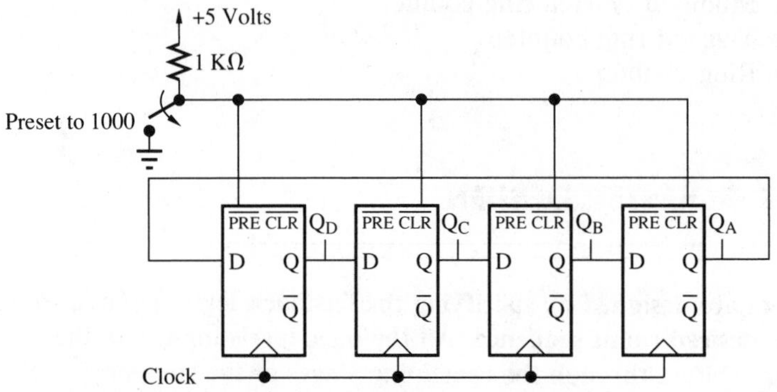

FIGURE 10-49 Example 10-21 Ring Counter Design ■

TABLE 10-21 Four-Bit Maximum Length Ring Counter Design

Q_D	Q_C	Q_B	Q_A	Feedback
1	0	0	0	0
0	1	0	0	0
0	0	1	0	1
1	0	0	1	1
1	1	0	0	0
0	1	1	0	1
1	0	1	1	0
0	1	0	1	1
1	0	1	0	1
1	1	0	1	1
1	1	1	0	1
1	1	1	1	0
0	1	1	1	0
0	0	1	1	0
0	0	0	1	1
1	0	0	0	(First state)
Nonessential state:				
0	0	0	0	1

■ EXAMPLE 10-22 Maximum Length Ring Counter Design

Problem: Design a maximum length ring counter to count according to the sequence given in Table 10-21. Design the counter so that the 0 0 0 0 state always leads to the 1 0 0 0 count state.

Solution: The feedback to produce the maximum length ring counter sequence must be defined in a truth table, and a logic expression obtained from the truth table. Table 10-21 shows the truth table definition for the essential count states, and the nonessential state of 0 0 0 0, which must lead to the 1 0 0 0 state.

The feedback can be mapped in a K-map as shown in Figure 10-50, and the logic function can be simplified.

$Q_D Q_C$ \ $Q_B Q_A$	0 0	0 1	1 1	1 0
0 0	1	1	0	1
0 1	0	1	0	1
1 1	0	1	0	1
1 0	0	1	1	1

$F = \overline{Q}_B Q_A + Q_B \overline{Q}_A + \overline{Q}_D \overline{Q}_C \overline{Q}_B + Q_D \overline{Q}_C Q_B$

FIGURE 10-50 Karnaugh Map for Maximum Length Ring Counter Design

The resulting logic equation for the feedback is:

$$F = \overline{Q}_B Q_A + Q_B \overline{Q}_A + \overline{Q}_D \overline{Q}_C \overline{Q}_B + Q_D \overline{Q}_C Q_B$$

The resulting circuit is shown in Figure 10-46. This circuit is functionally equivalent to the one shown in Figure 10-51.

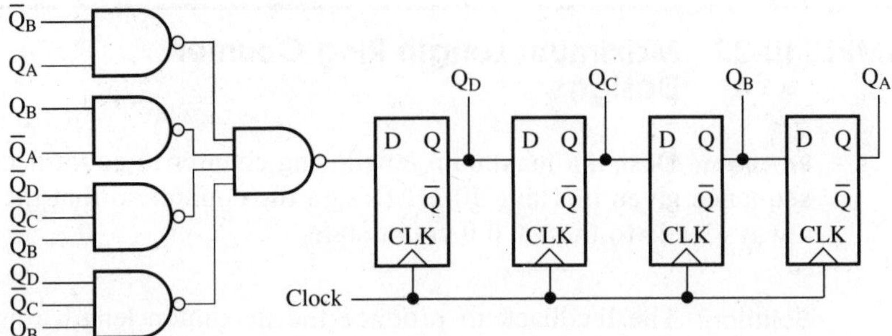

FIGURE 10-51 Example 10-22 Maximum Length Ring Counter Circuit

■

Section Self-Test

1. The nonessential states can be ignored when designing a ring counter circuit.
2. The nonessential states must lead into the essential states in the ring counter.
3. The nonessential states can be decoded to preset or clear the counter into an essential count state.

ANSWERS (Not necessarily in the order of the questions)

• False • False • True

10-11 RING COUNTER APPLICATIONS

Ring counter circuits are used in applications that require synchronization or time delay. A basic ring counter can produce output waveforms with equivalent frequencies with a fixed time delay between the occurrence of a pulse from one output to the next. Those output waveforms can be used as the clocks to other circuits that require a fixed delay between their operations. This time delay characteristic is seen in Figure 10-52.

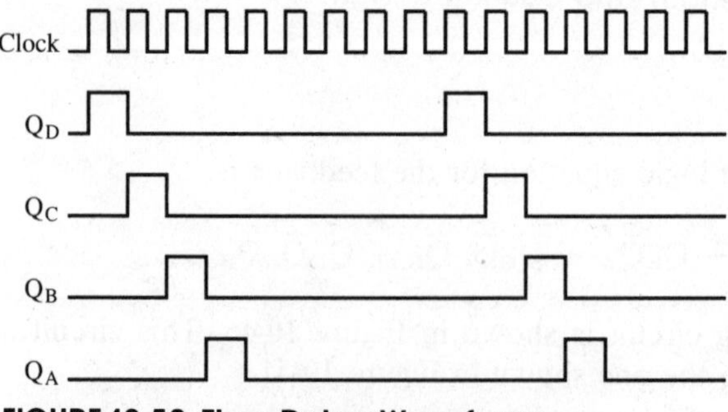

FIGURE 10-52 Time Delay Waveforms

■ EXAMPLE 10-23 Ring Counter Delay Circuit

Problem: The waveforms of Figure 10-52 are generated by a ring counter that is to create output pulses of 20 ms in duration. The output pulses have a frequency of 5 Hz. The Q_D pulse first occurs at a time of 0. The Q_C pulse occurs at a time of 20 ms. The Q_B pulse occurs at a time of 40 ms, and the Q_A pulse occurs at a time of 60 ms. The next Q_D pulse occurs at a time of 200 ms. The timing diagram is shown in Figure 10-53.

What input clock frequency is required? How many stages are required in the ring counter?

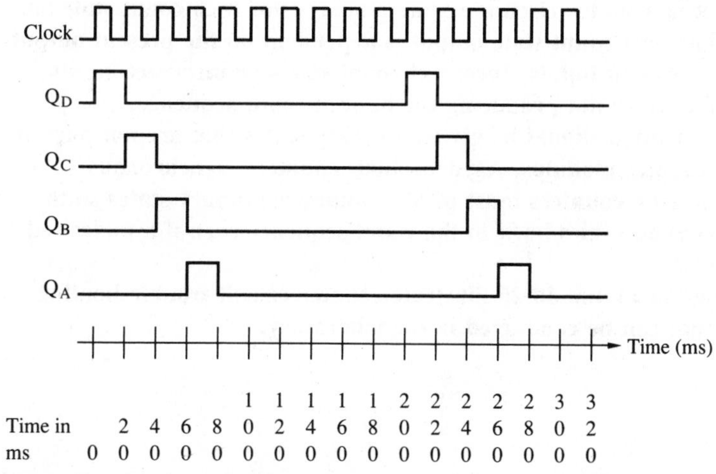

FIGURE 10-53 Example 10-23 Ring Counter Timing Diagram

Solution: Close inspection of the timing diagram in Figure 10-53 reveals that the input clock must run at a frequency of 50 Hz and ten stages are required in the ring counter to produce the required output waveforms. ■

Section Self-Test

1. Why are ring counters used in applications requiring waveforms to be generated that have specific time delay characteristics?
2. Given an input clock of frequency, f, what is the time duration of a pulse out of a ring counter?
3. Given an input clock frequency, f, and a ring counter of n stages, what is the frequency of the output waveforms?

ANSWERS (Not necessarily in the order of the questions)

- Pulse time duration = 1/f
- Output frequency = f/n
- The ring counter repetitively cycles a pulse of fixed duration through the circuit. This pulse is delayed from one stage to the next by the period of the input clock. The pulse can be used in applications requiring synchronous delayed clock pulses.

10-12 TROUBLESHOOTING COUNTER CIRCUITS

Troubleshooting counter circuits requires analysis of each count state and its inputs. The next count state output is dependent on the present output state and the present inputs. Incorrect count states or incorrect inputs result in the counter not producing the desired count sequence.

Special attention should be given to binary states that are not part of the desired counter modulus. Asynchronous counters, synchronous counters, and ring counters must process undesired binary states so that the counter circuit cycles back to the count sequence even if a undesired state occurs.

Examples 10-24 and 10-25 illustrate counter circuit troubleshooting techniques that can be conducted in the laboratory.

■ EXAMPLE 10-24 Ring Around a Counter

Problem: The ring counter of Figure 10-44 has proven to be unreliable when nonessential count states occur inadvertently. Analyze the counter to determine the complete state transition diagram for all 4-bit binary output combinations. Design the decoder circuitry to detect any nonessential state and set the ring counter back to the 1 0 0 0 state.

Solution: The analysis of the ring counter reveals the present state feedback table and state transition diagram shown in Figure 10-54.

A truth table is created to specify those states that must be decoded to reset the counter. The reset is active-LOW. The truth table for the reset function and the improved circuit is shown in Figure 10-55.

Present State Q_D	Q_C	Q_B	Q_A	Feedback to Q_D F	
0	0	0	1	1	Essential states
1	0	0	0	0	
0	1	0	0	0	
0	0	1	0	0	
0	0	0	1	1	
0	0	0	0	0	Locked at 0000
0	0	0	0	0	
0	0	1	1	1	Undesired count sequence
1	0	0	1	1	
1	1	0	0	0	
0	1	1	0	0	
0	0	1	1	1	
0	1	0	1	1	Undesired count sequence
1	0	1	0	0	
0	1	0	1	1	
0	1	1	1	1	Undesired count sequence
1	0	1	1	1	
1	1	0	1	1	
1	1	1	0	0	
0	1	1	1	1	
1	1	1	1	1	Locked at 1111
1	1	1	1	1	

(a)

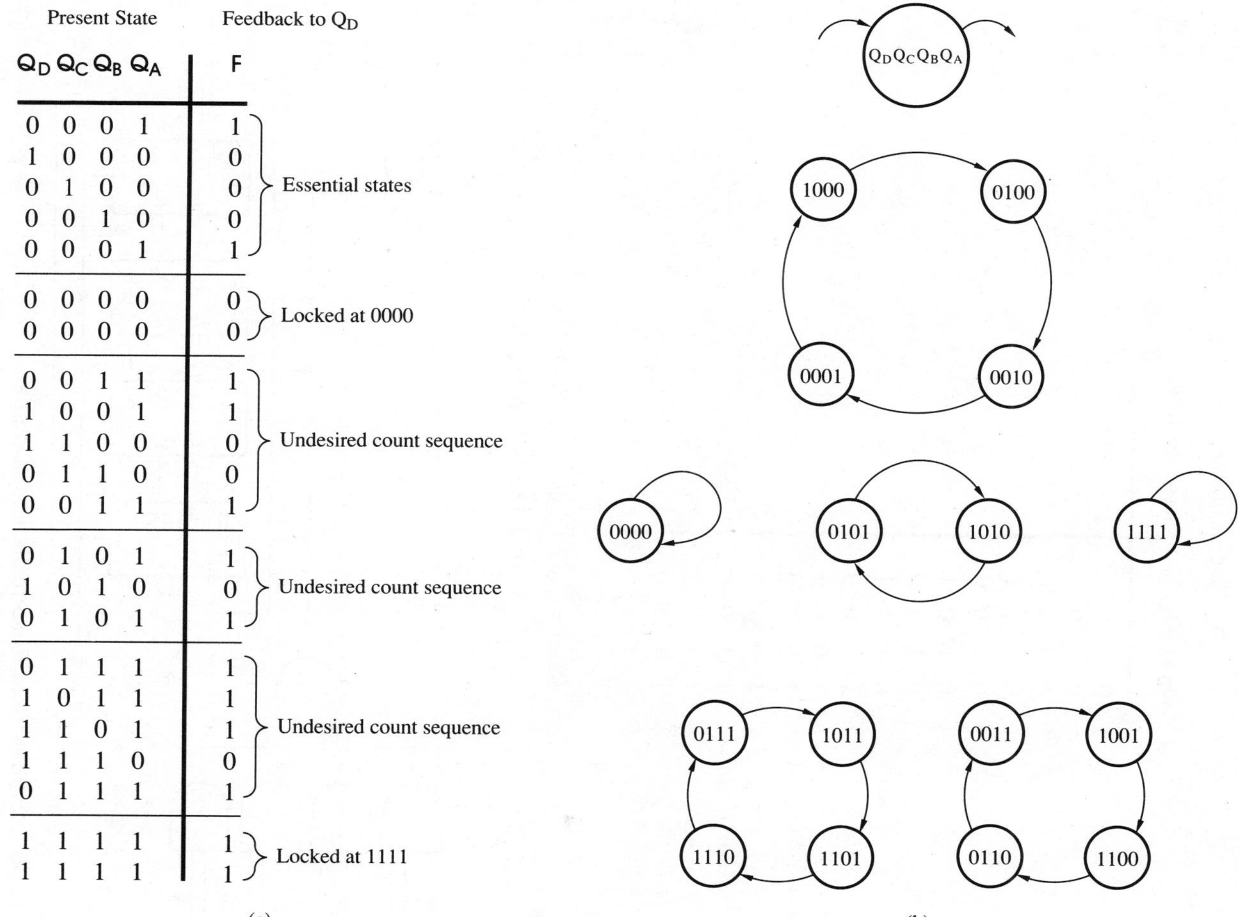

(b)

FIGURE 10-54 Example 10-23 Troubled Ring Counter Analysis

Decoder Circuit Design

Q_D	Q_C	Q_B	Q_A	$\overline{\text{Reset}}$ to 1000
0	0	0	0	0
0	0	0	1	1
0	0	1	0	1
0	0	1	1	0
0	1	0	0	1
0	1	0	1	0
0	1	1	0	0
0	1	1	1	0
1	0	0	0	1
1	0	0	1	0
1	0	1	0	0
1	0	1	1	0
1	1	0	0	0
1	1	0	1	0
1	1	1	0	0
1	1	1	1	0

$$\overline{\text{Reset}} = \overline{Q}_D\overline{Q}_C\overline{Q}_B Q_A + \overline{Q}_D\overline{Q}_C Q_B \overline{Q}_A + \overline{Q}_D Q_C \overline{Q}_B \overline{Q}_A + Q_D \overline{Q}_C \overline{Q}_B \overline{Q}_A$$

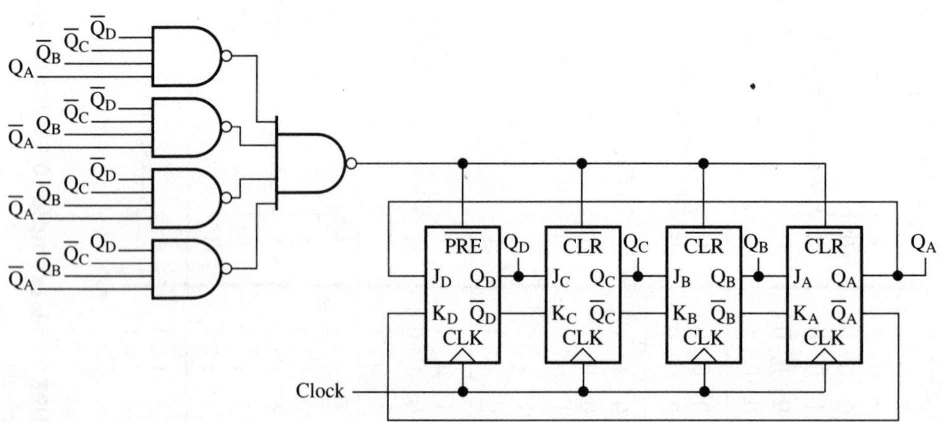

FIGURE 10-55 Example 10-24 Resettable Ring Counter

■ EXAMPLE 10-25 Unaccountable Counter

Problem: The synchronous counter circuit in Figure 10-28 produces the following count sequence: $Q_C\ Q_B\ Q_A$ = 1 1 1, 0 1 1, 1 0 1, 0 0 1, 1 1 1, and so on. The count state 0 1 0 is skipped. The circuit designers cannot account for the source of trouble in the circuit. You are called in to rectify the situation.

Solution: Construct a present state-present input-next state table to compare the expected circuit operation with the actual performance. The theoretical present state-present inputs-next state table is shown in Table 10-22. Another

TABLE 10-22 Example 10-26 Counter Analysis Theoretical

Present State-Present Inputs-Next State Table

Present State			Present Inputs						Next State		
Q_C	Q_B	Q_A	J_C	K_C	J_B	K_B	J_A	K_A	Q_C	Q_B	Q_A
0	0	0	0	0	0	0	1	0	0	0	1
0	0	1	1	1	1	1	1	0	1	1	1
0	1	0	0	0	0	0	1	0	0	1	1
0	1	1	1	1	1	1	1	0	1	0	1
1	0	0	0	0	0	0	1	0	1	0	1
1	0	1	1	1	0	0	1	0	0	0	1
1	1	0	0	0	0	0	1	1	1	1	1
1	1	1	1	1	0	0	1	1	0	1	0

TABLE 10-23 Example 10-26 Counter Analysis Observed Operation

Present State-Present Inputs-Next State Table

Present State			Present Inputs						Next State			
Q_C	Q_B	Q_A	J_C	K_C	J_B	K_B	J_A	K_A	Q_C	Q_B	Q_A	
0	0	0	0	0	0	0	1	0	0	0	1	
0	0	1	1	1	1	1	1	0	1	1	1	
0	1	0	0	0	0	0	1	0	0	1	1	
0	1	1	1	1	1	1	1	0	1	0	1	
1	0	0	0	0	0	0	1	0	1	0	1	
1	0	1	1	1	0	0	1	0	0	0	1	
1	1	0	0	0	0	0	1	0	1	1	1	See K_A
1	1	1	1	1	0	0	1	0	0	1	1	See K_A

present state-present inputs-next state table is derived to try to explain the observed operation. The last two rows in Table 10-23 indicate the source of the problem. K_A is to be HIGH, and the circuit is functioning as if K_A is a logic-LOW. The circuit is tested and the cause is determined: The output of the AND gate forming the Q_BQ_C term is shorted to ground. Therefore, K_A is always at a logic-LOW. The problem is corrected and the circuit functions as expected. ■

Section Self-Test

1. Troubleshooting counter circuits relies heavily on the counter analysis techniques.
2. All possible output states must be analyzed to define fully the operation of the counter.
3. Asynchronous inputs to clear and reset the counter can be used to detect unwanted states and force the counter back into its count modulus.

ANSWERS • True • True • True

SUMMARY

Counter circuits are complex synchronous logic functions that are important in many digital applications. Synchronous and asynchronous binary counters are flexible in their design to allow implementation of many specialized count sequences. Integrated circuit counters are available with many options for performance and features.

Ring counter circuits are a special type of synchronous counter circuits. Whereas the synchronous counter circuits are best known for producing specific combinations of output states, ring counters are known for producing time synchronous output waveforms with a fixed delay period.

ANALYSIS

Asynchronous and synchronous counters were analyzed and classified according to their modulus, frequency division, number of stages, number of bits, and triggering edge. The differences of asynchronous and synchronous counters were highlighted. Asynchronous counters have many glitches in their decoded outputs due to the timing delays in the clock. Synchronous counters operate with a common clock to all flip-flop stages, so extraneous glitches in the decoded outputs do not occur.

Integrated circuit counters, such as the 74193 and the 7490 were used in several examples. The 74193 is a 4-bit binary up or down counter. The 7490 is a BCD or biquinary decade counter.

APPLICATIONS

Several counter applications were investigated, including a digital time clock, digital lock, frequency dividers, and number sequence generators.

Counters can be cascaded to increase their modulus and thus their frequency division factor. The preset and clear inputs could be used in many applications to modify the count modulus as required for the application.

Ring counters are a special type of synchronous counters, often referred to as shift register counters. Ring counters are used in pulse delay, synchronization, and simplified decoding applications. The ring counters studied included the basic ring counter, twisted ring counter, modified twisted ring counter, and maximum length ring counter.

Several ICs were compared and evaluated according to selection criteria and application requirements. Several counter ICs are available with varying speed, input features, and count flexibility.

DESIGN

Asynchronous and synchronous counters were designed to count serial count sequences up or down, or to count a unique sequence of numbers. Design techniques for asynchronous counters relied heavily on waveform analysis and triggering requirements of the flip-flops or asynchronous IC counters. Synchronous counter design involved determining the required excitation on the inputs to produce the necessary count sequence. State transition diagrams and present state-next state tables were used to define the inputs needed.

Ring counters were designed based on the feedback requirements. The asynchronous preset and clear inputs to the counter were often critical elements of the design to ensure that the counter sequenced through the essential count states of the ring counter.

A large counter system design of a digital time clock was studied to determine how to cascade several different counters and how to display the results.

TROUBLESHOOTING

Counter circuits that functioned improperly were analyzed and diagnosed to determine the cause of the malfunction. Good analysis techniques are essential when troubleshooting. The waveform analysis, present state-present inputs-next state tables, and feedback tables are essential components of counter troubleshooting, along with the laboratory test devices that confirm the results of the analysis.

Counters will continue to be used in designs and applications throughout the remainder of the text. Chapter 12 covers counters from the standpoint of programmable logic devices (PLDs). Many PLDs are manufactured with a D flip-flop in each output stage. Because of this circuit architecture, many counter circuits will be redesigned as PLD counters based on D flip-flop operation instead of J-K flip-flop operations. The basics for the design will remain as they were defined throughout Chapter 10.

Programmable logic devices enable many counter designs to be implemented with a single chip, as opposed to the multiple ICs required to implement designs that were featured in this chapter. Although the PLD equations defining the flip-flop inputs may seem much more complex using the D flip-flop as the stages in the counter, the PLD can be easily programmed to implement these equations.

PROBLEMS

10-1 Digital Counter Applications—Application Problems

1. Cite three applications you find in the home for digital counter circuits.
2. Cite three applications you find in an automobile for digital counter circuits.

10-2 and 10-3 Counter Classification and Counter Analysis—Analysis Problems

*3. Refer to the waveforms in Figure 10-1. The frequency of the signal of output A is 1000 Hz. What is the frequency of the output D?

4. Refer to the waveforms in Figure 10-2. The frequency of the signal of output A is 1000 Hz. What are the frequencies of the outputs B, C, and D?

*5. Analyze the counter circuit shown in Figure 10-4, assuming that the flip-flops are master-slave devices. Show the clock waveform, output waveforms, and state transition diagram.

10-4 Count State Decoding—Application Problems

6. Use a 74154 to decode all count states from a 16-bit synchronous counter.
7. Select a BCD decoder to decode all BCD count states. Signal an error if a non-BCD count state occurs.

10-5 Asynchronous Counter Circuits—Analysis and Design Problems

*8. Design a 4-bit, MOD-16, asynchronous binary up counter using negative edge-triggered J-K flip-flops. Select a TTL flip-flop to use in the

---

* *See* Answers to Selected Problems.

design, and specify the part number. Indicate how many ICs are required to provide enough flip-flops to construct the counter circuit. Show the clock waveform, output waveforms, and the counter circuit.

9. If a 74154 were used to decode all count states from an asynchronous counter, list, in order, the decoded outputs that will be activated.

10. Design an asynchronous counter to count down from 1 1 1 1 to 0 0 0 0.

10-6 Synchronous Counters—Analysis and Design Problems

11. Redesign the circuit shown in Figure 10-21 that was analyzed in Example 10-13 so that it does not have a lockout loop. The state 1 0 0 should lead to the state 0 0 0. All other states remain as they are in the state transition diagram of Figure 10-21.

12. Design a MOD-10 synchronous down counter using J-K counters. Select a TTL J-K flip-flop IC for the design. Show the complete design with the counter excitation table and K-maps to determine the inputs to the J-K counters. Analyze the final counter circuit to show the complete state transition diagram for all possible output states.

10-7 Integrated Circuit Counters—Analysis and Design Problems

*13. Design a MOD-10 synchronous down counter using the 74LS193. Analyze the final counter circuit to show the complete state transition diagram for all possible output states.

14. Describe the differences between (or among) the following counters:
   a. The 74LS190 and the 74LS192
   b. The 74LS160 and the 74LS162
   c. The 74LS193 and the 74LS393
   d. The 74196, the 74LS196, and the 74S196

15. For the counter circuit of Example 10-16, change the clock to the "down clock" input and analyze the resulting counter. Show a complete state transition diagram.

10-8 Cascaded Counters—Analysis and Design Problems

16. Design a MOD-25 synchronous up counter using 74LS193s. Explain how the MOD-25 circuit functions, based on the count sequence and decoding operations performed.

*17. Design a MOD-25 asynchronous counter using 74LS90s. Explain how the MOD-25 circuit functions, based on the count sequence and decoding operations.

10-9 and 10-10 Ring Counters and Ring Counter Design—Analysis and Design Problems

18. Analyze the counter shown in Figure 10-44. Show the complete analysis for all possible count states in a present state-present inputs-next state table. Draw a state transition diagram of the count sequence.

*19. Redesign the ring counter shown in Figure 10-44 so that it is a self-starting counter where all output states lead back to the desired count sequence.

10-12 Troubleshooting Counter Circuits

20. Decode the output 0 0 0 0 from the asynchronous down counter in Figure 10-4 and reset the counter back to 1 1 1 1. The desired modulus is MOD-15, with a count sequence from 1 1 1 1 to 0 0 0 1. What is observed due to several decoding glitches that occur?

21. A 7476 is operated in a counter circuit with the clear and preset control inputs left floating. What happens?

22. A 7476 is operated with an input clock that is not a TTL compatible signal. What happens? What are the required parameters for the input clock signal to a 7476?

Chapter 11

Shift Registers

Upon completing and mastering the material in this chapter, you should be able to perform the following operations for the analysis, application, and design of shift register circuits:

ANALYSIS

1. Analyze shift register circuit input and output configurations for serial and parallel data transfer.
2. Analyze the shift direction of data through the register.
3. Determine the register capacity.
4. Predict the output waveforms generated by shifting data through the shift register.

APPLICATION

5. Identify common shift register TTL ICs.
6. Evaluate the capacity, speed performance, and shift modes of IC shift registers.
7. Use shift register circuits in applications involving temporary data shortage, serial-to-parallel format conversion, parallel-to-serial format conversion, timing delay, ring counters, multiplication, and division.

DESIGN

8. Design shift register circuits to meet application requirements.
9. Design shift register circuits using IC shift registers to perform temporary data storage functions, serial-to-parallel format conversion, parallel-to-serial format conversion, timing delay, ring counter functions, multiplication, or division.

TROUBLESHOOTING

10. Analyze incorrectly operating shift register circuits and correct the problem.

Shift registers are made up of an array of flip-flip stages to store and transport data. Shift registers are commonly used to hold several bits of data for storage or buffering prior to transmission, for conversion between serial and parallel formats, and for several data transfer applications.

This chapter studies shift registers as sequential logic systems built from basic flip-flop circuits. The flip-flops are connected to form data registers that can input and output data on a clock pulse, and that can temporarily store the data until it is transferred to a permanent memory storage device.

11-1 DATA STORAGE AND TRANSFER

Binary data must be transferred and stored in many logic applications. Bits that are generated or transferred one bit at a time are classified as serial data. Multiple bits that are generated simultaneously are classified as parallel data. In many applications data must be transmitted from one area of a large system in a serial format or in a parallel format. Data must be converted from a serial to a parallel format if the data is generated one bit at a time and must be processed in a parallel format. However, data must be converted from a parallel to a serial format in many data transmission applications.

Shift registers are digital routers that transfer data in serial or parallel formats and convert between the serial and parallel formats. Shift registers are used to control the flow of data to other digital devices through format conversion, data rate conversion, buffering, and the delay of the data.

A shift register consists of D flip-flop stages connected by a common clock that controls the input and output timing action of the flip-flops, as shown in Figure 11-1.

Although a common clock connects all the flip-flop stages, a shift register is not a counter. A shift register has no defined sequence. It is designed to accept data from a single input (serial input) or multiple inputs (parallel inputs) and to transfer the data to a single output (serial output) or to multiple outputs (parallel outputs).

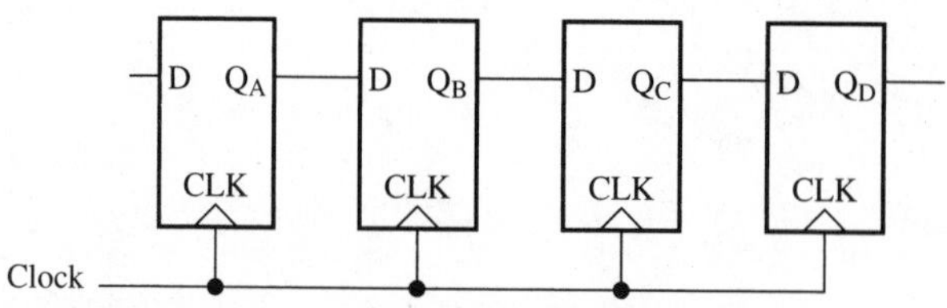

FIGURE 11-1 Four-Bit Shift Register

Shift registers are used to transfer data and to convert between the serial and parallel formats. Data enters the shift register and is transferred only on the triggering edge of the clock pulse. There are four categories of the shift register operation:

1. *Serial-In, Serial-Out.* Data enters the shift register 1 bit at a time and exits the shift register 1 bit at a time. With this type of operation, shift registers serve as temporary data storage devices. There is no format conversion.
2. *Serial-In, Parallel-Out.* Data enters the shift register 1 bit at a time and exits the shift register as a multibit binary word with all bits simultaneously available. In this type of operation the shift register converts from a serial to a parallel format and often serves as a data buffer. Serial computer communication systems commonly transmit data in a serial format. This data must be received and converted to a parallel format prior to arriving at the receiving device.
3. *Parallel-In, Parallel-Out.* Data enters the shift register as several simultaneous bits and exits the shift register as several simultaneous bits. No format conversion takes place. The shift register serves as a temporary data storage device.
4. *Parallel-In, Serial-Out.* Data enters the shift register as several simultaneous bits and exits the shift register 1 bit at a time. The shift register converts the data from a parallel format to a serial format and can temporarily store the data. Computer communication systems that transmit data in a serial format often require that parallel-to-serial conversion be performed by the transmitting device.

Serial data requires that several clock pulses be loaded into or out of a shift register. One clock pulse is required for each flip-flop stage of the register to load the data sequentially into the register or to transfer it out of the register. Only one input and output line is required for serial transmission.

Parallel data requires only one clock pulse to be loaded into or out of the shift register since all the bits are transferred simultaneously into or out of the flip-flops. Although parallel transmission is much quicker than serial transmission, an input line and an output line are required for each bit.

A hand-held calculator display operates like a shift register. When a number is entered with the keypad, that number is "read" into one stage of a shift register and displayed. As additional numbers are entered, the first entry shifts to the left while new values are read into the shift register. This is a serial shift left action. If an incorrect value was entered, the mistake can be corrected by pressing the "clear entry" button to erase the last entry. When this occurs, many calculators remove one value for each push of the clear entry button, and the value displayed shifts back to the right. This is a serial shift right action. When a value that has been previously loaded into the calculator memory is recalled, all numerals in the value are displayed simultaneously as the ''recall'' button is pressed. The display shift register has read all the numerals of the stored value. The value is still stored in the calculator memory, but the shift register is now also storing the value so that it can be displayed. The action of displaying all digits of the number is parallel output operation performed by the shift register. When a number that the user wants to store in the calculator memory has been entered by the keypad, the display shift register performs a parallel input operation to store the value into the memory of the calculator.

11.1.1 Register Capacity

Shift registers have a storage capacity equal to the number of flip-flop stages in the circuit. The stages are D flip-flops that can each hold 1 bit. Commonly available integrated circuit (IC) shift registers have a storage capacity for 4 or 8 bits and can be cascaded together to increase their capacity.

Shift registers are not memory devices even though they temporarily store binary data. Memory circuits have a complex architecture to allow the storage of many groups or words of binary data. They require addresses to specify the location of the data storage within the memory chip. Memory chips usually have complex control signals suited to interact with microprocessors. Finally, memory circuits are often manufactured using specialized IC techniques to increase the capacity or density of the memory chip while maintaining the same physical size of the piece of silicon.

11.1.2 Shift Register Analysis

The data transfer and format conversion operations of shift registers can be analyzed using a technique similar to counter analysis even though they do not have a defined sequence. The procedure consists of first analyzing the operation of the D flip-flops, and then analyzing the circuit formed by cascading the D flip-flops to form the register. D flip-flops are one of the easiest flip-flops to analyze: The next output state is always equal to the present input state, as shown in Table 11-1.

TABLE 11-1 D Flip-Flop

Present State-Next State Table

Present Input D_n	Present State Q_n	Next State Q_{n+1}	Action
0	0	0	Clear
0	1	0	
1	0	1	Set
1	1	1	

$$Q_{n+1} = D_n$$

In a shift register the output of one D flip-flop is the input to the next D flip-flop, which **shifts** the data from one stage in the register to the next, as shown in Figure 11-1. Shift registers are examined and classified in Sections 11.1.3 through 11.1.4 to analyze their operation better.

11.1.3 Input, Output, and Shift Operations

The input/output configuration of a shift register determines the way information is transferred into and out of the register from other logic systems. Parallel and serial input/output configurations are common on most shift registers. The shift operations of the register determine how the data contained in each flip-flop stage is transferred to the next flip-flop stage. Serial input registers enter the data into a serial input for shifting to the left or to the right. Parallel input registers enter the data simultaneously into each stage of the shift register.

Binary data is transferred out of a shift register in a serial or parallel format by clocking the data through the stages of the shift register. In serial data output operations the number of clock pulses required to shift one bit of data through the register is equal to the number of stages in the register. In parallel data output operations only one clock pulse is required to output simultaneously the data stored in each stage of the shift register.

The shift registers shown in Figures 11-2(a) and 11-2(b) are examples of parallel input and parallel output shift registers.

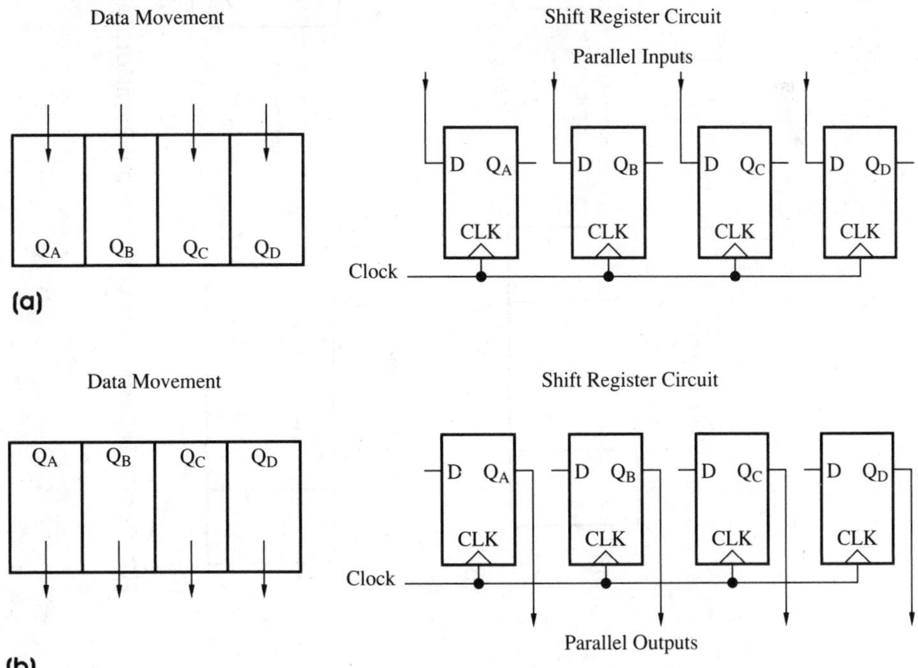

FIGURE 11-2 (a) Parallel Input Shift Register; (b) Parallel Output Shift Register

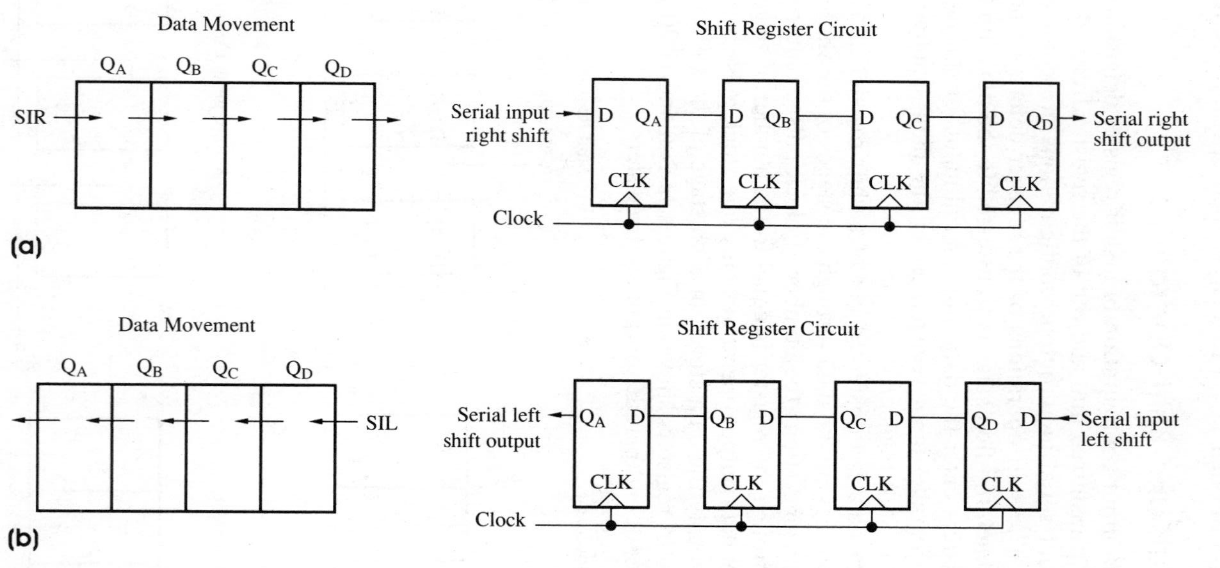

FIGURE 11-3 (A) Serial Input Shift Right Register; (b) Serial Input Shift Left Register

The shift registers shown in Figures 11-3(a) and 11-3(b) are examples of serial input shift registers that shift data to the right or to the left.

The shifting action performed by a shift register can be defined in a present state-next state table. Table 11-2 defines a 4-bit shift right register and a 4-bit shift left register corresponding to the circuits shown in Figure 11-3.

Bidirectional shift registers shift the data to either the left or the right according to a control input that determines the shifting direction of the data in the shift register. Table 11-3 is the present state-next state table that defines the shifting action for the bidirectional shift register. The control inputs of S_1 and S_0 determine the direction that data is transferred in the

TABLE 11-2 Present State-Next State Table

Shift Right Register

Serial Input Present Input	All Outputs Present State Q_n				All Outputs Next State Q_{n+1}			
Serial In	Q_A	Q_B	Q_C	Q_D	Q_A	Q_B	Q_C	Q_D
0	Q_A	Q_B	Q_C	Q_D	0	Q_A	Q_B	Q_C
1	Q_A	Q_B	Q_C	Q_D	1	Q_A	Q_B	Q_C

$$Q_{A_{n+1}} = \text{Serial In}$$
$$Q_{B_{n+1}} = Q_{A_n}$$
$$Q_{C_{n+1}} = Q_{B_n}$$
$$Q_{D_{n+1}} = Q_{C_n}$$

Shift Left Register

Serial Input Present Input	All Outputs Present State Q_n				All Outputs Next State Q_{n+1}			
Serial In	Q_A	Q_B	Q_C	Q_D	Q_A	Q_B	Q_C	Q_D
0	Q_A	Q_B	Q_C	Q_D	Q_B	Q_C	Q_D	0
1	Q_A	Q_B	Q_C	Q_D	Q_B	Q_C	Q_D	1

$$Q_{A_{n+1}} = Q_{B_n}$$
$$Q_{B_{n+1}} = Q_{C_n}$$
$$Q_{C_{n+1}} = Q_{D_n}$$
$$Q_{D_{n+1}} = \text{Serial In}$$

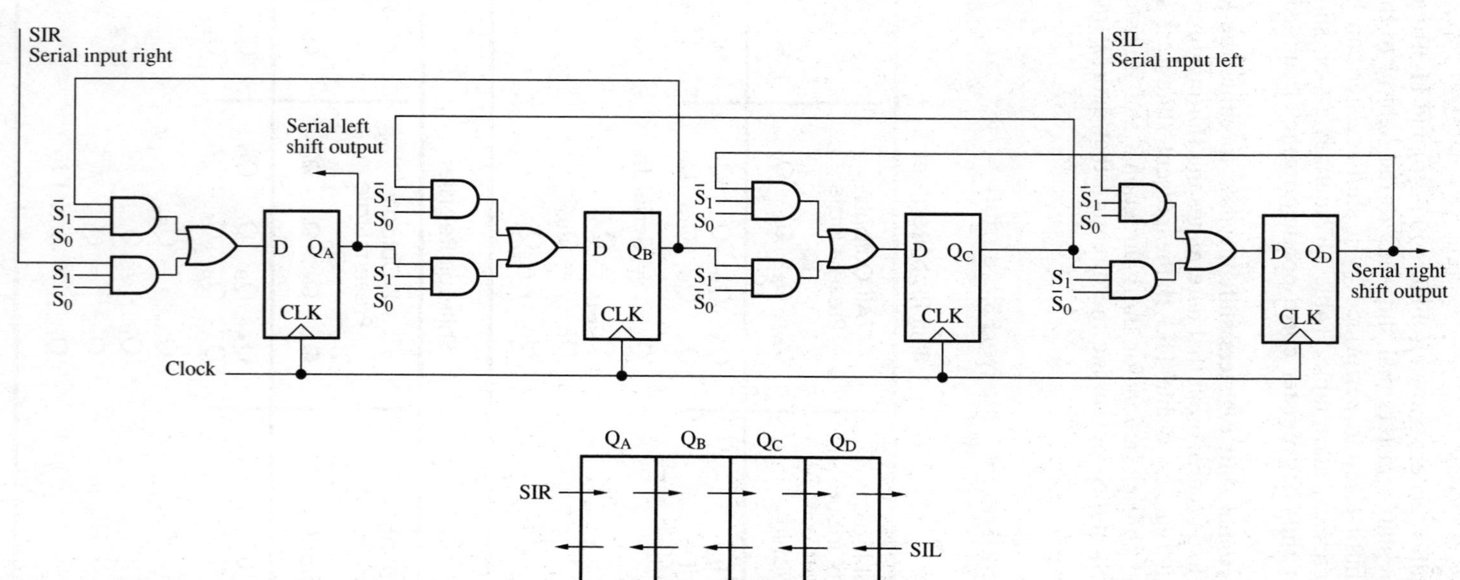

FIGURE 11-4 Bidirectional Shift Register

TABLE 11-3 Present State-Next State Table

Bidirectional Shift Register

Control Inputs S_1	S_0	All Outputs Present State Q_n Q_A	Q_B	Q_C	Q_D	All Outputs Next State Q_{n+1} Q_A	Q_B	Q_C	Q_D	Shift
0	1	Q_A	Q_B	Q_C	Q_D	Q_B	Q_C	Q_D	SIL	Left
1	0	Q_A	Q_B	Q_C	Q_D	SIR	Q_A	Q_B	Q_C	Right

$$D_n = Q_{n+1}$$

$$D_A = Q_{A_{n+1}} = \overline{S}_1 S_0 Q_B + S_1 \overline{S}_0 SIR$$
$$D_B = Q_{B_{n+1}} = \overline{S}_1 S_0 Q_C + S_1 \overline{S}_0 Q_A$$
$$D_C = Q_{C_{n+1}} = \overline{S}_1 S_0 Q_D + S_1 \overline{S}_0 Q_B$$
$$D_D = Q_{D_{n+1}} = \overline{S}_1 S_0 SIL + S_1 \overline{S}_0 Q_C$$

Serial input right: SIR
Serial input left: SIL

register. As defined in the truth table, this circuit shifts data to the left when S_1 S_0 control inputs are 0 1. The circuit shifts data to the right when the S_1 S_0 control inputs are 1 0.

The shift register defined in Table 11-3 has two serial inputs: a Serial Input Right for shifting to the right and a Serial Input Left for shifting to the left. From the present state-next state table the inputs to the D flip-flops are specified as sum of products (SOP) equations. Figure 11-4 shows the bidirectional shift register that performs the operation defined in Table 11-3.

■ EXAMPLE 11-1 Shift Register Analysis

Problem: Analyze the shift register circuit shown in Figure 11-3(a).

Solution: The shift register shown in Figure 11-3(a) is a 4-bit positive edge-triggered serial input shift right register. The data enters the register at the D_A input and is shifted right to the Q_D output. If a serial output is desired, the data is taken out of Q_D. If parallel outputs are desired, the data is taken out of the Q_A, Q_B, Q_C, and Q_D outputs. The data movement through this register is shown in the following table. The initial contents of each stage is assumed to be zero.

Clock Pulse Positive Edge	Serial Input D_A	Register Contents Q_A	Q_B	Q_C	Q_D
Initial state		0	0	0	0
1	1	1	0	0	0
2	0	0	1	0	0
3	0	0	0	1	0
4	0	0	0	0	1
5	0	0	0	0	0
6	1	1	0	0	0
7	1	1	1	0	0
8	0	0	1	1	0
9	1	1	0	1	1

There is no repeat pattern to a shift register. The input data is shifted through each flip-flop stage on the positive edge of the clock pulse. Four pulses are required to shift the data to the last stage of the register. ■

■ EXAMPLE 11-2 Shift Register Analysis

Problem: Analyze the shift register shown in Figure 11-3(b).

Solution: The shift register shown in Figure 11-3(b) is a 4-bit positive edge-triggered serial input shift left register. The data enters the register at the D_D input and is shifted left to the Q_A output. If a serial output is desired, the data is taken out of Q_A. If parallel outputs are desired, the data is taken out of the Q_A, Q_B, Q_C, and Q_D outputs. The data movement through this register is shown in the following table. The initial contents of each stage is assumed to be zero.

Clock Pulse Positive Edge	Serial Input D_D	Register Contents Q_A	Q_B	Q_C	Q_D
Initial state		0	0	0	0
1	1	0	0	0	1
2	0	0	0	1	0
3	0	0	1	0	0
4	0	1	0	0	0
5	0	0	0	0	0
6	1	0	0	0	1
7	1	0	0	1	1
8	0	0	1	1	0
9	1	1	1	0	1

■

■ EXAMPLE 11-3 Shift Register Analysis

Problem: Determine the movement of data through the bidirectional shift register shown in Figure 11-4.

Solution: The direction of data movement through the bidirectional shift register is determined by control inputs S_1 and S_0. According to Table 11-3, which defines the bidirectional shift register operation, the data is shifted to the right when the S_1 S_0 inputs are 1 0, and the data is shifted to the left when the S_1 S_0 inputs are 0 1. The data will shift on the positive edge of the clock pulse. The following table shows the movement of data through the register.

Positive Edge	S_1	S_0	SIR	SIL	Q_A	Q_B	Q_C	Q_D
Initial state					0	0	0	0
1	1	0	0	1	0	0	0	0
2	1	0	1	1	1	0	0	0
3	1	0	1	0	1	1	0	0
4	1	0	0	1	0	1	1	0
5	1	0	0	0	0	0	1	1
6	0	1	0	1	0	1	1	1
7	0	1	1	1	1	1	1	1
8	0	1	1	0	1	1	1	0
9	0	1	0	1	1	1	0	1

■

11.1.4 Timing and Waveforms

The shifting of data through the shift register is controlled by the clock and any control inputs, if they exist. Data moves through the shift register stages only on the triggering edge of the clock pulse. Waveforms are shown in Figures 11-5 and 11-6 to illustrate data movement through a shift register.

The data in Figure 11-5 is loaded serially into the register. The register can shift the data to either the left or the right. The data in Figure 11-6 is loaded in parallel into the register. The register in Figure 11-6 can also shift the data to either the left or the right.

One important function of shift registers is to delay an input pulse for a fixed time period. An input pulse is entered as data into the serial input of the shift register. The delay of the pulse experiences at each stage in the

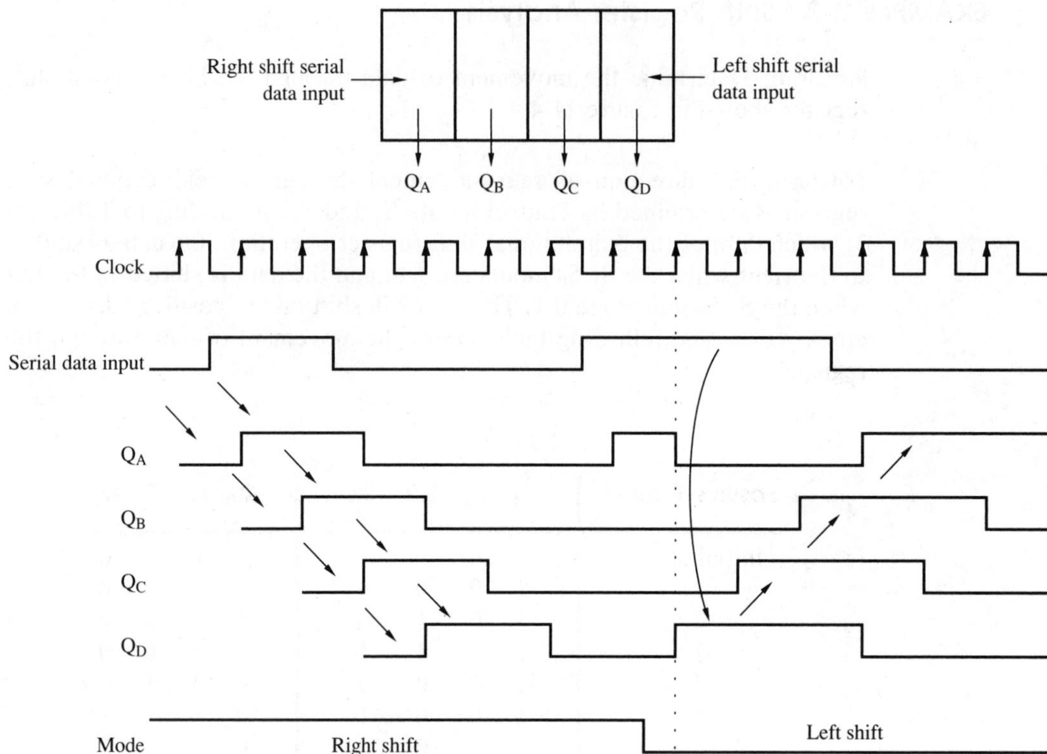

FIGURE 11-5 Serial Input Data Shifting

register is equal to the period of the clock waveform. The total delay through several stages of the shift register is equal to the number of stages the pulse is transferred through times the period of the input clock, as shown in Equation 11-1.

Eq. 11-1 $$T_{delay} = nT = \frac{n}{f}$$

n = number of stages

T = period of the input clock

f = frequency of the input clock

Figure 11-7 shows an example of an input pulse that is delayed as it is shifted through the shift register.

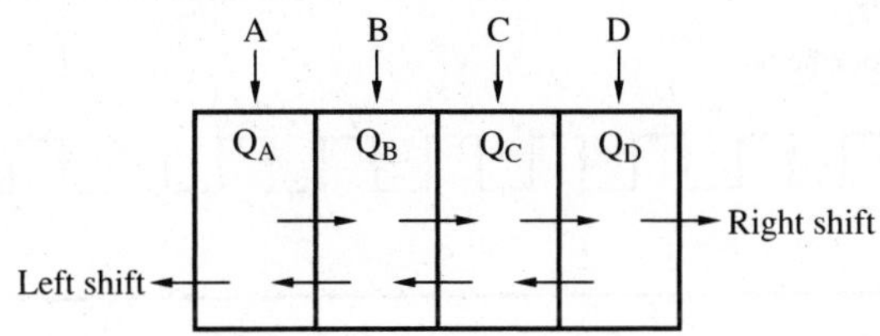

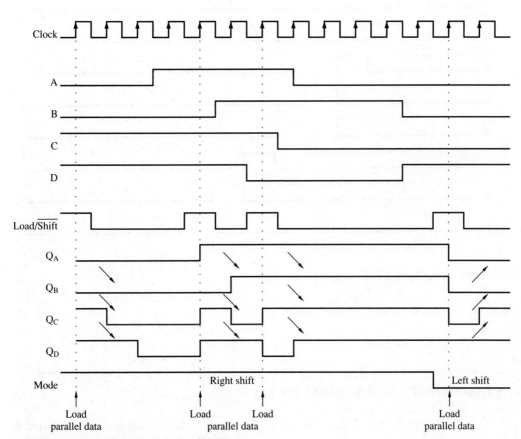

FIGURE 11-6 Parallel Input Data Shifting

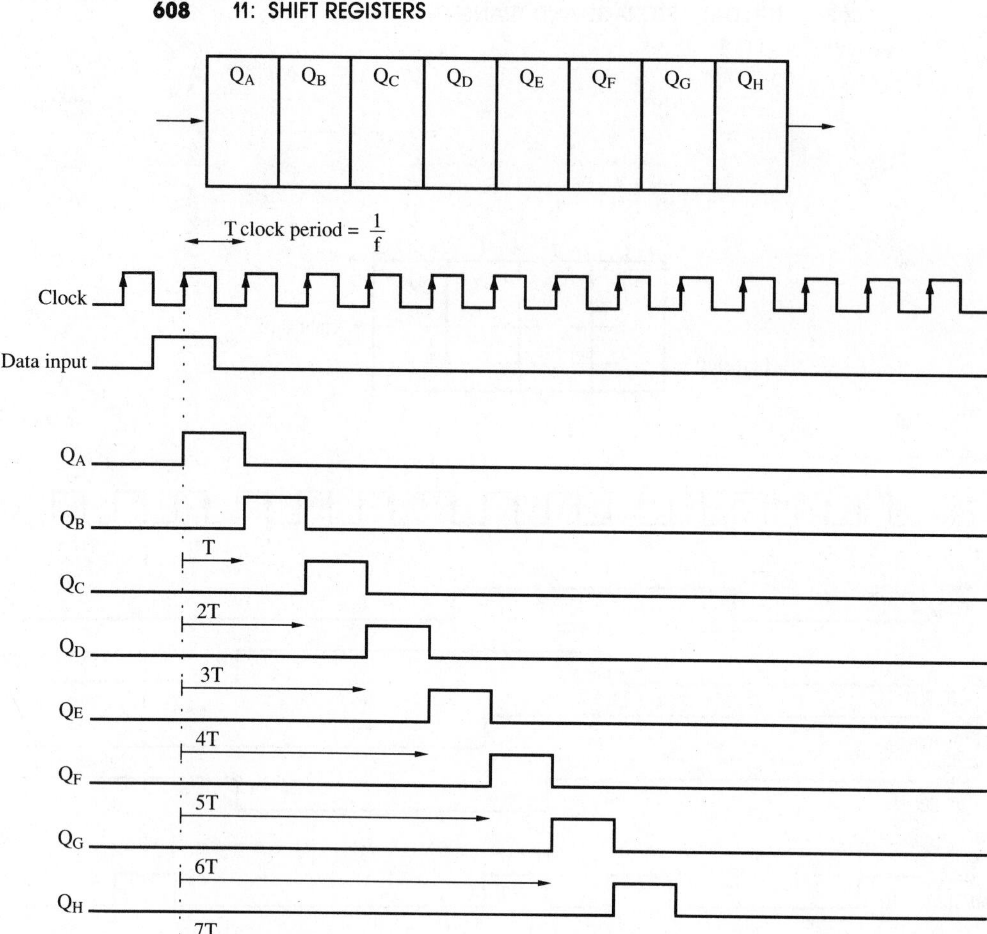

FIGURE 11-7 Time Delay Shift Register

■ EXAMPLE 11-4 Shift Register Timing

Problem: Draw the waveforms for the data input into the shift register in Example 11-1.

Solution: The shift register waveforms are shown here. Note that the outputs change only on the positive edge of the clock pulse.

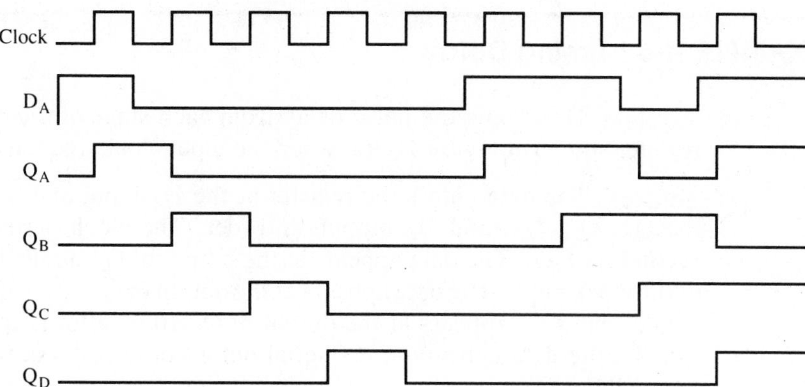

■

■ EXAMPLE 11-5 Shift Register Timing

Problem: Draw the waveforms for the data input into the shift register in Example 11-2.

Solution: The shift register waveforms are shown here. Note that the outputs change only on the positive edge of the clock pulse.

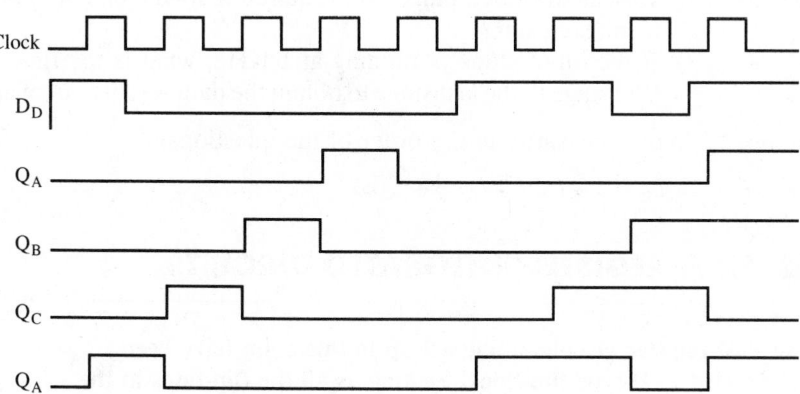

■

■ EXAMPLE 11-6 Timing Delay

Problem: Determine the pulse delay from each stage of the 4-bit shift right register shown in Figure 11-3(a) when the input clock frequency is 100 KHz.

Solution: The data enters the register at the D_A input and is transferred to the Q_A, Q_B, Q_C, and Q_D outputs in order. The clock period is 10 microseconds (10 μs). The data appears at the output of Q_A on the triggering edge of the clock pulse. The data appears at the output of Q_B 10 μs after it appeared at Q_A. The data appears at the output of Q_C 10 μs after it appeared at Q_B. Finally, the data appears at the serial output of Q_D 30 μs after it appeared originally at Q_A.

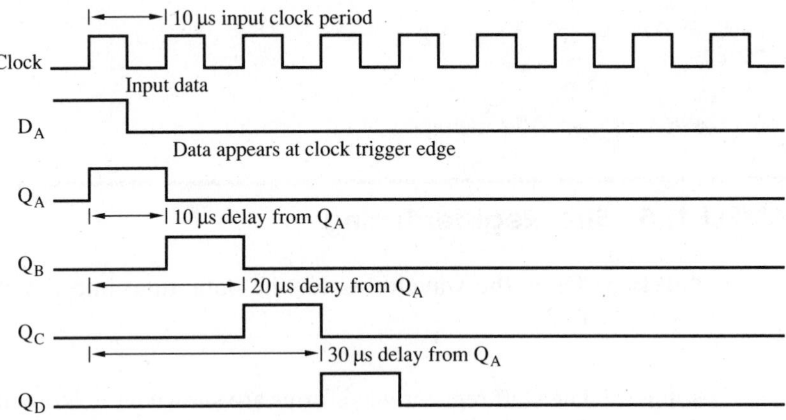

Section Self-Test

1. How many clock pulses are required to load 8 bits of data serially into a shift register?
2. How many clock pulses are required to load 8 bits of data in parallel into a shift register?
3. If the input clock is running at 1 KHz, what is the time delay from the first stage to the last stage to obtain the data serially out of an 8-bit register.

ANSWERS (Not necessarily in the order of the questions)

• 1 • 7 ms • 8

11-2 SHIFT REGISTER INTEGRATED CIRCUITS

The shift register circuits discussed up to this point have been constructed of D-type flip-flops. So long as all the flip-flops in the register triggered simultaneously, the register will shift the data as determined by the control inputs.

Integrated circuit shift registers are available to simplify the process

and to provide flexible data manipulation through the shift register without additional logic gates that were required for parallel and bidirectional operations, along with serial data shifting operations. Some IC shift registers are designated as universal shift registers. This means that the shift register can input and output data in a serial or parallel format, and that it can shift data to either the left or the right.

Table 11-4 is a listing of commonly available transistor-transistor logic (TTL) shift registers, the number of stages in each shift register, the input/output capabilities, and the shifting capabilities. Most shift registers are constructed of D-type flip-flop stages, but some, such as the 74195 and the 74199 have J-K inputs rather than a single serial input for expanded flexibility in applications that require J-K inputs.

TABLE 11-4 Integrated Circuit Shift Registers

Number	Stages	Input/Output	Shifting	Speed (MHz)
74LS91	8	Serial/Serial	Right	18
74LS95B	4	Parallel/Parallel	Right	36
74LS96	5	Parallel/Parallel	Right	25
74LS194	4	Universal	Universal	36
74S194	4	Universal	Universal	105
74LS195	4	Parallel/Parallel	Right	35
74198	8	Universal	Universal	35
74199	8	Universal	Universal	35

A critical factor of many sequential circuits is the maximum clock speed recommended. High speed data transmission applications require high speed shift registers. Shift register delay applications require the low speed circuits to minimize the number of stages required to achieve the necessary delay factor. The standard TTL and the low-power Schottky (LS) TTL have comparable performance speeds, ranging from 18 to 36 MHz for a maximum clock speed. The low-power TTL devices are much slower, with a maximum clock speed of approximately 5 MHz. The fastest TTL devices are the Schottky (S) TTL, with maximum clock speeds at 105 MHz. Not all logic subfamilies are available for each IC. The IC selection must be based on cost, availability, and operational and performance requirements.

11.2.1 The 74LS95B Shift Register

The 74LS95B shift register is a common register used in logic designs. The performance of the 74LS95 is listed in Table 11-4. The manufacturer's data sheets are shown in Figure 11-8.

SN5495A, SN54LS95B, SN7495A, SN74LS95B
4-BIT PARALLEL-ACCESS SHIFT REGISTERS

MARCH 1974 – REVISED MARCH 1988

TYPE	TYPICAL MAXIMUM CLOCK FREQUENCY	TYPICAL POWER DISSIPATION
'95A	36 MHz	195 mW
'LS95B	36 MHz	65 mW

SN5495A, SN54LS95B . . . J OR W PACKAGE
SN7495A . . . N PACKAGE
SN74LS95B . . . D OR N PACKAGE
(TOP VIEW)

Pin	Name	Pin	Name
1	SER	14	V_{CC}
2	A	13	Q_A
3	B	12	Q_B
4	C	11	Q_C
5	D	10	Q_D
6	MODE	9	CLK 1
7	GND	8	CLK 2

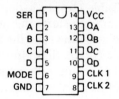

description

These 4-bit registers feature parallel and serial inputs, parallel outputs, mode control, and two clock inputs. The registers have three modes of operation:

Parallel (broadside) load
Shift right (the direction Q_A toward Q_D)
Shift left (the direction Q_D toward Q_A)

Parallel loading is accomplished by applying the four bits of data and taking the mode control input high. The data is loaded into the associated flip-flops and appears at the outputs after the high-to-low transition of the clock-2 input. During loading, the entry of serial data is inhibited.

Shift right is accomplished on the high-to-low transition of clock 1 when the mode control is low; shift left is accomplished on the high-to-low transition of clock 2 when the mode control is high by connecting the output of each flip-flop to the parallel input of the previous flip-flop (Q_D to input C, etc.) and serial data is entered at input D. The clock input may be applied commonly to clock 1 and clock 2 if both modes can be clocked from the same source. Changes at the mode control input should normally be made while both clock inputs are low; however, conditions described in the last three lines of the function table will also ensure that register contents are protected.

SN54LS95B . . . FK PACKAGE
(TOP VIEW)

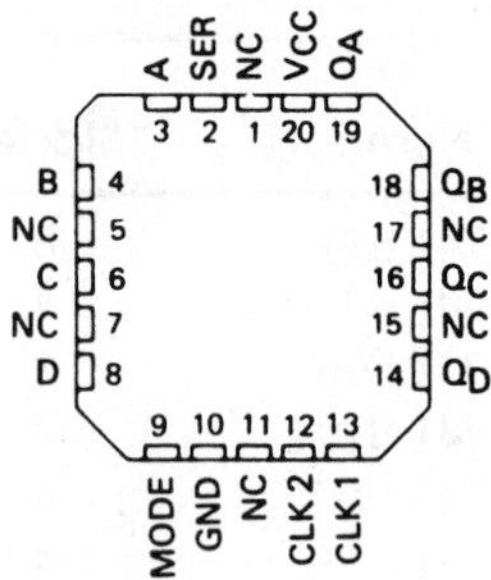

NC - No internal connection

FUNCTION TABLE

INPUTS								OUTPUTS			
MODE CONTROL	CLOCKS 2 (L)	CLOCKS 1 (R)	SERIAL	PARALLEL A	PARALLEL B	PARALLEL C	PARALLEL D	Q_A	Q_B	Q_C	Q_D
H	H	X	X	X	X	X	X	Q_{A0}	Q_{B0}	Q_{C0}	Q_{D0}
H	↓	X	X	a	b	c	d	a	b	c	d
H	↓	X	X	Q_B†	Q_C†	Q_D†	d	Q_{Bn}	Q_{Cn}	Q_{Dn}	d
L	L	H	X	X	X	X	X	Q_{A0}	Q_{B0}	Q_{C0}	Q_{D0}
L	X	↓	H	X	X	X	X	H	Q_{An}	Q_{Bn}	Q_{Cn}
L	X	↓	L	X	X	X	X	L	Q_{An}	Q_{Bn}	Q_{Cn}
↑	L	L	X	X	X	X	X	Q_{A0}	Q_{B0}	Q_{C0}	Q_{D0}
↓	L	L	X	X	X	X	X	Q_{A0}	Q_{B0}	Q_{C0}	Q_{D0}
↓	L	H	X	X	X	X	X	Q_{A0}	Q_{B0}	Q_{C0}	Q_{D0}
↑	H	L	X	X	X	X	X	Q_{A0}	Q_{B0}	Q_{C0}	Q_{D0}
↑	H	H	X	X	X	X	X	Q_{A0}	Q_{B0}	Q_{C0}	Q_{D0}

†Shifting left requires external connection of Q_B to A, Q_C to B, and Q_D to C. Serial data is entered at input D.
H = high level (steady state), L = low level (steady state), X = irrelevant (any input, including transitions)
↓ = transition from high to low level, ↑ = transition from low to high level
a, b, c, d = the level of steady-state input at inputs A, B, C, or D, respectively.
Q_{A0}, Q_{B0}, Q_{C0}, Q_{D0} = the level of Q_A, Q_B, Q_C, or Q_D, respectively, before the indicated steady-state input conditions were established.
Q_{An}, Q_{Bn}, Q_{Cn}, Q_{Dn} = the level of Q_A, Q_B, Q_C, or Q_D, respectively, before the most-recent ↓ transition of the clock.

FIGURE 11-8 74LS95B Manufacturer's Data Sheet (Courtesy of Texas Instruments)

SN5495A, SN54LS95B, SN7495A, SN74LS95B 4-BIT PARALLEL-ACCESS SHIFT REGISTERS

logic symbol†

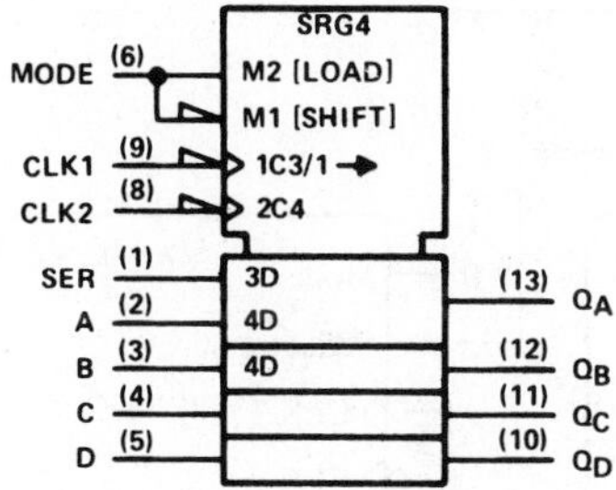

†This symbol is in accordance with ANSI/IEEE Std 91-1984 and IEC Publication 617-12.
Pin numbers shown are for D, J, N, and W packages.

logic diagram (positive logic)

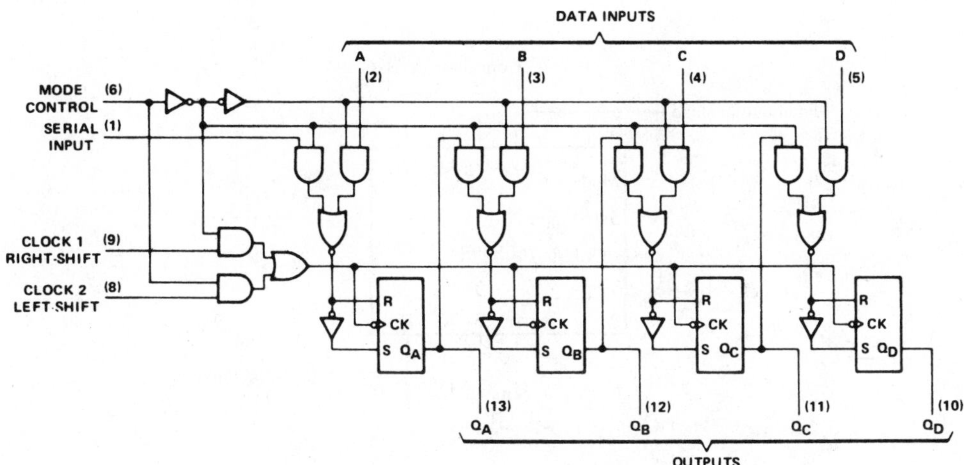

FIGURE 11-8 *(continued)*

The 7495 has two clocks, one to control serial input functions and the other to control parallel input functions. One serial input is provided for shifting data to the right. Four parallel inputs and four parallel outputs are also provided. Left shift operations can be accomplished through the use of parallel inputs and external connections. By externally connecting the Q_D output to the C input, the Q_C output to the B input, and the Q_B output to the A input, the contents of the stages can be shifted to the left.

The 74LS95s can be cascaded to build a shift register with a capacity of over 4 bits. Figures 11-9 and 11-10 show application circuits for the 74LS95B in both a right shift application and a left shift application.

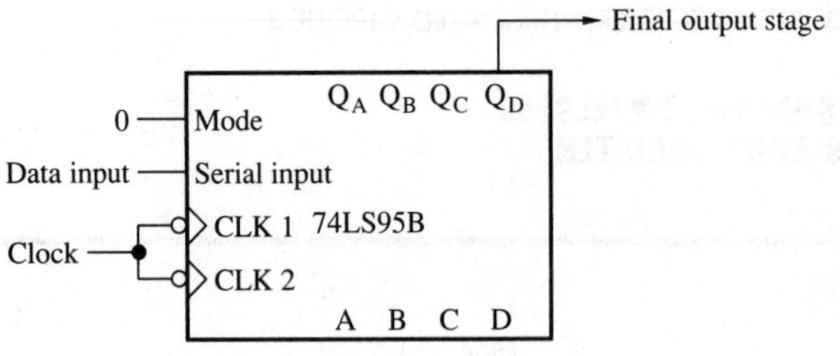

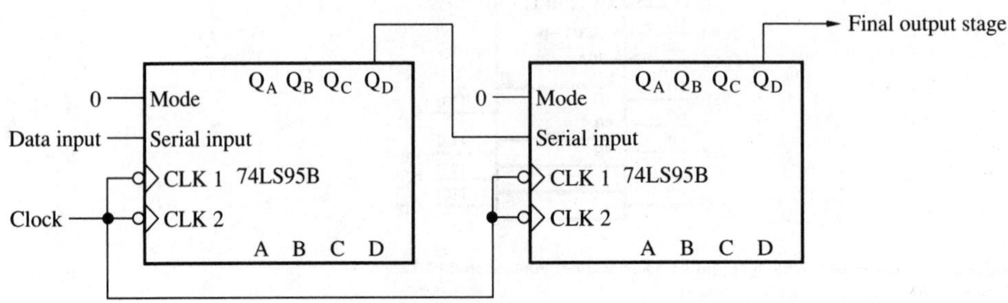

FIGURE 11-9 74LS95B Right Shift Application Circuits

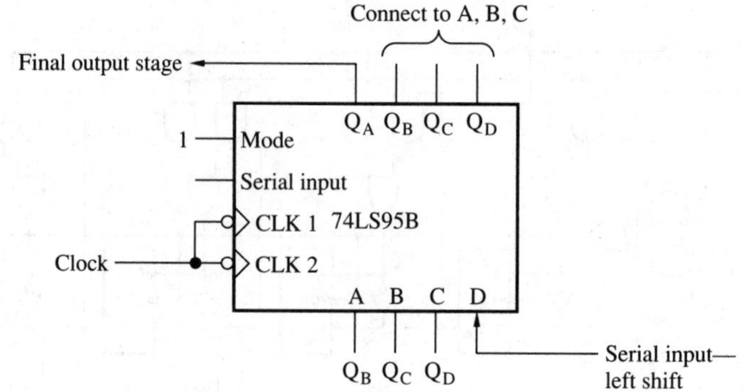

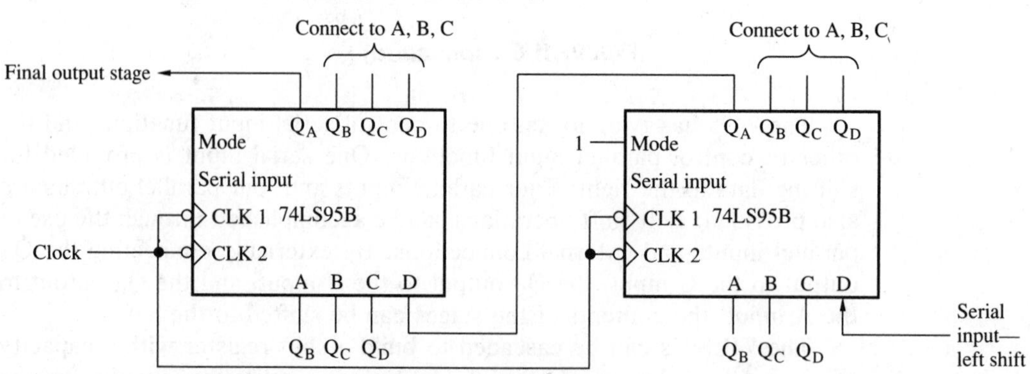

FIGURE 11-10 74LS95B Left Shift Application Circuits

■ EXAMPLE 11-7 The 74LS95 Bidirectional Shift Register Application

Problem: Use the 74LS95 shift register to perform according to Table 11-2.

Solution: The 74LS95 does not have S_1 or S_2 control inputs and has only one serial input. However, logic functions for the inputs to the 74LS95 can be derived as functions of S_1, S_0, and the serial inputs.

Control Inputs S_1	S_0	All Outputs Next State Q_{n+1} Q_A	Q_B	Q_C	Q_D	Shift	74LS95 Inputs M	C_2	C_1	Ser. In
0	1	Q_B	Q_C	Q_D	SIL	Left	1	C	x	x
1	0	SIR	Q_A	Q_B	Q_C	Right	0	x	C	SIR

The logic functions for the 74LS95 inputs are derived from the table presented here and from the function table in Figure 11-8. The resulting circuit is shown in Figure 11-11.

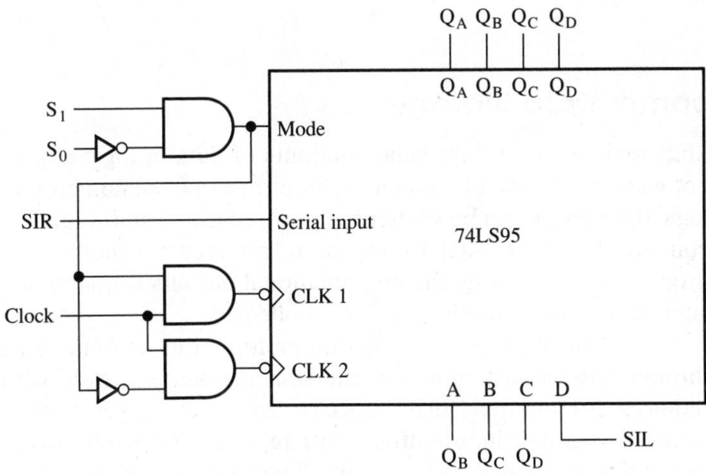

FIGURE 11-11 Example 11-7 Circuit

$M = \overline{S_1}\, S_0$

$C_2 = M \text{ clock} \qquad C_1 = \overline{M} \text{ clock}$

Serial input = SIR

Parallel inputs:

$D = \text{SIL} \qquad C = Q_D \qquad B = Q_C \qquad A = Q_B$ ■

Section Self-Test

1. Refer to Table 11-4 listing the IC shift registers. What is the minimum delay through four stages of the 74LS95?
2. Refer to Table 11-4 listing the IC shift registers. What shift register is needed for a minimum delay through four stages of 38.1 ns.
3. How many 74LS95 ICs are required to create a delay of 1 s when the input clock frequency is 1 KHz.

ANSWERS (Not necessarily in the order of the questions)

- .8 μs
- 250 (*Not* a practical method!)
- The 74S194

11-3 SHIFT REGISTER APPLICATIONS AND DESIGN

Shift register circuits can be used in a variety of applications to support the operation of microprocessors, memories, combinational circuits, and sequential logic circuits. The applications discussed in Section 11.3 include temporary data storage, data serial/parallel format conversion, ring counters, time delay circuits, and multiplication or division applications.

11.3.1 Temporary Data Storage

Shift registers can store small amounts of data in logic applications that do not warrant the use of a memory circuit. Data from numerous combinational logic operations can be sequentially stored into a shift register and then later converted to a parallel format or transferred to another logic circuit for processing. By storing the combinational outputs sequentially in a shift register, a history of the logic data is collected.

Logic operations that generate multiple bits of data can enter the data through the parallel inputs of the shift register and hold it there until it is required for another logic process. Arithmetic operations are especially suited to parallel input/output shift register operations to hold the values generated by an arithmetic circuit. The selection of the shift register to use in a serial or parallel application depends on the total storage capacity needed, the speed of the applications, and the operation required of the shift register. Figure 11-12 shows a block diagram of shift register data transfer applications.

11.3.2 Data Serial/Parallel Format Conversion

Shift registers can convert logic data from a serial format to a parallel format through the serial and parallel inputs and outputs on the register. In a serial format data is transmitted as a sequential bit stream over a single transmis-

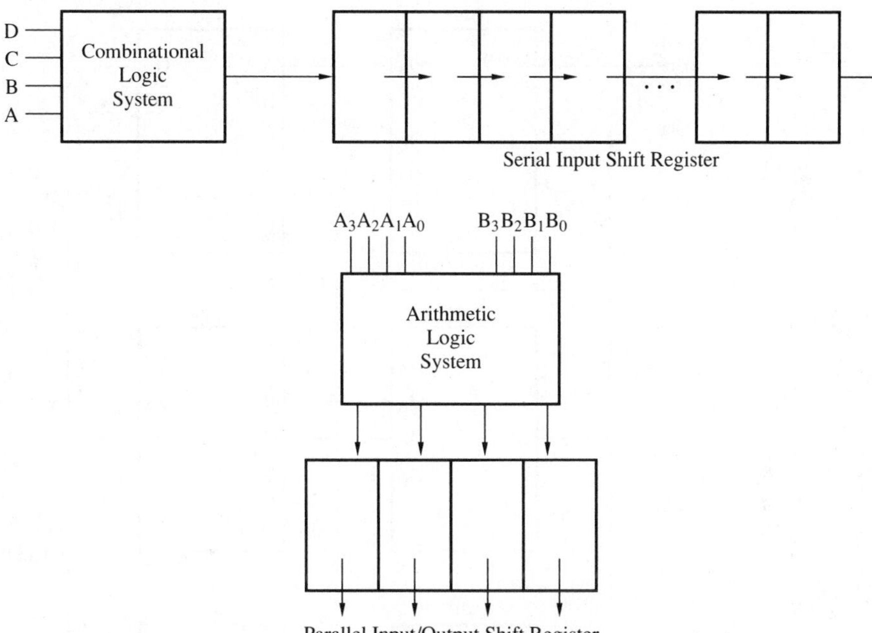

FIGURE 11-12 Shift Register Data Transfer Applications

sion line from the transmitter to the receiver. Data in a parallel format is transmitted as a word with multiple bits sent simultaneously from the transmitter to the receiver. Each bit in the word requires its own transmission line or conductor. Therefore, parallel transmission requires many conductors to transmit the bits. This format is very costly for long distance transmission, so the data must be converted to a serial format.

To perform serial-to-parallel conversion, data is entered into the shift register one bit at a time through the serial input to be shifted and stored in the stages of the register. When a complete word has been stored in the register, the contents of the stages can be output on the parallel outputs. To perform parallel-to-serial conversion, data is entered as a complete word through the parallel inputs of the shift register. It is then clocked through the stages and output through the final stage as a serial bit stream.

In some data transmission applications additional control bits are added at the beginning and end to **frame** each word as part of the serial transmission process. The most common serial transmission format is to have a **start bit** (logic LOW), the **data bits**, and two **stop bits** (logic HIGH). A shift register can be preset with the start and stop bits as required. The data bits of the word to be transmitted can be loaded in parallel into the appropriate bit positions in the register. Then the entire contents of the register can be serially output to produce a bit stream of the correct format. This function is performed in many computer communication systems by a special appli-

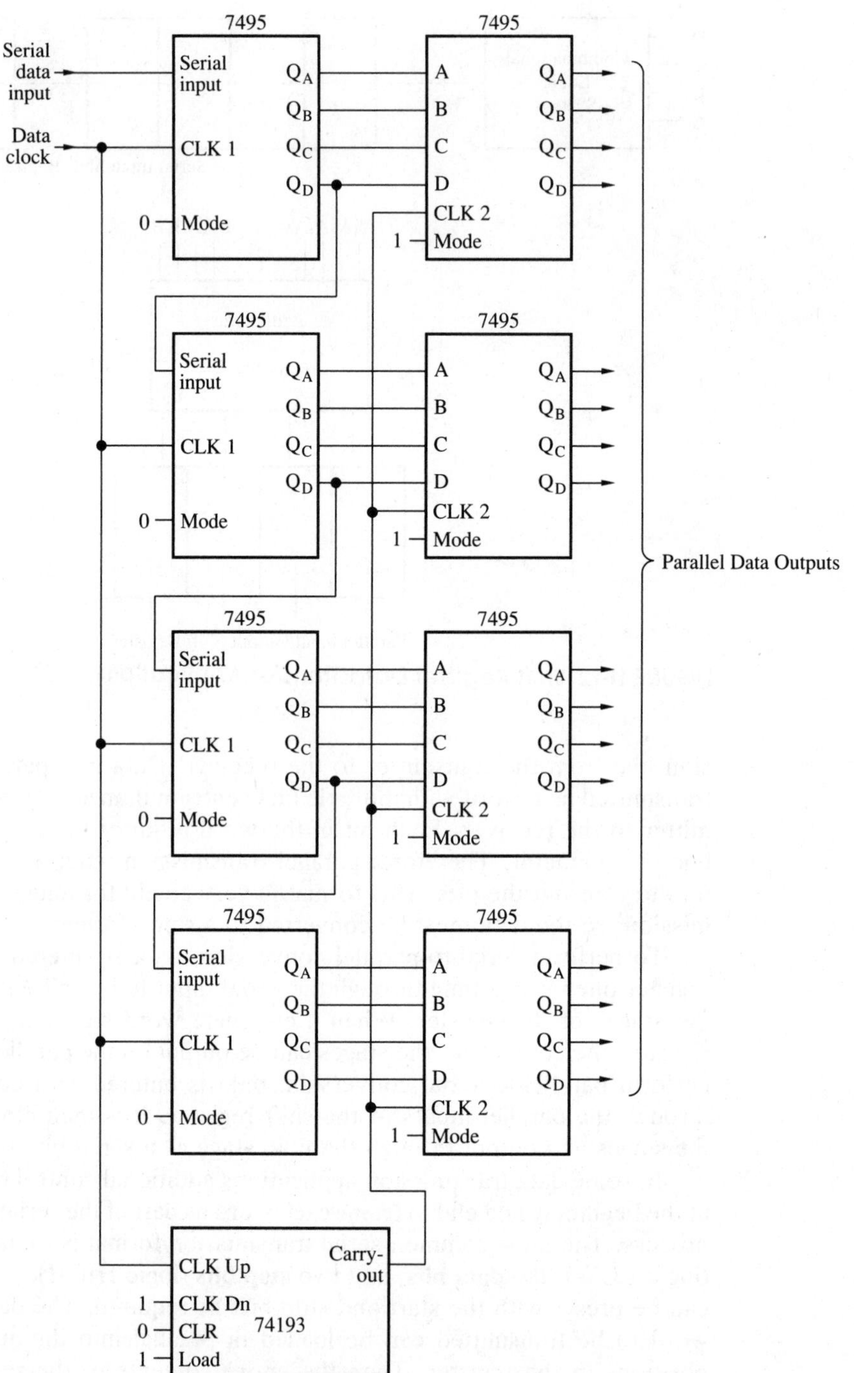

FIGURE 11-13 Example 11-8 16-Bit Data Transfer Circuit

cation shift register circuit, known as a **universal asynchronous receiver/transmitter (UART)**. UARTs are not covered in this textbook, but their operation is based on the parallel-to-serial format conversion capabilities of basic shift registers.

■ EXAMPLE 11-8 Data Storage Application with Serial-to-Parallel Conversion

Problem: A four-input combinational circuit is to produce data that will form 16-bit words. Design a shift register circuit to enter and store each 16-bit word.

Solution: A 16-bit serial input shift register is required to enter the 16-bit words produced by a combinational logic system, and a 16-bit parallel input shift register is required to store each word. Four 7495s must be cascaded together to obtain the required capacity for each register. The data is serially clocked into one 16-bit register, as shown in Figure 11-13. A counter counts up to 1 1 1 1 to determine when the shift register is filled. The carry-out pulse from the counter is used to load the contents of the register into a second 16-bit register to allow a new 16-bit word to be entered.

The clock signal that controls the input to the shift register must be triggered by the changes in the inputs to the combinational system. Any change in the inputs triggers the shift register clock to read the existing output data into the shift register. The new data will appear at the output after incurring the gate delays through the logic gates. ■

■ EXAMPLE 11-9 Parallel-to-Serial Data Conversion

Problem: Design a shift register to convert an 8-bit word to a serial output bit stream with one start bit and three stop bits framing each word. The start bit is a logic LOW. The stop bits are logic HIGH.

Solution: A 12-bit parallel input shift register is required to produce the required bit stream. Three 7495s can be cascaded together to obtain this capacity, as shown in Figure 11-14. The 74193 counter allows the shift register to load new data once every 12 clock pulses, after the existing data is clocked out of the shift register.

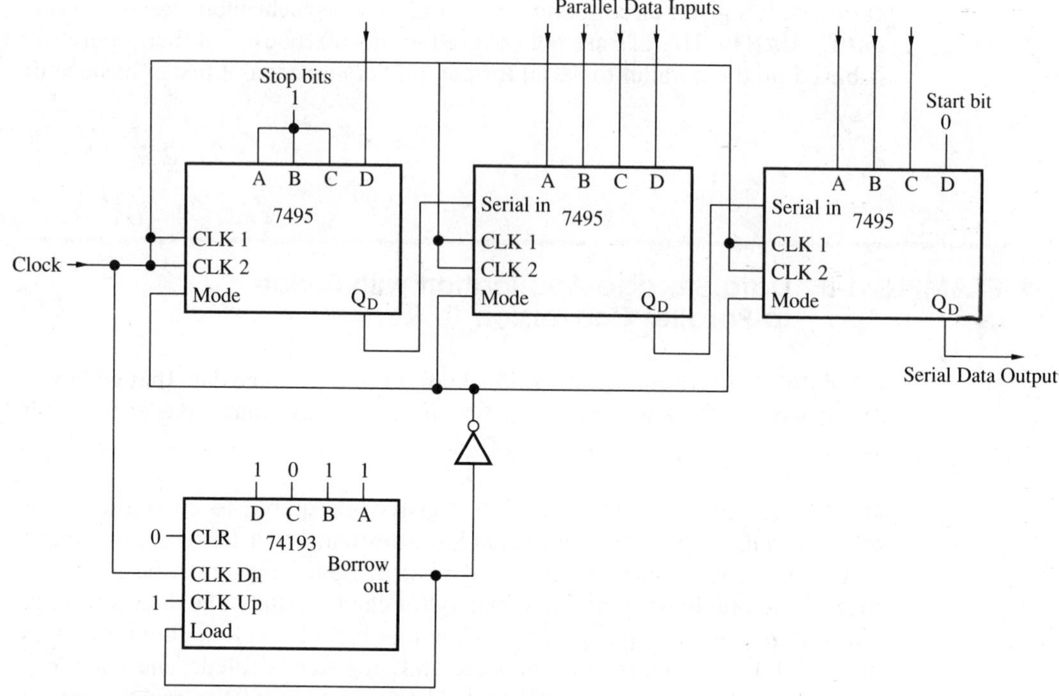

FIGURE 11-14 Example 11-9 Parallel-to-Serial Data Conversion ■

11.3.3 Ring Counter Circuits

Ring counter circuits, studied in Chapter 10, were the basic ring counter, the twisted ring counter, the modified twisted ring counter, and the maximum length ring counter. Ring counter circuits can be simplified by using IC shift registers and adding the necessary feedback with additional logic gates. Ring counters are often referred to as shift register counters because they are formed by adding a specific feedback function to a shift register.

■ EXAMPLE 11-10 Ring Counters

Problem: Use the 74LS85 IC shift register to construct a 4-bit basic ring counter and twisted ring counter. Each ring counter should be self-starting so that it generates the proper count sequence.

Solution: Each ring counter requires one 75LS95 IC. The self-starting feature can be accomplished by using the parallel inputs to load a count state. The circuits are shown in Figure 11-15.

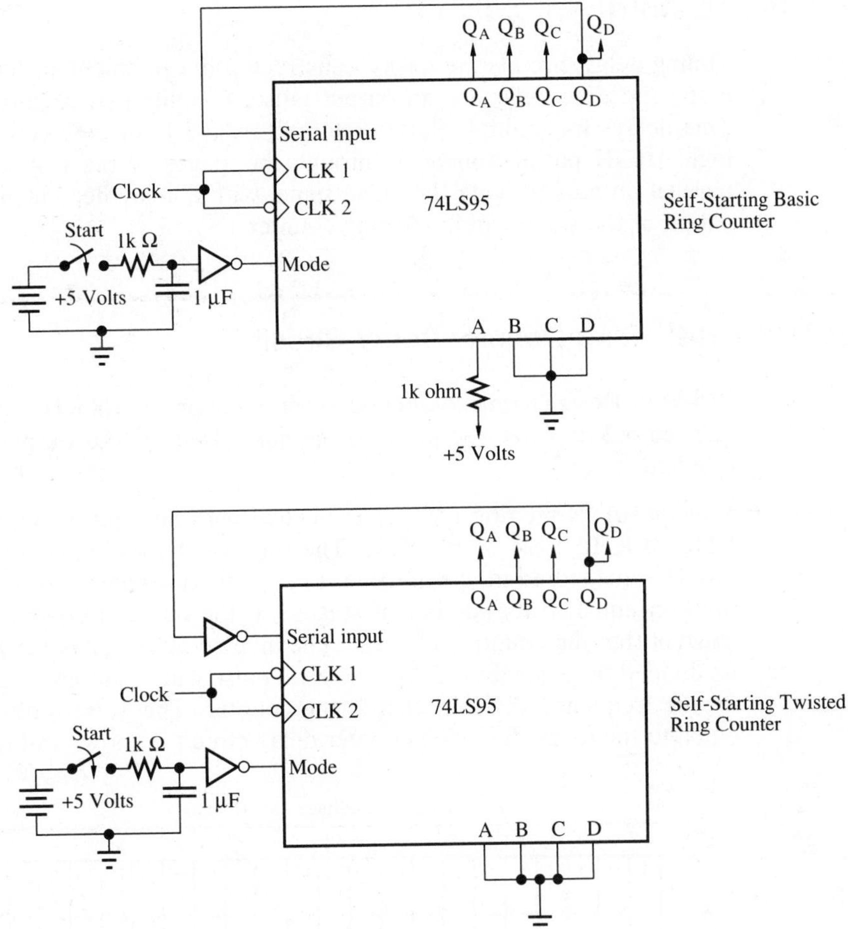

FIGURE 11-15 Example 11-10 Ring Counters

A circuit consisting of a resistor and a capacitor can be used to input the parallel data when the circuit is powered up and then allow the counter to cycle through the count states. When power is first applied, the initial voltage across the capacitor is 0 volt since the capacitor appears to be a short circuit. A logic HIGH is input into the mode control, M, and the starting state on the parallel inputs is loaded. When the capacitor charges, the voltage rises to V_{CC}. Once the capacitor charges, a logic LOW is input into the mode control, M, and the counter then inputs data from the serial input and shifts it to the right.

■

11.3.4 Timing Delay Circuits

Timing delay circuits are easily constructed out of shift registers to obtain a specific time delay for an output pulse. Circuits that require sequential time delays for multiple pulses are built from a basic ring counter. As the logic HIGH pulse sequences through the stages of the ring counter, the parallel outputs provide the pulse signal with a delay dependent on the location of the stage within the ring counter.

■ EXAMPLE 11-11 Ring Counter Delay Circuit

Problem: Design a ring counter delay circuit to produce 8 KHz output pulses delayed 5.2 μs from one pulse to the next. Twenty-four output pulses are required.

Solution: A 24-bit ring counter is needed with an input clock rate of 192 KHz. (8 KHz × 24 = 192 KHz) The ring counter will have a single logic-HIGH value stored in one of its 24 stages. The ring counter has a frequency division equal to its number of stages, so the output frequency from any stage of the ring counter is 8 KHz. The inverse of 8 KHz is 125 μs, and 125 μs divided by 24 stages is 5.2 μs, so each pulse will be automatically delayed by the frequency division of the ring counter. The pulse duration will be equal to the delay. The ring counter delay circuit is shown in Figure 11-16.

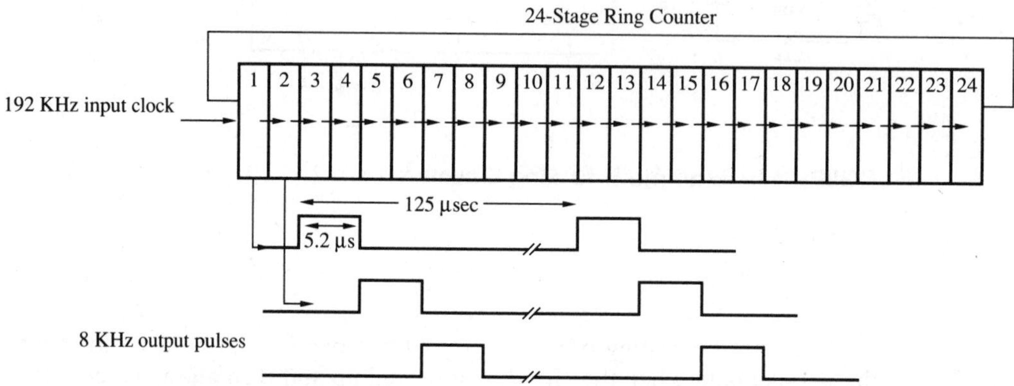

FIGURE 11-16 Example 11-11 Ring Counter Delay Circuit ■

11.3.5 Multiplication and Division Applications

Very simple multiplication and division by 2 applications can be performed by shifting numerical data in a shift register. To multiply by 2, shift the binary number to the higher bit weights and insert a zero into the least significant bit (LSB) position. To divide by 2, shift the binary number to the lower bit weights and insert a zero into the most significant bit (MSB) position.

Section Self-Test

1. How can a shift register be used to multiply or divide a binary number by 2?
2. How is a shift register used to generate timing waveforms of equal frequency that are out of phase with each other by a uniform delay?
3. How can a shift register be used to convert data from a parallel format to a serial format?

ANSWERS (Not necessarily in the same order as the questions)

- The parallel data is entered into the shift register. The data is clocked out of a single output as a serial data stream.
- A binary number is shifted to the left to multiply by 2; a binary number is shifted to the right to divide by 2.
- A basic ring counter produces output waveforms of equal frequency out of phase with each other by a specific delay. The output frequency is the input clock frequency divided by the number of stages. The phase delay from one output to the next is equal to the period of the input clock frequency.

11-4 TROUBLESHOOTING SHIFT REGISTER CIRCUITS

Troubleshooting shift register circuits is similar to troubleshooting counter circuits. The clock input, the serial inputs, parallel inputs, and control inputs must be properly connected for correct circuit operation. In cascaded operations it is important to tie all clocks and control inputs common, and to route the final stage output to the serial input of the subsequent shift register IC.

■ EXAMPLE 11-12 The Shift-Less Register

Problem: The 74LS95 shift register is needed for a shift register application requiring that data be shifted to the right and to the left. The shift register is only functioning in the right direction. When the direction of shift is changed to the left, the shift register maintains its last "shift right" output states. You are called in to debug this circuit. The circuit as it is wired is shown in Figure 11-17.

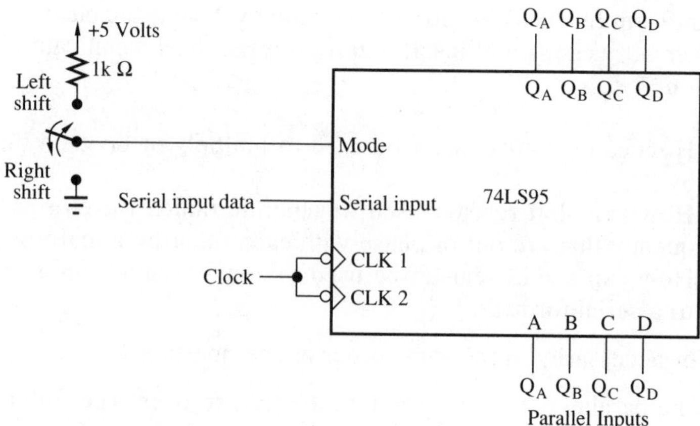

FIGURE 11-17 Example 11-12

Solution: Since the problem is with the left shift direction, check the clock input, mode input, and parallel inputs carefully. The mode input must be tied to a logic-HIGH for left shifting, which checks out. The C_1 clock controls the left shift action, and that is connected correctly. The problem lies with the parallel inputs. For left shifting to occur, the D input must be the serial input, the C input must receive the Q_D output data, the B input must receive the Q_C output data, and the A input must receive the Q_B output data. The problem in the wiring of the circuit in Figure 11-17 shows that the Q_D output is connected to the D input, the Q_C output is connected to the C input, the Q_B output is connected to the B input, and the Q_A output is connected to the A input. In this configuration, when the mode switches to the left shift operation, the last stages in the Q_A, Q_B, and Q_C outputs are loaded again into those same stages. Correct the wiring error and you will find that the circuit works according to the truth table in Figure 11-8. ■

■ EXAMPLE 11-13 Lost Data Shift Register

Problem: The shift register circuit shown in Figure 11-13 is modified to accept 12 bits of data in a serial format and convert it to a parallel format. The circuit as it has been modified is shown in Figure 11-18. When the parallel data is received, 4 bits of data are missing. You are identified as an expert shift register consultant to solve the problem.

Solution: As you suspected, when the original circuit was modified, the new timing requirements of converting 12 bits of serial data to a parallel format were not fully examined. The 74193 counter generates one carry-out pulse for every 16 data clock pulses. The carry-out pulse is used as the clock edge

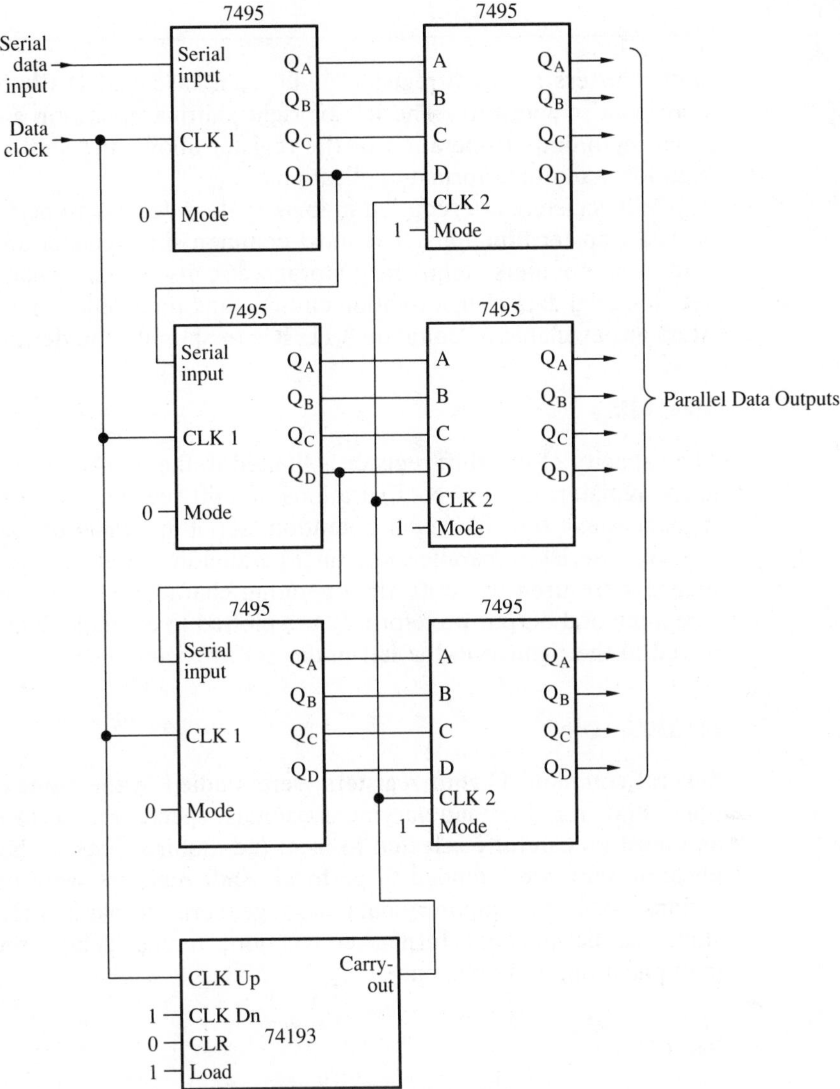

FIGURE 11-18 Example 11-13 Circuit with Errors

to load the data in parallel into the second bank of shift registers where it is temporarily stored. This caused four bits of data to be lost.

With the new application, the data should be loaded into the second bank of shift registers after the twelfth data clock pulse. To do this, the 74193 counter must be preset to 0 1 0 0. The counter will then count up from 0 1 0 0 to 1 1 1 1 and generate a carry-out pulse for every 12 data pulses. All the data will be correctly converted from a serial to a parallel format. ■

SUMMARY

Shift registers are data registers built from cascaded D flip-flop stages to store data temporarily. The left or right shifting operation and parallel or serial input/output operation of the register allows the shift register to be used for many data format applications.

Shift registers are required in logic system designs to perform a variety of data transfer functions. The most common shift register applications include ring counters, temporary storage circuits, serial-to-parallel and parallel-to-serial data transformation circuits, and time delay circuits. Shift registers are available as common TTL ICs to simplify the design process.

ANALYSIS

The capacity of the shift register is limited to the number of flip-flop stages in the register. Several configurations of shift registers were studied. Shift registers have four modes of operation: serial-in serial-out; parallel-in parallel-out; serial-in parallel-out; and parallel-in serial-out. Analysis techniques were used to verify the operating characteristics of shift registers. The input and output waveforms were plotted to examine data that is transferred to the right or to the left in the shift register.

APPLICATION

Several common IC shift registers were studied in the context of applications. Shift registers had varying capacities, speed, and performance limits and must be carefully selected to meet the requirements of the specific application they are intended to perform. Shift registers were used in applications involving temporary data shortage, serial-to-parallel format conversion, parallel-to-serial format conversion, timing delay, ring counters, multiplication, and division.

DESIGN

Shift register circuits were designed for applications to function as temporary data shortage devices, serial-to-parallel format converters, parallel-to-serial format converters, timing delay circuits, ring counters, multipliers, and dividers.

TROUBLESHOOTING

Incorrectly operating shift register circuits were analyzed to determine the cause of the problem. Critical wiring errors resulting in incorrect clock inputs, mode control inputs, serial data inputs, and parallel data inputs can result in the circuit not functioning. The source of the error is located through detailed analysis of the circuit operation and then is corrected.

PROBLEMS

11-1 Data Storage and Transfer—Analysis Problems

1. Show a functional block diagram of a calculator 13-bit shift register that controls the calculator display.

*2. Show the present state-next state truth table for a 4-bit shift register that has parallel inputs, parallel outputs, a serial input right, and a serial input left, and that performs the following operations with the given control signals. Figure 11-19 shows the block diagram of the data movement into and out of the shift register.

Control Inputs S_1	S_0	Operation
0	0	Hold the current data
0	1	Right shift
1	0	Left shift
1	1	Parallel input

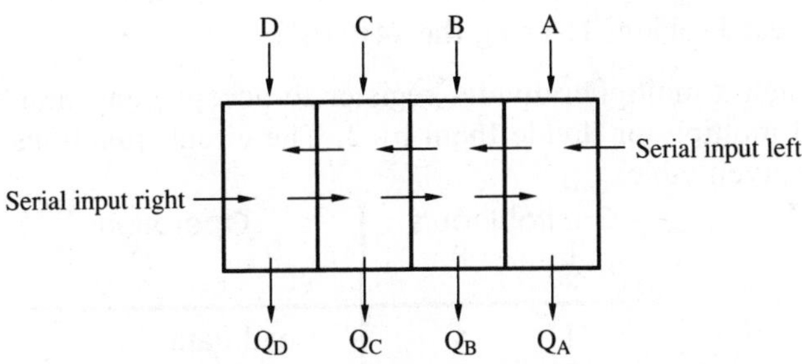

FIGURE 11-19 Problem Serial/Parallel Shift Register

11-2 Shift Register Integrated Circuits—Analysis Problems

3. Refer to the TTL data book to determine the following parameters for the 74LS95B IC.
   a. Maximum clock frequency
   b. Typical power dissipation
   c. Minimum width of the clock pulse.
   d. Minimum data setup time
   e. Minimum data hold time
   f. Time to enable clocks
   g. Maximum propagation delay
4. Repeat Problem 3 for the 74199 IC.

* *See* Answers to Selected Problems.

11-3 Shift Register Applications and Design—Application and Design Problems

*5. Design a time delay shift register, clocked at 100 KHz, to produce a time delay of .1 ms. Determine the number of stages required, and show the circuit built with 7495 shift registers.

6. Repeat Problem 5 using the 74199 shift register.

7. Design a serial-to-parallel conversion circuit to recover the 8-bit data word transmitted by the circuit of Example 11-9.

8. Design a "times 2" multiplier circuit to produce binary values up to 1022. Determine how many stages are required, and show the circuit built from 74199 ICs.

*9. Design an 8-bit Johnson counter using 7495s and any additional logic gates.

10. Repeat Problem 9 using the 74199 IC.

11. Design a 12-bit modified twisted ring counter using 7495s and any additional logic gates.

12. Repeat Problem 11 using the 74199 IC.

13. Design a multiplier/divider register to accept input numbers up to 63 and multiply or divide them by 2. The circuit functions according to the given table:

Control Inputs L	P	Operation
1	X	Load data
0	1	Multiply times 2
0	0	Divide by 2

14. Design a 4-bit parallel-input shift-right shift register using the asynchronous preset and clear inputs on J-K flip-flops to load the parallel data. The shift register should function according to the given table:

Control Input L	Operation
1	Load parallel data
0	Shift data right

11-4 Troubleshooting Shift Register Circuits—Troubleshooting Problems

*15. Determine the output of the basic ring counter circuit shown in Figure 11-15 if the C_1 clock input was tied to a constant logic-HIGH.

16. Determine the output of the basic ring counter circuit shown in Figure 11-15 if the C_2 clock input was tied to a constant logic-HIGH.

17. Determine the output of the twisted ring counter circuit shown in Figure 11-15 if the C_1 clock input was tied to a constant logic-HIGH.

18. Determine the output of the twisted ring counter circuit shown in Figure 11-15 if the C_2 clock input was tied to a contant logic-HIGH.

19. Determine the waveforms resulting from the operation of the bidirectional shift register in Figure 11-6 if the load/shift line was unintentionally inverted.

Part 6

LSI LOGIC AND MEMORY

Chapter 12

Programmable Logic Devices and Semiconductor Logic

Upon completing and mastering the material in this chapter, you should be able to perform the following operations for the analysis, application, design, and troubleshooting of programmable logic devices:

ANALYSIS

1. Describe the evolution of semiconductor logic, from standard logic to programmable logic devices (PLDs).
2. Analyze the architecture of PLDs to determine the input and output operations that a specific device is capable of performing.
3. Describe the capabilities and benefits of GAL devices as compared to PLA and PAL devices.
4. Define the three modes of operation of the GAL16V8A and the GAL16V8: simple, complex, and registered.
5. Describe the capabilities and limitations of the GAL16V8A and the GAL16V8 in its simple, complex, and registered mode of operation.

APPLICATION

6. Describe the application of full-custom logic, semicustom logic, gate arrays, and PLDs in logic system design.
7. Describe essential features of a PLD development system.
8. Describe the capabilities of the LC9000 and Logic Lab PLD development system by Programmable Logic Technologies.
9. Use the LC9000 logic compiler and Logic Lab PLD programmer to program the GAL16V8A or the GAL16V8.

DESIGN

10. Write source files to be compiled by the LC9000 for combinational and sequential PLD applications.
11. Design circuits using the GAL16V8 to implement logic functions such as code converters, multiplexers, decoders, latches, flip-flops, and shift registers.
12. Design circuits using the GAL16V8 to replace logic functions required for interfacing MSI and LSI circuits.

TROUBLESHOOTING

13. Debug PLD source files with errors associated with the architectural limitations of the PLD to be programmed.
14. Troubleshoot PLD circuits that are programmed correctly but are not operating correctly due to circuit construction errors.

Programmable logic devices (PLDs) are used extensively in digital logic design. PLDs give the designer complete flexibility in programming any desired logic function into a single IC. This chapter focuses on the analysis, application, and design of logic systems with PLDs.

Up to this point, all work in the text has focused on standard logic hardware. Logic functions had to be created out of available logic gates, flip-flops, and MSI logic chips such as adders, encoders, decoders, multiplexers, shift registers, and others. The fundamentals of digital logic are important in PLD applications and design. Key topics such as Boolean algebra, SOP equations, flip-flop operations, and logic functions specified in a truth table are important elements of PLD designs. Design problems in previous chapters that were implemented in standard logic are implemented in this chapter with PLDs.

The PLDs available on the market today include electrically erasable devices that can be programmed up to one hundred times. These devices can be programmed at a desktop or lab bench; there is no need for complex workstations or expensive hardware. The software and hardware required to complete the examples in this chapter consist of a PC with two floppy disk drives and 512 K of RAM, a PLD programmer, and the software compiler.

The material contained in this chapter, including the basic theory and application of PLDs, has been taught to freshmen at Purdue University by midsemester of their first digital logic class. The students program and use PLDs in the laboratory for approximately eight weeks each semester. The students include PLDs in their logic circuits with enthusiasm when they see the flexibility that they have when designing logic systems. Upon completing the material in this chapter, you should also be able to make design choices to incorporate PLDs into combinational and sequential logic circuits.

12-1 SEMICONDUCTOR LOGIC

In the early 1960s the electronics industry began commercially producing integrated circuits (ICs). As described in Chapter 1, ICs are semiconductor devices that have all the necessary components such as transistors, capacitors, and resistors, manufactured onto a single piece of semiconductor material known as an IC or chip. The types of semiconductor logic circuits available today include standard logic, custom logic, semicustom logic, application specific IC (ASIC) logic, gate arrays, and programmable logic. This section briefly covers the evolution of the semiconductor logic leading to the availability of programmable logic.

12.1.1 Standard Logic

The first commercially mass-produced transistor-transistor logic (TTL) ICs were the small scale integration (SSI) and medium scale integration (MSI) standard logic 7400 series ICs still in use today. The 4000 logic family was the first mass-produced complementary metal-oxide semiconductor (CMOS) logic ICs. The 7400/4000 families and associated subfamilies of logic are commonly referred to as **standard logic**. Up to this point in the text, standard logic devices have been the focus of the analysis, application, and design work. Small scale integration circuits such as basic logic gates and flip-flops and MSI circuits such as adders, multiplexers, decoders, encoders, counters, and registers have been used in logic designs.

12.1.2 Custom and Semicustom Logic (ASIC)

Very large and sophisticated logic designs and systems can be designed with standard logic. However, there are several disadvantages to large logic systems designed with only standard logic ICs—large power consumption, the large physical space needed, special ventilation and cooling requirements, and a high failure rate due to the large number of individual ICs used. Also, complex designs for computer, military, or industrial applications often require up to several hundred printed circuit boards of logic components, with each board containing up to 100 standard logic ICs.

To overcome the disadvantages of complex standard logic designs, companies contract with semiconductor manufacturers to design and fabricate a specific logic IC for a particular custom application. Or, a large corporation with internal semiconductor fabrication capabilities can design and fabricate a specific logic IC. These custom built logic ICs are known as **custom logic**, which is a category of **Application Specific Integrated Circuit** (**ASIC**) logic.

In custom logic ICs the logic functions are designed and then fabricated into a large scale integration (LSI) logic IC. The main advantage of custom logic is the integration of the function of many standard logic ICs into one or two custom ICs. However, custom logic has several disadvantages. Since ICs are unique, development and manufacturing costs are very expensive, and the time needed to design a full-custom IC is often a year or more than the time needed to design a system from standard logic. Design errors require a redesign and refabrication of a new custom IC.

The custom IC design cycle can be reduced by the use of cell libraries. **Cell libraries** are logic design blocks that will create a predetermined logic function. For example, instead of designing a custom J-K flip-flop, the designer would select a standard J-K flip-flop cell and place it in the design. In addition, it is possible to use computer programs known as **cell compilers** to reduce custom design time. Cell compilers take logic design schematics and automatically generate logic cells for the custom design. Even with cell libraries and cell compilers, custom logic is used only when absolutely necessary. A communications satellite is a good example of a complex system that may require custom logic due to power, space, and reliability constraints.

As personal computers and **Computer Aided Design** (CAD) have become available, a new type of custom logic, known as **semicustom logic**, was created. Semicustom logic is designed by the logic designer with the aid of CAD software and sent to a semiconductor manufacturer (often called a **foundry**) for the actual manufacture of the semicustom IC. Semicustom ICs typically have shorter development times than full-custom logic ICs.

Both custom and semicustom logic are referred to as ASIC logic. User programmable logic devices are also referred to as ASICs. In this text ASICs refer only to custom or semicustom logic, that is, ICs manufactured by the semiconductor manufacturer. All user programmable logic devices are referred to as PLDs.

12.1.3 Gate Arrays

Gate arrays are a special type of semicustom logic ICs that contain a large number of gates and special logic functions interconnected by metalization. A semicustom IC is created by selectively blowing open metal fuse connections to create the custom circuit. Gate arrays are available with the equivalent of over 50,000 logic gates. The logic designer can select logic functions and gates to be interconnected from a cell library. Typical cells are flip-flops, buffers, latches, adders, multiplexers, and counters.

There are four basic steps in the implementation of a gate array logic design:

1. Design acceptance
2. Layout
3. Test generation
4. Integrated circuit fabrication

Design acceptance is complete when the logic designer has selected all the logic functions and gates to be used on the gate array. The semicustom IC is then designed (layout) by the semiconductor manufacturer and logic functions are tested using CAD. Once the design function is verified, the gate array fuses are blown, creating the semicustom gate array IC.

Section Self-Test

1. What is the difference between standard logic and custom logic?
2. What are ASICs?
3. What are gate arrays?

ANSWERS

- Standard logic circuits are general purpose devices. Custom logic circuits are specifically manufactured for a single application.
- Application Specific Integrated Circuits
- A semicustom IC with functional cells. The user defines the final programming of the gate array by specifying the connections that will be made in the metalization applied as the final step in the IC manufacturing process.

12-2 PROGRAMMABLE LOGIC DEVICES

Recent advances in semiconductor and computer technology have led to the development of several types of user programmable logic devices (PLDs). These devices provide the logic designer the flexibility to produce custom circuits to be used in logic designs without the extensive cost and development time required for full-custom or semicustom logic.

Programmable logic devices are used extensively in digital logic systems to replace the hundreds of logic chips that perform the interfacing functions among major components in a logic system. As an example, computer systems require a microprocessor, memory ICs, a floppy disk controller IC, and numerous logic chips performing the functions needed to "glue" the entire system together. Hence, the term "glue chips" evolved. The general purpose standard hardware ICs originally used as glue chips require a great deal of space on the printed circuit board, and it takes many ICs to construct the necessary logic functions.

Used to replace glue chips in most digital systems, programmable logic devices can be programmed for the specific functions required. Computer manufacturers, such as Apple, have reduced the number of circuit boards needed for their Apple Macintosh by having PLDs perform many logic applications that ordinarily required several, if not hundreds, of standard hardware ICs.

Programmable logic devices are based on the operation of AND and OR gates connected in arrays that consist of hard-wired or **fixed** connections and **user programmable** connections, as shown in Figure 12-1. The array of AND and OR gates allow the PLD to implement sum of product (SOP) equations. The user programmable connections are defined at the time the device is programmed for the specific SOP function to be performed by the PLD. In some PLDs each AND and OR gate may have 128 or more inputs. The number of inputs is referred to as the **width** of the AND or OR array.

The logic gate notation for PLDs is slightly modified from the conventional logic schematic notation, as shown in Figure 12-2. The PLD notation

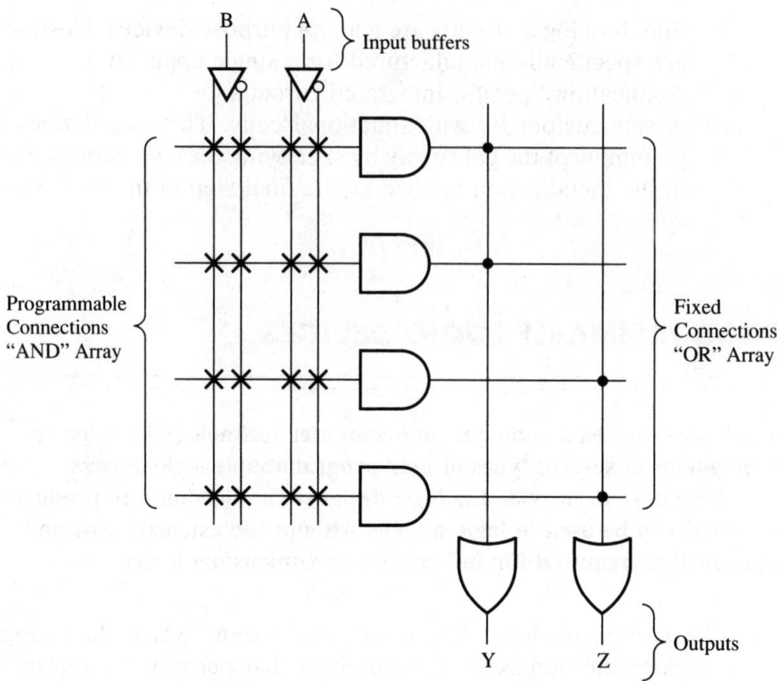

FIGURE 12-1 Basic Programmable Logic Device Architecture

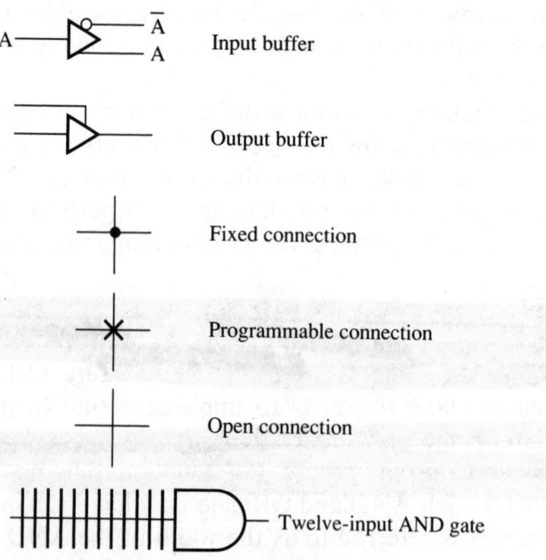

FIGURE 12-2 Programmable Logic Device Schematic Notation

is required to specify a **fixed connection**, a **programmable connection**, and a **multiple input gate**.

Original PLDs were bipolar devices that allowed a designer to program them once by opening fuse connections in the logic array. These devices could not be reprogrammed at a later time. They are referred to as **one time programmable (OTP)** devices.

Complementary metal-oxide semiconductor technology is used to manufacture **erasable PLDs (EPLDs)**. The first EPLDs could be erased by exposing the chip to ultraviolet (UV) light. This required the manufacturing of a device in a special package with a quartz window and a UV eraser to erase the device. The erasure process requires approximately 20 minutes to complete.

Now through CMOS technology **electrically erasable PLDs (E^2PLDs)** are available. These devices are electrically erased and programmed in a specially designed device programmer. The programmer applies voltage pulses of specified levels and durations to erase the PLD and to program a new set of functions. The E^2PLDs can be programmed up to 100 times, and they can be erased in 50 ms.

12.2.1 Programmable Read Only Memory (PROM)

The original PLDs are **Programmable Read Only Memories (PROMs)**. These devices consist of a fixed array of AND gates and a programmable array of OR gates, as shown in Figure 12-3. Every possible input combination is fixed as an output of an AND gate. For n inputs, 2^n AND gates are required to form the product terms.

Programmable read only memories are used primarily as memory devices. They are used extensively in microprocessor-based designs and often store user-generated programs to perform custom applications. Additional information about read only memories (ROMs) is covered in Chapter 13.

12.2.2 Programmable Logic Array (PLA)

The **Programmable Logic Array (PLA)** is a PLD designed for logic applications rather than for memory applications. It consists of both a programmable AND array and a programmable OR array, as shown in Figure 12-4.

The gate configuration of the PLA can be used to build any SOP logic function. The PLA allows the designer the most flexibility in specifying all the connections of the AND and OR arrays. However, the complexity of the PLA discouraged many designers from using it in digital circuit applications.

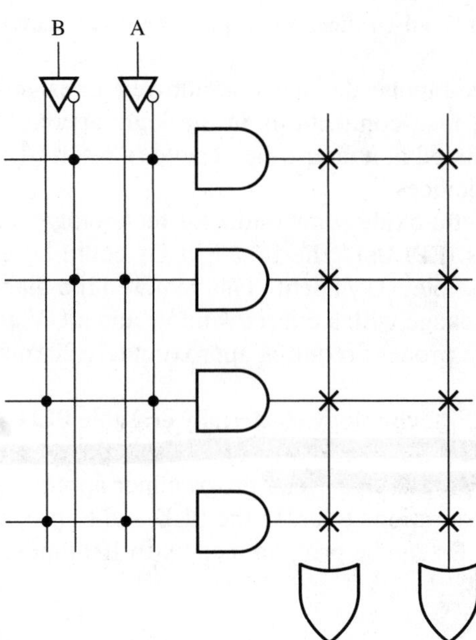

FIGURE 12-3 Basic Programmable Read Only Memory (PROM) Architecture

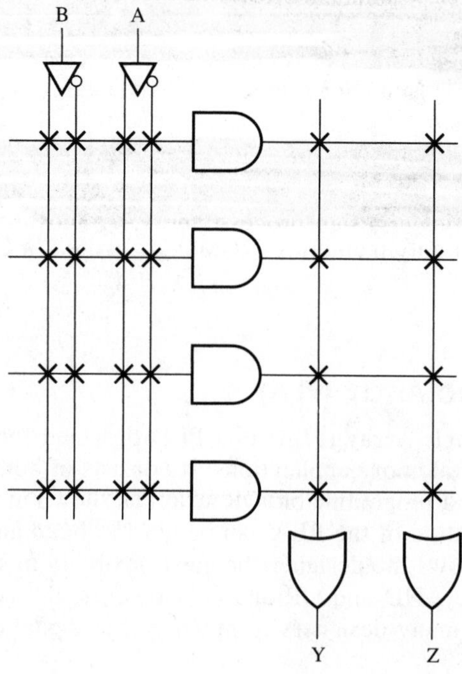

FIGURE 12-4 Basic Programmable Logic Array (PLA) Architecture

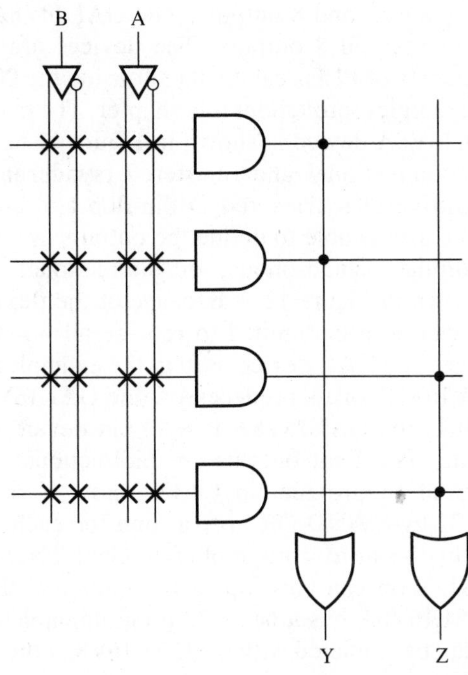

FIGURE 12-5 Basic Programmable Array Logic (PAL) Architecture

12.2.3 Programmable Array Logic (PAL)

Semiconductor manufacturers developed a simplified version of the PLA, which became known as the **Programmable Array Logic (PAL)**. The PAL consists of a programmable AND array and a fixed OR array, as shown in Figure 12-5.

To simplify the logic design process, the PAL allows the designer to program all input AND terms but limits the number of AND terms that can be ORed together. The PAL was originally developed by Monolithic Memories, Inc. (MMI).

12.2.4 Generic Array Logic (GAL)

Further developments of PAL devices include the **Generic Array Logic (GAL)**, as developed by Lattice Semiconductor Inc. The GAL has a programmable AND array, a fixed OR array, and a multifunction output stage referred to as the **Output Logic Macro Cell (OLMC)**. GAL devices are E^2PLDs.

Two general purpose GAL devices manufactured by Lattice Semiconductor are the GAL16V8A and the GAL20V8A. The GAL16V8A is a 20-

pin device with up to 20 inputs and 8 outputs. The GAL20V8A is a 24-pin device with up to 24 inputs and 8 outputs. The devices are functionally identical. Since the concepts of PLDs can be taught using the 20-pin IC, the GAL16V8A is used in examples throughout this chapter. The manufacturer's data sheet for the GAL16V8A device is shown in Figure 12-6.

The OLMC is a combinational and registered (synchronous) output stage. It contains a positive edge-triggered D flip-flop and combinational logic circuitry so that the user is able to define the outputs as active-HIGH, active-LOW, combinational, synchronous, or bidirectional input/output (I/O). The OLMC is shown in Figure 12-7. Because of the flexibility of the OLMC, GAL devices can be programmed to replace all other PLDs that have a fixed output stage. The GAL device used in the examples throughout this chapter is the GAL16V8A or its predecessor, the GAL16V8.

As mentioned earlier, the GAL16V8A is a 20-pin device that has ten inputs and eight outputs. The eight outputs are bidirectional I/Os, so the device can be configured to provide up to 18 inputs if required. The GAL16V8A has eight 32-by-8 AND-OR arrays, one for each output. The SOP equations formed by this array consist of up to eight AND terms ORed together, and each AND term can have up to 16 inputs and their complements. Overall, the GAL16V8A has a 64×32 programmable AND array. The PAL devices that can be emulated with the GAL16V8 or the GAL16V8A are listed in Table 12-1.

The array logic devices, whether PALs, GALs, or the many other variations, meet the logic designer's needs by supplying a single IC that can be easily programmed to perform many logic functions. These "array" programmable logic devices are referred to in the remainder of the chapter by the acronym **PLD**.

12.2.5 Device Architecture of the GAL16V8 and the GAL16V8A

The GAL16V8 and GAL16V8A have three modes of operation: simple, complex, and registered. The mode of operation determines the input/output features of the OLMC. Tables 12-2, 12-3, and 12-4 summarize the GAL16V8 and GAL16V8A pin functions in each of the three modes of operation.

The GAL16V8 is the predecessor of the GAL16V8A. It operates identically to the GAL16V8A in the registered and complex modes, but it differs from the GAL16V8A in the simple mode. Information about the GAL16V8 simple mode of operation is included in Table 12-2(b) in the event that some PLD software or hardware systems support only the GAL16V8 and not the GAL16V8A.

The **simple mode** of operation allows for combinational inputs and outputs. The output expressions can have up to eight product terms. The

GAL®16V8A
GAL®20V8A

Generic Array Logic™

U.S. Patents 4,761,768 and 4,766,569

FEATURES

- **HIGH PERFORMANCE E²CMOS™ TECHNOLOGY**
  - — 10 ns Maximum Propagation Delay
  - — Fmax = 62.5 MHz
  - — 8 ns Maximum from Clock Input to Data Output
  - — TTL Compatible 24 mA Outputs
  - — UltraMOS® III Advanced CMOS Technology
- **50% REDUCTION IN POWER**
  - — 75mA Typ I_{CC}
- **E² CELL TECHNOLOGY**
  - — Reconfigurable Logic
  - — Reprogrammable Cells
  - — 100% Tested/Guaranteed 100% Yields
  - — High Speed Electrical Erasure (<50ms)
  - — 20 Year Data Retention
- **EIGHT OUTPUT LOGIC MACROCELLS**
  - — Maximum Flexibility for Complex Logic Designs
  - — Programmable Output Polarity
  - — GAL16V8A Emulates 20-pin PAL® Devices with Full Function/Fuse Map/Parametric Compatibility
  - — GAL20V8A Emulates 24-pin PAL® Devices with Full Function/Fuse Map/Parametric Compatibility
- **PRELOAD AND POWER-ON RESET OF ALL REGISTERS**
  - — 100% Functional Testability
- **ELECTRONIC SIGNATURE FOR IDENTIFICATION**

GAL16V8A / GAL20V8A BLOCK DIAGRAM

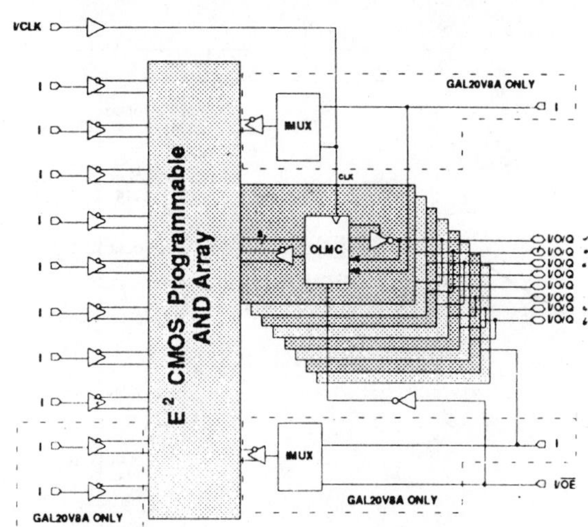

DESCRIPTION

The GAL16V8A and GAL20V8A, at 10 ns maximum propagation delay time, combine a high performance CMOS process with Electrically Erasable (E²) floating gate technology to provide the highest speed performance available in the PLD market. CMOS circuitry allows the GAL16V8A and GAL20V8A to consume just 75mA typical I_{CC} which represents a 50% savings in power when compared to their bipolar counterparts. The E² technology offers high speed (50ms) erase times, providing the ability to reprogram or reconfigure the devices quickly and efficiently.

The generic architecture provides maximum design flexibility by allowing the Output Logic Macrocell (OLMC) to be configured by the user. The GAL16V8A and GAL20V8A are capable of emulating standard 20 and 24-pin PAL® devices. The GAL16V8A is capable of emulating standard 20-pin PAL architectures with full function/fuse map/parametric compatibility. The GAL20V8A is capable of emulating standard 24-pin PAL architectures with full function/fuse map/parametric compatibility. On the right is a table listing the PAL architectures that the GAL16V8A and GAL20V8A can replace.

Unique test circuitry and reprogrammable cells allow complete AC, DC, and functional testing during manufacture. Therefore, Lattice guarantees 100% field programmability and functionality of all GAL products. Lattice also guarantees 100 erase/rewrite cycles and that data retention exceeds 20 years.

GAL16V8A / GAL20V8A ARCHITECTURE EMULATION

GAL20V8A PAL Architecture Emulation	GAL16V8A PAL Architecture Emulation
20L8	16L8
20H8	16H8
20R8	16R8
20R6	16R6
20R4	16R4
20P8	16P8
20RP8	16RP8
20RP6	16RP6
20RP4	16RP4
14L8	10L8
16L6	12L6
18L4	14L4
20L2	16L2
14H8	10H8
16H6	12H6
18H4	14H4
20H2	16H2
14P8	10P8
16P6	12P6
18P4	14P4
20P2	16P2

FIGURE 12-6 GAL16V8A Data Sheet (Courtesy of Lattice Semiconductor Corporation)

GAL16V8A BLOCK DIAGRAM

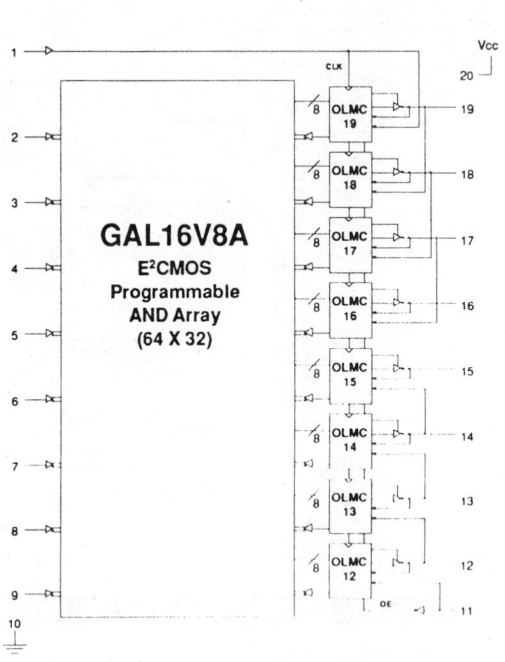

GAL20V8A BLOCK DIAGRAM

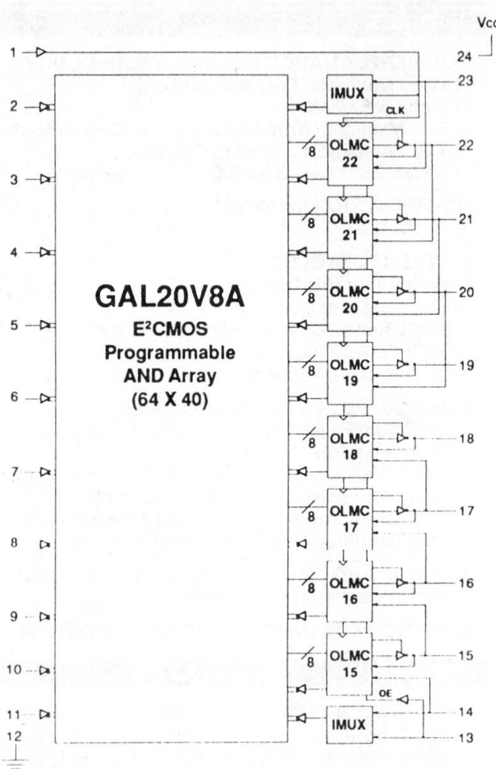

GAL16V8A PIN CONFIGURATION

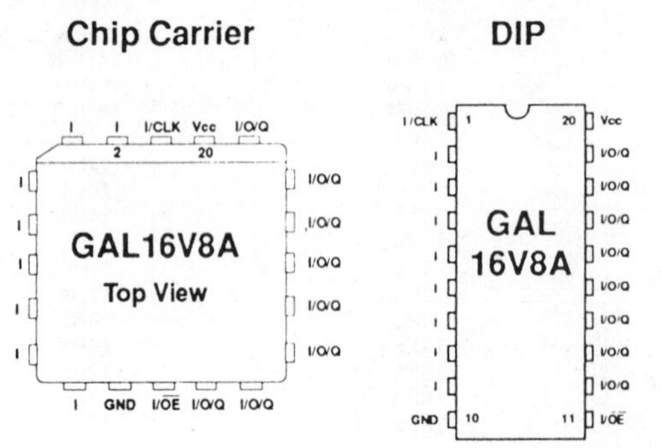

GAL20V8A PIN CONFIGURATION

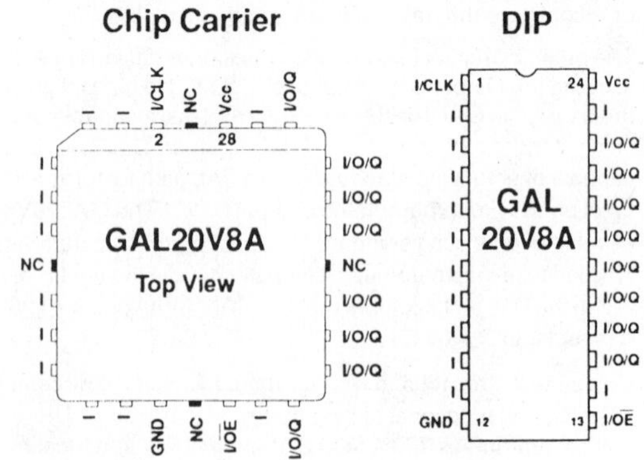

GAL16V8A LOGIC DIAGRAM

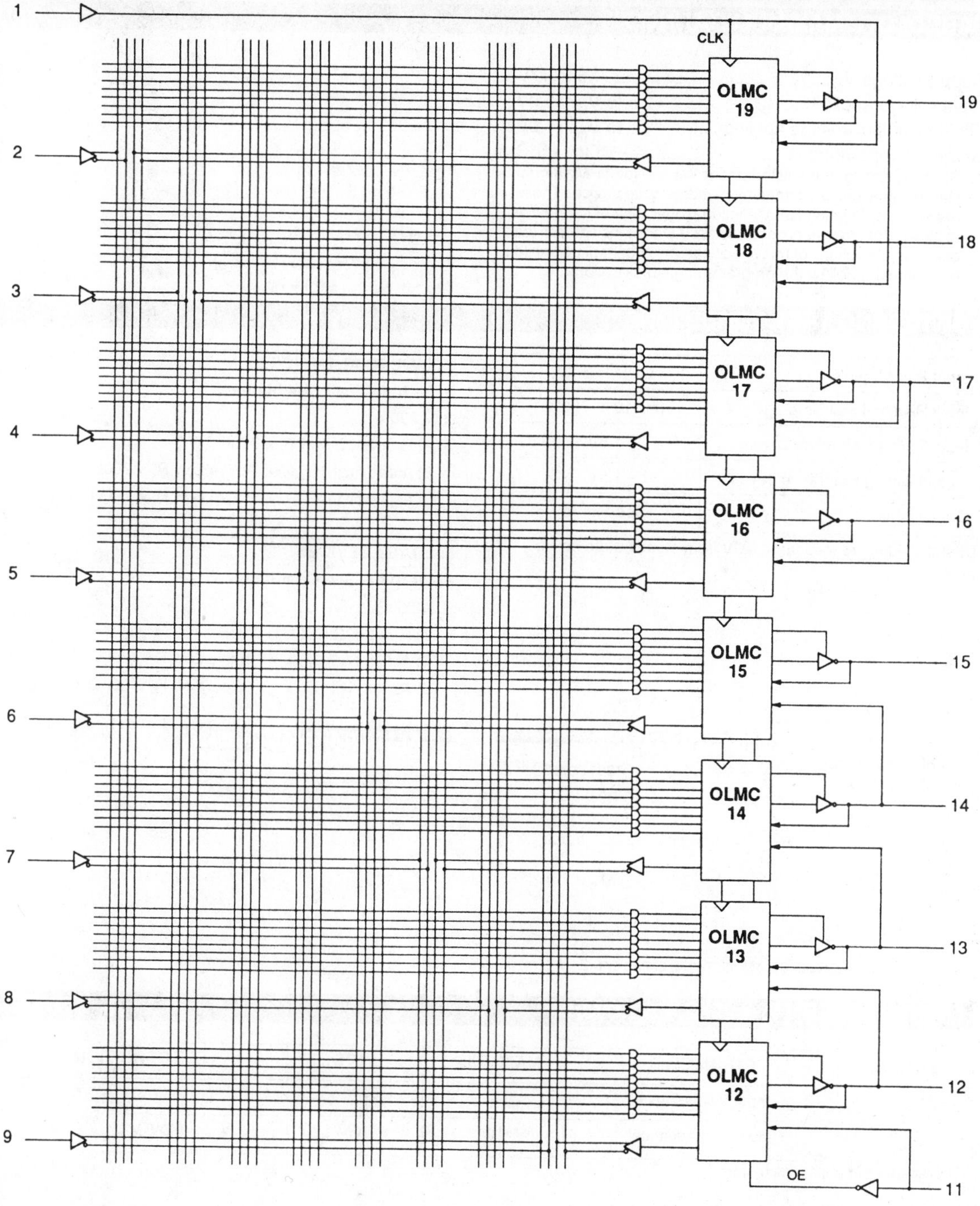

ABSOLUTE MAXIMUM RATINGS[1]

Supply voltage V_{CC} .... −.5 to +7V
Input voltage applied .... −2.5 to V_{CC} +1.0V
Off-state output voltage applied .... −2.5 to V_{CC} +1.0V
Storage Temperature .... −65 to 125°C

1. Stresses above those listed under the "Absolute Maximum Ratings" may cause permanent damage to the device. These are stress only ratings and functional operation of the device at these or at any other conditions above those indicated in the operational sections of this specification is not implied (while programming, follow the programming specifications).

SWITCHING TEST CONDITIONS

Input Pulse Levels	GND to 3.0V
Input Rise and Fall Times	3ns 10% – 90%
Input Timing Reference Levels	1.5V
Output Timing Reference Levels	1.5V
Output Load	See Figure

Tri-state levels are measured 0.5V from steady-state active level.

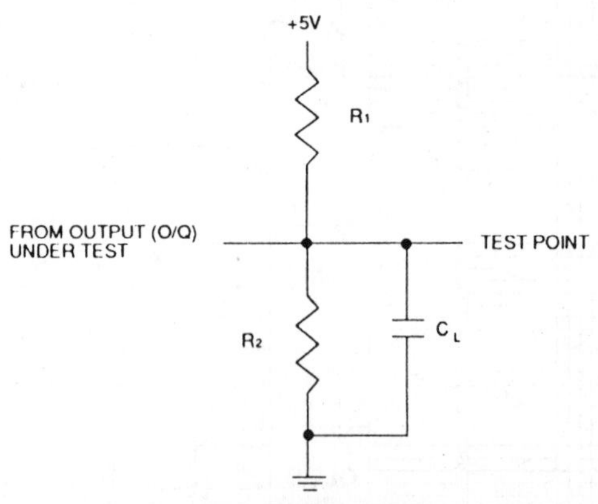

CL INCLUDES JIG AND PROBE TOTAL CAPACITANCE

COMMERCIAL DEVICES
Refer to AC Test Conditions: R_2 = 390Ω 1) R_1 = 200Ω and C_L = 50pF 2) Active High $R_1 = \infty$; Active Low R_1 = 200Ω C_L = 50pF 3) Active High $R_1 = \infty$; Active Low R_1 = 200Ω C_L = 5pF

MILITARY DEVICES
Refer to AC Test Conditions: R_2 = 750Ω 1) R_1 = 390Ω and C_L = 50pF 2) Active High $R_1 = \infty$; Active Low R_1 = 390Ω C_L = 50pF 3) Active High $R_1 = \infty$; Active Low R_1 = 390Ω C_L = 5pF

CAPACITANCE (T_A = 25°C, f = 1.0 MHz)

SYMBOL	PARAMETER	MAXIMUM*	UNITS	TEST CONDITIONS
C_I	Input Capacitance	8	pF	V_{CC} = 5.0V, V_I = 2.0V
$C_{I/O/Q}$	I/O/Q Capacitance	10	pF	V_{CC} = 5.0V, $V_{I/O/Q}$ = 2.0V

*Guaranteed but not 100% tested.

ELECTRICAL CHARACTERISTICS GAL16 / 20V8A-10L Commercial

Over Recommended Operating Conditions (Unless Otherwise Specified)

SYMBOL	PARAMETER	CONDITION	MIN.	TYP.	MAX.	UNITS
V_{OL}	Output Low Voltage		—	—	0.5	V
V_{OH}	Output High Voltage		2.4	—	—	V
I_{IL}, I_{IH}	Input Leakage Current		—	—	±10	µA
$I_{I/O/Q}$	Bidirectional Pin Leakage Current		—	—	±10	µA
I_{OS}[1]	Output Short Circuit Current	V_{CC} = 5V V_{OUT} = Gnd	–30	—	–150	mA
I_{CC}	Operating Power Supply Current	V_{IL} = 0.5V V_{IH} = 3.0V f_{toggle} = 25MHz	—	75	115	mA

1) One output at a time for a maximum duration of one second.

DC RECOMMENDED OPERATING CONDITIONS GAL16 / 20V8A-10L Commercial

SYMBOL	PARAMETER	MIN.	MAX.	UNITS
T_A	Ambient Temperature	0	75	°C
V_{CC}	Supply Voltage	4.75	5.25	V
V_{IL}	Input Low Voltage	Vss – 0.5	0.8	V
V_{IH}	Input High Voltage	2.0	Vcc+1	V
I_{OL}	Low Level Output Current	—	24	mA
I_{OH}	High Level Output Current	—	-3.2	mA

SWITCHING CHARACTERISTICS — GAL16 / 20V8A-10L Commercial

Over Recommended Operating Conditions

PARAMETER	#	FROM	TO	DESCRIPTION	TEST COND.[1]	MIN.	MAX.	UNITS
t_{pd}	1	I, I/O	O	Combinational Propagation Delay	1	3	10	ns
	2	CLK	Q	Clock to Output Delay	1	2	8	ns
t_{en}	3	I, I/O	O	Output Enable, Z → O	2	—	10	ns
	4	$\overline{OE}$	Q	Output Register Enable, Z → Q	2	—	10	ns
t_{dis}	5	I, I/O	O	Output Disable, O → Z	3	—	10	ns
	6	$\overline{OE}$	Q	Output Register Disable, Q → Z	3	—	10	ns

1) Refer to **Switching Test Conditions** section.

AC RECOMMENDED OPERATING CONDITIONS — GAL16 / 20V8A-10L Commercial

PARAMETER	#	DESCRIPTION	TEST COND.	MIN.	MAX.	UNITS
f_{clk}	7	Clock Frequency without Feedback	1	0	62.5	MHz
	8	Clock Frequency with Feedback	1	0	55.5	MHz
t_{su}	9	Setup Time, Input or Feedback, before CLK ↑	—	10	—	ns
t_h	10	Hold Time, Input or Feedback, after CLK ↑	—	0	—	ns
t_w	11	Clock Pulse Duration, High	—	8	—	ns
	12	Clock Pulse Duration, Low	—	8	—	ns

SWITCHING WAVEFORMS

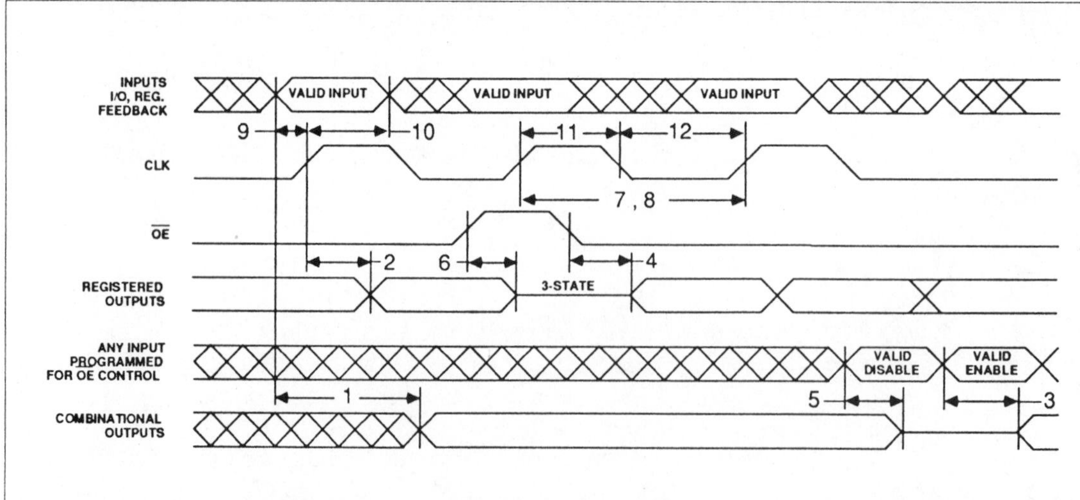

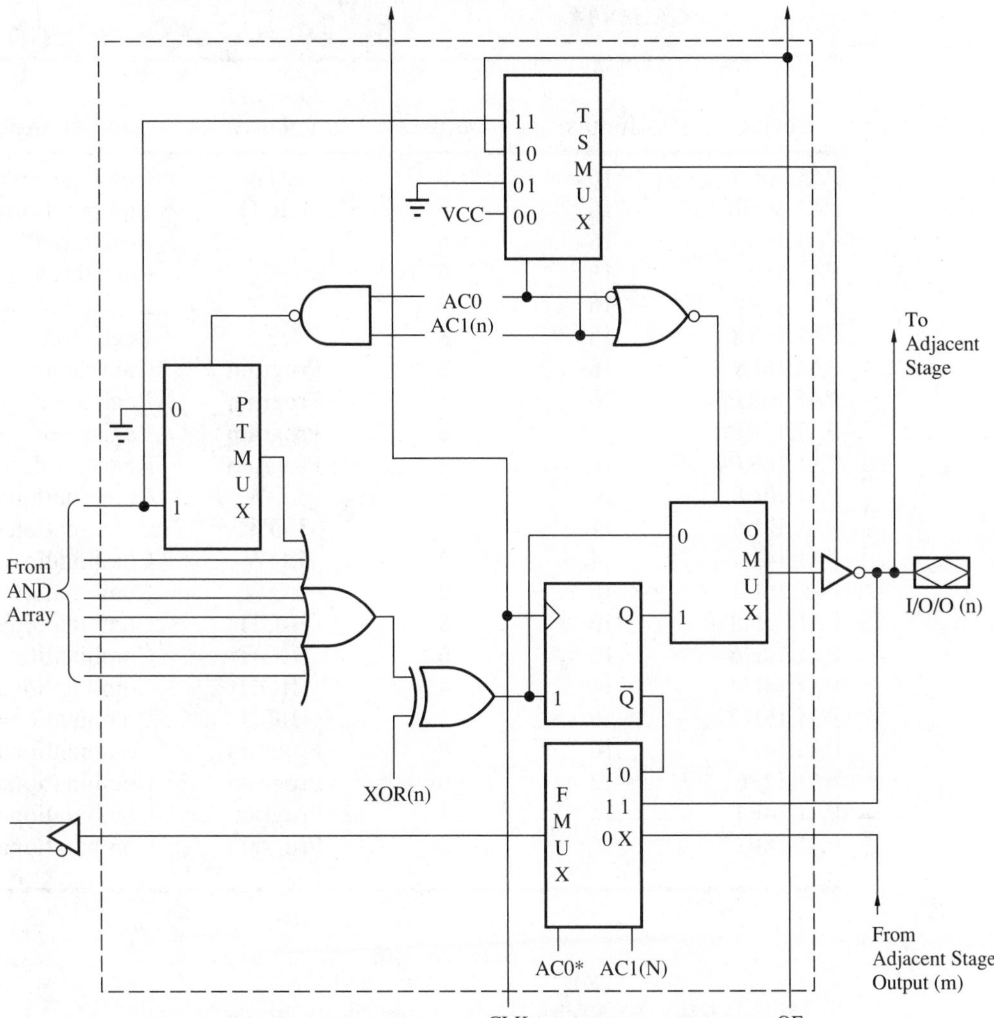

*Note: SYN replaces AC0 and SYN replaces AC1(m) as an input to the input FMUX in OLMC (12) and OLMC (19) to maintain full JEDEC fuse map compatibility with PAL® type device architectures.

FIGURE 12-7 GAL16V8A Output Logic Macro Cell (Courtesy of Lattice Semiconductor Corporation)

GAL16V8 does not allow any feedback in the simple mode. The GAL16V8A allows a feedback path to the AND array so that the output expression can be used as the input to other combinational logic functions.

In the simple mode pins 15 and 16 are outputs only and have no feedback. Pins 12 to 14 and 17 to 19 can be used as either inputs or outputs. Pins 1 to

TABLE 12-1 Programmable Array Logic Devices Emulated by the GAL16V8A

Device	Inputs	Outputs	Outputs Polarity	Output Type
PAL16L8	16	8	LOW	Combinational
PAL16H8	16	8	HIGH	Combinational
PAL16R8	16	8		Registered
PAL16R6	16	6		Registered
PAL16R4	16	4		Registered
PAL16R8	16	8		Registered
PAL16P8	16	8	Program	Combinational
PAL16RP8	16	8	Program	Registered
PAL16RP6	16	6	Program	Registered
PAL16RP4	16	4	Program	Registered
PAL10L8	10	8	LOW	Combinational
PAL12L6	12	6	LOW	Combinational
PAL14L4	14	4	LOW	Combinational
PAL16L2	16	2	LOW	Combinational
PAL10H8	10	8	HIGH	Combinational
PAL12H6	12	6	HIGH	Combinational
PAL14H4	14	4	HIGH	Combinational
PAL16H2	16	2	HIGH	Combinational
PAL10P8	10	8	Program	Combinational
PAL12P6	12	6	Program	Combinational
PAL14P4	14	4	Program	Combinational
PAL16P2	16	2	Program	Combinational

TABLE 12-2(a) GAL16V8A Device Operation: Simple Mode

Simple Mode: Combinational inputs and outputs; feedback allowed with the GAL16V8A; eight product terms allowed in each output expression.

Operation	GAL16V8A Pin Numbers
V_{CC}	20
GND	10
Input only	1–9, 11
Output only; no feedback	15, 16
Input or output with feedback	12–14, 17–19

TABLE 12-2(b) GAL16V8 Device Operation: Simple Mode

Simple Mode: Combinational inputs and outputs; no feedback with the GAL16V8; eight product terms allowed in each output expression.

Operation	GAL16V8 Pin Numbers
V_{CC}	20
GND	10
Input only	1–9, 11
Output only; no feedback	15, 16
Input or output; no feedback	12–14, 17–19

TABLE 12-3 GAL16V8/GAL16V8A Device Operation: Complex Mode

Complex Mode: Combinational inputs and outputs; output enable term required for feedback; seven product terms allowed in each output expression.

Operation	Pin Numbers
V_{CC}	20
GND	10
Input only	1–9, 11
Output only; no feedback	12, 19
Input or output with feedback	13–18

9 and 11 can serve only as inputs. The operational features of the GAL16V8A in the simple mode are summarized in Table 12-2(a). The operational features of the GAL16V8 in the simple mode are summarized in Table 12-2(b).

Figures 12-8 through 12-11 show the architecture of the GAL16V8A and the GAL16V8 in a single OLMC and in the entire chip operated in the simple mode.

TABLE 12-4 GAL16V8/GAL16V8A Device Operation: Registered Mode

Operation	Pin Numbers
V_{CC}	20
GND	10
Input only	2–9
Clock input pin	1
Active-LOW Output Enable input pin	11
Input or output with feedback	12–19

The **complex mode** allows for combinational inputs and outputs with feedback. All outputs must have an output enable term controlling their active state. Otherwise the outputs are in a high-impedance tristate mode. Output pins 13 to 18 have a feedback path back to the AND array; outputs 12 and 19 have no feedback path. The output expressions allow only seven product terms. The eighth term is used for the output enable control. The operational features of the GAL16V8 and GAL16V8A in the complex mode are summarized in Table 12-3. These two PLDs function identically in the complex mode.

The complex mode on the GAL16V8A is useful when each output term requires a separate enable condition, or when a PLD programming system does not support the feedback operation of the GAL16V8A. Otherwise the simple mode on the GAL16V8A allows for feedback without the need to specify an output enable term. The GAL16V8, however, does not have a feedback connection in the simple mode. If feedback is required for a combinational output using the GAL16V8, the complex mode must be used.

Figures 12-12 and 12-13 illustrate the GAL16V8A architecture of a single OLMC and of the entire chip operating in the complex mode.

The **registered mode** allows the PLD outputs to be synchronous (registered) or combinational with feedback. Both combinational and registered outputs can be programmed on a GAL16V8 and GAL16V8A IC operating in the registered mode.

The OLMC is configured with a D flip-flop for the synchronous outputs. Each registered or D flip-flop output expression is allowed up to eight product terms. Each combinational output expression is allowed up to seven product terms, and, in addition, requires an output enable term to enable the output buffer.

On the GAL16V8A or the GAL16V8 in the registered mode, pins 12 to 19 can function as inputs or outputs. Pins 1 to 9 and 11 serve only as inputs. The operational features of the GAL16V8 and GAL16V8A in the registered mode are summarized in Table 12-4. The GAL16V8 is identical to the GAL16V8A in the registered mode.

The synchronous outputs in the registered mode are positive edge-triggered D flip-flops. The clock signal to trigger the flip-flops must be input into pin 1. An active-LOW output enable function controls all registered outputs. The output enable function must be assigned to pin 11. To enable all registered outputs, a logic LOW must be applied to pin 11 during operation. All synchronous outputs on the chip are controlled by the common clock and active-LOW output enable signals on pins 1 and 11, respectively.

Figures 12-14 and 12-15 show the GAL16V8A architecture of a single OLMC and of the entire IC operating in the registered mode.

■ EXAMPLE 12-1 GAL16V8 Architecture

Problem: Determine the mode required and specify appropriate input and output pins for the GAL16V8 for each application specified.

APPLICATION I—COMBINATIONAL LOGIC SYSTEM

- Requires 12 inputs, 3 outputs, and no feedback.

APPLICATION II—COMBINATIONAL LOGIC SYSTEM

- Requires 12 inputs and 3 outputs with feedback, and individual output enable control is needed for each input.

APPLICATION III—SEQUENTIAL LOGIC SYSTEM

- Requires 10 input variables and 4 outputs from D flip-flops.

APPLICATION IV—SEQUENTIAL/COMBINATIONAL LOGIC SYSTEM

- Requires 10 input variables, 2 outputs from D flip-flops, and 2 combinational outputs.

Solution: Refer to Tables 12-2, 12-3, and 12-4 for the pin operations for each mode of operation for the GAL16V8.

Specifications **GAL16V8A**
GAL20V8A

SIMPLE MODE

In the Simple architecture mode pins are configured as dedicated inputs or as dedicated, always active, combinational outputs.

Architecture configurations available in this mode are similar to the common 10L8, 18H4 and 16P6 devices with many permutations of generic polarity output or input choices.

All ouputs are associated with 8 data product terms. In addition, each output has programmable polarity.

Pins 1 and 11 on a GAL16V8, and pins 1 and 13 on a GAL20V8, are always available as data inputs into the AND array. The "center" two macrocells (GAL16V8 pins 15 &16, GAL20V8 pins 18 & 19) cannot be used in the input configuration.

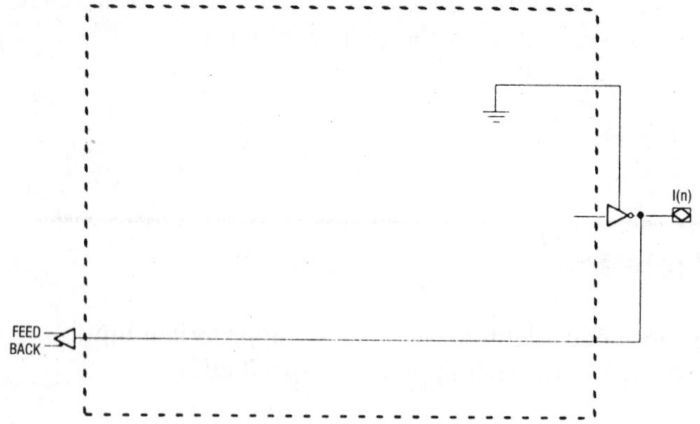

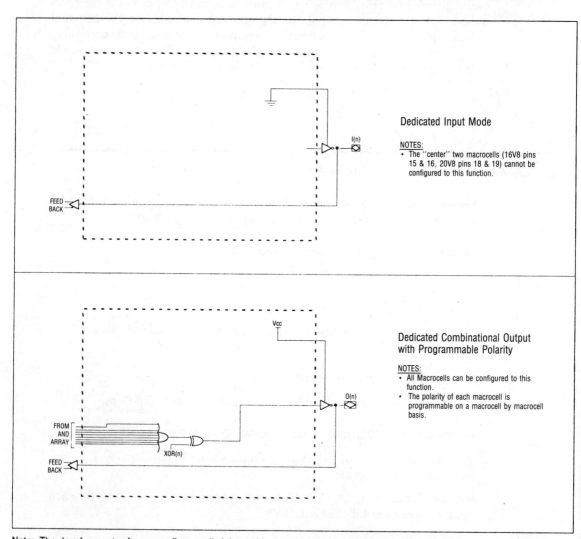

Dedicated Input Mode

NOTES:
- The "center" two macrocells (16V8 pins 15 & 16, 20V8 pins 18 & 19) cannot be configured to this function.

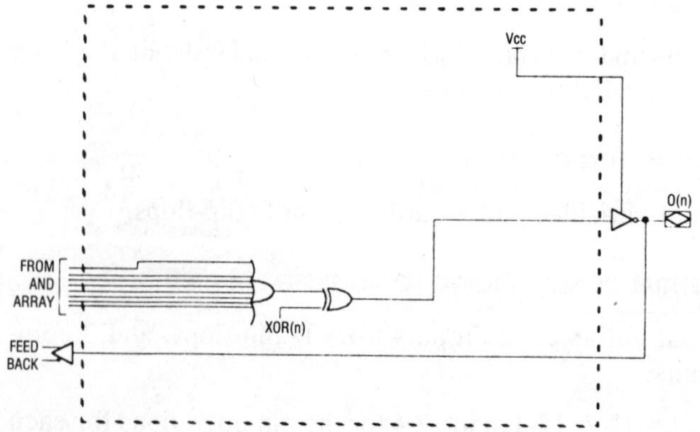

Dedicated Combinational Output with Programmable Polarity

NOTES:
- All Macrocells can be configured to this function.
- The polarity of each macrocell is programmable on a macrocell by macrocell basis.

Note: The development software configures all of the architecture control bits and checks for proper pin usage automatically.

FIGURE 12-8 GAL16V8A Architecture of the Output Logic Macro Cell in the Simple Mode of Operation (Courtesy of Lattice Semiconductor Corporation)

Simple Mode
GAL16V8A/16V8B
Feedback

Global	Output pins	
	XOR(n)	Polarity
SYN = 1 ACO = 0	0 1	Active low Active high

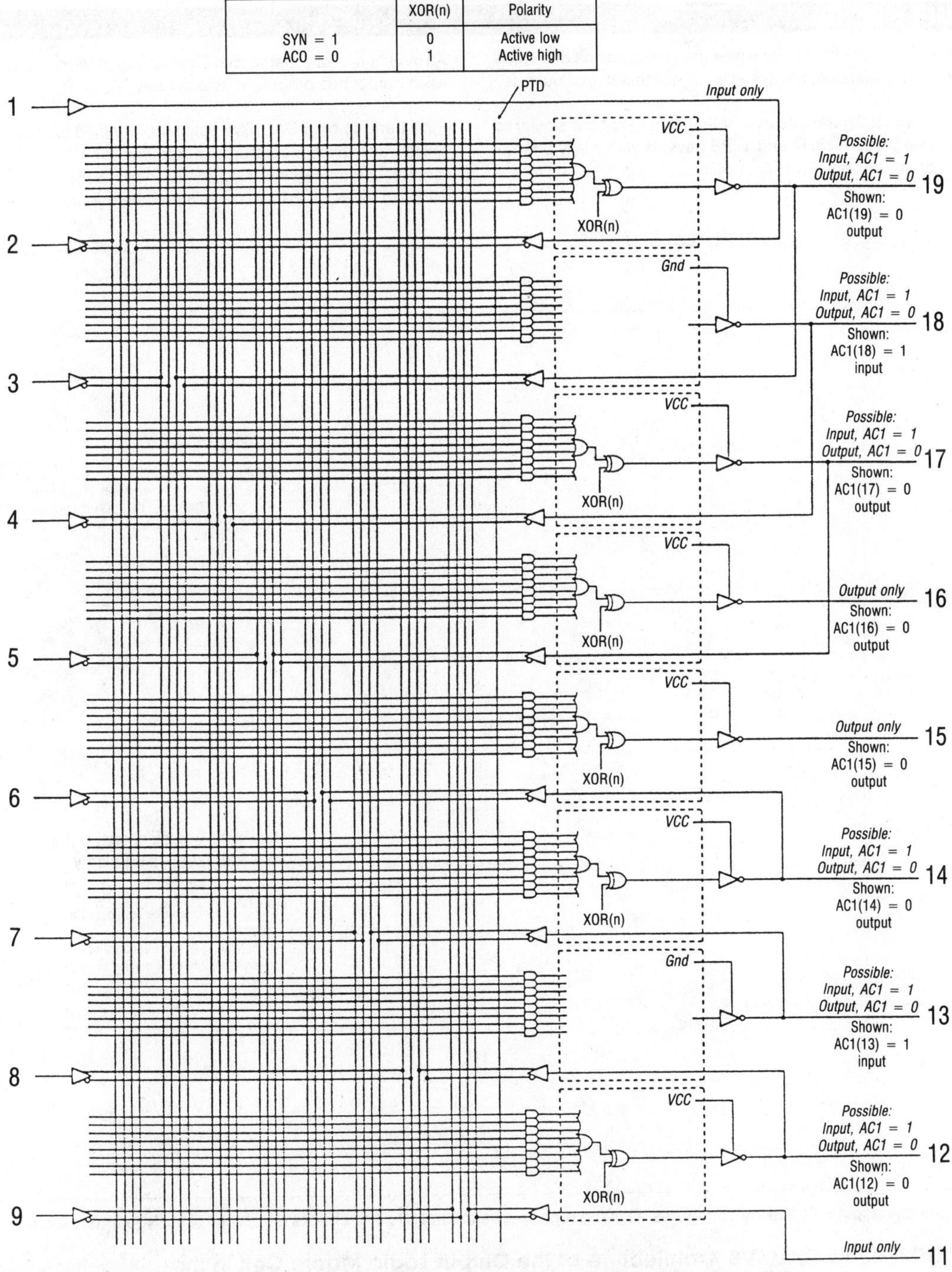

FIGURE 12-9 GAL16V8A Architecture of the Complete Integrated Circuit in the Simple Mode of Operation (Courtesy of Lattice Semiconductor Corporation)

SIMPLE MODE

In the Simple architecture mode pins are configured as dedicated inputs or as dedicated, always active, combinational outputs.

Architecture configurations available in this mode are similar to the common 10L8, 18H4 and 16P6 devices with many permutations of generic polarity output or input choices.

All ouputs are associated with 8 data product terms. In addition each output has programmable polarity.

Pins 1 and 11 on a GAL16V8, and pins 1 and 13 on a GAL20V8 are always available as data inputs into the AND array. The "center" two macrocells (GAL16V8 pins 15 &16, GAL20V8 pins 18 & 19) cannot be used in the input configuration.

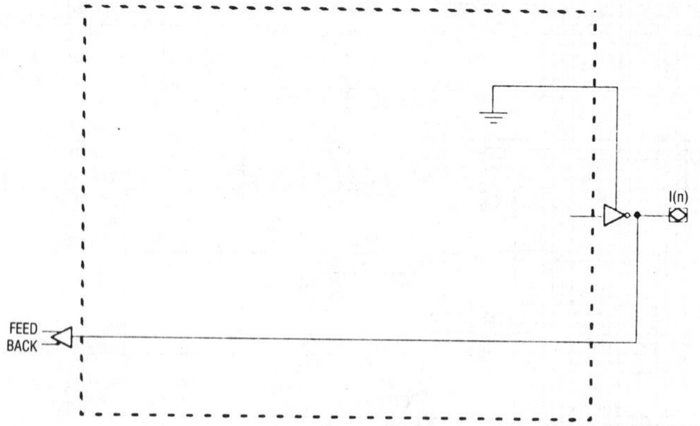

I(n)
FEED BACK

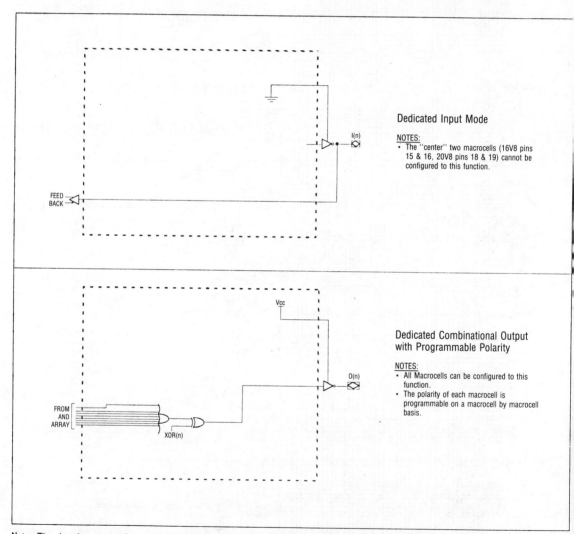

Dedicated Input Mode

NOTES:
- The "center" two macrocells (16V8 pins 15 & 16, 20V8 pins 18 & 19) cannot be configured to this function.

Vcc
O(n)
FROM AND ARRAY
XOR(n)

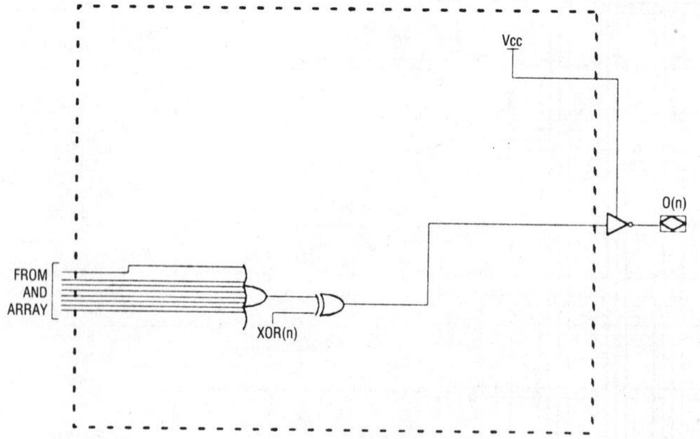

Dedicated Combinational Output with Programmable Polarity

NOTES:
- All Macrocells can be configured to this function.
- The polarity of each macrocell is programmable on a macrocell by macrocell basis.

Note: The development software configures all of the architecture control bits and checks for proper pin usage automatically.

FIGURE 12-10 GAL16V8 Architecture of the Output Logic Macro Cell in the Simple Mode of Operation (Courtesy of Lattice Semiconductor Corporation)

Simple Mode
GAL16V8
No Feedback

Global	Output pins	
	XOR(n)	Polarity
SYN = 1 ACO = 0	0 1	Active low Active high

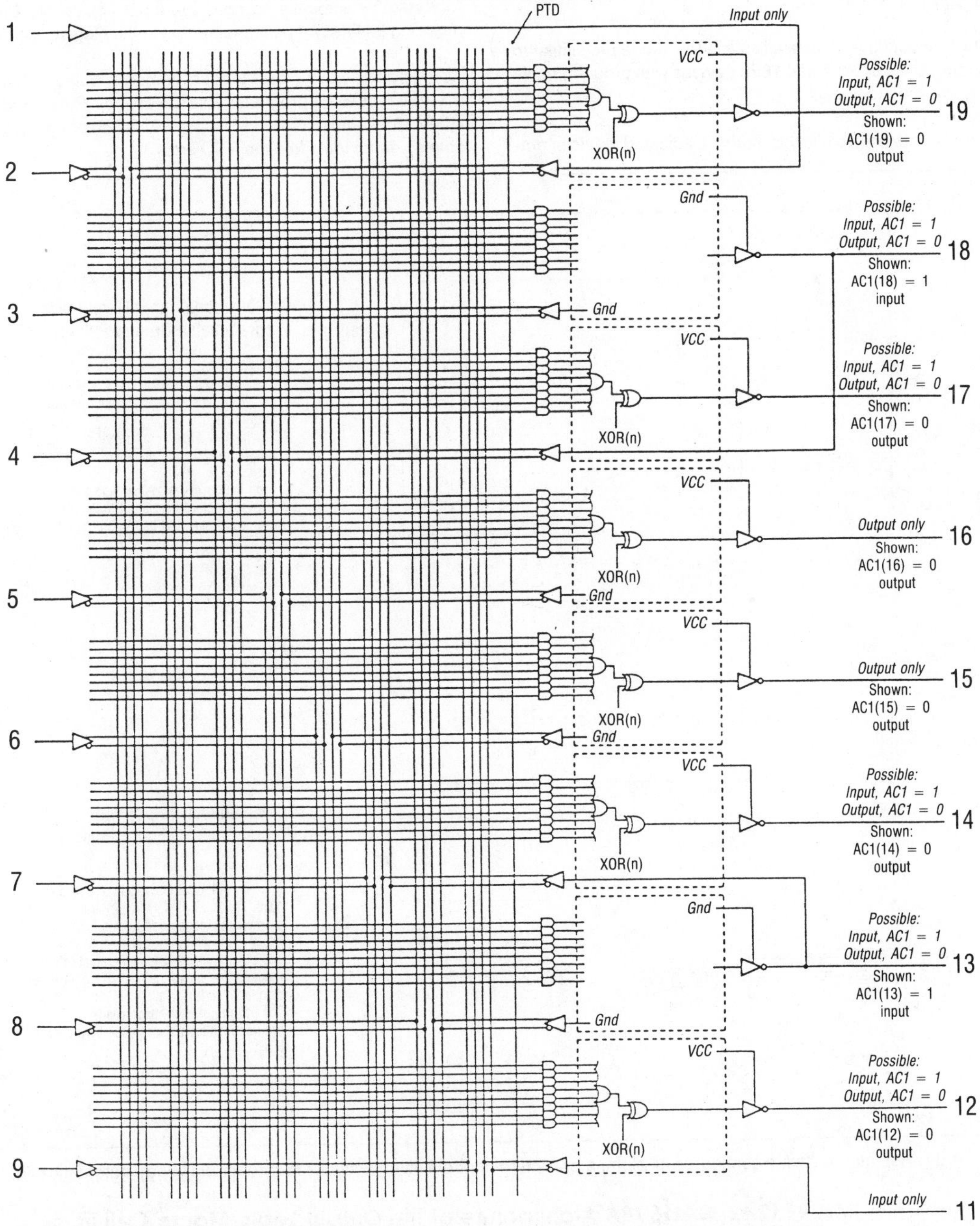

FIGURE 12-11 GAL16V8 Architecture of the Complete Integrated Circuit in the Simple Mode of Operation (Courtesy of Lattice Semiconductor Corporation)

COMPLEX MODE

In the Complex architecture mode macrocells are configured as output only or I/O functions.

Architecture configurations available in this mode are similar to the common 16L8, 20L8 and 16P8 devices with programmable polarity in each macrocell.

Up to 6 I/O's are possible in this mode. Dedicated inputs or outputs can be implemented as sub-sets of the I/O function. The two "outboard" macrocells do not have input capability. Designs requiring 8 I/O's can be implemented in the Registered mode.

All macrocells have 7 data product terms per output. One product term is used for programmable OE control. Pins 1 and 11 on a GAL16V8, and pins 1 and 13 on a GAL20V8, are always available as data inputs into the AND array.

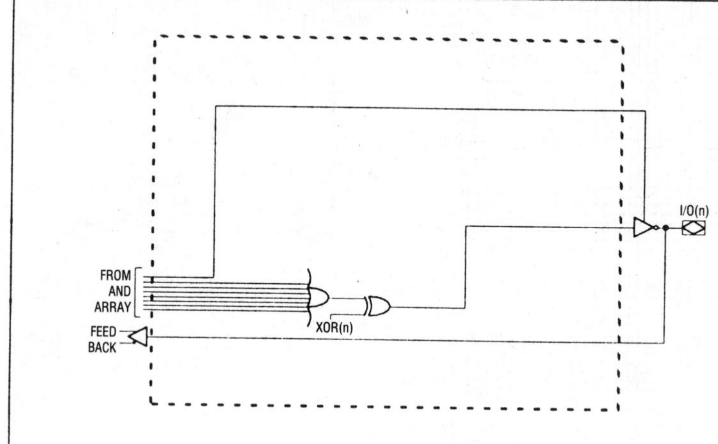

Combinational Input/Output with Programmable OE and Polarity

NOTES:
- The outboard macrocells (16V8 pins 12 & 19, 20V8 pins 15 & 22) cannot perform this function.
- The polarity of each macrocell is programmable on a macrocell by macrocell basis.
- Each marcocell has active high and active low feedback of the output buffer and/or device pin data into the AND array.

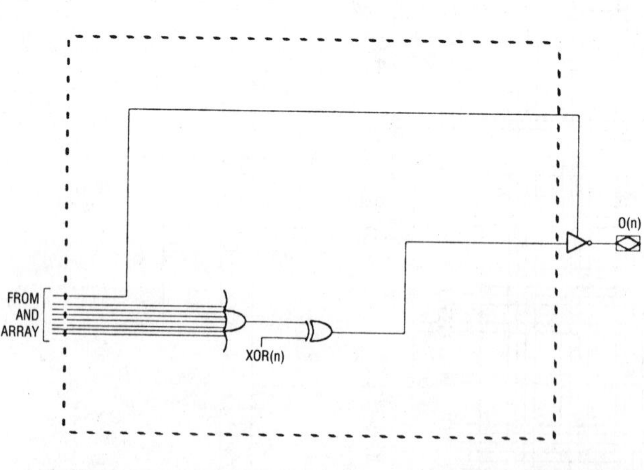

Combinational Output with Programmable OE and Polarity

NOTES:
- The two outboard macrocells (16V8 pins 12 & 19, 20V8 pins 15 & 22) are permanently configured to this function when in the Complex mode.
- The other 6 macrocells can emulate this mode by not using the feedback data as a data input to the array.
- The polarity of each macrocell is programmable on a macrocell by macrocell basis.

Note: The development software configures all of the architecture control bits and checks for proper pin usage automatically.

FIGURE 12-12 GAL16V8A Architecture of the Output Logic Macro Cell in the Complex Mode of Operation (Courtesy of Lattice Semiconductor Corporation)

Complex Mode
GAL16V8/16V8A/16V8B

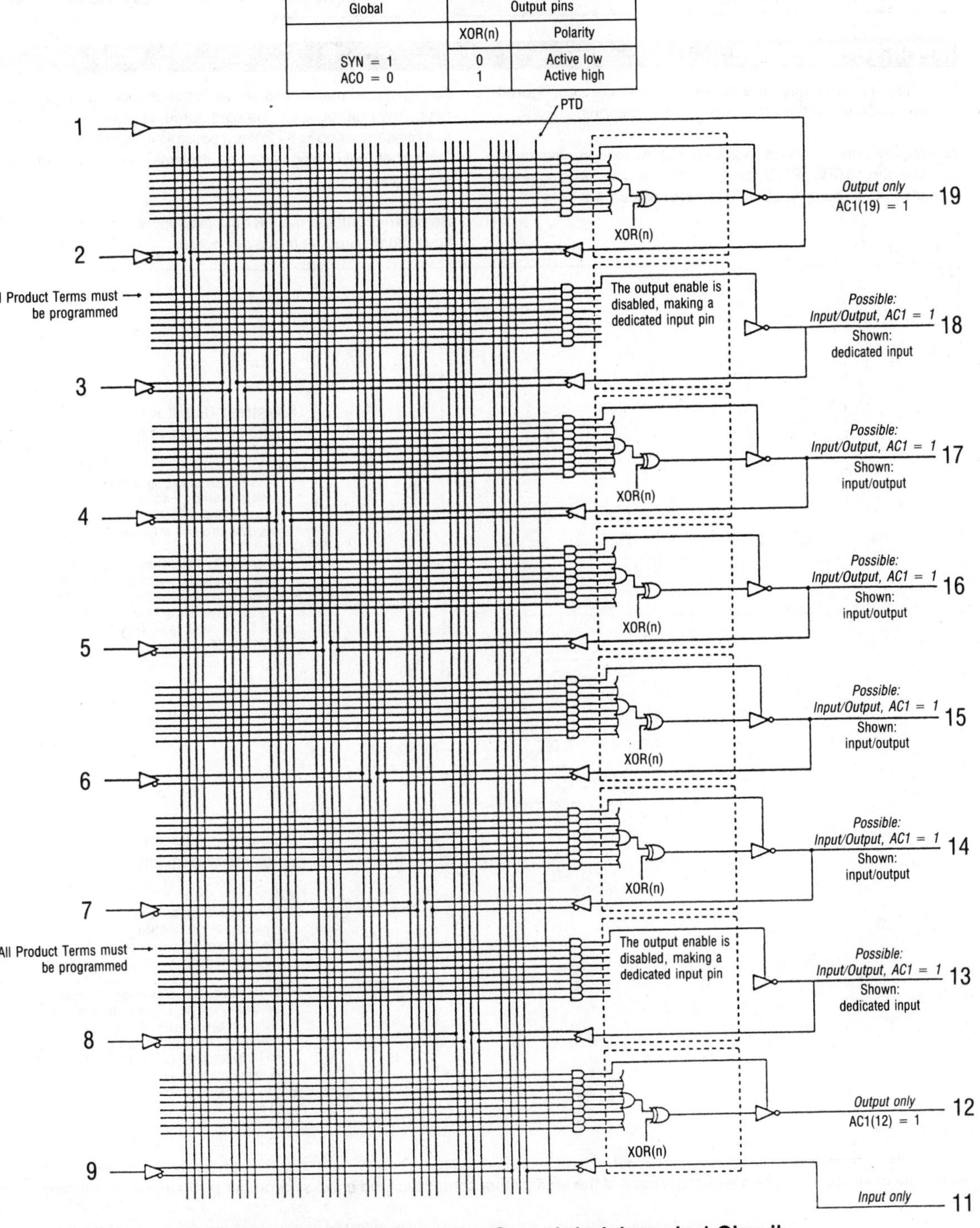

Global	Output pins	
	XOR(n)	Polarity
SYN = 1 ACO = 0	0 1	Active low Active high

FIGURE 12-13 GAL16V8A Architecture of the Complete Integrated Circuit in the Complex Mode of Operation (Courtesy of Lattice Semiconductor Corporation)

REGISTERED MODE

In the Registered architecture mode macrocells are configured as dedicated, registered outputs or as I/O functions.

Architecture configurations available in this mode are similar to the common 16R8, 20R6 and 16RP4 devices with various permutations of polarity, I/O and register placement.

All registered macrocells share common clock and $\overline{OE}$ control pins. Any macrocell can be configured as registered or I/O. Up to 8 registers or up to 8 I/O's are possible in this mode. Dedicated input or output functions can be implemented as sub-sets of the I/O function.

Registered outputs have 8 data product terms per output. I/O's have 7 data product terms per output.

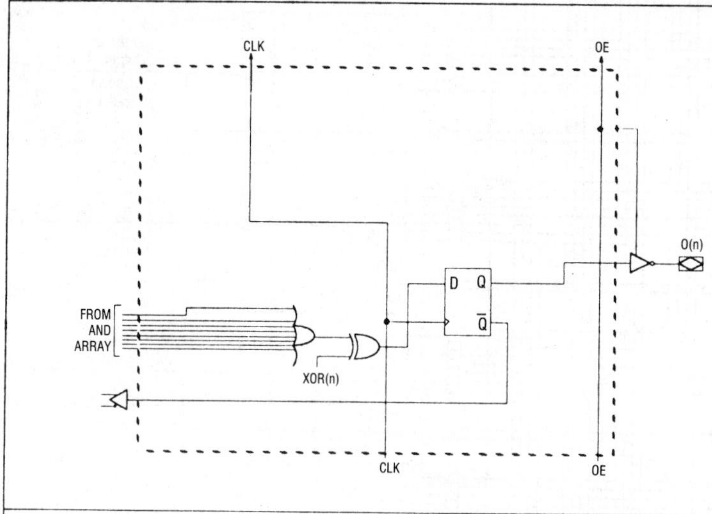

Registered Output with Programmable Polarity

NOTES:
- All macrocells can be individually configured to this function.
- Polarity of the register input is programmable on a macrocell by macrocell basis.
- Feedback into the AND array is from the $\overline{Q}$ signal of the register with active low and active high feedback paths provided.
- Registered macrocells have common clock (pin 1) and common $\overline{OE}$ (16V8 pin 11, 20V8 pin 13)

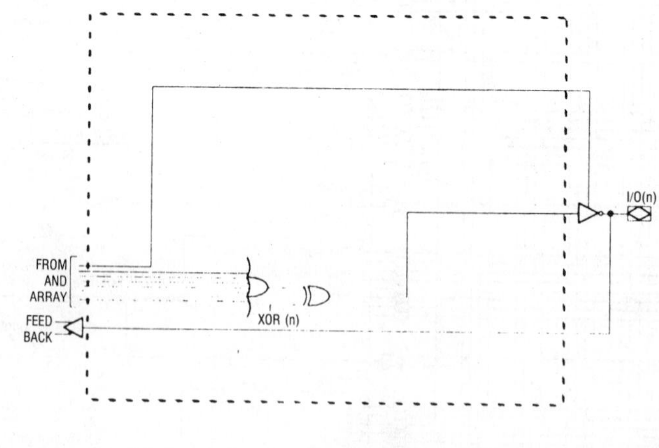

Combinational Input/Output with Programmable OE and Polarity

NOTES:
- All macrocells can be individually configured to this function.
- The polarity of each macrocell is programmable on a macrocell by macrocell basis.
- All macrocells have active high and active low feedback of the output buffer and/or device pin data into the AND array.
- When all 8 macrocells are configured into the I/O function the CLK and $\overline{OE}$ pins serve no valid logic function.

Note: The development software configures all of the architecture control bits and checks for proper pin usage automatically.

FIGURE 12-14 GAL16V8A Architecture of the Output Logic Macro Cell in the Registered Mode of Operation (Courtesy of Lattice Semiconductor Corporation)

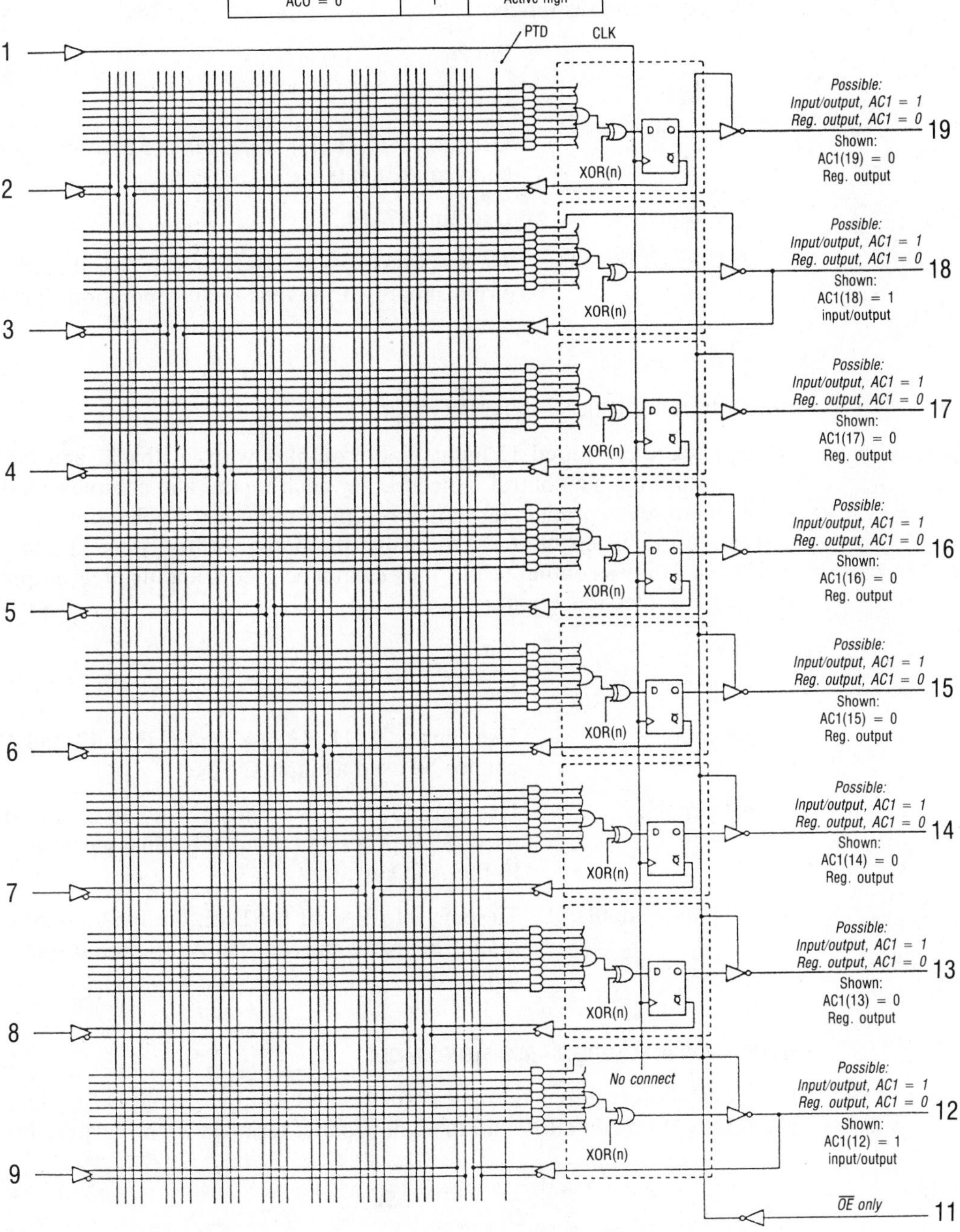

FIGURE 12-15 GAL16V8A Architecture of the Complete Integrated Circuit in the Registered Mode of Operation (Courtesy of Lattice Semiconductor Corporation)

APPLICATION I SOLUTION—SIMPLE MODE

The application required 12 inputs, 3 outputs, and no feedback. The simple mode allows up to eight product terms in each output equation. Pins 15 and 16 cannot be used as inputs:

- V_{CC}: Pin 20
- GND: Pin 10
- Inputs: Use pins 1–9, 11–13. *Note:* Pins 15 and 16 cannot be used as inputs.
- Outputs: Use pins 17–19.
- Unused inputs: Tie pin 14 to V_{CC} or GND on the breadboard or circuit board to prevent faulty operation due to noise.

APPLICATION II SOLUTION—COMPLEX MODE

The application required 12 inputs and 3 outputs with feedback, and individual output enable control is needed for each input. The complex mode allows up to seven product terms in an output expression. Each output needs a separate output enable term to enable the output buffer. Pins 12 and 19 can be used only as output terms; they cannot be used as inputs or as outputs that require a feedback path:

- V_{CC}: Pin 20
- GND: Pin 10
- Inputs: Use pins 1–9, 11, 13, 14. *Note:* Pins 12 and 19 cannot be used as inputs.
- Outputs: Use pins 15–17. *Note:* Pins 12 and 19 cannot be used as outputs that require a feedback path back to the AND array.
- Unused inputs: Tie pin 18 to V_{CC} or GND on the breadboard or circuit board to prevent faulty operation due to noise.

APPLICATION III SOLUTION—REGISTERED MODE

The application required 10 input variables and 4 outputs from D flip-flops. The registered mode allows up to eight product terms in each registered (D flip-flop) output expression. Pin 1 must be the clock input. Pin 11 must be the active-LOW output enable input controlling all registered outputs.

- V_{CC} — Pin 20
- GND: — Pin 10
- Clock: — Pin 1
- Output enable: — Pin 11 (Tie pin 11 to GND on the circuit board or breadboard so that all outputs are permanently enabled.)
- Inputs: — Pins 2–9 and 12–13
- Outputs: — Pins 16–19
- Unused input: — Pins 14–15 should be tied to V_{CC} or to GND on the breadboard or circuit board to prevent faulty operation due to noise.

APPLICATION IV SOLUTION—REGISTERED MODE

The application required 10 input variables, 2 outputs from D flip-flops, and 2 combinational outputs. The registered mode allows up to eight product terms in each registered (D flip-flop) output expression and up to seven product terms in each combinational output. Pin 1 must be the clock input. Pin 11 must be the active-LOW output enable input controlling all registered (D flip-flop) outputs. Each combinational term must have a separate output enable term to enable the output buffer.

- V_{CC}: — Pin 20
- GND: — Pin 10
- Clock: — Pin 1
- Output enable: — Pin 11 (Tie pin 11 to GND to enable the outputs at all times.)
- Inputs: — Pins 2–9 and 12–13
- Outputs: — Pins 16–19
- Unused input: — Pins 14–15 should be tied to V_{CC} or to GND on the breadboard or circuit board to prevent faulty operation due to noise. ■

Section Self-Test

1. State the three modes of operation of the GAL16V8 or GAL16V8A.
2. True or false: The GAL16V8 or GAL16V8A has programmable outputs that allow active-LOW and active-HIGH outputs on the chip at the same time.
3. True or false: The GAL16V8 or GAL16V8A allows combinational and registered outputs to be programmed on the chip at the same time.

ANSWERS

- (a) Simple (combinational inputs and outputs)
  (b) Complex (combinational inputs and outputs with output enable control of each output pin)
  (c) Registered (synchronous and combinational outputs on the chip at the same time)
- True
- True

12-3 PROGRAMMABLE LOGIC DEVICE PROGRAMMING SYSTEMS

A variety of computer-based hardware and software tools exist that can be used to program a PLD quickly and easily. This section examines the types of hardware and software tools that are most commonly used to program PLDs.

12.3.1 Logic Development Software

Software compilers are available to create the files required to program PLDs. Depending on the software, the PLD can be programmed by specifying Boolean equations, truth table operation, state transition diagrams, and even logic schematics, known as "schematic capture."

The compilers, or logic development systems, often perform several functions in addition to PLD programming. Complex logic compilers are usually equipped to simplify and minimize logic functions, to simulate the output function, to test the operation of the circuit, and to accept many logic function specifications in several formats. Simpler and less expensive compilers are capable of editing ASCII files, performing low-level simplification, and accepting logic functions specified in the form of Boolean equations.

The compiler must have **device libraries** specifying the architecture of the device specified in the source file. For instance, when a designer states in a source file that the GAL16V8 is to be programmed, the software accesses the GAL16V8 device library to determine the architecture of the chip.

The main task of the development software is to create a **JEDEC file** that specifies the **fuse map** of the PLD to be programmed. (JEDEC stands for Joint Electron Device Engineering Council that specifies a standard file format that can be read by device programmers.) The fuse map indicates which fuses in the device will be blown open and which will remain intact to create the desired logic function. The PLD is actually programmed when the JEDEC file is **downloaded** or transferred to a device programmed and then **programmed** into the device by applying the voltage levels necessary to blow open the appropriate fuses.

Development software often performs other tasks, such as creating pin diagrams and output files to document the programmed equations. These functions are useful to the designer but are not required to program the PLD.

The PLD development software described in detail in Section 12.4 is the LC9000 by Programmable Logic Technologies. The LC9000 is used with the Logic Lab hardware programmer, also by Programmable Logic Technologies. The examples in this chapter describe the use of both LC9000 and Logic Lab to program the GAL16V8 device. Refer to Appendix C for reference information on the LC9000 and Logic Lab.

12.3.2 Device Programmers

The device programmers required to program the PLDs must accept the JEDEC file created by the software compiler and then apply the required voltage levels to blow open fuses in the PLD. Some device programmers are general purpose and can be used to program memory devices as well as PLDs. Other programmers can only program specific PLDs.

Many device programmers have a specific communication software package that is used to control the communications and programming operations from a personal computer (PC). As with the development software that created the JEDEC fuse map, the device programmer software often has a device library that specifies exactly the devices that can be programmed.

The communication software links the device programmer to the PC and allows the user to select the functions for programming the device. First, a JEDEC file must be downloaded to the programmer. Then the correct device must be placed in the device socket. Finally, the device can be programmed. The program can be verified by comparing the resulting fuse configuration of the PLD with the contents of the JEDEC fuse map. For "secure" logic applications, the PLD programming can be performed with a security word that prevents anyone from reading the fuse configuration of the PLD.

System Self-Test

1. What type of file does the logic designer create in order to program a PLD?
2. What type of file must the development software create in order to program a PLD?

3. What type of file is downloaded to a device programmer and used to program a PLD?

ANSWERS

- Source file, specifying the device to be programmed, the pin assignments to the input and output variables, and the output expressions
- JEDEC file, specifying the fuse map
- JEDEC file is downloaded to the device programmer and then used to program the PLD

12-4 LC9000 LOGIC COMPILER AND LOGIC LAB PROGRAMMABLE LOGIC DEVICE PROGRAMMING SYSTEM

The LC9000 is a low-cost compiler designed for quick and simple programming of PLDs. The LC9000 accepts only the Boolean expressions of logic functions rather than other more complex methods of function entry. The compiler has an editor to assist in creating the ASCII source file. It is also capable of rudimentary simplification of Boolean equations.

Programming a GAL16V8 using the LC9000 compiler and Logic Lab software and programmer requires the following steps:

1. LC9000: Create a source file with Boolean equations.
2. LC9000: Compile the equations.
3. LC9000: Create a JEDEC file of the fuse map.
4. LC9000: Create a document file of the schematic of the PLD.
5. Logic Lab: Select the device to be programmed.
6. Logic Lab: Download the JEDEC file to the Logic Lab Programmer.
7. Insert the PLD into the socket of the programmer.
8. Logic Lab: Program the PLD.

The LC9000 and Logic Lab menu selections, the input files used, and the output files created for each operation are shown in Figure 12-16.

12.4.1 Getting Started with LC9000 and Logic Lab

The LC9000 is intended for use with an IBM compatible PC/XT/AT operating with DOS 2.0 or higher. The software can be used on a system with a hard drive or with two double density floppy disk drives. The computer must have at least 512 KBytes of RAM. The Logic Lab programmer is connected to the computer via the serial port.

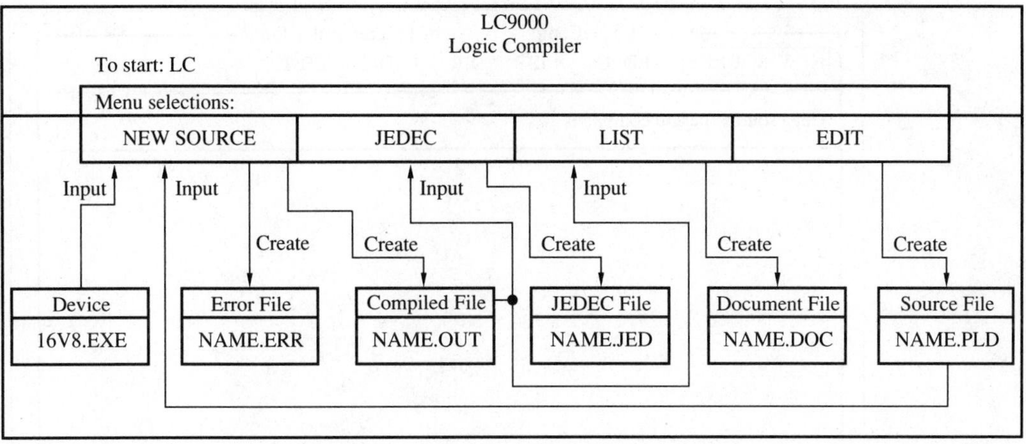

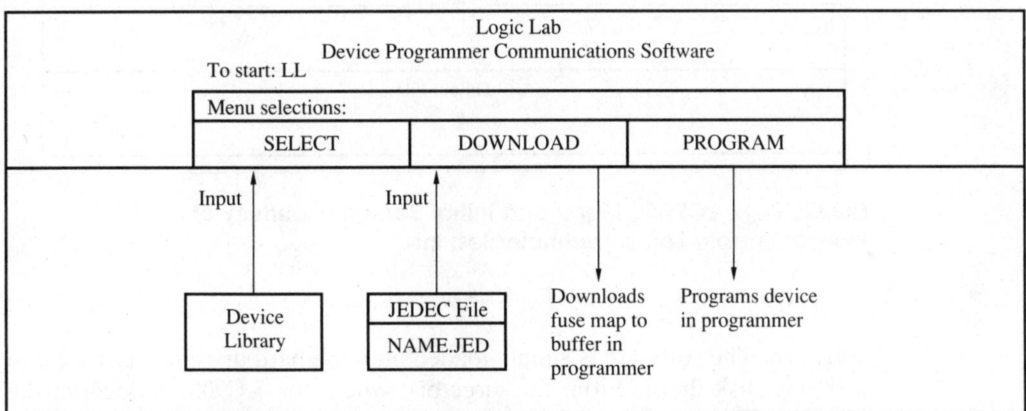

FIGURE 12-16 LC9000 and Logic Lab Menu Selections and Input/Output Files

The LC9000 software is used to create source files, compile source files, create JEDEC files, create document files with pin diagrams, and edit files. The Logic Lab software is used to establish communications between the PC and the programmer, download files to the programmer, and program the device. The two software packages are separate from each other. In general, the LC9000 is used first to create the source file and JEDEC files. After exiting the LC9000, the Logic Lab software is used to download the software to the programmer and to program the PLD.

Both the LC9000 and Logic Lab software packages are menu-driven and very easy to use. No installation is required of the LC9000 or Logic Lab

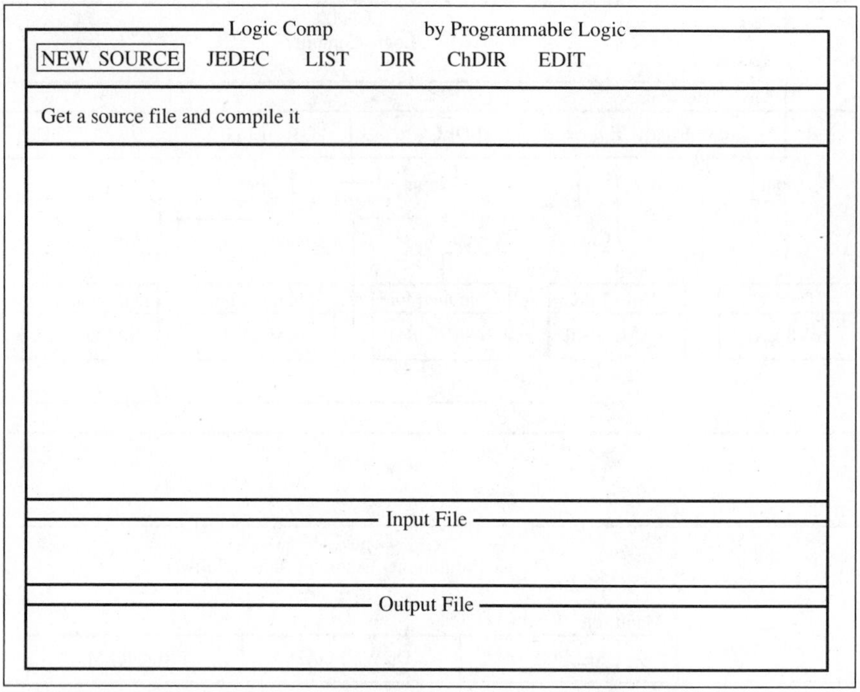

Logic Comp by Programmable Logic
NEW SOURCE JEDEC LIST DIR ChDIR EDIT
Get a source file and compile it
Input File
Output File

FIGURE 12-17 LC9000 Menu and Initial Screen (Courtesy of Programmable Logic Technologies, Inc.)

software. The software is simply loaded onto the hard drive or inserted into a floppy disk drive. From the directory where the LC9000 is located the user should type:

LC

and then hit the ENTER KEY. The LC9000 begins with the menu shown in Figure 12-17. The menu allows the user to select a source file, create a JEDEC file, create a document file, list the files in the current directory, change directories, and edit files.

12.4.2 Creating the Source File

The assembler software, the LC9000, requires a source file input to describe the logic function to be programmed into the PLD. The PLD source file can be created using any text editor that produces an ASCII file. The LC9000 has an editor that can be used to create the source file. The name of the

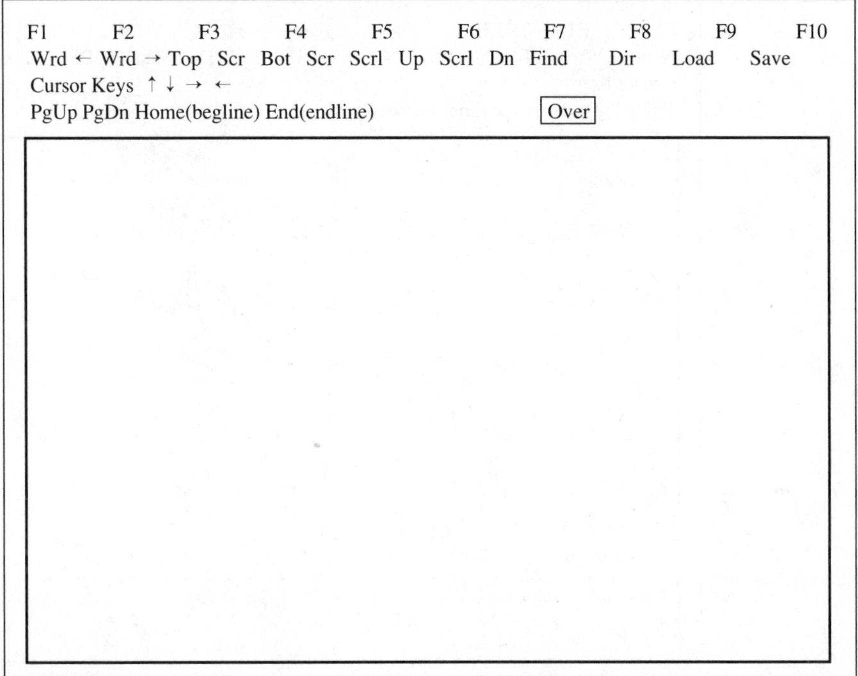

FIGURE 12-18 LC9000 Initial Editor Screen (Courtesy of Programmable Logic Technologies, Inc.)

source files must be limited to eight characters and have a filename extension of ".PLD".

To create or edit a source file using the LC9000, begin LC9000 by typing:

LC

from the directory where the LC9000 is located. When the menu appears, use the **ARROW KEYS** to move to the **EDIT** function. Then press the **ENTER KEY**. The first screen that will appear when one enters the LC9000 editor is shown in Figure 12-18.

The editor is in the "overwrite" mode. To change to the "insert" mode, hit the **INSERT KEY**. The editor screen in the insert mode is shown in Figure 12-19.

The source file can now be created by typing the appropriate commands with the editor in the insert mode. Save the source file by hitting the **F10** function key. The editor will ask for the name of the output file; enter the desired path and file name of the source file. The source file name is limited

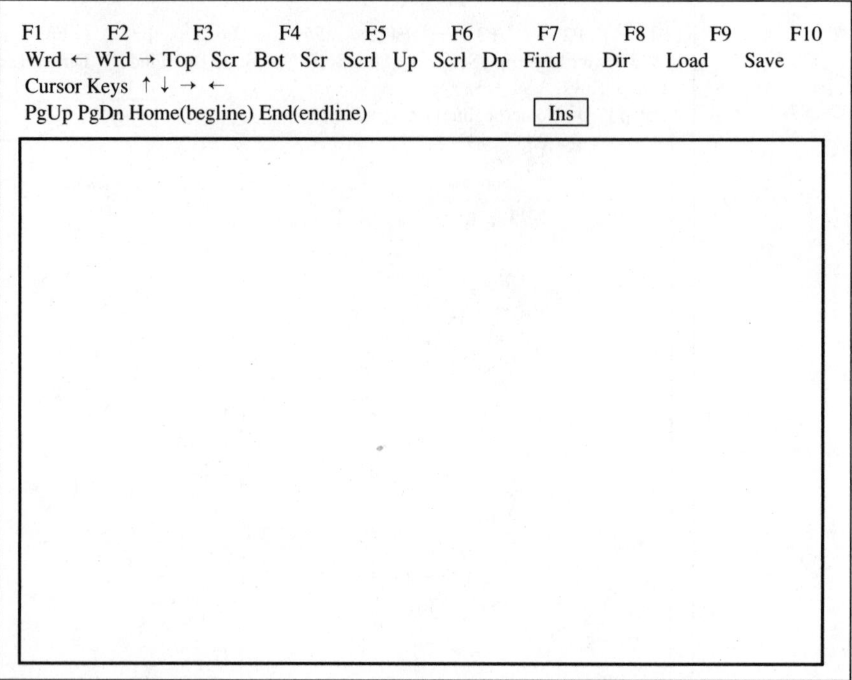

FIGURE 12-19 LC9000 Editor Screen in Insert Mode (Courtesy of Programmable Logic Technologies, Inc.)

to eight characters and must have the extension. **.PLD**. Exit the LC9000 editor by hitting the **ESCAPE KEY**.

The LC9000 editor does not create backup files, so be careful when editing files. Many functions are available for loading files, saving files, cutting, pasting, jumping to specific lines, and so on, through the function keys. The operation performed by each key is listed at the top of the editor screen. Additional functions are shown when the **SHIFT KEY** is pressed.

The source file defines the PLD to be programmed, the signal variable names, the input and output pin assignments, and the Boolean expressions to be programmed into the PLD. The LC9000 requires a specific file format for the source file. Key words must be used to specify the device and Boolean equations and to assign input and output variables to pins and other important parameters in the file. Table 12-5 lists the key words that are reserved for special use in source files compiled by LC9000.

The Boolean expressions must be specified in terms of symbols, or **operators**, that are recognized by the LC9000 software. These Boolean operators are shown in Table 12-6, and the formats required for the logic equations to program the GAL16V8 or GAL16V8A are shown in Table 12-7.

TABLE 12-5 LC9000 Key Words

DEVICE
TITLE
NAME
SIGNATURE
PIN
NODE
BURIED

All logic functions in the source file must be specified in the SOP form. Parentheses are allowed in individual product terms in the SOP function so long as the function does not exceed the number of product terms allowed by the architecture of the device for the specific operating mode. The product of sums (POS) form of logic expressions is not allowed.

Active-LOW SOP equations and active-LOW output logic functions such as NAND, NOR, and XNOR are specified with the ! symbol preceding the output variable name.

TABLE 12-6 LC9000 Boolean Operators

Operation	Symbol	Example
NOT	!	!A
AND	&	A & B
		A&B
OR	¦	A ¦ B
		A¦B
NAND		!(A&B)
NOR		!(A¦B)
XOR		!A & B ¦ A & !B
XNOR		!A & !B ¦ A & B

The ! symbol can be used to invert an input variable or to indicate active-LOW for an output variable.

TABLE 12-7 LC9000 Boolean Expression Formats to Be Used with the GAL16V8A

Input equation to a combinational output:

⟨Output Variable Name⟩ = ⟨Boolean Equation⟩*;

Input equation to a D flip-flip:
(This is required in the registered mode.)

⟨Output Variable⟩.D = ⟨Boolean Equation⟩;

Output Enable expression associated with a specific output pin:
(This is required for all outputs in the complex mode† and for combinational outputs in the registered mode.)

⟨Output Variable Name⟩.OE = ⟨Boolean Equation⟩;

* Boolean equations can extend beyond one line. When the equation is completed, it must end with a semicolon.

† In the complex mode the output enable line is active when the Boolean expression is true.

DeMorgan's theorems can be applied to convert logic functions from a POS format to the SOP format required by the LC9000. For instance, the logic equations in the GAL16V8 or GAL16V8A are limited to seven or eight terms, depending on the architecture of the specific operating mode. Karnaugh-mapping techniques, DeMorgan's theorems, and Boolean algebra rules can be applied to simplify equations and reduce the number of product terms.

The input and output signal variables, clock, and output enable signal must be assigned to the appropriate pins of the PLD. As specified in Table 12-4 for the GAL16V8 and GAL16V8A, the clock input for synchronous circuits must be assigned to pin 1. The output enable signal must be assigned to pin 11 when operating the device in the registered mode.

Assigning a variable to an input-only pin requires that it be used only as an input function. Assigning a variable to a bidirectional I/O pin allows it to be used as either an input or output in a sequential logic circuit. This feature is important in sequential logic designs when feedback terms in the logic equation are required.

Source files created for the LC9000 to program a GAL16V8 or GAL16V8A must have the following format. The semicolon at the end of each statement is required.

DEVICE 16V8;

TITLE (file title); The TITLE keyword is optional. If it is included, it will be printed at the top of each page of the document file.

NAME (file name); The NAME keyword is optional. It is treated like the TITLE.

PIN (first pin #) = (pin name);

⋮

PIN (last pin #) = (pin name);

The PIN statement assigns a name to each pin of the device. All variables to be used in Boolean equations must be assigned a pin. Unused pins do not require a name. The pin name must be unique and must begin with an alphabetic character. The name can include letters and numbers up to 16 characters. The program does not recognize the difference between uppercase and lowercase letters.

⟨Output Variable⟩ = ⟨Boolean Expression⟩;

Equations assign a Boolean expression to an output variable. The forms of the Boolean expressions and equations are listed in Table 12-7.

/*Comments ... */ Comments are denoted by the "star-slash" symbol. Comments can be placed on any line and can extend beyond one line so long as they end with the */ symbol.

An example PLD source file listing specifying basic logic gate functions is shown in Example 12-2, Table 12-8.

■ EXAMPLE 12-2 LC9000 Sample Source File

Problem: Create a source file appropriate for the LC9000 to program a PLD with the following output equations:

$M = A\,B$ $N = C + D$ $P = A\,B$

$Q = C + D$ $R = E \oplus F$ $S = E \oplus F$

TABLE 12-8 Programmable Logic Device Source File Example 12-2

```
DEVICE 16V8;
TITLE Example 12-2;
NAME Logic Gate Example Source File;

/*  2 Input Pins           */

PIN 1 = A;
PIN 2 = B;
PIN 3 = C;
PIN 4 = D;
PIN 5 = E;
PIN 6 = F;

/*     Output Pins          */

PIN 19 = M;
PIN 18 = N;
PIN 17 = P;
PIN 16 = Q;
PIN 15 = R;
PIN 14 = S;

/*     Power and Ground             */

/*     It is not required that these be specified.*/

PIN 20 = VCC;
PIN 10 = GND;

/*     Boolean Expressions              */

M = A & B;              /*      M = A AND B            */
N = C ! D;              /*      N = C OR D             */
!P = A & B;             /*      P = A NAND B           */
                        /*      The NAND function can be
                                specified as an
                                active-LOW AND         */
!Q = C ! D;             /*      P = C NOR D            */
                        /*      The NOR function can be
                                specified as an
                                active-LOW OR */
R = !E & F ! E & ! F;        /*    R = E XOR F      */
S = E & F ! !E & !F;         /*    S = E XNOR F     */
```

Solution: The equations are all combinational, so the GAL16V8 or GAL16V8A should be operated in the simple mode. Define the device, assign pin numbers to each input and output variable, and specify the Boolean equations using the allowed operators. The source file is shown in Table 12-8. The GAL16V8 pin diagram is shown in Figure 12-20.

Logic Comp by Programmable Logic
Example 12-2
Logic Gate Example Source File

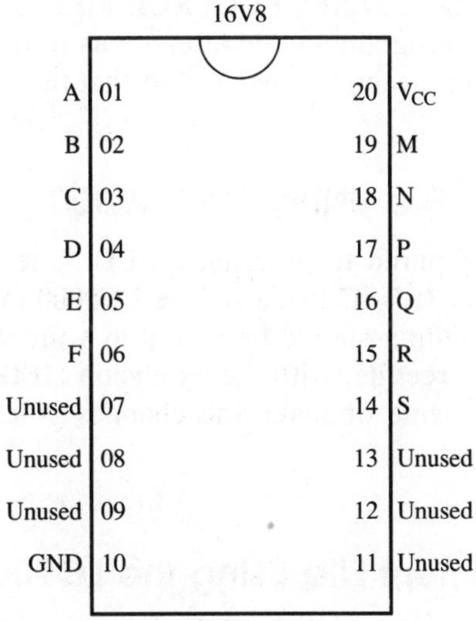

16V8

A	01	20	V_{CC}
B	02	19	M
C	03	18	N
D	04	17	P
E	05	16	Q
F	06	15	R
Unused	07	14	S
Unused	08	13	Unused
Unused	09	12	Unused
GND	10	11	Unused

FIGURE 12-20 Programmable Logic Device Pin Diagram Example 12-2

■

12.4.3 Compiling the Boolean Equations with LC9000

The Boolean equations listed in the source file must be compiled by the LC9000 prior to creating the JEDEC file for programming the PLD. If you are not already in LC9000, begin LC9000 by typing the command, **LC**, from the directory where the LC9000 program is located. If the LC9000 editor is used to create the source file, exit the editor and use the **ARROW KEYS** to highlight the menu option, **SELECT SOURCE FILE**, and hit the **ENTER KEY**. The system responds by asking for the name of the source file. Enter the path and file name of the source file, and hit the **ENTER KEY**.

If syntax errors exist in the source file, the program will respond:

Syntax errors. Compile aborted.

The errors are listed in an error file. The error file has the same file name as the source file, but with the extension **.ERR**. Inspect the error file by using the LC9000 editor. Load in the error file using the **F9** function key. After reading the error file, load in the source file, again using the **F9** function key, and make the necessary changes. (There is no need to exit the first file before loading the second one.) Be sure to save this new version of the source file by using the **F10** function key. Exit the editor using the **ESCAPE KEY**.

Compile the corrected source file again by using the **ARROW KEYS** to highlight the operation, **SELECT SOURCE FILE**. If the file has no syntax errors, the LC9000 program will update you as to the operations being performed. Within a few seconds it will report that the equations are compiled.

12.4.4 Creating a JEDEC File Using the LC9000

A JEDEC file is required to program a PLD. Use the **ARROW KEYS** to select the operation **JEDEC** listed on the LC9000 menu. The program will ask if the JEDEC output should be stored in a file with the same path and file name as the source file, with the extension **.JED**. Hit the **ENTER KEY** to accept this file name or make the changes you need and then hit the **ENTER KEY**.

12.4.5 Creating a Document File Using the LC9000

A document file is a verification of the equations that were compiled and used to create the JEDEC file. The document file includes a listing of the Boolean equations and a pin diagram showing the assigned pins on the PLD.

Create a document file by using the **ARROW KEYS** to highlight the **LIST** option on the LC9000 menu. The program will ask if the document file should be stored in a file with the same path and file name as the source file, with the extension **.DOC**. Hit the **ENTER KEY** to accept this file name or make the changes you need and then hit the **ENTER KEY**.

Exit the LC9000 program by hitting the **ESCAPE KEY**.

12.4.6 Programmable Logic Device Programmers

The JEDEC file compiled by the LC9000 must be **downloaded** or transferred to the hardware device where the programming will be done. The PLD programmer programs the PLD by applying voltage pulses to erase or eliminate any prior fuse connections. This erasure procedure takes 50 ms to complete for E^2PLDs such as the GAL devices. Following the erasure, the PLD is programmed as the programmer applies voltage pulses to create the fuse connections specified by the JEDEC file.

12.4.7 Programming the GAL16V8 Using the Logic Lab Programmer

The Logic Lab programmer by Programmable Logic Technologies is used at Purdue University to program the GAL16V8, the GAL16V8A, and other PLDs. Logic Lab software is used to download the JEDEC file and program the device.

The Logic Lab programmer has two sockets to program either the 20-pin or the 24-pin GAL devices. The serial cable on the programmer must be connected to the serial port on the PC, and the programmer must be plugged into the AC power. To establish communications between the PC and the programmer, type the following command from the directory where the Logic Lab software is located:

LL

When the communications link is established between the PC and the programmer, the Logic Lab menu appears, as shown in Figure 12-21.

The Logic Lab software allows you to select the device to be programmed, download the JEDEC file to the programmer, program the device, verify the accuracy of the fuses programmed in the PLD, and perform other operations. The **F1** function key provides a help directory.

To program the PLD using Logic Lab software, you should perform or select the following steps from the Logic Lab menu:

1. *Insert* the PLD into the device programmer and latch it into the socket.
2. *Select* the device number corresponding to the PLD you are using.
3. *Download* the JEDEC file to the buffer in the device programmer.
4. *Program* the PLD.
5. *Verify* the programming operation.
6. *Remove* the device from the programmer and verify its operation by testing the circuit.

```
              Logic Lab            Serial# 00000 : Device is 16V8
   Esc exit | F1 help | Checksum = 0000 | Device not secured after programming
 ---------------------------------- Main Menu ----------------------------------
 [Select] Clear Upload Download Edit LOAD VERIFY PROGRAM MASTER Secure

 Select a device (16V8, 20V8, 22V10, 39V18, 16Z8 or a RAL)
```

FIGURE 12-21 Logic Lab Menu (Courtesy of Programmable Logic Technologies, Inc.)

Use the **ARROW KEYS** to highlight the operation to be performed, and then hit the **ENTER KEY** to perform that operation. When the operation **DOWNLOAD** is to be performed, the Logic Lab software will ask for the name of the JEDEC file. Enter the entire path and file name of the JEDEC file.

Once the download is completed, be certain that the PLD is securely latched into the socket of the programmer. Pin 1 should be in the upper left corner. Select the **PROGRAM** operation and hit the **ENTER KEY**. The program counter will report how many times the device has been programmed.

Verify that the fuses programmed in the PLD match the JEDEC file in the buffer of the programmer. Use the **ARROW KEYS** to highlight the **VERIFY** operation and hit the **ENTER KEY**.

Once the device has been programmed and verified, it can be removed from the programmer socket and tested. Since the GAL device is a CMOS device, it should be handled with care and kept in conductive foam when being transported.

Section Self-Test

1. What is the purpose of the LC9000 software?
2. What is the purpose of the Logic Lab software?

ANSWERS

- The LC9000 is used to create a source file, compile the source file, create a JEDEC file, and create a document file.
- The Logic Lab software is used to control the Logic Lab programmer from the PC. It is used to select the device to be programmed, download the JEDEC file from the PC to the programmer, program the PLD in the socket of the programmer, and verify that the programmed fuses match the information in the JEDEC file.

12-5 DESIGN TECHNIQUES USING PROGRAMMABLE LOGIC DEVICES

Design techniques to include PLDs in hardware logic designs are based on defining the logic operations in terms of SOP equations. Other logic functions such as arithmetic, comparator, decoding, and encoding operations must all be specified as SOP logic equations.

Logic circuits designed for PLDs are not constrained by the standard logic hardware functions normally available. Now the PLD logic design must fit the architecture of the PLD selected.

The AND-OR array of the PLD determines the maximum number of product terms in SOP equations and the number of input variables allowed in the AND terms. The GAL16V8 and GAL16V8A PLDs allows up to eight product terms for each output in the simple mode, eight product terms for each registered output in the registered mode, seven product terms for each output in the complex mode, and seven product terms for each combinational output in the registered mode.

Boolean algebra, DeMorgan's theorems, and Karnaugh-mapping techniques can be used to simplify or modify logic equations that are too large for the AND-OR array of the PLD. However, in many logic designs no minimization of the SOP expression will be needed if the number of product terms in the truth table do not exceed the seven or eight allowed by the GAL16V8 or GAL16V8A.

The following steps should be taken when designing logic circuits for PLD implementation:

1. *Define the logic operation in a truth table or in a present state-next state table.*
2. *Select a PLD.* Be sure to check for a sufficient number of input pins, registered and combinational output pins, feedback, tristate output control, product term limitation, and clock or trigger characteristics. Also, examine the operating characteristics of the PLD, such as speed, current, power consumption, and so on.
3. *Determine the Boolean equations of the output functions.* Simplify and minimize the equations if necessary.
4. *Create a source file.* Assign the pin numbers and define the Boolean equations with the operators required by the development software.
5. *Compile the source file, create a JEDEC file, and create a document file.*
6. *Program the device.*
7. *Test the device.*

Section 12.6 features logic designs using the GAL16V8 or GAL16V8A in combinational circuit applications. Section 12.7 features logic designs using the GAL16V8 or GAL16V8A in sequential logic circuit applications.

12-6 PROGRAMMABLE LOGIC DEVICE COMBINATIONAL LOGIC APPLICATIONS

The combinational logic applications shown in this section include general combinational logic functions specified in a truth table, encoders, decoders, code converters, and multiplexers. Selected PLD source files and document files created for the LC9000 logic compiler are listed in Appendix D for reference.

The GAL16V8 and the GAL16V8A can be used to create combinational logic functions by operating in the simple mode. The architecture for the simple mode of operation was specified in Table 12-2(a) and in Figure 12-8 for the GAL16V8A, and in Table 12-2(b) and in Figure 12-9 for the GAL16V8.

12.6.1 Basic Logic Gate Functions Using Programmable Logic Devices

Programmable logic devices can be used as single-chip replacements for logic designs that consist of only basic logic functions, such as those discussed in Chapter 3. The PLD implementation of such designs begins with the truth table specification of the logic function. The SOP equations are specified directly from the truth table definition of the function if no simplification is required. K-maps or Boolean algebra techniques are used for simplification to reduce the number and size of AND terms if required, in order to fit the AND-OR array of the PLD.

■ EXAMPLE 12-3 Combinational Logic Functions

Problem: Implement the problems shown in Examples 3-26 and 3-28 with a GAL16V8 or GAL16V8A PLD.

Solution: The problems in Examples 3-26 and 3-28 consisted of a 3-input and a 4-input logic function. Both functions can be implemented with one PLD. The logic functions are defined in truth tables:

A	B	C	L
0	0	0	1
0	0	1	1
0	1	0	0
0	1	1	1
1	0	0	0
1	0	1	0
1	1	0	0
1	1	1	1

A	B	C	D	M
0	0	0	0	0
0	0	0	1	0
0	0	1	0	0
0	0	1	1	1
0	1	0	0	1
0	1	0	1	1
0	1	1	0	1
0	1	1	1	1
1	0	0	0	1
1	0	0	1	1
1	0	1	0	0
1	0	1	1	1
1	1	0	0	1
1	1	0	1	1
1	1	1	0	1
1	1	1	1	0

TABLE 12-9 Programmable Logic Device Source File Example 12-3

```
DEVICE 16V8;
TITLE Example 12-3;
NAME Combinational Logic Functions L and M;

/*      Inputs          */

PIN 1    =    A;
PIN 2    =    B;
PIN 3    =    C;
PIN 4    =    D;

/*      Outputs         */

PIN 12   =    L;
PIN 13   =    M;

PIN 20   =    VCC;
PIN 10   =    GND;

/*      Boolean Equations      */

L    =    !A & !B & !C ¦ !A & !B & C ¦
          !A & B & C ¦ A & B & C;

!M   =    !A & !B & !C & !D ¦ !A & !B & !C & D ¦
          !A & !B & C & !D ¦ A & !B & C & !D ¦
          A & B & C & D;

/*      L is defined as active-HIGH. M is defined as active-LOW in the
        Boolean Equations to eliminate the need for simplification      */
```

$$L = \bar{A}\,\bar{B}\,\bar{C} + \bar{A}\,\bar{B}\,C + \bar{A}\,B\,C + A\,B\,C$$

$$\bar{M} = \bar{A}\,\bar{B}\,\bar{C}\,\bar{D} + \bar{A}\,\bar{B}\,\bar{C}\,D + \bar{A}\,\bar{B}\,C\,\bar{D} + A\,\bar{B}\,C\,\bar{D} + A\,B\,C\,D$$

Although the equations can be reduced, no further simplification is required. Table 12-9 contains a PLD source file to program a GAL16V8 or GAL16V8A for the functions L and M to be used with the LC9000 assembler. The PLD pin diagram is shown in Figure 12-22.

To compare the PLD implementation of these logic functions with the design produced using standard logic, determine the number of ICs required to implement L and M using basic logic gates. If L were simplified with a K-map and built as a two-level NAND circuit, it would require two ICs: the 7400 and the 7404. If M were simplified with a K-map and built as a two-

Logic Comp by Programmable Logic
Example 12-3
Combinational Logic Functions L and M

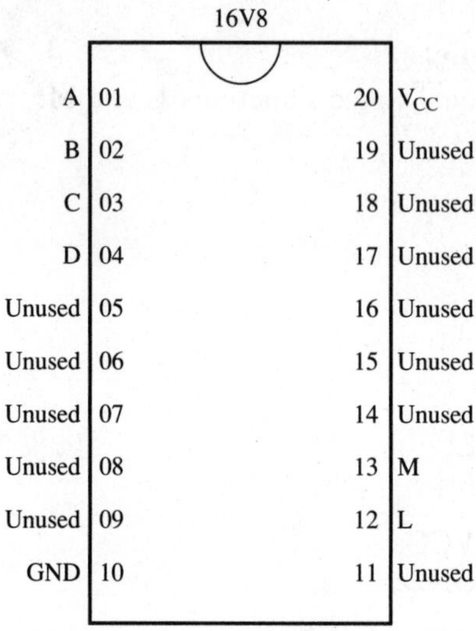

FIGURE 12-22 Programmable Logic Device Pin Diagram Example 12-3

level NOR circuit, it would require three ICs: the 7427, the 74260, and the 7404. The standard logic implementation of L and M requires five ICs; the PLD implementation of L and M requires one IC.

■

■ EXAMPLE 12-4 Ten-Input OR Function

Problem: Define the PLD equation to specify a 10-input OR function to be programmed into a GAL16V8.

Solution: A 10-input OR function can take on the following Boolean form:

$$Y = A + B + C + D + E + F + G + H + J + K$$

This form, however, cannot be used to program the GAL16V8 or GAL16V8A since it has more than eight terms that must be ORed together.

DeMorgan's theorems can be applied to convert the equation to a single term:

$$\overline{Y} = \overline{A}\,\overline{B}\,\overline{C}\,\overline{D}\,\overline{E}\,\overline{F}\,\overline{G}\,\overline{H}\,\overline{J}\,\overline{K}$$

The source file is shown in Table 12-10.

TABLE 12-10 Programmable Logic Device Source File Example 12-4

```
DEVICE 16V8;
TITLE Example 12-4;
NAME Ten-Input OR;

/*    This source file defines a ten-input OR
function as an active-LOW ten-input NOR.
The logic compiler, LC9000, converts the Boolean
expression to an equivalent ten-input AND function
according to DeMorgan's Theorem. The ten-input AND
function can be created with the GAL16V8
architecture.    */

/*    Inputs                    */

PIN  1 = A;
PIN  2 = B;
PIN  3 = C;
PIN  4 = D;
PIN  5 = E;
PIN  6 = F;
PIN  7 = G;
PIN  8 = H;
PIN  9 = J;
PIN 11 = K;

/*    Output                    */

PIN 12 = Y;

/*    Power and Ground          */

PIN 20 = VCC;
PIN 10 = GND;

/*    Boolean Equation          */

!Y = !A & !B & !C & !D & !E & !F & !G & !H & !J &
     !K;
```

■

12.6.2 Medium Scale Integration Combinational Logic Functions Using Programmable Logic Devices

Logic functions normally performed by MSI logic ICs can be programmed for PLDs by specifying the function in a truth table form and determining the Boolean expression for each output.

The Boolean definition for several MSI functions, such as decoding, encoding, code conversion, multiplexing, and demultiplexing, are specified in Chapter 3 in a number of example problems. Many other special functions performed by MSI circuits are defined in Chapters 4, 5, and 6. By specifying the logic function in a truth table format, these problems can be converted to PLD implementation.

Due to the simplicity and limitations of the LC9000 assembly software, functions requiring numerous levels of Exclusive-OR operations will be avoided since the expressions must be reduced to the basic SOP format with no parentheses. No Boolean operator is defined for the Exclusive-OR operation in the LC9000 assembler. Other assembler software could be used to implement Exclusive-OR operations.

■ EXAMPLE 12-5 Programmable Logic Device Decimal-to-Binary Priority Encoder

Problem: Design a priority encoder circuit to encode ten active-LOW input switches and output the binary value corresponding to that input switch.

Solution: Define the priority encoder in a truth table and specify the outputs as Boolean functions:

Input Switches										Outputs			
0	1	2	3	4	5	6	7	8	9	D	C	B	A
0	1	1	1	1	1	1	1	1	1	0	0	0	0
X	0	1	1	1	1	1	1	1	1	0	0	0	1
X	X	0	1	1	1	1	1	1	1	0	0	1	0
X	X	X	0	1	1	1	1	1	1	0	0	1	1
X	X	X	X	0	1	1	1	1	1	0	1	0	0
X	X	X	X	X	0	1	1	1	1	0	1	0	1
X	X	X	X	X	X	0	1	1	1	0	1	1	0
X	X	X	X	X	X	X	0	1	1	0	1	1	1
X	X	X	X	X	X	X	X	0	1	1	0	0	0
X	X	X	X	X	X	X	X	X	0	1	0	0	1

$$D = \overline{9} + \overline{8}\,9$$

$$C = \overline{7}\,8\,9 + \overline{6}\,7\,8\,9 + \overline{5}\,6\,7\,8\,9 + \overline{4}\,5\,6\,7\,8\,9$$

$$B = \overline{7}\,8\,9 + \overline{6}\,7\,8\,9 + \overline{3}\,4\,5\,6\,7\,8\,9 + \overline{2}\,3\,4\,5\,6\,7\,8\,9$$

$$A = \overline{9} + \overline{7}\,8\,9 + \overline{5}\,6\,7\,8\,9 + \overline{3}\,4\,5\,6\,7\,8\,9 + \overline{1}\,2\,3\,4\,5\,6\,7\,8\,9$$

The PLD source file appears in Table 12-11, and the PLD pin diagram is shown in Figure 12-23.

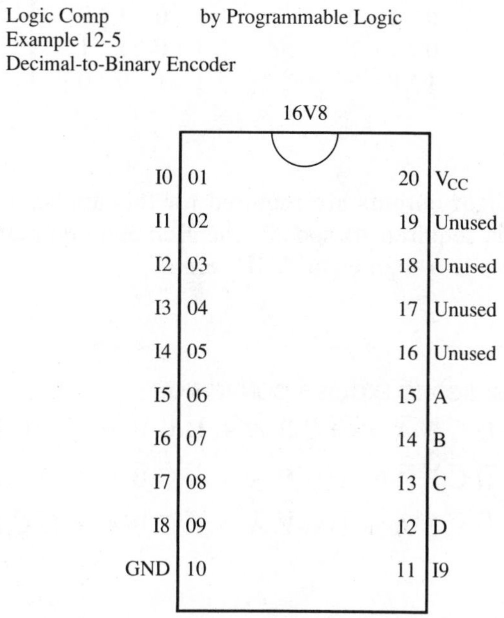

Logic Comp by Programmable Logic
Example 12-5
Decimal-to-Binary Encoder

16V8

I0	01	20	V_{CC}
I1	02	19	Unused
I2	03	18	Unused
I3	04	17	Unused
I4	05	16	Unused
I5	06	15	A
I6	07	14	B
I7	08	13	C
I8	09	12	D
GND	10	11	I9

FIGURE 12-23 Programmable Logic Device Pin Diagram Example 12-5

■

■ EXAMPLE 12-6 Binary Coded Decimal-Excess 3 Two-Way Code Converter

Problem: Design a two-way code converter to convert BCD to Excess-3 and to convert Excess-3 to BCD.

Solution: Define the code converter in a truth table and determine the output Boolean functions.

BCD to Excess-3

D	C	B	A	W	X	Y	Z
0	0	0	0	0	0	1	1
0	0	0	1	0	1	0	0
0	0	1	0	0	1	0	1
0	0	1	1	0	1	1	0
0	1	0	0	0	1	1	1
0	1	0	1	1	0	0	0
0	1	1	0	1	0	0	1
0	1	1	1	1	0	1	0
1	0	0	0	1	0	1	1
1	0	0	1	1	1	0	0

Excess-3 to BCD

R	S	T	U	H	G	F	E
0	0	1	1	0	0	0	0
0	1	0	0	0	0	0	1
0	1	0	1	0	0	1	0
0	1	1	0	0	0	1	1
0	1	1	1	0	1	0	0
1	0	0	0	0	1	0	1
1	0	0	1	0	1	1	0
1	0	1	0	0	1	1	1
1	0	1	1	1	0	0	0
1	1	0	0	1	0	0	1

Eight inputs and eight outputs are required for this application. However, no simplification is required to specify the Boolean equations since each SOP expression has less than eight AND terms.

BOOLEAN EQUATIONS: BCD TO EXCESS-3 CONVERSION

$$W = \overline{D}\,C\,\overline{B}\,A + \overline{D}\,C\,B\,\overline{A} + \overline{D}\,C\,B\,A + D\,\overline{C}\,\overline{B}\,\overline{A} + D\,\overline{C}\,\overline{B}\,A$$

$$X = \overline{D}\,\overline{C}\,\overline{B}\,A + \overline{D}\,\overline{C}\,B\,\overline{A} + \overline{D}\,\overline{C}\,B\,A + \overline{D}\,C\,\overline{B}\,\overline{A} + \overline{D}\,C\,\overline{B}\,A$$

$$Y = \overline{D}\,\overline{C}\,\overline{B}\,\overline{A} + \overline{D}\,\overline{C}\,B\,A + \overline{D}\,C\,\overline{B}\,\overline{A} + \overline{D}\,C\,B\,A + D\,\overline{C}\,\overline{B}\,\overline{A}$$

$$Z = \overline{A}$$

BOOLEAN EQUATIONS: EXCESS-3 TO BCD CONVERSION

$$H = R\,\overline{S}\,T\,U + R\,S\,\overline{T}\,\overline{U}$$

$$G = \overline{R}\,S\,T\,U + R\,\overline{S}\,\overline{T}\,\overline{U} + R\,\overline{S}\,\overline{T}\,U + R\,\overline{S}\,T\,\overline{U}$$

$$F = \overline{R}\,S\,\overline{T}\,U + \overline{R}\,S\,T\,\overline{U} + R\,\overline{S}\,\overline{T}\,U + R\,\overline{S}\,T\,\overline{U}$$

$$E = \overline{U}$$

The PLD implementation requires that the Boolean equations be converted to the operators recognized by the Logic Lab software in order to program the PLD. The source file for the BCD-Excess-3 converter is shown in Table 12-12, and the PLD pin diagram is shown in Figure 12-24.

TABLE 12-11 Programmable Logic Device Source File Example 12-5

```
DEVICE 16V8;
TITLE Example 12-5;
NAME Decimal-to-Binary Encoder;
/*    This source file defines a decimal-to-binary
priority encoder. The encoder accepts the inputs
from ten active-LOW switches and outputs the
corresponding binary value.    */

/*    Inputs        */

PIN  1 = I0;
PIN  2 = I1;
PIN  3 = I2;
PIN  4 = I3;
PIN  5 = I4;
PIN  6 = I5;
PIN  7 = I6;
PIN  8 = I7;
PIN  9 = I8;
PIN 11 = I9;

/*    Outputs       */

PIN 12 = D;
PIN 13 = C;
PIN 14 = B;
PIN 15 = A;

/*    Power and ground     */

PIN 20 = VCC;
PIN 10 = GND;

/*    Boolean Equations */

D = !I9 # !I8 & I9 ;

C = !I7 & I8 & I9 # !I6 & I7 & I8 & I9
    # !I5 & I6 & I7 & I8 & I9
    # !I4 & I5 & I6 & I7 & I8 & I9 ;

B = !I7 & I8 & I9 # !I6 & I7 & I8 & I9
    # !I3 & I4 & I5 & I6 & I7 & I8 & I9
    # !I2 & I3 & I4 & I5 & I6 & I7 & I8 & I9 ;

A = !I9 # !I7 & I8 & I9
    # !I5 & I6 & I7 & I8 & I9
    # !I3 & I4 & I5 & I6 & I7 & I8 & I9
    # !I1 & I2 & I3 & I4 & I5 & I6 & I7 & I8 & I9 ;
```

TABLE 12-12 Programmable Logic Device Source File Example 12-6

```
DEVICE 16V8;
TITLE Example 12-6;
NAME BCD-to-Excess 3 Code Converter;
/*      This source file defines a BCD-to-Excess 3 code converter.
        It converts BCD-to-Excess 3, as well as convert Excess 3-
        to-BCD.          */

/*      BCD-to-Excess 3 Inputs                */

PIN  1 = D;
PIN  2 = C;
PIN  3 = B;
PIN  4 = A;

/*      BCD-to-Excess 3 Outputs               */

PIN 19 = W;
PIN 18 = X;
PIN 17 = Y;
PIN 16 = Z;

/*      Excess 3-to-BCD Inputs                */

PIN  5 = R;
PIN  6 = S;
PIN  7 = T;
PIN  8 = U;

/*      Excess 3-to-BCD Outputs               */

PIN 15 = H;
PIN 14 = G;
PIN 13 = F;
PIN 12 = E;

/*      Power and Ground              */

PIN 20 = VCC;
PIN 10 = GND;

/*      BCD-to-Excess 3 Boolean Equations             */

W = !D & C & !B & A ! !D & C & B & !A ! !D & C & B & A
    ! D & !C & !B & !A ! D & !C & !B & A ;

X = !D & !C & !B & A ! !D & !C & B & !A ! !D & !C & B & A
    ! !D & C & !B & A ! D & !C & !B & A ;
```

TABLE 12-12 Programmable Logic Device Source File Example 12-6 *(continued)*

```
Y = !D & !C & !B & !A ¦ !D & !C & B & A ¦ !D & C & !B & !A
    ¦ !D & C & B & A ¦ D & !C & !B & !A;

Z = !A;

/*  Excess 3-to-BCD Boolean Equations           */

H = R & !S & T & U ¦ R & S & !T & !U;

G = !R & S & T & U ¦ R & !S & !T & !U
    ¦ R & !S & !T & U ¦ R & !S & T & !U;

F = !R & S & !T & U ¦ !R & S & T & !U
    ¦ R & !S & !T & U ¦ R & !S & T & !U;

E = !U;
```

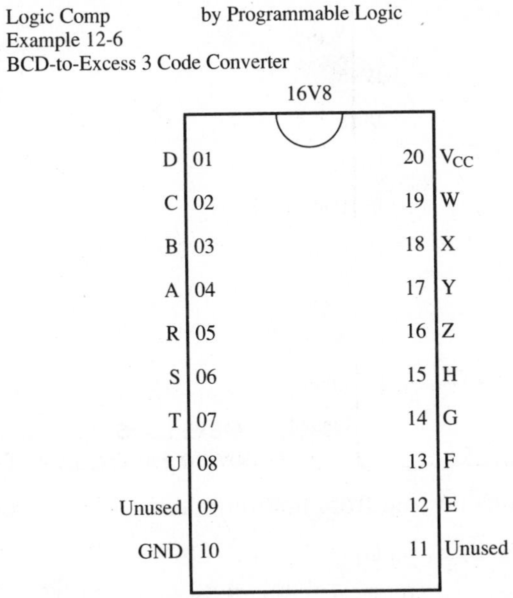

Logic Comp by Programmable Logic
Example 12-6
BCD-to-Excess 3 Code Converter

16V8

D	01	20	V_{CC}
C	02	19	W
B	03	18	X
A	04	17	Y
R	05	16	Z
S	06	15	H
T	07	14	G
U	08	13	F
Unused	09	12	E
GND	10	11	Unused

FIGURE 12-24 Programmable Logic Device Pin Diagram Example 12-6

■

■ EXAMPLE 12-7 Eight-to-One Multiplexer Programmable Logic Device (MUX)

Problem: Design an 8-to-1 multiplexer (MUX) to be implemented with the GAL16V8.

Solution: An 8-to-1 MUX requires three select inputs and eight data inputs. Two outputs can be provided for both the true and inverted outputs.

S_2	S_1	S_0	Y	W
0	0	0	D_0	$\overline{D_0}$
0	0	1	D_1	$\overline{D_1}$
0	1	0	D_2	$\overline{D_2}$
0	1	1	D_3	$\overline{D_3}$
1	0	0	D_4	$\overline{D_4}$
1	0	1	D_5	$\overline{D_5}$
1	1	0	D_6	$\overline{D_6}$
1	1	1	D_7	$\overline{D_7}$

Logic Comp by Programmable Logic
Example 12-7
8-to-1 Multiplier

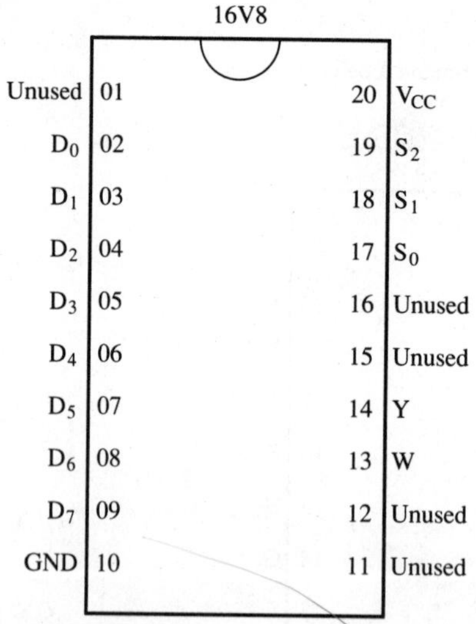

16V8

	Pin	Pin	
Unused	01	20	V_{CC}
D_0	02	19	S_2
D_1	03	18	S_1
D_2	04	17	S_0
D_3	05	16	Unused
D_4	06	15	Unused
D_5	07	14	Y
D_6	08	13	W
D_7	09	12	Unused
GND	10	11	Unused

FIGURE 12-25 Programmable Logic Device Pin Diagram Example 12-7

Multiplexer equations derived from the truth table:

$$Y = \overline{S}_2\,\overline{S}_1\,\overline{S}_0\,D_0 + \overline{S}_2\,\overline{S}_1\,S_0\,D_1 + \overline{S}_2\,S_1\,\overline{S}_0\,D_2$$
$$+ \overline{S}_2\,S_1\,S_0\,D_3 + S_2\,\overline{S}_1\,\overline{S}_0\,D_4 + S_2\,\overline{S}_1\,S_0\,D_5$$
$$+ S_2\,S_1\,\overline{S}_0\,D_6 + S_2\,S_1\,S_0\,D_7$$

$$W = \overline{Y}$$

■

TABLE 12-13 Programmable Logic Device Source File Example 12-7

```
DEVICE 16V8;
TITLE Example 12-7;
NAME 8-to-1 Multiplexer;

/*    This source file defines an 8-to-1 mux
      that has three select inputs, 8 data inputs,
      and both the true and complemented outputs.          */

/*    Data Inputs          */

PIN  2 = D0;
PIN  3 = D1;
PIN  4 = D2;
PIN  5 = D3;
PIN  6 = D4;
PIN  7 = D5;
PIN  8 = D6;
PIN  9 = D7;

/*    Select Inputs        */

PIN 19 = S2;
PIN 18 = S1;
PIN 17 = S0;

/*    Outputs              */

PIN 14 = Y;
PIN 13 = W;

/*    Power and Ground     */

PIN 20 = VCC;
PIN 10 = GND;

/*    Boolean Equations    */

Y =   !S2 & !S1 & !S0 & D0 ! !S2 & !S1 & S0 & D1
      ! !S2 & S1 & !S0 & D2 ! !S2 & S1 & S0 & D3
      ! S2 & !S1 & !S0 & D4 ! S2 & !S1 & S0 & D5
      ! S2 & S1 & !S0 & D6 ! S2 & S1 & S0 & D7;

!W =        !S2 & !S1 & !S0 & D0 ! !S2 & !S1 & S0 & D1
      ! !S2 & S1 & !S0 & D2 ! !S2 & S1 & S0 & D3
      ! S2 & !S1 & !S0 & D4 ! S2 & !S1 & S0 & D5
      ! S2 & S1 & !S0 & D6 ! S2 & S1 & S0 & D7;
```

■ EXAMPLE 12-8 Quad Two-Input Multiplexer

Problem: Design a quad 2-input multiplexer to be implemented with the GAL16V8 PLD.

Solution: Specify the device operation in the form of a truth table to derive the appropriate Boolean expressions. A quad 2-input multiplexer requires one select input, eight data inputs, and four outputs:

S	Y_3	Y_2	Y_1	Y_0
0	A_3	A_2	A_1	A_0
1	B_3	B_2	B_1	B_0

The Boolean expressions can be specified directly from the truth table:

$$Y_3 = \overline{S}\,A_3 + S\,B_3$$

$$Y_2 = \overline{S}\,A_2 + S\,B_2$$

$$Y_1 = \overline{S}\,A_1 + S\,B_1$$

$$Y_0 = \overline{S}\,A_0 + S\,B_0$$

The PLD source file for the quad 2-input multiplexer is shown in Table 12-14. The PLD pin diagram is shown in Figure 12-26.

■

Programmable logic devices are used in most digital systems as the "glue chips" required to interface one logic block to another. The logic blocks can be MSI circuits, such as adders, comparators, and other circuits studied earlier in the text, or they can be microprocessors, memory ICs, or other complex logic devices.

In Chapter 6 adder and comparator circuits were used in numerous applications that required additional logic gates. A single PLD, such as the GAL16V8 or the GAL16V8A, can be used to implement logic functions to be input into the MSI device.

TABLE 12-14 Programmable Logic Device Source File Example 12-8

```
DEVICE 16V8;
TITLE Example 12-8;
NAME Quad 2-input Multiplexer;

/*    This source file defines a four-output
      multiplexer that switches one of two inputs to each
      output.     */

/*    Data Inputs — A Word             */

PIN  2 = A3;
PIN  3 = A2;
PIN  4 = A1;
PIN  5 = A0;

/*    Data Inputs — B Word             */

PIN  6 = B3;
PIN  7 = B2;
PIN  8 = B1;
PIN  9 = B0;

/*    Select Input          */

PIN 19 = S ;

/*    Outputs          */

PIN 15 = Y3;
PIN 14 = Y2;
PIN 13 = Y1;
PIN 12 = Y0;

/*    Power and Ground            */

PIN 20 = VCC ;
PIN 10 = GND ;

/*    Boolean Equations           */

Y3 = !S & A3 ! S & B3;
Y2 = !S & A2 ! S & B2;
Y1 = !S & A1 ! S & B1;
Y0 = !S & A0 ! S & B0;
```

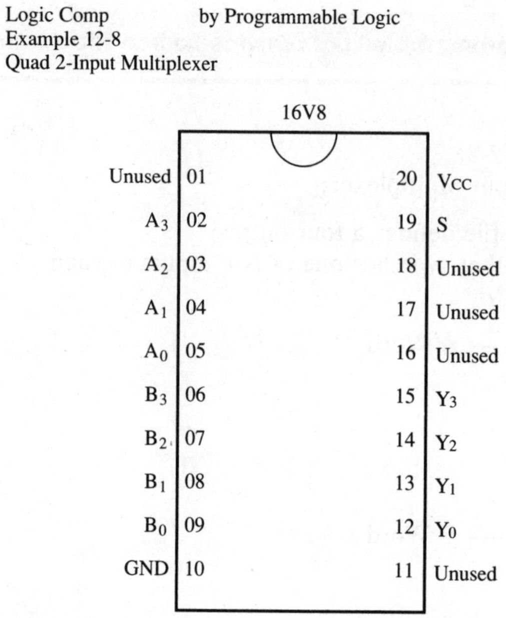

Logic Comp by Programmable Logic
Example 12-8
Quad 2-Input Multiplexer

16V8

Signal	Pin	Pin	Signal
Unused	01	20	Vcc
A_3	02	19	S
A_2	03	18	Unused
A_1	04	17	Unused
A_0	05	16	Unused
B_3	06	15	Y_3
B_2	07	14	Y_2
B_1	08	13	Y_1
B_0	09	12	Y_0
GND	10	11	Unused

FIGURE 12-26 Pin Diagram Example 12-8

■ EXAMPLE 12-9 Programmable Logic Device, Comparator, and Adder Circuit Application

Problem: Use the GAL16V8, the 7485 comparator, and the 74283 adder to design a circuit for the "difference circuit" application in Example 6-10. The circuit always subtracts the smaller of two 4-bit binary numbers from the larger number. The function tables are shown in Table 12-15.

Solution: Derive the logic equations required to perform the operations listed in function tables. The equations were derived in Example 6-13 and are listed in Table 12-16. Implement the logic equations using the GAL16V8. All eight outputs of the GAL16V8 are required for this application. The PLD source file is shown in Table 12-17. The PLD pin diagram is shown in Figure 12-27(a) and the schematic for the difference circuit is shown in Figure 12-27(b), ■

TABLE 12-15 Difference Circuit Function Tables

Difference Circuit—Function Table–Comparator

7485 Comparator Output	7485 Comparator Inputs	
Use output	$A_3\ A_2\ A_1\ A_0$	$B_3\ B_2\ B_1\ B_0$
$A > B_{out}$	$A_4\ A_3\ A_2\ A_1$	$B_4\ B_3\ B_2\ B_1$

Difference Circuit—Function Table–Adder

Control Input	Operation	74283 Adder Inputs	
$A > B_{out}$		$A_4\ A_3\ A_2\ A_1$	$B_4\ B_3\ B_2\ B_1\ \ C_0$
0	B − A	$\overline{A}_4\ \overline{A}_3\ \overline{A}_2\ \overline{A}_1$	$B_4\ B_3\ B_2\ B_1\ \ 1$
1	A − B	$A_4\ A_3\ A_2\ A_1$	$\overline{B}_4\ \overline{B}_3\ \overline{B}_2\ \overline{B}_1\ \ 1$

TABLE 12-16 Difference Circuit Equations

Adder Inputs

$$A_4 = \overline{A_4}\overline{D} + A_4D = \overline{A_4 \oplus D} \qquad C_0 = 1$$
$$A_3 = \overline{A_3}\overline{D} + A_3D = \overline{A_3 \oplus D}$$
$$A_2 = \overline{A_2}\overline{D} + A_2D = \overline{A_2 \oplus D}$$
$$A_1 = \overline{A_1}\overline{D} + A_1D = \overline{A_1 \oplus D}$$
$$B_4 = B_4\overline{D} + \overline{B_4}D = B_4 \oplus D$$
$$B_3 = B_3\overline{D} + \overline{B_3}D = B_3 \oplus D$$
$$B_2 = B_2\overline{D} + \overline{B_2}D = B_2 \oplus D$$
$$B_1 = B_1\overline{D} + \overline{B_1}D = B_1 \oplus D$$

D is the A > B output from the 7485 comparator.

TABLE 12-17 Programmable Logic Device Source File Example 12-9

```
DEVICE 16V8;
TITLE Example 12-9;
NAME Difference Circuit;

/*     This example problem was originally seen in
       Chapter 6, Example 6-10. The circuit is to
       compare two numbers and subtract the smaller
       number from the larger number. The results
       obtained in Chapter 6 required the use of the
       7485 comparator, the 74283 adder, and
       considerable additional circuitry in the form
       of XOR and XNOR gates.              */

/*     This source file will define the equations for
       a GAL 16V8 to replace the XOR and XNOR
       circuits. The GAL 16V8 will be used in
       combination with the 7485 comparator and the
       74283 adder.        */

/*     Inputs          */

PIN  1 = D;          /*     Note: D is a control value that
                            comes from the A > B output of the
                            7485 comparator. When D is a
                            logic-HIGH the circuit will
                            subtract B from A. When D is a
                            logic-LOW, the circuit will
                            subtract A from B.          */

PIN  2 = A4;
PIN  3 = A3;
PIN  4 = A2;
PIN  5 = A1;

PIN  6 = B4;
PIN  7 = B3;
PIN  8 = B2;
PIN  9 = B1;

/*     Outputs          */

/*     These outputs will be input to the 74283 adder
       to form the two's complement of either A or B,
       whichever is to be subtracted.          */

PIN 19 = ADDER_A4;
PIN 18 = ADDER_A3;
PIN 17 = ADDER_A2;
PIN 16 = ADDER_A1;
```

TABLE 12-17 Programmable Logic Device Source File Example 12-9 *(continued)*

```
PIN 15 = ADDER_B4;
PIN 14 = ADDER_B3;
PIN 13 = ADDER_B2;
PIN 12 = ADDER_B1;

/*      Power and Ground                */

PIN 20 = VCC ;
PIN 10 = GND ;

/*      Boolean Equations               */

ADDER_A4 =        !A4 & !D # A4 & D;
ADDER_A3 =        !A3 & !D # A3 & D;
ADDER_A2 =        !A2 & !D # A2 & D;
ADDER_A1 =        !A1 & !D # A1 & D;
ADDER_B4 =        !B4 & D # B4 & !D;
ADDER_B3 =        !B3 & D # B3 & !D;
ADDER_B2 =        !B2 & D # B2 & !D;
ADDER_B1 =        !B1 & D # B1 & !D;
```

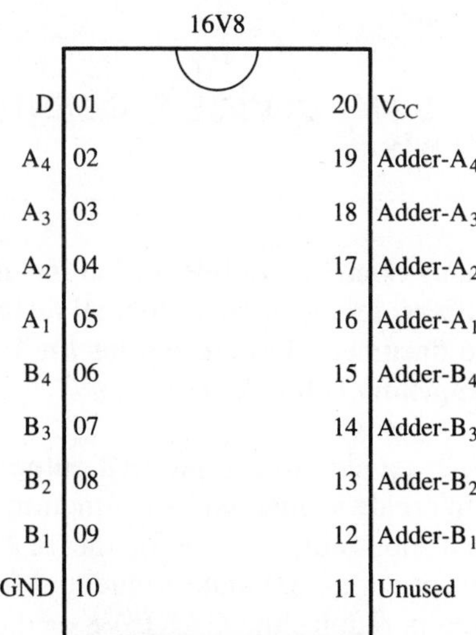

FIGURE 12-27 (a) Programmable Logic Device Pin Diagram Example 12-9

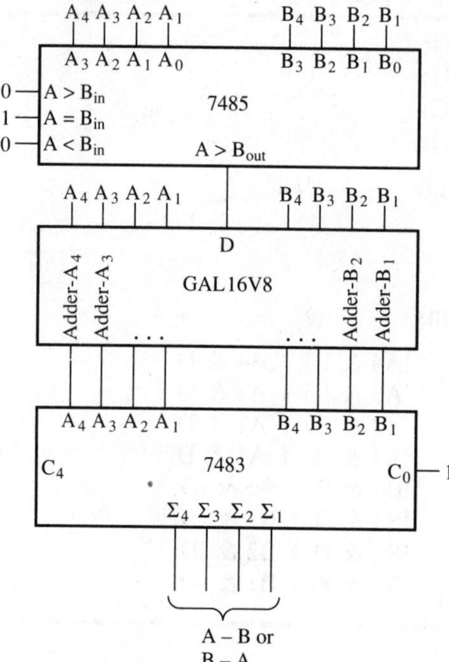

FIGURE 12-27 (b) Schematic for Example 12-9

12-7 PROGRAMMABLE LOGIC DEVICE SEQUENTIAL LOGIC APPLICATIONS

The sequential logic applications examined in this section include latches, flip-flops, counters, shift registers, and general sequential logic circuits. Selected PLD source files and document files created for the LC9000 logic compiler are listed in Appendix D for reference.

Programmable logic devices with **registered outputs**, such as a D-type flip-flop, can be used to create sequential logic functions. The feedback structure of the bidirectional input/outputs I/Os of the PLD is especially suited for implementing present state-next state sequential functions.

Sequential circuits require the GAL16V8 or the GAL16V8A to operate in either the complex mode or registered mode. The operating characteristics of the complex mode are listed in Table 12-3. The architecture of the

GAL16V8A in the complex mode is shown in Figures 12-12 and 12-13. The operating characteristics of the registered mode are listed in Table 12-4. The architecture of the GAL16V8A in the registered mode is shown in Figures 12-14 and 12-15.

The GAL16V8 and the GAL16V8A include a positive edge-triggered D flip-flop in each Output Logic Macrocell (OLMC) to produce **registered outputs**. The registered outputs operate synchronously with a clock that is input on pin 1 and with an active-LOW output enable function that is input on pin 11. The common clock input on pin 1 synchronizes all eight registered outputs. When pin 11 is tied to GND, the output enable function enables the output buffers of all eight registered outputs are enabled.

The combinational logic AND-OR array feeds into the D flip-flops so that any type of sequential logic may be defined from a truth table definition of the present inputs, present state, and next state requirements of the function. Designing sequential circuits with D flip-flops eliminates the need to design sequential circuits around the constraints of J-K, toggle, or master-slave-type flip-flops.

D flip-flops are the simplest sequential logic function. By definition of the D flip-flop, the output is always equal to the input on the trigger edge of the clock. Any sequential logic function can be described in a truth table that includes the present inputs, present state, and next state of the function. The Boolean expression for the function using D flip-flops is derived by simply defining the next state output in an SOP format.

Numerous sequential logic examples are shown in this section illustrating how the GAL16V8 or the GAL16V8A can be used to implement individual latches, flip-flops, shift registers, and counters.

12.7.1 Latch and Flip-Flop Functions Using Programmable Logic Devices

Latches are sequential devices that respond to inputs immediately when the device is enabled. The latch output is not synchronous with an input clock.

The latch applications to be implemented with a PLD are specified in a truth table with present inputs, present state, and next state outputs of the latch. The Boolean expressions for the next state output are combinational logic expressions that are functions of the present inputs and present state of the latch.

The combinational logic expressions require a feedback path to the AND-OR array in the PLD. With the GAL16V8, the feedback must be accomplished with either the complex mode or the registered mode. With the GAL16V8A, the feedback can be accomplished in either the simple, complex, or registered mode.

■ EXAMPLE 12-10 Programmable Logic Device Latches

Problem: Define the following latches in truth tables and implement their operation using the GAL16V8.

a. Active-LOW S-R latch
b. Gated D latch

Solution:

(a) Active-LOW S-R Latch

Present Inputs S	Present Inputs R	Present State Q_n	Next Output Q_{n+1}	Next Output $\overline{Q_{n+1}}$	
0	0	0	1	1	Invalid
0	0	1	1	1	
0	1	0	1	0	Set
0	1	1	1	0	
1	0	0	0	1	Reset
1	0	1	0	1	
1	1	0	0	1	Hold
1	1	1	1	0	

$Q_{n+1} = \overline{S} + S\,R\,Q_n;\ \ \overline{Q_{n+1}} = \overline{R} + S\,R\,\overline{Q_n}$

(b) Gated D Latch

Present Inputs En	Present Inputs D	Present State Q_n	Next Output Q_{n+1}	Next Output $\overline{Q_{n+1}}$	
0	0	0	0	1	
0	0	1	1	0	
0	1	0	0	1	Hold
0	1	1	1	0	
1	0	0	0	1	
1	0	1	0	1	
1	1	0	1	0	Latch
1	1	1	1	0	

$$Q_{n+1} = \overline{En}\, Q_n + En\, D; \qquad \overline{Q_{n+1}} = \overline{En}\, \overline{Q_n} + En\, \overline{D}$$

The PLD source file can be compiled for each of these sequential devices by converting the Boolean expressions into a form that is recognizable by the LC9000 assembler. The latch equations should be specified as combinational logic expressions. No time relationships need to be specified in the expressions since the present state feeds back to the AND-OR array by the GAL16V8A architecture.

The GAL16V8 must operate in the complex mode. The output equations must have output enable functions in order to obtain the feedback operation. The PLD source file for the latches appears in Table 12-18, and the pin layout is shown in Figure 12-28.

As an alternate solution, this problem could be implemented using the GAL16V8A in the simple mode. The PLD source file for the GAL16V8A implementation, requiring the simple mode, is shown in Table 12-19.

■

Programmable logic devices with registered outputs can be programmed to perform synchronous flip-flip operations. The GAL16V8 and the GAL16V8A have a positive edge-triggered D-type flip-flops in the OLMC. For the synchronous operation, all outputs defined for the PLD are clocked

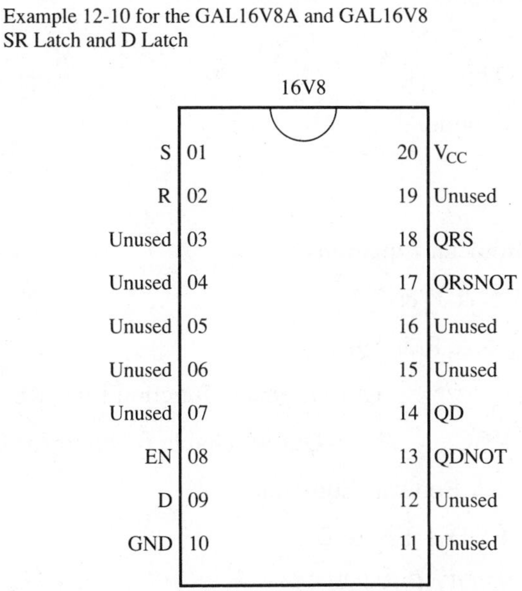

Example 12-10 for the GAL16V8A and GAL16V8
SR Latch and D Latch

16V8

Signal	Pin	Pin	Signal
S	01	20	V_{CC}
R	02	19	Unused
Unused	03	18	QRS
Unused	04	17	QRSNOT
Unused	05	16	Unused
Unused	06	15	Unused
Unused	07	14	QD
EN	08	13	QDNOT
D	09	12	Unused
GND	10	11	Unused

FIGURE 12-28 Programmable Logic Device Pin Diagram Example 12-10

TABLE 12-18 Programmable Logic Device Source File Example 12-10 for the GAL16V8

```
DEVICE 16V8;
TITLE Example 12-10 for the GAL 16V8;
NAME SR Latch and D Latch;

/*      This source file defines an active-LOW SR latch
        and an active-HIGH D latch.      */

/*      The GAL 16V8 must operate in the complex mode
        in order to have feedback in the combinational
        output logic expressions.     */

/*      SR Latch Inputs             */

PIN  1 = S;
PIN  2 = R;

/*      D Latch Inputs             */

PIN  8 = EN;
PIN  9 = D;

/*      D Latch Outputs             */

PIN 14 = QD;
PIN 13 = QDNOT;

*/      SR Latch Outputs             */

PIN 18 = QRS;
PIN 17 = QRSNOT;

/*      Power and Ground             */

PIN 20 = VCC;
PIN 10 = GND;

/*      SR Latch Boolean Equations             */

QRS =        !S ! S & R & QRS;

QRSNOT = !R ! S & R & !QRS ;

QRS.OE = VCC;     /*     Output enable function for QRS          */

QRSNOT.OE = VCC;     /*     Output enable function for QRSNOT     */

/*      Gated D Latch Boolean Equations             */

QD =        !EN & QD ! EN & D ;

QDNOT = !EN & !QD ! EN & !D ;

QD.OE = VCC;     /*     Ouput enable function for QD          */

QDNOT.OE = VCC;     /*     Output enable function for QDNOT     */
```

TABLE 12-19 Programmable Logic Device Source File Example 12-10 for the GAL 16V8A

```
DEVICE 16V8;
TITLE Example 12-10 for the GAL 16V8A;
NAME SR Latch and D Latch;

/*   This source file defines an active-LOW SR latch
     and an active-HIGH D latch.        */

/*   SR Latch Inputs          */

PIN  1 = S;
PIN  2 = R;

/*   D Latch Inputs          */

PIN  8 = EN;
PIN  9 = D;

/*   D Latch Outputs          */

PIN 12 = QD;
PIN 13 = QDNOT;

/*   SR Latch Outputs          */

PIN 18 = QRS;
PIN 19 = QRSNOT;

/*   Power and Ground          */

PIN 20 = VCC;
PIN 10 = GND;

/*   SR Latch Boolean Equations          */

QRS      = !S # S & R & QRS;

QRSNOT = !R # S & R & QRS ;

/*   Gated D Latch Boolean Equations          */
QD       = !EN & QD # EN & D ;

QDNOT = !EN & !QD # EN & !D ;
```

on the positive edge of the clock. Synchronous clear, preset, and output enable functions can be specified to control all synchronous outputs. These operations also occur on the positive edge of the clock.

In conventional logic circuits the J-K, T, and S-R flip-flops are manufactured as flip-flop ICs. With the GAL16V8 and the GAL16V8A, all flip-flop operations are designed using D flip-flops. The flip-flop operation is specified in a present input-present state-next state table. The next state output is derived as a function of the present inputs and present states and is written in an SOP format. This next state equation is then specified in the PLD source file as the input to the D flip-flop.

■ EXAMPLE 12-11 Programmable Logic Device Flip-Flops

Problem: Program the GAL16V8 for operation as a D flip-flop, a toggle flip-flop, and a J-K flip-flop. The flip-flops are positive edge-triggered and should have common synchronous preset and clear inputs.

Solution: Define the flip-flops in truth tables and implement their operation using the GAL16V8.

D Flip-Flop—Positive Edge-Triggered

Present Inputs			Present State	Next Output		State
PRE	CLR	D	Q_n	Q_{n+1}	$\overline{Q_{n+1}}$	
0	0	X	X	1	1	Invalid
0	1	X	X	1	0	Preset
1	0	X	X	0	1	Clear
1	1	0	0	0	1	
1	1	0	1	0	1	Latch
1	1	1	0	1	0	
1	1	1	1	1	0	

$Q_{n+1} = \overline{PRE} + CLR\ D;\qquad \overline{Q_{n+1}} = \overline{CLR} + PRE\ \overline{D}$

For a synchronous PLD operation, a synchronous clock must be assigned to pin 1 and an output enable must be assigned to pin 11. Since the output enable function is not used in these equations, pin 11 should be tied to GND for proper operation.

Toggle Flip-Flop—Positive Edge-Triggered

Present Inputs			Present State	Next Output		State
PRE	CLR	T	Q_n	Q_{n+1}	$\overline{Q_{n+1}}$	
0	0	X	X	1	1	Invalid
0	1	X	X	1	0	Preset
1	0	X	X	0	1	Clear
1	1	0	0	0	1	Hold
1	1	0	1	1	0	
1	1	1	0	1	0	Toggle
1	1	1	1	0	1	

$$Q_{n+1} = \overline{PRE} + CLR\,\overline{T}\,Q_n + CLR\,T\,\overline{Q_n}$$

$$\overline{Q_{n+1}} = \overline{CLR} + PRE\,\overline{T}\,\overline{Q_n} + PRE\,T\,Q_n$$

For a synchronous PLD operation, a synchronous clock must be assigned to pin 1 and an output enable must be assigned to pin 11. Since the output enable function is not used in these equations, pin 11 should be tied to GND for proper operation.

J-K Flip-Flop—Positive Edge-Triggered

Present Inputs				Present State	Next Output		State
PRE	CLR	J	K	Q_n	Q_{n+1}	$\overline{Q_{n+1}}$	
0	0	X	X	X	1	1	Invalid
0	1	X	X	X	1	0	Preset
1	0	X	X	X	0	1	Clear
1	1	0	0	0	0	1	Hold
1	1	0	0	1	1	0	
1	1	0	1	0	0	1	Reset
1	1	0	1	1	0	1	
1	1	1	0	0	1	0	Set
1	1	1	0	1	1	0	
1	1	1	1	0	1	0	Toggle
1	1	1	1	1	0	1	

$$Q_{n+1} = \overline{PRE} + CLR\,\overline{J}\,\overline{K}\,Q_n + CLR\,J\,\overline{K} + CLR\,J\,K\,\overline{Q_n}$$

$$\overline{Q_{n+1}} = \overline{CLR} + PRE\,\overline{J}\,\overline{K}\,\overline{Q_n} + PRE\,\overline{J}\,K + PRE\,J\,K\,Q_n$$

For a synchronous PLD operation, a synchronous clock must be assigned to pin 1 and an output enable must be assigned to pin 11. Since the output enable function is not used in these equations, pin 11 should be tied to GND for proper operation.

The Boolean expressions must be converted to a form that is readable by the LC9000, indicating a synchronous operation. This is accomplished by specifying the Boolean functions as inputs to D flip-flops. The feedback of the present state output of D flip-flops will be accomplished by the feedback architecture of the GAL16V8. The source file for the PLD flip-flops is Table 12-20. The PLD pin layout is shown in Figure 12-29.

■

TABLE 12-20 Programmable Logic Device Source File Example 12-11

```
DEVICE 16V8;
TITLE Example 12-11;
NAME PLD Flip-Flops;

/*      This source file defines a D flip-flop, and toggle
        flip flop, and a JK flip flop. Each flip-flop
        is a positive edge-triggered device with synchronous
        preset and clear inputs.            */

/*      The output enable is an active-LOW input. A logic LOW on pin 11
        enables all registered outputs. A logic HIGH on pin 11 disables all
        registered outputs by putting them into a high-impedance
        state          */

/*      Clock and Enable Inputs             */

PIN  1 = CLK;
PIN 11 = OE;

/*      Common Preset and Clear Inputs              */

/*      These preset and clear inputs will preset and clear
        all registered outputs on the rising edge of the clock pulse.   */

PIN  2 = PRE;
PIN  3 = CLR;

/*      D Flip-Flop Inputs            */

PIN  4 = D;
```

TABLE 12-20 Programmable Logic Device Source File Example 12-11 *(continued)*

```
/*      D Flip-Flop Outputs                */

PIN 19 = QD;
PIN 18 = QDNOT;

/*      Toggle Flip-Flop Inputs            */

PIN  5 = T;

/*      Toggle Flip-Flop Outputs           */

PIN 17 = QT;
PIN 16 = QTNOT;

/*      J-K Flip-Flop Inputs               */

PIN  6 = J;
PIN  7 = K;

/*      J-K Flip-Flop Outputs              */

PIN 15 = QJK;
PIN 14 = QJKNOT;

/*      D Flip-Flop Boolean Equations           */

QD.D =          !PRE # CLR & D ;

QDNOT.D =       !CLR # PRE & !D ;

/*      Toggle Flip-Flop Boolean Equations      */

QT.D =          !PRE # CLR & !T & QT # CLR & T & !QT ;

QTNOT.D =       !CLR # PRE & !T & !QT # PRE & T & QT ;

/*      J-K Flip-Flop Boolean Equations         */

QJK.D =         !PRE # CLR & !J & !K & QJK # CLR & J & !K
                # CLR & J & K & !QJK ;

QJKNOT.D =      !CLR # PRE & !J & !K & !QJK # PRE & !J & K
                # PRE & J & K & QJK ;
```

Logic Comp by Programmable Logic
Example 12-11
PLD Flip-Flops

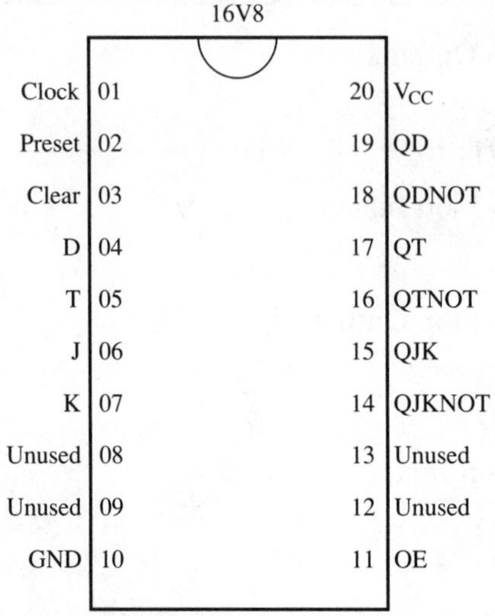

16V8

Signal	Pin	Pin	Signal
Clock	01	20	V_{CC}
Preset	02	19	QD
Clear	03	18	QDNOT
D	04	17	QT
T	05	16	QTNOT
J	06	15	QJK
K	07	14	QJKNOT
Unused	08	13	Unused
Unused	09	12	Unused
GND	10	11	OE

FIGURE 12-29 Programmable Logic Device Pin Diagram Example 12-11

12.7.2 Counter and Shift Register Functions Using Programmable Logic Devices

Sequential circuits that consist of several flip-flops such as counters and shift registers can be implemented with a PLD by defining the application in a present input-present state-next state truth table. The equations required for the next state output are derived from the truth table as functions of the present state and present inputs. The next state equations are specified as inputs to the D flip-flops that form the registered outputs of the PLD. On the trigger edge of the clock the next state output will be produced. Examples are shown using the GAL16V8 for shift registers, counters, and general synchronous logic circuits.

■ EXAMPLE 12-12 Universal Shift Register

Problem: Design a 4-bit shift register capable of parallel and serial inputs and outputs, and capable of shifting either right or left. All outputs should be at a high-impedance level if the output enable function is at a logic HIGH.

Solution: Define the circuit operation in a truth table according to the specifications given. Derive the synchronous Boolean logic equations to implement the circuit with D flip-flops.

- Mode control: S_1, S_0
  - 0, 0 Hold
  - 0, 1 Shift left
  - 1, 0 Shift right
  - 1, 1 Parallel load
- Parallel inputs: P_3, P_2, P_1, P_0
- Serial input right: SIR
- Serial input left: SIL
- Parallel outputs: Q_3, Q_2, Q_1, Q_0

Output Enable OE	Mode Control S_1	S_0	Parallel Outputs Q_3	Q_2	Q_1	Q_0
1	X	X	Z	Z	Z	Z
0	0	0	Q_3	Q_2	Q_1	Q_0
0	0	1	Q_2	Q_1	Q_0	SIL
0	1	0	SIR	Q_3	Q_2	Q_1
0	1	1	P_3	P_2	P_1	P_0

$$Q_3 = \overline{S_1}\,\overline{S_0}\,Q_3 + \overline{S_1}\,S_0\,Q_2 + S_1\,\overline{S_0}\,SIR + S_1\,S_0\,P_3$$

$$Q_2 = \overline{S_1}\,\overline{S_0}\,Q_2 + \overline{S_1}\,S_0\,Q_1 + S_1\,\overline{S_0}\,Q_3 + S_1\,S_0\,P_2$$

$$Q_1 = \overline{S_1}\,\overline{S_0}\,Q_1 + \overline{S_1}\,S_0\,Q_0 + S_1\,\overline{S_0}\,Q_2 + S_1\,S_0\,P_1$$

$$Q_0 = \overline{S_1}\,\overline{S_0}\,Q_0 + \overline{S_1}\,S_0\,SIL + S_1\,\overline{S_0}\,Q_1 + S_1\,S_0\,P_0$$

The PLD source file must have the clock input assigned to pin 1 and the output enable function assigned to pin 11. Connect pin 11 to the output enable switch for operation. Pin 11 must be a logic LOW for operation. The PLD source file for this shift register is shown in Table 12-21. The PLD pin diagram is shown in Figure 12-30.

■

TABLE 12-21 Programmable Logic Device Source File Example 12-12

```
DEVICE 16V8;
TITLE Example 12-12;
NAME Universal Shift Register;

/*     This source file defines a four-bit shift register
       that has four modes of operation. It can hold data,
       shift left, shift right, or parallel load.       */

/*     The shifting takes place on the rising edge of the
       clock pulse.     */

/*     The outputs are enabled when Pin 11 is a logic-LOW.
       The outputs are in a high-impedance state when Pin 11 is a
       logic-HIGH.     */

/*     Clock and Output-Enable Inputs       */

PIN  1 = CLK;
PIN 11 = OE;

/*     Mode Control Inputs             */

PIN  2 = S2;
PIN  3 = S1;
PIN  4 = S0;

/*     Parallel Data Inputs            */

PIN  5 = P3;
PIN  6 = P2;
PIN  7 = P1;
PIN  8 = P0;

/*     Serial Input for Shifting Right Input       */

PIN  9 = SIR;

/*     Serial Input for Shifting Left Input        */

PIN 12 = SIL;

/*     Parallel Outputs              */

PIN 19 = Q3;
PIN 18 = Q2;
PIN 17 = Q1;
PIN 16 = Q0;
```

TABLE 12-21 Programmable Logic Device Source File Example 12-12 *(continued)*

```
/*      Boolean Equations              */

Q3.D =  !S1 & !S0 & Q3 ! !S1 & S0 & Q2
        ! S1 & !S0 & SIR ! S1 & S0 & P3;

Q2.D =  !S1 & !S0 & Q2 ! !S1 & S0 & Q1
        ! S1 & !S0 & Q3 ! S1 & S0 & P2;

Q1.D =  !S1 & !S0 & Q1 ! !S1 & S0 & Q0
        ! S1 & !S0 & Q2 ! S1 & S0 & P1;

Q0.D =  !S1 & !S0 & Q0 ! !S1 & S0 & SIL
        ! S1 & !S0 & Q1 ! S1 & S0 & P0;
```

Logic Comp by Programmable Logic
Example 12-12
Universal Shift Register

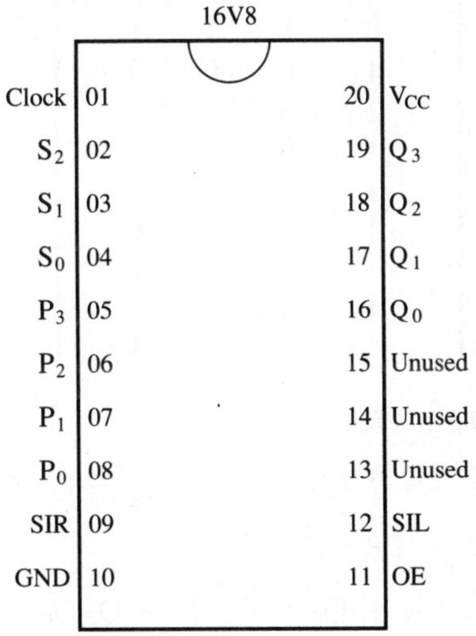

16V8

Clock	01	20	V_{CC}
S_2	02	19	Q_3
S_1	03	18	Q_2
S_0	04	17	Q_1
P_3	05	16	Q_0
P_2	06	15	Unused
P_1	07	14	Unused
P_0	08	13	Unused
SIR	09	12	SIL
GND	10	11	OE

FIGURE 12-30 Programmable Logic Device Pin Diagram Example 12-12

■ EXAMPLE 12-13 Four-Bit Up Counter

Problem: Design a 4-bit binary up counter with synchronous preset and clear inputs.

Solution: The 4-bit up counter must be completely specified in a truth table listing the present state, present inputs, and next state of the counter in order to derive the Boolean expressions. Boolean algebra can be used to simplify the expressions.

Present Inputs		Present State				Next Output State			
PRE	CLR	Q_3	Q_2	Q_1	Q_0	Q_3	Q_2	Q_1	Q_0
1	1	X	X	X	X	Q_3	Q_2	Q_1	Q_0
1	0	X	X	X	X	D_3	D_2	D_1	D_0
0	1	X	X	X	X	0	0	0	0
0	0	0	0	0	0	0	0	0	1
0	0	0	0	0	1	0	0	1	0
0	0	0	0	1	0	0	0	1	1
0	0	0	0	1	1	0	1	0	0
0	0	0	1	0	0	0	1	0	1
0	0	0	1	0	1	0	1	1	0
0	0	0	1	1	0	0	1	1	1
0	0	0	1	1	1	1	0	0	0
0	0	1	0	0	0	1	0	0	1
0	0	1	0	0	1	1	0	1	0
0	0	1	0	1	0	1	0	1	1
0	0	1	0	1	1	1	1	0	0
0	0	1	1	0	0	1	1	0	1
0	0	1	1	0	1	1	1	1	0
0	0	1	1	1	0	1	1	1	1
0	0	1	1	1	1	0	0	0	0

$$Q_3 = \text{PRE CLR } Q_3 + \text{PRE } \overline{\text{CLR}}\, D_3 + \overline{\text{PRE}}\, \overline{\text{CLR}}\, (\overline{Q_3}\, Q_2\, Q_1\, Q_0 + Q_3\, \overline{Q_2} + Q_3\, \overline{Q_1} + Q_3\, \overline{Q_0})$$

$$Q_2 = \text{PRE CLR } Q_2 + \text{PRE } \overline{\text{CLR}}\, D_2 + \overline{\text{PRE}}\, \overline{\text{CLR}}\, (\overline{Q_2}\, Q_1\, Q_0 + Q_2\, \overline{Q_1} + Q_2\, \overline{Q_0})$$

$$Q_1 = \text{PRE CLR } Q_1 + \text{PRE } \overline{\text{CLR}}\, D_1 + \overline{\text{PRE}}\, \overline{\text{CLR}}\, (\overline{Q_1}\, Q_0 + Q_1\, \overline{Q_0})$$

$$Q_0 = \text{PRE CLR } Q_0 + \text{PRE } \overline{\text{CLR}}\, D_0 + \overline{\text{PRE}}\, \overline{\text{CLR}}\, \overline{Q_0}$$

The counter outputs must be specified as synchronous outputs in the PLD source file, the clock input must be assigned to pin 1, and an output enable must be assigned to pin 11. Connect pin 11 to GND for operation. The PLD source file is shown in Table 12-22. The PLD pin diagram is shown in Figure 12-31.

■

TABLE 12-22 Programmable Logic Device Source File Example 12-13

```
DEVICE 16V8;
TITLE Example 12-13;
NAME Four-Bit Binary Up Counter;

/*      This source file defines a four-bit binary up counter.
        The counter has synchronous control inputs that clear
        or preset each output on the rising edge of the clock.
        Individual data inputs are provided to preset each
        counter stage individually.    */

/*      The counter is a positive edge-triggered device.     */

/*      To enable all outputs, Pin 11 must be a logic LOW.
        To disable all outputs and put them in a high-impedance
        state, Pin 11 should be a logic-HIGH.     */

/*      Clock and Output-Enable Inputs          */

PIN  1 = CLK;
PIN 11 = OE;

/*      Preset and Clear Control Inputs         */

PIN  2 = PRE;
PIN  3 = CLR;

/*      Preset Load Data Inputs         */

PIN  4 = D3;
PIN  5 = D2;
PIN  6 = D1;
PIN  7 = D0;

/*      Counter Outputs         */

PIN 19 = Q3;
PIN 18 = Q2;
PIN 17 = Q1;
PIN 16 = Q0;
```

TABLE 12-22 Programmable Logic Device Source File Example 12-13 *(continued)*

```
/*      Power and Ground              */

PIN 20 = VCC ;
PIN 10 = GND ;

/*      Boolean Equations             */

Q3.D =  PRE & CLR & Q3                              /*      Hold      */
        ! PRE & ! CLR & D3                          /*      Preset    */
        ! !PRE & !CLR &
              (!Q3 & Q2 & Q1 & Q0 ! Q3 & !Q2 ! Q3 & !Q1 !
               Q3 & !Q0);

Q2.D =  PRE & CLR & Q2                              /*      Hold      */
        ! PRE & !CLR & D2                           /*      Preset    */
        ! !PRE & !CLR &
              (!Q2 & Q1 & Q0 ! Q2 & !Q1 ! Q2 & !Q0);

Q1.D =  PRE & CLR & Q1                              /*      Hold      */
        ! PRE & !CLR & D1                           /*      Preset    */
        ! !PRE & !CLR &
              (!Q1 & Q0 ! Q1 & !Q0);

Q0.D =  PRE & CLR & Q0                              /*      Hold      */
        ! PRE & !CLR & D0                           /*      Preset    */
        ! !PRE & !CLR & !Q0 ;
```

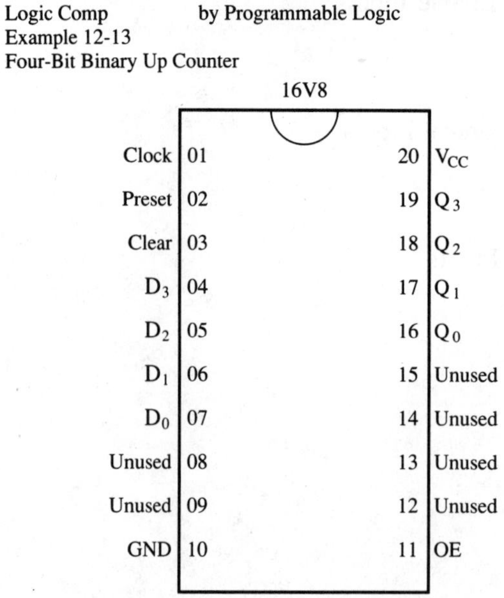

Logic Comp by Programmable Logic
Example 12-13
Four-Bit Binary Up Counter

16V8

Signal	Pin	Pin	Signal
Clock	01	20	V_{CC}
Preset	02	19	Q_3
Clear	03	18	Q_2
D_3	04	17	Q_1
D_2	05	16	Q_0
D_1	06	15	Unused
D_0	07	14	Unused
Unused	08	13	Unused
Unused	09	12	Unused
GND	10	11	OE

FIGURE 12-31 Programmable Logic Device Pin Diagram Example 12-13

■ EXAMPLE 12-14 Four-Bit Down Counter

Problem: Design a 4-bit binary down counter with synchronous preset and clear inputs.

Solution: The 4-bit down counter must be completely specified in a truth table listing the present state, present inputs, and next state of the counter. The Boolean equations can be derived and simplified as necessary from the truth table.

Present Inputs		Present State				Next Output State			
PRE	CLR	Q_3	Q_2	Q_1	Q_0	Q_3	Q_2	Q_1	Q_0
1	1	X	X	X	X	Q_3	Q_2	Q_1	Q_0
1	0	X	X	X	X	D_3	D_2	D_1	D_0
0	1	X	X	X	X	0	0	0	0
0	0	0	0	0	0	1	1	1	1
0	0	0	0	0	1	0	0	0	0
0	0	0	0	1	0	0	0	0	1
0	0	0	0	1	1	0	0	1	0
0	0	0	1	0	0	0	0	1	1
0	0	0	1	0	1	0	1	0	0
0	0	0	1	1	0	0	1	0	1
0	0	0	1	1	1	0	1	1	0
0	0	1	0	0	0	0	1	1	1
0	0	1	0	0	1	1	0	0	0
0	0	1	0	1	0	1	0	0	1
0	0	1	0	1	1	1	0	1	0
0	0	1	1	0	0	1	0	1	1
0	0	1	1	0	1	1	1	0	0
0	0	1	1	1	0	1	1	0	1
0	0	1	1	1	1	1	1	1	0

$$Q_3 = \text{PRE CLR } Q_3 + \text{PRE } \overline{\text{CLR}}\, D_3 + \overline{\text{PRE}}\ \overline{\text{CLR}}\,(\overline{Q_3}\,\overline{Q_2}\,\overline{Q_1}\,\overline{Q_0} + Q_3 Q_2 + Q_3 Q_1 + Q_3 Q_0)$$

$$Q_2 = \text{PRE CLR } Q_2 + \text{PRE } \overline{\text{CLR}}\, D_2 + \overline{\text{PRE}}\ \overline{\text{CLR}}\,(\overline{Q_2}\,\overline{Q_1}\,\overline{Q_0} + Q_2 Q_1 + Q_2 Q_0)$$

$$Q_1 = \text{PRE CLR } Q_1 + \text{PRE } \overline{\text{CLR}}\ D_1 + \overline{\text{PRE}}\ \overline{\text{CLR}}\ (\overline{Q_1}\ \overline{Q_0} + Q_1 Q_0)$$

$$Q_0 = \text{PRE CLR } Q_0 + \text{PRE } \overline{\text{CLR}}\ D_0 + \overline{\text{PRE}}\ \overline{\text{CLR}}\ \overline{Q_0}$$

As with the up counter, the outputs of the down counter must be specified as synchronous outputs in the PLD source file, and the clock input must be assigned to pin 1. The PLD source file follows in Table 12-23, and the PLD pin layout is identical to the up counter shown in Figure 12-31.

TABLE 12-23 Programmable Logic Device Source File Example 12-14

```
DEVICE 16V8;
TITLE Example 12-14;
NAME Four-Bit Binary Down Counter;

/*    This source file defines a four-bit binary down counter.
      The counter has synchronous control inputs that
      clear or preset each output on the rising edge of the
      clock. Individual data inputs are provided to preset
      each counter stage individually.    */

/*    The counter is a positive edge-triggered device.    */

/*    To enable all outputs, Pin 11 must be a logic LOW.
      To disable all outputs and put them in a high-impedance state, Pin
      11 should be a logic HIGH.    */

/*    Clock and Output-Enable Inputs    */

PIN  1 = CLK;
PIN 11 = OE;

/*    Preset and Clear Control Inputs    */

PIN  2 = PRE;
PIN  3 = CLR;

/*    Preset Load Data Inputs    */

PIN  4 = D3;
PIN  5 = D2;
PIN  6 = D1;
PIN  7 = D0;
```

TABLE 12-23 Programmable Logic Device Source File Example 12-14 *(continued)*

```
/*      Counter Outputs          */

PIN 19 = Q3;
PIN 18 = Q2;
PIN 17 = Q1;
PIN 16 = Q0;

/*      Power and Ground          */

PIN 20 = VCC ;
PIN 10 = GND ;

/*      Boolean Equations         */

Q3.D =  PRE & CLR & Q3                          /*    Hold      */
        ! PRE & !CLR & D3                       /*    Preset    */
        ! !PRE & !CLR &
             (!Q3 & !Q2 & !Q1 & !Q0 ! Q3 & Q2 ! Q3 & Q1 !
              Q3 & Q0);

Q2.D =  PRE & CLR & Q2                          /*    Hold      */
        ! PRE & !CLR & D2                       /*    Preset    */
        ! !PRE & !CLR &
             (!Q2 & !Q1 & !Q0 ! Q2 & Q1 ! Q2 & Q0);

Q1.D =  PRE & CLR & Q1                          /*    Hold      */
        ! PRE & !CLR & D1                       /*    Preset    */
        ! !PRE & !CLR &
             (!Q1 & !Q0 ! Q1 & Q0);

Q0.D =  PRE & CLR & Q0                          /*    Hold      */
        ! PRE & !CLR & D0                       /*    Preset    */
        ! !PRE & !CLR & !Q0 ;
```

■

■ EXAMPLE 12-15 Binary Sequence Counter

Problem: Design a 4-bit binary sequence counter to produce the following sequence: 2, 3, 7, 5, 8, 10, 14, 12. (As an application note, this type of sequence could be your Social Security number, your telephone number, or a security code.) The counter should be self-correcting so that if any unwanted state occurs, the sequence counter goes immediately to the first count in the sequence to begin again.

Solution: The sequence counter can be completely specified in a truth table by listing the present state and the corresponding next state in the sequence. For any unwanted present output states, the next output state is specified to be the binary value 0 0 1 1. The Boolean expressions can be obtained and simplified from the table.

Present State				Next State			
Q_3	Q_2	Q_1	Q_0	Q_3	Q_2	Q_1	Q_0
0	0	0	0	0	0	1	0
0	0	0	1	0	0	1	0
0	0	1	0	0	0	1	1
0	0	1	1	0	1	1	1
0	1	0	0	0	0	1	0
0	1	0	1	1	0	0	0
0	1	1	0	0	0	1	0
0	1	1	1	0	1	0	1
1	0	0	0	1	0	1	0
1	0	0	1	0	0	1	0
1	0	1	0	1	1	1	0
1	0	1	1	0	0	1	0
1	1	0	0	0	0	1	0
1	1	0	1	0	0	1	0
1	1	1	0	1	1	0	0
1	1	1	1	0	0	1	0

The Boolean expressions can accept up to eight terms. The equations can be specified directly off the truth table without any simplification necessary:

$$Q_3 = \overline{Q_3}\,Q_2\,\overline{Q_1}\,Q_0 + Q_3\,\overline{Q_2}\,\overline{Q_1}\,\overline{Q_0} + Q_3\,\overline{Q_2}\,Q_1\,\overline{Q_0} + Q_3\,Q_2\,Q_1\,\overline{Q_0}$$

$$Q_2 = \overline{Q_3}\,\overline{Q_2}\,Q_1\,Q_0 + \overline{Q_3}\,Q_2\,Q_1\,Q_0 + Q_3\,\overline{Q_2}\,Q_1\,\overline{Q_0} + Q_3\,Q_2\,Q_1\,\overline{Q_0}$$

$$\overline{Q_1} = \overline{Q_3}\,Q_2\,\overline{Q_1}\,Q_0 + \overline{Q_3}\,Q_2\,Q_1\,Q_0 + Q_3\,Q_2\,Q_1\,\overline{Q_0}$$

$$Q_0 = \overline{Q_3}\,\overline{Q_2}\,Q_1\,\overline{Q_0} + \overline{Q_3}\,\overline{Q_2}\,Q_1\,Q_0 + \overline{Q_3}\,Q_2\,Q_1\,Q_0$$

Notice that the active-LOW specification for Q_1 was given in the Boolean expressions. This version had only three terms in the equation, thus requiring no simplification. The PLD source file is listed in Table 12-24, and the PLD pin diagram is shown in Figure 12-32.

TABLE 12-24 Programmable Logic Device Source File Example 12-15

```
DEVICE 16V8;
TITLE Example 12-15;
NAME Binary Sequence Generator;

/*    This source file defines a binary sequence
      generator. The circuit generates a four-bit
      output of the following sequence: 2, 3, 7, 5, 8,
      10, 14, 12, 2, 3, etc. Any unwanted four-bit
      combinations force the sequence generator to
      the count value of 2 so that the circuit is
      self-correcting.   */

/*    The sequence generator changes count states on
      the rising edge of the clock. All outputs are
      active when Pin 11 is a logic LOW. All outputs
      are in a high-impedance state when Pin 11 is
      a logic HIGH.         */

/*    Clock and Output-Enable Control Inputs      */

PIN  1 = CLK;
PIN 11 = OE;

/*    Outputs          */

PIN 19 = Q3;
PIN 18 = Q2;
PIN 17 = Q1;
PIN 16 = Q0;

/*    Power and Ground             */

PIN 20 = VCC ;
PIN 10 = GND ;

/*    Boolean Equations            */

Q3.D = !Q3 & Q2 & !Q1 & Q0 ! Q3 & !Q2 & !Q1 & !Q0
       ! Q3 & !Q2 & Q1 & !Q0 ! Q3 & Q2 & Q1 & !Q0 ;

Q2.D = !Q3 & !Q2 & Q1 & Q0 ! !Q3 & Q2 & Q1 & Q0
       ! Q3 & !Q2 & Q1 & !Q0 ! Q3 & Q2 & Q1 & !Q0 ;

!Q1.D = !Q3 & Q2 & !Q1 & Q0 ! !Q3 & Q2 & Q1 & Q0
       ! Q3 & Q2 & Q1 & !Q0 ;

Q0.D = !Q3 & !Q2 & Q1 & !Q0 ! !Q3 & !Q2 & Q1 & Q0
       ! !Q3 & Q2 & Q1 & Q0 ;
```

```
Logic Comp          by Programmable Logic
Example 12-15
Binary Sequence Generator

                     16V8
          ----------------------------
   Clock | 01                   20 | Vcc
  Unused | 02                   19 | Q3
  Unused | 03                   18 | Q2
  Unused | 04                   17 | Q1
  Unused | 05                   16 | Q0
  Unused | 06                   15 | Unused
  Unused | 07                   14 | Unused
  Unused | 08                   13 | Unused
  Unused | 09                   12 | Unused
     GND | 10                   11 | OE
          ----------------------------
```

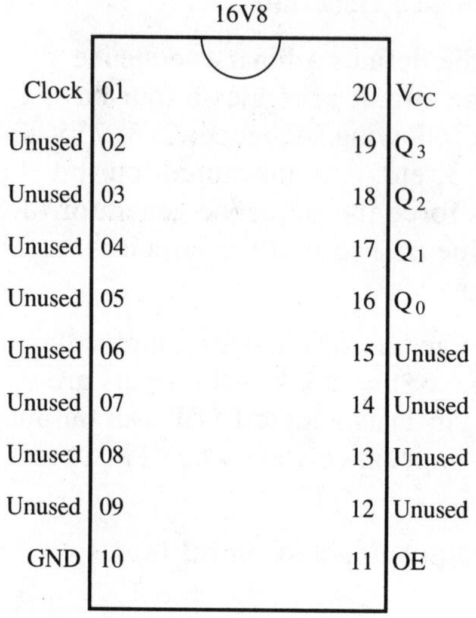

FIGURE 12-32 Programmable Logic Device Pin Diagram Example 12-15 ■

Section Self-Test

1. Combinational output equations are always allowed eight product terms with the GAL16V8 or GAL16V8A.
2. Feedback operations require the complex mode of operation.
3. Only sequential outputs are available on the GAL16V8 or GAL16V8A when it is operating in the registered mode.

ANSWERS

- False. Combinational outputs in the simple mode are allowed eight product terms. Combinational outputs in the complex mode and the registered mode are allowed only seven product terms. An output enable term is required by the combinational outputs in the complex and registered modes; this term takes up one product term in the AND-OR array of the GAL16V8 or GAL16V8A.
- False. The GAL16V8A allows feedback in the simple, complex, and registered modes. The GAL16V8 allows feedback in the complex and registered modes.
- False. Combinational outputs are allowed when the GAL16V8 or GAL16V8A is operating in the registered mode. The combinational outputs must be enabled with their separate output enable term.

12-8 TROUBLESHOOTING PROGRAMMABLE LOGIC DEVICE CIRCUITS

Troubleshooting PLD circuits requires analysis of the source file, programming techniques, and circuit construction to determine the source of the error. This section reviews areas of PLD circuit design and application that are likely sources of error.

A designer using PLDs must adhere to the constraints of the device architecture, the software and hardware development systems used to program the PLDs. In addition, the CMOS PLDs require careful handling to prevent them from being damaged due to electrostatic voltage.

The major constraints of a PLD are the number of inputs, the number of outputs, whether or not outputs are combinational or registered, feedback, and the number of product terms allowed by the AND-OR array. More complex PLDs exist that were not discussed in this chapter, but they allow the designer buried nodes to perform intermediate logic functions.

The constraints of the device architecture of the GAL16V8 and GAL16V8A listed in detail in Tables 12-2, 12-3, and 12-4. The devices have three modes of operation: the simple, complex, and registered. In each mode specific pins function as inputs, outputs, or bidirectional inputs/outputs (I/Os). Some outputs require an output enable function for each pin, whereas other outputs are enabled as a group with a common output enable control.

The LC9000 software development package used throughout this text is a very basic and low-cost system that enables a designer to program a PLD by specifying the Boolean expression for each output function. More complex and expensive systems are available that allow programming of the PLD through specification of the truth table, a present state-next state table, or other methods.

Some of the complex PLD software development systems can perform logic simulation and PLD device testing. Programmable logic device testing is normally performed by specifying ''test vectors'' of prescribed test states. When testing the device, outputs are preset to the prescribed test state and the operation is verified to ensure that the device produces the appropriate next state values. All possible logic output states should be tested.

Common errors encountered by students when working with PLD software development systems include the following:

1. Syntax errors
2. Device operating mode errors
3. Incorrect specification of Boolean expressions
4. Incorrect specification of input or output pins
5. Incorrect specification of output enable functions
6. Incorrect application of feedback signals that violate the device architecture constraints

The hardware programming system must be compatible for the specific device chosen for programming. The Logic Lab programming system selected for use in this chapter can be used to program electrically erasable CMOS GAL devices: the GAL16V8, GAL20V8, ispGAL16Z8, GAL6001, and GAL22V10. These GAL devices can be programmed to emulate numerous PAL devices.

Other hardware programmer systems are general purpose systems that can be used to program EPROMs and PLDs from many manufacturers. Programmers also exist to program the UV erasable PLDs. Still another type of PLD is the "in-system-programmable" PLD. The ispGAL16Z8 is an example of such a device. It is architecturally equivalent to the GAL16V8 with four additional pins for programming via a latch and a serial cable connected to the PC. In-system-programmable PLDs do not require separate hardware programming systems; they can be programmed while they are in their digital system.

The errors commonly encountered by students using the PLD hardware programming systems include the following:

1. Programmer not powered
2. No serial connection between the computer and the programmer
3. Incorrect device specified
4. Device in the socket incorrectly
5. Incorrect JEDEC file downloaded to the programmer
6. Program downloaded but the device is not programmed
7. Incorrect programming procedure. Example: A student downloads, then loads, then programs. (In the download the JEDEC fuse map is loaded into the buffer. In the load the old fuse connections in the PLD in the programmer socket are loaded into the buffer, overwriting the data intended for programming. In the program operation the fuse data loaded from the PLD into the buffer is now programmed into the PLD instead of the intended data.)

The GAL16V8, GAL16V8A, and other electrically erasable PLDs are CMOS devices that require special handling to prevent damage to the device. CMOS devices can be damaged by electrostatic voltages. To ensure device viability, these devices should be transported in conductive foam or conductive tubing at all times. When wiring the circuit, you should connect a ground strap at your wrist and then attach it to a ground connection and work on a conductive mat to prevent any build up of electrostatic charge at the laboratory bench. A typical logic lab error statement encountered when attempting to program an ESD damaged PLD is "device not recognized."

The circuit should be carefully wired in the breadboard while the power is off. All unused inputs and bidirectional I/O pins should be connected to V_{CC} or to GND to prevent electromagnetic noise from impairing the operation of the circuit.

The following examples illustrate common error conditions that are often encountered in the laboratory by students working with PLDs.

■ EXAMPLE 12-16 Source File Faults

Problem: Find as many errors as possible in the source file shown in Table 12-25.

Solution: The error file produced by LC9000 when trying to compile this source file is listed in Table 12-26. All these errors must be corrected before the file can be compiled. The LC9000 editor can be used to load the error file, jump to the line numbers with the errors, and make the corrections.

In addition to the errors found by the LC9000, a clock input must be assigned to pin 1 and an output enable function must be assigned to pin 11. The preset and clear inputs do not appear in any equation and can even be removed from the file. ■

■ EXAMPLE 12-17 Flashing Light Output

Problem: Once the source file from Example 12-16 is corrected and compiled, the PLD is programmed but does not operate correctly. The PLD is described by the student as "not working but all the lights flash." Suggest some items to check to determine the source of error.

Solution: The described symptom is often observed when the unused inputs and outputs are left floating. All unused inputs and outputs should be tied to V_{CC} or to GND. When this is done, the circuit should operate correctly. ■

Section Self-Test

1. State three common errors in a GAL16V8 or GAL16V8A source file to be compiled by the LC9000.
2. State three common errors associated with the device programmer and programming procedures.

ANSWERS

- (a) Forgetting the ";" at the end of each line
  (b) Assigning pin 15 or 16 as inputs in the simple mode
  (c) Having more than seven product terms in expressions requiring an output enable function with that output pin (complex mode outputs or combinational outputs in the registered mode)
- (a) Incorrect programming procedure
  (b) Device not latched in the socket
  (c) Device in the socket incorrectly (For example, with the Logic Lab, pin 1 must be in the top left corner, but it is possible to load the device incorrectly and damage the device while programming.)

TABLE 12-25 PLD Source File Example 12-16

```
Device 16V8;
TITLE Example 12-16;
NAME Source File Faults;

/*      This source file has numerous errors. Try to
        find the errors.          */

/*      Inputs          */

PIN  1 = PRE;
PIN  2 = CLR;

/*      Outputs         */

PIN 19 = Q5
PIN 18 = Q4
PIN 17 = Q3
PIN 16 = Q2
PIN 15 = Q1
PIN 14 = Q0
PIN 13 = C1
PIN 12 = C2

/*      Power and Ground          */

PIN 20 = VCC ;
PIN 10 = GND ;

/*      Boolean Equations          */

Q5.D = (Q0 # Q2)&(Q1 # Q4);

Q4.D = Q3 * Q2 * !Q1 # D4 * !Q3 # !Q2 & !Q0;

Q3.D = !Q3 Q2 & !Q1 & Q0 # Q3 & !Q2 & !Q1 & !Q0
       # Q3 & !Q2 & Q1 & !Q0 # Q3 & Q2 & Q1 & !Q0

Q2.D = !Q3 & !Q2 & Q1 & Q0 # !Q3 & Q2 & Q1 & Q0
       # Q3 & !Q2 & Q1 !Q0 # Q3 & Q2 & Q1 & !Q0 ;

!Q1.D = !Q3 & Q2 & !Q1 & Q0 # !Q3 & Q2 & Q1 & Q0
        Q3 Q2 & Q1 & !Q0 ;

Q0.D = !Q3 & !Q2 & Q1 & !Q0 # !Q3 & !Q2 & Q1 & Q0
       # !Q3 & Q2 & Q1 & Q0 ;

C1   = Q3 # Q2 & (Q1 # !Q0);

C0   = !Q5 & !Q4 & Q3 & Q0;
```

TABLE 12-26 LC9000 Error File Example 12-16

Missing ; Prior to Name statement on line #3
Invalid syntax in pin equation on line #16
Missing ; Prior to assignment operator on line #16
Missing ; Prior to Pin statement on line #17
Invalid syntax in pin equation on line #18
Missing ; Prior to assignment operator on line #18
Missing ; Prior to Pin statement on line #19
Invalid syntax in pin equation on line #19
Invalid syntax in pin equation on line #20
Missing ; Prior to assignment operator on line #20
Missing ; Prior to Pin statement on line #21
Invalid syntax in pin equation on line #22
Missing ; Prior to assignment operator on line #22
Missing ; Prior to Pin statement on line #26
Missing ; Prior to assignment operator on line #38

SUMMARY

Programmable logic devices are powerful logic circuits now available as low-cost, reliable, and easy to program ICs. They are used extensively in large logic systems as the interface circuits with specific logic functions required for a particular application. For example, PLDs are often seen in microprocessor systems to interface decoders, memory circuits, encoders, and other standard logic devices.

The flexibility of PLDs allows them to be used in numerous combinational and sequential logic applications. Erasable PLDs such as the GAL devices by Lattice Semiconductor are especially well suited to logic applications requiring numerous hardware modifications to the original design.

The following topics were covered in detail in the PLD analysis, application, and design examples in Chapter 12.

ANALYSIS

The evolution of semiconductor logic was described to acquaint the student with the types of logic devices available, from standard logic to PLDs, custom logic, and gate array devices. The chapter focused on user programmable logic devices, referred to as PLDs.

The Generic Array Logic (GAL) devices by Lattice Semiconductor were emphasized for their ease in programming, erasing, and emulating numerous other PLDs on the market. The GAL devices are the most appropriate for use in an educational laboratory setting as they can be programmed one hundred times, are low cost, reliable, and very flexible in their application features.

A crucial operating factor for all PLDs is the device architecture. The GAL devices used in examples in this chapter had three modes of operation: simple, complex, and registered. These modes allow the device to provide seven or eight product terms in output expressions and allow outputs to be combinational, or sequential, with or without feedback.

APPLICATION

Programming a PLD requires the use of software and hardware development systems. The software package selected for use in the example problems is the LC9000 by Programmable Logic Technologies. The LC9000 provides a simple, low-cost solution to programming the GAL devices that is appropriate for business or educational environments.

The Logic Lab PLD programmer by Programmable Logic Technologies is used to program the fuses in GAL devices. The Logic Lab programmer can program the 20-pin or 24-pin GAL devices. These devices emulate numerous other PAL devices on the market.

DESIGN

Several examples of logic applications were designed for implementation with the GAL16V8 or GAL16V8A. The applications included combinational logic circuits such as encoders, decoders, multiplexers, and general combinational logic functions. The sequential logic circuit applications included latches, flip-flops, counters, shift registers, and general sequential logic systems.

The source files for all designs were written in a format appropriate to be compiled by the LC9000 logic compiler. Selected source files are listed in Appendix D for reference.

TROUBLESHOOTING

PLD circuit errors and source file errors can occur as a result of the constraints of the software development system, the hardware device programmer, and the architecture of the PLD itself. A thorough understanding of the PLD and all programming and hardware tools associated with the device must be thoroughly understood to prevent errors. Crucial PLD circuits should undergo rigorous and formal quality testing to document the operation of the device in all logic states.

PLDs will replace most standard logic gates and MSI logic ICs. They are currently an important design choice to improve design flexibility and to conserve board space required for a logic system. Programmable logic devices can be incorporated in fundamental digital logic courses along with standard logic devices so that students are able to select the most appropriate type of logic device for a given application or system that they are designing.

PROBLEMS

The following problems should be completed using the GAL16V8 or GAL16V8A and the LC9000 PLD logic compiler software. The devices can be tested by programming with the Logic Lab PLD programmer.

12-2 Programmable Logic Devices—Analysis Problems

*1. Determine the following parameters from the GAL16V8A data sheet:
   a. V_{CC} operating range
   b. Switching input and output timing reference levels
   c. Output low and high voltages
   d. Input low and high voltages
   e. Fan-out
   f. Maximum frequency for synchronous and asynchronous operation
   g. Clock period and width of clock high and clock low levels
   h. Data setup time for input or feedback

12-6 PLD Combinational Logic Applications—Application and Design Problems

2. Design an 8-bit binary to gray code converter.

*3. Design an 8-bit gray to binary code converter.

4. Design a BCD to binary code converter for binary values 0 through 31.

5. Design a binary to BCD code converter for binary values 0 through 31.

*6. Design a quad 3-input multiplexer.

7. Design a code encypherer as described by Problem 3-118.

8. Design a code decypherer to recover the original code after the encryption of Problem 7.

* *See* Answers to Selected Problems.

9. Design a decimal to binary priority encoder with an output strobe that performs according to the function table of the 74148 encoder.

10. Design the display decoder driver circuit described in Problem 5-21.

11. Design the display decoder driver circuit described in Problem 5-22.

12. Design the display decoder driver circuit described in Problem 5-23.

12-7 PLD Sequential Logic Applications—Application and Design Problems

*13. Design a 5-bit R-S latch PLD with true outputs.

14. Design a six-stage toggle flip-flop PLD with preset and clear inputs that control all six stages.

15. Design a 6-bit shift register with mode controls for shifting right, shifting left, parallel loading the data, and holding the data. The design should include serial and parallel inputs and parallel outputs.

16. Design a 4-bit MOD-16 up/down counter.

*17. Design a 4-bit decade up/down counter.

18. Design a synchronous sequence generator that repeatedly generates the following sequence of binary numbers: 2, 3, 6, 5, 8, 9, 13, 12.

19. To the sequence generator of Problem 18, add a self-correcting feature so that the counter starts again back at 2 if any unwanted states occur.

20. Design an 8-bit ring counter.

21. Design a 6-bit modified twisted ring counter.

*22. Design a 6-bit Johnson counter.

23. Design an 4-bit maximum length ring counter.

Chapter 13

Semiconductor Memory Technology

Upon completing and mastering the material in this chapter, you should be able to understand semiconductor memory devices and how they are used in digital logic systems in the following areas of analysis, application, and design:

ANALYSIS

1. Be familiar with memory storage characteristics.
2. Compare and contrast volatile and nonvolatile memory operation.
3. Understand NMOS, CMOS, and bipolar memory types.
4. Understand read only memories.
5. Understand read–write memories.
6. Understand static and dynamic memories.
7. Interpret memory specifications and data sheets.
8. Understand memory capacity and organization.
9. Understand memory timing and operation.

APPLICATION AND DESIGN

10. Select the appropriate memory for an application.
11. Determine memory design criteria and parameters.
12. Develop a memory system design.
13. Apply memory systems to microprocessor based systems.

As logic designs become more complex, the need for the storage of digital information increases. Previous chapters illustrated how latches and flip-flops are used in small storage applications as counters and shift registers. Larger logic system ICs are specifically designed to retain large amounts of data. On a relative scale of speed and performance, semiconductor logic devices are some of the fastest electronic devices available. To utilize fully the speed of semiconductor logic, semiconductor memory must be used for storage. Other forms of storage, mostly magnetic media-based such as hard disk drives and floppy disk drives, are too slow to be used interactively with semiconductor logic.

This chapter introduces semiconductor memory concepts and emphasizes the practical selection and use of available memory ICs compatible with logic designs. Most advanced memory ICs are combined with the microprocessor in the design of powerful logic systems. The tremendous computing power available in personal computers (PCs) is a direct result of the availability of semiconductor memory and microprocessor logic.

13-1 INFORMATION STORAGE

Digital computers were invented to perform calculations rapidly. An integral part of the process is the ability to store numbers being operated on, including the intermediate and final results of the calculations. Since the operations are performed by using binary arithmetic processes, it is logical to perform the storage in binary form as well.

13.1.1 Evolution of Memory Technology

Memory technology progressed through a rapidly paced evolution that began in the 1940s with the first electronic digital computers and vacuum tube technology. In the 1950s bits of information were stored using discrete transistor circuits, magnetic core technology, and magnetic tape. In the 1960s several key inventions allowed bits of information to be represented and stored as electrical charge in transistor circuits that were no longer discrete, but were integrated onto small ceramic packages, about one-half inch square. Also, about this time removable magnetic disk packages were invented that stored large amounts of data for later access. Two distinct branches of memory were evolving: slower mass storage using magnetic media and much faster charge storage devices for internal computer memory. Figure 13-1 illustrates the evolution of memory technology.

In the 1970s the first monolithic memory chip was fabricated. With monolithic technology, all the circuits are fabricated onto a single silicon wafer. The silicon wafers, from 4 to 8 inches in diameter, are then diced (cut) into

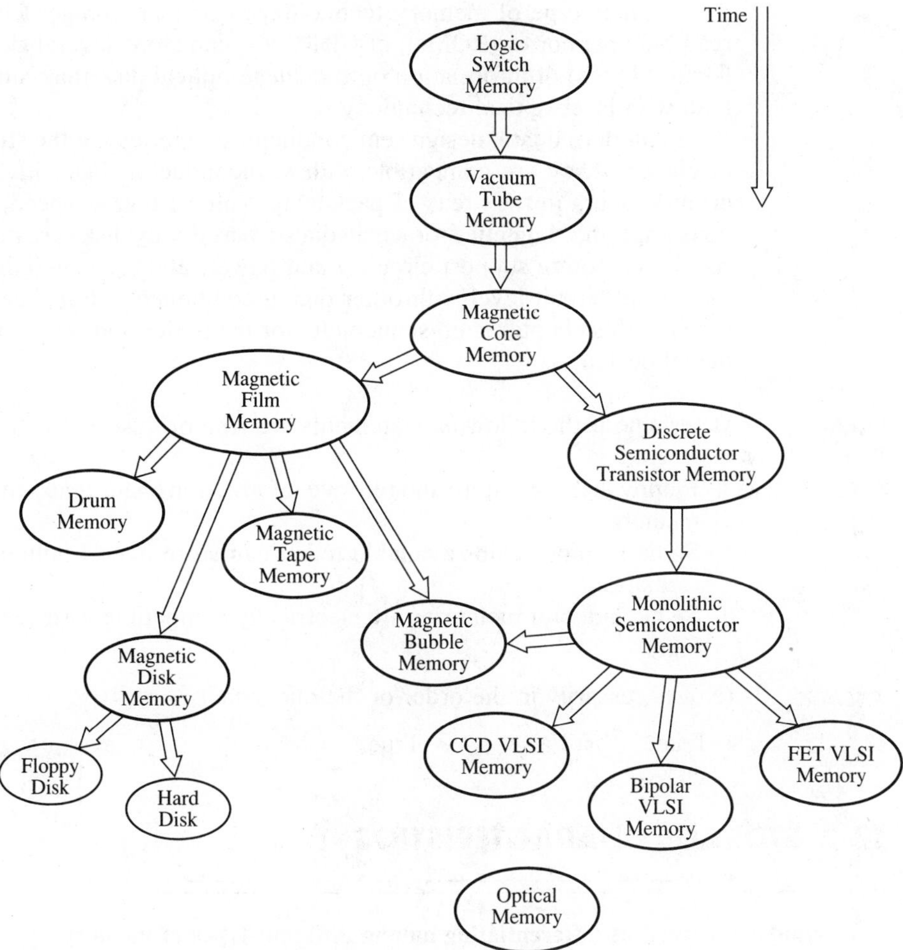

FIGURE 13-1 Evolution of Memory Technology

individual memory chips. Each silicon wafer may contain hundreds of memory chips.

The first monolithic memory chips had only eight individual memory bits per chip. In 1978 memory chips were manufactured that had over 64,000 memory bits (64 kilobits) (64 Kb) per chip. Today 4 megabit (4 Mb) memory chips with over 4 million memory bits are mass produced, 16 Mb memory chips are experimentally fabricated, and development work is underway for 64 Mb memory chips.

In the magnetic media branch of memory technology, floppy disks were invented in 1970 with the capability of storing hundreds of thousands of bytes of information. Today floppy disk technology allows well over one million bytes of information to be stored onto a disk.

Another type of memory technology is optical storage. Compact disk read only memories (ROMs), or CDROMs, can store several gigabytes (billions of bytes) of information onto a single optical disk that can be quickly read with laser optical technology.

In modern digital design semiconductor memories are the storage media of choice. They are compatible with semiconductor logic, PLDs, and microprocessors in the areas of packaging, voltage levels, speed, and power consumption. Magnetic storage media such as floppy disks are much slower, require elaborate support circuitry and power, and are generally incompatible at the circuit level with other digital components. For this reason, the focus of this chapter is on semiconductor memories and their application to digital design.

Section Self-Test

Determine if the following statements are true or false:

1. Floppy disks can store and retrieve information faster than semiconductor memory.
2. Some memory chips available today can store over 4 million bits of information.
3. Semiconductor memories are electrically compatible with semiconductor logic.

ANSWERS (Not necessarily in the order of the questions)

- True
- False
- True

13-2 STORAGE CHARACTERISTICS

A standard method of differentiating among different types of memory devices is to categorize them according to their storage characteristics. Semiconductor memories can retain the binary information stored in memory cells for varying amounts of time depending on the type of memory. The four major storage characteristics are volatile, non-volatile, dynamic, and static.

13.2.1 Volatile and Non-volatile Memories

Semiconductor memories that lose their stored information when power is removed are called **volatile** memories. The internal transistor circuits that store the information in these types of memories require a constant supply voltage to operate. Circuits of this type are referred to as **active storage** circuits. If the power to a volatile memory is interrupted or removed, the entire memory contents will be lost. Therefore, volatile memory is most suitable for applications requiring temporary memory storage.

Non-volatile memory retains stored information even when power to the memory is removed. The internal transistor circuits in non-volatile memories are designed to store binary bits permanently without active transistor action. This is sometimes referred to as **passive storage.** Non-volatile memories are ideally suited to applications requiring permanent memory storage. Computer and microprocessor software operating programs are stored in non-volatile memory. When computers are turned off, the operating system software will still be stored, allowing the computer to "boot up" or start when the power is restored.

13.2.2 Static and Dynamic Memories

Semiconductor memories are further differentiated by two additional storage characteristics, dynamic and static operations.

Dynamic memories are memory devices that require periodic refreshing of the stored information. **Refresh** is restoring binary data stored in a particular memory location. The internal circuitry of dynamic memories uses a very simple capacitive charge storage circuit. The simplicity of the circuit allows for a very large number of memory bits to be fabricated onto the semiconductor chip, but the penalty for the simple circuitry is that the capacitive charge "leaks." If a binary 1 is stored in the memory as 200 femtocoulombs (fC) (200×10^{-15} Coulombs), in a few milliseconds enough charge will leak away so that the stored binary 1 will be lost. Refreshing the memory cell every few milliseconds restores the original charge and the stored bit integrity is maintained. Internal circuitry of dynamic memories restores the charge to every bit in a systematic manner and the contents of the entire memory is maintained. It may be helpful to think of a bit of information stored in a dynamic memory as having a name, and if its name isn't called every few milliseconds, the bit will forget who it is!

Static memories are designed to store binary information without the necessity of periodic refreshes. This is accomplished through the use of more complicated storage circuitry for each binary bit of storage. Thus, static memories store less information per unit area of semiconductor material (silicon wafer) than dynamic memories. The number of bits per unit area is referred to as a chip's **bit density.**

In the vast majority of devices dynamic and static memories are also volatile memories.

Section Self-Test

Determine if the following statements are true or false:

1. Static memories retain their stored information even if the power to the memory chip is removed.
2. Dynamic memories lose the stored information if not periodically refreshed.

3. The storage circuitry for each bit of a dynamic memory is less complex than the storage circuitry for a static memory.

ANSWERS (Not necessarily in the order of the questions)

• False • True • True

13-3 MEMORY CAPACITY AND ORGANIZATION

Memory manufacturers have devised a system to indicate the amount of storage capacity and organization of each memory device. Memory devices are commonly labeled with shorthand notation such as 256K, 64 Kb × 8, and so on that must be understood in order to select the appropriate size and type of memory IC.

13.3.1 Memory Capacity

The **capacity** of a memory device is the total amount of information that the device can store. For example, a 3.5-inch floppy disk has a capacity of either 720 kilobytes (720 KB) or 1.4 megabytes (1.4 MB). Semiconductor memories have capacities that range from 256 bits to 16 MB. The units used to represent memory size are shown in Table 13-1.

The capacity of semiconductor memories is also often referred to as the **memory density.** In reality, the memory density or capacity quoted in data books is a shorthand term and does not actually represent the exact number of storage bits in the memory.

TABLE 13-1 Semiconductor Memory Units

Unit	Term	Capacity (bits)
b	bit	1
B	Byte	8
Kb	Kilobit	1,024
KB	Kilobyte	8,096
Mb	Megabit	1,048,580
MB	Megabyte	8,388,640
Gb	Gigabit	1,073,745,920
GB	Gigabyte	8,589,967,360

TABLE 13-2 Semiconductor Memory IC Capacities

Memory IC	Power of 2	Capacity (bits)
1 Kb	2^{10}	1,024
2 Kb	2^{11}	2,048
16 Kb	2^{14}	16,384
64 Kb	2^{16}	65,536
256 Kb	2^{18}	262,144
1 Mb	2^{20}	1,048,580
4 Mb	2^{22}	4,194,300
16 Mb	2^{24}	16,777,216

Binary in nature, semiconductor memories are always manufactured in powers of 2. A 16 Kb memory actually has 2 to the 14th power memory cells or bits of storage, a total of 16,384-bits. A 1 Mb memory has 2 to the 20th power, or 1,048,576 total memory bits of storage. Table 13-2 lists several common memory IC capacities. Further, note that these same capacities can also be used to describe several memory ICs combined into a memory system.

13.3.2 Memory Cells

The bits of a semiconductor memory device are stored in an area of the IC circuitry known as the **memory array, or cell area.** Each memory cell requires a combination of transistors and capacitance to accomplish the storage and allow for retrieval of the stored information. Dynamic RAMs, for example, require one transistor and a capacitor to store one bit of information. Static RAMs require four transistors to store one bit of information.

13.3.3 Memory Organization

It is possible to **store (write)** or **retrieve (read)** information one bit at a time, or several bits at a time. The term that describes the number of bits written or read to a memory IC during one input or output operation is **memory organization.**

If only one bit can be stored or retrieved at a time, the organization is "by 1," signified as "× 1." This is also referred to as a **serial** memory. If

8 bits are read or written at a time, the organization is "by 8," written as "× 8." Eight-bit organizations are also known as **byte organized memories.** Another common organization is by 4, referred to as a **nibble organized memory.** Nibble and byte organized memories are also called **parallel memories,** as more than one bit is output at the same time, or in parallel.

A 64 Kb memory IC, if byte organized, will be listed in data books as an 8K × 8 memory. In this example the total number of memory cells is 65,536, and 8 bits will be read from or written to at a time, in parallel.

■ EXAMPLE 13-1 Memory Capacity and Organization

Problem: A manufacturer lists a memory as having two possible organizations: 32K × 8 and 64K × 4. Find the total capacity, organization type, and number of bits for each input or output operation for each.

Solution: The 32K × 8 memory has a total capacity of 32K multiplied by the organization of by 8 or a capacity of 256 KB, or exactly 262,144 bits. It is byte organized with 8 bits input or output at a time. The 64K × 4 has exactly the same capacity but is nibble organized. ■

Note that in Example 13-1 the memories are referred to as 32K and 64K (instead of 32 Kb and 64 Kb). It is a common practice to drop the "b" or "B" designation, and care must be taken to differentiate between bits and bytes when discussing semiconductor memories. The best practice is to completely specify the bit capacity and organization in any descriptions you may use.

Often eight bit organizations are referred to as **words.** A 64K × 8 memory organization can also be referred to as a 64K word with 8 bits per word. This unfortunate terminology has its origins in the jargon of microprocessors, since a word is defined as the actual number of bits that are operated on at one time by a microprocessor, or simply the size of a microprocessor's data bus. Using this definition, a word can range from 4 to 64 bits, as microprocessors are manufactured in 4, 8, 16, and 32, and 64 bit sizes. Always make sure to clearly define the size of the word when using "word" terminology.

Section Self-Test

Determine if the following statements are true or false:

1. A 64 KB memory has a capacity of 65,536 bits.
2. An 8 Kb × 4 memory is byte organized.
3. A one megabit serial memory will have an organization of 1 Mb × 1.

ANSWERS (Not necessarily in the order of the questions)

• True • False • False

13-4 MEMORY ARCHITECTURE

One of the important aspects of understanding the operation of semiconductor memory devices is understanding the way information is stored within the memory. Individual memory cells are combined with unique circuitry to give the memory its characteristics, known as memory architecture, or simply architecture.

The architecture of a memory affects its capacity, type, organization, and external pin connections. Addressing the memory chip is an important part of the architecture.

13.4.1 Addressing

Every type of memory chip has external pins or connections that are called addresses. **Addressing** is the application of a unique combination of HIGH and LOW logic levels to select a correspondingly unique memory location or locations. If the memory has a serial (by 1) organization, there will be one address for each memory cell in the array. If the memory has byte organization, eight memory cells (bits) will be selected.

13.4.2 Row/Column Decoding

For small capacity memories, there can be a unique external connection or pin for each address line. However, as memory capacities grew, it became impractical to provide an external connection (pin) for each address line. For example, a 1 Mb memory device requires 20 address lines to allow for unique selection of each memory bit. (Recall that 2 to the 20th power allows for the capacity of 1 Mb). The reason external connections must be kept to a minimum is that the package used for the memory chip can be kept as small as possible, otherwise the advantages of very large scale integration (VLSI) are reduced. A method known as **multiplexing** was invented to keep the external pin count to a minimum. Multiplexing is a circuitry technique that allows the same external connection to be used for two or more different signals, depending on the time at which the external connection is examined.

The most common way to multiplex memory chip pins is to use one half the number of address lines that are necessary for unique address selection. The memory will look for and latch the row address during the first part of the address cycle, then the memory chip will look for and latch the column address during the second part of the address. The total unique address can then be used by the memory chip as if it were supplied simultaneously.

Two signal pins are also associated with the multiplexed address operations. **Row address select, RAS,** is the signal that indicates the row address logic levels are being applied. **Column address select, CAS,** is the column address timing signal.

13.4.3 Input/Output Connections

The input/output (I/O) external connections are the part of the memory architecture that are related to memory organization. A serial memory has one I/O connection. A byte organized memory has eight I/O connections. The I/O connections are also referred to as the **data lines, data I/O,** or **data out** pins.

13.4.4 Relationship Between Architecture and Capacity

It is possible to determine the total capacity and organization of a semiconductor memory device by examining the memory architecture. The procedure is as follows:

1. Find the total number of address lines (pins).
2. Find the total number of I/O lines (pins).
3. Determine if there is any multiplexing being used.
4. If no multiplexing is being used, take 2 to the nth power, where n is the number of address lines.

   If multiplexing is being used, take 2 to the (2n)th power, where n is the number of address lines and 2 is the doubling result of the multiplexing. This is the total number of unique addresses for the memory chip.
5. Then multiply the total number of unique address locations times the number of I/O lines to obtain the organization.

The capacity is simply the result of performing the multiplication indicated by the organization.

■ EXAMPLE 13-2 Memory Capacity and Organizations

Problem: A DRAM has ten multiplexed address pins and one data I/O line. Determine the organization and total memory capacity for the IC.

Solution: If there are ten multiplexed address lines, the total number of unique address locations is 2^{20}, or 1,048,580 unique address locations. If there is only one I/O line, the organization is 1 Mb × 1. Thus, the total capacity is 1,048,580 × 1 = 1,048,580 bits of memory. ■

■ EXAMPLE 13-3 Memory Capacity and Organization

Problem: A memory IC has 16 nonmultiplexed address lines and 8 data I/O lines. Find the organization and total capacity for the memory IC.

Solution: The total number of unique address locations is 2^{16}, or 65,536 locations. Since there are 8 data I/O lines, the organization is 64K × 8. Thus, the total bit capacity is 65,536 × 8 = 524,288 bits. ■

■ EXAMPLE 13-4 Memory Organization

Problem: A memory IC has 12 multiplexed address lines and 4 data output lines. Find the organization of the memory IC.

Solution: The total number of unique address locations is 2^{24}, or 16 Mb locations, since multiplexing is used. Thus, the organization is 16 Mb × 4. ■

■ EXAMPLE 13-5 Memory Address Inputs

Problem: A nibble-organized memory has a total capacity of 1 Mb. If multiplexed address lines are used, what is the number of actual address pins for the memory IC?

Solution: Since there are four data lines (nibble organized), the memory must be 256 Kb × 4. To find the number of address lines, n, solve the equation $(2)^{2n} = 262{,}144$. With n = 9, thus there are nine address lines. ■

Section Self-Test Determine if the following statements are true or false:

1. The RAS is the refresh alternating signal.
2. A memory with multiplexed addressing has ten address lines and eight data I/O lines. The organization of the memory is 1 Mb × 8.
3. A 256-Kb serial memory has 16 data I/O lines.

ANSWERS (Not necessarily in the order of the questions)

• False • True • False

13-5 MEMORY TYPES AND TECHNOLOGIES

Up to this point semiconductor memories have been described in terms of their storage characteristics, capacity, organization, and architecture. It is important to categorize semiconductor memories further according to their type and the technologies used to fabricate them. Each type of memory operates differently, and its appropriate application in circuit design depends heavily on a thorough knowledge of the operation of each type.

First, the memory types are defined and described. In addition, the major fabrication technologies used today are discussed. Technology comparisons are made to differentiate further among memory types, aiding in the selection of the appropriate memory for an intended application or design.

There are two major types of memories: read only memory (ROM) and random access memory (RAM). Within these two major types, additional specific types are defined according to the memory device operation.

13.5.1 ROMS, PROMS, EPROMS, and EAPROMS

Read only memories (ROMs) are semiconductor memories that have binary information stored permanently within the memory cells. The stored information can be read by the memory user, but no information can be written into a standard ROM by the user. The information stored is **coded** into a ROM by the manufacturer. Coding a memory is often called **programming a memory.** Standard ROMs are preprogrammed by the manufacturer during the actual fabrication of the device. All semiconductors are fabricated in several processes, and each step is often referred to as a mask level.

A **semiconductor mask** is a section of glass or other material that has clear portions that transmit light and opaque portions that do not transmit light. Through optical and chemical processing, several mask levels are used to fabricate the semiconductor memory.

ROMs have their contents programmed during one of these masking steps, and therefore are also called **mask programmable ROMs.** ROMs are non-volatile.

Standard ROMs are used in applications when the same information must be used repeatedly. Personal computer operating systems and microprocessor software codes are examples of information that is coded into ROMs.

A special type of ROM, called a **programmable ROM** or **PROM,** gives the memory user the ability to program the memory as long as the memory IC is removed from the circuit application. A hardware device called a **PROM programmer** is used to store the user code into a PROM. This is often referred to as **"burning"** or **"coding"** the memory. A PROM is purchased from the manufacturer nonprogrammed and must be placed into a PROM programmer and coded before use. Standard PROMs are one time programmable; that is, they cannot be written to after the initial user programming. In some memory data books these devices are referred to as **one time programmable** or **OTP** devices.

Several types of PROMs are manufactured that can be erased and reprogrammed. This type of memory is an **erasable PROM** or **EPROM.** Currently there are two types of EPROMs available. **EEPROMs** are electrically erased by applying a high voltage (typically +20 volts) to the appropriate pins of the IC memory. Some types of EEPROMs can be erased and programmed while in their circuit application. Other types must be removed from the application and erased in a special hardware fixture. EEPROMs are also known as **electrically alterable programmable read only memories,** or **EAPROMs.**

A newly developed type of EEPROM, known as a **flash memory,** uses a single transistor device to provide an in-system electrical erasure of the memory. All memory cells are erased in parallel, and new information can be stored (programmed) randomly, a byte at a time.

UVEPROMs are erased by exposure to a concentrated ultraviolet (UV) light source. A UVEPROM can be identified by the transparent window in the plastic or ceramic IC packaging that allows for exposure to the UV light. The transparent window should be covered during normal use to prevent accidental erasure over time by the UV light present in ambient light sources. UVEPROMs are programmed with a PROM programmer just as normal one time PROMs.

Both EEPROMs and UVEPROMs have a limited number of times that they can be erased and reprogrammed. This parameter will be listed in the memory IC specifications. One major advantage of an EEPROM is that selected bits within the memory can be erased and reprogrammed. Every bit in a UVEPROM is erased when it is exposed to UV light.

EEPROMs also have several disadvantages as compared to UVPROMs. The cost per bit of memory is higher, and often the reliability of an EEPROM is less due to the application of the high voltages during erasure. Figure 13-2 illustrates the types of semiconductor ROM memories.

13.5.2 RAMs, SRAMs, DRAMs

The other major type of memory is the **random access memory,** or **RAM.** RAMs can be written to or read with essentially the same timing waveforms while in their circuit application. RAMs are valuable for applications where the data being stored is variable or changing.

Because of their read/write operation, RAM memories are also called **read–write** memories, or **RWMs.** RWM is a much more accurate description of the operation, as even ROMs have memory bits that can be randomly accessed. However, we will continue to use the term RAM for read–write memories since virtually all data books and manufacturers refer to this type of memory as a RAM. The important concept to remember is that RAMs can be written to and read from an unlimited number of times without removal from the circuit. The information written is stored for reading until the user decides to rewrite new information.

The major application for RAM memory is for the temporary storage of relatively large amounts of data. A latch can temporarily store one bit, while a shift register typically stores a byte of data. RAMs are used to store kilobytes or megabytes of information predominantly in microprocessor applications.

There are two major types of RAMs currently available, named according to their internal storage cell characteristics: a static RAM and a dynamic RAM.

A **static RAM,** or **SRAM** (pronounced ess-RAM), is designed with memory cells that retain stored binary information as long as power is applied to the device. Therefore, SRAMs are volatile memories.

A **dynamic RAM,** or **DRAM** (pronounced dee-RAM), is designed with memory cells that retain stored binary information for a limited amount of time as long as power is applied to the device. The cell storage time is typically 10 ms or less. In order to retain the stored information for actual usage, each memory cell must be **rewritten** or **refreshed** before the information is lost.

The amount of time a DRAM cell retains its stored information is called the **cell retention time.** Every cell in a DRAM must be refreshed within the cell retention time. If the cell retention time is 8 ms, every bit must be

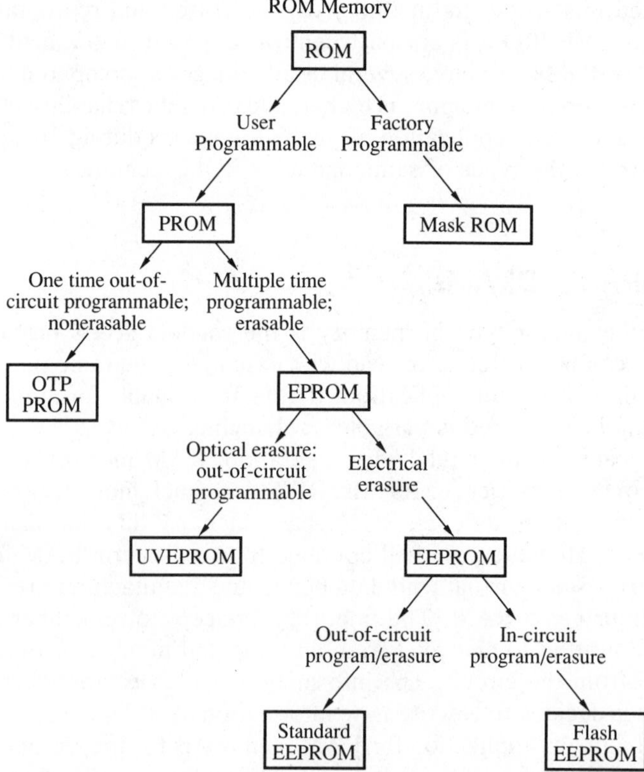

Figure 13-2 Semiconductor ROM Memories

refreshed in less than 8 ms. Fortunately, multiple bits can be refreshed at once.

Most DRAMs have internal addressing circuitry that automatically handles the addressing to ensure that all cells get refreshed. Thus, the user must only supply a pulse, as specified in the specification notes, to an external pin, often labeled refresh, to perform the refresh operation. The internal refresh circuitry is known as a **refresh address counter,** or **RAC.** The rate at which the user must supply a refresh pulse to a DRAM is known as the **refresh rate.** Again, the required refresh rate and cell retention time will be specified in a DRAM's specifications.

A valid question at this point is, "Why bother with the more complicated timing of a DRAM when a SRAM will store the information without refreshes?" To answer this question, it is necessary to understand the basic operation of the internal RAM circuitry.

Nearly all VLSI DRAM chips have a memory cell composed of one field-effect transistor (FET) and storage area in the form of capacitance, as shown in Figure 13-3. A 64 Kb memory has 65,536 transistor-capacitor cell devices, one for each bit of memory.

A logic 1 is represented by a small stored charge in the cell capacitor (typically 30 fC (30×10^{-15} C)), and a logic 0 is represented by a much lower level of charge, approaching zero in some designs. Because of its capacitive nature, the stored charge representing the logic levels eventually discharges (leaks) with time. When enough charge has leaked so that the memory circuitry can no longer tell a 1 from a 0, then the cell retention time has been exceeded.

Electrical engineers invented the SRAM storage cell to prevent the capacitive leakage by increasing the number of FET transistors used in each

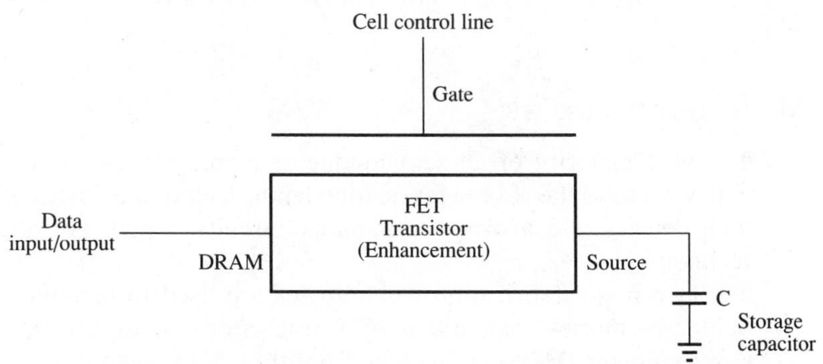

When the cell control line (CAS or RAS) is HIGH, the transistor is on, and the data on the data input/output line is stored in the capacitor C or retrieved from the capacitor.

Each bit of a DRAM requires one transistor and one capacitor. The actual circuit is more complex than the block diagram shown.

FIGURE 13-3 DRAM Memory Cell Symbolic Representation

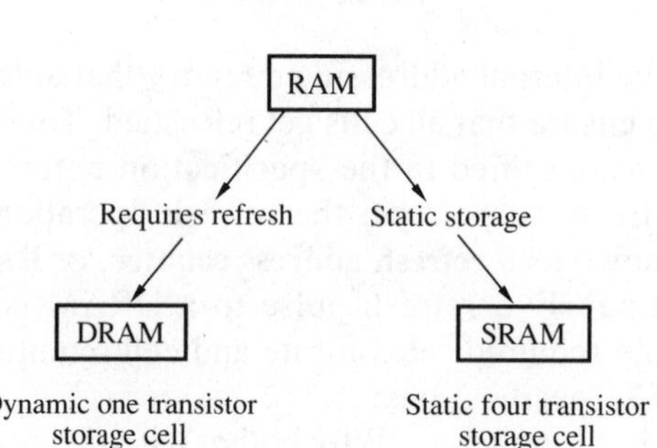

FIGURE 13-4 Semiconductor RAM Memories

storage cell from one to four or six. The penalty for using a circuit that can retain the cell charge without refresh is an increase in the circuit complexity and an increase in the size of each storage cell (since there are now four or six transistors for each memory cell instead of one). It takes more silicon area to produce a SRAM with the same memory capacity as a DRAM. Thus, DRAMs can be manufactured with higher densities, and in turn at a reduced cost.

SRAMs are used in smaller applications when the additional cost of an SRAM (vs. a DRAM) is less than the cost of refresh circuitry. DRAMs are used in applications when a large amount of memory is going to be used. In such cases the cost savings of purchasing DRAMs over SRAMs more than offsets the additional cost of refresh circuitry.

Figure 13-4 shows the different types of semiconductor RAM memories.

13.5.3 MOS Technologies

The vast majority of all semiconductor memories use FET transistor circuitry because the ease in fabrication lends itself to the design of very reliable high density and low-power memory circuits, which is critical for VLSI technology.

Two major fabrication technologies are used to manufacture semiconductor memories that utilize FET transistors. They are both **metal-oxide semiconductor (MOS)** technologies but they differ as to the type of FET that can be manufactured with the processing technology.

NMOS technology uses a type of FET transistor known as an **n-channel** device. Thus, NMOS is the process used to create n-channel FET transistors with MOS technology. NMOS, the first successful process for VLSI technology, is widely used for memory circuit fabrication. It is also a technology that produces transistors that can turn on and off very rapidly. NMOS transistors have typical switching speeds of less than 10 ns. Fast transistor switching speeds translate to fast data storage and retrieval.

Currently most manufacturers are fabricating semiconductor memories using the other major type of MOS technology, **complementary MOS** technology, or **CMOS.** CMOS circuits use both n-channel and **p-channel** FETs, and CMOS technology is capable of producing both types of transistors onto the same piece of silicon.

CMOS offers one very important advantage over NMOS. When both n-channel and p-channel transistors are used in circuitry, their operation complements each other such that the amount of current the circuit needs when the transistors are not switching is practically zero. The amount of non-switching current a circuit requires to maintain operation is referred to as the **standby** or **static** current. **Active** current is the current needed by a transistor circuit that is switching. Since there are thousands of transistor circuits on a typical memory chip, the total amount of current saved by using CMOS instead of NMOS can be substantial.

Historically, NMOS was cheaper to fabricate, produced faster memory, and was more reliable than CMOS. CMOS technology has matured to the point that the differences in cost, speed, and reliability are insignificant. Thus, CMOS is the technology most manufacturers use to manufacture semiconductor memories due largely to the reduced power consumption.

13.5.4 Bipolar Technology

Several semiconductor companies manufacture memories with circuitry that utilizes bipolar transistors. **Bipolar fabrication technology** is used to manufacture these devices.

The main advantage of bipolar memories is speed. Bipolar transistors can be designed to operate three to five times faster than MOS memories. The penalty for the increased speed is a dramatic increase in power consumption.

Section Self-Test

Determine if the following statements are true or false:

1. Bipolar memories are faster than FET memories.
2. A flash memory is a type of EEPROM.
3. A RAM can only be randomly accessed (read).

ANSWERS (Not necessarily in the order of the questions)

• False • True • True

13-6 MEMORY SPECIFICATIONS AND TIMING

As with logic devices, semiconductor manufacturers provide data sheet specifications with memory devices. Several parameters differ from logic device parameters, and in addition, there are parameters that apply only to specific types of memory devices. For example, only a DRAM will have timing waveforms associated with refresh cycles.

The organization of a memory device data book is examined. Also, specific device examples are used to explain the device parameters for SRAMs, DRAMs, ROMs, and PROMs.

13.6.1 Data Book Specifications

Memory data books are usually divided into sections based on the memory type and technology. Thus, typical section headings may be NMOS Static RAMs, CMOS Dynamic RAMs, or CMOS EPROMs, to name a few.

Within each section in a memory data book, the individual memory device specifications are listed. Table 13-3 lists the specification headings and a brief summary of the information found there.

TABLE 13-3 Memory Device Specification Headings

Specification Heading	Information Listed
Description	General description of the memory type and technology.
Features	Operational features of the device, including memory speed, power, and any unique features.
Pin connections	The number of pins, their names, and brief descriptions.
Block diagram	The internal block diagram of the memory device circuitry.
Absolute maximum ratings	The maximum physical and electrical conditions that can be applied to the device. Exceeding these maximums may damage the device. Typical parameters listed are maximum voltages, currents, and temperatures that may be applied to the pins.

Recommended operating conditions	The recommended voltages and currents to be applied for normal operation of the device.
DC electrical characteristics	The minimum and maximum voltages and currents the memory device will produce when DC biased. Typical parameters in this category are operating and standby currents, and I/O currents and voltages, including current leakages.
AC electrical characteristics	The AC operating timing signal values, listed by maximum and minimum time, and the complete timing requirements, showing timing waveform pulse widths, frequencies, and time relationships between timing waveforms. This section is used in conjunction with the next section, timing waveforms.
Timing waveforms	The timing waveforms are drawn for each of the different types of cycles the memory device can perform. These are the timing waveforms the user must supply to operate the chip. Various read and write timings are shown. If the chip is a DRAM, a refresh timing will be shown. Each waveform has the AC timing signals indicated, and the user must look up the symbols in the AC electrical characteristics to find the parameter value that corresponds to the symbol.
Capacitance	The input and output capacitance of each pin, typically 2–30 pF.
Application information	If included, this section contains valuable information on the operation of the memory device and helpful points on how to use the device in various circuit applications.
Physical information	This section often contains a listing and drawings of the different types of packages the manufacturer offers. Package size, pin spacing, and physical dimensions are indicated.

13.6.2 ROM Specifications

The first semiconductor memory specification to examine is the read only memory. ROMs have less complex specifications than most other memory devices since only the read operation can be performed with a ROM.

Every major section of the ROM is discussed in detail. Many specifications and parameters of ROMs are common to other types of memories. Thus, it is important to read and understand this section carefully since other specification sections build upon this information as the more complicated specifications and timings are examined.

The Hitachi HN62331 is a 1 Mb mask programmable ROM (PROM) organized as 128K × 8 bits. Its specification is presented in Appendix E. A detailed explanation of the HN62331 follows. The "features" section lists several important general specifications. First, the chip operates off a single +5 volt power supply, and the inputs and outputs are TTL compatible. The speed, listed as **access time,** is 120 ns. This means that it takes a minimum of 120 ns from the time an address is supplied to the chip until the contents of the memory at that address appears on the data out lines. Since this chip is byte organized, 8 bits are available for data output (read operation). In addition, the outputs are tristate, and the power consumption is low, using only 100 mW of active power.

The two photo/drawings shown at the top of the specification are the two types of packages available. The top picture is a standard dual-in-line package, or DIP, and Hitachi denotes this package by adding a P to the memory part number, HN62331P. The bottom package is a small outline package, or SOP, used in surface mount solder applications. Hitachi denotes this package by adding an F to the memory part number, HN62331F.

Below the package outlines, the pin placement for the two packages is shown. Both the DIP and SOP package have 32 pins. The number of pins and package size is in accordance with established semiconductor package standards.

The "block diagram" section serves to quickly indicate the number of address and data lines, the memory organization, and the operation of the chip enable.

The "absolute maximum ratings" section lists the limits on voltage and temperature that can be applied to the chip. Exceeding these limits will likely damage the device permanently. Also, note that the positive supply voltage and the ground connection are referred to symbolically as V_{CC} and V_{SS}, respectively.

The "recommended operating conditions" section lists the minimum and maximum DC supply voltages, input voltages, and operating temperatures. The minimum supply voltage is 4.5 volts, and the maximum supply voltage is 5.5 volts. These values represent the $\pm 10\%$ values of the single 5.0-volt supply. Ten percent is a standard minimum/maximum range for which semiconductor memory circuits are designed. The input HIGH level voltage, V_{IH}, is the voltage range that must be input to the address lines and chip enable for the chip to recognize that a HIGH is being applied. This value is a 2.4-volt minimum and has a maximum of V_{CC} + .3 volt. The input LOW level voltage, V_{IL}, is the range of voltages that must be input for the chip to recognize that a LOW is being applied. This value is a .45-volt maximum and has a minimum of −.3 volt.

The "DC electrical characteristics" section lists the DC operating conditions for the HN62331. Two parameters are used to describe the voltages that the memory chip will output to indicate a HIGH or LOW level. Output HIGH level voltage, V_{OH}, has a minimum of 2.4 volts for this chip. Thus, the chip will output at least 2.4 volts for a HIGH output, and although not listed, it will typically be in excess of 3 volts. The input LOW level voltage, V_{OL}, has a maximum of .4 volt. Thus, the chip will output .4 volt or lower when a LOW is output.

Several leakage current parameters are listed, and are important to consider when cascading devices. The designer must ensure that there is not enough leakage current that will flow within a circuit to activate or turn on the next device. When cascading devices, the leakage current is additive, and the current must be monitored more closely.

The supply currents are very important for calculating the amount of power that a particular device will require during operation and standby. Active currents are typically in the milliampere range for NMOS/CMOS devices and in the microampere range during standby.

■ EXAMPLE 13-6 Memory Power Requirements

Problem: What is the maximum amount of power that the HN62331 will require during active operation and standby?

Solution: The maximum active current is 50 mA. If the maximum V_{CC} voltage of 5.5 V is used, the maximum power is 50 mA × 5.5 V = 275 mW active power. The maximum standby current is 30 μA, and therefore the maximum standby power is 30 μA × 5.5 V = 165 μW. Thus, the active power requirement is over 1633 times the standby power requirement! ■

The input and output capacitances are shown in the "capacitance" section as maximum values, per pin, at 1 MHz. The 1 MHz is the indicated operating frequency, which in this case would be the frequency of the signal applied to the pin in question. The input capacitance for the HN62331 is 10 pF. These values are useful in calculating the amount of capacitive load that a device presents to a circuit and in determining the switching speed (propagation delay) of the device driving the memory input. Many capacitive loading calculations are currently made with circuit simulation programs, and these values would be input parameters for capacitance.

The "AC electrical characteristics" section shows the timing parameter values to be used in conjunction with the timing diagrams shown in the "timing waveform" section.

Since only read operations can be performed, the timing parameters are relatively simple. An analysis of the read cycle follows. First, the address lines must be set to indicate which bits within the chip are to be read. The address lines are always shown as two waveforms that cross. This is done since the timing diagram actually represents all the address lines; some of them are set HIGH, while some are set LOW. The point where the address lines cross is the reference point, which is considered the moment in time that the addresses are "set." Notice also that the chip select is an active LOW, $\overline{CE}$. This signal in essence turns the chip on and must be LOW when the addresses are set. With this chip, the access time is controlled by whichever occurs later, the addresses or $\overline{CE}$.

Recall that most standard decoders, such as the 74HC138, have active LOW outputs. Thus, decoders are designed to interface directly to active LOW $\overline{CE}$ memory inputs.

Two parameters indicate **access time.** t_{AA} is the access time from the addresses being valid (assuming $\overline{CE}$ is also active) and is 120 ns. t_{ACE} is the access time from the $\overline{CE}$ being active (assuming the addresses are already valid) and is 120 ns. If the addresses and $\overline{CE}$ are optimally switched, successive read cycles can be done every 120 ns. This is the **cycle time,** and for this chip the symbol is t_{RC}. For some memory devices, the cycle time is longer than the access time. That is, the very first read is performed at the access time, but successive read operations will take longer if done successively.

The **output hold times,** t_{DHL} and t_{DHA}, are both 0 ns. This indicates that the data will be valid until the next read cycle is performed by changing either the address lines or chip enable line. Thus, the data must be read by the device using the information before the next read cycle begins, or it must be latched in latches to prevent its loss once the next read cycle begins.

Some memory devices will have data hold times of 10 or 20 ns, indicating that the data will still be valid 10 or 20 ns after the next read cycle begins.

Also, notice that several parameters are associated with the data lines changing to a high impedance (HIGH Z) state. When not used, the data lines default to a high impedance state to prevent any type of bus contention problems with other memory devices that may be attached to the same data bus. This allows for more than one memory device to be attached to a common output bus. (See Chapter 15 for additional information on tristate outputs.)

13.6.3 EPROM Specifications

The next type of ROM to discuss is the programmable ROM (PROM). The PROM's basic operation (read cycle) is very similar to the ROM, so the discussion focuses on the programming and erasure specifications.

One advantage of a PROM is that the designer can program the memory. In addition, the memory can be reprogrammed a byte at a time to make changes in stored information. The entire memory can be erased by exposure to ultraviolet (UV) light.

The Hitachi HN27512G is a 512Kb UV erasable PROM (EPROM). It is byte organized, 65,536 × 8 bits, and packaged into a 28 pin DIP. The package has a transparent plastic window over the chip to allow for UV light erasure. The specification sheet is presented in Appendix E. The block diagram shows the memory array and address decoding circuitry. The diagram indicates that programming is accomplished through the use of only one programming pin, $\overline{OE}/V_{PP}$, in conjunction with the address and chip enable inputs. Also, notice from the pin arrangement diagram that the data pins are both input and output, labeled I/O_0 through I/O_7.

The programming of a PROM is accomplished one program cycle at a time. The HN27512G is byte organized, so 8 bits are programmed with each program cycle. It takes 65,536 program cycles to program the entire memory IC. Programming is accomplished by using the timing waveforms shown in the switching characteristics section and by following the programming flowchart shown in the data sheets. The memory address is first established. Then the 8 bits of data are placed on the data I/O pins. The byte of data is programmed into the chip by applying 12.5 volts to the V_{PP} pin and bringing the $\overline{CE}$ LOW for a minimum of .95 ms for the initial programming of the IC. Notice also that it takes a much longer time to program a PROM than it does to perform a read operation. The programming of a PROM is typically in the millisecond range for each bit or byte initially, and from 2 to 4 ms for each reprogram of the PROM. The entire HN27512G takes approximately 70 seconds to program.

The read cycle time (speed) of the HN27512G comes in two speed sorts, 250 and 300 ns. They are denoted by the addition of −25 and −30, respectively, to the IC part number. This is a typical practice among memory manufacturers. When the chips are fabricated, they are tested for speed and sorted. The faster chips are commonly higher priced.

There is also a high performance programming algorithm that can be applied to decrease the overall programming time when programming the entire chip. Manufacturers are very helpful in providing programs and assistance in setting up PROM programming devices for their particular chips.

■ EXAMPLE 13-7 Memory Programming Time

Problem: Assuming it takes 2.2 ms to perform one programming cycle, how long will it take using a normal programming cycle to program a 1 Mb byte organized PROM?

Solution: Byte organized PROMs are programmed 8 bits at a time. There are 1,048,576 bits in a 1 Mb chip. The total amount of time will be:

$(1{,}048{,}576/8) \times 2.2 \text{ ms} = 288 \text{ s}$ ■

All UVEPROM specifications list the amount of ultraviolet light necessary to completely erase the memory. In addition, the wavelength is typically listed. UV erasure devices are designed to output the necessary wavelengths of light for erasure, so the only parameter to be concerned about is exposure time. Since erasure lights have different intensities, the exposure time must be calculated from the minimum integrated dose listed in the specifications. The integrated dose is the UV intensity × the exposure time. For the HN27512G, the integrated dose is 15 W-s/cm^2. Complete erasure for this chip indicates that all bits are logic HIGH, or logic 1.

■ EXAMPLE 13-8 Ultraviolet Memory Erasure Time

Problem: What is the minimum exposure time necessary to erase completely a memory chip that requires a minimum integrated dose of 20 W-s/cm^2. Assume that the UV source has an output of 10 mW/cm^2.

Solution

$I = \text{UV intensity}$

$I \times T = D$

where D = Integrated dose, T = time in seconds. Solving for T, $T = D/I$, and thus at 20 W-s/cm^2

$T = 2000 \text{ s}$

$= 33.3 \text{ min}$ ■

13.6.4 SRAM Specifications

RAMs memories are no more difficult to understand operationally than ROM memories. The basic difference is the addition of timing parameters and waveforms for write cycles. Write cycles are very similar to the read cycles covered in ROM specifications. Only the parameter names and types change. The great advantage that a RAM memory offers over a ROM memory is that it takes the same amount of time to write to the memory as it does to read the memory. Thus, the contents of the memory can be changed an infinite number of times relatively rapidly. (Recall how slow the write, or program, operation of an EPROM is.) In addition, all write operations take place while the memory chip is in the circuit—another advantage over most PROMs.

The first RAM to examine is the Toshiba TC5563APL, 64K CMOS static RAM. This SRAM has an access time ranging from 100 to 150 ns, so it is considered a high speed CMOS memory device. It is organized 8K × 8, and has directly TTL compatible inputs and outputs, and comes in a standard .3 inch wide 28 pin DIP. Its specification is shown in Appendix E.

Examination of the pin diagram and pin names reveals that the data lines of this SRAM are labeled I/O_1 thru I/O_8. When data is written to the SRAM these lines are inputs, and when data is read from the SRAM these lines are outputs. The pin that controls the function of the I/O line is the read/$\overline{\text{write}}$ pin or R/$\overline{\text{W}}$ pin. A LOW level is applied to this pin during the write operation. This chip also has two chip enable inputs; CE_2 is active HIGH, and $\overline{CE_1}$ is active LOW. The timing diagrams show how these inputs can be used to control the write operation.

The maximum ratings and DC operating conditions are similar to those described for the ROM and will not be discussed in detail. However, always check these sections to ensure that the circuit application voltages, currents, and temperatures do not exceed the memory chip's limits.

The access time is the time from the application of the chip enable or valid address until valid data appears on the I/O lines. The TC5563APL has three types of access time parameters listed: t_{ACC} is the time from the setting of the address lines until valid data appears; t_{CO1} and t_{CO2} are the access times from the setting of the corresponding chip enable until valid data appears on the I/O lines. For this chip, the read cycle time is identical to the read access time. However, for many RAM memories, the cycle time exceeds the access time in order to allow the internal chip circuitry time to prepare for the next read cycle. In these instances the longer time between the access and cycle time governs the true memory speed.

The key parameter controlling the speed of writing to a RAM is the write cycle time. This is denoted for the TC5563APL as t_{WC} and is identical to the read cycle time for this chip (100, 120, or 150 ns). There are three write cycles shown for this chip, but they differ only in the signal that controls the write operation, either $\overline{\text{R}}$/W, $\overline{CE_1}$, or CE_2. The R/W-controlled write timing is described subsequently.

First, the address lines are input and set to the address being written to. Next, the R/W line is input as a LOW, indicating that a write is to take place. Next, both chip enables are active: a HIGH for CE_2 and a LOW for $\overline{CE_1}$. The parameter, t_{CW}, chip selection until the end of write, indicates that the chip selects must be active at least 80 ns before the end of the write pulse. The parameter, t_{DS}, data setup time, indicates that the data input to the I/O lines must be set at least 40 ns before the end of the write pulse. The write cycle is completed by bringing the R/W line HIGH, and the addresses can then be set to perform the next read or write operation.

It is interesting to note that several parameters are shown as having time widths on the timing chart, but their values in the AC parameter list are shown as 0 ns. One of these parameters is t_{WR}, write recovery time. Write recovery time is the time it takes for the memory chip circuitry to recover or setup for the next read or write cycle. Historically, this parameter was 10 to 30 ns. Through circuit innovation, the circuitry is automatically ready to read or write without any recovery time. But many chips still require this time, and manufacturers include it to indicate that this particular chip needs no recovery time.

Another interesting circuit innovation that the TC5563APL has is a mode called **data retention mode**. This feature is controlled by the current and voltage requirements of the chip.

In active mode the TC5563APL-10 requires a maximum of 45 mA when operated at its fastest speed and worst input levels, at a supply, V_{DD}, of 5.5 volts. In standby mode the same chip requires 3 mA at its worst input levels, with V_{DD} equal to 5.5 volts. Examination of the DC and operating specifications indicates lower typical current values and even lower current requirements if the TTL input levels are good (V_{IL} = .2 volt, and V_{IH} = V_{DD} − .2 volt)

Data retention mode is an innovation that allows the memory chip to retain its data at much lower current and voltage requirements. This is accomplished by turning off much of the chip's circuitry except for the critical memory cell circuitry. Since the SRAM is volatile, some power must be supplied to retain the memory. Data retention reduces the power to the absolute minimum needed to maintain data. For this chip, data retention mode is the application of as little as 2.0 volts for V_{DD}, and the standby current is thereby reduced to as little as 50 μA. Data retention mode is controlled by the chip enable timings shown in the specification sheets.

■ EXAMPLE 13-9 Memory Power Usage

Problem: Find the worst case power usage for the TC5563APL-10.

Solution: For the worst case data supplied for the TC5563APL-10, the power usage in the active mode is:

$5.5 \text{ V} \times 45 \text{ mA} = 247.5 \text{ mW}$

In the standby mode:

$5.5 \text{ V} \times 3 \text{ mA} = 16.5 \text{ mW}$

In the data retention mode:

$2.0 \text{ V} \times 50 \ \mu\text{A} = .1 \text{ mW}$ ■

13.6.5 DRAM Specifications

The last specification to consider is that of a dynamic RAM. The only unique specification parameters that a DRAM has in addition to those of an SRAM are those concerning the memory refresh and associated parameters.

One such parameter is availability. If a memory cell is being refreshed, it is not available for normal read or write cycles. Availability is defined as 100% minus the percentage of time the required refresh cycle interferes with read/write operations. Typically, the availability is 97 to 99+% and does not pose a design problem. Designers should be aware, however, that if a DRAM is used at its fastest cycle time for long periods of time, the manufacturers' application engineers should be contacted to aid in the assessment of availability problems.

The Toshiba TC514256 is a CMOS 1 Mb DRAM organized in the nibble mode as 256K × 4. Its data sheets are shown in Appendix E. The IC is available in a 20 pin DIP or small outline package, and has an access time of 100 ns in the fast sort. The read and write waveforms are similar to those a SRAM.

The TC514256 requires that a $\overline{RAS}$ pulse go active (LOW) to start the refresh process. The designer must ensure that $\overline{CAS}$ is inactive (HIGH) before the RAS is active, as shown by the parameter t_{CRP}. t_{CRP} is the CAS to RAS precharge time and must be at least 10 ns.

The timing waveforms also show that the address lines must be set at least t_{ASR} before the $\overline{RAS}$ goes active. t_{ASR} is 0 ns. This indicates that address lines can be set before or at the same time that $\overline{RAS}$ goes active (LOW).

The RAS pulse width, t_{RAS}, must be 100 ns or greater, with a minimum refresh cycle time equal to the read or write cycle time of 190 ns. Using this timing waveform, and cycling all of the address combinations for the nine address lines will ensure that the cell retention time of 8 ms will not be violated.

Section Self-Test

Determine if the following statements are true or false:

1. A typical DRAM has a cell retention time of approximately 100 ms.
2. Another name for the power consumption of a memory device being written to or read from is standby power.
3. The typical access time for a SRAM is from 80 to 300 ns.

ANSWERS (Not necessarily in the order of the questions)

• True • False • False

13-7 MEMORY COMPARISON AND DEVICE SELECTION

Often, deciding which memory device to choose for a particular application is difficult since there are over 20 major memory manufacturers, with each one offering several hundred memory devices. It is important to be able to select the appropriate memory device for a given application. This section describes important parameters that influence memory selection.

TABLE 13-4 Key Memory Parameters

Parameter	Description
Total capacity	Number of total memory bits
Organization needed	Bit, nibble, byte
Power requirements	NMOS, CMOS, or bipolar data retention mode
Volatility	ROM or RAM, battery backup
Speed	NMOS, CMOS, or bipolar
Packaging	SIP, DIP, flat pack, SOIC
Circuit use	ROM, PROM, EPROM, EEPROM, SRAM, DRAM
Cost	Design budget constraints
Reliability	Manufacturer dependent soft errors rates
Environment	Temperature, humidity, or radiation ranges

13.7.1 Selection Parameters

The first step is to determine the overall memory requirements for the circuit or system being designed. There are several key parameters to determine, which are listed in Table 13-4.

13.7.2 Capacity, Speed, Volatility, and Power Comparisons

One of the first parameters to consider for an intended application is total capacity. This controls the size of the memory devices to consider.

Related to capacity, the next parameter to determine is the organizational requirements. If it is a microprocessor application, byte organized chips will be needed. Serial memories are usually used by large system designers incorporating registers and redundancy schemes. Small system requirements are usually in multiples of 8 bits.

The next parameter to determine is the use of the memory in the intended application. Will the memory be used for one time storage of information, or will the information be changing? The answer to this question determines what type of memory to select. PROMs are often used for many small applications in the initial design phases. That way, if a mistake is made in the storage of, for example, a software program for a microprocessor, the PROM can be removed, erased, and reprogrammed. If the circuit is mass produced, the PROM code can then be given to a manufacturer to mass produce ROMs, which are cheaper than PROMs. If reading and writing is required, a SRAM is the likely choice for small system applications. No additional refresh timing is needed, and the cost savings of the DRAM over the SRAM is insignificant in small volumes.

If the design must be non-volatile, one can use a type of ROM or a SRAM with a battery circuit to supply power, when the rest of the circuitry is shut off. The data retention feature is a necessity for battery applications to ensure long battery life.

Speed is usually the next parameter considered. How fast must the memory operate? Keep in mind that faster memories are higher in price. Bipolar memories have speeds in the 5 to 50 ns range, NMOS in the 50 to 400 ns range, and CMOS in the range of 60 to 500 ns.

Power an important consideration if using bipolar memories that have high power requirements. Calculate power requirements using the worst case current and voltage parameters for design operating margin.

13.7.3 Quality, Packaging, Cost, and Environment

The remaining parameters—cost, packaging, quality, and environment—differ among individual manufacturers once a particular memory device has been selected.

The traditional standard package for a memory device is the **dual-in-line package,** or **DIP.** They come in standard pin counts and widths for compatibility with other memory and logic devices. Higher memory capacities forced manufacturers to invent other types of packaging to accommodate the larger number of pins required to operate the devices.

DIPs are mounted on circuit boards through holes and either **wire-wrapped** or **soldered.** This is called **pin-thru-hole board technology.** This technology limits the number of components that can be placed onto a circuit board since only one side of the board can be used for physical component placement.

Surface mount technology utilizes **small outline integrated circuits,** or **SOICs.** These packages are soldered directly onto a circuit board. The pins are bent to provide a flat surface for soldering. SOICs have a smaller package dimension than DIPs, allowing for smaller circuit board sizes for the same circuit board function.

Several types of packages were invented to increase the number of pins per package. **J-lead packages** are surface mountable devices (SMDs) in a square package with the pins bent into a "J" shape. All four sides have pins to provide more pin connections for high capacity memory devices.

Pin grid arrays are packages that have the pins directly under the package. They are used for high pin count devices and pin-thru-hole technology.

Plastic chip carriers, or **PCCs,** are another type of package for high pin count devices. Leads extend from all four sides of the package, but the leads are straight instead of bent as with the J-lead packages. This type of package is used in automated card assembly.

Flat packs are another type of SMD. Many types of flat packs exist, some with pins on two sides and some with pins on four sides. Their intended application is also in the area of automated card assembly.

Memory manufacturers conduct extensive testing of their memory products' initial and long-term quality. The reliability of a memory device can be predicted through these tests. When comparing memory products, obtain the quality and reliability specifications from the manufacturer. These specifications are not normally provided in typical data book specifications, but are provided upon request. The lower the failure rates, the better the IC quality and reliability. In addition, manufacturers can increase the reliability of semiconductor devices by operating the devices at high temperatures, causing the poor quality devices to fail and be rejected before being sold. This technique is called **burn-in.** Burn-in information should be requested if one is purchasing a large amount of memory. Longer burn-in can be requested for higher reliability at an additional cost.

Costs among memory products are usually an easy comparison to make. Parameters that add cost are high speed, high reliability, high capacity, and special packaging (non-DIP). Thus, cost alone is not a good parameter on which to base memory selection.

Some memory manufacturers offer military grade devices intended for applications in severe temperature environments. These parts operate the standard parts identically but are especially tested to ensure operation at the military specification temperature ranges. These parts usually cost more than the standard components.

The latest and largest memory technology often costs more than a memory device that has been available for several years. For example, a 4 Mb DRAM may cost $200 each, whereas a 1 Mb DRAM may only cost $40 each. Thus, 4 Mb of memory can be purchased at $160 by purchasing four 1 Mb DRAMs instead of the latest and most dense 4 Mb DRAM. Conversely, one is giving up board space for cost, as four 1 Mb ICs take up more space than one 4 Mb IC. These are some of the tradeoffs that must be decided by the designer.

Section Self-Test

Determine if the following statements are true or false:

1. Memory speed is a key design parameter.
2. Manufacturers can operate memory ICs at high temperatures before their sale to increase reliability.
3. The type of memory package selected does not affect the cost of the memory.

ANSWERS

(Not necessarily in the order of the questions)

• True • True • False

13-8 MEMORY SYSTEMS

Memory systems are circuits and applications that utilize memory devices. The discussion here is limited to semiconductor memory systems, and, in addition, the emphasis is placed on multichip memory systems.

13.8.1 System Requirements

The overall selection of a memory device for an intended application was covered in Section 13.7. The discussion at that point was limited to single chip applications. The same criteria apply to the selection of memory devices for system applications. The major differences between single and multichip memory applications are the methods used to address and select (decode) the memory. Power requirements are also larger in multichip applications.

Most memory systems in use today are part of a microprocessor-based system. In these systems both ROM and RAM are utilized. EPROM is typically used as a type of ROM since its contents can be erased and reprogrammed at the hardware level. The microprocessor or computer operating system is always stored in some type of non-volatile ROM memory. In this way the microprocessor system can always initialize when power is applied. Subroutines and user programs are stored in RAM to allow for fast data manipulation and programming changes via software. However, when power is removed from the system, the contents of the volatile RAM memory is lost.

13.8.2 Multiple IC Memory Design

Although very large memory ICs are available, it is necessary to be able to combine memory ICs into a memory system. There are several valid reasons to combine memory ICs.

Several different types of memory ICs can be combined into one memory system. This is commonly done in a microprocessor system design, where an operating system program is stored permanently in ROM, and user programs are stored in RAM. A microprocessor typically needs access to both types of memory, and this is accomplished through the combination of the RAM and ROM into one memory system.

Another reason to combine memory ICs is to increase the number of bits that can be accessed at one time. Very few memory ICs are fabricated with an organization any greater than an 8 bit output. However, a 32 bit microprocessor can access and operate on 32 bits simultaneously. In the case of a 32 bit microprocessor, 4 of the (× 8) memory ICs can be connected to construct a (× 32) bit memory system. This is commonly referred to as increasing the **width** of a memory. An example of this is illustrated in section 13.8.5, "Memory System Design."

Often the capacity of an individual memory IC is insufficient for a given application. If, for example, a 1 MB memory system is needed, 8 Mb of memory would be required. At present 8 Mb ICs are unavailable. One possible solution is to combine eight 128 Kb × 8 chips into a 1 MB × 8 memory system. This is commonly referred to as increasing the **depth** of the memory. An example of this type of memory design is illustrated in Section 13.8.5.

It may also be necessary to add additional memory to an existing digital design. The addition of a decoder and some support logic can facilitate memory expansion.

Finally, it is often more economical to combine smaller ICs into a larger system than to purchase a high capacity IC directly. This is due to the fact that the high capacity ICs are leading edge devices and typically cost more per bit when initially introduced (the cost is higher due to a high demand and low supply).

13.8.3 Memory Addressing

Recall that each individual memory IC has address lines that allow for the unique selection of individual bits in the IC for the purpose of memory storage or retrieval. Similarly, it is necessary to be able to control access to the memory in a system by addressing.

In memory systems it is convenient to define memory addresses in hexadecimal notation. Each group of four binary address lines constitutes one hex address digit. For example, a 64K × 1 memory, if the addresses are not multiplexed, will have 16 address lines since $2^{16} = 65{,}536$. Starting at address 0, the lowest and highest addressing for this memory will be as follows:

Lowest Address

0000	0000	0000	0000	Binary
0	0	0	0	Hex

Highest Address

1111	1111	1111	1111	Binary
F	F	F	F	Hex

Thus, it is common to state that the memory has an **address range** from 0000H to FFFFH, and that the **size** of the memory is 10000H. Note that if you count from 0 to FFFFH, there are 10000H memory locations. This can be verified by converting 10000H to binary: $1 \times 16^4 = 65{,}536$.

In multiple IC memory systems each individual memory IC has an address range and an address size stated in hex notation. With this notation, an entire memory system can be described by listing the address range for each memory IC.

■ EXAMPLE 13-10 Address Range

Problem: Determine the address range and address size for the following memory ICs: (Start at address 0 for each IC).

a. 256K × 4 EPROM
b. 1 Mb serial DRAM

Solution: (a) There are 18 address lines; therefore, the lowest hex address is 00000H and the highest address is 3FFFFH. The address size is 40000H. The × 4 indicates that 4 bits are output at each memory address.
(b) There are 20 address lines; therefore, the lowest address is 00000H and the highest address is FFFFFH. The address size is 100000H. ■

■ EXAMPLE 13-11 Memory System Organization

Problem: A memory system has ROM byte-organized from 0000H to 3FFF, and RAM byte-organized from 4000H to C000H. There are two PROMS of equal capacity used for the ROM memory, and two SRAMs of equal capacity for the RAM memory. Determine the organization of the PROM and SRAM ICs. What is the total memory capacity for the system?

Solution: The total ROM address range is 4000H. Thus, each PROM must have an address size of 2000H. Converting the 2000H to decimal indicates the number of unique addresses:

$$2 \times 16^3 = 2 \times 4096 = 8192$$

Thus, each PROM, if byte organized, is 8K × 8. Likewise for the RAM, the RAM address range is 8000H, indicating that each SRAM has an address size of 4000H. Each SRAM is 16K × 8.

The total memory capacity for the system is:

2 ICs × (8K × 8) = 16K × 8 ROM (131,072 bits)

2 ICs × (16K × 8) = 32K × 8 RAM (262,144 bits)

Total memory capacity = 128 Kb ROM + 256 Kb RAM = 384 Kb memory (393,216 bits) ■

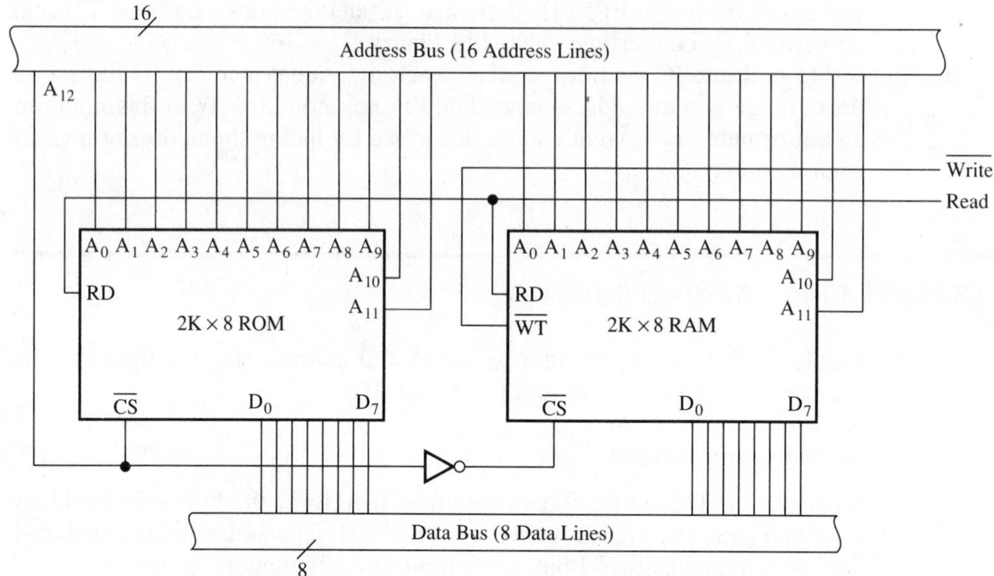

FIGURE 13-5 Basic Memory Decoding 4K × 8 Memory System

13.8.4 Memory Decoding

Closely related to memory addressing is memory decoding. **Memory decoding** is the use of logic gates or a decoder to select the appropriate memory ICs for a selected address range. In a memory system with multiple memory ICs, the logic designer must decode each memory IC through the use of address inputs into the decoding circuitry. This prevents bus contention that can occur without decoding. The decode logic output controls the chip select lines of each memory IC.

A simple example of memory decoding is illustrated in Figure 13-5. The memory system shown has an 2K × 8 ROM, a 2K × 8 RAM, and a total of 16 address lines. The address range of the ROM is from 0000H to 07FFH. The address range of the RAM is from 0800H to 0FFFH. Note that the common address lines for each IC are connected, with A0 to A0, A1 to A1, and so on. The data lines are also connected in the same manner. If an address is placed on the 11 address lines, the address will be input into *both* memory ICs. Decoding is necessary to select (turn on) the appropriate memory IC. To address 2K (2048) bits of memory, 11 address lines are needed. For the ROM in this example, 0000H is with all 11 address lines into the ROM IC at logic 0, and 07FFH is with all 11 address lines at logic 1. The other five address lines are all at logic 0. For the RAM, 8000H is with the 12th address line at a logic 1, and with the lower 11 address lines at a logic 0. The highest RAM address, 0FFFH, is with the 12th address line at logic

1, and with the lower 11 address lines at logic 1. Therefore, it is the 12th address line that changes between the two memories. This address line can be used to decode the memory ICs, as shown. Each IC has an active-LOW chip select. The ROM needs to be selected when the 12th address line is 0, and the RAM needs to be selected when the 12th address line is 1. This is accomplished by connecting the 12th address line directly to the ROM chip select and by using an inverter to decode the address line for connection into the RAM chip select. This same principle is used to decode any size memory system.

13.8.5 Memory System Design

Memory system design is a major part of the microprocessor system design and of more complex digital logic systems. Once the concepts of addressing and decoding are fully understood, the memory system design itself is straightforward. The designer has to consider also the important functional parameters and select the appropriate memory ICs for the application. The parameters of speed, voltage compatibility, power, and cost all influence the device selection. Several basic examples follow to illustrate further the addressing and decoding fundamentals.

■ EXAMPLE 13-12 Memory System Design

Problem: Design a 64K × 32 RAM memory system with a starting address of 0H. Use 64K × 8 ICs.

Solution: The width of the memory system is 32 bits. The width of the memory IC is 8 bits. Four of the ICs must be selected simultaneously to provide a 32 bit output. Thus, it takes four of the ICs to provide the needed memory system width. The depth of the memory system is 64K bits. The depth of the IC available is 64K bits. Thus, no additional ICs are needed for the depth. A total of four memory ICs are needed for the system design, as shown in Figure 13-6. No decoding is needed for this memory system since all four ICs are selected at the same time to provide the 32 bit output. ■

■ EXAMPLE 13-13 Memory System Design

Problem: Design a 48K × 8 memory system with 16K bytes of ROM and 32K bytes of RAM. Design the system with the ROM address starting at 0000H and the RAM address starting at 8000H. Use the following ICs:

8K × 8 EPROM   16K × 4 SRAM

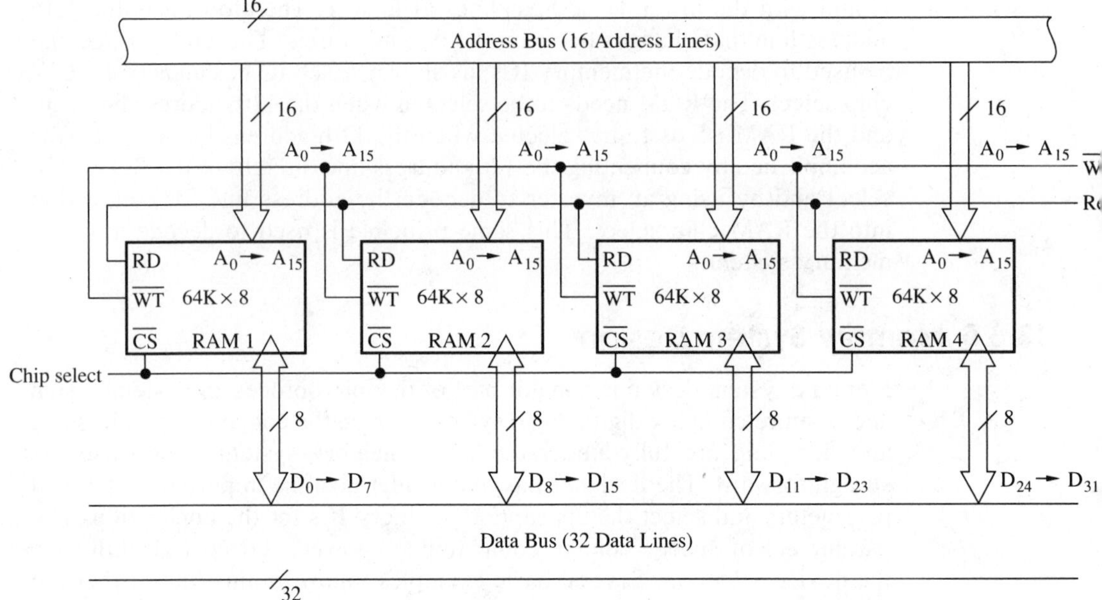

FIGURE 13-6 64 Kb × 32 Memory System

Solution: The width of the memory system is 8 bits. Since each EPROM is 8 bits wide, only 1 IC is needed to provide the system width. The depth of the memory system is 48K bits. The depth of the ROM in the system is 16K bits. The depth of each EPROM is 8K, so two ICs are needed for the 16K ROM depth. For the RAM, the width of the SRAM is 4 bits, so two ICs are needed to provide the 8 bit system width. The depth of the system RAM is 32K bits, and the depth of each SRAM is 16K bits. Thus, two SRAMs are needed to provide the system depth. A total of four SRAMs are therefore required, two ICs wide × two ICs deep. The address range of the ROM is 0000H to 3FFFH.

The address range of the RAM is 8000H to FFFFH. ■

It is helpful to construct a chart of all the address lines in the memory system to determine the decoding needed to provide the proper memory selection for the address ranges specified.

Table 13-5 can be used to select the appropriate address lines for decoding memory ICs. First note that A_{15} is always LOW for ROM and HIGH for RAM. A_{15} can be used to select between ROM and RAM. It is also necessary to decode between the individual ROM ICs and the individual RAM ICs once the ROM or RAM is decoded. Note that for the ROM, A_{13} is LOW for ROM IC 1 and HIGH for ROM IC 2. Thus, A_{13} in combination with A_{15} and additional logic gates can decode the two ROM ICs. The decode table using logic gates is shown in Figure 13-7a. Likewise for RAM, A_{14} is

ROM Decoding with Logic Gates

A_{15}	A_{13}	$\overline{CS1}$	$\overline{CS2}$	Comment
0	0	0	1	ROM 1 on; ROM 2 off
0	1	1	0	ROM 1 off; ROM 2 on
1	0	1	1	Both ROMs off
1	1	1	1	Both ROMs off

ROM Decode Hardware

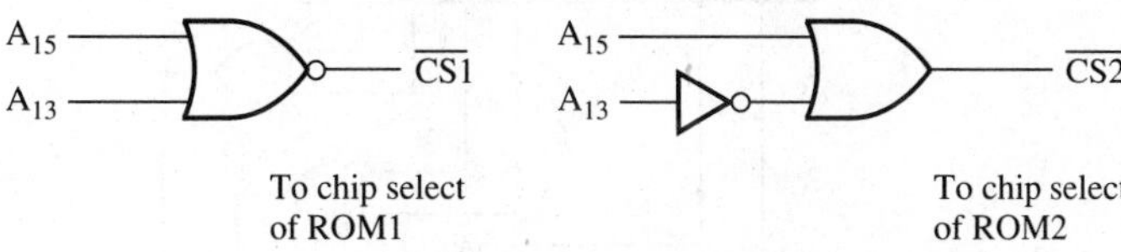

RAM Decoding with Logic Gates

A_{15}	A_{14}	$\overline{CSRAM1}$	$\overline{CSRAM2}$	Comment
0	0	1	1	Both RAMs off
0	1	1	1	Both RAMs off
1	0	0	1	RAMs 1 and 2 on; RAMs 3 and 4 off
1	1	1	0	RAMs 1 and 2 off; RAMs 3 and 4 on

RAM Decode Hardware

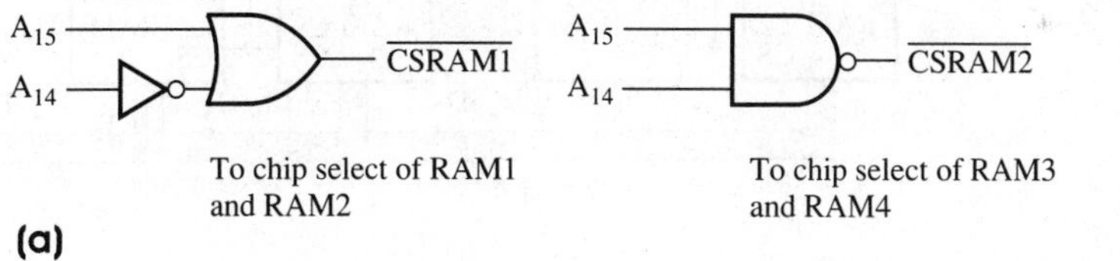

(a)

Decoding with a 3:8 Decoder

Select Lines C B A (A_{15} A_{14} A_{13})	Output	Comment	Address
0 0 0	$\overline{Y_0}$	ROM IC 1 CS	0000 — 1FFFH
0 0 1	$\overline{Y_1}$	ROM IC 2 CS	2000 — 3FFFH
1 0 0*	$\overline{Y_4}$	$\overline{Y_4}$, $\overline{Y_5}$ → RAM IC 1 and 2 $\overline{CS}$	8000 — BFFFH
1 0 1*	$\overline{Y_5}$		
1 1 0*	$\overline{Y_6}$	$\overline{Y_6}$, $\overline{Y_7}$ → RAM IC 2 and 3 $\overline{CS}$	C000 — FFFFH
1 1 1*	$\overline{Y_7}$		

* *Note:* Since the RAM is deeper than the ROM (8K for ROM, 16K for RAM), the decoder outputs for the RAM must be externally ORed to produce the circuit CS output.

(b)

FIGURE 13-7 (a) and (b) A 64K × 8 Memory System

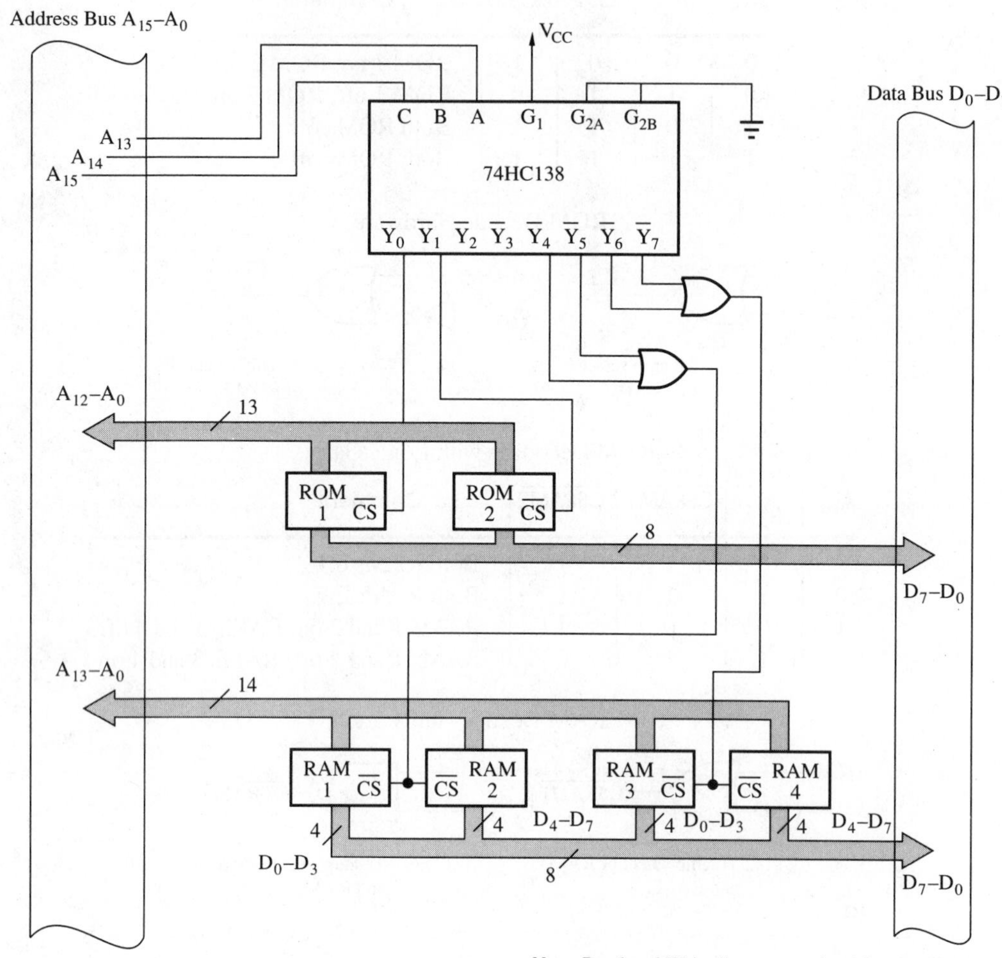

Note: Read and Write lines are omitted for simplicity.

FIGURE 13-7 (c) 64K × 8 Memory System Schematic

LOW for RAM ICs 1 and 2 and HIGH for RAM ICs 3 and 4. Thus, A_{14} in logic combination with A_{15} can decode the RAM ICs, also shown in Figure 13-7a.

Either discrete logic gates or a 74HC138 decoder can be used for decoding. It is often simpler to use a decoder for multiple IC memory systems by taking advantage of the binary select operation of a decoder. Figure 13-7b illustrates decoding with a 3:8 decoder.

A 74HC138 is used to select between the RAM ICs since this is one of the most commonly used decoders for a small memory system design. (A 2:4 decoder can be used as well.)

TABLE 13-5 Memory System Addressing

Binary Address Lines				HEX Address	Memory IC
A_{15} A_{14} A_{13} A_{12}	A_{11} A_{10} A_9 A_8	A_7 A_6 A_5 A_4	A_3 A_2 A_1 A_0		
0 0 0 0	0 0 0 0	0 0 0 0	0 0 0 0	0000H	ROM
0 0 0 1	1 1 1 1	1 1 1 1	1 1 1 1	1FFFH	IC 1
0 0 1 0	0 0 0 0	0 0 0 0	0 0 0 0	2000H	ROM
0 0 1 1	1 1 1 1	1 1 1 1	1 1 1 1	3FFFH	IC 2
1 0 0 0	0 0 0 0	0 0 0 0	0 0 0 0	8000H	RAM
1 0 1 1	1 1 1 1	1 1 1 1	1 1 1 1	BFFFH	ICs 1 and 2
1 1 0 0	0 0 0 0	0 0 0 0	0 0 0 0	C000H	RAM
1 1 1 1	1 1 1 1	1 1 1 1	1 1 1 1	FFFFH	ICs 3 and 4

The complete decoded memory system is shown in Figure 13-7c. Be sure to examine the decoder circuitry and verify the correct selection and operation of each memory IC in the system.

SUMMARY

ANALYSIS

Semiconductor memories are used for information storage in semiconductor logic designs. Non-volatile memories are used to store permanent information without the need for power to the memory ICs. Volatile memories lose their stored information if the power is removed from the IC.

Memories are described in terms of their overall bit capacity and memory organization. Today memory ICs with 4 megabits of capacity are available.

Two major processing technologies are used to fabricate semiconductor memories. Bipolar technology uses bipolar transistors in the design and manufacture of memories. Bipolar memories are the fastest type of semiconductor memories available, but they use relatively large amounts of power to achieve the speed.

MOS technology uses field-effect transistors (FETs) to fabricate memory ICs. CMOS is the major type of FET memory in use today. CMOS memories have sub-100 ns speeds, and much lower power usage than bipolar memories.

APPLICATION AND DESIGN

Several different types of semiconductor memories are available for use. They are selected for a particular design based on the application requirements for the design. These requirements include speed, power, packaging, cost, voltage and current compatibility, noise immunity, size, and operating characteristics.

ROMs are read only memories that have information stored in them before they are placed in a circuit. Once in the circuit, the information stored can only be retrieved (read). Several different types of ROMs are available, including PROMs, and EPROMs.

RAMs are read and write memories that have information stored or retrieved from them while in a circuit. DRAMs are the largest capacity memories available and have the highest storage density of any semiconductor memory. DRAMs are used primarily for large memory systems and require periodic memory cell refresh to retain stored information.

SRAMs have the same read/write features as DRAMS, but a more complex bit storage circuit is used to avoid the need for memory cell refresh. SRAMs are used in smaller memory systems that require in-circuit read and write memory.

Memory systems are combinations of memory ICs in a logic design. Addressing is used to control uniquely the access to each memory bit in the system. Decoding is used in conjunction with addressing to select the appropriate memory IC for a given address in the memory system.

Memory systems are used extensively as part of microprocessor systems. Microprocessors use the memory to store operating system instructions and the results of microprocessor operations. Chapter 14 introduces the concept of a microprocessor as an advanced programmable logic processing unit.

PROBLEMS

13-1 Information Storage—Application Problems

1. Define the following terms:
   a. information storage
   b. monolithic
   c. memory

13-2 Storage Characteristics—Analysis and Application Problems

2. a. Explain the difference between volatile and nonvolatile memory.
   b. Explain the difference between static and dynamic memories.

3. Define the following:
   a. chip density
   b. storage cell
   c. memory cell restore

4. List three applications for a nonvolatile memory.

5. List three applications for a volatile memory.

13-3 Memory Capacity and Organization—Analysis Problems

6. Define the following:
   a. memory capacity
   b. memory organization
   c. parallel memory
   d. serial memory
   e. byte, nibble, and word-organized memory

7. Explain the difference between memory read and memory write operations.

13-4 Memory Architecture—Analysis Problems

*8. Classify each of the following as serial or parallel organized memories and determine the number of address lines needed. (Assume no pin multiplexing is used.)
   (a) 64K × 1 (b) 256K × 4 (c) 1 Mb × 1 (d) 128K × 8

*9. What is the *exact* bit capacity for each of the memories listed in Problem 8 if no address line multiplexing is used?

10. Define the following:
   a. memory architecture
   b. addressing
   c. row/column decoding
   d. RAS and CAS
   e. multiplexing

13-5 Memory Types and Technologies—Analysis Problems

11. Define each of the following:
   (a) ROM (b) RAM (c) EPROM (d) SRAM
   (e) DRAM

*12. Explain each of the following. Be sure to explain to which memory technology each term applies:
   (a) mask levels (b) UV erasure (c) electrical erasure
   (d) refresh cycles (e) cell retention time

13. Use a memory data book to aid in finding two digital logic applications for each of the memory types in Problem 11.

---

* *See* Answers to Selected Problems.

14. Explain MOS technology. Describe the differences, advantages, and disadvantages of PMOS, NMOS, and CMOS.

15. Explain bipolar technology. Describe the advantages and disadvantages of bipolar technology as compared to MOS technology.

13-6 Memory Specifications and Timing—Analysis Problems

16. Use a memory data book to find a 1 Mb SRAM. Use Table 13-3 to create a specific memory specification sheet for the SRAM found.

17. Repeat Problem 16 for a 128K × 8 MASK ROM.

18. Repeat Problem 16 for a 1 Mb × 4 DRAM.

19. Repeat Problem 16 for a 64K × 8 EPROM.

*20. a. What is the minimum exposure time necessary to erase a UVEPROM that requires an integrated dose of 10 W-sec/cm^2 if the light source has an output of 10 mW/cm^2.
   b. Find a UVEPROM specification sheet. How does the number calculated in part (a) compare with the erasure time listed in the specification sheet? Explain any differences.

21. Refer to the Toshiba TC5563APL SRAM in the appendix. Copy the read timing specifications, and explain each waveform shown. Write the minimum (or maximum) time listed in the timing parameter section next to each timing parameter listed on the waveform timing diagram.

22. Repeat Problem 21 for the write cycle timing specification waveforms.

13-7 Memory Comparison and Device Selection—Application Problems

23. A designer has an application requiring data storage. She decides that a total memory capacity of 1 Mb is needed. Data is written to the memory 8 bits at a time in the application. Power is a concern, as only 200 mW of active power can be consumed by the memory ICs in the design. When the stored information is retrieved, it can take no longer than 200 ns. The circuit board on which the design is built uses pin-thru-hole technology.
   a. Use the preceding information to select the appropriate memory for the application. Be specific as to organization, capacity, and technology for the memory ICs.
   b. Use a memory data book to find a specific memory IC for the application. Construct a specification sheet for the IC.
   c. Several different types of memory ICs may be appropriate for the

design selection. Develop a list of questions you would ask the designer to specify more accurately the memory IC.

d. Contact a semiconductor vendor and determine the cost per IC and for the total number of ICs needed for the application.

e. What type of package did you select?

24. Repeat Problem 23 if the data must be read in 30 ns and power usage is not restricted.

25. Repeat Problem 23 with the following application changes: read time = 500 ns; memory capacity = 64 Kb; power consumption = 100 mW active; 1 mW standby.

13-8 Memory Systems—Application and Design Problems

26. a. What is a memory system?
    b. List three applications for a memory system.
    c. List four reasons why more than one memory IC would be used in a memory system.

*27. What would the highest address in hex be for each of the following ICs, if the lowest address starts at 0H?
(a) 2K × 8 (b) 16K × 8 (c) 256K × 1 (d) 256K × 4
(e) 1 Mb × 4

28. Find the highest address in hex for each of the memories listed in Problem 27, but with the starting address at 3000H.

29. What is the hex address size for each of the memories in Problem 27?

30. For each address size listed, determine the total organization of the memory system, assuming a byte wide organization.
(a) 1000 H (b) C000 H (c) 10000 H (d) 40000 H
(e) 100000 H (f) 800000 H

*31. What is the exact memory system capacity for each address size listed in Problem 30?

32. Explain the need for memory decoding.

*33. How many memory ICs can be uniquely selected by using only a 4:16 decoder?

34. Design a 128K × 16 ROM memory system.

35. Design a 128K × 16 RAM memory system.

36. Design a 256K × 16 memory system with 4 MB of RAM and 4 MB of ROM.

37. Design a 256K × 32 memory system with 64K words of EPROM and 192K words of SRAM. Each word is 32 bits.

38. Select actual memory ICs for Problem 34, and determine the amount of time it will take to read 16 bits of data from the system.

*39. a. How long will it take to read 16 bits of data from the memory system in Problem 35 if the access time of the IC chosen is 80 ns?
b. How long will it take to read 1 Kb of data given the same access time and a cycle time equal to the access time?
c. Repeat part (b) if the cycle time is 100 ms.

40. Repeat Problem 39, using the memory system of Problem 37. Use an access time of 100 ns for the RAM and ROM and a cycle time of 150 ns.

Chapter 14

Logic Design with Microprocessors

Upon completing and mastering the material in this chapter, you should be able to perform the following functions in the areas of analysis, application, and design of microprocessors:

ANALYSIS AND TROUBLESHOOTING

1. Understand the operation of a microprocessor.
2. Determine the size and speed of a microprocessor.
3. Understand how software instructions create programs to control microprocessors and perform logic functions.
4. Determine the basic parts and functions of a microprocessor system.
5. Select the appropriate troubleshooting equipment to test microprocessor-based circuitry.

APPLICATION AND DESIGN

6. Select the type of microprocessor needed for a given application.
7. Determine the types of peripheral devices needed for a microprocessor application.
8. Develop a complete microprocessor design by applying a set of systematic design guidelines to a given problem.
9. Compare the various types of hardware implementations available (logic gates, PLDs, microprocessors) to determine the appropriate type of hardware/software to use for an application.

Microprocessors are VLSI ICs used in systems to perform complex logic operations. It is no exaggeration to state that today's desktop personal computers, at a price of under $5,000, have more computing power than an entire room full of computers worth several million dollars in the early 1960s. The tremendous advances in computing are due to the invention of the VLSI microprocessor and VLSI memory.

This chapter serves to introduce the microprocessor as one option that is available for the implementation of logic functions. The material is introductory in the sense that it familiarizes one with the concept of a software program controlled type of logic, the microprocessor. Entire books are devoted to the details necessary actually to program and build microprocessor circuits, and this chapter does not intend to provide specific microprocessor details. However, a working knowledge of the terminology and aspects of microprocessors will serve as an ideal lead-in to any microprocessor course. Understanding the purpose and application of microprocessors will facilitate learning the detailed information contained in a microprocessor course.

14-1 MICROPROCESSOR LOGIC

The microprocessor is the logical evolution of the circuit designer's need for logic circuits that have more functionality. Logic gates can be used to make a flip-flop, but it is easier and more efficient to use a flip-flop IC. A memory device can be made from flip-flops, but it is easier and more efficient to use a memory IC. Likewise complex logic systems can be made from IC components, but the microprocessor was invented to integrate the function of many logic ICs into one multipurpose logic IC, the microprocessor.

14.1.1 Microprocessor Development History

The first integrated microprocessor was the 4 bit Intel 4004, introduced in 1971. In 1974 Intel was producing the first 8 bit microprocessor, the 8080. Motorola introduced a comparable 8 bit microprocessor, the 6800, in 1975, and the competitive microprocessor race had begun. Each of these microprocessors can execute a relatively complex logic function in less than 1 μs. The 8080 and 6800 are considered **first-generation microprocessors.**

Today both Intel and Motorola produce 32 bit microprocessors commercially, along with many other companies throughout the world. In addition to being able to operate on four times as many bits at a time (32 versus 8), the speed of the devices is over ten times faster! Currently microprocessors are **fourth-generation microprocessors**, with each jump in technology an increase in the generation of the microprocessor.

14.1.2 Logic Design Options

A logic designer has a wide range of design options and technologies available. Specific logic functions can be implemented with many different types of logic hardware. **Hardware** is the physical circuitry of a design, typically in the form of ICs.

A full adder, for example, can be built with several SSI logic gates, a single PLD, or a single MSI full adder IC. The hardware can also vary with the type of logic family or subfamily used.

At the system level an entire design can be built with logic gates, multiple PLDs, multiple MSI/LSI logic function ICs, or some combination of hardware. In addition, a logic system can be implemented with a VLSI logic IC known as a microprocessor.

14.1.3 Microprocessor Size

One way to refer to microprocessors is by the size of the data bus. Put another way, the size of the data bus is determined by the maximum number of bits of data that can be input to or output from the microprocessor. Thus, an 8 bit microprocessor has an 8 bit data bus in a logic system; a 16 bit microprocessor has a 16 bit data bus; and a 32 bit microprocessor has a 32 bit data bus. The larger the bus is, the more computing power the microprocessor has since it is capable of manipulating a larger number of bits simultaneously.

14.1.4 Functions, Codes, and Software

A **microprocessor** is a VLSI logic IC that can perform multiple logic functions, and in addition, can perform complex arithmetic, memory, and I/O operations. The symbolic shorthand for a microprocessor is "**μP.**"

The microprocessor is unique in that its logical function is controlled by an **instruction code**. An instruction code is a specific combination of logic bits needed for a microprocessor or computer to execute its logic operations. The instruction code is also known as an **operation code** or **op code**.

Depending on the type and complexity of the microprocessor, it will have from several to several hundred op codes available for a logic designer to use to control the microprocessor. The entire group of op codes for a microprocessor is collectively called the **instruction set**.

A designer selects the appropriate instruction code for the microprocessor to perform the desired logic function. The designer has available every instruction in the microprocessor instruction set and can select multiple instructions for the μP to execute. The selection of code in this manner is referred to as **programming,** and the code is a **program.** A program for execution by a microprocessor or computer is known as **software.** This term refers to the fact that the program can be changed, and the microprocessor will then perform different logic functions. Logic gate ICs are **hard-wired** (soldered into a circuit), and their logic function cannot be changed. A microprocessor is also hard-wired, but its logic function can be changed (i.e., is soft) with a program (software). The change in a program does not require any physical removal or manipulation of the microprocessor. It is the programming flexibility that is a major advantage a microprocessor offers over other types of logic.

Section Self-Test

Determine if the following statements are true or false:

1. An 8 bit microprocessor has an address bus that is 8 bits.
2. The 32 bit microprocessors available today are first-generation microprocessors.
3. An op code is a unique set of bits used to instruct the microprocessor how to operate.

ANSWERS (not necessarily in the order of the questions)

• True • False • False

14-2 MICROPROCESSOR INSTRUCTIONS

The microprocessor instruction set contains coded software instructions for the μP to perform specific operations. Although all the operations a microprocessor performs at the circuit level are digital logic, at the functional level the instructions are divided into groups. The instructions in each group perform a specific type of function, including arithmetic, logic, program control, input/output, register operations, memory operations, and microprocessor status.

14.2.1 Logic Operations

The seven basic logic operations of NOT, AND, NAND, OR, NOR, XOR, and XNOR are in this functional grouping. Other logical operations, such as compare, shift left, or shift right, may also be included in the instruction set.

14.2.2 Arithmetic Operations

Arithmetic operations a microprocessor may have in the instruction set include addition, subtraction, increment, decrement, division, and multiplication.

14.2.3 Input/Output Operations

A microprocessor can input and output data to devices connected to the microprocessor system bus. It is the input and output of coded data to external devices that allows a microprocessor to control physical functions. This feature, in turn, is used to control physical devices such as electric motors, automobile engines, speech devices, robotic arms, clocks, calculators, computers, microwave ovens, answering machines, and so on.

Data can be input or output (I/O) either one bit at a time, **serially**, or several bits at a time, in **parallel.** The place on a microprocessor or computer where data is input or output is known as a **port.** The port is the connection point of an external device to a microprocessor.

An 8 bit parallel port, for example, can be programmed to transfer 8 bits *into* the microprocessor from an external device, or *out of* the microprocessor to an external device. Some microprocessors allow for some bits to be input and for some bits to be output on the same port.

■ EXAMPLE 14-1 Microprocessor Ports

Problem: A logic designer wants to output from an 8 bit microprocessor two 8 bit numbers for simultaneous display on LEDs, then parallel input 8 bits of data from switches. Once the bits from the switches are input, output an indicator bit to a status LED. List the type and number of ports needed.

Solution: To display the 8 bit numbers from an 8 bit microprocessor, two 8 bit parallel ports must be configured as output ports. To input 8 bits of data in parallel, an 8 bit parallel port must be configured for input. The one bit of indicator status can be output on a serial port. Thus, three 8-bit parallel ports and one serial port will be required. ■

14.2.4 Register and Data Transfer Operations

Registers on a microprocessor are functionally the same as the logic registers (shift registers, e.g.) discussed earlier in the text. Registers are temporary memory storage locations used by the microprocessor. This temporary data may be the actual coded instruction (op code), the result of a logic or arithmetic operation, or any of a number of other types of data that a microprocessor uses in its operation.

For example, a special register, known as an **accumulator,** is often designated as the register that will contain the result of a microprocessor operation. On a conceptual level, if 5 and 4 were added, the result of 9 would be found in the accumulator. If this were performed in a microprocessor with an 8 bit accumulator, the actual contents of the accumulator would be 9 in binary, 0 0 0 0 1 0 0 1.

Register operations also include the movement of data from one register to another. In the preceding example, if the result of the first operation was to be temporarily saved before another addition occurred, it could be moved from the accumulator to another data register by using a register move instruction.

14.2.5 Memory Operations

A basic part of any microprocessor system is memory. A microprocessor has some **internal memory,** which is memory designed into the microprocessor IC. In addition, it may be necessary to add **external memory** to the microprocessor system to allow for additional data storage.

There are store instructions that save data from a microprocessor register to external memory, and there are retrieve instructions that get data from external memory and place it in a microprocessor register.

A special memory area, also used for temporary storage, is a **memory stack.** The memory stack is an area of memory that is used for the temporary storage and retrieval of data. As data is placed in the stack, a special register, known as the **stack pointer**, keeps track of the last memory address used in the stack. The microprocessor uses the stack pointer in combination with the memory operation instructions to store and retrieve data. A stack is needed for extra storage since microprocessors have a limited number of internal data registers.

14.2.6 Program Control

Program control instructions allow the programmer to change the order in which the instructions are executed by the μP. They include **jumps** from one part of the program to another, or execute a separate program known as a **subroutine.** A subroutine is a program that is designed to execute one specific function in support of a main program.

For example, consider a program written to count from 1 to 10, and display each number on a display for one second. It is appropriate to write a time subroutine that can wait one second, and execute or **call** the program from the main program ten times, one for each second of count display.

14.2.7 Microprocessor Status

Status instructions are used to determine the result of operations, exactly what the microprocessor is in the process of doing, or status condition of some I/O or memory device. They can be used to execute **conditional instructions.** Conditional instructions are instructions that are only executed if a particular condition previously occurred.

For example, a programmer may want a program to stop executing if the subtraction of two numbers results in a 0 value. If the result of the subtraction was not 0, then the program is to continue. Conditional instructions can be used for this purpose.

Section Self-Test

Determine if the following statements are true or false:

1. An accumulator is a type of internal register found in most microprocessors.
2. A stack pointer is used to count the number of op codes used in a microprocessor program.
3. The microprocessor port is used to perform arithmetic operations.

ANSWERS (not necessarily in the order of the questions)

- True
- False
- False

14-3 MICROPROCESSOR SYSTEM ARCHITECTURE

Microprocessors are software-controlled logic ICs capable of performing many complex logic functions. In order to be of practical use in digital logic applications, the microprocessor must be combined into a digital system with additional memory storage capacity and interface hardware to allow the microprocessor to communicate with its application environment. The combination of a microprocessor, memory, and input/output hardware is referred to as a microprocessor system.

14.3.1 Microprocessor System Functional Blocks

A microprocessor system is one type of computer system. All computer systems have three basic functional blocks: a **processing unit, memory,** and **input/output (I/O).** All microprocessor ICs have an internal processing unit, and depending on the degree of integration, they may also have internal memory and I/O ports. External processors, called **coprocessors,** may be added to the microprocessor system, as well as external memory and I/O ports. A coprocessor is used to share some of the processing functions a microprocessor must perform. By having two processors work simultaneously, the overall operations being performed by the microprocessor system can be completed faster. This is a basic type of **parallel processing.** Thus, the addition of a coprocessor can improve the performance (speed) of a microprocessor-based system.

The connections between the microprocessor IC and other external processor, memory, and I/O ICs are **bus lines,** collectively known as a **bus.** There are three basic microprocessor system buses; the **address bus,** the **data bus,** and the **control bus.** A block diagram showing the basic microprocessor system architecture is shown in Figure 14-1.

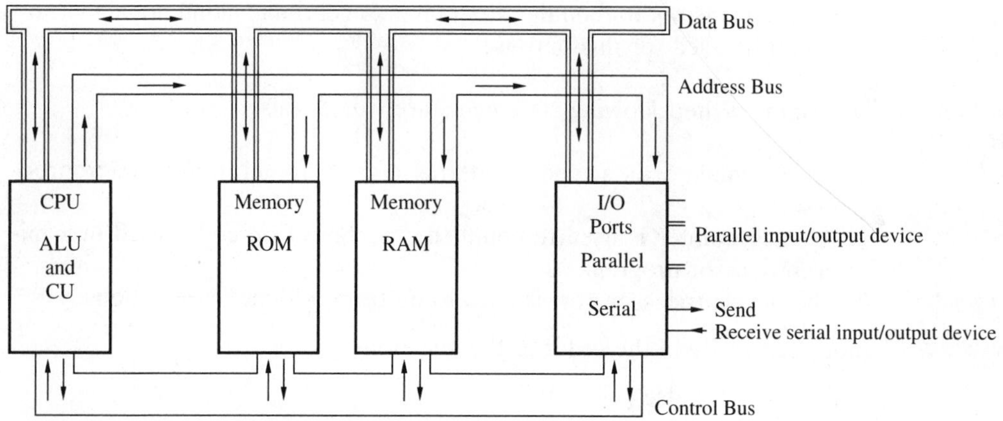

FIGURE 14-1 Basic Microprocessor System Architecture

14.3.2 Central Processor Unit (CPU)

The **central processor unit,** abbreviated **CPU,** performs the computational tasks of the microprocessor system and controls the operation and timing of the other microprocessor system blocks. The CPU has an **arithmetic/logic unit, ALU,** to process arithmetic and logic functions. The **control unit, CU,** does the overall system timing and operation control. The CU is responsible for executing the software program instructions.

Internal ROM in the CPU contains the coded instruction set for the microprocessor. Additional codes may be placed in the CPU by the manufacturer, depending on the type of microprocessor and the amount of internal memory available on the IC.

14.3.3 Read Only Memory

The read only memory (ROM) is external memory used to store information that will be used repeatedly by the μP. This information includes the operating system code to initialize (boot-up) the μP system, small programs and subroutines for frequently used functions, and various display and control system software. The ROM may be a PROM that can be changed to enhance or alter the operation of a microprocessor system. It is important that the operating system and control programs are stored in ROM, as they must be nonvolatile so that the system will always be operational upon power-up.

14.3.4 Random Access Memory

The random access memory (RAM) is external memory used to store the user programs and for external stack memory. The amount of RAM usually exceeds the amount of ROM in a μP system since it must allow for user programs of variable length. The RAM is volatile and will be lost if the power to the microprocessor system is removed.

14.3.5 Serial Input/Output

Serial input/output (SI/O) is an external device connected to the microprocessor system that requires bits be input to or output from the device one-bit at a time, or serially. The actual point where serial data goes in and out of the μP is called a **serial port.** Microprocessors may have one or more serial ports. In addition, it is possible to use a μP parallel port for serial I/O devices by using one bit of the parallel port.

Common I/O devices that are serial include modems, printers, and other peripherals such as a mouse on a PC. Many data communication devices, in addition to a modem, are also serial in operation. The PC disk operating system (DOS) standard refers to serial ports as **LPT n,** where n is the number of the port.

14.3.6 Parallel Input/Output

Parallel input/output (PI/O) is the transfer of data to or from an external device several bits at a time. Standard parallel ports are 8, 16, and 32 bits in size. Parallel I/O has an advantage over serial I/O since multiple bits of data can be simultaneously transferred. Thus, parallel operations are often faster than serial operations. However, the parallel interface often requires additional timing and control signals and buffers, adding complexity, as compared to serial I/O.

Common I/O devices that are parallel include printers and plotters, and speech peripherals. The personal computer disk operating system refers to parallel ports as **COM n** ports, where n is the number of the port. The first parallel port on a PC would be COM 1.

14.3.7. Address Bus

The address bus contains all the address lines of the microprocessor. All external memory and I/O devices requiring addressing are connected to the appropriate μP address lines via the address bus. The memory address bus, as described in Chapter 13, is the same as the microprocessor address bus.

The number of address lines available on the microprocessor determines the maximum number of memory bits or I/O devices that can be addressed by the microprocessor. For example, the Intel 8085, an 8 bit microprocessor, has 16 address lines. The maximum number of bytes of addressing, is 2^{16}, or 65,536 bytes. With this microprocessor, no more than 64 KB of external memory can be included in the μP system. For comparison, some of today's 32 bit fourth-generation microprocessors can address several gigabytes of memory.

The address bus is **unidirectional.** The μP sends address signals to the external memory and I/O. If signals are sent in two directions on a bus, the bus is **bidirectional.**

14.3.8. Data Bus

The transmission of data to and from the μP occurs on the **data bus.** This includes information stored to memory, information retrieved from memory, data to an I/O device, and data from an I/O device.

The size of the data bus determines the size of the microprocessor. A 32-bit μP has a 32 bit data bus. The data bus is bidirectional.

It is important to connect only devices to the μP system data bus that are tristate; otherwise bus contention can occur.

14.3.9 Control Bus

The **control bus** contains all the signals used by the CPU to control the μP system. Some typical control signals include **I/O and memory, READ/WRITE, RESET, interrupts, clocks, status,** and so on. Each of the signals is unidirectional, but some of the signals are unidirectional from the μP to memory or I/O, whereas others are unidirectional from memory or I/O to the μP. Therefore, the control bus is not referred to as unidirectional or bidirectional. It contains unidirectional signals transmitted either to or from the μP.

Section Self-Test

Determine if the following statements are true or false:

1. The ALU controls I/O operations in a microprocessor CPU.
2. A microprocessor system's data bus is bidirectional.
3. One way to improve the performance of a microprocessor system is by adding a coprocessor.

ANSWERS (not necessarily in the order of the questions)

• True • False • True

14-4 MICROPROCESSOR TYPES

Several different types of microprocessors are available. In addition to size and speed, what differentiates the microprocessor (μP) types is the amount of memory, I/O, and special functions that are integrated onto the μP IC. The three basic types of microprocessors are microcontrollers (μC), general purpose microprocessors, and custom microprocessors.

14.4.1 Microcontrollers

A **microcontroller (μC)** is a type of microprocessor designed for use in small digital systems, typically performing one type of control function. In addition to the CPU, microcontrollers usually have additional timers and some internal memory and ports.

Microcontrollers generally have less internal memory than general purpose microprocessors. The instruction set for a microcontroller is usually smaller, and the cost is less than that of a general purpose μP.

Microcontrollers are ideally suited for many industrial and consumer applications in which some process has to be controlled. Unlike general purpose microprocessors, the software code is written and optimized, then written into the memory of the system with no intention of running any other type of program on the μC.

Typical applications include controlling the ignition and fuel flow on internal combustion engines (automobiles), intelligent toys, appliances, and audio electronics. Microcontrollers are used due to the repetitive nature of mass production and the need for low-cost microprocessors. Once optimized, thousands or millions of the same μC system may be manufactured, all built with the same software program.

These types of applications are commonly referred to as **embedded applications.** Embedded applications are used when there is no longer any access to the microprocessor system circuitry to make functional changes unless new software is coded externally and the PROM memory is replaced. Microcontrollers are also referred to as **embedded controllers.**

14.4.2 General Purpose Microprocessors

General purpose microprocessors are designed to allow for programming flexibility. Unlike microcontrollers, general purpose microprocessors are designed to perform a greater variety of tasks and have additional internal memory and a larger instruction set. The Intel 8085, 8086, 80286, 80386, and 80486 are all general purpose microprocessors. The Motorola 6800 and 68000 are general purpose microprocessors.

Typical consumer applications include PCs, workstations, video recorders, and telecommunication products. Automated manufacturing uses microprocessors in robotic arms, automated testers, and component assembly equipment.

14.4.3 Custom Microprocessors

Custom microprocessors are microprocessors that are custom designed and fabricated by a semiconductor processing facility. Custom microprocessors are used mainly by corporations that have semiconductor manufacturing facilities to support internal product development.

The custom microprocessor can be designed to perform logic functions that are unavailable in vendor microcontroller and microprocessor products. This may include some unique size, such as 24 or 64 bits, or incorporate some unique programming instructions.

The advantage of a custom microprocessor is that it can be designed to function for a unique application or to perform some operation that a commercially available μP cannot do. The major disadvantages are the time it takes to produce a custom microprocessor and engineering design and development costs.

■ EXAMPLE 14-2 Microprocessor Selection

Problem: A logic designer for a toy company wants to design a low-cost stuffed toy that beeps when a noise is detected. What type of microprocessor would you recommend? Why?

Solution: Since this application is very specific and requires a small amount of memory and I/O with a low cost requirement, a microcontroller would be the appropriate type of device to consider. An application this simple may not need a μc, and other logic technologies may be appropriate. ■

Section Self-Test

Determine if the following statements are true or false.

1. A microwave oven is more likely to have a microcontroller than a general purpose microprocessor.
2. A custom microprocessor is less expensive to purchase than a microcontroller since the microcontroller has built-in memory and I/O circuitry.
3. The INTEL 80386 is a general purpose microprocessor.

ANSWERS (not necessarily in the order of the questions)

- False • True • True

14-5 MICROPROCESSOR SPECIFICATIONS

Microprocessor specifications can be divided into two broad categories: hardware specifications and software specifications.

14.5.1. Hardware Specifications

Microprocessor hardware specifications are similar to hardware specifications for other logic ICs. These include pin descriptions, a functional block diagram, modes of operation, DC and AC characteristics, and timing waveforms.

TABLE 14-1 Intel μP Instruction

Hex Code	Binary Code	Mnemonic	Operand(s)
41	01000001	MOV	B, C

One very important hardware specification is microprocessor speed. A 20 MHz microprocessor has a **clock cycle** of $\frac{1}{20\text{ MHz}}$, or 50 ns. It takes several microprocessor clock cycles to execute each instruction.

14.5.2. Software Specifications

Microprocessor software specifications include a detailed description of each instruction in the instruction set. Each instruction has a format code, which is the binary code that the microprocessor associates with a particular instruction. Each instruction also has a **mnemonic,** which is a letter code to aid the programmer in remembering the function of each instruction. Table 14-1 illustrates an actual Intel instruction.

The instruction in Table 14-1 indicates that the microprocessor is to take the contents of register C and move (copy) it to register B. The "MOV" is the mnemonic, and the registers involved, B, C, are the operands. Each instruction has a unique binary code and an associated hex code. When the code for the instruction is processed by the microprocessor, the indicated function is executed.

Also listed under the software specifications, next to each instruction, is the number of clock cycles it takes the microprocessor to execute the instruction. The instruction in Table 14-1, for example, takes five clock cycles to execute.

■ EXAMPLE 14-3 Microprocessor Instruction Execution Time

Problem: A given microprocessor has a speed of 12.5 MHz. The instruction to subtract one number from another takes four clock cycles.

a. How long does it take the microprocessor to subtract the two numbers?
b. How long would it take if the μP speed can be increased to 20 MHz?

Solution: (a) First, find the clock cycle. $\frac{1}{12.5\text{ MHz}} = 80$ ns. To execute four clock cycles, it takes:

4×80 ns, $= 320$ ns

(b) The new clock cycle is $\frac{1}{20\text{ MHz}}$, = 50 ns. Four clock cycles take 200 ns. ■

Writing a software program using microprocessor instruction code is called **assembly programming,** and the instruction set is referred to as **assembly language.** The programmer writes a program **source file** using the mnemonics for each instruction that uses some type of text or ASCII editor program, and a software program called an **assembler** translates the mnemonics into binary or hex code for the microprocessor. The **assembled file** that is loaded into the microprocessor is called a **hex, object,** or **executable file.** The process of loading a program into a microprocessor is called **downloading.**

It is also possible to write a microprocessor program in a **high level language,** such as C, Pascal, or PL1, which can be translated into assembly language and an executable file by using a software program called a **compiler.** The high level language has the advantage that it can perform more instructions per line of software code and is often less cryptic than assembly language. Assembly language, however, usually results in a faster program.

Section Self-Test

1. What is a compiler?
2. If a microprocessor has a processor cycle of 30 ns, how long will it take to execute an instruction that requires four clock cycles?
3. What is a downloading?

ANSWERS

1. A compiler is a software program that translates microprocessor instructions written in a microprocessor language into the actual code needed by the microprocessor for execution.
2. 30 ns × 4 = 120 ns
3. Downloading is sending a program in executable code to the microprocessor RAM for execution by the microprocessor.

14-6 LOGIC TECHNOLOGY SELECTION: GATES, PLDs, AND MICROPROCESSORS

It is important to be able to select the appropriate type of logic implementation for a given application. Often there are several solutions and the actual implementation choice may be based on design parameters in addition to operational specifications. These include cost, scheduling, design expertise, familiarity of the logic designer with a logic technology, the amount of technical support available, and the availability of the necessary support equipment to implement a design. This section makes some basic comparisons among logic gate, PLD, and microprocessor-based logic circuit implementation. The intention is to provide some

general guidelines so that a logic designer can select a technically feasible implementation.

14.6.1 Specification Development

The first task is to develop a specification for the given application. The larger the logic system is, the more important it is to develop a specification list. A complete list of specifications limits the number of redesigns or modifications needed. This saves time and money.

Once the application specification is completed, the three major types of logic implementation—logic gates, PLDs, and microprocessors—can be matched against the specification for feasibility. Keep in mind that the three are not necessarily exclusive approaches, as a PLD or microprocessor design likely needs some gate logic. It is the responsibility of the designer to be able to answer questions such as "Why did you use PLDs?" or, "Why didn't you use a microprocessor?" Comparing the technologies to the application specification aids in being able to answer such questions.

14.6.2 General Selection Guidelines

Beginning logic students first encounter logic designs implemented with logic gate ICs. This type of implementation is relatively easy, low cost, and requires no additional programming equipment.

The next step is the implementation of the same designs with PLDs. PLDs reduce the number of ICs needed, but they require program development support equipment, that is, an editor, assembler, and a PC. In addition, a hardware programmer is required.

PLDs offer a superior design solution for most small logic applications over using off-the-shelf logic gate ICs. However, PLDs may consume more power, are not as mechanically reliable as TTL IC's (due to their susceptibility to electrostatic discharge (ESD) damage), and require the additional programming support equipment. Also, PLDs are not presently available for very fast switching applications. Be sure to compare the required application speed to the PLD speed if a PLD approach is selected.

Microcontrollers are excellent small system solutions to any application requiring the control of a function through I/O and the use of small amounts of memory. Again, a similar type of software support is needed for μCs as for PLDs. Often an EPROM programmer is necessary for coding the system memory with the program.

Microprocessors are the technology of choice for larger memory systems and maximum programming flexibility. Microprocessors are also on the leading edge of the technology as far as integrated function and processing speed are concerned. Microprocessors are also used in designs requiring the control of several functions simultaneously, referred to as **multitasking.**

Section Self-Test

Determine if the following statements are true or false:

1. PLDs exist that have faster switching speeds than any other available type of logic.
2. The use of specification lists reduce the amount of time needed to make design modifications.
3. Microprocessors are used in multitasking logic systems.

ANSWERS (not necessarily in the order of the questions)

• True • False • True

14-7 PERIPHERAL COMPONENTS

When designing with microprocessors, some advanced functions can be accomplished with the use of microprocessor peripheral components. Microprocessor manufacturers develop these peripherals to reduce the complexity and design effort needed to develop a μP-based design. A few standard peripherals are listed here to familiarize the student with the type of functionality available in IC form.

14.7.1 Latches and Transceivers

Almost every microprocessor design needs latches. Latches are used to demultiplex address and data lines from the microprocessor and to isolate sections of the design.

Transceivers are useful to ensure that devices are properly isolated (tri-stated) from the buses. Transceivers can buffer data in two directions. They are **bidirectional buffers.**

14.7.2 Coprocessor

Coprocessors are used in a μP design to increase the performance (speed) of the system. This is accomplished by adding another CPU to help perform some of the more complex calculations. Two processors can complete the processing task in a shorter time than one processor for a larger number of logic applications. In addition, it may be useful to have the coprocessor optimized to execute a specific task while the main microprocessor executes other tasks.

14.7.3 Keyboard and Display Interface

Nearly every nonembedded microprocessor application needs some sort of interface to a keyboard for input and some type of display for output. A keyboard and display interface, connected to the μP system buses, performs these functions. For simpler designs, a hex key pad provides a low cost means to enter numerical data.

14.7.4 Memory Controllers

Memory controllers aid the CPU in controlling the operation of memory. One important function is the automatic performance of refresh operations for DRAMs. Other types of memory controllers are used to detect and correct memory bit errors that may occur.

14.7.5 Disk Controllers

One very large application area for μPs is in personal computers and workstations. Almost every PC and workstation has some type of disk, either a hard disk or floppy disk. This peripheral handles data transfer to and from the μP system semiconductor memory to the disks. Optical disk control ICs are also available.

14.7.6 Timers

Timers are used to provide additional clock signals to the microprocessor system components as needed. Many timers are programmable.

14.7.7 Terminal Controllers

Terminal controller peripherals are similar to keyboard/display interfaces, in that they control data input and output between the microprocessor and a peripheral. In this case the peripheral is an integrated keyboard and display, or a terminal.

14.7.8 Specialized Peripherals

Specialized peripherals exist for many different applications. There are telecommunication peripherals for modems, computer networks, and digital data networks. There are automation peripherals for robotic microprocessor systems. Many specialized audio and video peripherals exist for use in consumer electronic applications. Microprocessor and peripheral data books are an excellent source for the latest information on the types of peripherals available.

Section Self-Test

Determine if the following statements are true or false:

1. Dynamic RAM refresh can be accomplished by using a memory controller peripheral.

2. Latches are used for storing large amounts of data to be used by the microprocessor CPU.
3. Transceivers control the rate of microprocessor and coprocessor logic speed.

ANSWERS (not necessarily in the order of the questions)

• True • False • False

14-8 MICROPROCESSOR LOGIC DESIGN METHODOLOGY

Microprocessor systems are sufficiently complex to warrant a careful and systematic design approach. Independent of the type of microprocessor used, a systematic problem solution methodology reduces the design time and separates the design into specific activities. In a practical sense, this allows for more than one person to work on the design and more clearly defines tasks and time schedules, which are very important in industry.

14.8.1 Systematic Problem Solution Methodology

The following steps can be used to proceed systematically in the design of a microprocessor-based system:

1. *Determine the system requirements.* This includes developing the system functional specification, as discussed in Section 14.6.
2. *Define hardware.* After the system is specified, the type of technology, gates, PLDs, microcontroller, or microprocessor is selected, based on the system requirements.
3. *Design hardware circuitry.* Next, the circuits are designed, using the hardware technologies chosen in step 2. Hardware circuit analysis programs, such as SPICE, can be used at this point for analysis. Many manufacturers have ready-built microprocessor boards that may be suitable for a given application. This should be considered in order to simplify hardware construction and to test hardware, as explained in step 5.
4. *Design software.* The program needed to support the hardware (PLD or μP) is written and assembled. Software simulators that can test software, if available, can be used at this point.
5. *Build and test hardware.* This step can be done in parallel with step 4. The hardware is built and tested for electrical functionality. A known operational software test program is then executed to test the functionality of the hardware independent of the actual application software. Debugging the hardware is completed at this point.

6. *Debug software.* Sections of the software are tested on the hardware for functionality. Once each section of the software is debugged, the entire program can be executed and debugged on the system hardware.
7. *Verify the final system.* The entire system, both hardware and software, is operated at the specification limits set forth in step 1. Testing at several different conditions of voltage, and temperature, can be used to determine the operating range of the system.
8. *Documentation of steps 1 through 7.* Each step should not be considered complete until written documentation has been completed. There are several reasons for the necessity of having complete documentation. First, it aids in the debugging and troubleshooting of each task. It also is needed for communication among team members working on a design. In addition, once the design is completed, documentation is relied on for fixing or modifying the system. Often the original designers are no longer available, and only the documentation remains. The quality check for documentation should always be "can someone, given only the existing documentation, understand the system without any prior design knowledge?" If the answer to this question is "no," further documentation is needed.

Section Self-Test

Determine if the following statements are true or false:

1. Hardware should be selected before determining specification requirements.
2. Microprocessor hardware should be debugged before attempting to debug the software running on the hardware.
3. Documentation must be complete enough for someone who is not familiar with the design to understand its operation.

ANSWERS (not necessarily in the order of the questions)

- True • False • True

14-9 MICROPROCESSOR SYSTEM TROUBLESHOOTING

Microprocessor systems can be difficult to troubleshoot due to their complexity. This section is intended to provide an introduction to the tools and basic techniques used when performing microprocessor troubleshooting. Actual microprocessor troubleshooting is best learned in the laboratory using the appropriate equipment.

14.9.1 Troubleshooting Equipment

Microprocessor systems have many timing, data, and address signals that are constantly changing state during the operation of the microprocessor. A **logic analyzer** is used to monitor and display multiple waveforms simultaneously for analysis. As many as 64 different signals can be simultaneously analyzed with some of the more advanced logic analyzers. With this tool, the relationship among the address, data, and timing can be analyzed to determine if any problems exist. Logic analyzer personal computer boards are also available at a lower cost to display the waveforms on a PC under software control.

If a logic analyzer is not available, an oscilloscope can be used to examine the various signals. The limitation with the oscilloscope is that only a limited number of signals can be displayed and analyzed simultaneously.

A **signature analyzer** is a special type of logic analyzer designed to perform tests that are specific to the type of microprocessor or microcontroller being tested. It differs from a standard logic analyzer in that it has some automatic test features. These include the ability to read and write data to memories, address bus tests, data bus tests, control and timing tests, and other specialized tests.

14.9.2 Troubleshooting Techniques

Troubleshooting techniques for microprocessor systems differ from troubleshooting techniques for other types of logic devices. Microprocessors have a software program that can be a source of errors in both the actual program and the memory where the program is stored. These additional sources for problems are in addition to the hardware problems normally associated with any type of logic IC such as power, loading, fan-out, wiring, and so on. Microprocessor hardware is also more complex than many other types of logic, and the problems associated with the timing and large number of signals present adds further to the complexity associated with troubleshooting microprocessor-based systems.

The approach to take when troubleshooting microprocessor-based systems is to follow the systematic design approach presented in Section 14.8. First, verify that the hardware is working by testing the hardware with the available logic tools.

If possible, execute the program on a **simulator** to determine if the program is executing correctly. If a simulator is not available, the program can be executed on the debugged microprocessor hardware.

Special microprocessor programs are available to **single step** through a program that is loaded into a microprocessor. The single step program allows one instruction at a time to be executed. The program then suspends operation, and hardware status and software register contents can be examined to help determine the problems.

Section Self-Test

1. List four possible sources for errors in a microprocessor system.
2. List three tools that are used for microprocessor troubleshooting.

ANSWERS

1. Software program, hardware wiring, timing, memory failure
2. Oscilloscope, logic analyzer, signature analyzer

SUMMARY

This chapter introduces the microprocessor as another design alternative for logic designers. Microprocessor-based logic designs now exist in almost every major area of electronics, with PCs one of the largest application areas. The intention is to familiarize the student with microprocessor terminology and availability. The actual use and implementation of microprocessors require additional microprocessor specific course work. The information in this chapter can be used as a reading supplement during the study of microprocessors. It is important always to ask application questions and to become familiar enough with the technology so that logic design with microprocessors becomes an option that can be exercised.

Microprocessor design options should be carefully compared to logic gate IC and PLD design options to ensure that there are valid reasons for using a microprocessor-based approach. When a microprocessor approach is selected, check with manufacturers for ready-made boards to simplify hardware construction.

Microprocessor designs all have three basic functional blocks: the central processing unit, memory, and input/output. Three major buses are part of a microprocessor system: the address bus, the data bus, and the control bus.

Many peripherals exist to simplify microprocessor designs. These include memory controllers, terminal controllers, display controllers, timers, and special functions. The microprocessor manufacturers are an excellent source of specific component information.

Microprocessor designs are relatively complex in nature, and they require a systematic problem solution methodology. This methodology reduces the design time, aids in coordination and communication on team designs, and aids in the troubleshooting of microprocessor systems.

PROBLEMS

14-1 Microprocessor Logic—Analysis Problems

1. a. Define the term microprocessor size.

   b. Compare the size and speed of the microprocessors available in 1971 with the microprocessors available today.

2. Define the following as they pertain to μPs:
   (a) microprocessor (b) instruction code (c) op code
   (d) software (e) hardware (f) hard-wired

14-2 Microprocessor Instructions—Analysis Problems

*3. a. List the different types (groups) of microprocessor instructions.
   b. Use a microprocessor data book, and find two instructions for each group listed in part (c). Explain what each instruction does.

4. a. What is a port?
   b. What is the difference between serial and parallel I/O?

5. a. Use a microprocessor data book, and list all the registers of the microprocessor chosen.
   b. Next to each register, write the size (in bits) of the register.

6. Explain the difference between internal and external memory.

7. a. What are conditional instructions?
   b. Give two examples of conditional instructions.

14-3 Microprocessor System Architecture—Analysis Problems

*8. a. List and explain the major functional blocks of a μP system.
   b. List and explain the μP system buses.
   c. Draw a basic μP system.

9. Explain the function of a CPU, and detail its internal architecture.

10. a. What is a stack?
   b. How is it used?
   c. Refer to a μP data book, and explain the operation of the stack.

*11. a. Explain how a first in-first out (FIFO) stack operates. (*Hint:* The same principle as a FIFO shift register!)
   b. If the following data is stored in a FIFO stack, 05H, then C2H, then 5DH, which byte of data would be retrieved first?

12. a. Explain how a FILO stack operates. (*Hint:* The same principle as a FILO shift register)
   b. If the following data is stored in a FILO stack, 05H, then C2H, then 5DH, which byte of data would be retrieved first?

13. Explain the difference between unidirectional and bidirectional, and match these properties with each microprocessor system bus.

---

* *See* Answers to Selected Problems.

14-4 Microprocessor Types—Analysis Problems

*14. a. List the three types of μPs.
 b. Explain the difference between each type.
 c. List four applications for each type of μP.

15. Explain the term, "embedded controllers."

14-5 Microprocessor Specifications—Analysis Problems

16. Refer to a μP data book. List the important hardware specifications for an 8 bit general purpose μP.

17. Refer to a μP data book. List the important software specifications for an 8 bit general purpose μP.

*18. A microprocessor comes in four speeds: 12 MHz, 15 MHz, 20 MHz, and 25 MHz. Find the clock cycle for each.

19. Using the information from Problem 18, calculate how long it would take to execute an eight-clock cycle instruction for each microprocessor speed listed in Problem 18.

20. Refer to a μP data book. Find a conditional instruction, and determine the amount of time it will take to execute for a 25 MHz μP speed
 a. if the instruction conditionally executes
 b. if the instruction does not execute (but is processed by the μP)

*21. A software program has 260 instructions. Within these instructions, 90 require six clock cycles, 110 require eight clock cycles, and the remaining instructions require ten clock cycles. If the program is executed by a 10 MHz μP, how long does it take to execute the entire program?

22. a. What is the difference between an assembly language and a high level language?
 b. List three common assembly languages.
 c. List three common high level languages.

14-6 Logic Technology Selection: Gates, PLDs, and Microprocessors—Application Problems

23. List three important reasons for comparing logic technologies for implementation. Discuss each reason in detail.

24. List two advantages for implementing a design in
 (a) logic gates (b) PLD logic (c) μP logic

25. List two disadvantages for implementing a design in
(a) logic gates (b) PLD logic (c) μP logic

14-7 Peripheral Components—Design Problems

26. List six different types of μP peripheral components and explain the use and advantages of each.

27. Refer to a μP peripheral component data book. Find a keyboard/display controller.
   a. Write a brief explanation of the use of this IC.
   b. Determine how much power this IC uses.
   c. Draw a schematic of this IC as it would be used in a μP system, listing all pins.

28. Add an appropriate μP to the memory system design schematic of Chapter 15, Problem 34. Show all μP connections.

29. Add an appropriate μP to the memory system design schematic of Chapter 15, Problem 35. Show all μP connections.

30. Add an appropriate μP to the memory system design schematic of Chapter 15, Problem 36. Show all μP connections.

31. Add an appropriate μP to the memory system design schematic of Chapter 15, Problem 37. Show all μP connections.

14-8 Microprocessor Logic Design Methodology—Design Problems

32. List the steps for the systematic problem solution methodology for microprocessor based designs.

*33. Using the steps listed in Problem 32, write a specific methodology for the PLD editor, assembler, hardware programmer, and PLDs used in your curriculum.

34. Select a μP, and write specific solution steps for its implementation.

35. Explain how a systematic problem solution methodology aids in troubleshooting a PLD or μP logic system.

14-9 Microprocessor System Troubleshooting—Troubleshooting Problems

36. List a method to determine if a microprocessor system is functioning properly.

37. List a method to determine if a compiled microprocessor program is executing properly.

*38. Every time data is output from a parallel port to LEDs, the two least significant LEDs are always the same logic value, even when they are supposed to be different. Propose a reason that explains how this can occur?

39. A microprocessor program is stored at the hexadecimal location 8000H. Every time a student tries to access that memory location, the microprocessor goes to memory location F000H. List a reason how this can occur. (*Hint:* Think of each address line separately, and determine what would happen if the address lines were wired incorrectly.)

Part 7

LOGIC FAMILY PERFORMANCE AND INTERFACING

Part 1 **DIGITAL LOGIC FUNDAMENTALS**

Chapter 1 Digital Logic and Technology
Chapter 2 Number Systems and Arithmetic

Part 2 **COMBINATIONAL LOGIC**

Chapter 3 Logic Functions and Combinational Logic Circuits

Part 3 **ADVANCED COMBINATIONAL LOGIC DESIGN WITH MEDIUM SCALE INTEGRATION (MSI) LOGIC CIRCUITS**

Chapter 4 Multiplexers and Demultiplexers
Chapter 5 Decoders, Encoders, and Code Converters
Chapter 6 Arithmetic Circuits

Part 4 **SEQUENTIAL LOGIC**

Chapter 7 Monostable and Astable Circuits
Chapter 8 Latches
Chapter 9 Flip-Flops

Part 5 **ADVANCED SEQUENTIAL LOGIC DESIGN**

Chapter 10 Counter Circuits
Chapter 11 Shift Registers

Part 6 **LSI LOGIC AND MEMORY**

Chapter 12 Programmable Logic Devices and Semiconductor Logic
Chapter 13 Semiconductor Memory Technology
Chapter 14 Logic Design with Microprocessors

Part 7 **LOGIC FAMILY PERFORMANCE AND INTERFACING**

Chapter 15 Logic Families, Interfacing, and Device Selection
Chapter 16 Analog/Digital Conversion

Part 8 **LOGIC SYSTEM DESIGN**

Chapter 17 Digital Logic Design Projects

Chapter 15

Logic Families, Interfacing, and Device Selection

Upon completing and mastering the material in this chapter, you should be able to understand logic families, interfacing, and device selection in the following areas of analysis, application, and design:

ANALYSIS

1. Be familiar with the TTL technologies and subfamilies of ICs.
2. Understand the basics of TTL circuitry.
3. Be able to differentiate between totem-pole and open-collector output stages.
4. Be familiar with the CMOS technologies and subfamilies of ICs.
5. Understand the basics of CMOS circuitry.
6. Be able to calculate propagation delays.
7. Be able to calculate power consumption.
8. Be familiar with tristate outputs.
9. Be able to calculate pull-up resistor values.
10. Be able to interpret TTL and CMOS device data sheets.

APPLICATION AND DESIGN

11. Understand that specialized logic families such as ECL are available for digital design.
12. Be able to select the appropriate digital logic approach to designing a circuit for a given application.
13. Compare TTL, CMOS, PLD, and microprocessor design approaches.
14. Select the appropriate TTL subfamily for a given application based on the design parameters.
15. Select the appropriate CMOS subfamily for a given application based on the design parameters.
16. Interface between TTL and CMOS.
17. Interface digital logic circuits to displays.
18. Interface digital logic circuits to mechanical devices.
19. Design simple optical interfaces to digital circuits.

TROUBLESHOOTING

20. Troubleshoot TTL circuits.
21. Troubleshoot CMOS circuits.
22. Apply troubleshooting techniques to interface circuits.

Logic designs are predominately implemented with two types of logic families, TTL and CMOS. TTL ICs are fabricated with bipolar transistors, and CMOS ICs are fabricated with field effect transistors (FETs). Historically, most designs were built with TTL, but due to the superior power and noise parameters of CMOS, today most logic systems are built using CMOS logic.

It is important for logic designers to be familiar with both logic families and the different technologies used to implement TTL and CMOS. This chapter defines and explains TTL and CMOS logic families and the important selection and design parameters associated with each family and subfamily of logic.

Another important design technique is interfacing. Interface circuitry is often needed to interface logic families and digital logic with other digital and analog components such as microprocessors, memory, displays, and other peripherals.

The emphasis is on understanding the practical application and design parameters for each logic family and key interface requirements. In addition, overall comparisons in designing with discrete logic ICs, PLDs, and microprocessors are examined in order to determine the right approach for a given application.

15-1 TRANSISTOR-TRANSISTOR LOGIC (TTL)

One of the most widely used logic families for digital circuits is transistor-transistor logic, or TTL. The term "TTL" can refer to the type of logic family and its electrical characteristics, the input and output voltage level specifications for this particular type of IC device, or the transistor operating characteristics of the IC's internal circuitry.

15.1.1 TTL Logic Definition

Transistor-transistor logic, TTL, has voltage level conventions defined as shown in Table 15-1.

TABLE 15-1 TTL Voltage Levels

Signal	Parameter	Defined Voltage Range (volts)
Input LOW	V_{IL}	0.0–0.8
Input HIGH	V_{IH}	2.0–5.0
Output LOW	V_{OL}	0.0–0.4
Output HIGH	V_{OH}	2.4–5.0

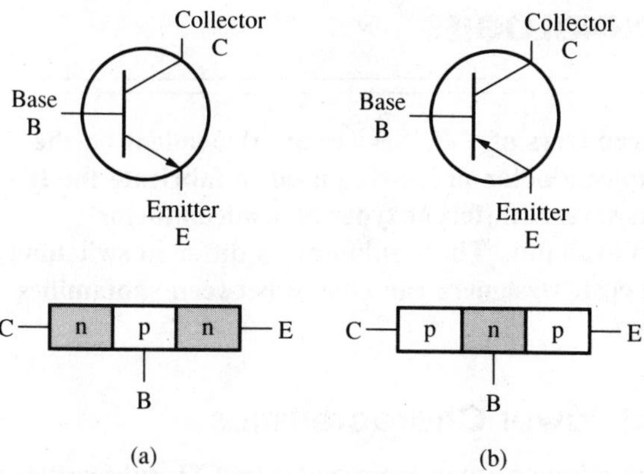

FIGURE 15-1 Bipolar Transistor Symbols (a) npn Bipolar Transistor; (b) pnp Bipolar Transistor

Devices that meet the I/O specifications listed in Table 15-1 are **TTL compatible.** TTL logic devices are indicated by the 5400 and 7400 numerical series designations. This is commonly known as the 54/74 TTL series, first introduced in 1965. The 7400 series of ICs represent devices with a temperature operating range of 0° to 70°C. The 7400 series ICs are known as commercial grade ICs. The 5400 series ICs have a wider temperature operating range, from −55° to 125°C, and are known as military grade or mil spec devices. The function and electrical characteristics of the 5400 and 7400 devices are both TTL compatible. However, the 5400 device is typically more expensive than its equivalent 7400 series device due to the additional testing and screening necessary to guarantee the greater temperature range.

15.1.2 Bipolar Transistor Technology

The internal circuitry of a TTL IC is designed using bipolar transistor technology. Each bipolar transistor has a base, collector, and emitter, as shown in Figure 15-1.

The type and size of the bipolar transistor, its switching characteristics, and the additional circuitry used for loading, current, and voltage control determine the operating characteristics of the particular type of TTL device.

Section Self-Test

Determine if the following statements are true or false:

1. The lowest TTL compatible input voltage is .4 volt.
2. The lowest TTL compatible output voltage is 2.4 volts.
3. The 5400 series TTL devices operate over a larger temperature range than the 7400 series TTL devices.

ANSWERS (Not necessarily in the order of the questions)

• False • True • True

15-2 TTL LOGIC TECHNOLOGIES

The power and speed parameters of TTL devices are dependent on the internal circuitry and semiconductor processing used to fabricate the ICs. The TTL logic family has several different types of semiconductor technologies (subfamilies) available. These subfamilies differ in switching speed, power usage, and cost. Designers can choose between subfamilies to customize a logic design.

15.2.1 TTL Speed and Power Characteristics

TTL logic technologies are categorized into **TTL subfamilies** that each have unique speed and power characteristics. These unique characteristics are a result of specialized bipolar transistor circuits and semiconductor processing techniques used to fabricate the TTL subfamily ICs.

Power refers to the voltage-current product or power used by a device, typically given in milliwatts (mW).

The **speed** of a logic device is controlled by the time it takes to switch from one logic level to another. The time it takes to switch logic levels is the **propagation delay,** also referred to as the **gate delay.** Logic gates often have different times for switching from a logic HIGH to LOW (t_{PHL}) versus switching from a logic LOW to HIGH level (t_{PLH}), as shown in Figure 15-2.

Sometimes it is useful to calculate an average propagation delay, which is the average of the HIGH to LOW and LOW to HIGH propagation delay times. Be sure to refer to the device specification sheets to determine gate or device propagation delay values. Propagation delay is also discussed as a design parameter in Section 15.10.

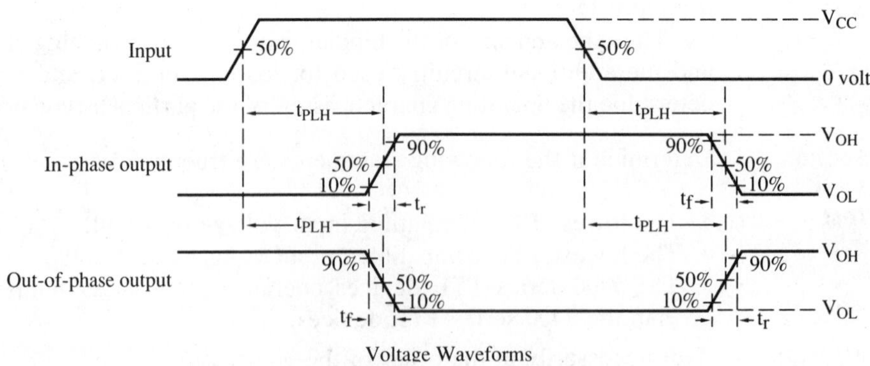

FIGURE 15-2 TTL Propagation Delay Waveforms

■ **EXAMPLE 15-1 Propagation Delay Parameters**

Problem:

a. Find the maximum HIGH to LOW propagation delay time for a 7402.
b. Find the maximum LOW to HIGH propagation delay time for a 7402.
c. Calculate the average propagation delay for a 7402.

Solution: Refer to the TTL data book for the AC electrical characteristics of a 7402 to find the switching parameters, t_{PHL}, and t_{PLH}.

(a) HIGH to LOW propagation delay time $= t_{PHL} = 15$ ns

(b) LOW to HIGH propagation delay time $= t_{PLH} = 22$ ns

(c) Average propagation delay time $= t_{Pav} = \dfrac{15 \text{ ns} + 22 \text{ ns}}{2} = 18.5$ ns ■

15.2.2 Standard TTL Logic

Standard logic is used as the power consumption and speed reference point. Standard TTL logic has a typical power consumption of 10 mW per gate and a device speed or propagation delay of 10 ns while driving a 15 pF/400 ohm load. The output load refers to the amount of capacitance and resistance that the device has to drive. A load of 15 pF and 400 ohms is a standard reference value for standard TTL logic. Other subfamilies use different resistive and capacitive loads to measure speed. Larger capacitive and resistive values on the output will reduce the actual speed of a device. Always check the data sheets to determine the capacitive and resistive loads the manufacturer uses when measuring device speed.

15.2.3 Low-Power Schottky (LS) TTL

The **low-power Schottky (54/74LS)** technology takes advantage of a unique input circuit design and high current gain bipolar transistors to achieve propagation speeds that are as good or better than standard TTL, using only about one-fifth the power. The LS subfamily has become one of the most widely used types of TTL logic.

15.2.4 Schottky (S) TTL

Schottky (54/74S) is one of the TTL logic subfamilies that uses the improved Schottky bipolar circuitry. The diodes are used to prevent oversaturation of the switching transistor, resulting in improved switching speeds that are typically three times faster than standard TTL logic, with only a 50% increase in the power consumption as compared to standard logic.

15.2.5 Advanced Schottky (AS) TTL

The **advanced Schottky (54/74AS)** subfamily is the fastest family of TTL ICs. Special bipolar fabrication techniques are used to produce circuits with very fast switching bipolar transistors. The logic gates and devices built with these circuits can have an average gate delay time of around 1 ns while driving a 50 pF/2K-ohm load. The power consumption is from 10 to 40% less than standard TTL.

15.2.6 Advanced Low-Power Schottky (ALS) TTL

Advanced low-power Schottky (54/74ALS) devices have the best combination of low-power consumption and speed of any of the TTL logic families. Typical speeds are 4 ns of propagation delay per gate, and typical power consumption is 1 mW per gate. As compared to standard TTL logic, this is a ten times decrease in the power and a doubling of the device speed.

15.2.7 Fast (F) TTL

Fast (F) TTL is another TTL subfamily. The performance of the fast TTL is better than Schottky but not so fast as advanced Schottky. Its internal circuitry provides it with relatively good power consumption as compared to standard TTL, and it has very good fan-out and loading characteristics.

15.2.8 Low-Power (L) TTL

The **low-power (54/74L)** TTL subfamily uses larger resistor values on the internal bipolar circuitry to reduce the circuit current usage. This typically results in a tenfold decrease in the current usage, and therefore a tenfold decrease in the power consumption for a 54/74L IC as compared to standard TTL. The penalty for less power usage is a reduction in the switching speed. Low-power TTL ICs are typically two to three times slower than standard TTL logic. Few low-power TTL ICs are produced today, having been replaced by other TTL subfamilies.

15.2.9 High Speed (H) TTL

High speed (54/74H) TTL devices are optimized to increase the switching speed of the logic, but the penalty is an increase in power consumption. Most semiconductor manufacturers no longer produce 74H devices, due to improvements in bipolar circuit design used in other logic families. Other TTL logic subfamilies (AS and ALS) are now used in place of 74H devices.

TABLE 15-2 TTL Logic Subfamilies

Subfamily	Prefix	Operating Characteristic
Standard	54/74	Nominal power, speed
Low-power Schottky	54/74LS	One fifth the power of standard; same speed as standard
Low-power	54/74L	One tenth the power of standard
High speed	54/74H	fast switching; higher power than standard
Schottky	54/74S	Three times faster than standard; higher power than standard
Advanced Schottky	54/74AS	Ten times the speed and less power than standard
Advanced low-power Schottky	54/74ALS	One tenth the power of standard; twice the speed of standard
Fast	54/74F	Approximately five times faster than standard; less power than standard

15.2.10 TTL Technology Comparisons

It is useful to be able to compare TTL subfamilies and to have a basic "design sense" in selecting the appropriate subfamily for a given application. The major differences are speed and power as summarized in Table 15-2.

All TTL logic subfamilies can be used in combination in logic circuit designs due to the voltage compatibility of all TTL devices. Sections of a design or an entire design can be optimized for speed, power consumption, or some combination through the use of available 54/74 logic families. However, there are several design considerations that have to be examined before interchanging the logic subfamilies. It is not as simple as replacing a 7402 NOR IC with a 74ALS02 to achieve increased speed and reduced power consumption in a circuit. Logic families and subfamilies may not have the same drive capability, which can result in faulty operation. The important design considerations will be discussed in Section 15.4, "Designing with TTL."

At this point it is important to have a general understanding of the overall speed and power relationships among the TTL logic subfamilies. Table 15-3 shows the relative power and speed of the TTL logic subfamilies.

TABLE 15-3 TTL Logic Power Consumption and Speed Comparisons

Power Consumption

Decreasing power consumption ⟶

High-power usage H .. S .. std .. AS .. F .. LS .. ALS .. L **Low-power usage**

Speed

Increasing speed ⟶

Slow L .. std .. LS .. ALS .. H .. S .. F .. AS **Fast**

Section Self-Test

Determine if the following statements are true or false:

1. The fastest TTL subfamily that is still manufactured today is high speed (H) TTL.
2. The larger the propagation delay is, the slower the device is.
3. Power consumption for TTL ICs is generally higher in fast TTL subfamilies as compared to slower TTL subfamilies.

ANSWERS (Not necessarily in the order of the questions)

- True
- False
- True

15-3 TTL CIRCUIT OPERATION: TOTEM-POLE AND OPEN-COLLECTOR OUTPUTS

Bipolar transistors are the basic circuit building blocks for all TTL logic devices. The operation of the bipolar transistor determines the operating characteristics of TTL devices. Detailed bipolar transistor operation is taught in the appropriate electronic circuit courses. The goal here is to understand bipolar transistor operation in terms of digital logic levels and TTL circuit operation in order to explain the two major types of TTL output stages, open-collector and totem pole.

15.3.1 Bipolar Transistor Basics

There are two major types of bipolar transistors: the **npn** and the **pnp**. The bipolar transistor is actually two diodes joined by the one type of common

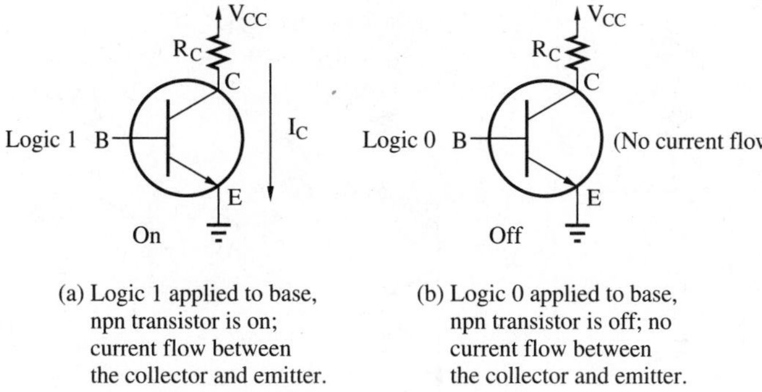

(a) Logic 1 applied to base, npn transistor is on; current flow between the collector and emitter.

(b) Logic 0 applied to base, npn transistor is off; no current flow between the collector and emitter.

FIGURE 15-3 Bipolar Transistor Operation

semiconductor material, either n or p, as shown in Figure 15-1. The description that follows is based on the npn transistor, used as a logic switch.

Figure 15-3 shows bipolar transistors with a V_{CC} applied to the collector and ground applied to the emitter. If logic 0 is applied to the base, the bipolar transistor is ''off'' since no current can flow from the collector to the emitter, as shown in Figure 15-3(a). If logic 1 is applied to the base, the bipolar transistor is ''on'' and current can then flow from the collector to the emitter.

Another way of examining the bipolar transistor is by analyzing the voltages at the transistor base, collector, and emitter. For silicon bipolar transistors, if the voltage from the base to the emitter, V_{BE}, is greater than approximately .7 volt, the transistor is on. If V_{BE} is less than .7 volt, the transistor is off.

The basic bipolar transistor circuit for digital logic is the inverter circuit shown in Figure 15-4. Modifications can be made from the inverter circuit to build all basic logic gate functions. Basic circuits for the NAND and NOR gate are also shown in Figure 15-4. Actual TTL logic circuits use additional transistors per logic function to improve device power and speed characteristics.

15.3.2 Totem-Pole Output Stage

There are several different types of bipolar circuits that can be used for the output or driver stage of a TTL device. The standard type of bipolar output stage is shown in Figure 15-5. This transistor combination provides internal connections via the two transistors in the output stage to both the logic HIGH and LOW levels. When the output is logic HIGH, T_1 is on and T_2 is off. T_1 provides the connection to V_{CC}. When the output is logic LOW, T_1 is off and T_2 is on. T_2 provides the connection to ground for logic LOW. No external circuitry is needed for this output logic operation.

The totem-pole output stage has good current drive capacity. The current drive capacity of a device or circuit is known as the **fan-out** of the device.

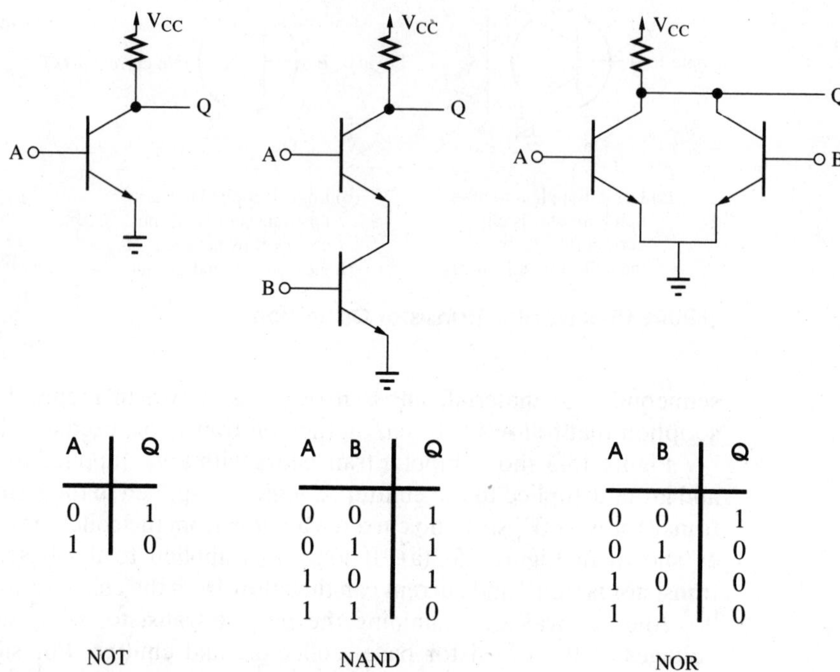

A	Q
0	1
1	0

A	B	Q
0	0	1
0	1	1
1	0	1
1	1	0

A	B	Q
0	0	1
0	1	0
1	0	0
1	1	0

FIGURE 15-4 Bipolar Transistor Circuit Logic

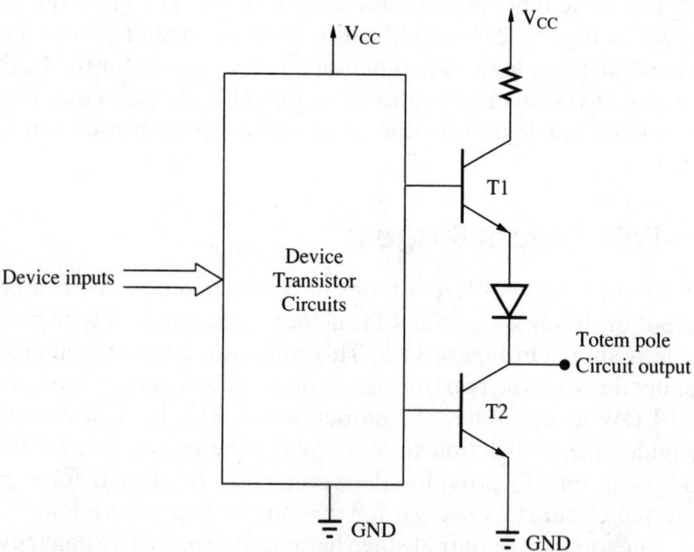

FIGURE 15-5 TTL Totem-Pole Output Stage

Device B output is HIGH and device A output is LOW. In this example the figure illustrates current flow from V_{CC} of device B to ground of device A, causing excess current flow in device A T2 transistor and device B T1 transistor.

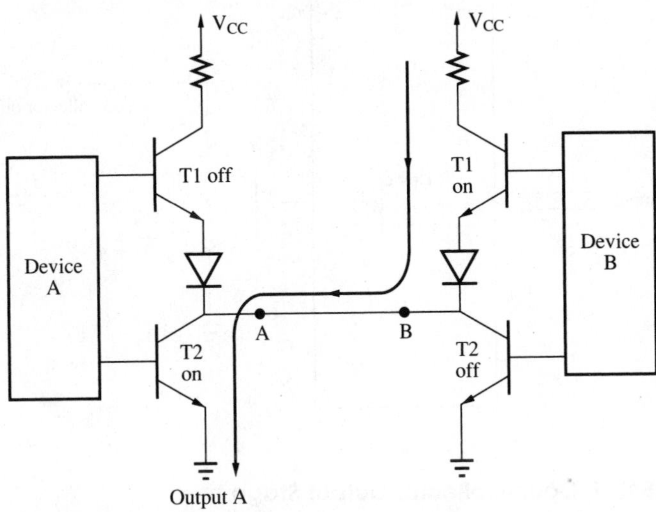

FIGURE 15-6 Improper Connection of Totem-Pole Outputs

The limitation associated with totem-pole output ICs is that two totem-pole outputs cannot be connected directly together. Examination of the circuit shown in Figure 15-6 indicates that when two of these circuits are connected together at the output stage, if one of the output stages is LOW while the other output stage is HIGH, excessive current flows from V_{CC} to ground in the output transistors and damages the circuitry. *Totem-pole outputs should never be connected together in any type of circuit where the outputs are both active at the same time.* This does not limit the usefulness of totem-pole outputs since there are many logic circuits that do not require the connection of two or more output stages.

15.3.3 Open-Collector Output Stage

Open-collector devices allow for the connection of outputs from several different circuits. Outputs can be tied together without causing damage to the internal circuitry because open-collector devices do not have the output stage connected to V_{CC}. Open-collector devices do not have a transistor connection to V_{CC}, as shown in Figure 15-7.

To obtain logic HIGH output from an open-collector device, an external connection to V_{CC} is required. This allows direct connection of open-collector device outputs. Open-collector devices also generate higher V_{OH} levels than totem-pole outputs.

Pull-up resistor would be attached from the open collector output to V_{CC}.

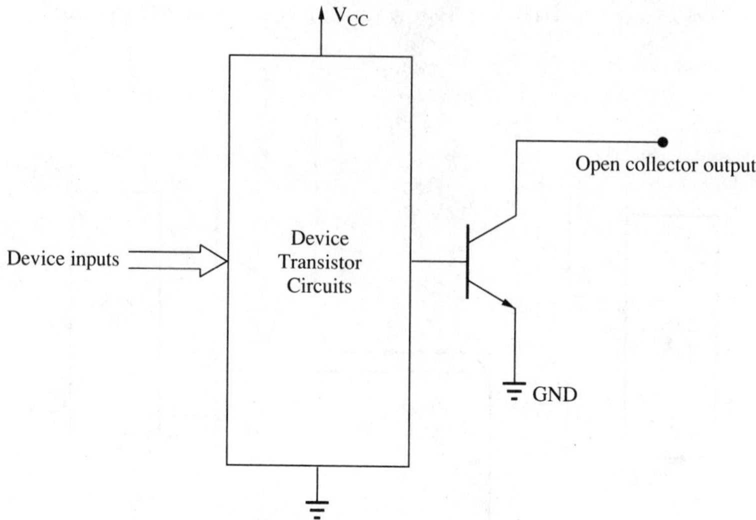

FIGURE 15-7 Open-Collector Output Stage

Logic gates with open-collector outputs are designated in traditional logic schematics by placing a diamond-bar symbol (◇̲) in the gate symbol. When using IEEE/ANSI logic symbols, the same diamond-bar symbol is placed inside the logic rectangle next to the open-collector output.

15.3.4 Pull-Up Resistors

The HIGH output for open-collector devices is achieved by adding an external **pull-up** resistor to the output of an open-collector IC. This provides a connection to V_{CC}. When the output transistor is on, the output is connected to ground for logic LOW. When the transistor is off, the output is connected through the external pull-up resistor to V_{CC} for logic HIGH. External current is supplied through the resistor to pull-up the output of the device to logic HIGH. Open-collector devices are usually indicated in the data book specification sheet descriptions for a device. However, another way to identify a specification for an open-collector device is by noting the absence of the V_{OH} parameter specification.

The value of the pull-up resistor must be calculated and selected by the designer to supply the necessary current and voltage to the next device. The pull-up resistor also limits the sink current through any LOW output while the other outputs are HIGH. This is to ensure that the $I_{OL(max)}$ current is not exceeded in the LOW output device. If $V_{CC} = 5$ volts, and the pull-up resistor, $R_p = 1K\ \Omega$, $I_{OL} = 5$ mA.

Another consideration in the selection of R_p is the effect that the pull-up resistor has on the switching speed of the device. The larger R_p is, the slower the device will switch since any capacitive load will be charged by the current supplied through R_p.

Equation 15-1 can be used to find the minimum value for a pull-up resistor, R_p. Any resistor value larger than R_{pmin} can be used, keeping in mind that the larger the value is, the larger the propagation delay will be, or the slower the open-collector circuit becomes. It is best to select a standard value pull-up resistor slightly larger than R_{pmin}.

Eq. 15-1 $$R_{pmin} = \frac{V_{CC} - V_{OL(max)}}{I_{OL(max)} - I_{IL(total)}}$$

where

V_{CC} = supply voltage
$V_{OL(max)}$ = source device maximum V_{OL}
$I_{OL(max)}$ = source device maximum I_{OL}
$I_{IL(total)}$ = total I_{IL} for all load devices connected to pull-up resistor

The maximum value for a pull-up resistor, R_{pmax}, can be found by using Equation 15-2. If the maximum value for a pull-up resistor is exceeded, the total leakage current for all input and output devices connected to the pull-up resistor may pull V_{OH} below the minimum TTL 2.4 volt specification.

Eq. 15-2 $$R_{pmax} = \frac{V_{CC} - V_{IH(min)}}{I_{IH(total)}}$$

where

V_{CC} = supply voltage
$V_{IH(min)}$ = load device minimum V_{IH}
$V_{IH(total)}$ = total I_{IH} for all load devices connected to the pull-up

Note that there is no I_{OH} in the R_{pmax} equation since all current is being supplied by the pull-up resistor.

■ EXAMPLE 15-2 Pull-Up Resistor Calculation

Problem: A 74LS01 NAND gate is driving eight 74LS04 inverters in an open-collector wired-AND configuration. Determine an appropriate value for a pull-up resistor. Use V_{CC} = 5 volts.

Solution: Find the parameters for Equation 15-1.

V_{CC} = 5 V

$V_{OL(max)}$ = .4 V

$$I_{OL(max)} = 8 \text{ mA}$$

$$I_{IL(total)} = 400\ \mu\text{A} \times 8 = 3.2 \text{ mA}$$

$$R_{p(min)} = \frac{5 - .4 \text{ V}}{8 - 3.2 \text{ mA}} = 958\ \Omega$$

Check the maximum R_p using Equation 15-2

$$V_{CC} = 5 \text{ V}$$

$$V_{IH(min)} = 2.0 \text{ V}$$

$$I_{IH(total)} = 20\ \mu\text{A} \times 8 = .16 \text{ mA}$$

$$R_{pmax} = \frac{5 - 2.4 \text{ V}}{.16 \text{ mA}} = 16.25\text{K}\ \Omega$$

■

Thus, any pull-up resistor between 958 and 16.25K Ω is acceptable. The current choice is a standard value as close to 958 ohms as possible to provide

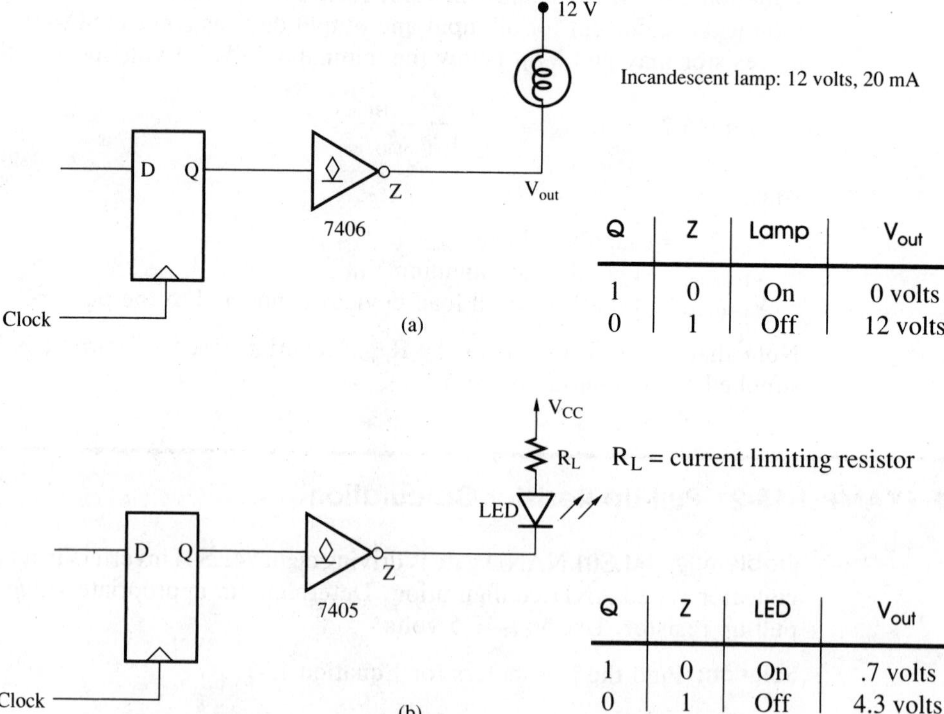

Q	Z	Lamp	V_{out}
1	0	On	0 volts
0	1	Off	12 volts

Q	Z	LED	V_{out}
1	0	On	.7 volts
0	1	Off	4.3 volts

FIGURE 15-8 Open-Collector Applications (a) Driving a Lamp Indicator; (b) Driving an LED Indicator

the best (fastest) propagation delay time. A 1K Ω resistor is an appropriate value.

A common error in the laboratory is to wire correctly all the pins for a circuit with open-collector ICs only to find that it will not output any logic HIGH values. This is always an indication to check for appropriate value pull-up resistors in the circuit.

Several open-collector applications requiring larger drive currents than can be provided by totem-pole outputs are shown in Figure 15-8. Note in the applications shown that a pull-up resistor is not required when the open-collector device is driving a lamp or LED since the load acts as a pull-up resistance.

TABLE 15-4 Open-Collector and Totem-Pole Comparisons

Totem-Pole Advantages	Open-Collector Advantages
No external pull-up resistor needed	Outputs can be directly connected (wired-AND)
Fast device switching speed as compared to open-collector outputs	Designer has control over fan-out through pull-up resistor size used.
More commonly available than open collector	Higher voltage for V_{OH} possible.
	High source/sink current
Totem-Pole Drawbacks	**Open-Collector Drawbacks**
Limited fan-out	Requires an external pull-up resistor.
Switching from a LOW to HIGH causes a 20–60 mA current spike in the V_{CC} supply current.	Slow device switching speed.
Outputs cannot be wired together.	Not all devices available with open-collector outputs
Limited output sink and source current	Once connected as wired logic, output cannot be used individually.

15.3.5 WIRED GATES

Open-collector devices that are connected together at the output are known as **wired gates.** Regardless of the type of gates being connected, the output of wired gates results in the Boolean AND operation, so the output is referred to as a **wired-AND** function. Figure 15-9 shows four open-collector NAND gates in a wired-AND configuration. It is common to indicate that the outputs are ANDed by the addition of an AND gate symbol at the wired output, as shown in Figure 15-9.

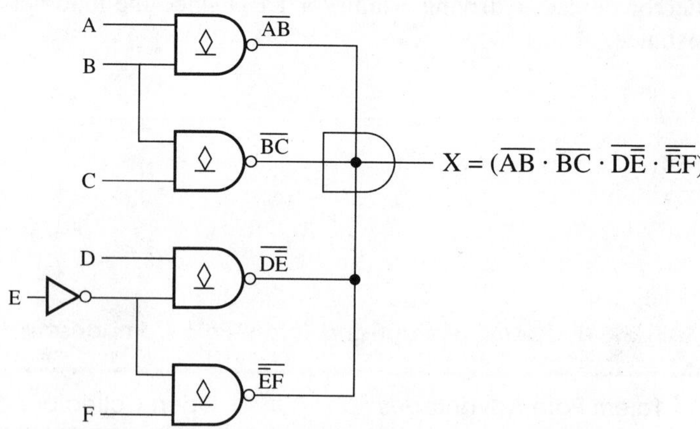

FIGURE 15-9 TTL Open-Collector Wired-AND Circuit

■ **EXAMPLE 15-3 Wired Gates**

Problem: Determine the output equation X for the circuit shown in Figure 15-10.

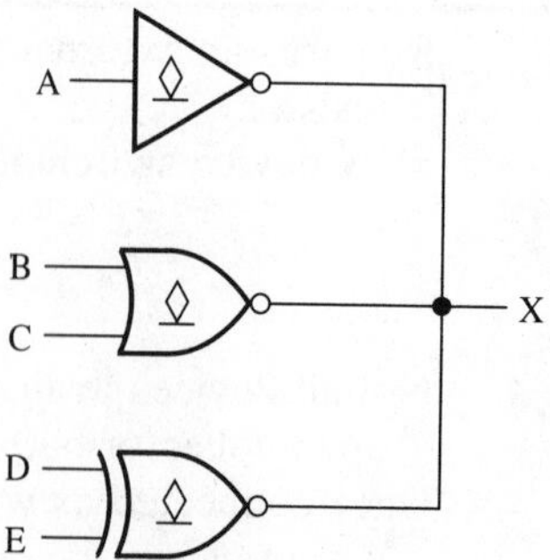

FIGURE 15-10 Wired-AND Circuit

Solution: Each of the open-collector outputs is wired together to form a wired-AND output. Thus:

$$X = \overline{A}\,\overline{(B + C)}\,\overline{(D \oplus E)}$$

■

15.3.6 Open-Collector and Totem-Pole Comparisons

A variety of digital IC functions are available with standard totem-pole or open-collector outputs. Table 15-4 summarizes the advantages and disadvantages of using totem-pole or open-collector devices.

15.3.7 Tristate Outputs

In addition to open-collector and totem-pole outputs, data books also list another type of output, known as **tristate,** or **3-state.** Tristate outputs are unique since in addition to having the normal HIGH and LOW logic output states, the output can also be in a very high impedance state. Electrically, this has the effect of disconnecting a tristate device from whatever it is connected to, even though the physical wiring connection is intact. This allows tristate outputs to be wired together. However, unlike open-collector wired circuits, only one tristate device can be electrically connected to a common output point. Section 15.14 discusses further the concept of tristate outputs.

Section Self-Test

Determine if the following statements are true or false:

1. Totem-pole outputs cannot be wired together.
2. Open-collector outputs require a pull-up resistor and a pull-up capacitor.
3. An npn bipolar transistor has its emitter tied to ground and its collector tied to V_{CC} through a resistor. If the voltage applied to the base of the transistor is 1 volt, the transistor is off.

ANSWERS (Not necessarily in the order of the questions)

• True • False • True

15-4 DESIGNING WITH TTL

The preceding material in this chapter provides an explanation of the different families of TTL ICs available, their operation, and the different types of input and output circuitry available. For simpler designs and

circuits, one wires the circuit correctly and applies the correct voltages, and the circuit should operate properly. For larger and more complex digital logic designs, additional design parameters must be considered. Several important parameters to consider are current sourcing and sinking, fan-out, grounding, decoupling, propagation delays, power usage, and logic IC interchangeability within the TTL subfamilies.

The initial discussion focuses on TTL logic devices. TTL offers the largest selection of ICs from which to choose and is the appropriate choice for many logic designs. However, most parameters that are explained for TTL will be applicable to other logic families such as CMOS and ECL as well.

15.4.1 Basic TTL Design Procedures

Several basic design procedures should be followed with any digital logic design. This includes connecting all unused inputs to a solid logic HIGH or LOW level, depending on the particular logic level needed. Unconnected inputs are referred to as **floating inputs.** Floating inputs should always be avoided, as floating inputs for TTL will float to a logic HIGH, but the input will not be a solid HIGH. A solid HIGH for TTL is 3.5 volts and higher; but a floating TTL input may only be at a 2.5 volt level. Because of this, floating inputs are susceptible to noise and are a constant source of troubleshooting problems in digital designs.

For example, the unused inputs of NAND devices should be connected to a logic HIGH level through a 1K Ω resistor. The resistor limits the amount of supply (V_{CC}) current into the unused input. Typically, a single 1K Ω resistor can be used to connect up to ten unused inputs to V_{CC}. Unused inputs can also be connected to an used input to avoid floating inputs.

The outputs of open-collector devices should be connected to pull-up resistors with values that fall within the values of $R_{P_{min}}$ and $R_{P_{max}}$, given by Equations 15-1 and 15-2, unless the data book for the device in use specifies using other equations.

To provide circuit immunity against low and high frequency noise on the V_{CC} supply, **decoupling capacitors** are used. Decoupling capacitors filter out the unwanted frequency components due to rapidly switching devices and current variations within the design. The decoupling capacitors prevent transient current spikes (such as those mentioned as a result of totem-pole outputs) from damaging the ICs or causing noise-related logic glitches. Usually, a large capacitor of 10 to 100 μF is used across the V_{CC} supply to filter out unwanted noise on the V_{CC} bus.

In addition, small device decoupling capacitors of .1 μF are connected between the V_{CC} pin and around each logic IC to filter out device switching noise. If standard or low-power logic devices are used, it is acceptable to use one decoupling capacitor for every two devices.

Proper grounding techniques should be used to minimize circuit noise.

This includes providing separate power and signal grounds and minimizing the wire length on V_{CC} and ground connections in critical applications involving signal waveforms. In addition, separate analog components from digital components by placing them on separate circuit boards. If this is not possible, provide separate ground and V_{CC} traces (wiring) for the analog and digital circuitry.

Good wiring practices on prototype breadboards are also necessary to prevent stray capacitance from affecting the digital circuitry. Wire lengths should be kept to a minimum. Challenge anyone who wires circuitry and uses wire of more than 1 inch in length for connections. The result will be poorly operating circuits and waveforms displayed on oscilloscopes will have signal **overshoot, undershoot,** and **capacitive charge** and **discharge** effects, as shown in Figure 15-11.

Data books are a good source of information on designing with TTL logic. In addition, many manufacturers supply application notes that cover in detail design considerations for specific applications. For example, an

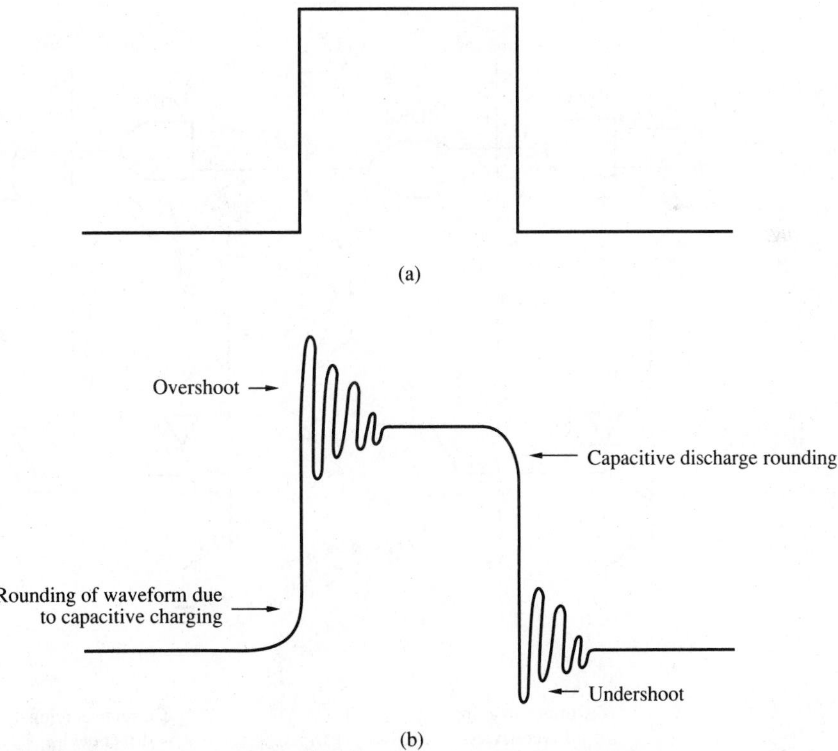

FIGURE 15-11 Waveform Capacitive Affects Due to Poor Circuit Wiring Techniques (a) Ideal Waveform Output; (b) Waveform Output from Poorly Wired Breadboard Circuit with Excessive Wire Lengths

application note on a synchronous data transmission circuit would include information on designing with bus drivers and receivers, transmission line termination, and other pertinent AC design considerations.

15.4.2 Fan-Out

It is not necessary when designing with TTL to stay strictly with one logic subfamily. One major advantage of TTL design is that most ICs are interchangeable if the proper design precautions are considered.

Fan-out is one parameter that varies within TTL logic subfamilies. Fan-out is the maximum number of inputs that can be driven by the output of a gate. It is calculated by dividing the total drive output current by the total load input current. A standard TTL gate has a fan-out of approximately 10, and the advanced Schottky subfamily has the highest typical TTL fan-out of from 30 to 50.

Many data books do not specifically list a fan-out parameter, so it must be calculated. This is very important, for if the fan-out capability of a gate

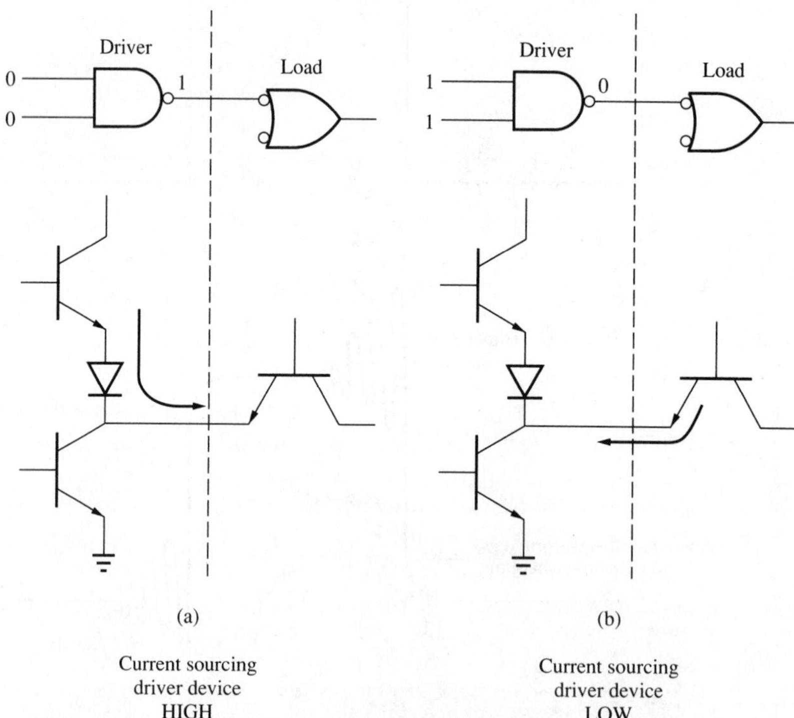

FIGURE 15-12 TTL Current Sourcing and Sinking (a) Current Sourcing Driver Device HIGH; (b) Current Sinking Driver Device LOW

is exceeded, it can be a very difficult type of problem to troubleshoot. In some instances the circuit may function properly, but in other cases there will be insufficient drive current causing a malfunction in the same previously working circuit.

In order to understand the calculation of fan-out, the current flow between the drive and source devices must first be defined: The fan-out of a device is actually a figure of merit related to the maximum amount of current a gate can source to and sink from gates attached to the output. When the output of a drive gate is a logic LOW, conventional current will flow *to the drive gate from the load gate* or gates. This action is known as **current sinking.** Figure 15-12(a) shows a driver and load gate with the driver sinking the current.

When the output of a drive gate is logic HIGH, conventional current will flow *from the drive gate to the load gate* or gates. This action is known as **current sourcing.** Figure 15-12(b) shows a driver and load gate with the driver sourcing the current.

In most cases TTL ICs can sink more current than they can source. The parameters of interest when calculating fan-out are the input and output HIGH and LOW voltages and currents. Each TTL gate has a maximum output LOWcurrent, I_{OL}, which determines the maximum amount of current the gate can sink. Conversely, each gate has a maximum output HIGH current, I_{OH}, which determines the maximum amount of current the gate can source. To complete the fan-out calculation, one must determine the input HIGH current, I_{IH}, and the input LOW current, I_{IL}, for each gate connected. Equations 15-3 and 15-4 can be used to determine fan-out, given that the loads are all of the same logic subfamily:

Eq. 15-3 $$\text{Fan-out}_{LOW} = \frac{I_{OL(\text{drive gate})}}{I_{IL(\text{load gate})}}$$

Eq. 15-4 $$\text{Fan-out}_{HIGH} = \frac{I_{OH(\text{drive gate})}}{I_{IH(\text{load gate})}}$$

Fan-out is a unitless positive whole number, and thus the negative sign for I_{IL} and I_{OH} indicating current polarity should be ignored when performing fan-out calculations. (Use the magnitude of the current.) The fan-out for logic LOW and HIGH will not always be the same, and the designer is limited by the smaller of the two numbers. It is also a wise design guardband to attach a few less gates than the maximum fan-out, if possible, for additional drive capacity and circuit operating margin.

■ EXAMPLE 15-4 Fan-Out Calculation

Problem: Calculate the fan-out of standard TTL driving standard TTL.

Solution

$I_{OL} = 16\text{ mA} \qquad I_{IL} = -1.6\text{ mA}$

$I_{OH} = -.4\text{ mA} \qquad I_{IH} = 40\ \mu\text{A}$

$$\text{Fan-out}_{LOW} = \frac{16\text{ mA}}{1.6\text{ mA}} = 10$$

$$\text{Fan-out}_{HIGH} = \frac{.4\text{ mA}}{.04\text{ mA}} = 10$$

$$\text{Fan-out} = 10$$

■

■ EXAMPLE 15-5 Fan-Out Calculation

Problem: Calculate the fan-out of standard TTL driving LS TTL.

Solution

$I_{OL} = 16\text{ mA} \qquad I_{OH} = -.4\text{ mA}$

$I_{IL(LS)} = -.4\text{ mA} \qquad I_{IH(LS)} = 20\ \mu\text{A}$

$$\text{Fan-out}_{LOW} = \frac{16\text{ mA}}{.4\text{ mA}} = 40$$

$$\text{Fan-out}_{HIGH} = \frac{.4\text{ mA}}{.02\text{ mA}} = 20$$

$$\text{Fan-out} = 20$$

since the lowest fan-out number determines overall fan-out. ■

■ EXAMPLE 15-6 Fan-Out Calculation

Problem: Calculate the fan-out of LS TTL driving standard TTL.

Solution

$I_{OL} = 8\text{ mA} \qquad I_{OH} = -400\ \mu\text{A}$

$I_{IL(std)} = -.4\text{ mA} \qquad I_{IH(std)} = 40\ \mu\text{A}$

$$\text{Fan-out}_{LOW} = \frac{8\text{ mA}}{.4\text{ mA}} = 20$$

$$\text{Fan-out}_{\text{HIGH}} = \frac{400\ \mu\text{A}}{40\ \mu\text{A}} = 10$$

$$\text{Fan-out} = 10$$

since the lowest fan-out number determines overall fan-out. ■

In designs where a drive gate is driving more than one type of logic family or subfamily load, the best way to guarantee proper circuit operation with respect to drive current is to ensure that the drive current always exceeds the load current.

15.4.3 Methods for Increasing Fan-Out

Often it is necessary to increase fan-out. There are several methods available to the logic designer for accomplishing this.

One easy solution that should be considered is first to compare logic subfamily parameters and then to select devices with a larger source and sink currents as the drive device and to select devices with smaller source and sink currents as the load devices.

■ EXAMPLE 15-7 Fan-Out Improvement

Problem: Improve the fan-out of Example 15-6 by selecting another logic subfamily.

Solution: If the standard subfamily is replaced by a subfamily with lower currents (LS or ALS, for example, the fan-out increases. Likewise, if the LS drive device is replaced by a standard TTL device, the fan-out can be increased further. Other solutions are possible. ■

Another method for increasing fan-out is to use additional gates or devices as interface buffers. For example, a 74LS125 is a noninverting buffer that can be used between the CMOS drive gate and the TTL loads. If a buffer is not available, and propagation delay is not a critical parameter, two inverters placed in serial between the drive output and the load inputs serve as a buffer to increase fan-out. These solutions are illustrated in Figure 15-13.

An additional circuit technique for increasing fan-out is to place two identical gates (commonly inverters or buffers) in parallel, as shown in Figure 15-14. This has the effect of doubling the fan-out. Typical applications include driving mechanical relays or other types of high current switches.

Current-limiting resistors, usually 50 ohms or less, are needed to balance the current sinking and sourcing of the devices. This will limit the possibility of one device sinking current from the other parallel device.

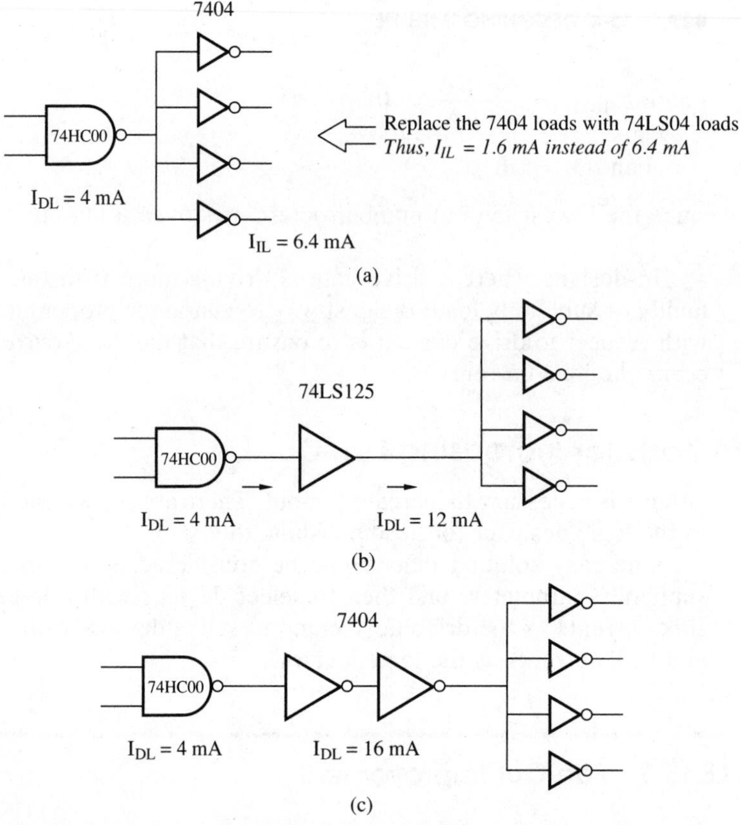

FIGURE 15-13 Increasing Fan-Out (a) Subfamily Substitution; (b) Add a Buffer; (c) Add Two Inverters as a Buffer

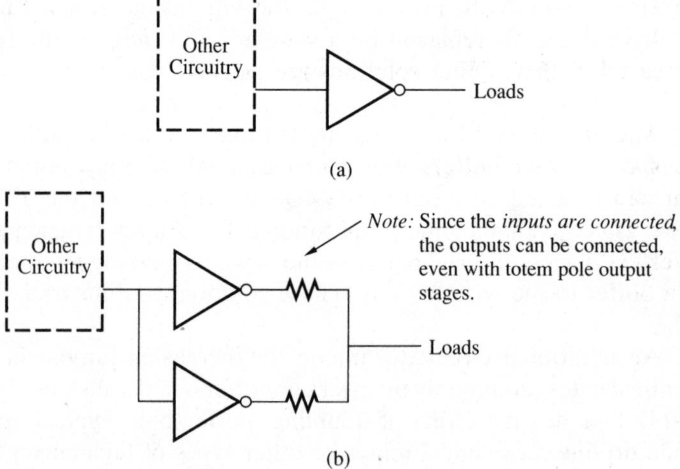

FIGURE 15-14 Parallel Inverter Interface (a) Circuit Gate Needing Additional Fan-Out; (b) Parallel Fan-Out Doubling

15.4.4 Unit Loads

Device currents can also be specified in **unit loads (ULs),** where one standard TTL UL is equal to 1.6 mA at a LOW logic level and 40 μA at a HIGH logic level. A Schottky UL is 50 μA I_{IH} and −2.0 mA I_{IL}, and a LS UL is defined as 20 μA I_{IH} and −0.4 mA I_{IL}.

■ EXAMPLE 15-8 Unit Loads

Problem: How much current will be represented by five LS TTL unit loads?

Solution: Each LS TTL UL is represented as follows:

$1\ UL_{LS\ LOW} = .4\ mA$

$1\ UL_{LS\ HIGH} = 20\ \mu A$

5 ULS: $5 \times .4\ mA = 2\ mA$ LS LOW

$5 \times 20\ \mu A = 100\ \mu A$ LS HIGH ■

■ EXAMPLE 15-9 Unit Loads

Problem: Determine the standard TTL UL represented by a 7475 D-latch clock input.

Solution: For standard TTL ULs:

$1\ UL_{STD\ LOW} = 1.6\ mA$

$1\ UL_{STD\ HIGH} = 40\ \mu A$

For the 7475 clock input, the current specifications are:

$I_{IH} = 80\ \mu A$

$I_{IL} = 6.4\ mA$

Divide the current values by the UL values:

$$\text{LOW:} \quad \frac{6.4\ mA}{1.6\ mA} = 4\ UL$$

$$\text{HIGH:} \quad \frac{80\ \mu A}{40\ \mu A} = 2\ UL$$

Thus, each 7475 clock input should be equated in value with the four ULs, the larger value. Each 7475 clock input is equivalent to four NAND gate equivalent inputs. ■

15.4.5 Mixed Logic

Mixed logic refers to the usage of more than one type of family or subfamily in the same logic design. An important concern when mixing TTL logic is the speed parameters. Within a design, race conditions must be avoided and propagation delays calculated from inputs to outputs for each section of the circuit design. If variations in excess of one half a gate delay exist, check for timing hazards. Also, the speed and switching parameters are often measured to different standard loads. As much as possible, try to standardize or estimate gate propagation delays based on a standard load for the design. Data books specify the type of resistive and capacitive loads used to test and measure the devices in the parameter measurement section of a data book.

Power usage can vary considerably between families, and care must be taken to ensure that the current parameters selected are appropriate to each IC.

Section Self-Test

Determine if the following statements are true or false:

1. LS TTL driving standard TTL has a fan-out of 10.
2. The 74ALS devices and 74S devices cannot be used on the same circuit board due to possible grounding problems.
3. If the load TTL logic subfamily in a design were changed from 74S to 74 ALS, the fan-out will increase.

ANSWERS (Not necessarily in the order of the questions)

• False • True • False

15-5 COMPLEMENTARY METAL-OXIDE SEMICONDUCTOR (CMOS) LOGIC

CMOS logic is the second most widely used logic family after TTL. If the growth in CMOS usage continues, CMOS logic will surpass TTL as the dominant logic family. This is due to the successful invention of reliable CMOS circuits with speeds comparable to TTL and with lower power consumption and better noise immunity characteristics. In addition, nearly all VLSI memory components are manufactured using some form of CMOS processing, which significantly reduces the cost of producing logic components with the same technology.

The original CMOS logic family was the 4000 series of CMOS ICs. The improved version is known as the 4000B series. Today TTL compatible CMOS exists that can be used directly with TTL devices. The available CMOS logic families and subfamilies are discussed in this section.

15.5.1 FET Technology

CMOS logic ICs are designed using **field-effect transistors (FETs).** The semiconductor process used to fabricate FETs is a metal and oxide process. The oxide most often used is silicon dioxide, which provides electrical isolation. Connection between devices are processed using a metal, such as aluminum, or similar material with electrical conduction properties.

Two major types of FETs can be fabricated, **n-type** and **p-type.** The n-type and p-type refer to the semiconductor impurities or **doping** used in the semiconductor material. Semiconductor materials that are n-type have excess electrons in their molecular structure, and materials that are p-type have an excess of holes (absence of electrons) in their molecular structure. The n-type and p-type transistors have different operating characteristics. Figure 15-15 shows the symbols for several types of FETs.

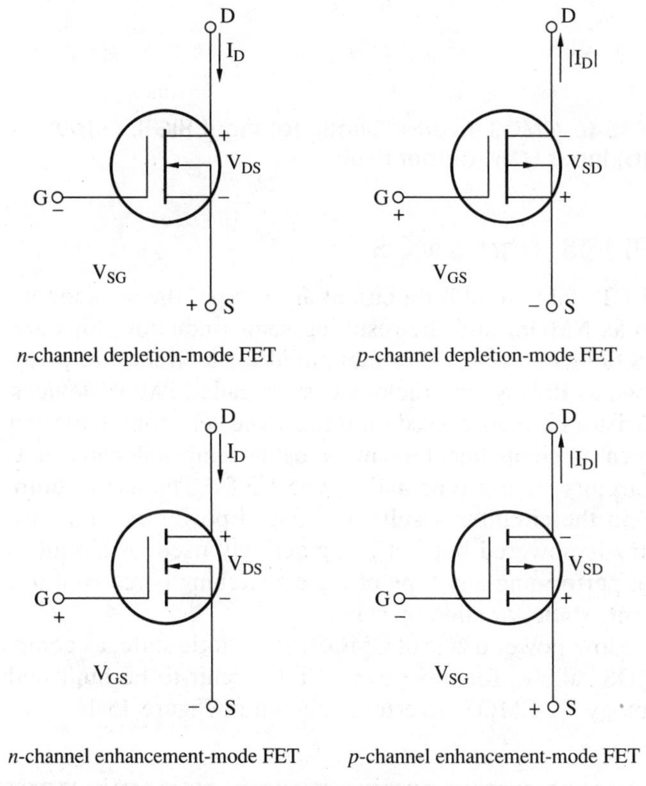

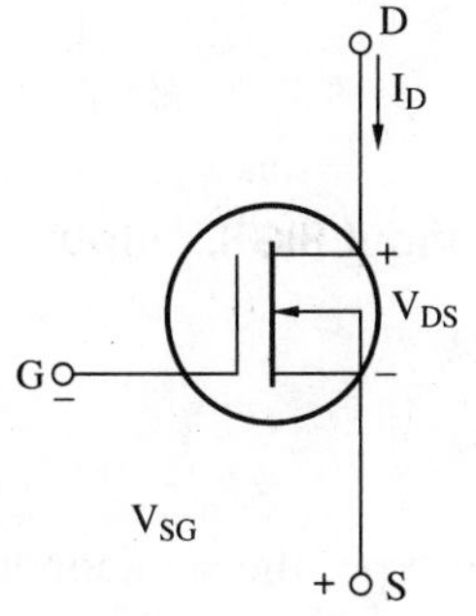

D
I_D
+
V_{DS}
G
−
V_{SG}
+ S
n-channel depletion-mode FET
D
$|I_D|$
−
V_{SD}
G
+
V_{GS}
− S
p-channel depletion-mode FET
D
I_D
+
V_{DS}
G
+
V_{GS}
− S
n-channel enhancement-mode FET
D
$|I_D|$
−
V_{SD}
G
−
V_{SG}
+ S
p-channel enhancement-mode FET

D = drain　　V_{SG} = voltage, source to gate
G = gate　　V_{GS} = voltage, gate to source
S = source　　V_{SD} = voltage, source to drain
　　V_{DS} = voltage, drain to source

FIGURE 15-15 FET Symbols

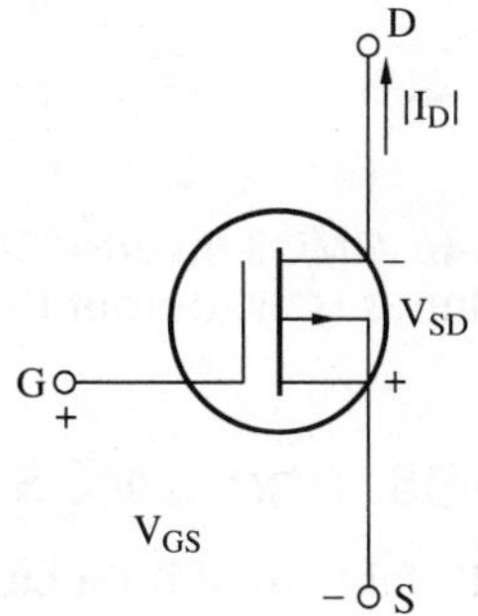

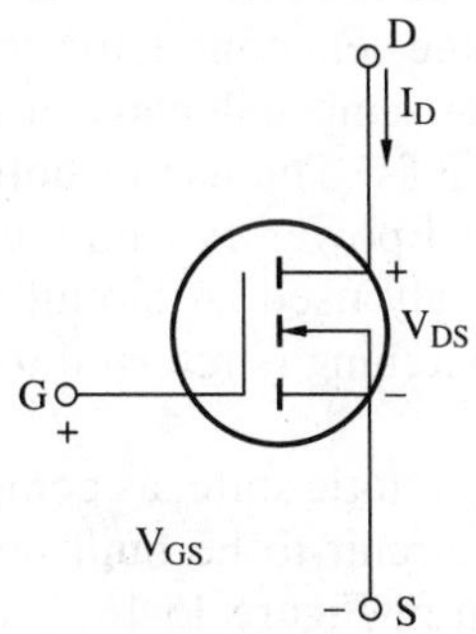

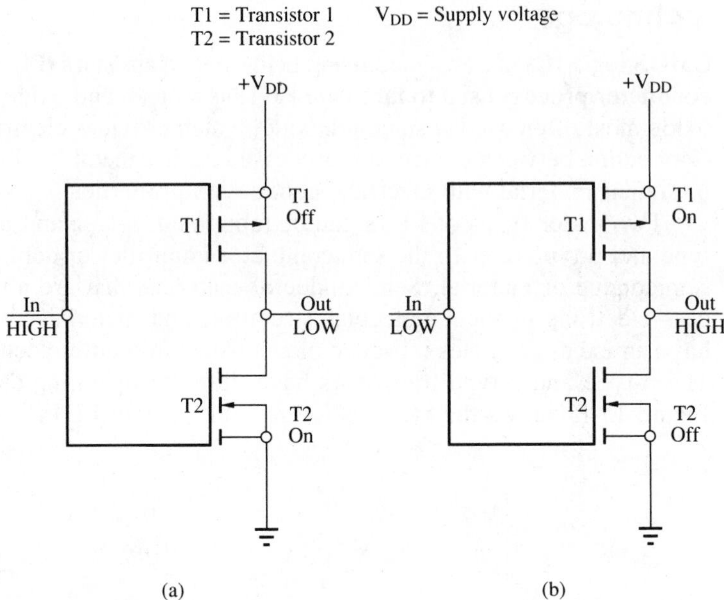

FIGURE 15-16 CMOS Inverter Circuit (a) Input HIGH, output LOW, (b) Input LOW, output HIGH

15.5.2 NMOS, PMOS, and CMOS

If all FETs fabricated for a circuit are n-type, the semiconductor process is known as **NMOS,** and the resulting semiconductor chips are simply called NMOS devices. If all FETs fabricated for a circuit are p-type, the process is known as **PMOS,** and the devices are called PMOS devices. If both types of transistors are processed onto the same semiconductor chip, this process is known as **complementary metal-oxide semiconductor,** or **CMOS.** CMOS logic circuits have n-type and p-type FETs. The use of both types of transistors in the circuitry results in reduced power consumption when the IC circuitry is powered but not being actively used. A circuit that is powered but not performing any type of logic switching is referred to as being in the **quiescent, static,** or **standby state.**

The low-power usage of CMOS in the static state, as compared to NMOS or PMOS, allows for low-power FET circuit to be built with CMOS FET technology. A CMOS inverter is shown in Figure 15-16.

■ EXAMPLE 15-10 TTL and CMOS Power Consumption

Problem: How does the power consumption of a 74138 TTL 3:8 decoder compare with a 74HC138 CMOS 3:8 decoder?

Solution: Operating both circuits at 5 volts, the typical power consumption in the operating mode for the TTL 74138 is:

$I_{CC(typ)} \times V_{CC} = 75\text{ mA} \times 5\text{ V} = 375\text{ mW}$ active

For the CMOS 74HC138 in the active mode:

$I_{CC(typ)} \times V_{CC} = 50\text{ mA} \times 5\text{ V} = 250\text{ mW}$ active

Note: The I_{CC} for CMOS is very dependent on the operating temperature, operating frequency, and load capacitance. (This will be discussed later in the chapter.)

For the 74HC138 in the standby (quiescent) mode:

$I_{CC(qui)} \times V_{CC} = 4\ \mu\text{A} \times 5\text{V} = 20\ \mu\text{W}$ standby

Thus, the active power usage for the CMOS for a 74HC138 decoder is approximately 33% less than the equivalent TTL device, but on the same order of magnitude. The standby power, however, is only 20 μW, three orders of magnitude less than for TTL. ■

15.5.3 CMOS Voltage Specifications

CMOS is based on FET technology, and TTL is based on bipolar transistor technology. The internal circuitry of CMOS is designed to provide input and output HIGH and LOW voltages that differ from TTL. The supply voltage for CMOS devices is $\mathbf{V_{DD}}$, and the ground reference is known as $\mathbf{V_{SS}}$. Standard CMOS (4000B) input and output voltages vary with V_{DD}, and V_{DD} has a wide acceptable range of values, from 3.0 to 15.0 volts. Table 15-5 shows the standard CMOS input and output voltage level specifications. Note that CMOS voltage vary considerably from TTL.

Devices that meet the I/O specifications listed in Table 15-5 are **CMOS compatible.** Note that CMOS circuits will recognize both a LOW and a HIGH over a wide range of voltage. Also, note the large amount of voltage between a CMOS LOW and HIGH. For a supply voltage of 5 volts, the input LOW will be from 0 to 1.5 volts, the input HIGH can range from 3 to 5 volts, and

TABLE 15-5 Standard CMOS Voltage Levels

Signal	Parameter	Defined Voltage Range (volts)
Input LOW	V_{IL}	0.0–(30% of V_{DD})
Input HIGH	V_{IH}	(60% of V_{DD})–V_{DD}
Output LOW	V_{OL}	0.0–(1% of V_{DD})
Output HIGH	V_{OH}	(99% of V_{DD})–V_{DD}

there is a minimum nonvalid logic voltage of 1.5 volts between HIGH and LOW logic levels.

CMOS circuits output a HIGH and LOW within a very tight 1% tolerance of the supply voltage. The wide range of input voltages and the accurate output voltages result in CMOS logic having good noise immunity characteristics and a better noise immunity than TTL, since TTL only has a nominal 400 mV difference between input and output voltages.

Thus, the major advantages CMOS logic provides are low-power consumption, excellent noise immunity, and a wide power supply voltage range of operation. These advantages allow the use of less expensive power supplies (nonregulated) and battery supply operation.

Section Self-Test

Determine if the following statements are true or false:

1. Standard CMOS can be operated at a supply voltage equal to that of TTL.
2. CMOS ICs have less noise immunity than TTL ICs due to the large undefined logic voltage range of CMOS.
3. CMOS ICs use several orders of magnitude less power than TTL ICs in the active power mode.

ANSWERS (Not necessarily in the order of the questions)

• False • True • False

15-6 CMOS LOGIC TECHNOLOGIES

CMOS logic ICs were first offered by the RCA Corporation in 1967. At that time they introduced the 4000 series of CMOS logic. Many of the same logic functions available in TTL had a 4000 series equivalent. These logic devices had superior power parameters to TTL, often using hundreds of times less power than TTL in some applications.

Many advances in processing technology and CMOS circuit design have resulted in several new and advanced CMOS logic families with superior power parameters as compared to many TTL subfamilies and equivalent speed.

15.6.1 CMOS Speed and Power Parameters

CMOS technology has evolved and now competes successfully with TTL ICs in speed comparisons, with lower power usage in most applications. CMOS devices, however, require special handling precautions because of their susceptibility to damage due to electrostatic discharge (ESD). In many laboratory and educational settings TTL devices are preferred for their durability and reliability.

TABLE 15-6 4000B CMOS Logic Gate ICs

Number	Description
4069B	Hex inverter
4019B	Quad AND/OR select
4011B	Quad 2-input NAND
4001B	Quad 2-input NOR
4070B	Quad XOR
4077B	Quad XNOR

15.6.2 4000/4000B CMOS

The 4000/4000B series is seldom used for new logic designs, having been replaced by newer CMOS logic technologies. However, many existing designs use 4000/4000B logic, so it is important to have some understanding of the technology.

The 4000 series, as mentioned, has lower power usage than equivalent TTL ICs. Compared to standard TTL at 10 mW per gate 4000 series, CMOS has power usage in the microwatt (μW) to nanowatt (nW) range, a three to six order of magnitude reduction in the power usage per gate.

However, the 4000 series has less fan-out than TTL, is not pin compatible at the device level with TTL, and is usually slower than TTL. Typical 4000 series propagation delay times are from 20 to 500 ns per gate. Table 15-6 shows the basic gates available in the 4000B CMOS logic subfamily.

15.6.3 74C CMOS

To overcome the problem with pin compatibility between TTL and CMOS, another CMOS logic series was created, the 74C00 subfamily. The 74C00 CMOS ICs were designed to be pin and number compatible with the TTL family of logic. This enables logic designers to convert TTL designs to CMOS. However, the input and output voltage levels are still incompatible. The 74C CMOS devices are no longer commonly manufactured.

15.6.4 74HC CMOS

Dramatic improvements in CMOS semiconductor processing have led to the development of the 74HC00 CMOS logic subfamily. These devices not only offer excellent low power parameters and noise immunity, but also have a typical DC noise margin three times better than TTL. The propagation delay speeds are typically or better than 6 to 10 ns per gate. This speed is equivalent the standard and LS TTL logic subfamily speeds. The 74HC subfamily has CMOS input switching levels of V_{IL} = 30% V_{CC} and V_{IH} = 70% V_{CC} and operates with a supply voltage of 2 to 6 volts.

15.6.5 74HCT CMOS

The 74HCT CMOS logic subfamily is designed to be directly compatible with LS TTL. The HCT devices have TTL input switching levels of .8 and 2.0 volts and operate within the standard TTL supply voltage range of 4.5 to 5.5 volts. An important use for the HCT ICs is interfacing between TTL and CMOS ICs.

15.6.6 Advanced CMOS Logic (ACL)

One of the newer CMOS logic families is the **advanced CMOS logic (ACL)** technology. ACL logic is available in two subfamilies, the **advanced CMOS (AC)** logic and the **advanced CMOS-TTL (ACT)** logic. These devices are intended to offer the speed of the advanced bipolar (TTL) technologies while maintaining the low-power usage of CMOS.

The AC subfamily has CMOS compatible inputs, with switching speeds that are from 1.5 to 10 ns, depending on the supply voltage used. The ACT subfamily also has TTL compatible inputs, with switching speeds from 1.5 to 10 ns.

TABLE 15-7 CMOS Logic Subfamilies

Subfamily	Prefix	Operating Characteristic
Standard CMOS	4000	Excellent power; slow speed
Buffered CMOS	4000B	Excellent power; slow speed, better fan-out than standard CMOS
TTL pin compatible CMOS	74C	Excellent power; better speed than standard
High speed CMOS	74HC	Very good power; equivalent speed of standard TTL
High speed CMOS; TTL compatible	74HCT	Very similar to 74HC; can be driven directly by TTL
Advanced CMOS	74AC	Higher speed replacement for 74HC
Advanced CMOS; TTL compatible	74ACT	Higher speed replacement for 74HCT

15.6.7 CMOS Logic Technology Comparisons

As with TTL, it is important that the logic designer be familiar with the different CMOS logic technologies and have a basic understanding of which method to select for a given application. Table 15-7 summarizes the different types of CMOS logic available. Consult the manufacturer's data book to determine which ICs are available in each CMOS family and subfamily.

Section Self-Test

Determine if the following statements are true or false:

1. The 74ACT ICs are TTL compatible.
2. A hex inverter IC in the 4000B series is a 4004B.
3. Some CMOS logic subfamily ICs are faster than comparable low-power Schottky TTL ICs.

ANSWERS (Not necessarily in the order of the questions)

- True
- False
- True

15-7 CMOS CIRCUIT OPERATION: FET INVERTERS AND OPEN-DRAIN

Field-effect transistors (FETs) are the basic building blocks for CMOS circuits. Unlike a bipolar transistor that operates as a result of currents produced from applying voltage (biasing) to the base, collector, and emitter, the FET's operation is based on the application of a voltage to the gate that, through an insulator, sets up an electric field used to control the flow of current between two points: the source and gate.

15.7.1 Field Effect Transistors

FETs have a gate, drain, and source, as shown in Figure 15-17. Depending on the type of FET, a **threshold voltage, V_t,** is applied to the gate to turn the transistor either on or off.

15.7.2 Enhancement Mode FET

Enhancement mode FETs are normally off. A threshold voltage is applied to the gate to turn the transistor on. If the enhancement FET is an **n-channel** device, a *positive* threshold voltage of greater than 1 volt will turn the transistor on. If the enhancement FET is a **p-channel,** a *negative* threshold voltage of less than -1 volt (e.g., -1.5 volts) will turn the transistor on.

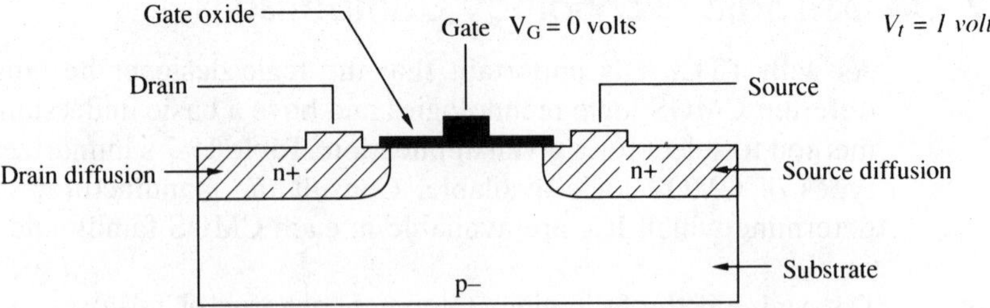

(a) npn enhancement mode FET cross section. Since $V_G < V_t$ no conduction path exists between the drain and source (no channel). The transistor is off.

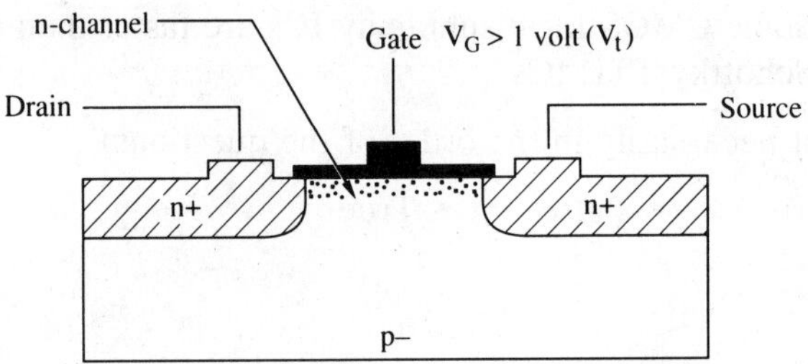

(b) npn enhancement mode FET cross section. Since $V_G > V_t$ a conduction path of electrons exists between the drain and source (*n*-channel). The transistor is on.

FIGURE 15-17 FET

15.7.3 Depletion Mode FET

Depletion mode FETs are normally on. A threshold voltage is applied to turn the transistor off once the threshold voltage is applied to the gate. As with enhancement mode devices, there are p-channel and n-channel depletion mode devices. Table 15-8 summarizes the FET switching characteristics.

TABLE 15-8 FET Switching Characteristics

FET Type	Channel	Transistor State, No Gate Voltage Applied	Transistor State, V_t Applied to Gate	Type V_t (volt)
Enhancement	n	Off	On	+1
Enhancement	p	Off	On	−1
Depletion	n	On	Off	+1
Depletion	p	On	Off	−1

15.7.4 CMOS Output Stage: Open Drain

Logically, CMOS and TTL ICs function identically, but the operating characteristics (speed, power, etc.) differ. Just as with TTL, normal CMOS outputs should not be connected together. The same problem that occurs when bipolar totem-pole TTL outputs are connected occurs when FET inverter CMOS outputs are connected together.

If one of the outputs is driving a HIGH and is connected to an output driving a LOW, the shorted output voltage will be in an undefined region of operation. For common (tied) output connection, CMOS has **open-drain** devices that are functionally equivalent to TTL open-collector devices. Open-drain CMOS ICs require pull-up resistors to supply the current for a logical HIGH output. The value of the required pull-up resistor is calculated just as with TTL open-collector devices. The wired-AND operation is the same as for TTL.

Many CMOS logic ICs, especially those designed to function with microprocessor and memory designs, have tristate outputs. As with TTL, this prevents nonactive ICs connected to a common bus from loading the bus and interfering with the operation of an active device at the common output point (bus).

Section Self-Test

Determine if the following statements are true or false:

1. The CMOS equivalent of a TTL open-collector output is an open-drain.
2. A depletion n-channel FET has 5 volts applied to its gate. The transistor is on.
3. An enhancement mode p-channel FET has 5 volts applied to its gate. The transistor is on.

ANSWERS (Not necessarily in the order of the questions)

• False • True • False

15-8 DESIGNING WITH CMOS

The same design considerations that were explained when discussing TTL design apply to CMOS designs as well. CMOS has parameters on power, speed, fan out, noise, I/O voltages, and loading that are analogous to TTL. Basic design rules that applied to TTL also apply to CMOS, such as the connection of all unused inputs to avoid floating inputs.

In addition, CMOS has some parameters that differ from TTL, including a large increase in power consumption as the frequency of operation increases, susceptibility to ESD damage, and latch-up.

15.8.1 Power Consumption

As the frequency of operation of CMOS circuits increases so does the power consumption, approaching TTL power consumption numbers at very high frequencies (greater than 20 MHz). Most low power advantages of CMOS are a result of very low currents of the CMOS inverter circuit when the FETs are not switching, that is, are in standby. If the transistors are required to switch at faster rates, the device currents are active for a larger percentage of the time and the average power usage for the device increases significantly. The active current can be calculated by using Equation 15-5:

$$\text{Eq. 15-5} \qquad I_{CC\ active} = I_T \text{ per gate}$$

$$= (C_{pd} \times V_{CC} \times f) + \frac{I_{CC}}{n}$$

where I_{CC} = operating current
C_{pd} = power dissipation capacitance
V_{CC} = operating voltage
f = switching frequency
n = number of gates per IC

The point to remember is that power consumption for CMOS increases as the operation frequency increases, and that the current values listed in typical CMOS IC specifications are for low frequency use. All current values should be carefully calculated at the frequency of operation in actual CMOS design applications. Figure 15-18 shows a chart of the power consumption of HC CMOS and LS TTL versus the frequency of operation. Note how CMOS and TTL approach the same power usage as the operating frequency increases.

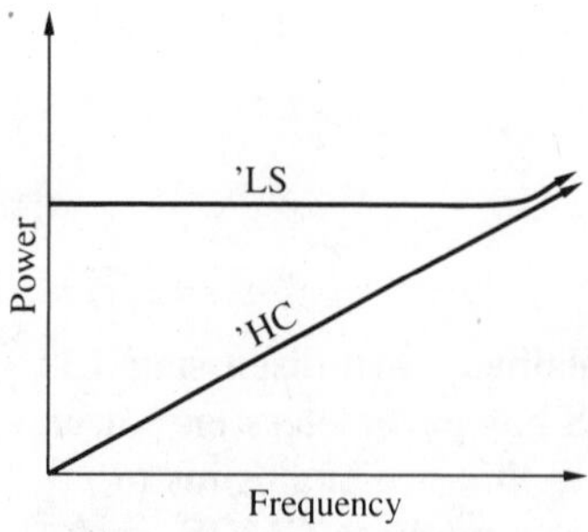

FIGURE 15-18 CMOS and TTL Power Usage Versus Frequency of Operation

Boolean equation: $A\overline{B} + CD = X$

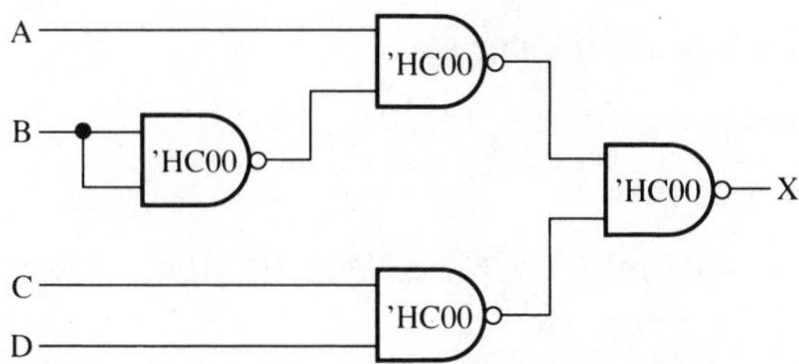

FIGURE 15-19 Example 15-11 CMOS Circuit

EXAMPLE 15-11 CMOS Power Calculations

Problem: a. Select one CMOS IC to build the circuit shown in Figure 15-19.
b. Determine the allowable frequency range of operation for the circuit.
c. Calculate the static (standby) power usage for the circuit at 4.5 volts.
d. Calculate the transient (active) power usage for the circuit at 4.5 volts and 100 KHz.
e. Calculate the transient power usage for the circuit at 4.5 volts and 10 MHz.

Solution: (a) A 74HC00 can be used, with one NAND wired as an inverter.
(b) At 4.5 volts the maximum propagation delay time, t_{PD}, is 23 ns. Thus:

$$f_{max} = \frac{1}{23 \text{ ns}} = 43.5 \text{ MHz.}$$

(c) The static or quiescent power is:

$V_{CC} \times I_{CC} = 100 \text{ nA} \times 4.5 \text{ V} = 4.5\ \mu\text{W}$

(d) $C_{pd} = 20$ pF per gate

$$I_T = (20 \text{ pF} \times 100 \text{ KHz} \times 4.5 \text{ V}) + \frac{100 \text{ nA}}{4}$$

$$= 9\ \mu\text{A} + 24 \text{ nA} = 9\ \mu\text{A per gate}$$

The transient power per gate is:

$9\ \mu\text{A} \times 4.5 \text{ V} = 40.6\ \mu\text{W}$

For four gates, $4 \times 40.6\ \mu\text{W} = 162.4\ \mu\text{W}$ at 100 KHz.

(e) Repeating the calculation of part (d) but now with the frequency at 10 MHZ yields:

I_T = .9 mA + 25 nA = .9 mA per gate

The transient power per gate is:

.9 mA × 4.5 V = 4.05 mW

For four gates, 4 × 4.05 mW = 16.2 mW at 10 MHz. ■

15.8.2 CMOS Fan-Out

The fan-out of CMOS is generally much larger than that of TTL. A drive gate or output from some CMOS subfamilies can theoretically drive several hundred loads from the same subfamily, according to the current and voltage fan-out equations. Other practical design factors, however, such as propagation delay, make this impractical.

■ EXAMPLE 15-12 CMOS Fan-Out Calculations

Problem: Calculate the theoretical fan-out of the 74HC CMOS logic subfamily.

Solution: Refer to a CMOS data book, and find the input and output maximum current parameters. For the HC subfamily of CMOS:

I_{OL} = 4 mA $\quad$ I_{OH} = −4 mA

I_{IL} = −1 μA $\quad$ I_{IH} = 1 μA

$$\text{Fan-out}_{LOW} = \frac{4\text{ mA}}{1\ \mu\text{A}} = 4000$$

$$\text{Fan-out}_{HIGH} = \frac{4\text{ mA}}{1\ \mu\text{A}} = 4000$$

$$\text{Fan-out} = 4000$$

Note, however, that such a high fan-out cannot be practically achieved due to the effect capacitive loading has on propagation delay and the practical wiring and reliability considerations. ■

15.8.3 CMOS Latch-up

CMOS has some unique design considerations. One of the most widely researched operating phenomenon associated with CMOS is a failure mechanism called **latch-up**, which prevents the IC from functioning.

Latch-up occurs when a particular set of voltages is applied to CMOS circuits. Internally, high currents conduct between V_{DD} and V_{SS}, which cause the inverter circuit to stop operating or latch-up. When the power is removed from a circuit in latch-up, it will once again be functional unless the latch-up currents destroy the FETs. This often occurs when power is initially applied to a CMOS IC, or upon the application of any noise spike that brings the output of the device at least .7 volt below V_{SS}.

Many circuit and semiconductor processing innovations have reduced the problems once associated with CMOS circuits, but some types of CMOS devices may still latch-up and become nonoperational if a unique set of voltages are applied. Therefore, always consult the specification sheets on CMOS devices to check for any application information concerning the avoidance of latch-up.

15.8.4 Electrostatic Discharge (ESD)

Another characteristic of CMOS ICs due to their very high input resistance is the susceptibility to damage by **electrostatic discharge (ESD)**. ESD damage is caused by the discharge of electrostatic charge into CMOS ICs due to

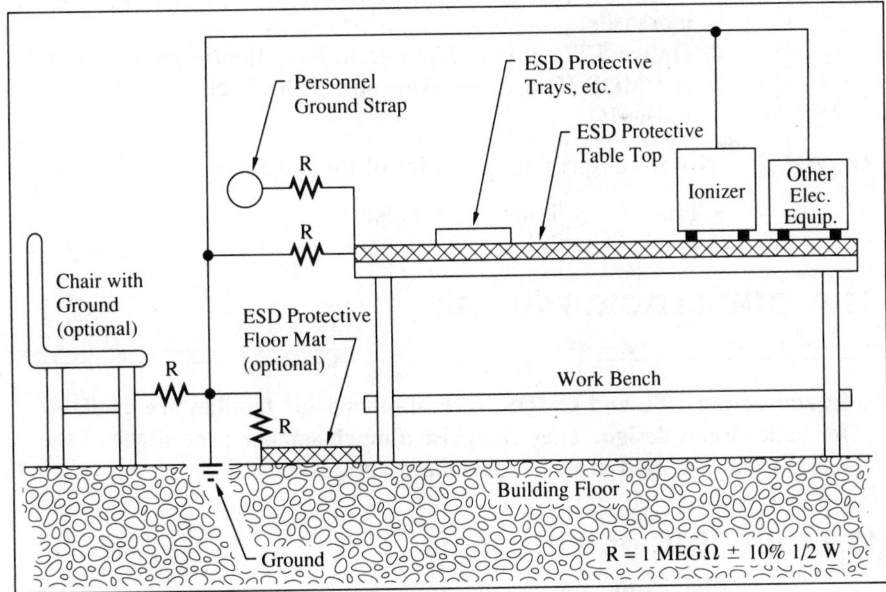

All electrical equipment sitting on the conductive table top must be hard grounded but must be isolated from the conductive table top.

Note: Earth ground is not computer ground or RF ground or any other limited type ground.

FIGURE 15-20 Static-Free Workstation (Courtesy of Texas Instruments)

improper handling techniques. A large voltage placed across the very high input resistance of a MOS circuit produces internal voltages that are sufficient to destroy the gate oxide of the input FETs.

Static charge sufficient to damage CMOS ICs is prevalent in low humidity environments, and increasing the relative humidity level is one method used to reduce the possibility of ESD damage in large CMOS manufacturing areas. CMOS ICs are packaged in conductive foam, and the parts should never be handled in bare, nongrounded hands. Anyone building circuits using CMOS ICs should at the very minimum use a grounding strap attached around the wrist and connected to a ground. Antistatic work mats are also very good at reducing the risk of ESD damage to CMOS ICs.

Many CMOS ICs now have circuits with built-in ESD protection. However, this does not always prevent ESD damage, and device damage can result by walking across a carpet in a low humidity environment and touching the pins of a CMOS IC. Inserting a CMOS IC into styrofoam or some similar nonconducting foam can also produce enough ESD to damage a CMOS device. A static-free workstation is shown in Figure 15-20.

Section Self-Test

Determine if the following statements are true or false:

1. As the frequency of operation increases, the power usage of a CMOS IC increases.
2. Unlike TTL, it is acceptable to have floating inputs on CMOS ICs.
3. A CMOS IC can be taken out of the latch-up state by removing power to the IC.

ANSWERS (Not necessarily in the order of the questions)

• True • True • False

15-9 OTHER LOGIC FAMILIES

In addition to TTL and CMOS, several other logic families are available for logic circuit design. They comprise a much smaller percentage of the market and are used in more specialized applications.

15.9.1 RTL , DTL, and HTL Logic

Some of the first bipolar logic devices were **resistor-transistor logic,** or **RTL, diode-transistor logic,** or **DTL,** and **high-threshold logic,** or **HTL.** RTL, DTL, and HTL are mentioned for a historical perspective but are no longer used in current logic design. TTL and its subfamilies have replaced RTL and DTL, and the excellent noise immunity of CMOS has virtually eliminated the need for the good noise margin HTL.

15.9.2 Integrated-Injection Logic (IIL)

Integrated-injection logic, IIL, or **I-squared L,** is a type of bipolar logic that is used in LSI and VLSI designs because its simple circuitry allows the manufacture of very dense logic devices on silicon. However, it is not used to manufacture discrete logic ICs, as other logic families have superior switching speed.

15.9.3 Emitter-Coupled Logic

Emitter-coupled logic, or **ECL,** is the other bipolar logic family that is used to make SSI and MSI ICs for logic designers. ECL is also known as **current mode logic (CML).**

ECL logic is used in very high speed applications. These include real-time applications such as the monitoring of nuclear phenomenon, time bases in oscilloscopes (how else can you measure the propagation delay of TTL and CMOS!), and any application requiring the measurement of time in less than 1 ns increments.

ECL circuits are designed to prevent the bipolar transistors from operating in the saturation region, which increases the transistor switching speed. This is also known as current mode switching, as a fixed current is switched between the input and output transistors while keeping both transistors out of saturation.

One advantage of ECL logic is that the propagation delay is fairly constant over a large range of frequencies, and ECL gates can often operate at well above 1000 MHz. The typical propagation delay time is less than 1 ns. ECL has a typical gate power of 40 to 50 mW. None of the TTL subfamilies can offer this speed/frequency performance. In addition, ECL has good fan-out (usually 20 to 30) and the availability of both true and complement outputs.

Even though the power usage is high by TTL LS standards, the power usage is fixed over a wide frequency range. This is an important advantage that ECL has over TTL. In addition, the internal circuitry requires about the same amount of current to produce a HIGH or LOW. This is an advantage since there are no large current transients associated with logic level switching.

ECL also has several disadvantages as compared to TTL and CMOS. ECL has relatively high power consumption and low noise immunity. Since the logic levels are based on negative voltages, a negative power supply voltage must be available. This is incompatible with CMOS and TTL designs unless the additional power supply reference voltage circuitry is added.

A binary 0 is represented in ECL logic as −1.7 volts, and a logic 1 is represented by −0.8 volt. It is important to note that ECL to TTL interface circuits are needed due to the voltage incompatibility between ECL and TTL. Special ICs exist to interface bidirectionally from ECL to CMOS or

TABLE 15-9 ECL IC Number Classification

Logic Function	ECL Number (with the prefix 10 or 100)
Basic gates	100–109
Complex gates	110–119
Interfaces	120–129
Latches, flip-flop counters	130–139
Registers, memory multiplexers	140–155
Encoders, decoders, other MSI	156–179
Arithmetic circuits	180–189
Interfaces	190–399
High capacity memory	400–499
Military ICs	500–699
Microprocessors and peripherals	800–899

from ECL to TTL. Also, ECL is susceptible to ESD and precautions must be taken when handling ECL ICs.

ECL devices are available in several subfamilies, including 10K, 100K, and 10KH. Some manufacturers use the subfamily designator of 10E and 100E—10E corresponds to 10KH and 100E corresponds to 100K. The differences between the subfamilies are the supply voltages and how much the speed parameters vary with temperature.

The availability of logic functions in the ECL family is much more limited than for CMOS and TTL. The IC numbering system also varies from that of CMOS and TTL, as shown in Table 15-9.

Section Self-Test

Determine if the following statements are true or false:

1. ECL is a good logic family to select for high speed applications.
2. ECL is a good logic family to select for low-power applications.
3. ECL is a good logic family to select for high noise applications.

ANSWERS (not necessarily in the order of the questions)

- False • True • False

15-10 LOGIC COMPARISON AND SELECTION

Now that the logic families and their characteristics have been thoroughly examined, it is appropriate to make some overall comparisons among all

different types of logic available. PLDs should be considered and compared to TTL, CMOS, and microprocessor designs in terms of important design parameters of input and output voltages and currents, power, speed, and other design criteria.

15.10.1 Technology Comparison and Selection

The first major design decision involves consideration of PLDs and microprocessors as one possible solution to a given application, in addition to the use of logic family ICs. If the decision is made to use a PLD or microprocessor, then fan-out and other interfacing parameters must be considered for any additional discrete or MSI logic used. A common term used for small numbers of logic gates needed in larger microprocessor or PLD based designs is **glue logic.** In simpler designs, consideration still must be given to the selection and interfacing required for TTL, CMOS, and ECL logic.

After determining these basic requirements, the design can be optimized within the selected logic family by reviewing the information in the preceding sections and the up-to-date data specifications for the logic family or families chosen.

An overall comparison by parameter will be given, including supply voltages, propagation delay, power dissipation, fan-out, noise margins, and maximum frequency of operation. Exact comparisons are not practical, as these parameters will vary with manufacturer, improvements in the process, and even the invention of new logic subfamilies with improved parameters. Thus, these comparisons are to be used only as a guide to initiate the overall design selection and to develop an overall understanding of the capabilities of the available digital logic devices. Figure 15-21 shows an overall com-

TECHNOLOGY‡	SILICON-GATE CMOS	METAL GATE CMOS	STD TTL	LOW-POWER SCHOTTKY TTL	SCHOTTKY TTL	ADVANCED LOW-POWER SCHOTTKY TTL	ADVANCED SCHOTTKY TTL
Device series	SN74HC	4000	SN74	SN74LS	SN74AS	SN74ALS	SN74AS
Power dissipation per gate (mW)							
Static	0.0000025	0.001	10	2	19	1	8.5
At 100 kHz	0.17	0.1	10	2	19	1	8.5
Propagation delay time (ns) (C_L = 15 pF)	8	105	10	10	3	4	1.5
Maximum clock frequency (MHz) (C_L = 15 pF)	40	12	35	40	125	70	200
Speed/Power product (pJ) (at 100 kHz)	1.4	11	100	20	57	4	13
Minimum output drive (mA) (V_O = 0.4 V)							
Standard outputs	4	1.6	16	8	20	8	20
High-current outputs	6	1.6	48	24	64	24/48	48/64
Fan-out (LS loads)							
Standard outputs	10	4	40	20	50	20	50
High-current outputs	15	4	120	60	160	60/120	120/160
Maximum input current, I_{IL} (mA) (V_I = 0.4 V)	±0.001	–0.001	–1.6	–0.4	–2.0	–0.1	–0.5

‡Family characteristics at 25°C, V_{CC} = 5 V; all values typical unless otherwise noted. This table is provided for broad comparisons only. Parameters for specific devices within a family may vary. For detailed comparisons, please consult the appropriate data book.

FIGURE 15-21 Comparison of CMOS and TTL Technologies

parison between CMOS and TTL technologies, which is useful once all the parameters listed are understood.

15.10.2 Supply Voltage

TTL logic has a nominal supply voltage of 5 volts and ground. The 7400 series (commercial grade) has a ±5% supply tolerance (250 mV) and the 5400 series (military grade) has a ±10% supply tolerance (500 mV). The absolute maximum V_{CC} voltage for TTL is 7.0 volts.

CMOS 4000 and 4000B logic subfamilies have a recommended supply voltage range from 3 to 15 volts. The CMOS 74HC, 74HC, and 74HCT subfamilies have a recommended supply voltage range from 2 to 6 volts, and a maximum rating of from −.5 to 7 volts.

PLDs are available that are TTL or CMOS compatible. Thus, PLDs are designed to operate within the respective TTL or CMOS design voltages.

ECL has a typical V_{EE} supply of −5.2 volts and a maximum V_{EE} supply of −7 volts. In both cases V_{EE} is referenced to V_{CC}, which is typically ground (0 volt).

In comparison, CMOS has the largest voltage supply tolerance, and this family is ideal for designs when the power supply may vary. Two examples are nonregulated supplies and battery supplies. TTL has a relatively small supply tolerance of 5 to 10%, and TTL designs must have regulated power supplies. ECL requires a negative supply. Notice that TTL and CMOS can easily be used in the same design from a supply voltage standpoint as long as the necessary interfacing is designed. Table 15-10 summarizes the logic family voltage supply parametrics.

TABLE 15-10 Voltage Supply Parametrics

		VOLTAGES (VOLTS)	
Logic	Subfamily	Range	Absolute Maximum
TTL	All 74XXX	4.75 – 5.25	7.0
TTL	All 54XXX	4.50 – 5.50	7.0
CMOS	4000/4000B	3.0 – 15.0	– .5 – 7.0
CMOS	74C/HC/HCT	2.0 – 6.0	– .5 – 7.0
ECL	100K	−4.5 – 0.0	−7.0 – .5

XXX denotes individual IC numbers in the subfamily.

TABLE 15-11 Power Dissipation Parametrics

Logic	Subfamily		POWER DISSIPATION (1 NAND) Typical*	Worst Case
TTL	74		10 mW	29 mW
TTL	74L		1 mW	3 mW
TTL	74H		21 mW	50 mW
TTL	74S		19 mW	47 mW
TTL	74LS		4 mW	6 mW
TTL	74AS		16 mW	23 mW
TTL	74ALS		2 mW	4 mW
CMOS†	4000B		2 μW	‡
CMOS†	74HC	static	1 mW	12 μW
		active	550 μW	‡
CMOS†	74HCT	static	2 μW	20 μW
		active	1 mW	‡
ECL	10K		30 mW	35 mW
ECL	100K		45 mW	50 mW

* "Typical" assumes nominal supply voltage and that the output is HIGH 50% of the time. The "worst case" is the maximum V_{CC}, with the output in the worst case logic level.
† CMOS calculations are at 5.0 volts V_{CC} and at 1 MHz for the active power.
‡ The worst case for CMOS is frequency dependent.

15.10.3 Power

Power calculations are most often calculated on a per gate basis for a given technology. This type of calculation will yield a fairly accurate power calculation for a given design. The major difference between TTL and CMOS is that the power dissipation per gate with TTL is constant in the static and transient states, whereas CMOS has very low power usage in the static state and low power usage as compared to TTL in the active or transient state, increasing with increasing frequency. TTL power dissipation per gate is in the milliwatt range, whereas CMOS has a static power dissipation in the nanowatt range and an active power in the microwatt range. However, the active power increases linearly with the switching frequency as shown in Figure 15-18.

TTL uses approximately three orders of magnitude more power than CMOS in the active mode and six orders of magnitude more power than CMOS in the static mode. ECL, like TTL, has a fixed per gate power dissipation, typically 20 to 50 mW, or two to five times more than standard TTL. Table 15-11 summarizes the logic family power parametrics.

15.10.4 Propagation Delay

Propagation delay is one of the most important parameters to consider for any logic design. As previously mentioned, the speed of the device is dependent on the voltage of operation and the resistive and capacitive loads applied to the output. For HC CMOS devices, for example, each picofarad of load capacitance adds approximately .66 ns to the propagation delay value. Table 15-12 summarizes the propagation delay parameters for a NAND gate in each technology. Other devices have different propagation delay times.

For TTL, the standard input capacitance is approximately 5 pF. Thus, each TTL input adds 5 pF of capacitance that must be driven by the drive output.

TABLE 15-12 Propagation Delay Parametrics

			PROPAGATION DELAY (NAND)	
Logic	Subfamily	t_P	Typical (ns)	Worst Case (ns)
TTL	74	LH	12	22
		HL	7	15
TTL	74L	LH	35	60
		HL	31	60
TTL	74H	LH	5.9	10
		HL	6.2	10
TTL	74S	LH	4	7
		HL	5	8
TTL	74LS	LH	8	15
		HL	8	15
TTL	74AS	LH	1	4
		HL	1	4
TTL	74ALS	LH	3	11
		HL	2	8
CMOS	4000B	LH	75	150
		HL	75	150
CMOS	74HC	LH	10	18
		HL	10	18
CMOS	74HCT	t_{pD}	13	23
ECL	10K/100K	LH	.2	.6
		HL	.2	.6

Note: V_{CC} = 5 volts, C_L = 50 pF, R_L = 500 ohms.
LH = LOW to HIGH delay; HL = HIGH to LOW.

For CMOS, the standard input capacitance is approximately 10 pF. Thus, each CMOS input adds 10 pF of capacitance that must be driven by the drive output.

■ EXAMPLE 15-13 CMOS Propagation Delay Calculation

Problem: A 74HC138 has a propagation delay time from the enable to the output of 39 ns at V_{CC} = 4.5 volts. Determine the following:
a. Propagation delay at 2 volts
b. Propagation delay at 6 volts
c. Propagation delay for 100 HC loads at 4.5 volts

Solution: (a) From a CMOS data book, T_{PD} at 2 volts = 195 ns.
(b) t_{PD} at 6 volts = 33 ns.
(c) The values listed for propagation delay in the data book are for a capacitive load of 50 pF. Each HC input has a capacitive load of 10 pF. Thus, there are 100 − 5 = 95 capacitive loads that must be added to the 4.5-volt propagation delay of 39 ns:

$$(95 \times 10 \text{ pF}) \times .66 \text{ ns/pF} = 627 \text{ ns!!}$$

Therefore, even though the fan-out allows for up to 500 HC loads, the propagation delay at such a large loading is unacceptable. In this case the propagation delay went from 39 to 627 ns, a 1500% increase in propagation delay! ■

15.10.5 Fan-Out

The fan-out for a given logic device is dependent on the I_{OH} and I_{OL} of the device in question, along with the I_{IL} and I_{IH} of each device to be driven by the gate. Thus, exact fan-out calculations require the current parametrics from the data specification sheets, as discussed in Section 15.7.1. However, within a logic subfamily, output currents are somewhat standardized, so approximate fan-out can be given for each subfamily. Table 15-13 shows a comparison of the fan-out (load) parametrics.

■ EXAMPLE 15-14 HC CMOS to LS TTL Fan-Out Calculation

Problem: How many 74LS TTL gates can be driven by a 74HC CMOS gate?

Solution:

$I_{OL(CMOS)}$ = 4mA $\qquad$ $I_{IL(LS\ TTL)}$ = −.4 mA

TABLE 15-13 Fan-Out Parametric Comparison

Load Device →→→→ / Drive Device ↓↓	STD TTL	LS TTL	S TTL	F TTL	74HC*	74HCT*
STD TTL	10	40	8	26	400	400
LS TTL	5	20	4	13	400	400
S TTL	12	50	10	33	1000	1000
F TTL	12	50	10	33	1000	1000
74 HC CMOS	2	10	2	6	4000	4000
74 HCT CMOS	2	10	2	6	4000	4000

* For illustrative purposes only. These fan-out numbers agree with the fan-out equations but are not possible in actual digital circuits due to the effects of other parameters, especially propagation delay.

CMOS loads take only 1 μA of current. This table illustrates that fan-out is not a concern with CMOS loads.

To use this table, first select the drive device from the vertical column. Then select the load device from the horizontal column. The intersection is the fan-out if all load devices are the same subfamily.

Example: 74LS TTL has a fan-out of four 74S TTL loads.

$$I_{OH(CMOS)} = -4 \text{ mA} \qquad I_{IH(LS\ TTL)} = 20\ \mu\text{A}$$

$$\text{Fan-out}_{LOW} = \frac{4 \text{ mA}}{.4 \text{ mA}} = 10$$

$$\text{Fan-out}_{HIGH} = \frac{4 \text{ mA}}{.02 \text{ mA}} = 200$$

$$\text{Fan-out} = 10$$

■

■ EXAMPLE 15-15 HC CMOS to TTL Fan-Out Calculation

Problem: How many 74 TTL gates can be driven by a 74HC CMOS gate?

Solution

$$\text{Fan-out}_{LOW} = \frac{4 \text{ mA}}{1.6 \text{ mA}} = 2.5$$

$$\text{Fan-out}_{HIGH} = \frac{4\text{ mA}}{.04\text{ mA}} = 100$$

$$\text{Fan-Out} = 2$$

since fan-out is in unit gate increments. ■

■ EXAMPLE 15-16 HCT CMOS to TTL Fan-Out Calculation

Problem: How many standard TTL loads can be driven by a CMOS HCT output?

Solution: Since it is the CMOS LOW output that determines the fan-out, only this number needs to be calculated.

$$\frac{4\text{ mA}}{1.6\text{ mA}} = 2.5$$

Since loads are even numbers, only two standard TTL loads can be driven by a CMOS HCT output. ■

15.10.6 Noise Margin

Noise is any unwanted signal. It can be induced by electromagnetic fields between wires of a logic circuit or introduced by power supplies and logic switching transient currents. **Noise immunity** or **noise margin** refers to the maximum amount of noise that a device can tolerate and still operate correctly. The high state noise margin is defined as:

Eq. 15-6 $$V_{NH} = V_{OH(min)} - V_{IH(min)}$$

The low state noise margin is defined as:

Eq. 15-7 $$V_{NL} = V_{IL(max)} - V_{OL(max)}$$

LS TTL has a typical HIGH noise margin of .7 volts. CMOS has a typical HIGH noise margin of 30% of V_{CC}, or 1.5 volts at 5 volts V_{CC}. ECL has only a 250-mV HIGH noise margin, V_{NH}. Thus, CMOS has the best noise immunity of any logic family. Figure 15-22 shows a comparison of HC CMOS and LS TTL noise margins versus supply voltage.

■ EXAMPLE 15-17 Noise Margin Calculation

Problem: Use Figure 15-22 to determine the following noise margins:

a. LS TTL HIGH noise margin
b. LS TTL LOW noise margin

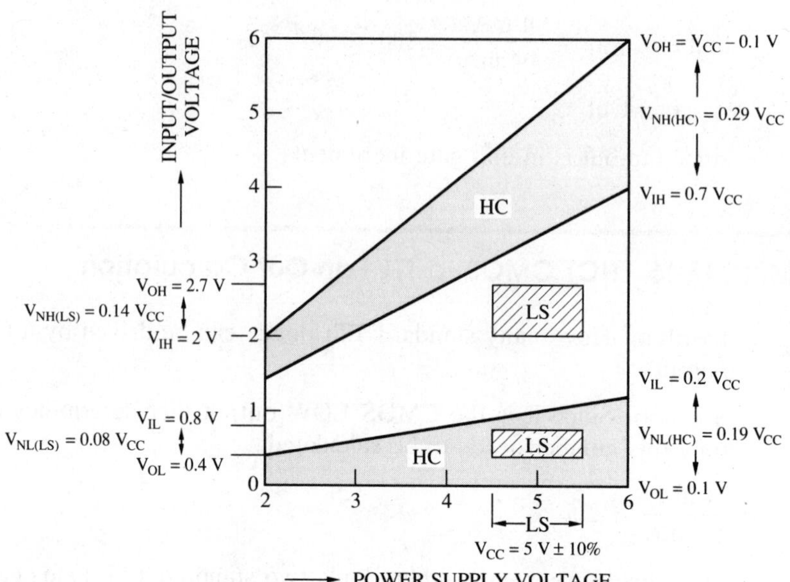

FIGURE 15-22 HC CMOS and LS TTL Noise Margins (Courtesy of Texas Instruments)

c. HC CMOS HIGH noise margin at $V_{CC} = 5.0$ V
d. HC CMOS LOW noise margin at $V_{CC} = 5.0$ V

Solution

$$V_{NH(LS\ TTL)} = 2.7\ V - 2.0\ V = .7\ V$$

$$V_{NL(LS\ TTL)} = .8\ V - .4\ V = .4\ V$$

$$V_{NH(HC\ CMOS)} = .29\ V_{CC}; \quad \text{at } 5.0\ V = 1.45\ V$$

$$V_{NL(HC\ CMOS)} = .19\ V_{CC}; \quad \text{at } 5.0\ V = .95\ V$$

Note that the CMOS ICs have over two times the noise margin of TTL ICs at equivalent voltages. ■

15.10.7 Operating Frequency

The maximum operating frequency for many logic devices is listed in the data specification sheets of many logic devices. This parameter is listed as $\mathbf{f_{max}}$, or as the **maximum clock rate.** Some device manufacturers, however, do not list the maximum operating frequency. In these cases the maximum operating frequency can be estimated by taking the reciprocal of the total worst case (maximum) propagation delay time, $t_{PHL} + t_{PLH}$. If only one propagation delay is listed, then the total propagation delay for maximum switching frequency would be two times p_D.

For some ICs, other circuit characteristics may reduce the maximum operating frequency to a value less than the value predicted by the propagation delay frequency. For other ICs, the calculated maximum frequency will be a conservative estimate. Thus, if the maximum operating frequency is a critical design parameter in a given application, always check the device specifications for an f_{max} parameter, or contact the manufacturer.

■ EXAMPLE 15-18 Maximum Operating Frequency

Problem: Determine the maximum operation frequency for each of the following ICs. Use V_{CC} = 4.5 volts for HC CMOS, V_{CC} = 5.0 volts for LS TTL, and V_{CC} = 5.5 volts for HCT CMOS.

a. 74LS20 b. 74LS138 c. 74HC27 d. 74HC112
e. 74HCT138

Solution

(a) $$\frac{1}{t_{Pmax}} = \frac{1}{(22 \text{ ns} + 15 \text{ ns})} = 27 \text{ MHz}$$

(b) 30 MHz (listed in specification)

(c) $$\frac{1}{[2t_{PD(max)}]} = \frac{1}{2(23) \text{ ns}} = 21.7 \text{ MHz}$$

(d) 20 MHz (listed in specification)

(e) $$\frac{1}{[2t_{PD(max)}]} = \frac{1}{66 \text{ ns}} = 15 \text{ MHz}$$ ■

It is also important to remember that the maximum operating frequency is dependent on the amount of capacitive load that the device is driving. Data books list operating frequencies and propagation delays for relatively low capacitive loads. As the capacitive load increases, the propagation delay time increases and the maximum operating frequency decreases. Added capacitance makes the device switch slower.

■ EXAMPLE 15-19 Maximum Frequency and Input Capacitance

Problem: a. What is the maximum operating frequency for a CMOS 74HC74 D flip-flop?

b. What is the capacitive load used to measure the maximum frequency and propagation delay for the 74HC74?

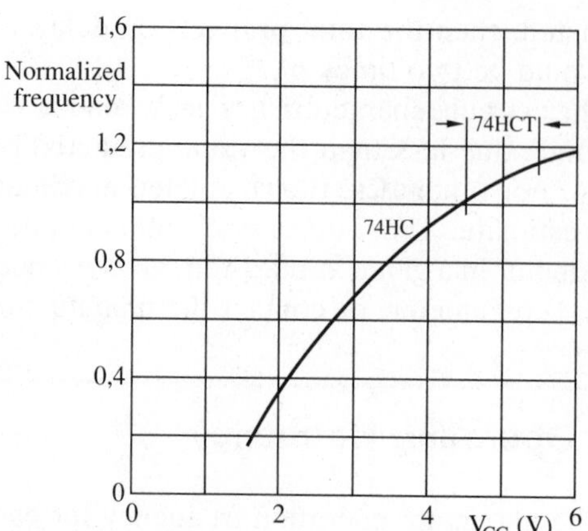

FIGURE 15-23 CMOS Operation Frequency Versus Supply Voltage

c. What is the input capacitance of an HC CMOS inputs?
d. How many HC CMOS loads can a 74HC74 output drive and still maintain the maximum frequency as answered in part (a)?
e. What is the fan-out of HC CMOS driving HC CMOS?
f. What do you expect will happen to the maximum operating frequency if the maximum fan-out load were attached to the 74HC74?

Solution

(a) $f_{max} = 25$ MHz ~ $V_{CC} = 4.5$ V
(b) 50 pF
(c) 10 pF
(d) five loads
(e) approximately 500
(f) The device propagation delay will increase and the maximum operating frequency will decrease with additional loads. ■

TTL and ECL power consumption is fairly constant over the allowed operating frequencies, while CMOS logic has a proportional dependence on frequency. As the CMOS frequency of operation increases, the power consumption increases. In addition, the maximum operating frequency of CMOS is dependent on the supply voltage. Figure 15-23 is a typical data book graph showing supply voltage vs. maximum frequency of operation.

15.10.8 Mixed Logic

Most logic designs should be done in one major logic family. There are few reasons to mix logic within a design. However, one design may have been done in CMOS and must interface with another design done in TTL. Another problem that can occur with inadequate project planning is to begin a design in one logic family such as HC CMOS and then find that a particular IC needed for the design is only available in TTL. As discussed, the input and output voltages are different for each type of logic, and interface circuits must match the output level of one logic type to the input level of the other logic type. For this reason, these interface circuits are often called **level shifters.** The following sections address the reasons and needed circuitry for interfacing the logic families and subfamilies. The advent of CMOS logic ICs with TTL compatible inputs and outputs has eliminated the need for some of the specialized interface circuitry, but the concepts are very important for interfacing mixed logic when the need arises.

Section Self-Test

Determine if the following statements are true or false:

1. ECL is the fastest logic family available.
2. Each input of a TTL device has an equivalent capacitance of 100 pF.
3. CMOS has better noise margin than TTL.

ANSWERS (Not necessarily in the order of the questions)

- True
- True
- False

15-11 LOGIC INTERFACING

Interfacing is the hardware and/or software needed to convert information in one form to another form. Hardware interface circuits are often referred to as the glue that holds a design together. For this reason, it is difficult to discuss any type of circuit design without discussing some interfacing concepts.

The following sections reinforce the information learned on TTL and CMOS logic families, selection, and design since interfacing relies on a good working knowledge of important parameters and concepts, including open-collector and totem-pole outputs, wired gates, and fan-out.

15.11.1 Interface Applications

If all circuits were of the same type, with the same specifications, and were to be used in the same application, there would be no need to interface. Interfacing circuits are required to allow one type of circuit or device to operate correctly with another type of circuit and to allow information in a form that is difficult to assimilate to be converted into a form that is easier to comprehend.

15.11.2 Analog-to-Digital and Digital-to-Analog Interface Circuits

Digital logic provides a way to represent physical quantities for electronic design and implementation. It is important to recognize that since digital electronics is a representation, digital information must eventually be converted to some analog form for human comprehension and use.

Analog-to-digital (A/D) and **digital-to-analog (D/A)** circuits are used to convert information from one representation to another. A/D and D/A circuits, by definition, are interface circuits. The specific details of A/D and D/A conversion are examined in Chapter 16, but by necessity they are mentioned here in the context of I/O interfacing.

A/D and D/A circuits are used for electrical, mechanical, and optical I/O interfacing to digital circuitry. Many interfaces are single chip ICs, with names indicating their function, including display controllers, optical couplers, and coder/decoders (codecs).

15.11.3 Logic Family Interface Requirements

Each logic family has unique voltage and current specifications with additional variations within logic subfamilies. Within the same logic subfamily, no interfacing is needed, as long as the fan-out limitations of the subfamily are not exceeded. In mixed family logic voltages and currents must be matched, often requiring interface circuitry. Frequently a designer finds it necessary to connect circuits from different logic families.

In smaller systems a design may be mostly CMOS, but a particular IC that a designer needs to use is only available in TTL. Thus, an interface is needed for its use in the CMOS design.

In larger systems a designer may want to optimize a section of the system for speed and optimize another part of the system for low power, necessitating a mixed logic family design. This may require interface circuitry.

The two major logic families, TTL and CMOS, require interface circuitry for joint circuit functionality. The exact interfacing needed depends on whether the TTL is driving the CMOS or whether the CMOS is driving the TTL. Interfacing to other logic families such as ECL is also possible.

When interfacing logic, three basic conditions need to be met:

- *Condition 1.* The drive device must be able to **source** a sufficient amount of output current to meet the combined input requirements of all load devices attached. (Equation 15-4)
- *Condition 2.* The drive device must be able to **sink** the combined maximum currents from all attached load devices. (Equation 15-3)
- *Condition 3.* The drive device output voltage must be within the allowed range of the load device(s) input voltage specification. This includes both logic LOW and logic HIGH voltages.

Conditions 1 and 2 are **fan-out** conditions, as discussed in Section 15.4. Condition 3 is a voltage compatibility condition. Other parameters such as noise tolerance, input and output capacitance, and switching speed also need to be considered in some designs.

Section Self-Test

Determine if the following statements are true or false:

1. No interface circuitry is needed when interfacing CMOS and TTL.
2. Current and voltage are the two primary interface parameters to consider.
3. Information is converted from analog to digital form for display purposes.

ANSWERS (Not necessarily in the order of the questions)

• True • False • False

15-12 CMOS TO TTL INTERFACE

CMOS to TTL interfacing is the condition when the drive device is CMOS and the loads are TTL. The voltages in this case are compatible and no additional voltage interface circuitry is needed. To determine current interfacing, the fan-out equations are used.

The equivalent output circuit for CMOS driving TTL is shown in Figure 15-24. Note that the CMOS drive device sources current to the TTL loads in

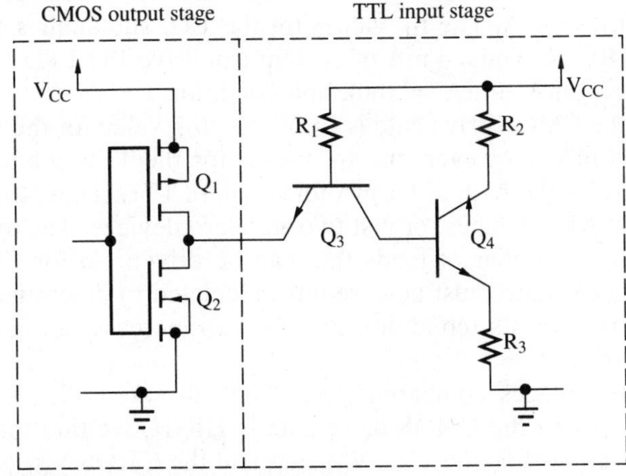

FIGURE 15-24 CMOS to TTL Interface

TABLE 15-14 TTL and CMOS Interface Parameters

Logic Family →	TTL			CMOS	
Subfamily →	74	74LS	74ALS	74HC	74HCT
$I_{IH(max)}$	40 μA	20 μA	20 μA	1 μA	1 μA
$I_{IL(max)}$	1.6 mA	400 μA	100 μA	1 μA	1 μA
$I_{OH(max)}$	400 μA	400 μA	400 μA	4 mA	4 mA
$I_{OL(max)}$	16 mA	8 mA	8 mA	4 mA	4 mA
$V_{IH(min)}$	2.0	2.0	2.0	3.5	2.0
$V_{IL(max)}$	.8	.8	.8	1.0	.8
$V_{OH(min)}$	2.4	2.7	2.7	4.9	4.9
$V_{OL(max)}$	.4	.5	.4	.1	.1

V_{CC} = 5 volts, T_a = 25°C.

The worst case parameters are used in the calculations.

the HIGH output state. In the LOW output state the CMOS drive device sinks current from the TTL loads.

Table 15-14 lists the parameters of interest when interfacing CMOS to TTL, or TTL to CMOS, for the most commonly used CMOS and TTL subfamilies.

The parameters in Table 15-14 can be used to determine if the three basic conditions for interfacing are met.

When the CMOS drive gate is HIGH, the I_{OH} value for the HC and HCT CMOS is 4 mA. The I_{IH} values for the TTL subfamilies shown ranges from 20 to 40 μA. Thus, 4 mA of current can drive 100 TTL 74 loads in the HIGH state (4 mA/40 μA = 100), and condition 1 is met.

When the CMOS drive gate is LOW, the I_{OL} value for the HC and HCT devices is 4 mA. However, the I_{IL} values for the TTL subfamilies ranges from 100 μA for the ALS to 1.6 mA for standard TTL. Thus, 4 mA of current can drive 40 ALS devices, or just two standard devices. The overall fan-out is the smallest number of loads that can be driven, so for CMOS driving TTL, the LOW state must be carefully calculated to determine if sufficient sinking current exists (condition 2). Ways to increase fan-out will be discussed shortly.

Are the voltages compatible for CMOS driving TTL? Examining the parameters, when the CMOS drive gate is HIGH, we find that the CMOS $V_{OH(min)}$ is larger than the TTL $V_{IH(min)}$, and the CMOS $V_{OL(max)}$ is smaller than the TTL $V_{IL(max)}$. Thus, the voltages are compatible, and condition 3 is met.

■ EXAMPLE 15-20 CMOS to TTL Interfacing

Problem: A logic circuit has a CMOS gate driving four standard TTL inputs. All inputs are from different MSI ICs: a flip-flop, two decoders, and a latch, making it impractical to change all the devices to LS TTL.

a. Is this circuit interfaced correctly?

b. If not, modify the design as needed without changing the four existing load devices.

Solution:

(a) A quick check indicates that fan-out is exceeded in this design: I_{OL} = 4 mA, $I_{IL(total)} = 4 \times 1.6$ mA = 6.4 mA. The circuit is not interfaced correctly for reliable operation in the LOW output condition.

(b) Since there is a restriction on part replacement in this design, a logical alternative is to add a buffer between the CMOS drive and the four load inputs. A 74LS125 will appear as only one load to the CMOS drive gate and becomes the drive gate for the four standard TTL loads, with I_{OL} = 8 mA. With this change, there is an operating margin of 8 mA − 6.4 mA = 1.4 mA for the four-device loads. A much improved design! ■

■ EXAMPLE 15-21 CMOS to TTL Interfacing

Problem: A 74HC00 gate has one standard TTL inverter and six 74LS inputs attached to its output. Is the fan-out of the CMOS gate exceeded?

Solution: Again, the LOW CMOS output is the gating factor (pun intended!) Thus:

- One standard TTL input, I_{IL} = 1.6 mA
- Six LS inputs, $I_{IL} = 6 \times 400\ \mu$A = 2.4 mA
- Total I_{IL} = 1.6 mA + 2.4 mA = 4.0 mA

In this design $I_{OL} = I_{IL}$ = 4 mA. The fan-out is not exceeded, but the operating margin is 0 mA, a poor design practice. ■

Section Self-Test

Determine if the following statements are true or false:

1. CMOS HC devices can drive more TTL devices than CMOS HCT devices.
2. When CMOS is driving TTL, it is the LOW state that determines the overall fan-out.

3. No voltage interfacing circuitry is needed to interface CMOS driving TTL because the voltages are compatible.

ANSWERS (Not necessarily in the order of the questions)

• False • True • True

15-13 TTL TO CMOS INTERFACE

TTL to CMOS interfacing is the condition when the drive device is TTL and the loads are CMOS. When TTL is driving CMOS, the voltage levels are incompatible and a pull-up resistor voltage interface is needed. The HCT subfamily of CMOS eliminates this need if it is used instead of other types of CMOS ICs.

The voltage parameters for CMOS and TTL shown in Table 15-14 indicate that there is an incompatibility between the TTL output voltage levels and the CMOS HC input voltage levels in the HIGH TTL output state. The $V_{OH(min)}$ for TTL is 2.7 volts and the $V_{IH(min)}$ for HC CMOS is 3.5 volts.

15.13.1 Pull-up Resistor Interfacing

The TTL driving CMOS solution is to use a **pull-up** resistor to interface the voltage levels, as shown in Figure 15-25. The pull-up resistor to V_{CC} will pull the TTL output voltage up to a HIGH of approximately 5 volts.

The size of the pull-up resistor is determined by the number of load devices and the current parameters of the TTL drive and CMOS loads. The same equations used for calculating the size of the pull-up resistor for fan-out, Equations 15-1 and 15-2, apply, as explained in Section 15.3.4.

15.13.2 TTL to HCT CMOS

The HCT CMOS subfamily is designed to be voltage compatible with TTL. When using HCT CMOS, no additional interfacing is needed for connection to TTL as long as the fan-out requirements are met. In fact, the use of an HCT device is one form of interfacing TTL to CMOS. By using an HCT device as the interface, voltage compatibility is achieved without the use of a pull-up resistor.

Since HCT CMOS operates at a lower voltage than HC CMOS, HCT CMOS logic has slower switching speeds than HC CMOS and also consumes additional power over HC CMOS. Thus, there is a speed and power penalty for the convenience of direct TTL to CMOS interfacing. This illustrates one of many design trade-off decisions to be made when designing logic circuitry.

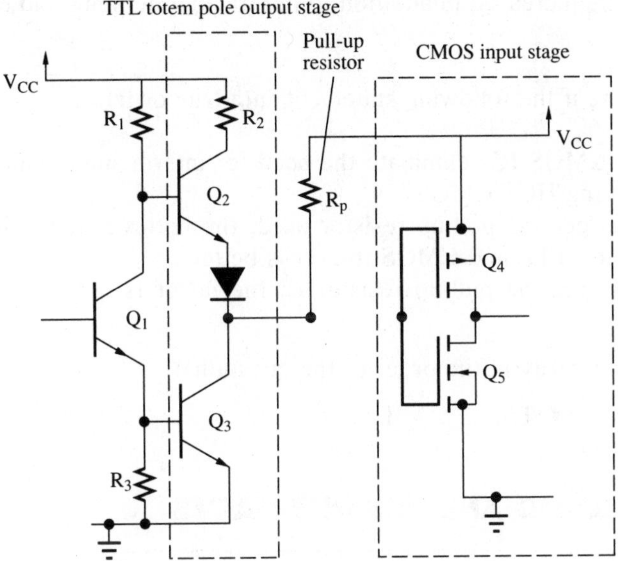

TTL to SN54/74HC Interface with a Pull-Up Resistor

FIGURE 15-25 TTL to CMOS Interface (Courtesy of Texas Instruments)

The internal transistors of HCT devices use additional current over HC devices. Many data books list a DC parameter, delta-I_{CC}, (ΔI_{CC}), which indicates the additional I_{CC} current that the HCT device uses over the same type of device in the HC subfamily. Although higher in power consumption than the HC subfamily, the HCT subfamily consumes much less power at most switching frequencies than TTL.

15.13.3 Voltage Level Shifters

A **level shifter** is a circuit designed to take an input voltage and either raise or lower it to another voltage. The HCT subfamily, for example, does level shifting when used as an interface between TTL and HC CMOS.

Some manufacturers offer ICs specifically designed for level shifting. The CMOS 40104 is an example of a level shifter that can convert a TTL input voltage into a high voltage (greater than 5 volts) for input into CMOS ICs.

15.13.4 Open-Collector Buffer

Another method used to interface TTL to CMOS circuits is the use of an open-collector noninverting buffer, such as the 7407. With this method, fan-out can be increased in addition to interfacing the input and output voltage levels.

Section Self-Test

Determine if the following statements are true or false:

1. HCT CMOS ICs eliminate the need for interfacing circuitry when TTL is driving HCT CMOS.
2. The larger the pull-up resistor used, the better is the voltage interface between TTL and CMOS (bigger is better).
3. The larger the pull-up resistor is, the faster is the device propagation delay.

ANSWERS

(Not necessarily in the order of the questions)

• False • True • False

15-14 TRISTATE LOGIC AND BUS INTERFACES

Some of the more advanced LSI logic devices, especially those used in microprocessor and memory applications, require special output circuits that switch to a high impedance state when not in use. These devices have three logic conditions and are called tristate devices.

15.14.1 Tristate Logic

Tristate logic or **3-state logic** has a third logic state in addition to the two normal logic states of HIGH and LOW. The **high impedance state,** or **high-Z state,** is the third state in addition to the logic HIGH and LOW states.

When a device switches to the high-Z state, the device is effectively disconnected from the point at which it is connected to a circuit, known as the **bus.** This prevents unused devices from loading the bus and allows for multiple devices to be connected to a common bus, with only one active device driving the bus at any one time.

Figure 15-26 illustrates a memory circuit with three memory ICs that have eight one-bit outputs. Only the data line connections are shown for clarity. All D_0 lines are connected to a common point (bus); all D_1 lines are connected to a common output bus; and so on. Thus, there are eight bus lines, each one having three physical connections. Each of the eight memory IC data lines for each of the nonselected ICs will switch to the high-Z state. Only the data lines for the decoder-selected IC will be driving their respective bus with either a logic HIGH or logic LOW. There is only one electrical connection to each data output bus line at any one time.

If the memory ICs do not have tristate outputs, more than one data line attempts to drive the bus with a logic level, resulting in a condition known as **bus contention.** Non-TTL logic levels can result, in addition to possible damage to the output drivers of each of the contending devices.

Several data book parameters will be listed for devices with tristate capability. The high level tristate output current is I_{OZH}, and I_{OZL} is the low level tristate output current. These values will typically be in the μA range. Memory devices and certain microprocessor signal lines will have parameters that specify the minimum time it takes for a line to switch to its high impedance or tristate condition. This is an especially important parameter since no other devices can use a common bus in a design until the last device that used the bus goes into the high-Z state.

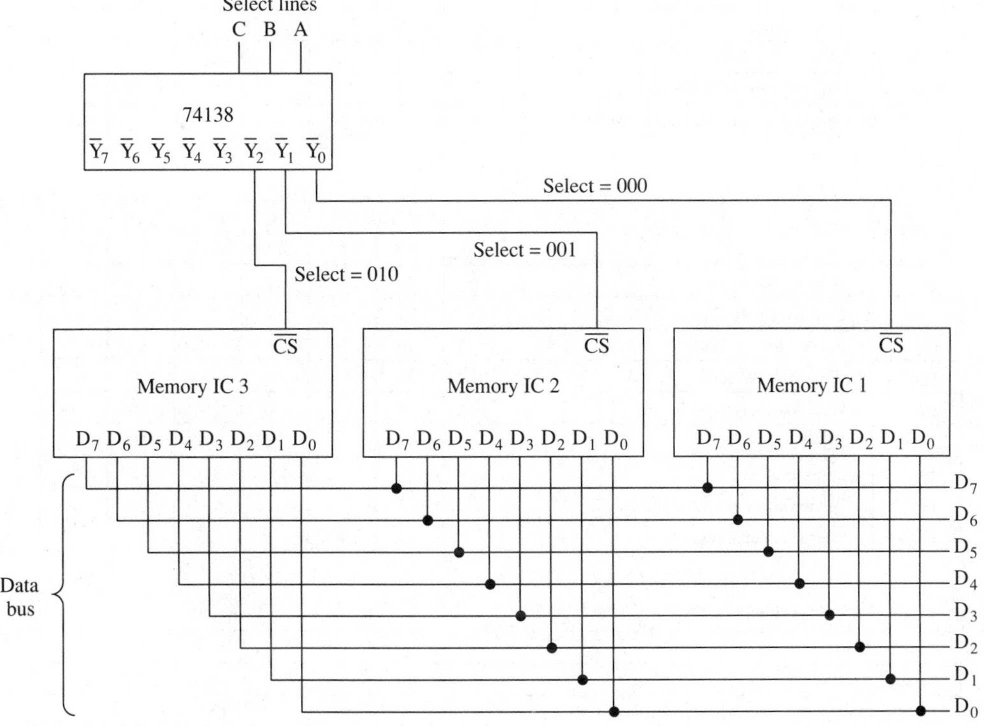

FIGURE 15-26 Tristate Memory Circuit

■ EXAMPLE 15-22 Tristate Parameters

Problem: Examine the parameter specification list provided in Figure 15-27, and determine the worst case time that is needed for this memory IC to switch into the high-Z state.

A. C. CHARACTERISTICS (Ta = 0~70°C, V_{CC} = 5V ± 10%)

Read Cycle

SYMBOL	PARAMETER	TMM2064P-10		TMM2064P-12		TMM2064P-15		UNIT
		MIN.	MAX.	MIN.	MAX.	MIN.	MAX.	
t_{RC}	Read Cycle Time	100	–	120	–	150	–	ns
t_{ACC}	Address Access Time	–	100	–	120	–	150	
t_{CO1}	$\overline{CS_1}$ Access Time	–	100	–	120	–	150	
t_{CO2}	CS_2 Access Time	–	100	–	120	–	150	
t_{OE}	$\overline{OE}$ Access Time	–	40	–	50	–	60	
t_{OH}	Output Data Hold Time from Address Change	10	–	10	–	10	–	
t_{CLZ}	$\overline{CS_1}$ or CS_2 to Output in Low-Z	10	–	10	–	10	–	
t_{CHZ}	$\overline{CS_1}$ or CS_2 to Output in High-Z	–	40	–	40	–	55	
t_{OLZ}	$\overline{OE}$ to Output in Low-Z	5	–	5	–	5	–	
t_{OHZ}	$\overline{OE}$ to Output in High-Z	–	35	–	35	–	50	
t_{PU}	Chip Selection to Power Up Time	0	–	0	–	0	–	
t_{PD}	Chip Deselection to Power Down Time	–	50	–	60	–	60	

Write Cycle

SYMBOL	PARAMETER	TMM2064P-10		TMM2064P-12		TMM2064P-15		UNIT
		MIN.	MAX.	MIN.	MAX.	MIN.	MAX.	
t_{WC}	Write Cycle Time	100	–	120	–	150	–	ns
t_{CW}	Chip Selection to End of Write	80	–	100	–	120	–	
t_{AS}	Address Set Up Time	10	–	10	–	10	–	
t_{WP}	Write Pulse Width	70	–	85	–	100	–	
t_{WR}	Write Recovery Time	0	–	0	–	0	–	
t_{DS}	Data Set Up Time	40	–	50	–	60	–	
t_{DH}	Data Hold Time	0	–	0	–	0	–	
t_{WLZ}	$\overline{WE}$ to Output in Low-Z	5	–	5	–	5	–	
t_{WHZ}	$\overline{WE}$ to Output in High-Z	–	30	–	35	–	40	

A. C. TEST CONDITIONS

Input Pulse Levels	V_{IH} = 2.2V, V_{IL} = 0.6V
Input Rise and Fall Time	10ns
Input and Output Reference Levels	1.5V
Output Load	1 TTL Gate & C_L = 100pF

FIGURE 15-27 Memory IC Parameters (Courtesy of Toshiba Corp.)

Solution: There are two high-Z parameters shown, t_{CHZ} and t_{OHZ}. If the chip select pin is used, the maximum time is t_{CHZ} = 40 ns. If the output enable is used, the maximum time is t_{OHZ} = 35 ns. That is, 35 or 40 nS of time must elapse before another device can drive the bus. ■

It may be desirable to connect several MSI devices such as counters or shift registers to a common output bus. However, not all these devices have tristate outputs. One solution is to use a latch or flip-flop with a tristate output as a bus interface IC. The 74LS373 is an 8 bit D-latch with tristate outputs, and the 74AS825 is an 8-bit flip-flop with tristate outputs. Many other latches and flip-flops, in 8, 9, and 10 bit configurations exist for bus interfacing.

As described in Chapter 14, a **bus** is a grouping of input or output lines, with each line connected to more than one device input or output. Only one device can drive a bus. If more than one device attempts to drive a bus simultaneously, bus contention occurs, resulting in invalid data.

To prevent bus contention and to isolate devices electrically from the bus to reduce capacitive loading, **buffer ICs** are utilized. If a buffer is used to send data from the drive to the load, it is known as a **bus driver.** If a buffer is used to receive data, it is known as a **bus receiver.** If a buffer can both transmit and receive data, it is known as a **bus transceiver.** Look for these descriptive terms in the data books when selecting a buffer IC.

Figure 15-28 illustrates a simple example of two-way digital data transmission over a single transmission line. When digital data is transmitted from device A to device B, the transmit buffer (bus driver) of A is enabled and the receive buffer of B is enabled. When digital data is transmitted from

Data Transmission	TBE_A	RBE_A	TBE_B	RBE_B
Device A to device B	1	0	0	1
Device B to device A	0	1	1	0

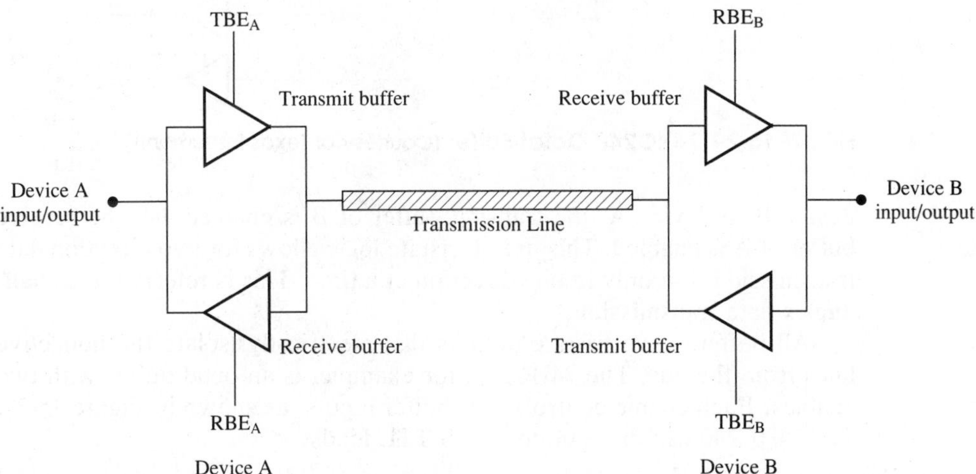

RBE = receive buffer enable (active HIGH)
TBE = transmit buffer enable (active HIGH)

FIGURE 15-28 Half-Duplex Digital Data Transmission Using Tristate Buffers

'HC240
(EACH BUFFER)

INPUTS		OUTPUT
$\overline{G}$	A	Y
L	H	L
L	L	H
H	X	Z

logic symbols†

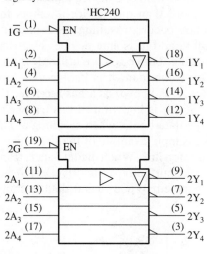

'HC240

$1\overline{G}$ (1) EN
$1A_1$ (2) — (18) $1Y_1$
$1A_2$ (4) — (16) $1Y_2$
$1A_3$ (6) — (14) $1Y_3$
$1A_4$ (8) — (12) $1Y_4$
$2\overline{G}$ (19) EN
$2A_1$ (11) — (9) $2Y_1$
$2A_2$ (13) — (7) $2Y_2$
$2A_3$ (15) — (5) $2Y_3$
$2A_4$ (17) — (3) $2Y_4$

†These symbols are in accordance with ANSI/IEEE Std 91-1984 and IEC Publication 617-12.

logic diagrams (positive logic)

'HC240

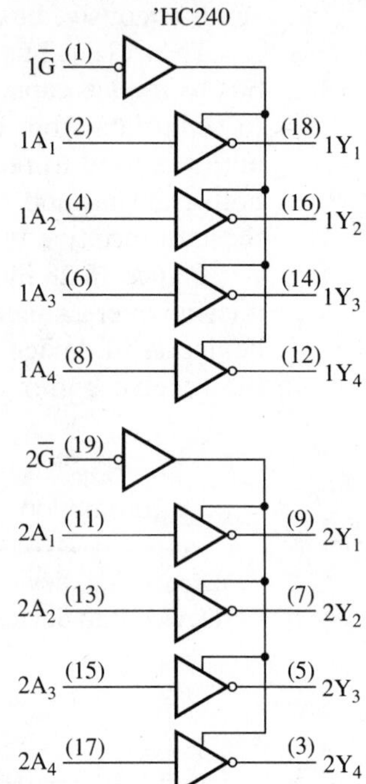

FIGURE 15-29 74HC240 Octal Buffer (Courtesy of Texas Instruments)

device B to device A, the transmit buffer of B is enabled and the receive buffer of A is enabled. This use of tristate logic allows for two direction data transmission, but only in one direction at a time. This is referred to as **half-duplex** data transmission.

All buffers have tristate outputs that electrically isolate the nonactive lines from the bus. The 74HC240, for example, is an octal buffer with two enables. Each enable controls four buffer inputs, as shown in Figure 15-29. The 74HC240 can drive up to 15 LS TTL loads.

15.14.2 Bilateral Transmission Gates

FETs are quite useful as switches. Consequently, CMOS ICs are available that can transmit a signal through a gate in either direction. These special circuits are called **bilateral transmission gates, bilateral switches,** or **bidirec-**

tional buffers. The signal can be applied to either one of the two I/O connections for bilateral operation. Transmission is controlled by an additional control input to each gate. If the control line is logic 0, the device is off and will not allow signal propagation. If the control line is logic 1, the device allows signal propagation with the addition of a small resistance.

SN54HC242, SN54HC243
SN74HC242, SN74HC243
QUADRUPLE BUS TRANSCEIVERS WITH 3-STATE OUTPUTS

logic symbols†

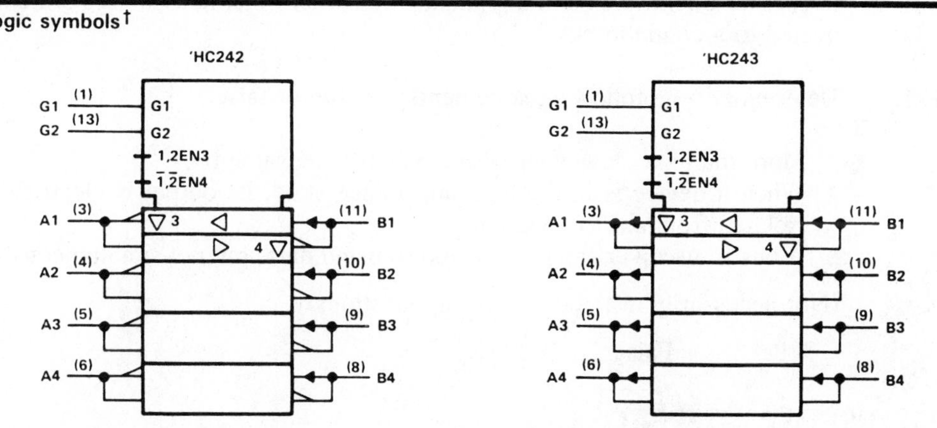

†These symbols are in accordance with ANSI/IEEE Std 91-1984 and IEC Publication 617-12

logic diagrams (positive logic)

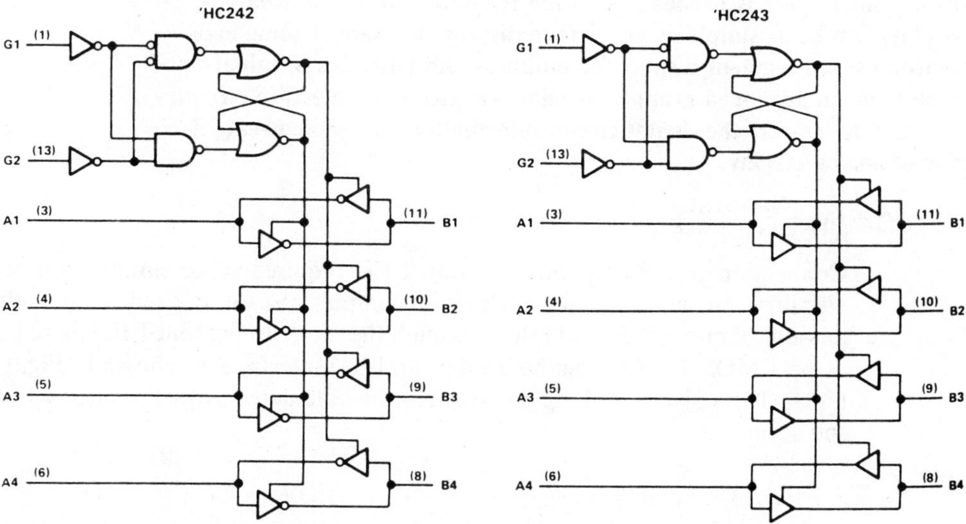

Pin numbers shown are for D, J, and N packages.

FIGURE 15-30 CMOS Quad Bilateral Switch (Courtesy of Texas Instruments)

The bilateral gates can be used to transmit both analog and digital signals. These types of devices increase fan-out, which is the reason they are also called buffers. There is some propagation delay, which can range from 10 to over 1000 ns. The 74HC242 is a high speed CMOS quad bilateral switch. Its pin assignment/functional diagram is shown in Figure 15-30. When used with analog signals, these bilateral switches have maximum input frequencies, attenuation and cross-talk specifications, and maximum directional control switching frequencies.

Buffers are used in many different types of bus interface applications, including memory and microprocessor systems (Chapters 13 and 14), register to register operations, and any application where multiple devices are connected to a common bus.

Section Self-Test

Determine if the following statements are true or false:

1. More than one device can drive a bus at the same time.
2. When a device is in the high impedance state, its output is electrically isolated from any connection.
3. A bus transceiver can receive and transmit data, but not simultaneously.

ANSWERS (Not necessarily in the order of the questions)

• True • False • False

15-15 DISPLAY INTERFACES

Display interfacing is needed to provide readable output information. Displays can be as simple as an LED to display the state of some logic device, a seven segment display for numbers and letters, a terminal display, or an advanced graphics display. In each case interface circuitry is needed to convert the digital circuit information into some eventual type of analog display.

15.15.1 Driving an LED

Connection of a circuit output to an LED requires some simple interface circuitry. In most instances a **current-limiting resistor** is used to limit the amount of current that will flow through the diode to prevent LED damage.

A CMOS 74HC04 can be used as an LED interface, as shown in Figure 15-31. The current-limiting resistor can be calculated with Equations 15-8 and 15-9:

Eq. 15-8 $$R = \frac{V_{OH} - V_f}{I_d}$$ LOW = on

Eq. 15-9 $$R = \frac{V_{CC} - V_f - V_{OL}}{I_d}$$ LOW = off

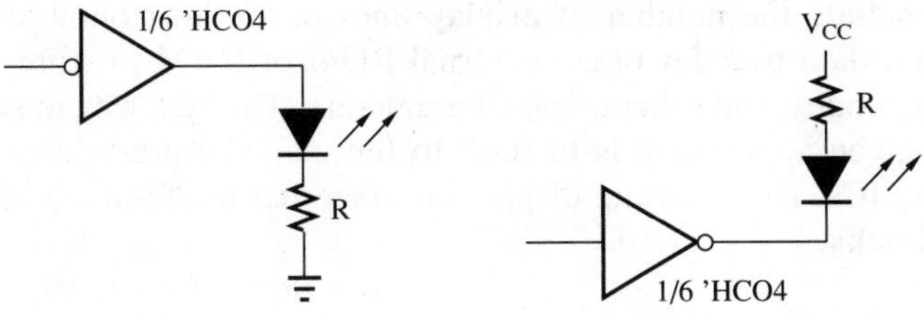

FIGURE 15-31 74HC04 Driving an LED (Courtesy of Texas Instruments)

where

I_d = diode current,
V_f = diode forward voltage
V_{OH} and V_{OL} are not $V_{OH(min)}$ and $V_{OH(max)}$ Typical values are used, based on the diode current.

■ EXAMPLE 15-23 LED Interface Circuit

Problem: A circuit is needed to turn on an LED when a HIGH CMOS circuit output occurs. Use a 74HC04 to design interface circuit. Use I_d = 10 mA, V_f = 2.2 V, and V_{CC} = 5 V.

Solution: For a HIGH = on, Equation 18-2 applies.

$$R = \frac{5 - 2.2 - .4}{10\text{ mA}}\text{ V} = 240\ \Omega$$

The circuit is shown in Figure 15-32. ■

15.15.2 Display Interface Parameters

There are many parameters in addition to voltage and current requirements that need to be matched when interfacing a display to a digital circuit. These

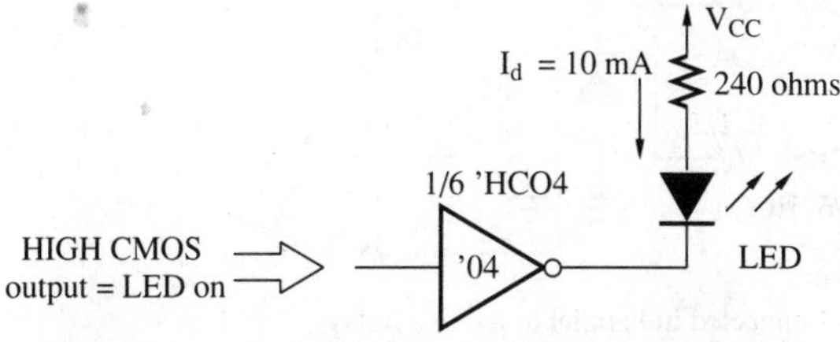

FIGURE 15-32 Example 15-23 LED Interface Circuit

may include the number of display lines in the horizontal and vertical direction, data transfer rates, external ROM or RAM to store alphanumeric display codes, and other display parameters. The best way to select a display for a given application is to refer to the manufacturer's data books listing display ICs. Displays and display interface ICs are found in optoelectronics data books.

Section Self-Test

Determine if the following statements are true or false.

1. The larger the LED current-limiting resistor is, the brighter an LED will illuminate.
2. Display parameters are found in fiber optic data books.
3. An LED can be driven using CMOS or TTL devices.

ANSWERS (Not necessarily in the order of the questions)

- True • False • False

15-16 MECHANICAL INTERFACES

There are many different types of digital circuits used to control mechanical functions. These functions may include controlling a motor position or speed, turning a relay on or off; controlling fluid flow through a valve, or using assembly line processes, robotic machines, and other factory automation equipment.

As with display interfaces, many mechanical interfaces are specific in nature, and specialized ICs are available.

One common mechanical interface function is the control of a relay. Relays have voltage and current input specifications that must be met. Operational amplifiers are often used in relay applications to provide the necessary D/A voltage and current interface.

Small relay circuits can be adequately driven with a parallel inverter

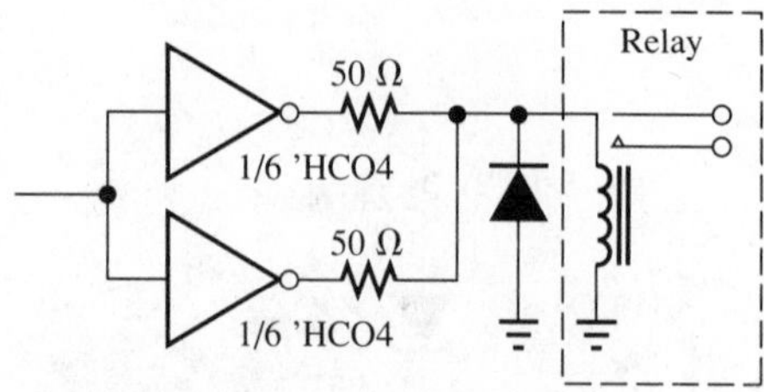

SN54/74HC04 Gates Connected in Parallel to Drive a Relay

FIGURE 15-33 Mechanical Relay Driver
(Courtesy of Texas Instruments)

drive circuit. Figure 15-33 shows a relay symbol and diode and a parallel inverter interface.

15-17 OPTICAL INTERFACES

Another type of interface circuit is the optical interface. The optical interface provides an excellent type of electrical isolation.

An optical interface is an interface that converts electrical signals into optical signals. Optical interfaces are particularly useful in isolating a noise-sensitive section of circuitry. Noise coupling from another part of a circuit is commonly referred to as **common mode noise.**

In addition to noise isolation, optical interfaces can be used to interface between logic families. Applications include data signal buffering, motor controls, power supply switching, AC to DC interfacing, data transmission and reception, ground isolation, and relay control.

15.17.1 Optocouplers

Optical interface ICs, commonly known as **optocouplers,** or **optoisolators,** have the internal optical isolation circuitry combined internally into one package, typically an 8 pin DIP. The input to the device is an **optical transmitter,** commonly an LED with anode and cathode connections. The output circuitry consists of an **optical detector,** a bipolar phototransistor, and ad-

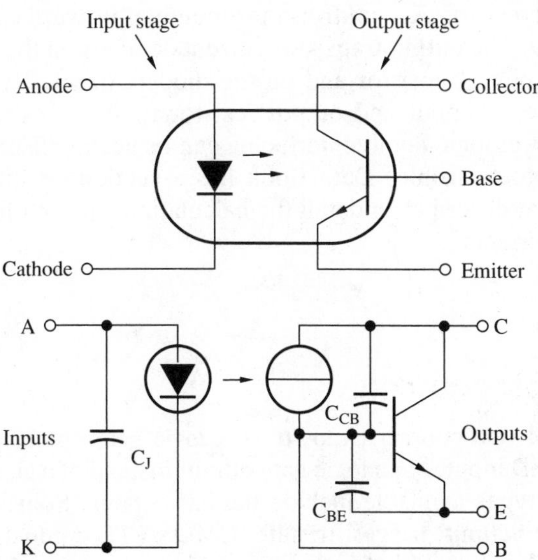

FIGURE 15-34 Optocoupler Equivalent Circuit

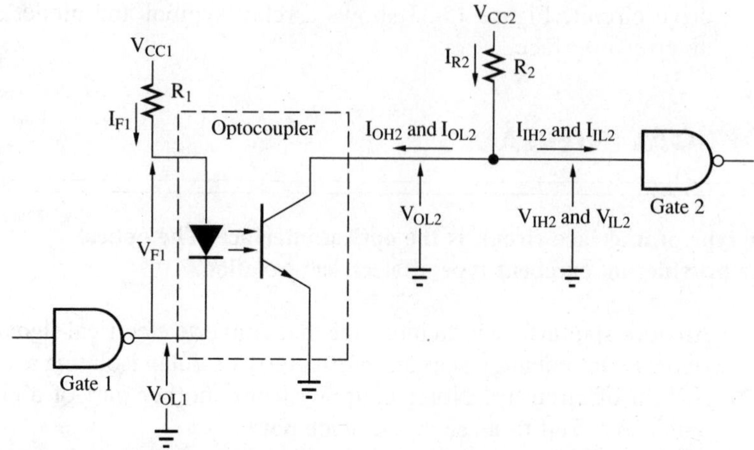

Note: V_{OL2} = Low-level output voltage of coupler when coupler is on
V_{IL2} = Low-level input voltage specified for gate 2

FIGURE 15-35 Optocoupler Interface Circuit

ditional transistor circuitry to control the output current, depending on the type of optocoupler. The basic optocoupler circuit has a high speed transistor output. The equivalent circuit for a transistor output optocoupler is shown in Figure 15-34.

Figure 15-35 shows a transistor output optocoupler interface circuit. The size of the input resistor, R_1, controls the amount of forward current through the emitter LED. The output transistor current depends on the current transfer ratio of the phototransistor and on the diode current. By selecting the appropriate external input and output resistor (pull-up resistor) values, a wide assortment of logic family interfacing can be accomplished. The Texas Instruments Optoelectronics Data Book has a section on interfacing with optocouplers that describes in detail the calculations needed for this type of optocoupler interfacing.

15.17.2 Logic Gate Optocouplers

Another type of optocoupler, known as a **logic gate optocoupler,** has the same type of LED input, but a logic gate output instead of a simple transistor output. Output types available include the basic gates. Some of the output features include Schmitt trigger, tristate, CMOS/TTL compatible, and high speed optocouplers capable of switching speeds in excess of 60 MHz.

Section Self-Test

Determine if the following statements are true or false:

1. Optocouplers are used to isolate a circuit from noise sources.
2. Optocouplers can be used to interface logic families.

ANSWERS

• True • True

SUMMARY

ANALYSIS

Two major logic families are currently in use for digital logic design at the circuit board level using ICs: TTL and CMOS. Within each of these major logic families, several subfamilies have been manufactured that optimize one or more of the operational parameters such as power or propagation delay.

TTL is based on bipolar transistor technology and has the following logic subfamilies presently available: standard, Schottky, low-power Schottky, advanced Schottky, and advanced low-power Schottky. Totem-pole outputs are the most common type of output, but open-collector outputs with the appropriate pull-up resistor can be used for wired logic applications or to increase V_{OH}.

CMOS is based on FET technology and has the following logic subfamilies: standard, buffered, TTL pin compatible, advanced, high speed, and high speed TTL compatible. CMOS has superior power parameters as compared to TTL. The low power usage makes CMOS useful for low power applications such as battery-operated devices. CMOS also has better noise immunity than TTL.

ECL, another bipolar technology, is a specialized family used for very high speed applications with switching speeds of less than 500 ps.

APPLICATION AND DESIGN

Selection of the appropriate logic family for use in a logic system is based on design requirements with regard to voltage supplies available, noise margins, operation frequency, and power usage. Additional considerations such as the need for open-collector outputs or ESD protection affect the choice of individual logic devices. The most important point to remember is that up-to-date logic data specifications must be used in order to be able to make the most informed and intelligent choices of logic components. Calculations of important parameters should always be made before the construction of any digital hardware in order to select correctly the appropriate ICs for the intended application.

Interfacing is an important part of most designs. Interface circuitry is necessary for designs that mix TTL and CMOS logic circuits. In addition to logic family and logic subfamily interfacing, bus, display, mechanical and optical interfacing are an important part of the logic designer's responsibilities. Specialized ICs are available for the majority of these types of interface applications. Data books, as always, are a valuable source of design information.

A/D and D/A conversion are two types of interface circuits which are discussed in Chapter 16.

Both CMOS and TTL ICs are available with tristate outputs. Tristate outputs allow for the physical connection of multiple devices to a bus. The tristate devices can be enabled individually so that each device appears to have a unique electrical connection when the other devices are in the high impedance state. Tristate circuits are very common in memory and microprocessor logic applications.

PROBLEMS

15-1 Transistor-Transistor Logic (TTL)—Analysis Problems

1. Explain the difference between the 7400 and the 5400 series TTL ICs.
2. What is meant by the term "TTL compatible"?
3. a. What type of transistor is used to fabricate TTL ICs?
   b. Draw and label the schematic for the transistor of part (a).

15-2 TTL Logic Technologies—Analysis Problems

*4. Find t_{PHL} and t_{PLH} for:
   (a) 7400 (b) 74LS00 (c) 74L00 (d) 74S00
   (e) 74ALS00
5. Find the power (typ) at 5.0 V for each of the ICs listed in Problem 4.
6. a. Which TTL subfamily consumes the most power?
   b. Which TTL subfamily consumes the least power?
   c. Which TTL subfamily is the fastest?
   d. Which TTL subfamily is the slowest?

15-3 TTL Circuit Operation: Totem-Pole and Open-Collector Outputs—Analysis Problems

7. a. Explain the difference between totem-pole and open-collector outputs.

b. List three reasons to use totem-pole outputs.
c. List three reasons to use open-collector outputs.

8. Examine the circuit in Figure 15-36.
   a. Determine the output if logic 1 is input.
   b. Determine the output if logic 0 is input.

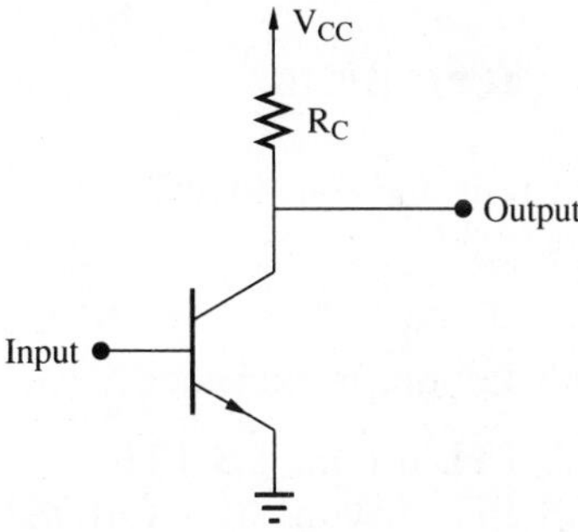

FIGURE 15-36 Problem 8

9. Refer to a TTL data book and find an open-collector TTL IC for:
   (a) inverters (b) NAND gates (c) NOR gates (d) latches
   (e) flip-flops
10. Why is a pull-up resistor needed for open-collector devices? Explain in terms of current and voltage.

*11. Determine the Boolean equation for X in the circuit in Figure 15-37.

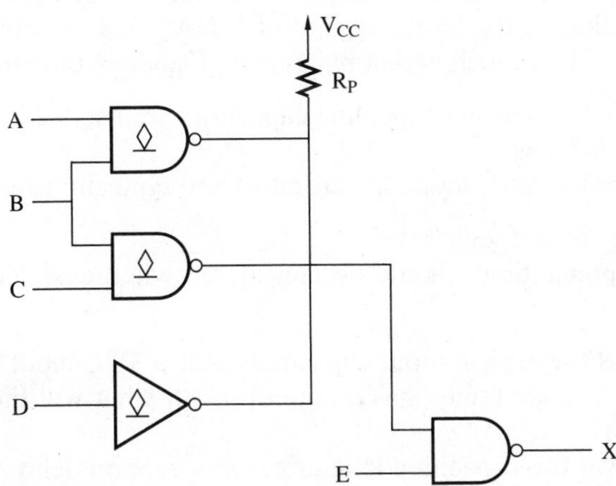

FIGURE 15-37 Problem 11

12. For the TTL circuit in Problem 11, use $V_{CC} = 5.0$ V and find:
(a) $R_{p(min)}$ (b) $R_{p(max)}$

13. Repeat Problem 12 for $V_{CC} = 4.5$ V. Calculate the percent difference between the results in the two problems.

15-4 Designing with TTL Design Problems

14. Define fan-out in terms of current and unit loads.

15. a. Explain current sourcing.
b. Explain current sinking.
c. What happens if a device's fan-out is exceeded?

*16. a. What is the fan-out for LS TTL driving LS TTL?
b. What is the fan-out for LS TTL driving HCT CMOS?
c. What is the fan-out for LS TTL driving standard TTL?
d. What is the fan-out for LS TTL driving S TTL?

17. A 74LS00 has two 7404s, three 74LS00s, and one 74S00 attached to its output.
a. Is the fan-out of the drive gate exceeded?
b. If the fan-out is exceeded, propose a circuit change to correct the problem. If the fan-out is not exceeded, how many additional LS gates can be attached?

*18. Determine how many 74LS193 data inputs can be driven with a 74LS00.

19. Determine how many J or K inputs of a 74113 can be driven with a 74LS13.

*20. Refer to a TTL data book and find a buffer IC. Compare the output current value of the buffer to that of a NAND gate within the same subfamily. How much additional current (%) does the buffer output?

21. a. Explain the reason decoupling capacitors are needed in digital logic circuit designs.
b. What value of decoupling capacitors are typically used?

22. a. What is mixed logic?
b. What precautions should be considered when designing in mixed logic?

*23. a. What is the typical input capacitance for a TTL input?
b. If a TTL logic family has a fan-out of 10, what will the capacitive load be?
c. How will the capacitive load affect propagation delay?

15-5 Complementary Metal-Oxide Semiconductor (CMOS) Logic—Analysis Problems

24. a. What is CMOS logic?
    b. What type of transistor is CMOS logic based on?

25. a. What are three advantages of CMOS logic over TTL logic?
    b. What are three disadvantages of CMOS logic as compared to TTL?

26. What is meant by the term "CMOS compatible"? List specific voltage values in your explanation.

27. What is the difference between and NMOS and a PMOS transistor?

15-6 CMOS Logic Technologies—Analysis Problems

28. a. What CMOS subfamily is known as "TTL compatible"?
    b. Compare the speed of an HC CMOS device to that of an LS TTL device.

*29. If $V_{CC} = 5.5$ V, what are the minimum V_{IH} and maximum V_{IL} values for a 74HC CMOS device?

15-7 CMOS Circuit Operation: FET Inverters and Open Drain—Analysis Problems

30. What is meant by the term "open drain?"

31. a. Explain the difference between enhancement mode and depletion mode FETs.
    b. How does threshold voltage relate to FETs? (Explain the operation of FETs in terms of V_t)

32. Find three CMOS ICs with tristate outputs. List the relevant tristate parameters, and explain the significance of each parameter.

33. A 74HC open drain inverter has eight LS TTL inputs attached to its output. What size should the pull-up resistor be?

34. a. What is the noise margin for CMOS?
    b. How does it compare to the noise margin for TTL?
    c. Do all CMOS subfamilies have the same noise margin? Explain.

15-8 Designing with CMOS—Design Problems

*35. Calculate the following for a 74HC163:
    a. active power at 5.0 V
    b. static power at 5.0 V

For Problems 36 and 37, refer to a CMOS specification sheet for a 74HC163.

*36. What is the typical power dissipation capacitance? How is the parameter used?

37. a. What is the active power at 100 KHz and 5 V?
 b. What is the active power at 10 MHz and 5 V?

38. Repeat Problem 36 for a 74AC75.

39. Repeat Problem 37 for a 74HC75.

40. Repeat Problem 37 for a 74HCT75.

41. a. What is CMOS latch-up?
 b. How can latch-up be avoided?

42. a. What is ESD?
 b. How can the effects of ESD be minimized?

15-9 Other Logic Families—Application Problems

43. a. What is IIL logic?
 b. What applications is IIL used for?

*44. a. What is ECL logic?
 b. List three specific applications for ECL logic.
 c. How much faster (in %) is ECL than LS TTL?

45. a. What are the advantages of using ECL?
 b. What are the disadvantages of using ECL?

15-10 Logic Comparison and Selection—Application and Design Problems

46. A simple cross-coupled NAND circuit is to be constructed as a switch de-bounce. The decision needs to be made whether to build this circuit with a PLD, TTL, or CMOS IC.
 a. As a designer, what important operating parameters should be considered before making the technology choice?
 b. Are there any reasons to use a PLD? Explain.

47. On the same graph, chart the supply voltage ranges for TTL, CMOS 4000B, CMOS 74HC, CMOS and 74HCT.

48. Calculate the average power consumption for a 74107 in each of the following logic families:
 (a) std TTL (b) 74LS (c) 74HC (d) 74HCT

*49. Calculate the average propagation delay for each of the ICs in Problem 48.

50. Repeat Problem 48 for *1 NAND gate* (not a NAND IC) to determine the typical per gate power consumption for each subfamily listed.

51. a. Define noise margin.
b. Why does CMOS have a better noise margin than TTL?
c. What is the typical noise margin for TTL?
d. What is the typical noise margin for CMOS?

*52. Explain how operating frequency affects the power consumption of CMOS ICs.

53. Refer to a CMOS data book.
a. What is the fastest frequency of operation for a 74HC573 at 25°C and V_{CC} = 5.0 V
b. How does the result of part (a) compare to the operating frequency of a typical CMOS microprocessor at 25 MHz?
c. Will this latch be an appropriate choice to latch data for a 32 bit microprocessor at the speed in part (b)?
d. How many 74HC573s will be needed to latch the data bus of a 32 bit microprocessor?

54. What are some of the precautions necessary when designing in mixed logic?

55. Refer to a CMOS data book, and find the data sheets for a 74HC243.
a. Graph the propagation delay as a function of V_{CC}. Comment on how the supply voltage affects the propagation delay.
b. Draw the IEEE/ANSI logic symbol for a 74HC243, and explain each qualifying symbol shown.
c. Compare the propagation delay of a 74HC243 with that of a 74243, and determine the percent difference between the speed of the two ICs.

56. a. List and describe the various methods to increase fan-out.
b. Compare the methods, and list two advantages and two disadvantages of each method.

57. A 74LS123 output is driving five standard TTL inputs.
a. Will this circuit operate properly?
b. If needed, recommend a specific design modification for correct operation.

58. How many LS TTL loads can a 74HCT00 drive?

*59. How many LS TTL loads can a 74HC00 drive?

15-11 Logic Interfacing—Application and Design Problems

60. a. Define interfacing.
    b. List five common examples of interfacing.
61. a. List three reasons to interface.
    b. List and describe the conditions required for proper operation of interfaced circuits.
62. Define the following terms, and explain their relevance to interfacing:
    (a) source (b) sink (c) drive (d) load (e) fan-out
    (f) receiver (g) voltage level

15-12 and 15-13 CMOS to TTL Interface and TTL to CMOS Interface—Design and Troubleshooting Problems

63. How do the requirements for interfacing between CMOS and TTL differ, depending on which logic family is the drive device?
64. What are the eight important voltage and current parameters to consider when interfacing CMOS and TTL? List and describe each.
65. Write a concise design guideline for interfacing standard TTL to HC CMOS. Describe any interface hardware needed, and determine the fan-out number. Comment on the speed and power parameters of the interfaced circuit.
66. Repeat Problem 65 for LS TTL to HC CMOS.
67. Repeat Problem 65 for ALS TTL to HC CMOS.
68. Repeat Problem 65 for LS TTL to 4000 CMOS.
69. Write a concise design guideline for interfacing HC CMOS to standard TTL. Include any interface hardware needed. Comment on the speed and power parameters of the interfaced circuit.
70. Repeat Problem 69 for HC CMOS to LS TTL.
71. Repeat Problem 69 for HC CMOS to ALS TTL.
72. Repeat Problem 69 for 4000 CMOS to LS TTL.
73. Write a concise design guideline for interfacing E^2PLD devices to LS TTL. Include any interface hardware needed. Comment on the speed and power parameters of the interfaced circuit.
74. Repeat Problem 73, but interface LS TTL driving E^2PLD inputs (Lattice GAL16V8A, e.g.).

*75. A 74LS138 is driving 14 HC CMOS gate inputs.
  a. What size pull-up resistor is needed?
  b. Draw your final interface circuit.

76. Repeat Problem 75 for six HC CMOS gate inputs.
  a. What is the new size of the pull-up resistor?
  b. Can you draw any conclusions about the number of loads for this type of interface and the size of the pull-up resistor?

77. a. What is a level shifter?
  b. List five applications for a level shifter.

78. Complete the following matrix by filling in the fan-out number for each intersecting CMOS and TTL subfamily. If an exact number cannot be given (pull-up resistor, e.g.), place an * in the square and explain below the chart.

Drive Output		Load Input				
		TTL STD	TTL LS	TTL ALS	CMOS HC	CMOS HCT
TTL	STD	10				
TTL	LS					
TTL	ALS					
CMOS	HC					
CMOS	HCT					

*79. Two 74LS04s are combined in parallel to drive 16 HC CMOS loads. Calculate the size of the pull-up resistor needed.

80. Review the operation of the internal input and output circuitry of CMOS and TTL ICs.
  a. If the fan-out of a TTL driver (output stage) is exceeded, explain how the circuit malfunctions.
  b. When troubleshooting a TTL circuit, explain how the condition of fan-out exceeded would be discovered. List any troubleshooting equipment needed and what type of measurements should be made.

81. a. If the fan-out of a CMOS driver (output stage) is exceeded, explain how the circuit malfunctions.
  b. When troubleshooting a CMOS circuit, explain how the condition of fan-out exceeded would be discovered. List any troubleshooting equipment needed and what type of measurements should be made.

82. A CMOS to TTL interface is not functioning. List the steps you would use to troubleshoot the circuit.

83. A TTL to CMOS interface is not functioning. List the steps you would use to troubleshoot the circuit.

15-14 Tristate Logic and Bus Interfaces—Application and Design Problems

84. a. Explain how tristate devices operate in terms of logic levels and impedance.
    b. List three applications requiring tristate devices.

85. a. What is bus contention?
    b. What problems can it cause in a digital circuit?
    c. How can it be avoided?

*86. Memory device 1 has t_{CHZ} = 20 ns and memory device 2 has t_{CHZ} = 25 ns. Memory devices 1 and 2 share a common output bus and a common address bus. If the access time for each memory IC is 100 ns, determine how long it would take to access memory device 1, then memory device 2, then memory device 1. Consider the tristate and access time parameters given, and draw a timing diagram (waveforms) to aid in the analysis.

87. a. What are bidirectional buffers?
    b. List three applications for bidirectional buffers.

88. Define and explain the following:
    (a) bus driver (b) bus receiver (c) bus transceiver

89. What conditions should be met when connecting multiple devices to a bus?

90. List five bus applications. Be specific.

15-15 Display Interfaces—Design Problems

*91. Design a circuit to drive an LED with V_f = 2.5 V and I_d = 4.5 mA. Use V_{CC} = 5.0 V. LED on = LOW. Draw your final circuit.

92. Repeat Problem 96 if LED on = HIGH.

93. Refer to a data book specification for the LED you use in your digital laboratory. Use allowable V_f and I_d values, and design a circuit that will turn the LED on when the output of a 7476 is HIGH.

15-16 Mechanical Interfaces—Application Problems

94. List five applications for a digital circuit mechanical interface. Be specific.

15-17 Optical Interfaces—Application and Design Problems

95. List five applications for a digital circuit optical interface. Be specific.

96. Refer to a Texas Instruments Optoelectronic Data Book or its equivalent, and calculate the values for R_1 and R_2 to interface optically a 74LS04 driving a 74LS00, using the circuit of Figure 15-35. Use a value of $I_{diode(forward)} = 20$ mA.

97. Repeat Problem 96, using a diode forward current of 10 mA.

**See* Answers to Selected Problems.

Chapter 16

Analog/Digital Conversion

Upon completing and mastering the material in this chapter, you should be able to perform the following operations related to the analysis, application, and design of digital-to-analog and analog-to-digital conversion circuits:

ANALYSIS

1. Determine the resolution, dynamic response, percent accuracy, and maximum sampling rate of D/A and A/D converters.
2. Analyze the operation of resistor ladder network D/A converters.
3. Analyze the operation of IC D/A converters using the resistor ladder method of conversion.
4. Analyze the operation of multiplying D/A converters.
5. Analyze the operational and performance characteristics of A/D and D/A converters to select the appropriate device for a given application.
6. Determine the maximum sampling frequency for an A/D converter from the manufacturers' data sheets when the sampling frequency is not explicitly stated.
7. Analyze the operation of successive approximation A/D converters.
8. Analyze the operation of flash A/D converters.

APPLICATION

9. Use D/A and A/D converters in logic systems interfacing to standard logic or to microprocessors.
10. Use the DAC-08B to perform unipolar and dipolar D/A conversion.
11. Use the DAC-08B to scale an input analog quantity by a digital word and output a new analog value.
12. Use the AD557 in latched and transparent applications for D/A conversion.
13. Use the ADC-830 in free-running A/D conversion applications.
14. Use the TLC0820 in stand-alone A/D conversion applications.

DESIGN

15. Design A/D circuits using the ADC-830 to meet A/D application specifications.
16. Design A/D circuits using the TLC0820 to meet A/D application specifications.
17. Design D/A circuits using the AD557 to meet D/A application specifications.
18. Design D/A circuits using the DAC-08B to meet application specification for fixed reference D/A applications.
19. Design D/A circuits using the DAC-08B to meet application specifications for varying reference D/A applications and multiplying D/A applications.
20. Employ good circuit construction techniques when laying out D/A and A/D circuits on breadboards and printed circuit boards.

TROUBLESHOOTING

21. Analyze operational data of D/A and A/D circuits to determine the wiring error causing the faulty circuit operation.
22. Given operational conditions, determine the output of D/A and A/D circuits.
23. Determine methods to correct the faulty operation of D/A and A/D circuits.

This chapter is intended to provide students with an introduction to digital/analog conversion so that they can interface their digital systems with analog systems. However, it is not intended to be an exhaustive treatment of digital/analog conversion techniques. For an in-depth treatment of digital/analog conversion, students should refer to the 700-page book, *Analog-Digital Conversion Handbook*, published by Prentice-Hall, Inc., Englewood Cliffs, NJ.

16-1 FUNDAMENTALS OF DIGITAL AND ANALOG CONVERSION

Digital logic circuits require special interfacing techniques to input and output analog data. Physical quantities with an infinite range of values, such as temperature, pressure, fluid flow, velocity, acceleration, and voltage are analog quantities. Analog-to-digital (A/D) conversion is the process of converting analog values to digital codes representing the analog value. Digital-to-analog (D/A) conversion is the process of converting digital codes to proportional analog values. Digital audio, digital sampling, and music synthesis equipment are some exciting examples of A/D and D/A applications.

A basic D/A converter is shown in Figure 16-1. The D/A converter accepts a 4-bit input code and outputs an analog current. The current can be converted to an analog voltage with a resistor. Table 16-1 lists hypothetical values of the D/A converter shown in Figure 16-1. A graph of the input code to output voltage is shown in Figure 16-2 as the input code changes with time.

Figure 16-3 shows a basic A/D converter. The A/D converter accepts an analog input voltage and converts it to a 4-bit digital code. Table 16-2 shows the digital code produced by the analog input voltage for the A/D converter in Figure 16-3.

Analog-to-digital (A/D) and digital-to-analog (D/A) conversion operations are required at the inputs to and outputs from digital processing circuits,

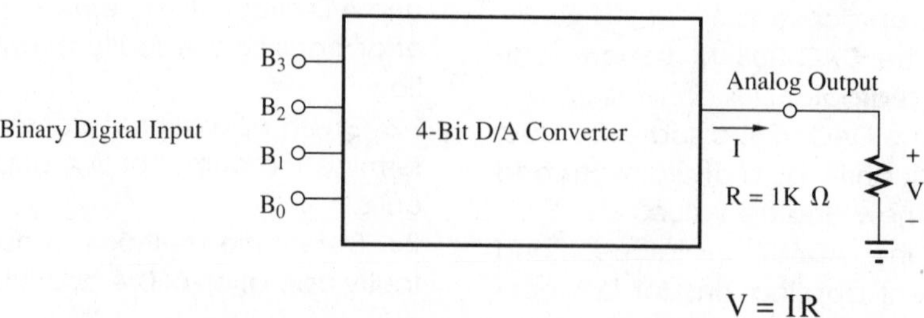

FIGURE 16-1 Basic Digital-to-Analog (D/A) Converter

TABLE 16-1 Digital-to-Analog Conversion

Input Code	Output Current (mA)	Output Voltage (volts)
0 0 0 0	0	0
0 0 0 1	1	1
0 0 1 0	2	2
0 0 1 1	3	3
0 1 0 0	4	4
0 1 0 1	5	5
0 1 1 0	6	6
0 1 1 1	7	7
1 0 0 0	8	8
1 0 0 1	9	9
1 0 1 0	10	10
1 0 1 1	11	11
1 1 0 0	12	12
1 1 0 1	13	13
1 1 1 0	14	14
1 1 1 1	15	15

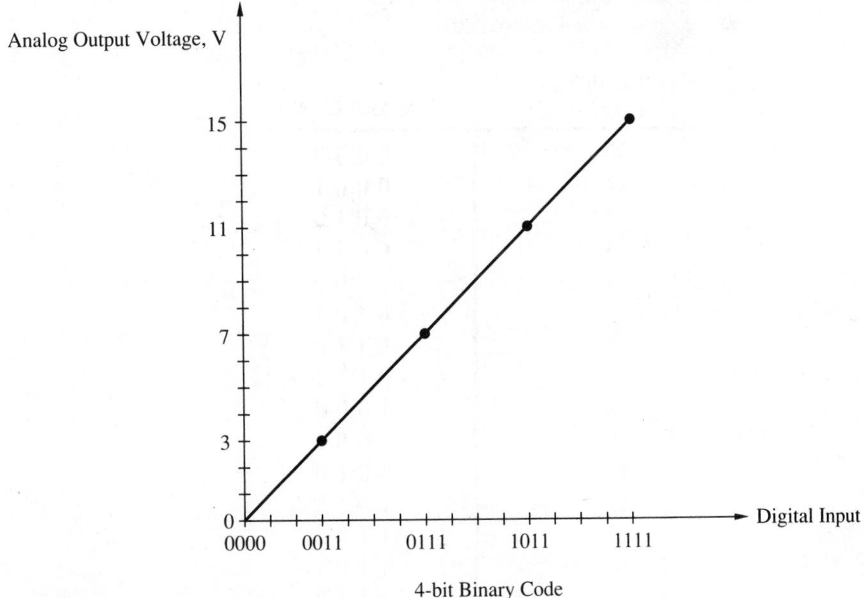

FIGURE 16-2 D/A Conversion Graph

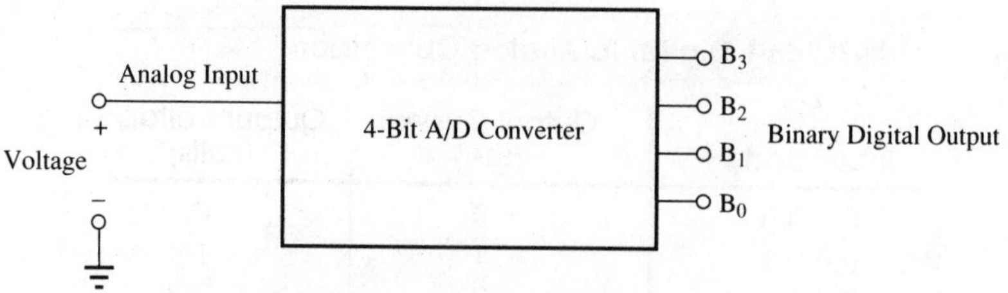

FIGURE 16-3 Basic Analog-to-Digital (A/D) Converter

digital controller circuits, and digital transmission circuits. Figure 16-4 shows a generic block diagram of the analog and digital signal conversion operations that must take place within a system.

Most physical quantities are analog. Analog data must be converted to a digital code in order to be processed in a digital system. The results of the processing must be displayed on an output display. Older output displays are analog, with dials or other continuously varying indicators that require D/A conversion in order to activate the analog output meter. Modern displays are digital and display discrete values. Examples of digital displays are digital clocks, digital speedometers, and digital voltmeters. Digital dis-

TABLE 16-2 Analog-to-Digital Conversion

Input Voltage (mV)	Output Code
0	0 0 0 0
1	0 0 0 1
2	0 0 1 0
3	0 0 1 1
4	0 1 0 0
5	0 1 0 1
6	0 1 1 0
7	0 1 1 1
8	1 0 0 0
9	1 0 0 1
10	1 0 1 0
11	1 0 1 1
12	1 1 0 0
13	1 1 0 1
14	1 1 1 0
15	1 1 1 1

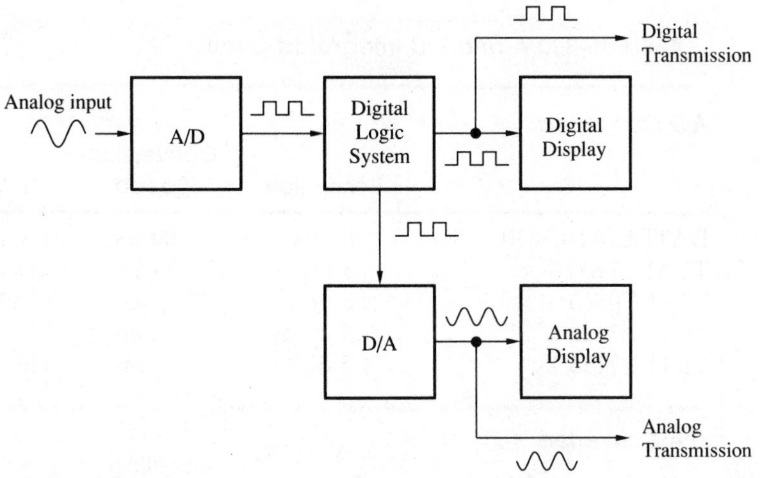

FIGURE 16-4 A/D and D/A Functions Within a Digital System

plays are often easier for the consumer to read. The accuracy of digital displays depends on the accuracy of the A/D conversion.

Analog and digital transmission systems also require A/D and D/A conversion operations. In the case of voice and video processing a very high-quality A/D converter converts the analog voice or video to a digital signal. The digital system processes the signal that represents the voice or video message. In a digital transmission system the digital representation of the analog quantities can be transmitted with the appropriate line drivers and other transmission circuits. (Additional information on digital transmission is contained in Appendix C.)

Analog transmission of digital information requires that the digital codes be converted to analog signals prior to transmission. Although analog systems are still in existence, they are quickly being replaced by improved digital systems.

Numerous D/A and A/D ICs are available to aid in making the conversion from a digital processing system to an analog world. Table 16-3 lists a small sample of the many A/D and D/A circuits available.

16.1.1 Performance Criteria

The performance criteria of any data acquisition system that converts between digital and analog signals are **resolution, sampling rate, speed,** and **linearity.**

The **resolution** of a digital or analog conversion system is the smallest change in voltage that can be detected by the system and represented as a digital code. The resolution determines the total number of digital codes or

TABLE 16-3 D/A and A/D Integrated Circuits

A/D Converters

IC	Resolution	Conversion Speed	Data Format
DATEL ADC-830	8 bits	100 μs	Parallel
TI ADC0831	8 bits	84 μs	Serial
TI TLC0820	8 bits	1 μs	Parallel
TI TLC7136	3.5 digits	333 ms	With LCD drivers
TI TLC7135	4.5 digits	34 ms	With BCD output

D/A Converters

IC	Resolution	Settling Time	Data Format
DATEL DAC-08	8 bits	.85 μs	Parallel
Analog Devices AD557	8 bits	1.5 μs	Parallel

A/D and D/A Interface IC

IC	Resolution	Conversion Speed	Data Format
TI TLC32040	14 bits	52 μs	Serial

quantization levels that will represent all possible analog values. Many analog or digital conversion systems specify the resolution in terms of the number of bits in the digital code. An n-bit code allows for 2^n quantization levels, or 2^n-1 steps between quantization levels, as shown in Equation 16-1. The voltage resolution is a function of the full-scale voltage and the number of quantization steps, as shown in Equation 16-2. Figure 16-5 shows a comparison between A/D systems with 2-, 3-, and 4-bit resolution.

Eq. 16-1 $\quad$ n bits $\rightarrow 2^n$ quantization levels; 2^n-1 quantization steps

Eq. 16-2
$$\text{voltage resolution} = \frac{\text{full-scale voltage}}{2^n - 1}$$

The system resolution can be specified as the number of bits in the allowed digital code, as the voltage between quantization levels, or as a percent. The percent resolution of a system can be defined by Equations 16-3 and 16-4.

Eq. 16-3
$$\%\ \text{resolution} = \frac{\text{step size}}{\text{full-scale voltage}} \times 100\%$$

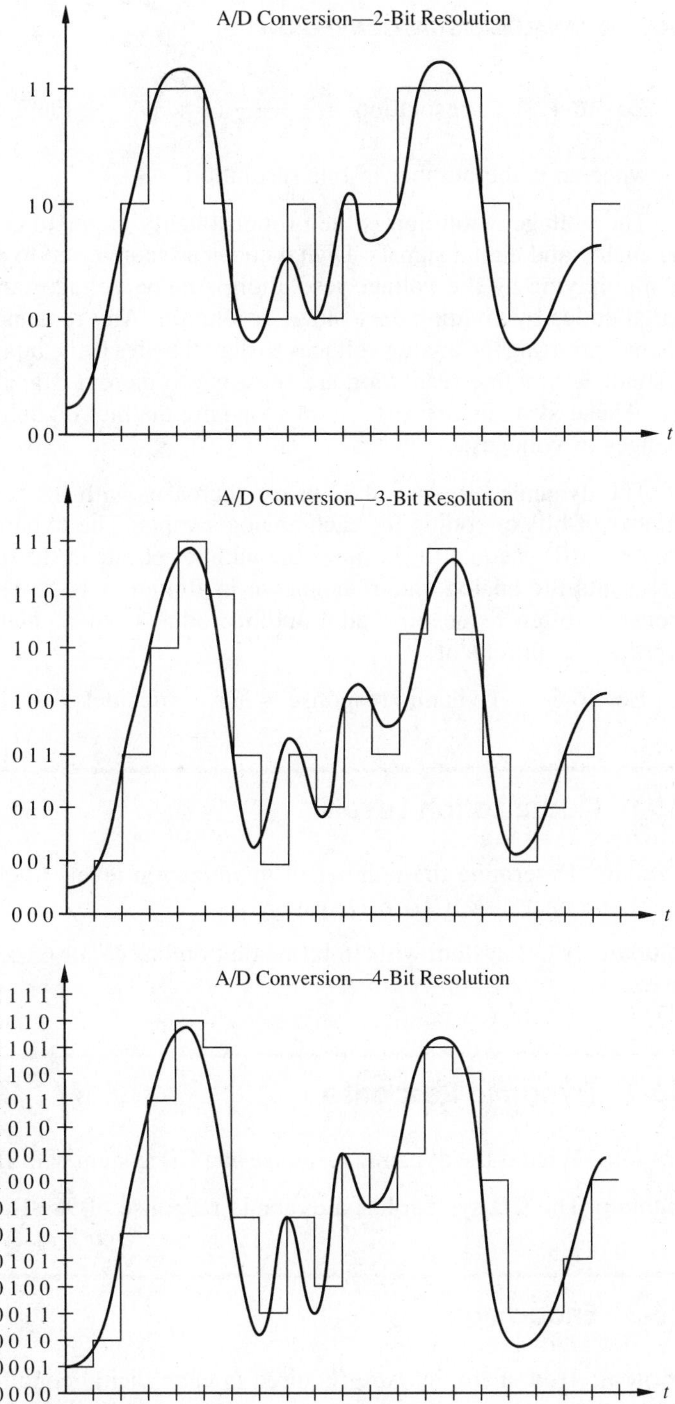

FIGURE 16-5 A/D Comparison of Resolution at a Low Sampling Rate

Eq. 16-4 $$\% \text{ resolution} = \frac{1}{2^n - 1} \times 100\%$$

where n is the number of bits resolution.

The voltage resolution is the proportionality factor to convert between the analog and digital signals. Digital codes are converted to analog voltages by multiplying by the voltage resolution. Analog voltages are converted to digital codes by dividing the voltage resolution. Any remainder that occurs when converting the analog voltages to digital codes is the quantization error. Systems with a fine resolution are sensitive to incremental changes in voltage. These systems are capable of assigning distinct digital codes to small changes in voltages.

The **dynamic response** of a system increases with the resolution or the number of bits of coding for each analog sample. The dynamic response in decibels (dB) is equal to six times the number of bits in the digital code that represents the analog value, as shown in Equation 16-5. The dynamic response is often listed on digital audio products where high fidelity is an important requirement.

Eq. 16-5 $$\text{Dynamic response} = 6n \quad \text{decibels (dB)}$$

■ EXAMPLE 16-1 Quantization Levels

Problem: Determine the number of quantization levels (digital codes) in a 16-bit compact disk (CD) A/D system.

Solution: A CD system with 16-bit resolution has 2^{16} or 65,536 quantization levels. ■

■ EXAMPLE 16-2 Dynamic Response

Problem: What is the dynamic response of a CD system with 16-bit encoding.

Solution: The CD system has a dynamic response of 96 dB. ■

■ EXAMPLE 16-3 Encoding

Problem: How many bits are required in each digital code for a system to have a dynamic response greater than or equal to 70 dB.

Solution: To determine the number of bits required, divide 70 by 6. The response is 11.666. Therefore, each digital code must have 12-bits in order to represent the analog value and meet the dynamic response requirements. The actual dynamic response of this system is 72 dB. ■

The resolution of the system is the analog voltage step size between two consecutive digital codes. The voltage resolution of a system can be calculated by dividing the analog range by the number of quantization levels. The quantization levels represent the distinct digital codes that are assigned to the analog voltages. Any error resulting due to the approximation between the actual analog voltage and the resulting digital code is referred to as the **quantization error.**

■ EXAMPLE 16-4 Voltage Resolution

Problem: Determine the voltage resolution of a CD system with a 16-bit resolution and a ±10 volt analog input range.

Solution: A 16-bit A/D system has $2^n - 1$ steps between quantization levels. Therefore, 65,535 voltage steps must be spread over the total analog input signal range of −10 to +10 volts. This 20-volt range must have 305.18 μV between each quantization level. Thus, the voltage resolution is 305.18 μV. ■

■ EXAMPLE 16-5 A/D Coding

Problem: An A/D system with an 8-bit resolution can accept input voltages of 0 to 5 volts. What is the digital code representing an analog input value of 2.5 volts?

Solution: This A/D system has 255 quantization steps and a voltage resolution of 19.608 mV. An input voltage of 2.5 volts is divided by the voltage resolution to determine the digital code to represent that input voltage:

$$\frac{2.5 \text{ volts}}{19.608 \text{ mV}} = 127.499$$

To represent this analog input voltage with an allowed digital code, round this value down to $(127)_{10}$ and represent it by the 8-bit binary code of 0 1 1 1 1 1 1 1. A quantization error occurred due to the rounding error. To calculate the actual voltage represented by the code, multiply the resulting digital code by the voltage resolution:

$$127 \times 19.608 \text{ mV} = 2.4902 \text{ volts}$$

■

The **linearity** of a data acquisition system is the accuracy in the analog or digital conversion throughout the operating range. Linear analog or digital conversion systems have a constant step size between quantization levels throughout the entire operating range. In linear conversion systems the graphed function of input vs. output should result in a straight line. The straight line can be the "best straight line" achieved by equalizing the gain or offset of the converter, or it can be the straight line through the end points of the operating range.

Linearity error is any deviation of the measured analog valued from a straight line in a plot of the conversion relationship. The degree of linearity of a system can be specified by percent linearity or parts per million of full-scale range, or fractions of the LSB. In IC A/D and D/A converters the linearity is specified over a defined operating range. Operation outside this range will result in nonlinear conversion and distortion.

Monotonicity is the operation of the converter so that the output increases as a single-valued function of the input. A linear system is monotonic. As with linearity, an operating range is often specified by the manufacture for monotonic performance.

The **sampling rate** is usually a quantity specified for A/D conversion. The sampling rate is the number of times per second that the analog signal is converted into a digital code. For proper A/D conversion, the minimum sampling rate is twice the highest analog frequency. This minimum sampling rate is also known as the Nyquist sampling rate. Figure 16-6 shows the results of A/D conversion illustrated in Figure 16-5 performed at twice the original sampling rate.

If the sampling frequency is less than twice the highest analog frequency, **aliasing** occurs. Aliasing produces severe distortion of high frequency components of the signal due to the spectral content of the sampled signal. Aliasing is a phenomenon caused when frequency components generated by the sampled signal interfere with the frequency content of the signal being sampled. Aliasing is not studied in this chapter, but it can be avoided by using a sampling frequency of at least twice the maximum analog frequency. Antialiasing filters are used in complex A/D systems that prefilter the analog signal prior to sampling.

Oversampling is a technique used in compact disk and digital audiotape systems when a very high degree of accuracy is needed to obtain the desired sound quality. Oversampling is used to reconstruct an analog signal from a digital code, so it is referred to as a D/A reconstruction technique.

In oversampling, the frequency used to reconstruct an analog signal from the digitized signal is an integral multiple of the original sampling frequency. Common oversampling frequencies are two, four, or eight times the original sampling frequency. In high fidelity audio systems a very high-order or sharp low-pass filter is required to remove unwanted noise from the audio signal to be recovered. The unwanted noise is centered at the recovery sampling frequency. Thus, by using a higher frequency to recover the signal, the unwanted noise occurs at frequencies considerably higher than the signal to be recovered. This reduces filter requirements to recover the signal with minimal distortion at the high frequencies.

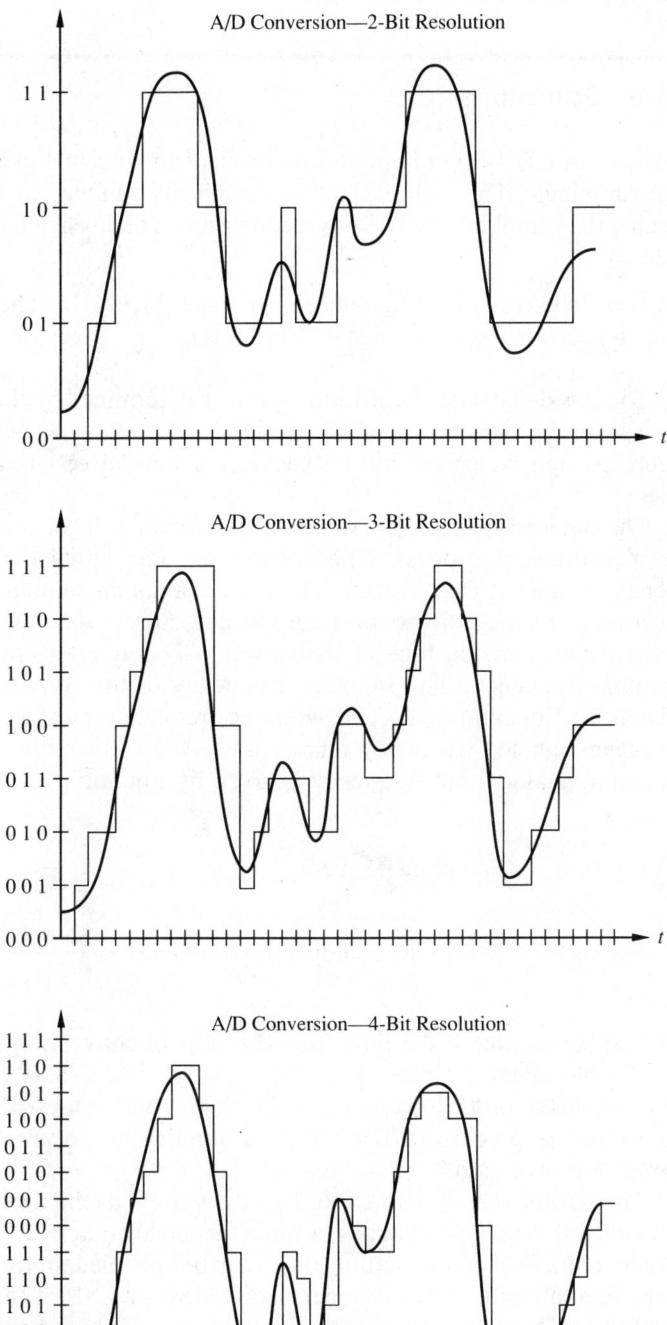

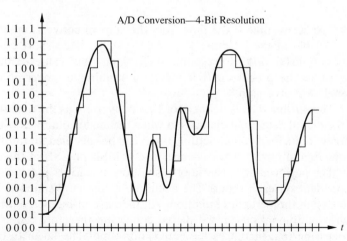

FIGURE 16-6 A/D Conversion at a High Sampling Rate

■ EXAMPLE 16-6 Sampling Rate

Problem: A CD system is said to recover an audio signal using "four times oversampling." The audio signal was originally sampled at 44.1 KHz. Determine the sampling rate used to reconstruct an audio signal from the digital code.

Solution: The oversampling rate is four times 44.1 KHz. The sampling rate used to recover the audio signal is 176.4 KHz. ■

The **speed** of a data acquisition system is determined by the time required to perform the conversion between the analog value and digital code. The speed is often measured by the **conversion time, access time,** and **settling time.**

The **conversion time** is the time required for an A/D converter to complete the measurement process. The conversion time limits the sampling frequency in most A/D converters since the maximum sampling frequency is the inverse of the conversion time. Manufacturers data sheets frequently report the conversion time of the slower A/D converters rather than their sampling frequency. The sampling frequency of the converter can be calculated by Equation 16-6. The sampling frequency must be at least twice the highest analog frequency for accurate A/D conversion. Therefore, the maximum analog input frequency is given by Equation 16-7.

Eq. 16-6 $$\text{Sampling frequency} = \frac{1}{\text{conversion time}}$$

Eq. 16-7 $$\text{Maximum analog input frequency} = \frac{\text{sampling frequency}}{2}$$

The **access time** is the time from the start of conversion until valid data is available at the outputs. Fast A/D systems have short conversion and access times in order to respond to changing input values. Due to the complexity of the process, A/D conversion requires a longer conversion time than D/A conversion.

The **settling time** is defined for D/A converters as the time from a change in the digital data input changes to when the analog output is within a defined percent of its final value. Settling times can be specified for full-scale changes in the digital input, or for changes in the MSB or LSB of the digital code.

The performance criteria of resolution, linearity, and speed are closely dependent on each other. The accuracy of the conversion is improved by increasing the percent resolution. An increase in the percent resolution requires additional bits in the digital code, and therefore requires additional processing that increases the conversion time. The linearity of the system should be nearly equivalent to the resolution of the system.

■ EXAMPLE 16-7 Sampling Frequency

Problem: Determine the minimum allowable sampling frequency required to digitize analog systems whose highest frequency is given.

ANALOG SYSTEM	MAXIMUM ANALOG FREQUENCY
Voice	4 KHz
Audio	22 KHz
Measurements	1 KHz

Solution: The minimum sampling frequency must be twice the highest analog frequency. The resulting sampling frequencies are given.

ANALOG SYSTEM	MAXIMUM ANALOG FREQUENCY	MINIMUM SAMPLING FREQUENCY
Voice	4 KHz	8 KHz
Audio	22 KHz	44 KHz
Measurements	1 KHz	2 KHz

■

■ EXAMPLE 16-8 Conversion Time

Problem: Determine the maximum allowable conversion time for each analog system in Example 16-7.

Solution: The conversion time can be no more than the reciprocal of the sampling frequency. The maximum conversion times are given.

ANALOG SYSTEM	MINIMUM SAMPLING FREQUENCY	MAXIMUM CONVERSION TIME
Voice	8 KHz	125 μs
Audio	44 KHz	22.727 μs
Measurements	2 KHz	500 μs

■

16.1.2 Selection Criteria for Analog/Digital Converters

Hundreds of A/D and D/A converters are available, with prices ranging from a few dollars to over a hundred dollars each. The selection of the appropriate type of A/D converter is based on the application requirements of the system, performance requirements, and cost.

A designer should examine the system requirements and obtain answers to the following questions in order to select the appropriate A/D converter:

1. What are the input and output requirements for the system? Specify all signal current and voltage ranges, logic levels, input and output impedances, digital codes, data rates, serial or parallel data format.
2. What level of accuracy is required? Determine the resolution needed throughout the analog voltage range, the dynamic response, the degree of linearity, and the number of bits encoding. Also, determine what types of error the system will tolerate, such as nonlinearity error, missed codes, and so on.
3. What speed is required? Determine the maximum analog input frequency for sampling in an A/D system, the number of bits for encoding each analog sample, and the rate of change of input digital codes in a D/A system.
4. What is the operating environment of the system? Obtain information on the temperature range and power supply to select a converter that is stable over the operating range.

Final selection of A/D and D/A converters should be made by consulting manufacturers to obtain their technical specifications of the devices. Major manufacturers of digital and analog converter circuits include (in alphabetical order) Analog Devices, Burr-Brown, DATEL, National, Philips Components, Signetics, Sony, Texas Instruments, Ultra Analog, and Yamaha.

16.1.3 Circuit Design Considerations for A/D and D/A Converter Circuits

Circuit layout and design considerations are required to achieve the manufacturers' performance ratings of A/D and D/A converters. Circuit design is critical since both analog and digital signals must be processed and are in close proximity to each other. All electrical signals emit electromagnetic interference, often referred to as noise. This noise is induced in the signals that must be processed by the A/D and D/A converters, resulting in faulty conversion or failure of the device to operate at all. Good circuit construction techniques should be followed at all times, but they are especially critical when dealing with A/D and D/A converters. The following is a checklist of items to be reviewed by the circuit designer. It is not an exhaustive list of circuit design criteria, but rather a starting point to eliminate the most common errors found in student projects and laboratory experiments:

1. Group digital signals together and keep them as far as possible from analog inputs.
2. Shield all analog inputs.
3. Keep analog input leads as short as possible.
4. Use a single analog ground point that is separate from the digital ground. The analog and digital ground should interconnect only at the main power supply.

5. Use separate analog and digital voltage supply lines. Their only common point should be at the main power supply.
6. Bypass all IC supply inputs to ground. V_S, V_{CC}, and V_{EE} inputs should have a tantalum capacitor as close as possible to the supply input connected to the digital ground. The value of the capacitor is usually 10, 1, or .1 μF but should be selected according to the manufacturer's recommendations.
7. Make sure that external clocking capacitors (if any) are tied to digital ground.
8. For analog inputs to A/D converters, keep the input source resistance below 5K ohms and do not use input bypass capacitors.
9. Adhere to the manufacturer's recommended component values and loads. Buffers must be used to drive loads that exceed the recommended values.
10. Follow the manufacturer's recommended circuit configurations, especially concerning unused input and output pins.
11. Use sockets in PC board layout design.
12. Make sure that the PC board has a large ground plane and supply plane to minimize parasitic reactance and resistance.

Section Self-Test

1. Determine the minimum sampling frequency of a system whose maximum analog frequency is 10 KHz.
2. How many bits encoding are required to obtain 1% resolution?
3. What is the maximum voltage step size for a system with 1% resolution with an analog range of 0 to 2.55 volts?

ANSWERS (Not necessarily in the order of the questions)

- 25.5 mV
- 20 KHz
- 7 bits

16-2 DIGITAL-TO-ANALOG CONVERSION

Digital-to-analog conversion is required when a digital code must be represented as an analog signal. The analog signal can be used to control an output level of a system, such as a flow level in a fluid system or a volume level on a stereo system.

A digital code can be converted to an analog value by assigning a voltage weight to each bit in the code and then summing the voltage weights. This process is electrically equivalent to the conversion from binary to decimal number systems by multiplying each bit value by its bit weight and summing.

A general D/A converter consists of a network of precision resistors, input switches, and level shifters to activate the switches to convert a digital code to an analog voltage or current. A D/A converter may also contain input or output buffers, amplifiers, and internal references.

D/A converters commonly have a fixed or variable reference level. The reference level can be generated internally or externally. It determines the switching threshold of the precision switches that form a controlled impedance network, which controls the value of the output signal.

Fixed reference D/A converters have current or voltage output values that are proportional to the digital input. **Multiplying D/A converters** produce an output signal that is proportional to the product of a varying reference level and a digital code.

D/A converters can produce bipolar, positive or negative polarity signals. A four-quadrant multiplying D/A converter allows both the reference signal and the value of the binary code to have a positive or negative polarity. The four-quadrant multiplying D/A converter produces bipolar output signals according to the rules of multiplying signed numbers.

The D/A converters studied in this section include a resistor ladder circuit, a fixed reference D/A IC, and a multiplying D/A IC.

16.2.1 D/A Ladder Circuit

A very basic D/A converter can be designed with an operational amplifier and a resistor ladder network as shown in Figure 16-7.

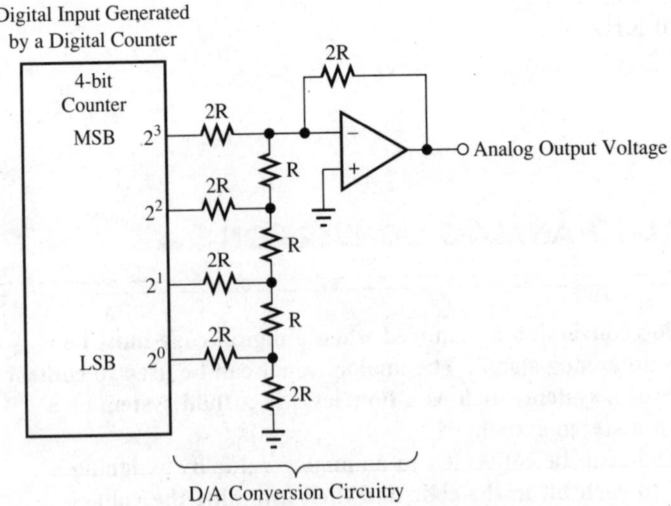

FIGURE 16-7 D/A Converter R/2R Ladder Network

Digital Counter

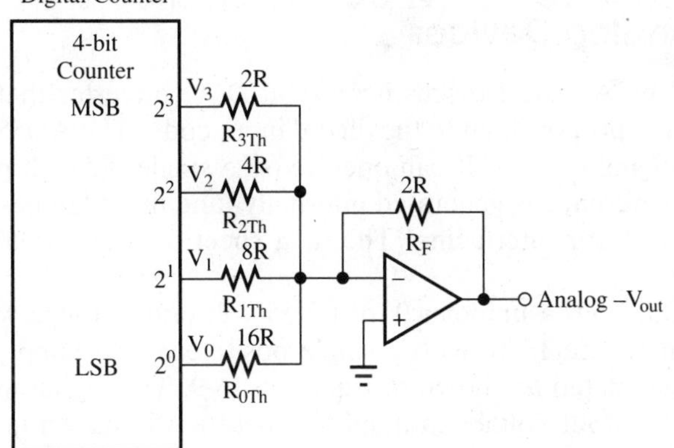

$$-V_{out} = 2R\left(\frac{V_3}{2R} + \frac{V_2}{4R} + \frac{V_1}{8R} + \frac{V_0}{16R}\right) = V_3 + \frac{V_2}{2} + \frac{V_1}{4} + \frac{V_0}{8}$$

FIGURE 16-8 Thevenin Equivalent Circuit for the R/2R Resistor Ladder Circuit

Only two values of resistors are required for the ladder network: R and 2R. The resistors weight the digital output bits so that the LSB has a weight of 2^0 and the most significant nth bit has a weight of $2^{(n-1)}$. The circuit of Figure 16-7 is equivalent to a binary proportional voltage summing network. The Thevenin equivalent circuit for the binary proportional voltage summing network is shown in Figure 16-8. The analog output voltage of the R/2R network is a negative value, calculated according to Equation 16-8.

Eq. 16-8
$$-\text{Analog } V_{out} = \frac{V_{b(n-1)}}{2^0} + \frac{V_{b(n-2)}}{2^1} + \cdots + \frac{V_{b0}}{2^{n-1}}$$

where $V_{b(n-1)}$ is the output voltage of the MSB of the digital code and V_{b0} is the output voltage of the LSB of the digital code.

For linear performance of the D/A resistor ladder conversion circuit, it is necessary to select a digital output device such as a transistor switch that produces consistent voltage values for a logic HIGH level and 0 volts for a logic-LOW level. One possible solution is to buffer the digital logic circuit with an open-collector output stage. With open-collector outputs, the logic HIGH is pulled up to +5 volts through the pull-up resistors, and the logic LOW is at 0 volts.

Linear operation of the R/2R ladder circuit also requires that the resistors forming the network are precisely calibrated to produce the proper voltage division. System temperature effects must also be taken into account as resistance increases with higher temperatures.

16.2.2 Fixed Reference Level D/A Converter: The AD557 by Analog Devices

The AD557 by Analog Devices is an 8-bit D/A converter that produces an output voltage proportional to the digital input code. The AD557 can be used easily in a digital system. It can operate off a single +5-volt power supply, the voltage reference is generated internally, and input latches are available for microprocessor interfacing. The data sheet for the AD557 is shown in Figure 16-9.

The AD557 has a unipolar 0 to +2.55 volt output range when operated as shown in Figure 16-10 with a single positive power supply. The output voltage is calculated as shown in Equation 16-9. The digital input code and the resulting output voltage in unipolar operation is shown in Table 16-4.

Eq. 16-9 AD557 UNIPOLAR OPERATION

$$V_{out} = (\text{decimal equivalent of input code}) \times 0.1 \text{ Volts}$$

The AD557 has input latches to simplify interfacing synchronous circuits and microprocessor systems to the AD557 for D/A conversion. The input latches are controlled by the chip select, $\overline{CS}$, and chip enable, $\overline{CE}$, inputs. If the latches are not required, the chip select and chip enable inputs are tied LOW.

Table 16-5 shows the latched input operation of the AD557. Data is latched into the input latches on the positive edge of either $\overline{CS}$ or $\overline{CE}$. The data is held in the input latch until both $\overline{CS}$ and $\overline{CE}$ return to a logic LOW level. When both $\overline{CS}$ and $\overline{CE}$ are at the logic LOW level, the data is transferred from the input latch to the D/A converter for conversion to an analog voltage.

TABLE 16-4 AD557 D/A Conversion 0 to +2.55 Volt Output

Digital Input Code			Output Voltage (volts)
Binary	Hex	Decimal	
0000 0000	00	0	0
0000 0001	01	1	0.01
0000 0010	02	2	0.02
0000 1111	0F	15	0.15
0001 0000	10	16	0.16
0001 1111	1F	31	0.31
0111 1111	7F	127	1.27
1000 0000	80	128	1.28
1111 0000	F0	240	2.40
1111 1111	FF	255	2.55

DACPORT Low-Cost Complete μP-Compatible 8-Bit DAC

AD557

FEATURES
Complete 8-Bit DAC
Voltage Output – 0 to 2.56V
Internal Precision Band-Gap Reference
Single-Supply Operation: +5V (±10%)
Full Microprocessor Interface
Fast: 1μs Voltage Settling to ±1/2LSB
Low Power: 75mW
No User Trims Required
Guaranteed Monotonic Over Temperature
All Errors Specified T_{min} to T_{max}
Small 16-Pin DIP or 20-Pin PLCC Package
Low Cost

AD557 FUNCTIONAL BLOCK DIAGRAM

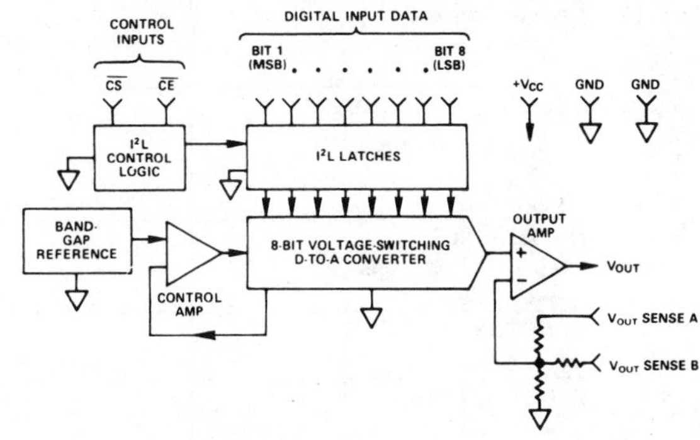

PRODUCT DESCRIPTION

The AD557 DACPORT™ is a complete voltage-output 8-bit digital-to-analog converter, including output amplifier, full microprocessor interface and precision voltage reference on a single monolithic chip. No external components or trims are required to interface, with full accuracy, an 8-bit data bus to an analog system.

The low cost and versatility of the AD557 DACPORT are the result of continued development in monolithic bipolar technologies.

The complete microprocessor interface and control logic is implemented with integrated injection logic (I^2L), an extremely dense and low-power logic structure that is process-compatible with linear bipolar fabrication. The internal precision voltage reference is the patented low-voltage band-gap circuit which permits full-accuracy performance on a single +5V power supply. Thin-film silicon-chromium resistors provide the stability required for guaranteed monotonic operation over the entire operating temperature range, while laser-wafer trimming of these thin-film resistors permits absolute calibration at the factory to within ±2.5LSB; thus, no user-trims for gain or offset are required. A new circuit design provides voltage settling to ±1/2LSB for a full-scale step in 800ns.

The AD557 is available in two package configurations. The AD557JN is packaged in a 16-pin plastic, 0.3"-wide DIP. For surface mount applications, the AD557JP is packaged in a 20-pin JEDEC standard PLCC. Both versions are specified over the operating temperature range of 0 to +70°C.

PRODUCT HIGHLIGHTS

1. The 8-bit I^2L input register and fully microprocessor-compatible control logic allow the AD557 to be directly connected to 8- or 16-bit data buses and operated with standard control signals. The latch may be disabled for direct DAC interfacing.
2. The laser-trimmed on-chip SiCr thin-film resistors are calibrated for absolute accuracy and linearity at the factory. Therefore, no user trims are necessary for full rated accuracy over the operating temperature range.
3. The inclusion of a precision low-voltage band-gap reference eliminates the need to specify and apply a separate reference source.
4. The AD557 is designed and specified to operate from a single +4.5V to +5.5V power supply.
5. Low digital input currents, 100μA max, minimize bus loading. Input thresholds are TTL/low voltage CMOS compatible.
6. The single-chip, low power I^2L design of the AD557 is inherently more reliable than hybrid multichip or conventional single-chip bipolar designs.

DACPORT is a trademark of Analog Devices, Inc.
Covered by U.S. Patent Nos. 3,887,863; 3,685,045; 4,323,795; other patents pending.

FIGURE 16-9 AD557 D/A Converter Data Sheet (Courtesy of Analog Devices, Inc.)

SPECIFICATIONS (@ T_A = +25°C, V_{CC} = +5V unless otherwise specified)

Model	AD557J Min	Typ	Max	Units
RESOLUTION			8	Bits
RELATIVE ACCURACY[1]				
0 to +70°C		±1/2	1	LSB
OUTPUT				
Ranges		0 to +2.56		V
Current Source	+5			mA
Sink		Internal Passive Pull-Down to Ground[2]		
OUTPUT SETTLING TIME[3]		0.8	1.5	μs
FULL SCALE ACCURACY[4]				
@25°C		±1.5	±2.5	LSB
T_{min} to T_{max}		±2.5	±4.0	LSB
ZERO ERROR				
@25°C			±1	LSB
T_{min} to T_{max}			±3	LSB
MONOTONICITY[5]				
T_{min} to T_{max}		**Guaranteed**		
DIGITAL INPUTS				
T_{min} to T_{max}				
Input Current			**±100**	μA
Data Inputs, Voltage				
Bit On – Logic "1"	2.0			V
Bit On – Logic "0"	0		0.8	V
Control Inputs, Voltage				
On – Logic "1"	2.0			V
On – Logic "0"	0		0.8	V
Input Capacitance		4		pF
TIMING[6]				
t_W Strobe Pulse Width	225			ns
T_{min} to T_{max}	**300**			ns
t_{DH} Data Hold Time	10			ns
T_{min} to T_{max}	**10**			ns
t_{DS} Data Setup Time	225			ns
T_{min} to T_{max}	**300**			ns
POWER SUPPLY				
Operating Voltage Range (V_{CC})				
2.56 Volt Range	**+4.5**		**+5.5**	V
Current (I_{CC})		15	**25**	mA
Rejection Ratio			**0.03**	%/%
POWER DISSIPATION, V_{CC} = 5V		75	125	mW
OPERATING TEMPERATURE RANGE	0		+70	°C

NOTES

[1]Relative Accuracy is defined as the deviation of the code transition points from the ideal transfer point on a straight line from the offset to the full scale of the device. See "Measuring Offset Error" on AD558 data sheet.

[2]Passive pull-down resistance is 2kΩ.

[3]Settling time is specified for a positive-going full-scale step to ± 1/2LSB. Negative-going steps to zero are slower, but can be improved with an external pull-down.

[4]The full-scale output voltage is 2.55V and is guaranteed with a +5V supply.

[5]A monotonic converter has a maximum differential linearity error of ± 1LSB.

[6]See Figure 7.

Specifications shown in **boldface** are tested on all production units at final electrical test.

Specifications subject to change without notice.

PIN CONFIGURATIONS

DIP

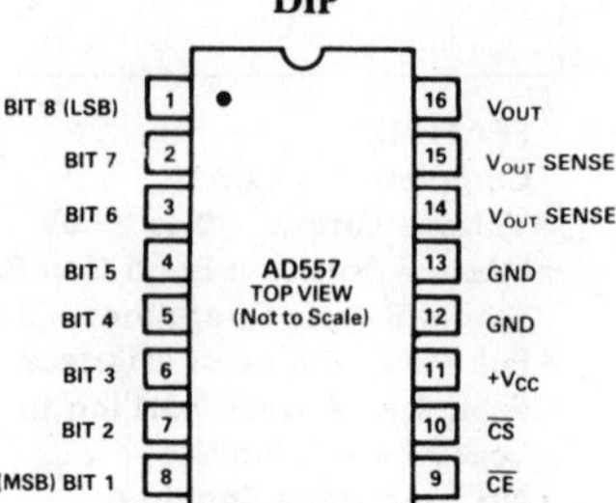

PLCC

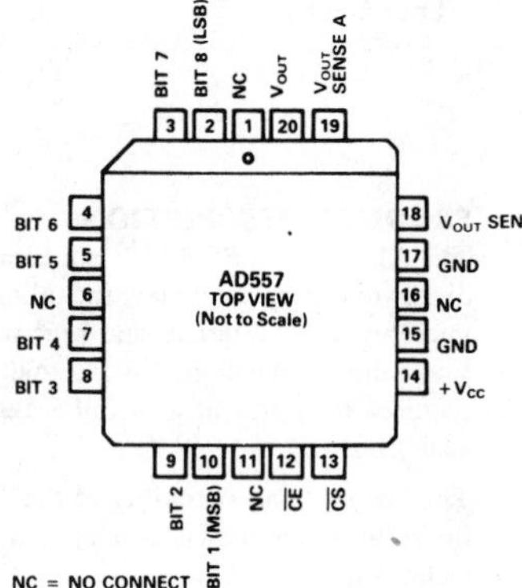

AD557 ORDERING GUIDE

Model	Package Options*	Temperature
AD557JN	Plastic (N-16)	0 to +70°C
AD557JP	PLCC (P-20A)	0 to +70°C

*See Section 14 for package outline information.

ABSOLUTE MAXIMUM RATINGS*

V_{CC} to Ground . . . . 0V to +18V
Digital Inputs (Pins 1-10) . . . . 0 to +7.0V
V_{OUT} . . . . Indefinite Short to Ground
Momentary Short to V_{CC}
Power Dissipation 450mW
Storage Temperature Range
N/P (Plastic) Packages . . . . −25°C to +100°C
Lead Temperature (soldering, 10 sec) . . . . 300°C

Thermal Resistance
Junction to Ambient/Junction to Case
N/P (Plastic) Packages . . . . 140/55°C

*Stresses above those listed under "Absolute Maximum Ratings" may cause permanent damage to the device. This is a stress rating only and functional operation of the device at these or any other conditions above those indicated in the operational sections of this specification is not implied. Exposure to absolute maximum rating conditions for extended periods may affect device reliability.

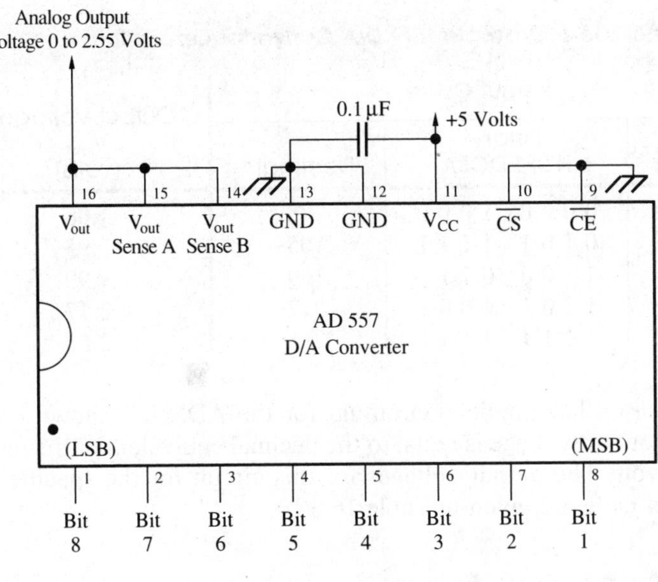

FIGURE 16-10 AD557 Unipolar Output Configuration 0- to 2.55-Volt Operation

TABLE 16-5 AD557 Input Latch Operation

Input Data	$\overline{CE}$	$\overline{CS}$	D/A Converter Data	Latch Condition
0	0	0	0	"Transparent"
1	0	0	1	"Transparent"
0	↑	0	0	Latching
1	↑	1	1	Latching
0	0	↑	0	Latching
1	0	↑	1	Latching
x	1	x	Previous data	Latched
x	x	1	Previous data	Latched

■ EXAMPLE 16-9 AD557 Application

Problem: Use the AD557 D/A converter to produce an output voltage for 8-bit input binary values. The binary inputs are HGFE DCBA, from MSB to LSB. Show the circuit used with a +5 volt supply. Determine the voltage output for hexadecimal input codes of 08, 5F, A7, D9, and FF.

TABLE 16-6 Example 16-9 D/A Converter Operation

Input Code			Output Voltage
Hex	Binary HGFE DCBA	Decimal	V_{out} (volts)
08	0000 1000	8	.08
5F	0101 1111	95	.95
A7	1100 0111	199	1.99
D9	1101 1001	217	2.17
FF	1111 1111	255	2.55

Solution: The application circuit for the AD557 is shown in Figure 16-11. The output voltage is equal to the decimal equivalent of the input code times .01 volt. The output voltages for this circuit for the specified hexadecimal input code are given in Table 16-6.

■

16.2.3 Varying Reference Level D/A Converter: The DAC-08B by DATEL

The DAC-08B is an 8-bit multiplying D/A converter. The D/A conversion process of the DAC-08B produces an output current that is a product of an 8-bit digital input word and input reference current. The data sheet for the DAC-08B is shown in Figure 16-12.

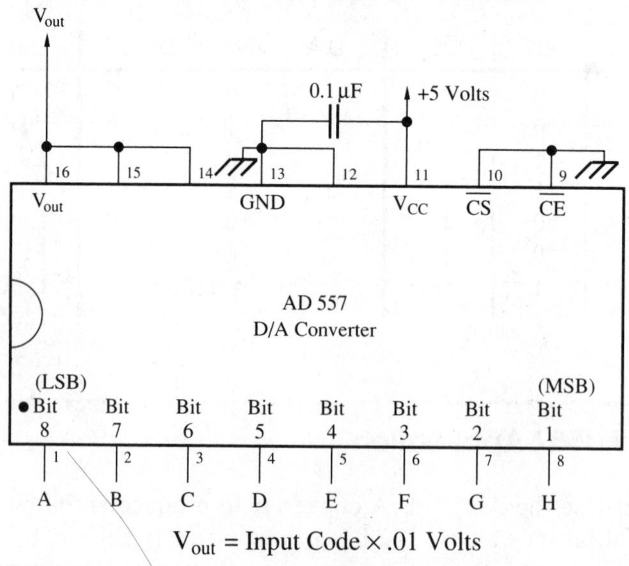

FIGURE 16-11 Example 16-9 AD557 Application Circuit

The output current range for the DAC-08B is 0 to −2 mA. Both positive and negative current outputs are provided. The full-scale current output is the sum of the positive output current and the negative output current, as shown in Equation 16-10. Application circuits for the DAC-08B will be shown later in this section for proper connection of the current outputs.

Eq. 16-10 DAC-08B FULL-SCALE OUTPUT CURRENT

$$I_{FS} = I_o + \overline{I_o}$$

The output current is a product of the current reference and the binary input word. The nominal reference current is 2 mA, but the reference current can range from 4 mA to 100 μA for monotonic operation. The full-scale output current is obtained when the binary input word is $(1\,1\,1\,1 \quad 1\,1\,1\,1)_2$, which is $(255)_{10}$. Equations 16-11 and 16-12 show the calculation to obtain the output current for a given input code and the full-scale output current.

Eq. 16-11 DAC-08B OUTPUT CURRENT

$$I_{out} = \frac{\text{decimal equivalent of the input code}}{256} \times I_{REF}$$

where I_{REF} is the current at pin 14 on the DAC-08B.

Eq. 16-12 DAC-08B MAXIMUM FULL-SCALE OUTPUT CURRENT

$$I_{FS} = \frac{255}{256} \times I_{REF}$$

The settling time for the DAC-08B is typically 85 ns when operated with a reference current of 2 mA. The settling time increases when the reference current drops below 1 mA. The maximum settling time is 150 ns for a minimum bias current of −1 μA.

The DAC-08B can operate from a single or dual power supply. The total supply voltage should range from ±4.5 to ±18 volts. A symmetrical supply is not required. If the supply voltage is ±5 volts or less, the reference current should be no more than 1 mA. Positive and negative supply inputs, V_{CC} and V_{EE}, respectively, should always have a bypass capacitor to ground of at least .1 μF.

Four application circuits for the DAC-08B are shown in Figures 16-13 through 16-16 to illustrate four modes of operation. Analog output current can be converted to an output voltage by using a resistor at the outputs. Tables 16-7 and 16-8 show the resulting output currents and voltages for unipolar and bipolar operation. Notice that the negative polarity on the current is determined by the direction of current flow. Positive current flows into a device, as specified by IEEE current notation. Negative current flows out of the device.

DAC-08B High Speed, 8-Bit Monolithic Digital-to-Analog Converter

FEATURES

- 85 Nanoseconds settling time
- −10 to +18V compliance
- ±4.5 to ±18V supply
- 8-Bit resolution
- 1- or 2-Quadrant multiplication
- Low cost

GENERAL DESCRIPTION

The DAC-08BC and DAC-08BM provide very high speed performance coupled with low cost and application flexibility. These units have guaranteed full 8-bit monotonicity with nonlinearity of 0.19% over the full operating temperature range. High-speed current steering switches achieve 85 nanoseconds settling time with a very low glitch for full-scale changes. A large output voltage compliance range (−10 to +18V) allows direct current to voltage conversion with just an output resistor, omitting the need for an operational amplifier in many cases.

The DAC-08 consists of 8 fast-switching current sources, a diffused R-2R resistor ladder, a bias circuit, and a reference control amplifier. The diffused resistor ladder gives excellent temperature tracking, resulting in a gain temperature coefficient of 10 ppm/°C. The monolithic fabrication results in excellent linearity and tempco, fast output settling and low cost. Linearity is ±½ LSB.

An external reference current of 2 mA nominal programs the scale factor of the DAC. This reference current can also be varied, resulting in one or two quadrant multiplying operation. The output voltage can be unipolar or bipolar dependent upon the connection of the two complementary output sink currents.

DAC-08 applications include fast A/D converters, waveform generators, audio encoder and attenuators, CRT display drivers, and high-speed modems.

Power supply requirements are ±4.5V to ±18V. Operating temperature range is 0°C to 70°C for the DAC-08BC and −55°C to +125°C for the DAC-08BM. These models have equivalent specifications and pinouts to industry standard DAC-08's.

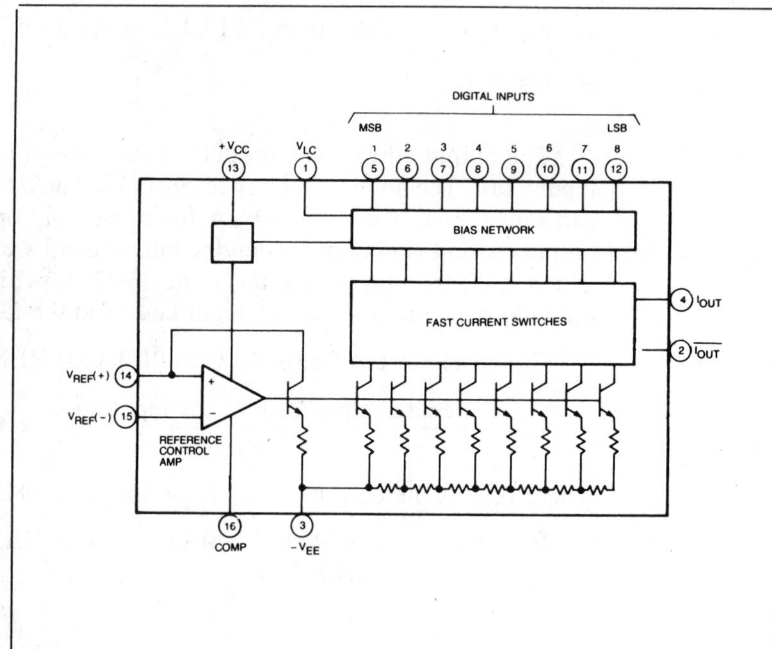

MECHANICAL DIMENSIONS INCHES (MM)

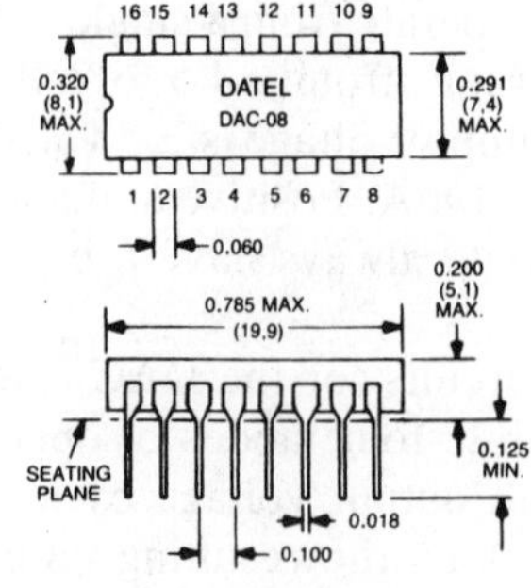

INPUT/OUTPUT CONNECTIONS

PIN	FUNCTION
1	THRESHOLD CONTROL (VLC)
2	$\overline{I_{OUT}}$
3	VEE
4	IOUT
5	BIT 1 IN (MSB)
6	BIT 2 IN
7	BIT 3 IN
8	BIT 4 IN
9	BIT 5 IN
10	BIT 6 IN
11	BIT 7 IN
12	BIT 8 IN (MSB)
13	VCC
14	VREF+
15	VREF−
16	COMPENSTION

FIGURE 16-12 DAC-08B Data Sheet (Reprinted by permission of DATEL, Inc.)

ABSOLUTE MAXIMUM RATINGS

V_{CC} Supply to V_{EE} Supply	36V
Digital Input Voltage	$-V_{EE}$ to $-V_{EE}$ plus 36V
V_{LC}	$-V_{EE}$ to $+V_{CC}$
Reference Input Voltage	$-V_{EE}$ to $+V_{CC}$
Reference Input Current	5.0 mA

FUNCTIONAL SPECIFICATIONS

Typical at 25°C, V_S = ±15V, I_{REF} = 2.0 mA unless otherwise noted.

INPUTS	
Resolution	8 Bits
Coding, Unipolar Output	Straight Binary
Coding, Bipolar Output	Offset Binary
Input Logic Level, Bit ON ("1")	+2.0V minimum at +10.0 μA
Input Logic Level, Bit OFF("0")	+0.8V maximum at −10.0 μA[1]
Nominal Reference Current	2.0 mA
Reference Bias Current	−1.0 μA
Reference Input Slew Rate	8 mA/μsec.
OUTPUTS	
Output Current, I_{REF} = 2.0 mA	1.99 mA ±0.05 mA[2]
Output Current Range, V_{EE} = −5V	0 to 2.1 mA
Output Current Range, V_{EE} = −7 to −18V	0 to 4.2 mA
Output Current, all bits OFF	±0.2 μA typical ±2.0 μA maximum
Full-Scale Symmetry	±1.0 μA typical ±8.0 μA maximum
Output Voltage Compliance	−10 to +18V
PERFORMANCE	
Relative Accuracy	±½ LSB (±0.19%) maximum
Nonlinearity	±½ LSB (±0.19%) maximum
Differential Nonlinearity	±½ LSB (±0.19%)
Full-Scale Tempco	±10 ppm/°C typical ±50 ppm/°C maximum
Settling Time, 2 mA to ½ LSB	85 nsec. typical 150 nsec. maximum
Propagation Delay	60 nsec. maximum
Power Supply Sensitivity, I_{REF} = 1 mA	±0.002%/%
POWER REQUIREMENTS	
V_{CC}	+4.5V to +18V
V_{EE}	−4.5V to −18V
Power Supply Current, I_{REF} = 1.0 mA V = ±5V	+3.8, −5.8 mA maximum
Power Supply Current, I_{REF} = 2.0 mA V = +5V, −15V	+3.8, −7.8 mA maximum
V = ±15V	+3.8, −7.8 mA maximum
PHYSICAL/ENVIRONMENTAL	
Operating Temperature Range	
DAC-08BC	0°C to +70°C
DAC-08BM	−55°C to +125°C
Storage Temperature Range	−65°C to +150°C
Package	16 Pin Dip

FOOTNOTES

1. For TTL, DTL Interface, V_{LC} = 0V. For other digital interfaces see TECHNICAL NOTE 3.
2. I_{OUT} (Pin 4) + $\overline{I_{OUT}}$ (Pin 2) = Output Current

TECHNICAL NOTES

1. The DAC-08 series is a multiplying D/A converter in which the output current is a product of the digital word and the input reference current. Excellent performance is obtained for I_{REF} from 4.0 mA to 4.0 μA. Monotonic operation is maintained from 4.0 mA to 100 μA. The full-scale output current is a linear function of the reference current and is given by:

$$I_{FS} = \frac{255}{256} \times I_{REF} \text{ } (I_{REF} \text{ is current at Pin 14})$$

2. **Reference Amplifier Set-up.** If a regulated power supply is used as the reference, a resistor divider should be used with the junction by-passed to ground with a 0.1 μf capacitor. TTL logic supplies are not recommended to be used as the reference. AC and dc reference applications will require the reference amplifier to be compensated using a capacitor (C_C) from pin 16 to V_{EE}. For fixed reference application (dc), a 0.01 μF capacitor is recommended. For AC reference applications, the value of C_C depends on the impedance present at pin 14. For R_{REF} values of 1.0, 2.5 and 5.0 KΩ, minimum values of C_C are 15, 37 and 75 pf respectively. Larger values of R_{14} require proportionately increased values of C_C for proper phase margin. See Graph on Reference Input Frequency Response. Low R_{REF} values enable small C_C achieving highest throughput on V_{REF}. If pin 14 is driven by a high impedance such as a transistor current source, the amplifier must be heavily compensated which will decrease overall bandwidth and slew rate. For R_{REF} = 1.0 KΩ and C_C = 15 pf, the reference amplifier slews at 4.0 mA/microsecond, enabling a transition from I_{REF} = 0 to I_{REF} = 2.0 mA in 500 nanoseconds.

3. **Interfacing Various Logic Families.** The DAC-08 design incorporates a unique logic input circuit which enables direct interface to all popular logic families and provides maximum noise immunity. A large input swing capability allows adjustable logic threshold voltage and 200 μA maximum source current on pin 1. Mimimum input logic swing and minimum logic threshold voltage is given by V_{EE} + (I_{REF} x 1.0 KΩ) + 2.5V. Logic threshold is adjusted by appropriate voltage at V_{LC}. The Interfacing Various Logic Families Diagram shows appropriate connections. Fastest settling times are obtained when V_{LC} sees a low impedance. Use 0.01 μF by-pass capacitors whenever possible.

4. **Analog Output Currents.** Both true and complemented output sink currents are provided, $I_O + \overline{I_O} = I_{FS}$. Both outputs can be used simultaneously. If one of the outputs is not required, it must be connected to ground or a point capable of sourcing I_{FS}. **Do not leave unused output pin (I_O or $\overline{I_O}$) open.** The compliance voltage is the voltage swing on output pin without affecting DAC accuracy. Positive compliance is 36V above V_{EE} and is independent of V+. Negative compliance is V_{EE} + (I_{REF} x 1 KΩ) +2.5V.

5. **Settling Time.** The DAC-08 is capable of extremely fast settling times, typically 85 nanoseconds at I_{REF} = 2.0 mA. Judicious circuit design and careful board layout must be employed to obtain full performance. The output capacitance of the DAC including the package is approximately 15 pf, therefore the output RC time constant dominates at R_L > 500 Ω.

   Settling time remains essentially constant for I_{REF} values down to 1.0 mA, with gradual increases for lower I_{REF} values. The switching transients (glitches) are very low and may be further reduced by small capacitive loads at the output. Settling time will be increased slightly.

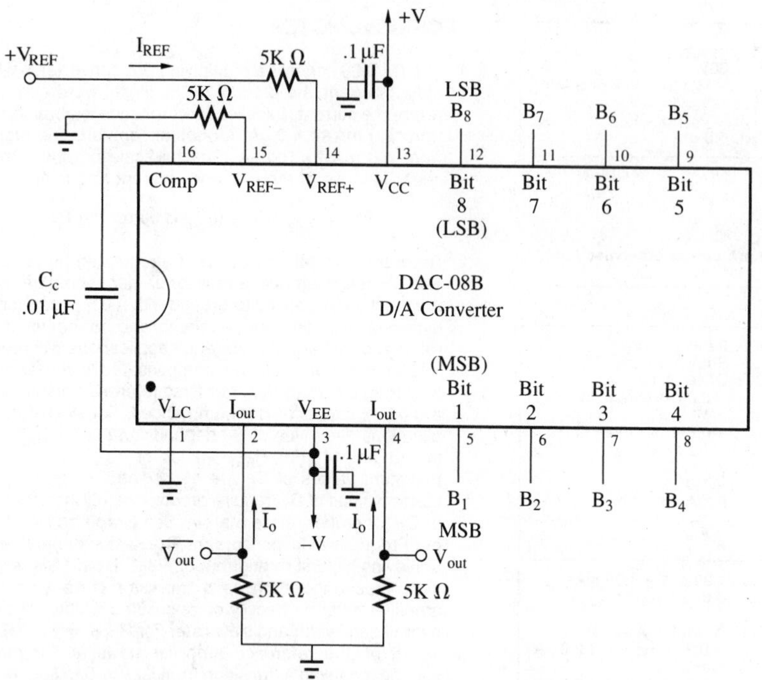

$$I_0 + \overline{I_0} = I_{FS}$$

$$I_{FS} = \frac{+V_{REF}}{R_{REF}} \times \frac{255}{256}$$

Typical Values
+V = +15 Volts
–V = –15 Volts
V_{REF+} = 10 Volts
I_{REF} = 2 mA

Basic Unipolar Negative Operation with a Fixed Positive Reference Voltage
(*Note:* Change C_c to 75 pF for a varying reference voltage.)

$$I_{out} = \frac{\text{Input Code}}{256} \times I_{REF}$$

FIGURE 16-13 DAC-08B Application Circuit: Basic Unipolar Operation

Table 16-7 DAC-08B Unipolar Operation (Refer to Figure 16-14)

Input Code	Output Current (mA)		Output Voltage (volts)	
	I_o	$\overline{I_o}$	V_o	$\overline{V_o}$
1111 1111	1.992	0.000	−9.961	0.000
1100 0000	1.500	0.429	−7.500	−2.461
1000 0000	1.000	0.992	−5.000	−4.961
0100 0000	0.500	1.492	−2.500	−7.461
0000 0000	0.000	1.992	0.000	−9.961

Note: I_{REF} = 2 mA

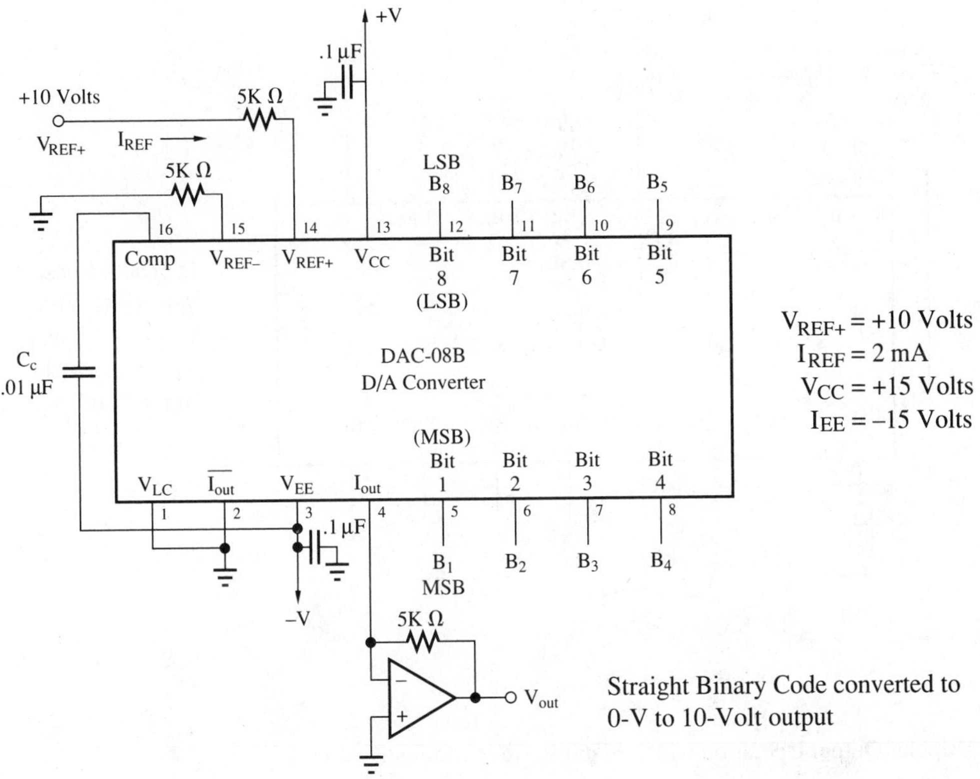

$$V_{out} = \frac{-\text{Input Code}}{256} \times I_{REF} \times 5 \times 10^3$$

FIGURE 16-14 DAC-08B Application Circuit: Straight Binary Code to +10-Volt Conversion

TABLE 16-8 DAC-08B Bipolar Operation with Offset Binary Coding (Refer to Figure 16-16)

Input Code	Output Voltage (volts)	
	V_o	$\overline{V_o}$
1111 1111	− 9.922	+10.000
1100 0000	− 5.000	+ 5.078
1000 0000	0.000	+ 0.078
0100 0000	+ 5.000	− 4.922
0000 0000	+10.000	− 9.922

Note: I_{REF} = 2 mA

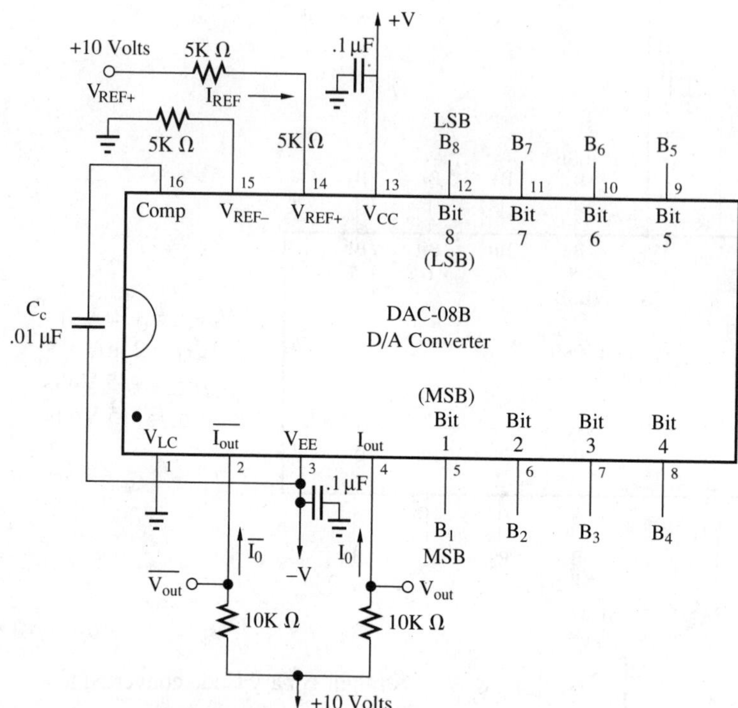

Typical Values
V_{CC} = +15 Volts
V_{EE} = –15 Volts
V_{REF+} = +10 Volts
I_{REF} = 2 mA

Basic Bipolar Output Operation with a Fixed Positive Reference Voltage

FIGURE 16-15 DAC-08B Application Circuit: Basic Bipolar Operation

■ EXAMPLE 16-10 DAC-08B Application

Problem: Use the DAC-08B in an application to produce a bipolar output voltage from an 8-bit binary input code. The circuit should operate with V_{CC} at +5 volts and V_{EE} at ground. Determine the output voltages for selected binary input codes.

Solution: For bipolar operation, design a circuit similar to the one shown in Figure 16-16. However, the reference current must be reduced to 1 mA since the supply voltage is only +5 volts. The resistor and capacitor values shown are recommended by the manufacturer for fixed (DC) reference applications. The circuit is shown in Figure 16-17. The resulting voltages will be half the magnitude of the values shown in Table 16-8 due to the 1 mA reference current.

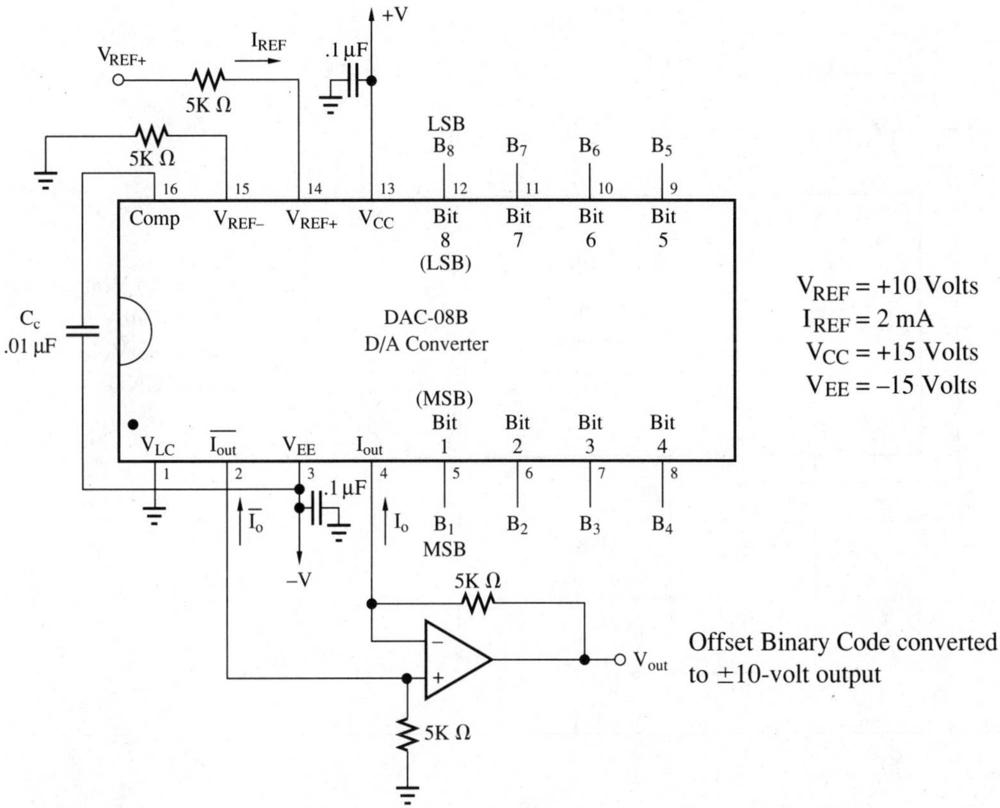

FIGURE 16-16 DAC-08B Application Circuit: Offset Binary Code to ±10-Volt Conversion

Input Code	Output Voltage (volts)	
	V_o	$\overline{V_o}$
1111 1111	−4.811	+5.000
1100 0000	−2.500	+2.539
1000 0000	0.000	+0.039
0100 0000	+2.500	−2.461
0000 0000	+5.000	−4.861

■

■ EXAMPLE 16-11 DAC-08B Application

Problem: Use the DAC-08B to scale an analog input current by an amount specified by an 8-bit binary code. The analog input current can range from 4 mA to 4 μA.

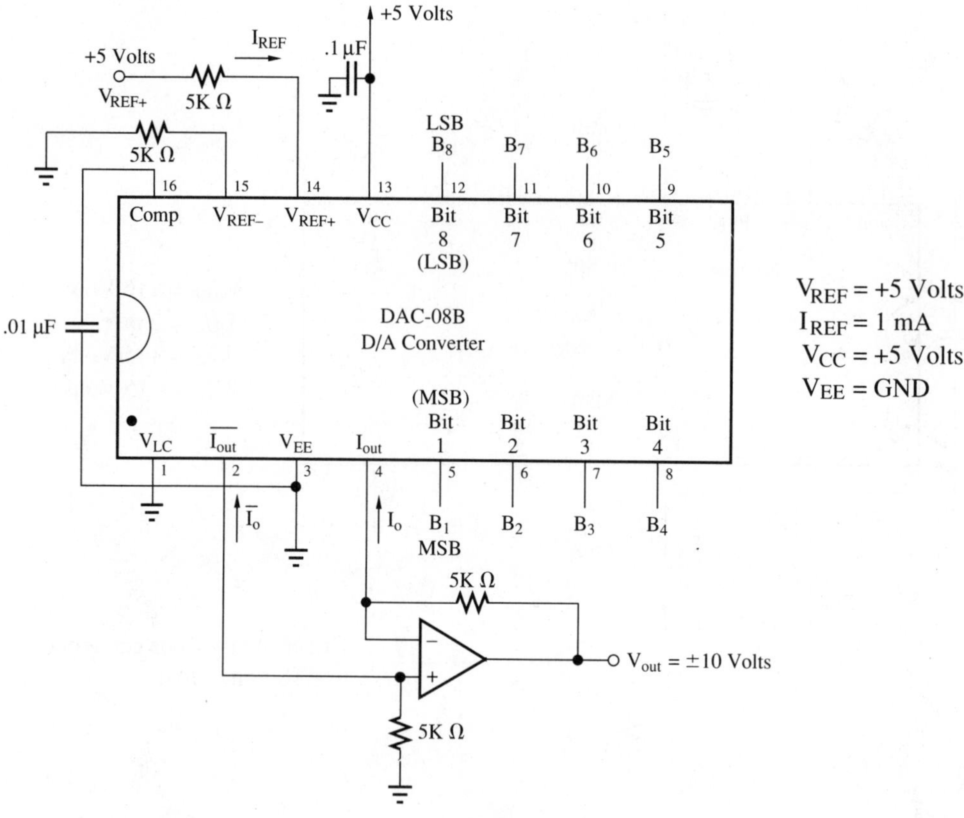

FIGURE 16-17 Example 16-10 DAC-08B Conversion Circuit with a TTL Power Supply

Solution: In this application the DAC-08B produces an output current equal to the product of a varying input current and an 8-bit binary code. The 8-bit binary code is a digital scaling factor for the current; in essence the DAC-08B is acting as a digitally programmable attenuator. The circuit for this application is shown in Figure 16-18. The values of the resistors and capacitors are recommended by the manufacturer for varying (AC) reference applications.

■

Section Self-Test

For the following problems, assume that the logic HIGH level is 3.5 volts and that a logic LOW level is .2 volt.

1. For a digital input code of $(1101)_2$, determine the output voltage from the D/A converter in Figure 16-8.

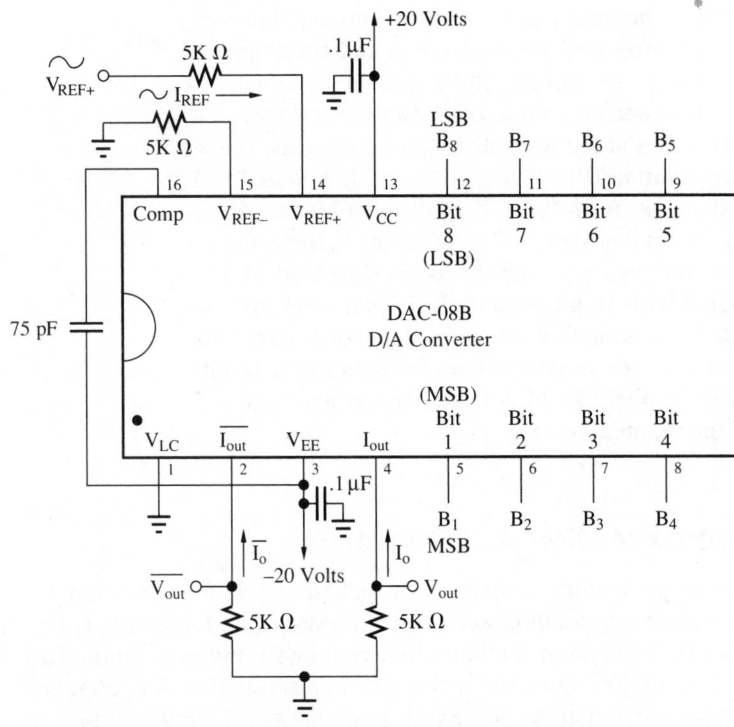

FIGURE 16-18 Example 16-10 DAC-08B AC Reference Application

2. For a digital input code of $(0D)_{16}$, determine the output voltage from the D/A converter in Figure 16-11.
3. For a digital input code of $(0D)_{16}$, determine the output voltage from the D/A converter in Figure 16-14.

ANSWERS (Not necessarily in the order of the questions)

- −5.738 volts
- +.13 volt
- −507.8 mV

16-3 ANALOG-TO-DIGITAL CONVERSION

Analog-to-digital (A/D) conversion is required to process any analog quantity in a digital system, whether that digital system is a simple logic circuit, a microprocessor, or a complex computer system. The A/D conversion techniques described in this section are used primarily in data acquisition systems and applications that do not require the precision of a

digital voice or audio system. The primary A/D conversion techniques used in these applications are successive approximation and simultaneous (or flash) A/D conversion. These techniques will be studied along with specific A/D converter ICs that perform these conversion techniques.

For very high resolution digital audio or digital voice systems, the technique of pulse code modulation (PCM) is used for both A/D and D/A conversion. The PCM systems perform the A/D conversion by sampling, quantizing, and encoding the analog signal. CD recording systems use a high-quality linear PCM technique, sampling the audio signals at 44.1 KHz and encoding the signal with 16-bit resolution. Digital voice systems use a nonlinear PCM technique, sampling the voice signal at 8 KHz and encoding it with an 8-bit word with an effective performance of a 12-bit resolution system. Information about PCM A/D and D/A converters should be obtained from the manufacturers.

16.3.1 Successive Approximation A/D Conversion

A commonly used technique in medium to high speed data acquisition applications is **successive approximation A/D conversion.** The technique is one of the fastest A/D conversion methods that requires a minimal amount of circuitry. The conversion times for successive approximation A/C converters commonly range from 10 to 300 μs on systems with 8-bit resolution to convert analog signals of frequencies up to 50 and 5 KHz, respectively.

Successive approximation is a "divide-and-conquer" technique of assigning a digital code to an analog input voltage. A number guessing game is illustrative of the successive approximation method. To guess a specific number that a person is thinking of, for instance between 1 and 12, guess 6 and ask if the value is above or below 6. Proceed by asking if the number is above or below the midpoint of the known range where the number must fall. If it is above 6, then determine if it is above the midpoint of the range from 6 to 12, or 9. If it is above 6 but below 9, the next guess should be 7.5. The guessing can continue until the desired degree of accuracy or resolution is achieved.

The successive approximation A/D converter can approximate the analog signal to form an n-bit digital code with only n steps. The **successive approximation register,** or **SAR,** repeatedly compares an analog input voltage to the midpoint of the known range where the value must fall. The SAR determines if the analog input is above or below the midpoint and sets the bits of the digital code accordingly. The system assigns the bits beginning with the MSB. The MSB is set to 1 if the analog input is greater than the midpoint voltage, or to 0 if it is less than the midpoint voltage. The SAR then moves to the next bit and sets it to 1 or 0 based on the results of comparing the analog input with the midpoint of the allowed range.

The SAR must perform one approximation for each bit in the digital code. Therefore, an n-bit digital code requires n approximations. The circuitry for the A/D converter consists of four functional blocks shown in Figure 16-19: the successive approximation register (with a control shift register), the analog comparator, a D/A converter, and a clock.

The control shift register begins the conversion process by setting the MSB of the SAR to 1 and all remaining bits to 0. The D/A resistor ladder network converts the code back to an analog value, in this case the midpoint voltage, to serve as the threshold voltage of the comparator. The analog comparator compares the analog input voltage to the midpoint voltage. If the input voltage is greater than the threshold, the MSB remains set as 1. If the input voltage is less than the midpoint, the MSB is reset to 0. The first approximation cycle is complete when the final value of the MSB is

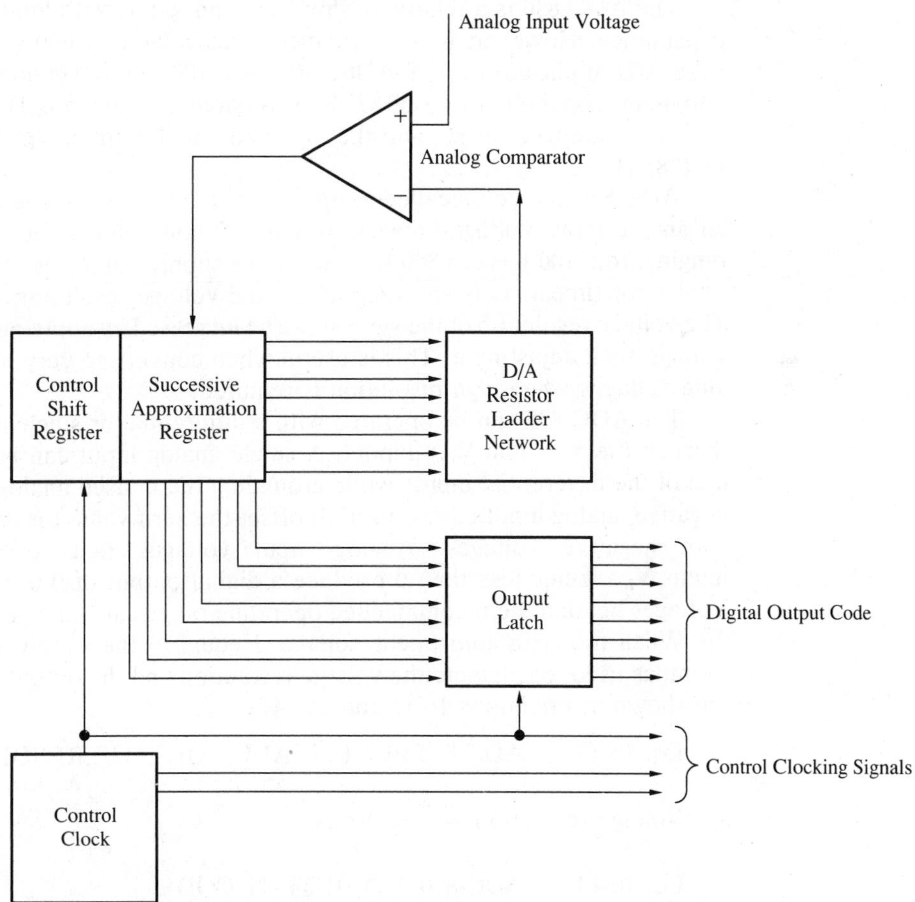

FIGURE 16-19 Successive Approximation A/D Converter

stored in the output latch. The control shift register then sets the next MSB of the SAR to 1, and the conversion process continues. The clock circuitry controls the process and generates pulse signals that indicate the beginning and end of the conversion process.

16.3.2 Successive Approximation Converter IC: The ADC-830 by DATEL

The ADC-830 is an 8-bit successive approximation A/D converter. It is a low-cost A/D converter with control inputs and output latches for easy interfacing to microprocessor systems and with differential analog inputs for ease in analog interfacing. The manufacturer's data sheet for the ADC-830 is shown in Figure 16-20. This A/D converter is a replacement for Texas Instruments' ADC 0803.

The ADC-830 is a relatively slow A/D converter, with limited sampling capabilities. However, its performance is acceptable in many general purpose A/D applications. The ADC-830 has a 100 μs conversion time and a maximum conversion rate of 8770 conversions per second. This limits the sampling rate to 8770 Hz and the maximum analog input signal frequency to 4385 Hz.

ADC-830 is recommended to operate with a supply voltage of +5 volts, an analog input voltage between 0 and +5 volts, and a clock frequency ranging from 100 KHz to 800 KHz when the supply voltage is +5 volts. The total error (linearity) is specified as $\pm\frac{1}{2}$ the voltage resolution of the LSB. The voltage resolution of the system can be increased by applying an external voltage span adjustment. This is useful when converting very low level analog voltages when high resolution is required.

The ADC-830 can be operated with a differential or single analog input through the V_{in+} and V_{in-} inputs. A single analog input can be applied to one of the differential inputs while grounding the unused analog input. The negative analog input can be used to offset the zero value for analog inputs with negative voltages. Analog input voltages that result in V_{in+} minus V_{in-} being less than 0 produce a digital output of 0 0 0 0 0 0 0 0. Voltages beyond the recommended operating range can damage the device.

When the span adjustment voltage is equal to the supply voltage, the formulas used to calculate the voltage resolution and the output digital code are shown in Equations 16-13 and 16-14.

Eq. 16-13 ADC-830 FULL SCALE VOLTAGE RESOLUTION

$$\text{Voltage resolution} = \frac{V_{CC}}{255}\ \text{Volts}$$

Eq. 16-14 ADC-830 A/D OUTPUT CODE

$$\begin{array}{c}\text{Decimal equivalent of}\\ \text{the binary output code}\end{array} = \frac{\text{input voltage}}{\text{voltage resolution}}$$

ADC-830
Microprocessor-Compatible 8-Bit A/D Converter

ATURES

- icroprocessor-compatible
- ½ LSB total adjustment error
- 0 Microseconds conversion time
- ifferential analog inputs
- atiometric operation
- ingle-supply operation

NERAL DESCRIPTION

EL's ADC-830 is a low cost, 8-bit, OS A/D converter designed to operate ctly with the 8080A control bus via e-state outputs. The device appears a memory location or I/O port to the oprocessor and thus does not require rfacing logic. The ADC-830's digital trol inputs, $\overline{CS}$, $\overline{RD}$, and $\overline{WR}$, are active and are available in all microproc- or memory systems. Upon completion conversion, an Interrupt signal is gen- ed at the converter's output. The -830 will operate as a normal A/D for -microprocessor based applications.

ng the successive approximation tech- e and a modified potentiometric stor ladder, the ADC-830 achieves an conversion in 100 microseconds with aximum total adjusted error of only LSB. No zero adjust is required. Also, differential analog input allows the user ncrease the common mode rejection offset the zero value of the analog t.

er features include single supply oper- n and an internal clock generator. The k generator requires only an external network or, it may be driven by an ex- al clock. The clock frequency range is kHz to 1.2 MHz. In addition, the -830 operates ratiometrically or with a dc, 5V dc, or, to allow the encoding of ller analog input voltage ranges, an og-span-adjusted reference.

ADC-830 is packaged in 20-pin plastic and operates over the 0°C to +70°C mercial temperature range. Power re- ement is +5V dc. With it's combina- of low cost, small size, ease of digital rfacing, and versatility of analog inter- ng, the ADC-830 is the ideal choice for ny process control and instrumentation lications.

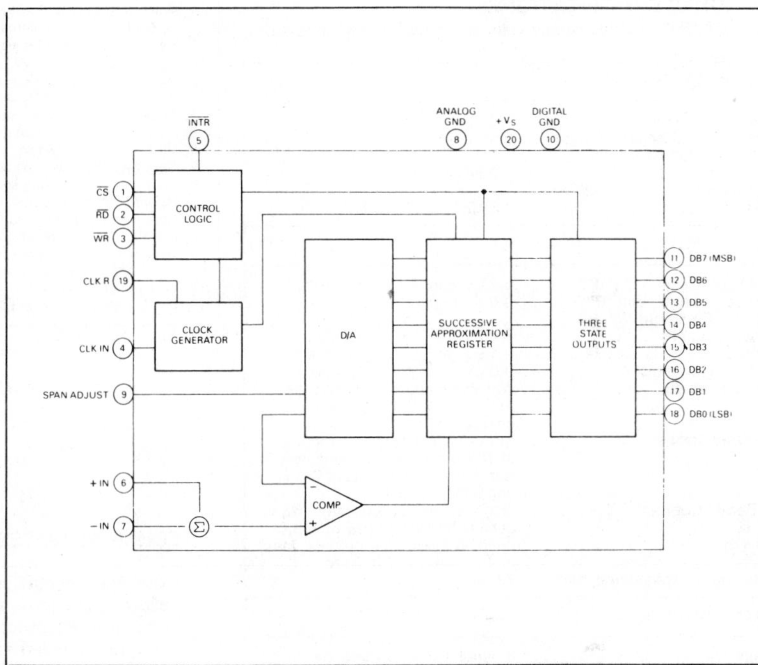

MECHANICAL DIMENSIONS INCHES (MM)

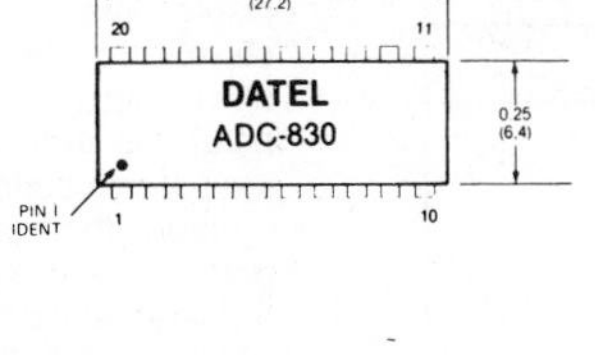

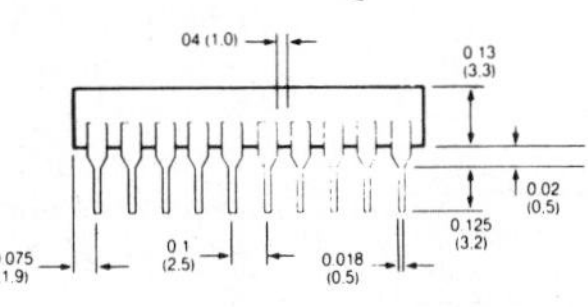

INPUT/OUTPUT CONNECTIONS

PIN	FUNCTION	PIN	FUNCTION
1	$\overline{CS}$ (CHIP SELECT)	11	DB 7 (MSB)
2	$\overline{RD}$ (READ STROBE)	12	DB 6
3	$\overline{WR}$ (WRITE STROBE)	13	DB 5
4	CLOCK IN	14	DB 4
5	$\overline{INTERRUPT}$	15	DB 3
6	+ ANALOG IN	16	DB 2
7	− ANALOG IN	17	DB 1
8	ANALOG GROUND	18	DB 0 (LSB)
9	SPAN ADJUST	19	CLOCK RETURN
10	DIGITAL GROUND	20	+V SUPPLY

FIGURE 16-20 ADC-830 Data Sheets (Reprinted by permission of DATEL, Inc.)

ABSOLUTE MAXIMUM RATINGS	
Supply Voltage	+6.5V
Digital Input Voltage	−0.3V to +18V
Analog Input Voltage	−0.3V to (V_S +0.3V)
Package Dissipation	875 mW

FUNCTIONAL SPECIFICATIONS

Typical at +25°C, +5V dc supply voltage, unless otherwise noted.

ANALOG INPUTS	
Analog Input Range[1]	−0.05V to +V_S +0.05V
Common Mode Voltage Range	Gnd to +V_S
Common Mode Rejection, dc, max.	±2.44 mV
Input Resistance, Span Adjust, min.	2.5 kΩ
DIGITAL INPUTS	
Input Logic Level, Vin ("1")[2]	+2.0V min. to +15V max.
Input Logic Level, Vin("0")[3]	+0.8V max.
Clock IN Threshold Voltage[4],	
Pos.	+2.7V min. to +3.5V max.
Neg.	+1.5V min. to +2.1V max.
Clock IN Hysteresis[4]	+0.6V min. to +2.0V max.
$\overline{CS}$ (Chip Select)	Active low state, enables the ADC-830 for read and write operations.
$\overline{WR}$ (Write Strobe)	Start conversion pulse. Input low of 100 nsec. min., in conjunction with a low on $\overline{CS}$, resets S.A.R. and shift register.
$\overline{RD}$ (Read Strobe)	Ouput enable pulse. Input low, in conjunction with a low on $\overline{CS}$, enables three-state outputs. Max. enable delay is 200 nsec.
Digital Input Capacitance, max.	7.5 pF
DIGITAL OUTPUTS	
Parallel Output Data	8 parallel lines of three-state, gateable output data.
$\overline{INT}$ (Interrupt)	Device status signal. Low when conversion complete. High when conversion in progress and when output data enabled.
Output Logic Level,	
Vout ("1")[5]	+2.4V min. at −360 μA
Vout ("0")[6]	+0.4V max. at 1.6 mA
Output Short Circuit Current,	
Gnd, min.	4.5 mA
Vs., min.	9.0 mA
Off-State Output Current	±3 μA
Digital Output Capacitance, max.	7.5 pF
PERFORMANCE	
Resolution	8 binary bits
Total Adjusted Error[7], max.	±½ LSB
Conversion Time[8]	100 μsec.
Conversion Rate[9], max.	8770 CPS
Clock Frequency Range[10]	100 kHz to 1.2 MHz
Output Enable Delay[11], max.	200 nsec.
Three-State Control Delay[12], max.	250 nsec.
Interrupt Output Delay, max.	450 nsec.
Power Supply Sensitivity[13]	±2.44 mV
POWER REQUIREMENTS	
Supply Voltage Range	+4.5V dc to +6.3V dc
Supply Current, max.	1.8 mA

PHYSICAL/ENVIRONMENTAL	
Operating Temperature Range	0°C to 70°C
Storage Temperature Range	−65°C to +150°C
Package Type	20 pin plastic DIP

FOOTNOTES

1. When −Analog IN (Pin 7) is ≥ + Analog IN (Pin 6), the digital output code will be 0000 0000. Two internal diodes are connected to each analog input which will forward conduct for input voltages one diode drop below ground or above V_S.
2. V_S = +5.25V dc, at V_S = +5V dc, high level input current = 1 μA maximum.
3. V_S = +4.75V dc, at V_S = +5V dc, low level input current = 1 μA maximum.
4. Clock IN (Pin 4) is the input of a Schmitt Trigger circuit.
5. V_S = +4.75V. For Vout ("1") = 4.5V high level output current = −10 μA.
6. V_S = +4.75V. Low level output current for the $\overline{\text{Interrupt}}$ Output is 1.0 mA.
7. Specified after full-scale adjustment.
8. With an asynchronous start pulse, up to 8 clock periods may be required before conversion starts.
9. Conversion rate in free-running mode; $\overline{INTR}$ (Pin 5) connected to $\overline{WR}$ (Pin 3), CS (Pin 1) = OV, and f_{clk} = 740 kHz.
10. V_S = +6V. Clock frequency range at V_S = +5V is 100 kHz to 800 kHz.
11. C_L = 100 pf, use bus driver for large C_L.
12. C_L = 10 pf, R_L = 10 KΩ.
13. V_S = +5V ±10% over full analog input range.

TECHNICAL NOTES

1. The digital control inputs ($\overline{CS}$, $\overline{RD}$, and $\overline{WR}$) are active low to allow easy interface to microprocessor control busses. For non-microprocessor based applications, the $\overline{CS}$ input (Pin 1) can be grounded and the standard A/D START function is obtained by an active low pulse on the $\overline{WR}$ input (Pin 3) and the Output ENABLE function is obtained by an active low pulse on the $\overline{RD}$ input (Pin 2).
2. The ADC-830 has a differential analog voltage input (Pins 6 & 7). The switching time between the inputs is 4.5 clock periods. The maximum error voltage due to this sampling delay is ΔV_e (maximum) = $(V_P)(2\pi f_{cm})(4.5/f_{clk})$ where: ΔV_e is the error voltage due to sampling delay, V_P is the peak value of the common-mode voltage, and f_{cm} is the common-mode frequency. Because of this internal switching action, displacement currents will flow at the analog inputs. These current transients occur at the leading edge of the internal clock, rapidly decay, and do not cause errors as the comparator is strobed at the end of the clock period. However, if the voltage source applied to Ana. IN + (Pin 6) exceeds V_S by more than 50 mV, a large current may flow through a parasitic diode to V_S. If these currents could exceed 1 mA, an external diode should be connected between Ana. IN + (Pin 6) and V_S (Pin 20).
3. The leads to the analog inputs should be kept as short as possible to prevent noise pickup. The source resistance for these inputs should be kept below 5 kΩ. Input bypass capacitors should not be used as they will average the transient input switching currents of the converter causing scale errors.

FIGURE 16-20 (Continued)

Four timing and control signals plus a clock input are provided to interface the ADC-830 with microprocessor systems. The on-board clock generator can be used to supply a clock frequency of $(1.1RC)^{-1}$ Hz with an externally connected resistor and capacitor. The resistor should be selected with a nominal value between 10K and 50K ohms. An external clock signal can be applied through the external clock input if greater precision is required.

The conversion time required is 100 μs. A conversion cycle requires 66 to 73 clock cycles. Equation 16-15 or 16-16 should be used to determine the clock frequency required in order to sample an incoming analog signal above the Nyquist minimum sampling rate.

Eq. 16-15 ADC-830 SAMPLING FREQUENCY

$$f_{sampling} = \frac{f_{clock}}{73} \geq 2 \times f_{max\ analog}$$

$$f_{sampling} \leq 8770 \text{ Hz}$$

(Limited by the maximum number of conversions per second in a free-running mode of operation)

Eq. 16-16 ADC-830 CLOCK FREQUENCY

$$f_{clock} \geq 73 \times 2 \times f_{max\ analog}$$

$$100 \text{ KHz} \leq f_{clock} \leq 800 \text{ KHz}$$

The $\overline{CS}$, $\overline{RD}$, $\overline{WR}$, and $\overline{INTR}$ are the timing and control signals in addition to the clock that control the A/D conversion process. These signals correspond to microprocessor control signals to allow for easy interfacing to microprocessors. The function of these timing signals is explained in detail.

1. **Conversion start, $\overline{CS}$,** is an active-LOW input required to enable the output latch and clear the control shift register to begin the conversion process.
2. **Read, $\overline{RD}$,** is an active-LOW input that works with the $\overline{CS}$ to enable the tristate output latch so that the data can be read.
3. **Write, $\overline{WR}$,** is an active-LOW input that works with the $\overline{CS}$ to clear the control shift register at the start of the conversion process. The $\overline{WR}$ input should be low at power-up to ensure that the circuit will start up under all conditions.
4. **Interrupt, $\overline{INTR}$,** is an active-LOW output signal that signals the end of the conversion process. This interrupt signal can be used by a microprocessor or other logic systems that require a signal at the completion of the A/D conversion.

The conversion process begins when the $\overline{CS}$ and $\overline{WR}$ are both LOW, followed by a LOW-to-HIGH transition on the $\overline{WR}$ input. While the con-

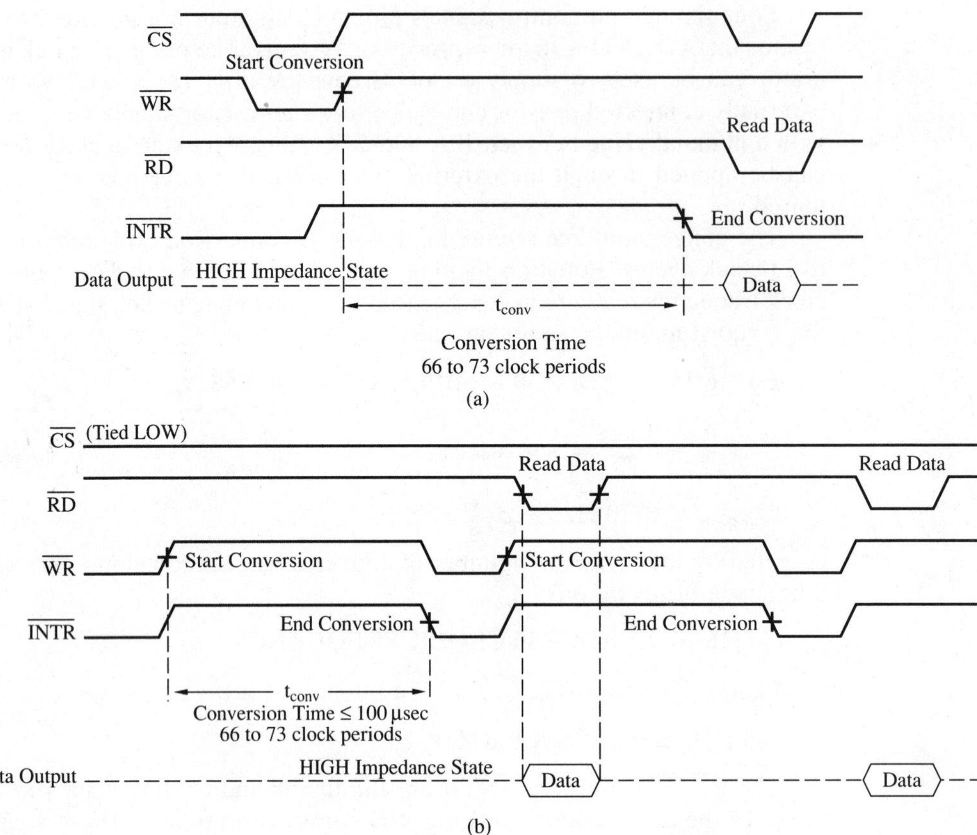

FIGURE 16-21 ADC-830 Timing Waveforms

version process is performed, the $\overline{\text{INTR}}$ output is at a logic HIGH level. The resulting digital data can be read anytime after the conversion is completed, which is signaled by the $\overline{\text{INTR}}$ output going to a logic LOW state. Data can be read when the $\overline{\text{CS}}$ and $\overline{\text{RD}}$ are at a logic LOW state. At any time that the $\overline{\text{CS}}$ or $\overline{\text{RD}}$ controls are at a logic HIGH level, the output latch is in its high impedance state and data cannot be read. The timing conditions and waveforms are shown in Figure 16-21.

Several modes of operation are possible with the ADC-830, but the simplest is the free-running mode of operation. In the free-running mode the $\overline{\text{INTR}}$ output is connected to the $\overline{\text{WR}}$ input and the $\overline{\text{CS}}$ is tied to a logic-LOW level. The $\overline{\text{WR}}$ and $\overline{\text{INTR}}$ should be forced to a logic LOW momentarily at power-up to guarantee operation. To read the data, the $\overline{\text{RD}}$ must receive a logic LOW pulse. When the $\overline{\text{RD}}$ input is a logic HIGH, the tristate output latch is in a high impedance state for bus interfacing.

Figure 16-21 shows the timing signals for both a generic and a free-running mode of operation for the ADC-830. Figure 16-22 shows an application circuit of the ADC-830 in the free-running mode of operation. Figure 16-23 shows an application circuit for interfacing the ADC-830 to a microprocessor in the free-running mode.

■ EXAMPLE 16-12 ADC-830 Application

Problem: Use the ADC-830 to design an A/D conversion circuit to convert an incoming voltage ranging from 0 to +5 volts to a digital code. The input frequency will range from DC to 4 KHz.

Solution: The ADC-830 can be configured to accept a single analog input. The minimum sampling frequency allowed must be 8 KHz in order to convert the high frequency analog signals without aliasing. Therefore, the minimum

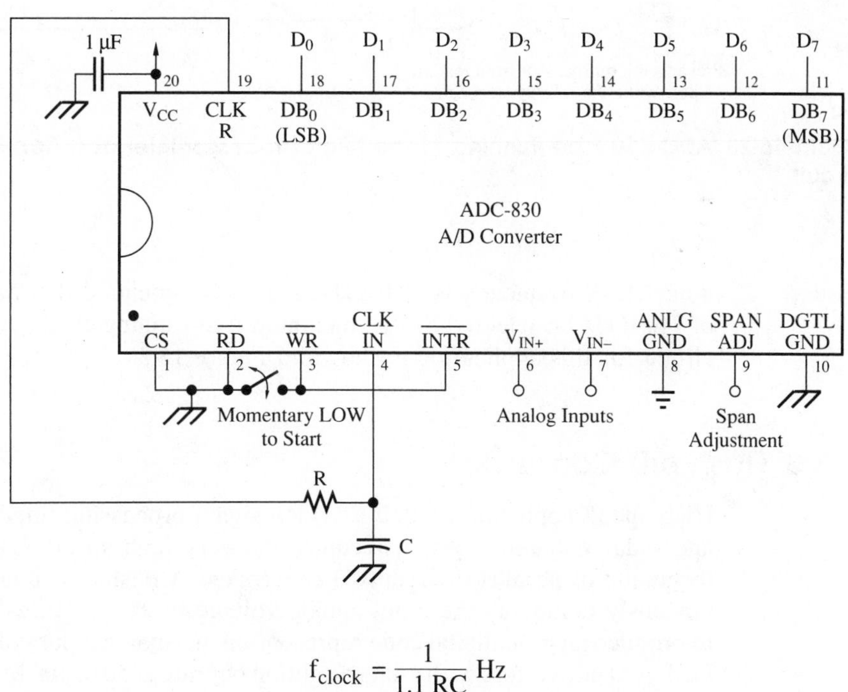

FIGURE 16-22 ADC-830 Free-Running Mode Application Circuit

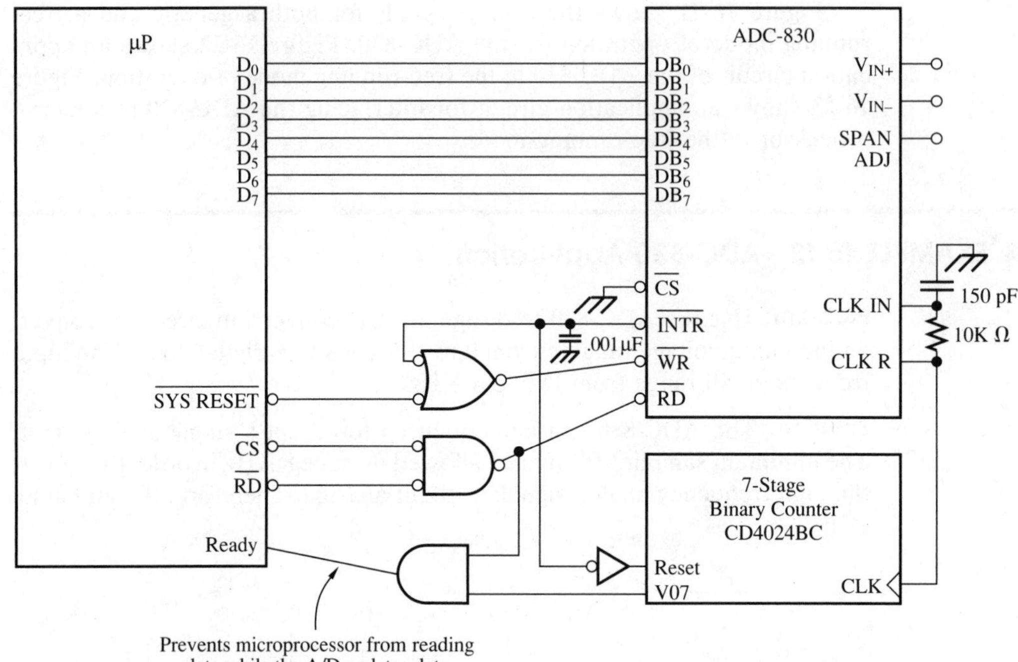

FIGURE 16-23 ADC-830 Free-Running Mode Microprocessor Interface Application Circuit

input clock frequency is 584 KHz. It is recommended that an input clock of 740 KHz be selected as the maximum free-running clock frequency. The circuit for this application is shown in Figure 16-24.

■

16.3.3 Flash A/D Conversion

High speed applications such as video signal processing, medical imaging, and radar detection systems require the very high speed A/D conversion technique of **parallel** or **flash A/D conversion.** A flash A/D converter simultaneously compares the input analog voltage to $2^n - 1$ threshold voltages to produce an n-bit digital code representing the analog input voltage. Typical flash A/D converters with 4-bit resolution operate at 50 to 100 MHz. A typical flash A/D converters with 8-bit resolution operates at 20 MHz.

The functional blocks of a flash A/D converter are shown in Figure 16-25. The circuitry consists of a precision resistor ladder network, $2^n - 1$ analog comparators, and a digital priority encoder. The resistor network establishes threshold voltages for each allowed quantization level. The an-

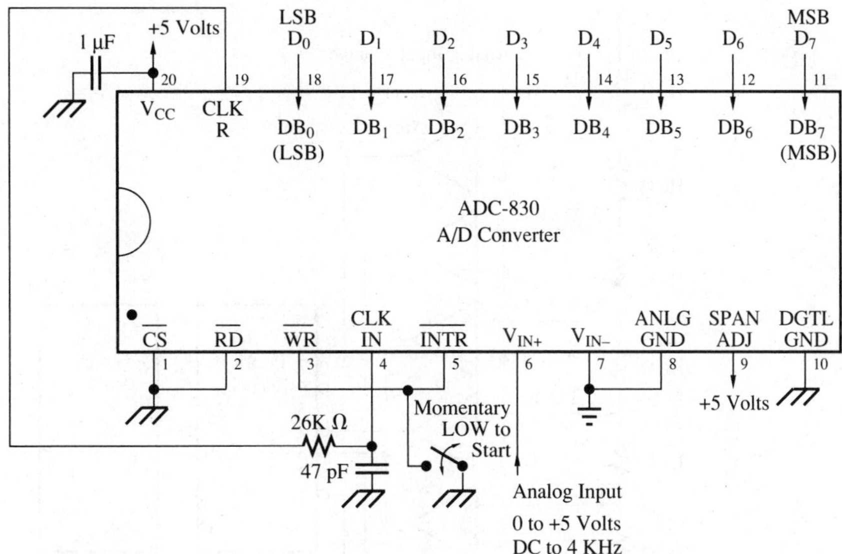

FIGURE 16-24 Example 16-12 ADC-830 Application Circuit

alog comparators indicate whether or not the input analog voltage is above or below the threshold at each level. The output of the analog comparators is input to the digital priority encoder. The priority encoder produces the final digital output code that is stored in an output latch.

A 4-bit flash A/D converter requires 15 analog comparators. An 8-bit flash A/D converter requires 255 comparators. The cost of high resolution A/D converters escalates as the circuit complexity and the number of analog converters rise by $2^n - 1$.

16.3.4 Modified Flash A/D Converter: The TLC0820 by Texas Instruments

The TLC0820 is an 8-bit A/D converter that consists of two 4-bit flash A/D converters. The flash A/D conversion operation is performed in two steps to reduce the amount of circuitry required. Since the technique does not simultaneously determine all digital outputs, it is referred to as a modified flash A/D or half-flash A/D conversion. No external clock or oscillator components are required. The data sheet for the TLC0820 is shown in Figure 16-26.

The recommended input voltage range to be converted by the TLC0820 is 0 to V_{CC}. Analog signals below −.1 volt are converted to the binary word 0 0 0 0 0 0 0 0, and analog signals above V_{CC} + .1 volt are converted to the binary word 1 1 1 1 1 1 1 1. With V_{CC} of +5 volts, the TLC0820 has

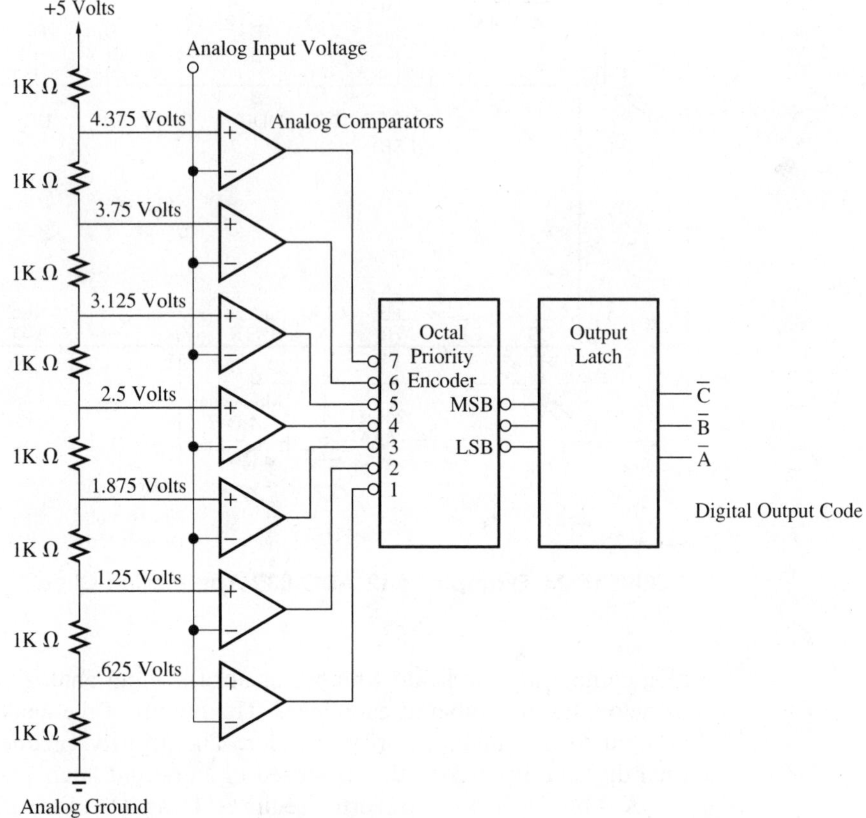

Resistor Ladder Network

FIGURE 16-25 Flash A/D Converter

an input voltage range from -0.1 to $+5.1$ volts. The equation to compute the digital output code is shown in Equation 16-17.

Eq. 16-17 TLC0820 A/D OUTPUT CODE

$$\text{Decimal equivalent of the digital code} = \frac{\text{input voltage}}{V_{CC}} \times 255$$

The TLC0820 has differential reference inputs, REF+ and REF−, which can be used to reduce the reference span and increase the sensitivity of the conversion. The voltage range over which the conversion takes place is REF+ to REF−.

The REF− input can also be used to offset zero. The voltage at REF− establishes the input level that produces a digital output of zero. Although the TLC0820 does not have a differential analog input, application of the REF− input to offset the zero provides the same flexibility as would a differential analog input.

TLC0820A, TLC0820B, ADC0820B, ADC0820C Advanced LinCMOS™ HIGH-SPEED 8-BIT ANALOG-TO-DIGITAL CONVERTERS USING MODIFIED "FLASH" TECHNIQUES

D2873, SEPTEMBER 1986–REVISED FEBRUARY 1989

- **Advanced LinCMOS™ Silicon-Gate Technology**
- **8-Bit Resolution**
- **Differential Reference Inputs**
- **Parallel Microprocessor Interface**
- **Conversion and Access Time Over Temperature Range**
  Write-Read Mode . . . 1.18 μs and 1.92 μs
  Read Mode . . . 2.5 μs Max
- **No External Clock or Oscillator Components Required**
- **On-Chip Track-and-Hold**
- **Low Power Consumption . . . 50 mW Typ**
- **Single 5-V Supply**
- **TLC0820B is Direct Replacement for National Semiconductor ADC0820B/BC and Analog Devices AD7820L/C/U; TLC0820A is Direct Replacement for National Semiconductor ADC0820C/CC and Analog Devices AD7820K/B/T**

ALL TYPES . . . DW OR N PACKAGE
TLC0820_M . . . J PACKAGE
(TOP VIEW)

Signal	Pin	Pin	Signal
ANLG IN	1	20	VCC
(LSB) D0	2	19	NC
D1	3	18	OFLW
D2	4	17	D7 (MSB)
D3	5	16	D6
WR/RDY	6	15	D5
MODE	7	14	D4
RD	8	13	CS
INT	9	12	REF +
GND	10	11	REF −

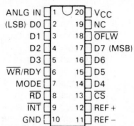

TLC0820_M . . . FK PACKAGE
TLC0820_I, TLC0820_C . . . FN PACKAGE
ADC0820_CI, ADC0820_C . . . FN PACKAGE
(TOP VIEW)

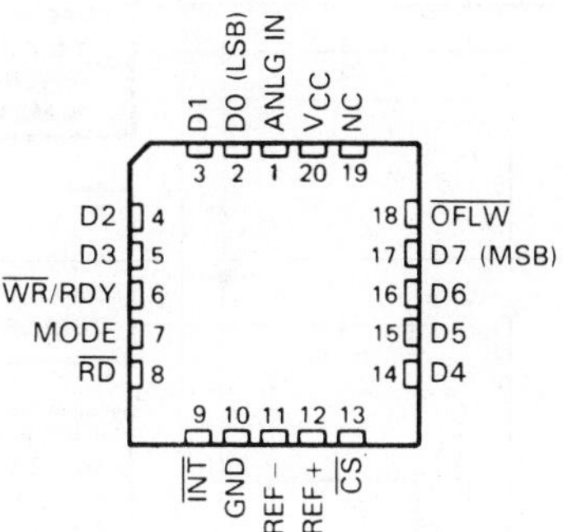

NC – No internal connection

description

The TLC0820A, TLC0820B, ADC0820B, and ADC0820C are Advanced LinCMOS™ 8-bit analog-to-digital converters each consisting of two 4-bit "flash" converters, a 4-bit digital-to-analog converter, a summing (error) amplifier, control logic, and a result latch circuit. The modified "flash" technique allows low-power integrated circuitry to complete an 8-bit conversion in 1.18 μs over temperature. The on-chip track-and-hold circuit has a 100 ns sample window and allows these devices to convert continuous analog signals having slew rates of up to 100 mV/μs without external sampling components. TTL-compatible three-state output drivers and two modes of operation allow interfacing to a variety of microprocessors. Detailed information on interfacing to most popular microprocessors is readily available from the factory.

The M-suffix devices are characterized for operation over the full military temperature range of −55 °C to 125 °C. The I-suffix devices are characterized for operation from −40 °C to 85 °C. The C-suffix devices are characterized for operation from 0 °C to 70 °C. See Available Options.

FIGURE 16-26 TLC0820 Data Sheet (Courtesy of Texas Instruments)

TLC0820A, TLC0820B, ADC0820B, ADC0820C Advanced LinCMOS™ HIGH-SPEED 8-BIT ANALOG-TO-DIGITAL CONVERTERS USING MODIFIED "FLASH" TECHNIQUES

AVAILABLE OPTIONS

SYMBOLIZATION†		OPERATING	TOTAL
DEVICE	PACKAGE SUFFIX	TEMPERATURE RANGE	UNADJUSTED ERROR
TLC0820AC	DW, FN, N	0°C to 70°C	±1 LSB
TLC0820AI	DW, FN, N	−40°C to 85°C	±1 LSB
TLC0820AM	DW, FK, J, N	−55°C to 125°C	±1 LSB
TLC0820BC	DW, FN, N	0°C to 70°C	±0.5 LSB
TLC0820BI	DW, FN, N	−40°C to 85°C	±0.5 LSB
TLC0820BM	DW, FK, J, N	−55°C to 125°C	±0.5 LSB
ADC0820BC	DW, FN, N	0°C to 70°C	±0.5 LSB
ADC0820BCI	DW, FN, N	−40°C to 85°C	±0.5 LSB
ADC0820CC	DW, FN, N	0°C to 70°C	±1 LSB
ADC0820CCI	DW, FN, N	−40°C to 85°C	±1 LSB

†In many instances, these ICs may have both TLC0820 and ADC0820 labeling on the package.

functional block diagram

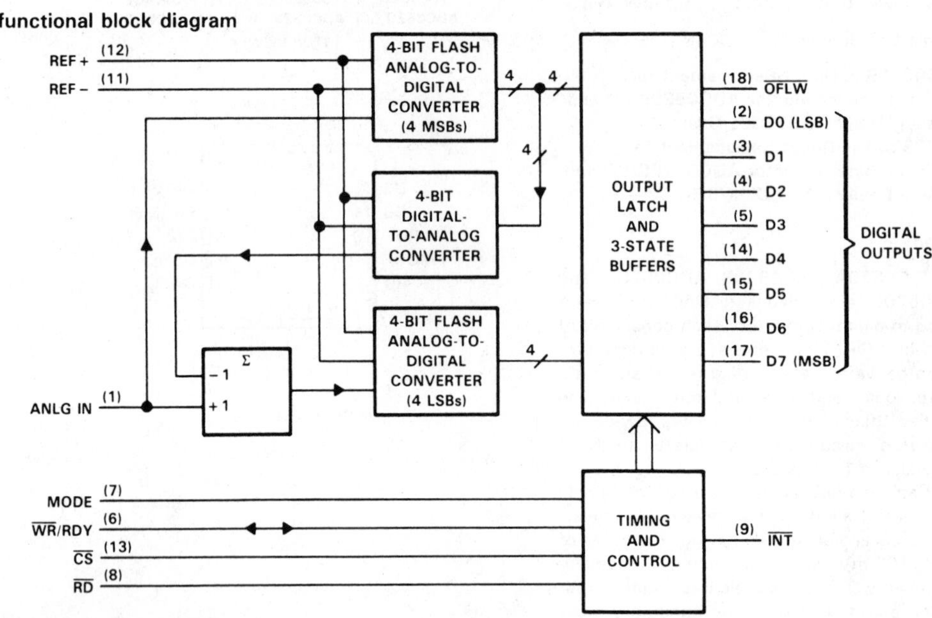

FIGURE 16-26 (Continued)

The TLC0820 has two modes of operation: read mode and write–read mode. The modes are controlled by the MODE signal and timing signals $\overline{CS}$, $\overline{WR}$/RDY, $\overline{RD}$, and $\overline{INT}$. The signals are explained in detail.

1. The **MODE** input is set to a logic LOW level for operating in the read mode and set to a logic HIGH level for operating in the read–write mode.
2. The **conversion start, $\overline{CS}$,** is an active-LOW input that is taken LOW to begin the conversion process.

3. The **write/ready, $\overline{\text{WR}}$/RDY**, functions as an input in the write–read mode and as an output in the read mode. In the write–read mode with the $\overline{\text{CS}}$ at a logic LOW level $\overline{\text{WR}}$ goes LOW to begin the conversion process. In the read mode RDY is an output that goes LOW after the falling edge of $\overline{\text{CS}}$. The RDY then goes into a high impedance state when the conversion result is strobed into the output latch. The RDY output is used to interface to a microprocessor system. The RDY output is an open-drain output that requires a pull-up resistor.
4. The **read input, $\overline{\text{RD}}$**, goes LOW to begin the conversion process in the read mode or to activate the latched outputs in the write–read mode.
5. The **interrupt output, $\overline{\text{INTR}}$**, goes LOW to indicate that the conversion result is latched in the output latches. The $\overline{\text{INTR}}$ output is reset by the rising edge of either $\overline{\text{RD}}$ or $\overline{\text{CS}}$.

The read mode is useful for microprocessors with a "wait" state to control the entire conversion operation through the read input. The microprocessor can start the conversion, wait, and read the data with a single "read" instruction.

The conversion time in the read mode is typically 1.6 μs but can extend up to 2.5 μs. The maximum delay to the next conversion is 500 ns. This establishes the maximum sampling frequency in the read mode as 333 KHz.

To operate in the read mode, the mode pin is logic LOW. When the RDY output and the $\overline{\text{CS}}$ are both logic LOW, the device is busy. Conversion begins on the negative edge of the $\overline{\text{RD}}$ pulse. The interrupt output, $\overline{\text{INTR}}$, goes LOW when the conversion is complete and the data is latched in the output latches. The $\overline{\text{INTR}}$ is reset on the rising edge of $\overline{\text{RD}}$ or $\overline{\text{CS}}$. The timing waveforms for the read mode are shown in Figure 16-27.

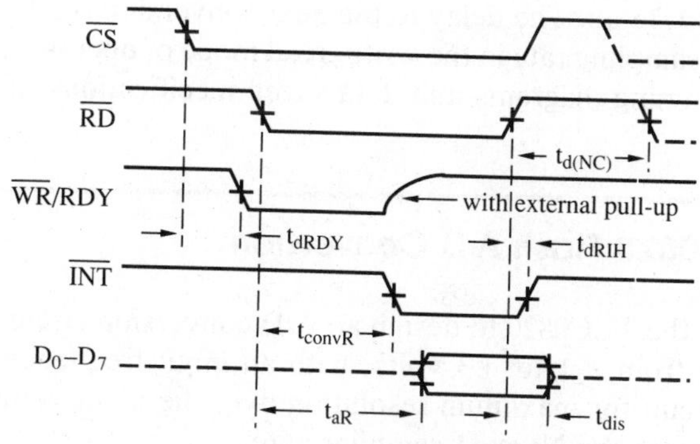

FIGURE 16-27 TLC0820 Timing Waveforms Read Mode (Courtesy of Texas Instruments)

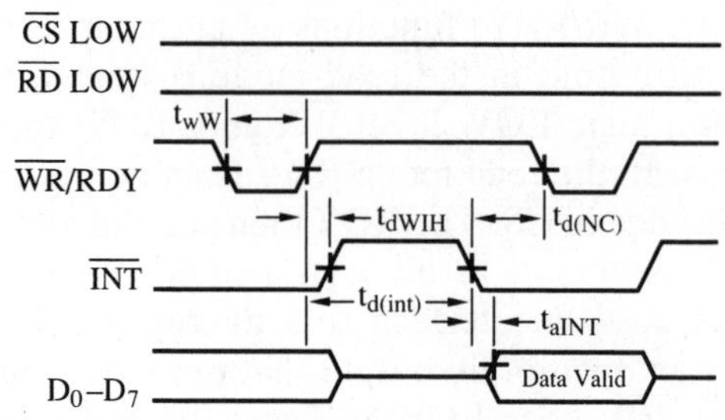

Write-Read Mode Waveforms
(Stand-Alone Operation, MODE Pin HIGH, and RD LOW)

FIGURE 16-28 TLC0820 Timing Waveforms Write–Read Mode, Stand-Alone Operation (Courtesy of Texas Instruments)

The write–read mode uses the write input to initiate the conversion and the read input is used to transfer the data to the output latch and to read it. The write–read mode can also be used to place the TLC0820 in a stand-alone operating mode.

To operate in the write–read mode, the mode pin is tied to a logic HIGH level. Stand-alone operation is performed when the $\overline{CS}$ and $\overline{RD}$ inputs are tied to a logic-LOW level. The conversion is started when the $\overline{WR}$ input goes LOW. The $\overline{INTR}$ output goes LOW when the conversion result is latched in the output latches. The timing waveforms for stand-alone operation in the write–read mode are shown in Figure 16-28. An application circuit of the TLC0820 in stand-alone operation is shown in Figure 16-29.

The pulse width of the write pulse, required to begin the conversion, is between .6 and 50 μs. The conversion begins on the rising edge of the write pulse. The conversion time in the write–read mode is typically .82 μs and at a maximum 1.35 μs. The delay to the next conversion is 500 ns. This sets the maximum sampling rate in the write–read mode of operation at 555 KHz. (Refer to the timing diagrams and data sheet specifications to verify these values.)

■ EXAMPLE 16-13 TLC0820 Flash A/D Conversion

Problem: Use the TLC0820 to design an A/D conversion circuit for an input signal ranging from +1 to +3 volts, with an input frequency of 10 KHz. Design the circuit for maximum resolution over the input voltage span and to sample at twice the Nyquist sampling rate.

Solution: The A/D converter can operate in the stand-alone mode. To obtain maximum voltage resolution, the REF+ should be +3 volts and the REF−

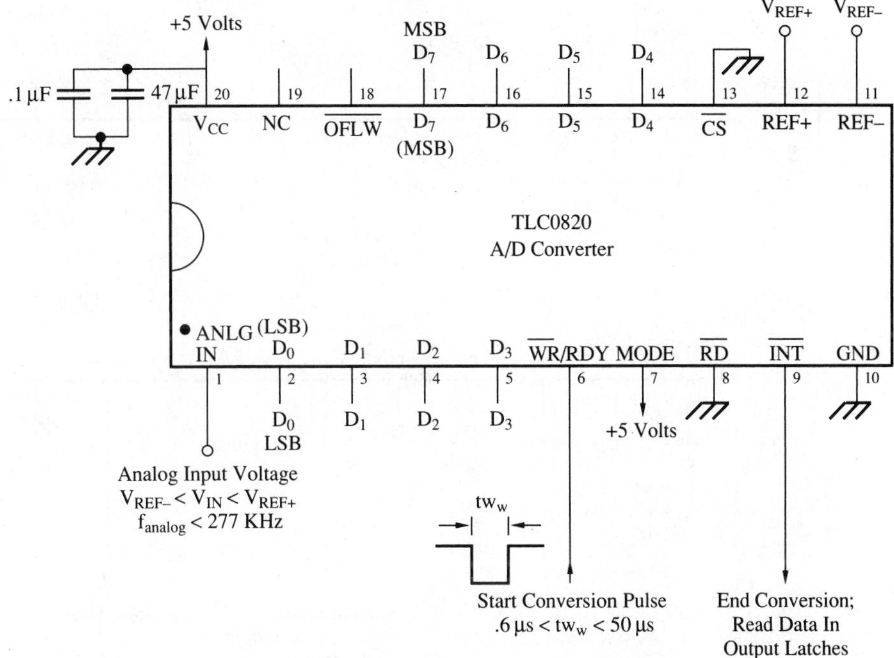

FIGURE 16-29 TLC0820 Application Circuit Write–Read Mode, Stand-Alone Operation

should be +1 volt. A precision voltage reference should be used to establish these values. If a precision voltage reference is not available, a resistor divider network will suffice. The sampling frequency is established by providing a write signal with a frequency of 40 KHz. The pulse width of the active-LOW write pulse must be at least .6 μs, which requires an active-LOW duty cycle of at least 2.4%. (See Figure 16-30.) ■

Section Self-Test

1. What is the voltage resolution of the circuit in Figure 16-30?
2. What would be the voltage resolution of the TLC0820 if the REF+ was +5 volts and the REF− was 0 volt?
3. Why is the maximum sampling rate of the ADC-830 or the TLC0820 less than the inverse of the conversion time?

ANSWERS (Not necessarily in the order of the questions)

- Additional time delays occur to extend the time period between conver-

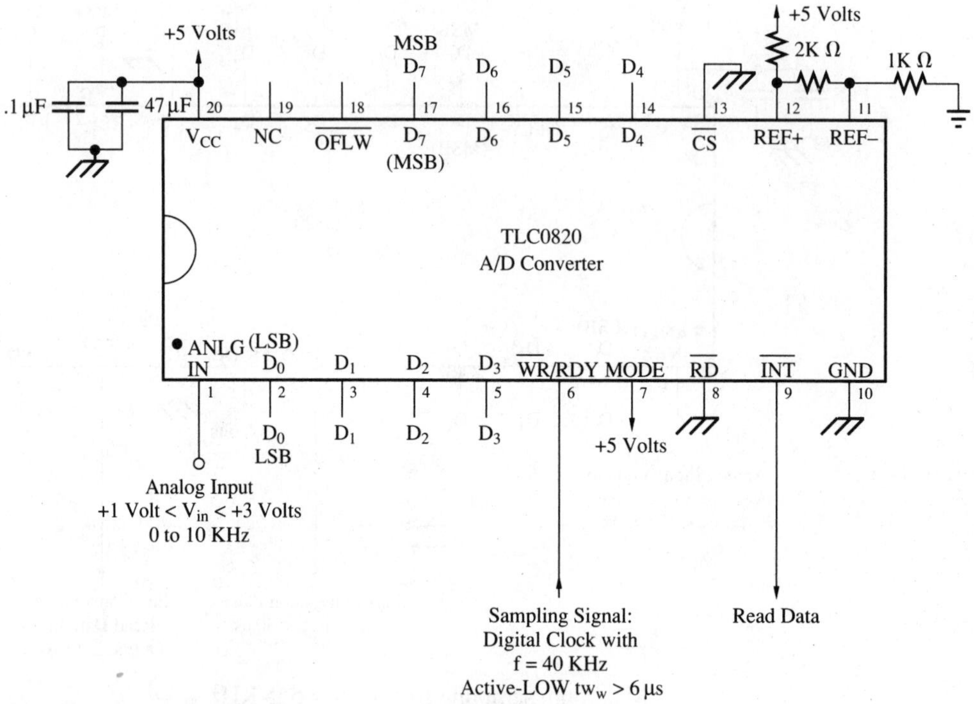

FIGURE 16-30 Example 16-13 Application Circuit

sions. Therefore, the sampling frequency is the inverse of the total delay time between conversions.

- 19.608 mV
- 7.843 mV

16-4 TROUBLESHOOTING A/D AND D/A CIRCUITS

Troubleshooting techniques for A/D and D/A circuits must include testing the operation of both the digital and analog portions of the circuit. Due to the complexity of the devices, there are numerous sources of error that result in faulty conversions. A checklist of common sources of circuit errors is listed as a starting point for troubleshooting D/A and A/D circuits.

D/A Converter Troubleshooting Checklist

1. Is a reference input required? If so, it is within the correct operating range?
2. Are the digital inputs connected to the proper circuit inputs?

3. Do the power supply connections have a bypass capacitor to ground?
4. Are all external component values appropriate as suggested by the manufacturer?
5. Are the timing and control signals tied to appropriate logic levels?
6. Is the chip enabled?
7. Are the latches enabled?
8. Is the circuit configured to operate in a "free-running" mode?
9. Is the input signal stable during the conversion period?

A/D Converter Troubleshooting Checklist

1. Is the analog input within the allowed voltage range? Be sure to check DC offset as well as peak values.
2. Is the analog input a differential or single input signal?
3. Is the analog input within the allowed frequency range?
4. Is a voltage input reference required? If so, is it within the correct operating range?
5. Do the power supply connections have a bypass capacitor to ground?
6. Were power-up procedures followed correctly?
7. Are all external component values appropriate as suggested by the manufacturer?
8. Is the sampling frequency at least twice the maximum analog input frequency?
9. Is the system clock running at an appropriate frequency to obtain the correct sampling frequency?
10. Are the timing and control signals tied to appropriate logic levels?
11. Is the chip enabled?
12. Are the latches enabled?
13. Is the circuit configured to operate in a "free-running" mode?

The examples that follow are intended to illustrate common errors often made by students when using A/D and D/A circuits.

■ EXAMPLE 16-14 Random Coding D/A Converter: AD557

Problem: A D/A converter is built to perform according to the operation shown in Table 16-6. However, when the circuit is built, the output performs according to Table 16-9, with the same results graphed in Figure 16-31. The AD557 is connected as shown in Figure 16-32. The student who built the circuit believes it is a faulty device and is ready to purchase another one.

TABLE 16-9 Random Output DAC Operation

Input Code			Measured Output Voltage
Hex	Binary HGFE DCBA	Decimal	V_{out} (volts)
00	0 0 0 0 0 0 0 0	0	0.0
08	0 0 0 0 1 0 0 0	8	.16
5F	0 1 0 1 1 1 1 1	95	2.50
C7	1 1 0 0 0 1 1 1	199	2.27
D9	1 1 0 1 1 0 0 1	217	1.55
FF	1 1 1 1 1 1 1 1	255	2.55

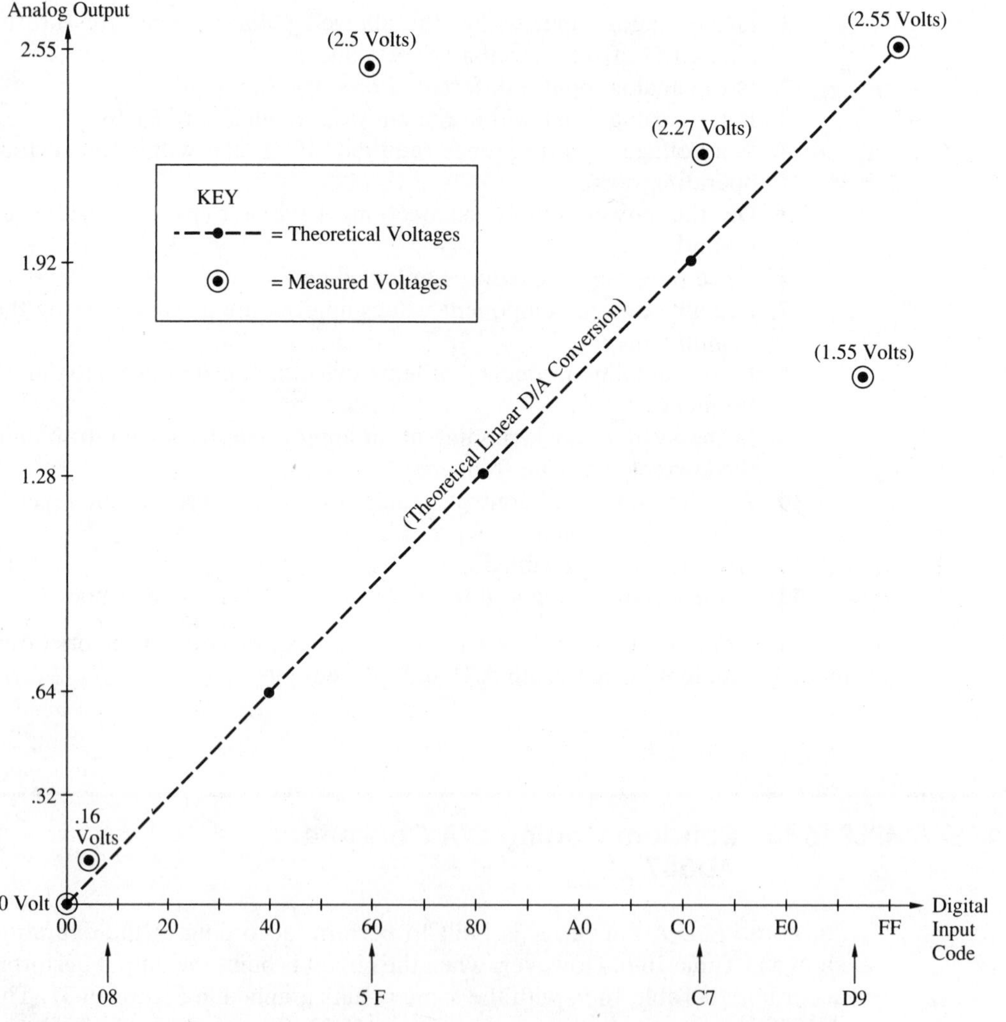

FIGURE 16-31 Example 16-14 Random Coding D/A Converter Operational Measurements

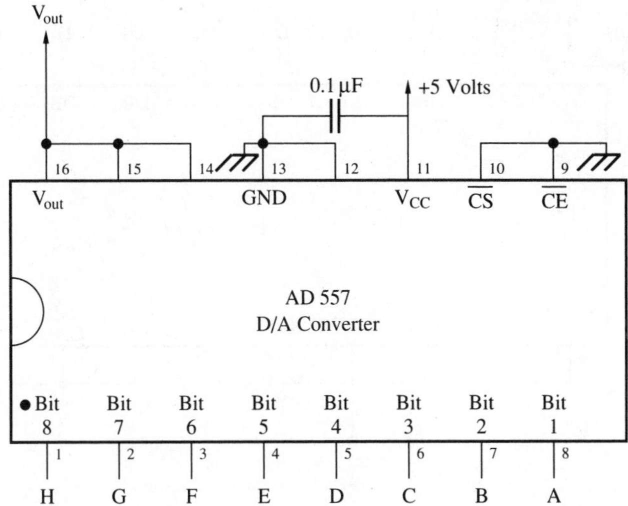

FIGURE 16-32 Example 16-14 Random Coding D/A Converter

Before your fellow student spends his money on an IC, determine the wiring error that has caused the circuit to behave in this way.

Solution: Notice that the maximum and minimum input values are correct, but nothing in between seems to work. Your first suspicion is correct: The binary input code is connected to the chip inputs backward. The correct circuit is shown in Figure 16-11. ■

■ EXAMPLE 16-15 Zero-Out A/D Converter

Problem: The ADC-830 is connected by a student to perform an A/D conversion operation on a slowly changing input voltage. The input voltage is only a 200 Hz signal. The circuit only puts out logic LOW values from the digital outputs. The circuit that is built is shown in Figure 16-33. Determine the cause of the problem.

Solution: Several problems arise with this circuit. To verify the analog input, you display the signal on a oscilloscope, and find that it is a $4V_{PP}$ signal with a -3 volt DC offset. Therefore, the signal falls between the values of -1 to -5 volts. This is one reason for the constant 0 0 0 0 0 0 0 0 reading in the output registers. Another problem with the circuit is that the span adjust input is tied to ground. The span adjust input should be tied to V_{CC}. Finally, the input clock frequency is set by the RC components as 193 Hz. The minimum clock frequency as specified in the data sheets is 100 KHz. The

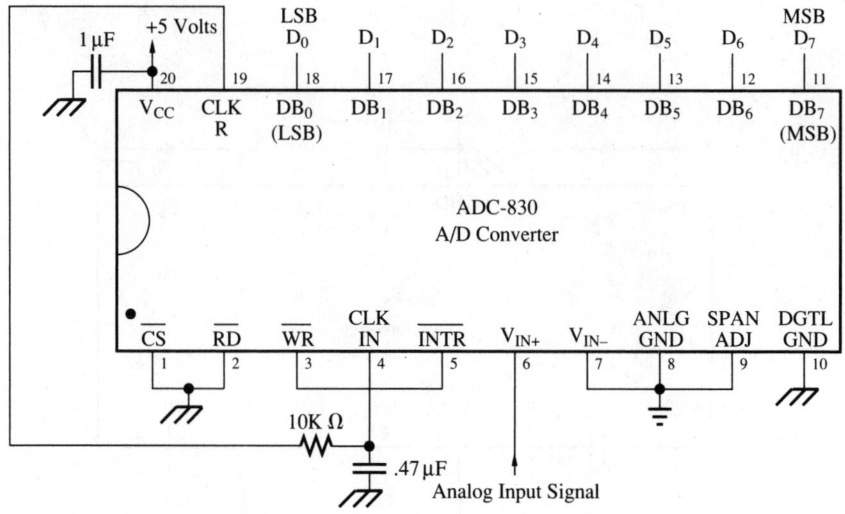

FIGURE 16-33 Example 16-15 Zero-Out A/D Converter

circuit problems are corrected by applying the analog input to the V_{IN-} input, grounding the V_{IN+} input, selecting R and C values for an input clock of nearly 200 KHz, and connecting the span adjust input to V_{CC}. The corrected circuit is shown in Figure 16-34.

■

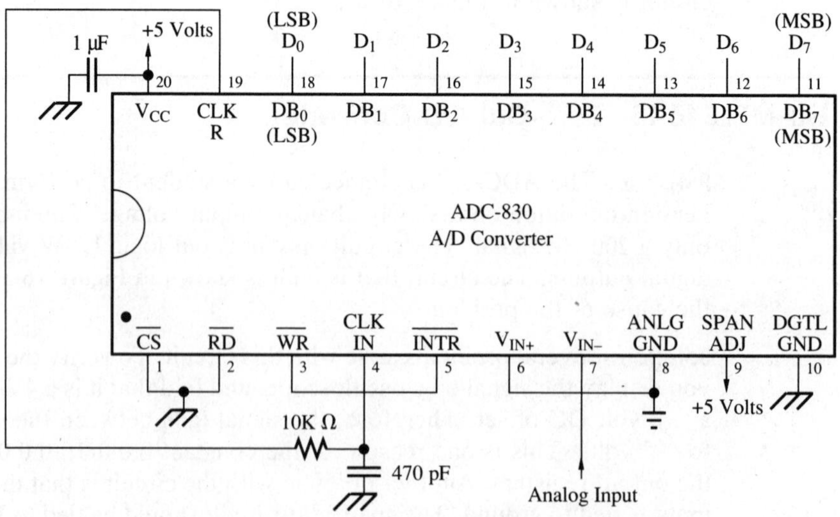

FIGURE 16-34 Example 16-15 Zero-Out A/D Converter Corrected Circuit

Section Self-Test

Determine if the following statements are true or false:

1. Although the circuit is properly constructed, the A/D or D/A converter may still not function due to poor circuit board design techniques.
2. An A/D circuit can convert a digital word to an analog quantity by inputting digital values.
3. A D/A circuit can convert an analog value to a digital word by inputting an analog value.
4. Noise can be induced in the circuit if the analog and digital grounds are connected.

ANSWERS (Not necessarily in the order of the questions)

• True • False • False • True

SUMMARY

The selection and use of appropriate data acquisition A/D and D/A converters is dependent on the application constraints for resolution, speed, and cost. The most commonly used D/A and A/D techniques of resistor ladder networks, successive approximation, and parallel conversion were discussed. The successive approximation A/D conversion is adequate for moderate to high speed data acquisition applications that do not require a high degree of resolution. Flash A/D conversion is used for very high speed applications.

The following topics were covered throughout the chapter as part of the analysis, application, and design of A/D and D/A circuits.

ANALYSIS

The performance characteristics of A/D and D/A converters were analyzed to determine the resolution, speed, accuracy, dynamic response, and sampling rate of many A/D and D/A converters. Those circuits analyzed in detail included resistor ladder network D/A converters, multiplying D/A converters, successive approximation A/D converters, and flash A/D converters. The specific ICs used in applications throughout the text included the AD557 D/A converter, the DAC-08B multiplying D/A converter, the ADC-830 successive approximation A/D converter, and the TLC0820 modified flash A/D converter.

APPLICATION

Selection criteria for A/D and D/A converters were examined to select the appropriate circuit for a given application. Application examples using the AD557, the DAC-08B, the ADC-830, and the TLC0820 were examined in detail. The application constraints of each circuit were studied, such as the maximum sampling rate or voltage ranges allowed.

The application examples in this chapter showed that the AD557 D/A converter for general purpose applications is very easy to use. The DAC-08B is a multiplying D/A converter that can be used in fixed as well as varying reference applications. The AD-830 is an easy-to-use A/D converter that has control inputs designed to simplify microprocessor interfacing applications. The TLC0820 is a modified flash A/D converter that can be used in moderately high speed A/D applications.

DESIGN

System design criteria were studied to design A/D and D/A circuits to meet application performance requirements. Circuit construction criteria were studied to determine the appropriate layout of each A/D and D/A circuit. The circuit construction was critical to ensure operation according to manufacturers' specifications. Special attention had to be given to eliminate noise induced by digital signals into analog inputs in A/D converter designs.

Specific D/A interface circuits were designed using the AD557, DAC-08B, ADC-830, and the TLC0820 to meet application and performance specifications.

TROUBLESHOOTING

Troubleshooting techniques for D/A and A/D circuits must examine both digital and analog signals to determine the source of error. Check lists were provided to aid in the troubleshooting of these complex devices.

Troubleshooting examples focused on examining operational data to decipher the cause of faulty circuit operation. Once the cause of the error is located, the circuit is corrected to work properly.

The circuits used in the examples produced digital codes in a parallel format. A/D converters also exist that produce the digital codes in a serial format and that can multiplex several analog inputs at one A/D converter. The serial A/D converters are required for data transmission applications when parallel techniques are not practical.

For additional information on A/D and D/A converters and other data acquisition devices, refer to manufacturers data books published by Texas Instruments, DATEL, Signetics, Analog Devices, National Semiconductor, and others. An in-depth reference is the 700-page book, *Analog-Digital Conversion Handbook*, published by Prentice-Hall, Inc., Englewood Cliffs, NJ.

PROBLEMS

16-1 Fundamentals of Digital and Analog Conversion—Analysis Problems

*1. How many quantization levels are defined in an A/D system with a 12-bit resolution?

2. What is the resolution of a commercial quality digital voice system with 256 quantization levels?

*3. What is the voltage resolution of a 16-bit CD system with an allowable input voltage range of 2 volts?

4. What is the voltage resolution of an 8-bit data acquisition A/D system with an allowable input voltage range of 2 volts?

5. Compare the percent resolution of the 16-bit CD A/D converter with that of the 8-bit data acquisition A/D converter.

16-2 Digital-to-Analog Conversion—Analysis Problems

*6. Refer to the data sheet of the AD557 to determine the following:
   a. resolution
   b. settling time
   c. dynamic response
   d. power dissipation

7. Refer to the data sheet of the DAC-08B to determine the following:
   a. resolution
   b. settling time
   c. dynamic response
   d. power dissipation

16-2 Digital-to-Analog Conversion—Application and Design Problems

8. Use the AD557 in a D/A conversion application where the output from an 8-bit binary counter is converted to an analog voltage only on the falling edge of the system clock.

9. Use the AD557 to design a D/A converter to convert an 8-bit binary input to an analog output current.

10. Use the AD557 to design a D/A converter to convert an 8-bit binary input to an analog output voltage.

11. Use the DAC-08B to design an D/A converter to convert an 8-bit binary input to an analog output current.

12. Use the DAC-08B to design an D/A converter to convert an 8-bit binary input to an analog output voltage.

* *See* Answers to Selected Problems.

*13. Use the DAC-08B to design a D/A converter that scales an input analog current ranging from 10 μA to 3 mA by an 8-bit digital word.

16-3 Analog-to-Digital Conversion—Analysis Problems

*14. Refer to the data sheet of the ADC-830 to determine the following:
   a. resolution
   b. maximum conversion time
   c. free-running conversion rate
   d. dynamic response
   e. minimum input clock frequency
   f. maximum input clock frequency
   g. minimum clock pulse width
   h. maximum clock pulse width
   i. power dissipation.

15. Refer to the data sheet of the TLC0820 to determine the following:
   a. resolution
   b. maximum conversion time in the read mode
   c. maximum conversion time in the write–read mode
   d. maximum sampling rate in the read mode
   e. maximum sampling rate in the write–read mode
   f. dynamic response
   g. minimum write pulse width to begin conversion in the write–read mode
   h. maximum write pulse width to begin conversion in the write–read mode
   i. power dissipation

16-3 Analog-to-Digital Conversion—Application and Design Problems

*16. Use the ADC-830 to design an A/D converter to convert the analog input voltage of 1 KHz to an 8-bit digital word.

17. Use the ADC-830 to design an A/D converter to convert a 2 KHz analog input current to an 8-bit digital word.

18. Use the ADC-830 to design an A/D converter to convert a 3 KHz analog input voltage ranging from +1 to +4 volts to an 8-bit digital word. Design the converter to produce the maximum resolution.

19. Use the ADC-830 to design an A/D converter to convert a 2 KHz analog input voltage ranging from −1 to −4 volts to an 8-bit digital word. Design the converter to produce the maximum resolution.

20. Use the TLC0820 to design an A/D converter to convert an analog input voltage of 100 KHz to an 8-bit digital word.

21. Use the TLC0820 to design an A/D converter to convert a 25 KHz analog input current to an 8-bit digital word.

22. Use the TLC0820 to design an A/D converter to convert a 30 KHz analog input voltage ranging from +1 to +4 volts to an 8-bit digital word. Design the converter to produce the maximum resolution.

23. Use the TLC0820 to design an A/D converter to convert a 150 KHz analog input voltage ranging from −1 to −4 volts to an 8-bit digital word. Design the converter to produce the maximum resolution.

16-4 Troubleshooting D/A and A/D Circuits—Analysis Problems

24. Determine the output of the AD557 when the chip select or chip enable inputs are left floating.

25. Explain what happens if one of the I_o outputs on the DAC-08B is left unconnected.

26. Determine the output of the ADC-830 if the analog input exceeds the reference voltage.

27. When the ADC-830 is connected in a free-running mode, why is it recommended that the write input be taken to a logic LOW level momentarily as part of the power-up procedure?

28. An analog input signal vs. time is shown in Figure 16-35. Determine the output from the A/D converter if the sampling rate is 1 KHz. Determine the sampling period and state the times each sample is taken. Assume that the first sample is taken at t = 0.

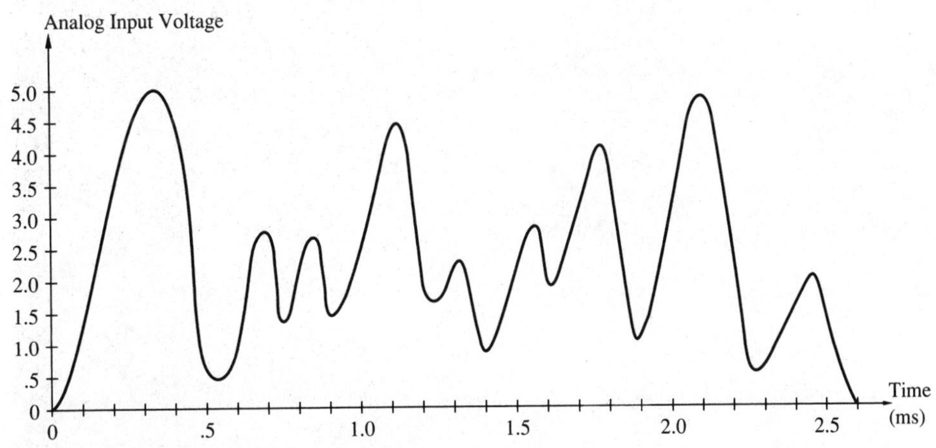

FIGURE 16-35 Analog Voltage Versus Time

29. Repeat Problem 28 with a sampling frequency of 5000 samples per second.

30. Repeat Problem 28 with the maximum sampling frequency possible for the ADC-830.

31. Repeat Problem 28 with the maximum sampling frequency possible for the TLC0820.

32. Determine the output from the circuit in Figure 16-11 if the input word, HGFE DCBA, were connected to the following inputs:

INPUT BIT	IC INPUT
H	Bit 5 (pin 4)
G	Bit 6 (pin 3)
F	Bit 7 (pin 2)
E	Bit 8 (pin 1)
D	Bit 1 (pin 8)
C	Bit 2 (pin 7)
B	Bit 3 (pin 6)
A	Bit 4 (pin 5)

Part 8

LOGIC SYSTEM DESIGN

Chapter 17

Digital Logic Design Projects

Upon completing and mastering the material in this chapter, you should be able to apply your digital skills to design projects as they relate to the areas of analysis, application, and design:

ANALYSIS

1. Learn how to document a project properly.
2. Learn how to formulate a project proposal.
3. Learn how to create a development plan.
4. Learn how to plan for testing a project.
5. Understand the importance of user/operator documentation.

APPLICATION AND DESIGN

6. Learn how to develop a functional block diagram.
7. Determine performance specifications.
8. Develop input and output specifications.
9. Understand the importance of cost analysis.
10. Learn how to develop schedules and timetables.

Digital logic design projects are an exciting and rewarding endeavor for students who have acquired a fundamental knowledge of digital logic circuits. Throughout this textbook combinational logic, sequential logic, programmable logic, memory devices, interface components, and A/D conversion devices have been studied in terms of analyzing and applying the circuit operation to digital system design requirements. This study should equip students with a solid knowledge in digital logic components so that they can successfully design and build a digital logic system.

Careful planning, investigation, analysis, design, testing, and attention to detail are required to complete a fully operational, economical, and efficient digital system. Chapter 17 explores the logic system design from project specification, planning, development, implementation, and testing. The principles and techniques described apply to small individual projects, team projects, industry application and development projects, or multimillion dollar government contract projects.

17-1 PROJECT DOCUMENTATION

It is important to document all project work from the initial design concept through to project completion. This is true in all professional fields, but often takes on additional relevance to engineers and technologists since over the course of a multiyear project frequently several different groups and people may become involved.

An engineering notebook with both ruled and graph paper is used to keep engineering records. A computer can also be used to record information about the project. Several different types of software are available to aid in the documentation and planning of projects. It is important to keep backup copies of personal computer information to prevent the loss of information due to disk failure.

Project documentation is used to track the history and evolution of a project. It should list all business and consulting contacts with addresses and phone numbers and any reference material that is used when developing the design. The documentation must contain all circuit designs, including rough draft sketches, test data, and analysis of the data to meet performance specifications. The documentation provides a thorough record of the work and can be used as evidence of the work for legal action, such as obtaining a patent, defending a patent infringement dispute, or as part of a negligence lawsuit if damage or injury is caused by the final product. More commonly, an engineering notebook is often useful in documenting your work and accomplishments for periodic performance reviews with management.

17-2 PROJECT SCOPE

Before beginning a project, one needs to estimate the resources necessary to initiate and complete the project. This is especially important in industry, where manpower and capital resources must be projected before any work on the project begins.

The written resource estimate, including project rationale, goals, schedule, dependencies, and funding, form a **project proposal.** The proposal should have enough information for making a business decision as to the financial and technical soundness of the proposal.

On a smaller scale, such as a student project, the proposal should focus less on the financial and more on the technical aspects of the project. This can help determine if the student has the expertise to complete the project or what additional technical resources the student may need. These resources may include library research on the project or consulting with other students, faculty, or industry experts.

17.2.1 Development Plan

Once a project is approved, the next step is to create a **development plan**—a document that includes the project specification, performance criteria, a project timetable, and test and packaging requirements. The development plan is an expansion of the technical information in the project proposal. Think of a development plan as a road map for the project, from beginning to end. Detailed descriptions of the important parts of the development plan follow.

17-3 PROJECT SPECIFICATION

The operational specification of the final digital system is the most important requirement for successful logic system design. The project must be described in excruciating detail, as if it were fully operational and available as an off-the-shelf project. The project specification must include a functional block diagram description of the system, the performance specifications, the input and output signal requirements, and the detailed operation of every hardware and software function in the system.

17.3.1 Functional Block Diagram

The **operation** of the digital system is specified as a **functional block diagram.** A functional block diagram description of the logic system is an appropriate starting point in the design process. Whether the end product is a satellite or a clock radio, it is important to define the operation of each functioning block in the system.

An initial block diagram should be a high level or general description of the logic system. Next, an intermediate block diagram should define the major functional blocks that make up the logic system. A final block diagram should divide each major function into subsystems and components. It can be used directly to produce circuit schematics for each subsystem.

As part of the documentation necessary to support the functional block diagram, each subsystem should be defined in terms of the hardware and software operations required. Figure 17-1 illustrates the functional block hierarchy.

In addition to specifying the function of the blocks, the methods used to test each block to verify its operation must be defined and documented. If a block cannot be tested, then it cannot be verified as working.

Cost estimates should be obtained for each functional block as well as time estimates for completing the design, building, and testing of each block. The cost and time analysis information is important in tracking and preventing job overruns or time schedule slips.

17.3.2 Performance Specifications

A very critical description of the function of the logic system is the **performance specification.** Large business and government contract disputes are battled by the designers to define and ensure acceptable performance of the functional blocks that comprise the total system.

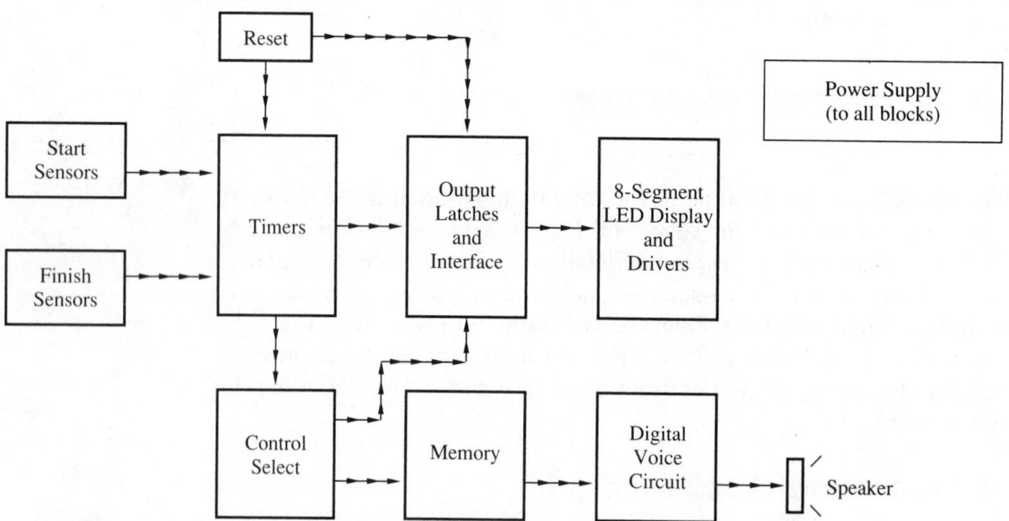

FIGURE 17-1 Functional Block Diagram Hierarchy

The **performance** of a system complements the operation of the system. Performance specifications define the electrical and procedural requirements of each operational block in the system. The performance is specified in terms of the final outcome of the block as well as the required electrical characteristics and operating conditions during operation. The performance specification must also be linked to the testing procedures planned for each functional block in the system.

Technical performance parameters include output voltages, output currents, access times, delay times, switching characteristics, the sampling rate, the input data capacity, the processing time, the maximum data rate, the operating data rate, the margin of acceptable error, power supply requirements, and the temperature operating range.

Procedural performance parameters describe the actions or operation of the system in quantitative terms, such as data transmission, data retrieval, or control operations.

17.3.3 Input and Output Requirements

The input and output requirements at each functional block must be thoroughly defined also in terms of procedural operation and electrical characteristics. Many digital systems are developed as modular subsystems that will later be connected together to form the total operational system. The definition and adherence to the input and output requirements at each functional block is critical for total system operation.

17-4 COST ANALYSIS

There is never a lack of ideas for projects in most engineering departments. However, there is never enough funding for all possible ideas. Therefore, an important part of any project is to develop a cost analysis. For student projects, the focus is on the total cost of the parts. For business engineering projects, additional factors such as manpower cost, facilities cost, and return on investment are also considered.

A cost analysis must be developed in the initial stages of the project design. Initial cost estimates for each block diagram and for the overall system packaging are important for planning the project. The project concept may be modified if functional blocks reach unreasonable cost levels.

Cost estimates should include development, testing, and construction costs associated with the project, as well as overhead charges for services provided by support groups or equipment suppliers. Accurate cost estimates are vital for budgeting purposes, for obtaining approval for the project, and for obtaining the necessary support to launch the project.

The final costs can be determined as the project progresses, but they should remain within a very close margin of the original cost estimates.

17-5 PROJECT TIMETABLE

Time is money. The project timetable must accurately plan and schedule all project operations, their sequence of completion, and their impact on all other steps in the project. The two questions that together comprise "the bottom line" of projects are:

- **Is the project on schedule?**
- **Is the project under cost?**

(The assumption is made that the project will be operational to performance specifications.)

A **time action plan** is used to track the progress of the individual steps within the total project. Each step should be indicated by an estimated start date and stop date. The actual start and stop dates are then added to the time action plan as they occur to monitor the project development.

17-6 LOGIC SELECTION

Logic selection involves selecting the design approach, the type of logic family, and the type of components for a given project.

Logic design approaches include discrete IC logic, PLD logic, and microprocessor-based logic. Logic families include TTL, CMOS, and ECL. Within each logic family, additional subfamilies can be selected to optimize a design for speed, power, or other operating characteristics.

These selections should be based on the complexity of the design, resources available, performance specifications, cost, and availability of components. Any interfacing between logic families should be noted so that the appropriate steps can be taken to ensure proper operation at the interface point. Power levels, voltage and current compatibility, fan-out, noise margins, timing requirements, and other critical performance parameters should be analyzed to verify that they are met with the logic family selected for the design. Chapter 15 covers the specific details of logic families, interfacing, and device selection.

17-7 CIRCUIT DESIGN AND PLANNING

Circuit design is one of the more interesting steps in the design process. This is when individual creativity and design talents often come into play. There may be several or several hundred different ways to actually build a circuit to perform a block function. The selection often involves the use of a circuit simulation to verify predicted circuit operation.

The circuit design and planning should correspond to the operation of each functional block. System troubleshooting and modification is greatly simplified if the circuits corresponding to each operational block are organized and built as separate circuit blocks. When at all possible, do not combine circuit functions from one operational block to another. Separate the functions into distinct circuit boards or areas on the board. Table 17-1 shows the steps to be taken in the circuit design process.

A function table and state transition diagram should be developed to indicate the inputs and resulting outputs to produce the necessary function. The logic functions should then be derived from the function table. The logic functions should be analyzed to verify that they perform according to the specifications stated for that block function. Components can then be selected to implement the logic functions so that a prototype breadboard design can be built and tested.

TABLE 17-1 Circuit Planning and Design Steps

Circuit function definition	Develop a function table and state transition diagram for each block operation.
Logic function design	Derive the Boolean functions.
Simulate the design	If available, use simulation software, such as MICROLOGIC, PCSILOS, or PSPICE, to verify on the PC the operation of the circuit.
Component selection	Select components.
Prototype implementation	Breadboard the components for each functional block.

17-8 TESTING

Testing is an important process that must be incorporated into the total digital system design procedures. However, it is often overlooked or pushed to the end of the project. Only by testing the project against the specifications can one be sure that each block functions properly.

Testing must be done at the breadboard stage of each operational block, at the block interconnections, as well as in the end when the project is fully constructed. Every circuit should be fully breadboarded, tested, and approved as meeting performance specifications before the circuit is used in the final design.

Test procedures that were defined for each functional block should be followed specifically to ensure the proper operation of the circuits within that block. Hardware and software blocks must be tested throughout the design process. Any portions that do not pass the testing must be redesigned, and the time action plan for the total design must be updated to reflect the slip in the schedule.

Careful attention should be given to the test conditions and test equipment so that valid data is obtained. During testing the operational limits of the devices should be determined so that a full report can be developed on the performance of the system.

17-9 CIRCUIT ASSEMBLY

Circuit assembly refers to the construction of the project from its prototype stage (breadboard) to its final stage (PC board).

The circuit assembly for the final system begins only after all breadboarded circuits have passed the performance testing. The final circuit assembly method must be determined based on the environmental requirements of the circuits to keep them in working order for the specified period of the life of the completed system. Custom printed circuit board design, wire-wrap, or point-to-point wiring and soldering must be evaluated based on cost and performance of the constructed system. Digital projects involving high frequencies or that are sensitive to wiring capacitance should not be constructed with a wire-wrap method. Special consideration should be given to minimize noise effects and electromagnetic interference effects within the final system. This includes separating digital and analog sections of the system and separate ground planes for each circuit board to prevent ground loops. The circuit construction must be robust to withstand normal wear and tear.

17-10 PACKAGING

Often the quality of a project is judged by its packaging. In addition to the aesthetic aspects of a project package, it must be functional to provide access to internal circuit boards for test and repair and durable enough to withstand its environment.

The packaging of the digital system must be designed to allow for easy insertion or maintenance of the circuit boards, displays, and power supplies—power cords, batteries, and protection fuses. Proper ventilation, grounding, and shielding from electromagnetic interference must be included in the design of the system package. For systems to be used outdoors or in hostile environments, special waterproof packaging is required to prevent moisture from damaging the components.

17-11 FINAL TESTING

Once assembled, the digital system must undergo final testing as the last verification of meeting system performance requirements.

The project testing must verify the complete operation of the system as compared to the specifications developed for the project. This should include both correct and incorrect user operational sequences. The final testing should ideally include both a laboratory test period and an "in-the-field" test period. Commercial products require Underwriters' Laboratory (UL) testing to ensure against electrical shock or fire hazard. Operational problems resulting from the laboratory test, UL test, or field test should be corrected before the project is put into actual service. Caution must be taken with any project intended for consumer safety as additional product liabilities apply.

17-12 USER/OPERATOR PROJECT DOCUMENTATION

User or operator documentation is important to describe safely the use of the digital system to the user and to prevent harm to the user or the system.

The user documentation should include the proper operating steps, proper care and storage of the device, acceptable operation conditions, and simple troubleshooting steps to take if the device does not function properly. Improper user manual information can result in legal suits brought against the designer in the event that damage to individuals or property is caused by the device.

17-13 DESIGN EXAMPLES

The preceding methodology for project design can be applied to any digital system. Practice in project design is a useful tool in mastering the techniques of digital logic design.

Table 17-2 lists many design projects undertaken by students and completed as operational projects. The designs are primarily digital systems, but they may incorporate additional analog or communications circuits as well. This list of examples is intended only as a starting point for individuals searching for design project ideas.

17-14 DIGITAL PROJECT CASE STUDY

The following project is used to demonstrate the principles presented in this chapter. There are several right ways to approach most problems,

TABLE 17-2 Design Project Examples

Computer interface for data storage
Tone decoder and switcher
Satellite receiver modem with a computer interface
Model rocket launcher with automatic countdown timer
Temperature controller
Programmable timer
Digital displays
Digital combination lock
Digital scorekeeper
Digital priority input indicator (tie-breaker switch)
Event timer
Digitized speech storage
Digital meters (voltage, current, resistance, speed)
Home security systems
Microcontroller-based projects
Microprocessor-based projects

and this case study is no exception. As with most learned abilities, practice makes perfect!

STUDENT PROJECT: Model Car Autotimer

A student has just completed a two-semester course using this textbook. Ready to embark on the exciting world of digital design, the student recalls that there is a rather popular wooden model car race at the hometown fall festival. This is a contest where wooden car models are made and raced down an inclined ramp.

Unfortunately, all of the timing and judging is done by hand and eyesight, with a timer hitting a stopwatch and declaring a winner. Many disputes result. The student decides to put digital logic to work!

DESCRIPTION OF THE APPLICATION

The wooden model cars are 18 inches long and weigh no more than 2 pounds each. The cars are placed at the top of a 20-foot inclined ramp and held in place by a "chief race steward" who removes a small barrier that allows gravity to propel the model cars down the ramp. There are eight lanes and eight cars race in each "heat." The winners of each heat race against each other, eight at a time. The winner of the final heat is the champion.

1. Project Documentation. The student buys a log book for the project and writes down some initial ideas on how to improve the timing and determination of a winner. The student thinks that each lane should have a timer, and that all eight lane times should be displayed at the same time, with all timing done automatically. A feature that the student would also like to have is a digital voice that announces the winning lane and time.

Research is the next step. The student uses the technical library of a nearby university to review pertinent literature and books on event timers and associated electronics. The student also calls several manufacturers of timer components for information. The availability, function, and cost of any commercially available units is also researched. All information is recorded in the project logbook, with a bibliography.

The student calls those in charge of the festival model car race to propose the project, along with asking questions about the details of the application that may be needed to make design decisions during the project. For example, how long does it take the cars from start to finish? How much time usually separates each car? Is there access to a 120-volt AC power? The questions and answers, and all pertinent phone numbers and contacts, are neatly entered in the logbook for future use.

The initial response the student gets from the festival chairman is encouraging, but more information willl be needed before any decisions are made.

2. Project Scope. The next step is for the student to determine the scope of the project and to formulate a project proposal and development plan. A brief outline of the proposal follows. The development plan will contain additional technical details as needed for the project, as shown in Table 17-3.

The student sends a copy of the proposal to the festival race chairman, and explains some of the details of the autotimer. The chairman is sufficiently impressed that he has agreed to purchase the timer for $350.00, if it is successfully demonstrated to the festival committee.

The student proceeds by getting commitments for all the dependencies listed in the proposal.

3. Project Specifications. The next step is the development of project specifications. This includes a functional block diagram of the project, performance specifications, and I/O requirements. The functional block diagram is shown in Figure 17-2.

There are ten functional blocks in the functional block diagram of this project. Each block has a well-defined function. This is important in order to be able to test the functionality of each block separately.

The student next develops an I/O specification for each block, listing all power and signaling going into and out of each block.

TABLE 17-3 Model Car autotimer Development Plan

Goal	Automate the timing of a model car race.	
Rationale	Eliminate the inaccuracies of the present race scoring by applying digital design techniques to a real-world application.	
Manpower	One student, 160 hours of work (estimate)	
Cost	$350.00 (estimate)	
Dependencies	Student's expertise	
	Access to laboratory equipment	
	University library for research	
	Mail-order parts suppliers	
	Festival committee approval	
Schedule	Start:	May 1992
	Finish:	July 1992
	Planned Use:	September 1992

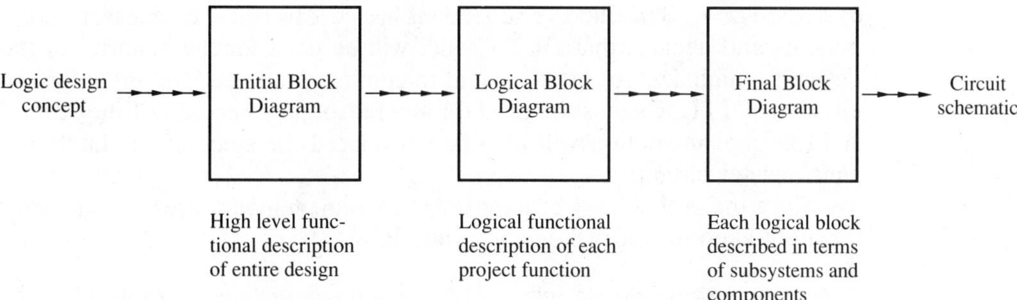

FIGURE 17-2 Functional Block Diagram

Some of the overall performance specifications that the student determines are power consumption of less that 2 watts, timer accuracy of ± 10 ms, a short voice message stating which lane won the race, and the display of each model car's race time immediately after the car finishes the race.

4. Cost Analysis. The student has already done a rough estimate of the cost of materials for the project at $350.00. Detailed cost estimates are shown in Table 17-4.

5. Project Timetable. The student next develops a time action plan that lists all the necessary steps in the construction and testing of the project. The student has estimated that it will take 160 hours of actual work. Ten weeks have been allocated for the project, and so the student must plan to work an average of 16 hours per week on the project.

Adequate time must be allocated for the ordering of parts, testing of each individual block, packaging, and final testing. The estimated time for each task will be recorded in a time action plan.

TABLE 17-4 Cost Estimates

Item	Cost
Wiring and breadboards	$ 40.00
IC components	70.00
Digital voice chipset	40.00
Eight-segment LED displays	40.00
Packaging	70.00
Sensors	40.00
Power supply	30.00
Speaker	10.00
Miscellaneous parts	10.00
Total estimated cost	$350.00

6. Logic Family Selection. The student has researched the necessary components and decides that HCT CMOS will be used for the majority of the design to minimize power usage and to eliminate the need for any interface circuitry if TTL ICs must be used for any reason in some part of the design. A PLD implementation will also be considered for some of the latch and shift register circuitry.

Since the project may be exposed to extreme temperatures outside, care must be taken to select the appropriate ICs.

7. Circuit Design and Planning. Following the guidelines in Table 17-1, the student develops circuitry for each functional block. Without going into detailed circuitry, the circuitry needed for each block is summarized in Table 17-5.

8. Testing. Each functional block is breadboarded and tested to ensure full functionality as compared to specifications and I/O requirements. Noncompliant blocks are redesigned, or functional specifications may have to be modified.

9. Circuit Assembly. After each circuit is tested, the circuitry is placed on circuit boards, either using a wire-wrap technique or soldering. The student decides to use wire-wrap, and sockets for the key ICs to allow for easy replacement.

10. Packaging. The student decides to package the circuitry in a waterproof package since it may be exposed to the elements. In addition, the displays must be visible to a crowd. The student decides to package the display separate from the rest of the circuitry to allow for some flexibility in the placement of the display (on a tower, e.g.).

11. Final Test. After the entire project is completed, the student performs several tests in the laboratory to measure the accuracy of the timers and displays. Satisfied that all is working, the student schedules a time to install the project and field test the project.

12. Documentation. Throughout the course of the project, the student has been keeping a logbook of all project-related activities and results. The student finalizes the project by producing a professional technical report that will be delivered with the project, along with a user's manual on how to operate and maintain the autotimer.

13. Customer Acceptance. The student has field tested the autotimer and schedules a demonstration for the festival committee. The autotimer performs to all specifications, and the committee decides to buy and use the autotimer immediately.

TABLE 17-5 Project Circuitry

Functional Block	Description of Circuitry
Start sensors	Eight normally open micro-mechanical switches.
Finish sensors	Eight normally open micro-mechanical switches.
Reset	Pushbutton switch to reset all eight timers.
Timers	Eight timer circuits, one for each lane, keeping track of seconds, tenths, and hundredths of a second. (Counters or specialized timer ICs)
Output latches/coding	Each timer output is latched and converted to the appropriate coding to interface with the driver/display block.
Control/Select	This block uses shift registers to load one of eight preprogrammed addresses into the memory to select the appropriate code for the lane that won the race. This circuitry also controls the output latch enables, as needed.
Memory	This circuit is a small EPROM memory that contains the 8-bit codes needed by the voice circuitry chipset to announce a phrase.
Voice Circuitry	A commercial digital talking chipset and control signals. An 8-bit code is needed for each word the voice circuitry must announce. There are eight phrases, such as "Lane three won."
LED drivers/displays	Large eight-segment LED displays and driver circuitry that shows the time for each lane immediately after the car crosses the finish line.
Power supply	A 120-volt AC, switching 5-volt supply, rated at 3 watts.

The student now realizes that an improvement to the project would be the addition of an amplifier circuit between the voice circuitry and the speaker, as on the outside with crowd noise, it is difficult to hear the digital voice. Other improvements may also be added at a later date.

SUMMARY

Student design projects are both challenging and rewarding. In addition to the technical skills of digital logic design, successful projects all have additional requirements for success. This includes carefully planning and researching the project, detailed documentation throughout the project, specification development, cost analysis, and realistic schedules. The final project must be thoroughly tested and professionally packaged.

Several possible student projects are provided. The project example illustrates the detailed steps in the planning, building, and testing of a relatively simple practical digital project. After mastery of the information in this text, you have the tools to design some rather complex digital systems.

PROBLEMS

1. Define the following terms:
   a. development plan
   b. project proposal
   c. project performance
   d. time-action plan

Problems 2 through 7 are design problems from previous chapters. Apply the design methodology outlined in this chapter to the design. Include the following:

- Project proposal
- Project specifications
- Functional block diagrams
- Estimated cost analysis
- I/O requirements
- Select a logic family/subfamily
- User/test documentation

2. Flip-flop design problem of Problem 9-22.
3. MOD-25 counter of Problem 10-16.
4. Times two multiplier circuit of Problem 11-18.
5. Sequence generator of Problem 12-18.
6. Memory system of Problem 13-37.
7. Microprocessor system of Problem 14-30.
8. List five reasons why complete project documentation is important.

9. Select one of the project design examples from Table 17-2. Use the techniques described in Chapter 17, and construct a development plan.
10. Repeat Problem 9 for a different project.
11. Select your own project and construct a development plan.

Appendix A

Interpreting Data Sheet Information

The manufacturers' data sheets for integrated circuits provide the most comprehensive information about the performance and operation of the IC. Data sheets can also provide application circuits for recommended circuit configurations. It is important to know how to find the information in the data sheet and how to interpret the information in terms of logic device performance and operation.

The data sheet shown in Figure A-1 is for the 7402 2-input NOR gate. It is used as an example to explain the information listed on the data sheet.

Device Part Numbers. Note the logic families listed at the top of the page. The electrical operating conditions, electrical characteristics, and switching characteristics vary with the logic family of the device.

Part Description/Title. The title often indicates how many gates are contained on the chip.

Function Table. Defines the inputs and outputs produced by the circuit.

Logic Diagram. The standard logic symbol.

Logic Equation. The Boolean equation describing the operation.

Pin Diagram. Note the specific part numbers indicated for each pin diagram to ensure proper circuit connection.

Schematics. Note the output stage.

Absolute Maximum Ratings over Free-Air Temperature Range. Do not operate the device at these ratings. They are the maximum ratings that will not damage the circuit, but operation is not guaranteed.

Recommended Operating Conditions. The conditions that must be maintained for proper operation. Carefully note the voltage and current levels for interfacing to other logic devices.

Electrical Characteristics over Recommended Free-Air Temperature Range. Note the voltage, current, and supply current characteristics. These values are given for free-air temperatures. Few devices operate in free air. Proper steps should be taken to ensure proper heat sinking and ventilation in the enclosure.

Switching Characteristics. The gate propagation delays are specified with specific test circuit conditions.

DEVICE PART NUMBERS — **SN5400, SN54LS00, SN54S00, SN7400, SN74LS00, SN74S00**

PART DESCRIPTION — **QUADRUPLE 2-INPUT POSITIVE-NAND GATES**

DECEMBER 1983—REVISED MARCH 1988

- **Package Options Include Plastic "Small Outline" Packages, Ceramic Chip Carriers and Flat Packages, and Plastic and Ceramic DIPs**
- **Dependable Texas Instruments Quality and Reliability**

SN5400 . . . J PACKAGE
SN54LS00, SN54S00 . . . J OR W PACKAGE
SN7400 . . . N PACKAGE
SN74LS00, SN74S00 . . . D OR N PACKAGE
(TOP VIEW)

	Pin	Pin	
1A	1	14	V_{CC}
1B	2	13	4B
1Y	3	12	4A
2A	4	11	4Y
2B	5	10	3B
2Y	6	9	3A
GND	7	8	3Y

THREE DIFFERENT PIN DIAGRAMS

SN5400 . . . W PACKAGE
(TOP VIEW)

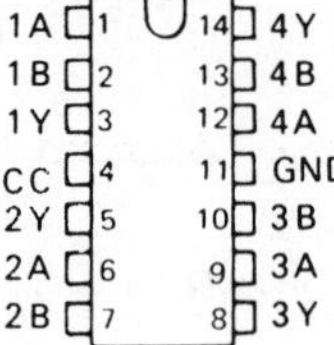

SN54LS00, SN54S00 . . . FK PACKAGE
(TOP VIEW)

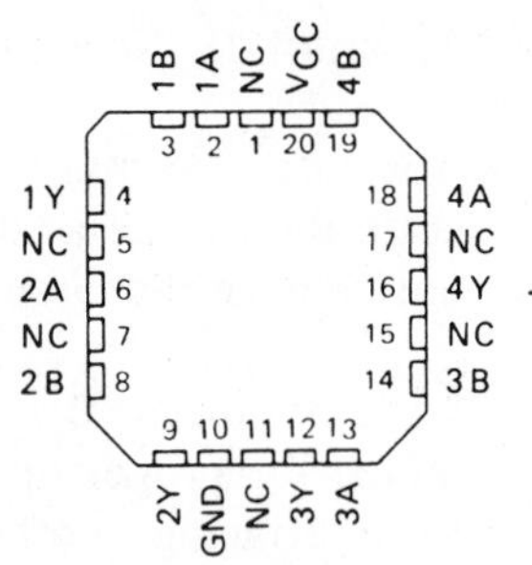

NC - No internal connection

description

These devices contain four independent 2-input-NAND gates.

The SN5400, SN54LS00, and SN54S00 are characterized for operation over the full military temperature range of −55°C to 125°C. The SN7400, SN74LS00, and SN74S00 are characterized for operation from 0°C to 70°C.

FUNCTION TABLE (each gate)

INPUTS		OUTPUT
A	B	Y
H	H	L
L	X	H
X	L	H

logic symbol†

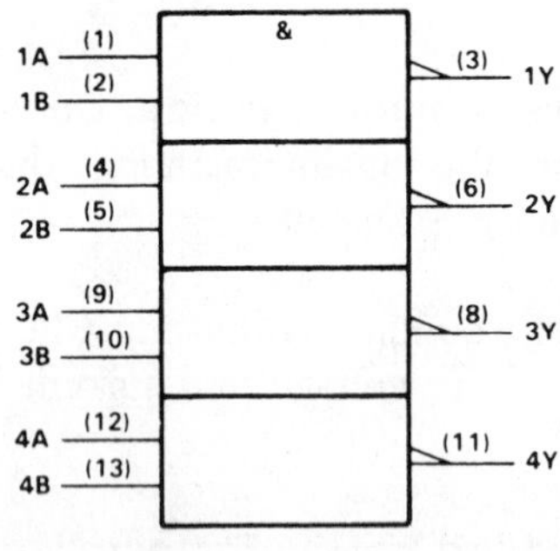

†This symbol is in accordance with ANSI/IEEE Std. 91-1984 and IEC Publication 617-12.
Pin numbers shown are for D, J, and N packages.

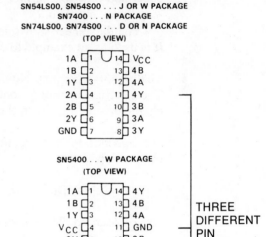

logic diagram (positive logic)

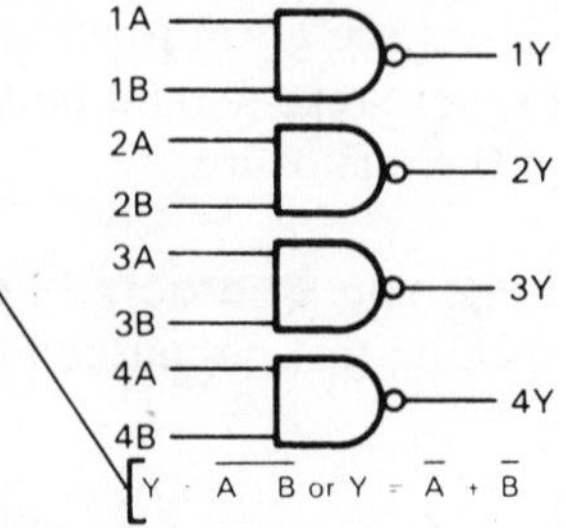

LOGIC EQUATION

$Y = \overline{A\ B}$ or $Y = \overline{A} + \overline{B}$

FIGURE A-1 Data Sheet. (Courtesy of Texas Instruments.)

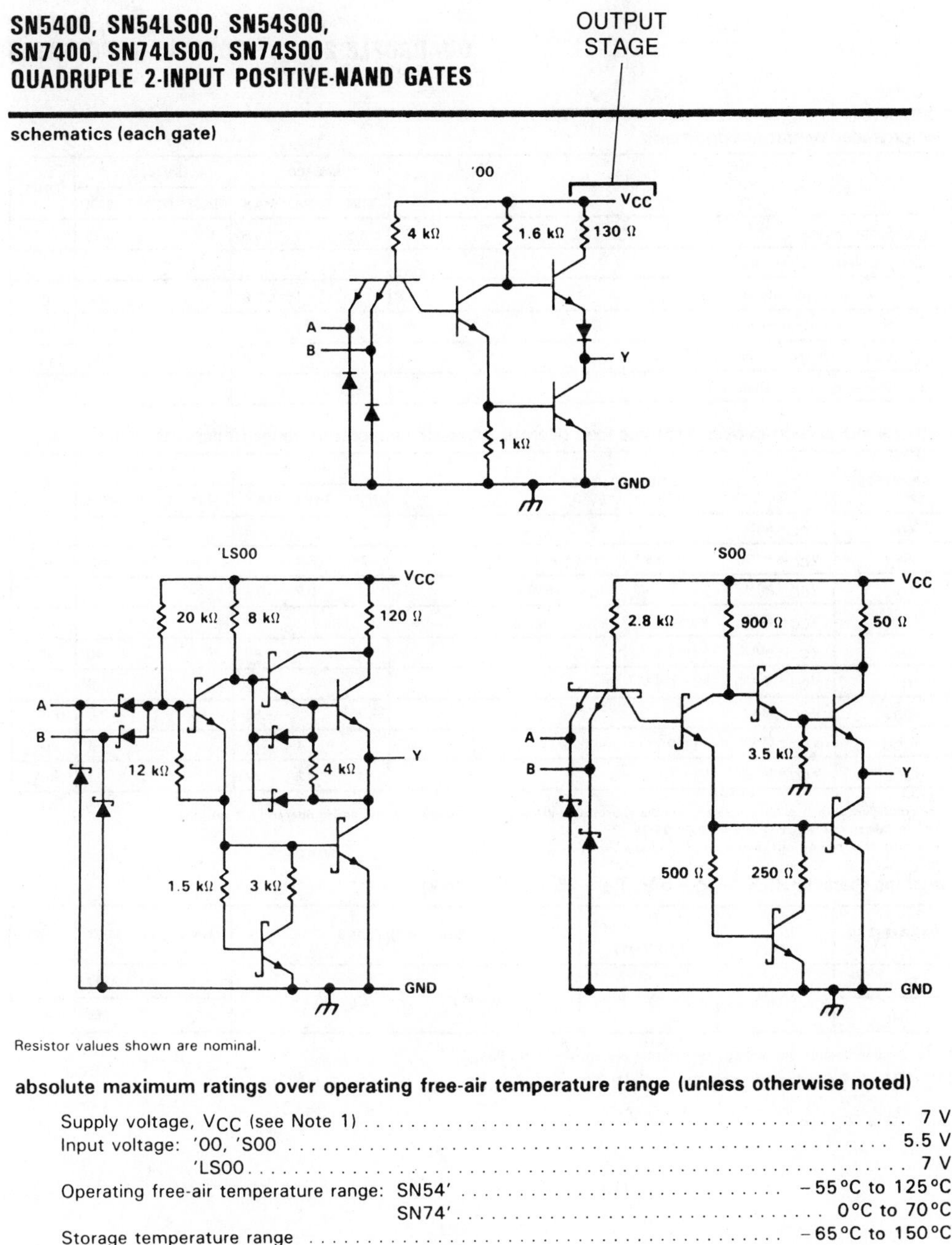

Resistor values shown are nominal.

absolute maximum ratings over operating free-air temperature range (unless otherwise noted)

Supply voltage, V_{CC} (see Note 1)		7 V
Input voltage:	'00, 'S00	5.5 V
	'LS00	7 V
Operating free-air temperature range:	SN54'	−55°C to 125°C
	SN74'	0°C to 70°C
Storage temperature range		−65°C to 150°C

NOTE 1: Voltage values are with respect to network ground terminal.

FIGURE A-1 Data Sheet (cont'd). (Courtesy of Texas Instruments.)

SN5400, SN7400
QUADRUPLE 2-INPUT POSITIVE-NAND GATES

recommended operating conditions

		SN5400			SN7400			UNIT
		MIN	NOM	MAX	MIN	NOM	MAX	
V_{CC}	Supply voltage	4.5	5	5.5	4.75	5	5.25	V
V_{IH}	High-level input voltage	2			2			V
V_{IL}	Low-level input voltage			0.8			0.8	V
I_{OH}	High-level output current			− 0.4			− 0.4	mA
I_{OL}	Low-level output current			16			16	mA
T_A	Operating free-air temperature	− 55		125	0		70	°C

electrical characteristics over recommended operating free-air temperature range (unless otherwise noted)

PARAMETER	TEST CONDITIONS †	SN5400			SN7400			UNIT
		MIN	TYP‡	MAX	MIN	TYP‡	MAX	
V_{IK}	V_{CC} = MIN, I_I = − 12 mA			− 1.5			− 1.5	V
V_{OH}	V_{CC} = MIN, V_{IL} = 0.8 V, I_{OH} = − 0.4 mA	2.4	3.4		2.4	3.4		V
V_{OL}	V_{CC} = MIN, V_{IH} = 2 V, I_{OL} = 16 mA		0.2	0.4		0.2	0.4	V
I_I	V_{CC} = MAX, V_I = 5.5 V			1			1	mA
I_{IH}	V_{CC} = MAX, V_I = 2.4 V			40			40	µA
I_{IL}	V_{CC} = MAX, V_I = 0.4 V			− 1.6			− 1.6	mA
I_{OS}§	V_{CC} = MAX	− 20		− 55	− 18		− 55	mA
I_{CCH}	V_{CC} = MAX, V_I = 0 V		4	8		4	8	mA
I_{CCL}	V_{CC} = MAX, V_I = 4.5 V		12	22		12	22	mA

† For conditions shown as MIN or MAX, use the appropriate value specified under recommended operating conditions.
‡ All typical values are at V_{CC} = 5 V, T_A = 25°C.
§ Not more than one output should be shorted at a time.

switching characteristics, V_{CC} = 5 V, T_A = 25°C (see note 2)

PARAMETER	FROM (INPUT)	TO (OUTPUT)	TEST CONDITIONS	MIN	TYP	MAX	UNIT
t_{PLH}	A or B	Y	R_L = 400 Ω, C_L = 15 pF		11	22	ns
t_{PHL}					7	15	ns

NOTE 2: Load circuits and voltage waveforms are shown in Section 1.

FIGURE A-1 Data Sheet (cont'd). (Courtesy of Texas Instruments.)

SN54LS00, SN74LS00
QUADRUPLE 2-INPUT POSITIVE-NAND GATES

recommended operating conditions

		SN54LS00			SN74LS00			UNIT
		MIN	NOM	MAX	MIN	NOM	MAX	
V_{CC}	Supply voltage	4.5	5	5.5	4.75	5	5.25	V
V_{IH}	High-level input voltage	2			2			V
V_{IL}	Low-level input voltage			0.7			0.8	V
I_{OH}	High-level output current			−0.4			−0.4	mA
I_{OL}	Low-level output current			4			8	mA
T_A	Operating free-air temperature	−55		125	0		70	°C

electrical characteristics over recommended operating free-air temperature range (unless otherwise noted)

PARAMETER	TEST CONDITIONS †			SN54LS00			SN74LS00			UNIT
				MIN	TYP‡	MAX	MIN	TYP‡	MAX	
V_{IK}	V_{CC} = MIN,	I_I = −18 mA				−1.5			−1.5	V
V_{OH}	V_{CC} = MIN,	V_{IL} = MAX,	I_{OH} = −0.4 mA	2.5	3.4		2.7	3.4		V
V_{OL}	V_{CC} = MIN,	V_{IH} = 2 V,	I_{OL} = 4 mA		0.25	0.4		0.25	0.4	V
	V_{CC} = MIN,	V_{IH} = 2 V,	I_{OL} = 8 mA					0.35	0.5	
I_I	V_{CC} = MAX,	V_I = 7 V				0.1			0.1	mA
I_{IH}	V_{CC} = MAX,	V_I = 2.7 V				20			20	μA
I_{IL}	V_{CC} = MAX,	V_I = 0.4 V				−0.4			−0.4	mA
I_{OS}§	V_{CC} = MAX			−20		−100	−20		−100	mA
I_{CCH}	V_{CC} = MAX,	V_I = 0 V			0.8	1.6		0.8	1.6	mA
I_{CCL}	V_{CC} = MAX,	V_I = 4.5 V			2.4	4.4		2.4	4.4	mA

† For conditions shown as MIN or MAX, use the appropriate value specified under recommended operating conditions.
‡ All typical values are at V_{CC} = 5 V, T_A = 25°C
§ Not more than one output should be shorted at a time, and the duration of the short-circuit should not exceed one second.

switching characteristics, V_{CC} = 5 V, T_A = 25°C (see note 2)

PARAMETER	FROM (INPUT)	TO (OUTPUT)	TEST CONDITIONS		MIN	TYP	MAX	UNIT
t_{PLH}	A or B	Y	R_L = 2 kΩ,	C_L = 15 pF		9	15	ns
t_{PHL}						10	15	ns

NOTE 2: Load circuits and voltage waveforms are shown in Section 1.

FIGURE A-1 Data Sheet (cont'd). (Courtesy of Texas Instruments.)

SN54S00, SN74S00
QUADRUPLE 2-INPUT POSITIVE-NAND GATES

recommended operating conditions

		SN54S00			SN74S00			UNIT
		MIN	NOM	MAX	MIN	NOM	MAX	
V_{CC}	Supply voltage	4.5	5	5.5	4.75	5	5.25	V
V_{IH}	High-level input voltage	2			2			V
V_{IL}	Low-level input voltage			0.8			0.8	V
I_{OH}	High-level output current			−1			−1	mA
I_{OL}	Low-level output current			20			20	mA
T_A	Operating free-air temperature	−55		125	0		70	°C

electrical characteristics over recommended operating free-air temperature range (unless otherwise noted)

PARAMETER	TEST CONDITIONS †			SN54S00			SN74S00			UNIT
				MIN	TYP‡	MAX	MIN	TYP‡	MAX	
V_{IK}	V_{CC} = MIN,	$I_I = -18$ mA				−1.2			−1.2	V
V_{OH}	V_{CC} = MIN,	V_{IL} = 0.8 V,	$I_{OH} = -1$ mA	2.5	3.4		2.7	3.4		V
V_{OL}	V_{CC} = MIN,	V_{IH} = 2 V,	I_{OL} = 20 mA			0.5			0.5	V
I_I	V_{CC} = MAX,	V_I = 5.5 V				1			1	mA
I_{IH}	V_{CC} = MAX,	V_I = 2.7 V				50			50	μA
I_{IL}	V_{CC} = MAX,	V_I = 0.5 V				−2			−2	mA
I_{OS}§	V_{CC} = MAX			−40		−100	−40		−100	mA
I_{CCH}	V_{CC} = MAX,	V_I = 0 V			10	16		10	16	mA
I_{CCL}	V_{CC} = MAX,	V_I = 4.5 V			20	36		20	36	mA

† For conditions shown as MIN or MAX, use the appropriate value specified under recommended operating conditions.
‡ All typical values are at V_{CC} = 5 V, T_A = 25°C.
§ Not more than one output should be shorted at a time, and the duration of the short-circuit should not exceed one second.

switching characteristics, V_{CC} = 5 V, T_A = 25°C (see note 2)

PARAMETER	FROM (INPUT)	TO (OUTPUT)	TEST CONDITIONS		MIN	TYP	MAX	UNIT
t_{PLH}	A or B	Y	R_L = 280 Ω,	C_L = 15 pF		3	4.5	ns
t_{PHL}						3	5	ns
t_{PLH}			R_L = 280 Ω,	C_L = 50 pF		4.5		ns
t_{PHL}						5		ns

NOTE 2: Load circuits and voltage waveforms are shown in Section 1.

FIGURE A-1 Data Sheet (cont'd). (Courtesy of Texas Instruments.)

Operating Conditions and Characteristics

V_{CC} Supply voltage
I_{CC} Supply current in to the V_{CC} supply
I_{CCH} Supply current with the outputs HIGH
I_{CCL} Supply current with the outputs LOW

V_{OH} Logic HIGH output voltage produced
V_{OL} Logic LOW output voltage produced
V_{IH} Logic HIGH input voltage required
V_{IL} Logic LOW input voltage required
I_{OH} Logic HIGH output current produced
I_{OL} Logic LOW output current produced
I_{IH} Logic HIGH input current required
I_{IL} Logic LOW input current required

f_{max} Maximum clock frequency allowed for stable operation
t_{PHL} Propagation delay occurring when the output changes from a logic-HIGH to a logic-LOW
t_{PLH} Propagation delay occurring when the output changes from a logic-LOW to a logic-HIGH
t_W Pulse width required
t_h Hold time required after a transition
t_{SU} Set-up time required of a signal input prior to the transition of the trigger input
t_{acc} Access time occurring between an input signal and a valid output signal resulting from the input

FIGURE A-1 Data Sheet (cont'd). (Courtesy of Texas Instruments.)

Appendix B

Data Transmission

Digital data is sensitive to many sources of error during transmission caused by electromagnetic interference, cross talk, attenuation, pulse spreading, and other impairments. A digital signal requires a very wide bandwidth to transmit the pulses without distortion. All transmission systems have a limited bandwidth that results in limiting the speed of the data that can be transmitted.

B-1 DIGITAL TRANSMISSION TECHNIQUES

The quality of transmission is dependent on the transmission media, the rate or speed of the digital data, and the distance of transmission. Digital and analog data conversion and encoding techniques are used to transmit digital data reliably between a source and a receiver. Frequently, line driver circuits are required to convert standard TTL or CMOS voltage and current levels to other levels better suited for transmission.

Digital transmission can take place in a digital format, known as **baseband** transmission, or the digital data can modulate an analog waveform (or carrier) to be transmitted as an analog signal, as shown in Figure B-1. Most computing devices and computer peripherals, such as printers, plotters, and other devices transmit digital data in a baseband form over ribbon cable, twisted pair, coaxial cable, or optical fiber cable. Long distance transmission on systems intended for analog signals often requires the use of modems. Modems are modulators/demodulators that convert the digital data to an analog signal for transmission and that convert the received analog signal back to digital data at the end device.

Long distance transmission systems are converting to digital transmission, but many analog transmission systems still remain. Current telephone networks, for example, require a modem to transmit digital data from one computer or facsimile machine to another. The digital data must be con-

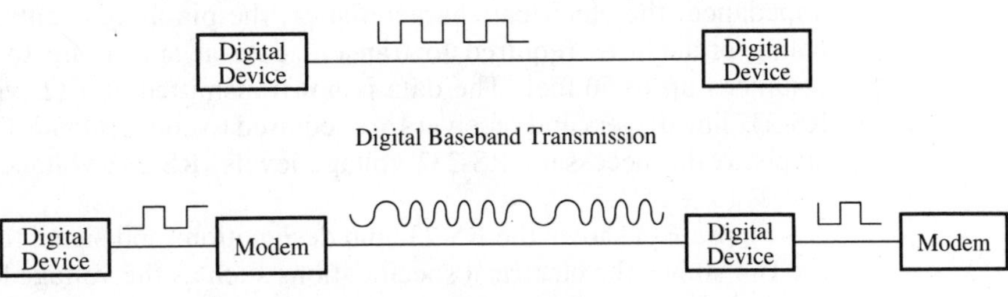

FIGURE B-1 Digital Transmission

verted to a "voiceband" signal that conforms to the frequency and amplitude of an analog voice signal. Typical data rates achievable by current modems on existing analog telephone networks range from 1200 bits per second (bps) on standard dial-up lines to 19,200 bps on specially conditioned phone lines. The development of digital telephone networks such as the Integrated Services Digital Network (ISDN) will allow digital transmission at speeds ranging from 64 to 1544 Kbps on standard telephone lines.

Local area networks (LANs) are specially designed computer networks intended to transmit high-speed digital data within a small geographic region, up to approximately 2 miles. Most LANs transmit digital data in a baseband form, but some LANs modulate an analog carrier with the digital data. Typical LAN transmission speeds are up to 16 Mbps on copper wire systems, and up to 100 Mbps on fiber optic systems.

B-2 TRANSMISSION MEDIA

B.2.1 RS-232 Serial Transmission Standard

The transmission media selected determines the maximum speed and the maximum distance for error-free transmission of digital data. Ribbon cable is used in many serial data transmission applications. One common serial data transmission standard is RS-232. The RS-232 standard is intended to connect a computing device to a communications device, such as a modem. However, it is commonly used and misused throughout the computer industry to connect computers to printers.

Figure B-2 shows RS-232 configurations for baseband transmission and for modem transmission. Baseband transmission refers to the RS-232 interface being used to connect two digital devices, such as a computer and a printer. Modem transmission refers to the case when RS-232 interface is being used to connect a digital device, such as a computer, to a modem.

The RS-232 specification defines the voltage levels, the terminating impedance, the electrical characteristics, the pin assignments, and the signaling procedures required to transmit data at speeds up to 20 Kbps for distances up to 50 feet. The data is not transmitted at TTL voltage levels. RS-232 line drivers and receivers are required to convert from TTL or CMOS levels to the necessary RS-232 voltage levels. RS-232 voltages range from $-25V$ to $+25V$.

Figure B-3 shows the RS-232 pin designations and signal functions. Figure B-4 shows the electrical specifications such as the voltage levels defined for the driver (transmitter) and terminator (receiver). Figure B-5 shows the DB25 connector that is commonly used with RS-232 transmission. The data sheet for an RS-232 driver/receiver is shown in Figure B-6.

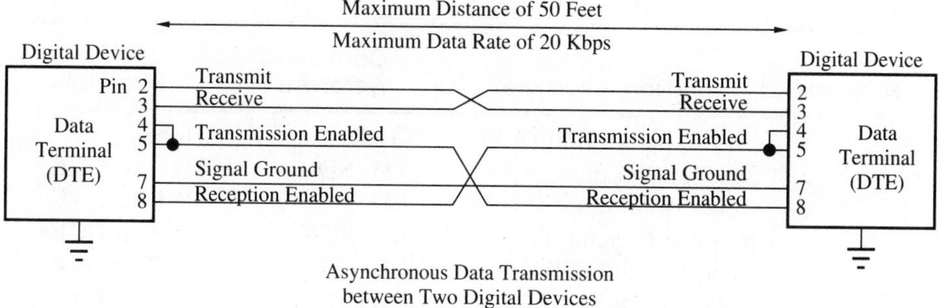

Asynchronous Data Transmission between Two Digital Devices

Baseband Transmission

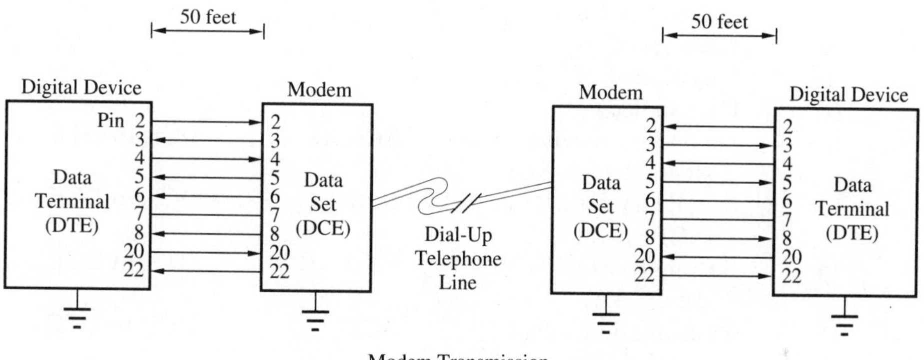

Modem Transmission

(Data rate is limited by telephone line and modem characteristics. Typical data rates are 1200 bps, 2400 bps, and 9600 bps.)

FIGURE B-2 RS-232 Configuration

B.2.2 Twisted Pair

Twisted pair is an inexpensive transmission media used extensively in the telephone network and in many local area networks (LANs). It provides minimal shielding from electrical interference. The digital pulses are highly susceptible to attenuation and distortion as a function of frequency, with increased distortion occurring as the speed of the data increases. Data is commonly transmitted through a modem on a dial-up line at rates of 1200 to 2400 bps. Higher rates up to 9600 bps and 19.2 Kbps require specially conditioned phone lines. Digital transmission rates on specifically designed digital loop carriers and trunk lines are typically 1.544 to 3.15 Mbps. Some LANs use twisted pair cable to transmit data in a baseband format at 10 Mbps, but special signal processing is performed at the transmitting and receiving devices.

EIA RS-232C Pin Designations

Pin Number	EIA Nomenclature	Common Acronym	Direction
1	Protective ground (AA)	GND	None
2	Transmitted data (BA)	TD, SD	DTE to DCE
3	Received data (BB)	RD	DCE to DTE
4	Request to send (CA)	RS, RTS	DTE to DCE
5	Clear to send (CB)	CS, CTS	DCE to DTE
6	Data set ready (CC)	DSR, MR	DCE to DTE
7	Signal ground (AB)	GND	None
8	Received line signal detect (CF)	RLSD	DCE to DTE
9	Unassigned		
10	Unassigned		
11	Unassigned		
12	Secondary received line signal detect (SCF)	SRLSD	DCE to DTE
13	Secondary clear to send (SCB)	SCS	DCE to DTE
14	Secondary transmitted data (SBA)	STD	DTE to DCE
15	Transmission signal element timing (DB)	SCT	DCE to DTE
16	Secondary received data (SBB)	SRD	DCE to DTE
17	Receiver signal element timing (DD)	SCR	DCE to DTE
18	Unassigned		
19	Secondary request to send (SCA)	SRS	DTE to DCE
20	Data terminal ready (CD)	DTR	DTE to DCE
21	Signal quality detector (CG)	SQD	DCE to DTE
22	Ring indicator (CE)	RI	DCE to DTE
23	Data signal rate selector (CH)	DSRS	DTE to DCE
24	Transmit signal element timing (DA)	SCTE	DTE to DCE
25	Unassigned		

FIGURE B-3 RS-232 Serial Data Transmission Standard—Pin Designations

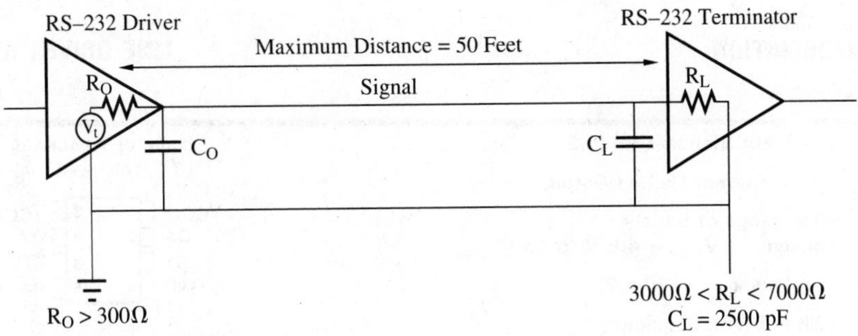

RS 232	Voltages Logic 1; OFF	Logic 0; ON
Driver	–5 to –15 V	+5 to +15 V
Terminator	–3 to –25 V	–3 to –25 V

FIGURE B-4 RS-232 Serial Data Transmission Standard—Electrical Specifications

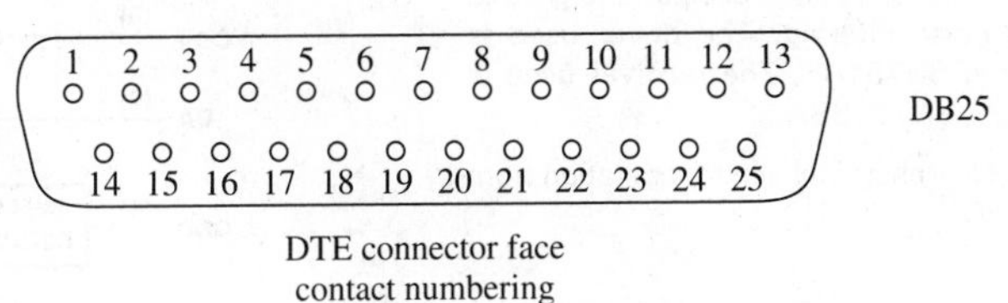

Typical RS–232 Connector

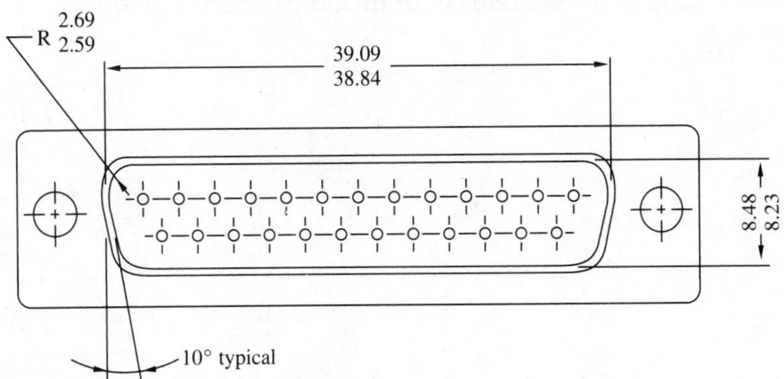

FIGURE B-5 DB25 Connector

ADVANCE INFORMATION

SN75155 LINE DRIVER AND RECEIVER

D2951, JULY 1986

- **Meets EIA Standard RS-232-C**
- **10-mA Current Limited Output**
- **Wide Range of Supply Voltage . . . V_{CC} = 4.5 V to 15 V**
- **Low Power . . . 130 mW**
- **Built-In 5-Volt Regulator**
- **Response Control Provides:**
  Input Threshold Shifting
  Input Noise Filtering
- **Power-Off Output Resistance . . . 300 Ω Typ**
- **Driver Input TTL Compatible**

D, JG, OR P PACKAGE (TOP VIEW)

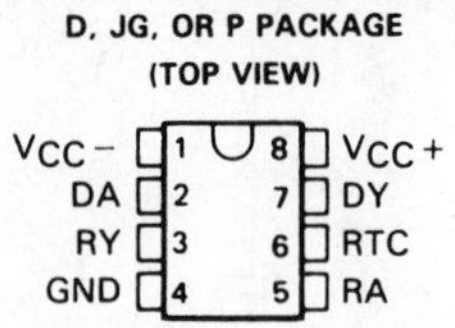

description

The SN75155 is a monolithic line driver and receiver that is designed to satisfy the requirements of the standard interface between data terminal equipment and data communication equipment as defined by EIA standard RS-232-C. A Response Control input is provided for the receiver. A resistor or a resistor and a bias voltage can be connected between the response control input and ground to provide noise filtering. The driver used is similar to the SN75188. The receiver used is similar to the SN75189A.

The SN75155 is characterized for operation from 0°C to 70°C.

logic symbol†

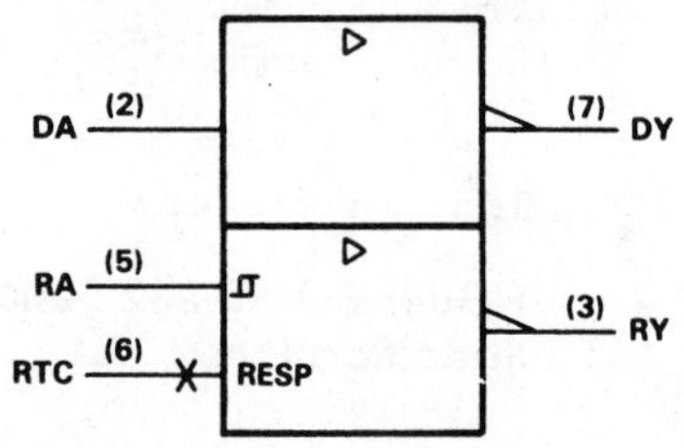

†This symbol is in accordance with ANSI/IEEE Std 91-1984 and IEC Publication 617-12

logic diagram

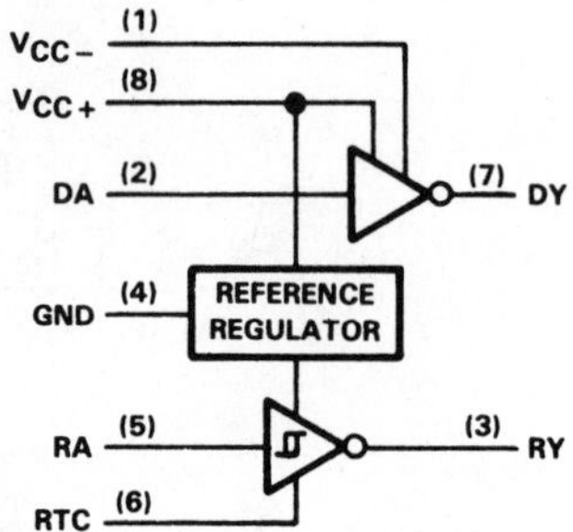

FIGURE B-6 RS-232-C Driver/Receiver Data Sheet. (Courtesy of Texas Instruments.)

SN75155
LINE DRIVER AND RECEIVER

ADVANCE INFORMATION

schematic

DA (2)
V_{CC+} (8)
35 kΩ
3.5 kΩ
RA (5)
8.5 kΩ
GND (4)
RTC (6)
V_{CC-} (1)
60 Ω
(7) DY
300 Ω
55 Ω
(3) RY

All resistor values shown are nominal.

absolute maximum ratings over operating free-air temperature range (unless otherwise noted)

Supply voltage, V_{CC+} (see Note 1) . . . . . . 15 V
Supply voltage, V_{CC-} (see Note 1) . . . . . . −15 V
Input voltage range: Driver . . . . . . −15 V to 15 V
Receiver . . . . . . −30 V to 30 V
Output voltage range (Driver) . . . . . . −15 V to 15 V
Continuous total dissipation at (or below) 25°C free-air temperature (see Note 2):
D package . . . . . . 725 mW
JG package . . . . . . 825 mW
P package . . . . . . 1000 mW
Operating free-air temperature range . . . . . . 0°C to 70°C
Storage temperature range . . . . . . −65°C to 150°C
Lead temperature 1,6 mm (1/16 inch) from case for 60 seconds, JG package . . . . . . 300°C
Case temperature for 60 seconds, FK package . . . . . . 260°C
Lead temperature 1,6 mm (1/16 inch) from case for 10 seconds, D or P package . . . . . . 260°C

NOTES: 1. All voltage values are with respect to network ground terminal.
2. For operation above 25°C free-air temperature, refer to Dissipation Derating Table. In the JG package, SN75155 chips are glass mounted.

DISSIPATION DERATING TABLE

PACKAGE	T_A = 25°C POWER RATING	DERATING FACTOR	ABOVE T_A	T_A = 70°C POWER RATING
D	725 mW	5.8 mW/°C	25°C	464 mW
JG	825 mW	6.6 mW/°C	25°C	528 mW
P	1000 mW	8.0 mW/°C	25°C	640 mW

FIGURE B-6 RS-232-C Driver/Receiver Data Sheet (cont'd). (Courtesy of Texas Instruments.)

ADVANCE INFORMATION

SN75155 LINE DRIVER AND RECEIVER

recommended operating conditions

PARAMETERS	MIN	NOM	MAX	UNIT
Supply voltage, V_{CC+}	4.5	12	15	V
Supply voltage, V_{CC-}	−4.5	−12	−15	V
Input voltage, driver, $V_{I(D)}$			±15	V
Input voltage, receiver, $V_{I(R)}$	−25		25	V
High-level input voltage, driver, V_{IH}	2			V
Low-level input voltage, driver, V_{IL}			0.8	V
Response control current			±5.5	mA
Output current, receiver, $I_{O(R)}$			24	mA
Operating free-air temperature, T_A	0		70	°C

electrical characteristics over recommended operating free-air temperature range (unless otherwise noted)

total device

PARAMETERS		TEST CONDITIONS			MIN	TYP[†]	MAX	UNIT
I_{CCH+}	High-level supply current	V_{CC+} = 5 V,	V_{CC-} = −5 V,	$V_{I(D)}$ = 2 V,		6.3	8.1	mA
		V_{CC+} = 9 V,	V_{CC-} = −9 V,	$V_{I(R)}$ = 2.3 V,		9.1	11.9	
		V_{CC+} = 12 V,	V_{CC-} = −12 V,	Output open		10.4	14	
I_{CCL+}	Low-level supply current	V_{CC+} = 5 V,	V_{CC-} = −5 V,	$V_{I(D)}$ = 0.8 V,		2.5	3.4	mA
		V_{CC+} = 9 V,	V_{CC-} = −9 V,	$V_{I(R)}$ = 0.6 V,		3.7	5.1	
		V_{CC+} = 12 V,	V_{CC-} = −12 V,	Output open		4.1	5.6	
I_{CC+}	Supply current	V_{CC+} = 5 V,	V_{CC-} = 0,	$V_{I(R)}$ = 2.3 V,		4.8	6.4	mA
		V_{CC+} = 9 V,	V_{CC-} = 0,	$V_{I(D)}$ = 0		6.7	9.1	
I_{CCH-}	High-level supply current	V_{CC+} = 5 V,	V_{CC-} = −5 V,	$V_{I(D)}$ = 2 V,		−2.4	−3.1	mA
		V_{CC+} = 9 V,	V_{CC-} = −9 V,	$V_{I(R)}$ = 2.3 V,		−3.9	−4.9	
		V_{CC+} = 12 V,	V_{CC-} = −12 V,	Output open		−4.8	−6.1	
I_{CCL-}	Low-level supply current	V_{CC+} = 5 V,	V_{CC-} = −5 V,	$V_{I(D)}$ = 0.8 V,		−0.2	−0.35	mA
		V_{CC+} = 9 V,	V_{CC-} = −9 V,	$V_{I(R)}$ = 0.6 V,		−0.25	−0.4	
		V_{CC+} = 12 V,	V_{CC-} = −12 V,	Output open		−0.27	−0.45	

[†] All typical values are at T_A = 25°C.

FIGURE B-6 RS-232-C Driver/Receiver Data Sheet (cont'd). (Courtesy of Texas Instruments.)

SN75155
LINE DRIVER AND RECEIVER

ADVANCE INFORMATION

electrical characteristics over recommended operating free-air temperature range, $V_{CC+} = 12$ V, $V_{CC-} = -12$ V (unless otherwise noted)

driver section

PARAMETER		TEST CONDITIONS		MIN	TYP†	MAX	UNIT
V_{OH}	High-level output voltage	$V_{IL} = 0.8$ V, $R_L = 3$ kΩ	$V_{CC+} = 5$ V, $V_{CC-} = -5$ V	3.2	3.7		V
			$V_{CC+} = 9$ V, $V_{CC-} = -9$ V	6.5	7.2		
			$V_{CC+} = 12$ V, $V_{CC-} = -12$ V	8.9	9.8		
V_{OL}	Low-level output voltage (see Note 3)	$V_{IH} = 2$ V, $R_L = 3$ kΩ	$V_{CC+} = 5$ V, $V_{CC-} = -5$ V		−3.6	−3.2	V
			$V_{CC+} = 9$ V, $V_{CC-} = -9$ V		−7.1	−6.4	
			$V_{CC+} = 12$ V, $V_{CC-} = -12$ V		−9.7	−8.8	
I_{IH}	High-level input current	$V_I = 7$ V				5	μA
I_{IL}	Low-level input current	$V_I = 0$			−0.73	−1.2	mA
I_{OSH}	High-level short-circuit output current	$V_I = 0.8$ V, $V_O = 0$		−7	−12	−14.5	mA
I_{OSL}	Low-level short-circuit output current	$V_I = 2$ V, $V_O = 0$		6.5	11.5	15	mA
R_O	Output resistance with power off	$V_O = -2$ V to 2 V			300		Ω

receiver section

PARAMETER		TEST CONDITIONS		MIN	TYP†	MAX	UNIT
V_{T+}	Positive-going threshold voltage			1.2	1.9	2.3	V
V_{T-}	Negative-going threshold voltage			0.6	0.95	1.2	V
V_{hys}	Hysteresis			0.6			V
V_{OH}	High-level output voltage	$V_I = 0.6$ V, $I_{OH} = 10$ μA	$V_{CC+} = 5$ V, $V_{CC-} = -5$ V	3.7	4.1	4.5	V
			$V_{CC+} = 12$ V, $V_{CC-} = -12$ V	4.4	4.7	5.2	
		$V_I = 0.6$ V, $I_{OH} = 0.4$ mA	$V_{CC+} = 5$ V, $V_{CC-} = -5$ V	3.1	3.4	3.8	
			$V_{CC+} = 12$ V, $V_{CC-} = -12$ V	3.6	4	4.5	
V_{OL}	Low-level output voltage	$V_I = 2.3$ V, $I_{OL} = 24$ mA			0.2	0.3	V
I_{IH}	High-level input current	$V_I = 25$ V		3.6	6.7	10	mA
		$V_I = 3$ V		0.43	0.67	1	mA
I_{IL}	Low-level input current	$V_I = -25$ V		−3.6	−6.7	−10	mA
		$V_I = -3$ V		−0.43	−0.67	−1	mA
I_{OS}	Short-circuit output current	$V_I = 0.6$ V			−2.8	−3.7	mA

†All typical values are at $T_A = 25°C$.

NOTE 3: The algebraic limit system, in which the more positive (less negative) limit is designated as maximum, is used in this data sheet for logic voltage levels only, e.g., if −8.8 V is the maximum, the typical value is a more negative value.

FIGURE B-6 RS-232-C Driver/Receiver Data Sheet (cont'd). (Courtesy of Texas Instruments.)

ADVANCE INFORMATION

SN75155 LINE DRIVER AND RECEIVER

switching characteristics over recommended operating free-air temperature range, V_{CC+} = 5 V, V_{CC-} = −5 V, C_L = 50 pF (unless otherwise noted)

driver section (see Figure 2)

PARAMETER		TEST CONDITIONS	MIN	TYP	MAX	UNIT
t_{PLH}	Propagation delay time, low-to-high-level output	R_L = 3 kΩ		250	480	ns
t_{PHL}	Propagation delay time high-to-low-level output			80	150	
t_r	Output rise time	R_L = 3 kΩ		67	180	ns
		R_L = 3 kΩ to 7 kΩ, C_L = 2500 pF		2.4	3	μs
t_f	Output fall time	R_L = 3 kΩ		48	160	ns
		R_L = 3 kΩ to 7 kΩ, C_L = 2500 pF		1.9	3	μs

receiver section (see Figure 3)

PARAMETER		TEST CONDITIONS	MIN	TYP	MAX	UNIT
t_{PLH}	Propagation delay time, low-to-high-level output	R_L = 400 Ω		175	245	ns
t_{PHL}	Propagation delay time, high-to-low-level output			37	100	
t_r	Output rise time	R_L = 400 Ω		255	360	ns
t_f	Output fall time	R_L = 400 Ω		23	50	ns

†All typical values are at T_A = 25°C.

PARAMETER MEASUREMENT INFORMATION

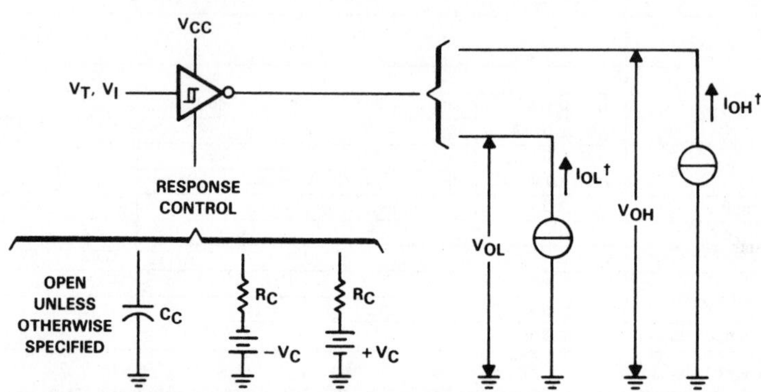

†Arrows indicate actual direction of current flow. Current into a terminal is a positive value.

FIGURE 1. RECEIVER SECTION TEST CIRCUIT (V_{T+}, V_{T-}, V_{OH}, V_{OL})

FIGURE B-6 RS-232-C Driver/Receiver Data Sheet (cont'd). (Courtesy of Texas Instruments.)

B.2.3 Coaxial Cable

Coaxial cable is a more expensive transmission media, but it provides improved shielding to electromagnetic interference. Coaxial cable is used extensively in CATV networks and LANs. Digital data can be transmitted in a baseband format or through a modem at rates up to 16 Mbps with coaxial cable.

B.2.4 Optical Fiber Cable

Optical fiber cable is the most expensive transmission media, but it has the best performance characteristics for high speed and long distance transmission. Optical fiber transmission requires converting from an electrical signal to an optical signal for transmission and detecting an optical signal at the receiver and converting it back to an electrical signal. Fiber optic transmitters are light emitting diodes (LEDs) and lasers. Fiber optic receivers are PIN diodes and avalanche photodiodes.

Optical fiber has very low loss and distortion characteristics, so it is capable of transmitting digital data at the highest rates and for the farthest distance. Current optical fiber transmission systems transmit data at speeds exceeding 2 Gbps. The fiber optic LAN standard, Fiber Distributed Data Interface (FDDI) is intended to transmit data over optical fiber at 100 Mbps. Low-cost fiber optic systems are available to transmit digital data at 5 to 30 Mbps. The HP Fiber Optic Evaluation Kit is one example of a low-cost system, as shown in Figure B-7.

The transmitter and receivers included in the HP Fiber Optic Evaluation Kit operate at TTL-compatible voltage levels. Interface drivers are required to increase the current to a level that will drive the LED.

Numerous sources of information are available on data transmission techniques. All data transmission applications should be thoroughly analyzed to ensure that the transmission techniques and performance are compatible with industry specifications.

LOW COST FIBER OPTIC COMPONENTS WITH ST* PORTS

HFBR-0400 ST SERIES

TECHNICAL DATA JULY 1987

Features

- LOW COST TRANSMITTERS AND RECEIVERS
- 820 NANOMETRE WAVELENGTH TECHNOLOGY
- GUARANTEED WITH 62.5/125, 100/140, and 50/125 μm FIBER SIZES
- QUICK TWIST DELIVERS LOCKING AND SPRING LOADED CONNECTION
- REPEATABLE ST CONNECTIONS WITHIN 0.2 dB TYPICALLY
- UNIQUE OPTICAL PORT DESIGN FOR EFFICIENT COUPLING
- AUTO-INSERTABLE AND WAVE SOLDERABLE
- NO MOUNTING HARDWARE REQUIRED

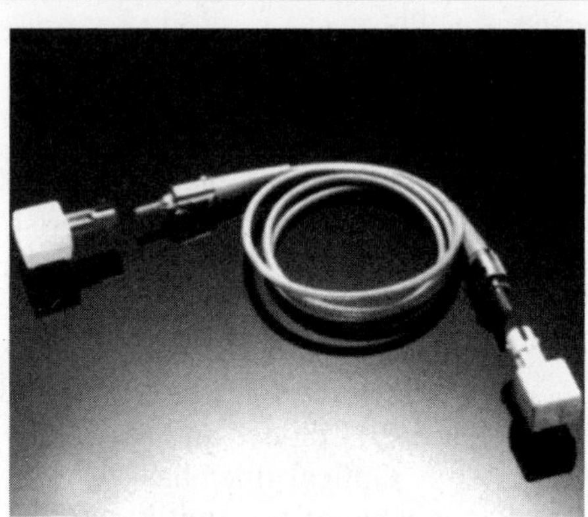

Applications

- COMPUTER TO PERIPHERAL LINKS
- LOCAL AREA NETWORKS
- CENTRAL OFFICE SWITCH LINKS
- PBX LINKS
- COMPUTER MONITOR LINKS
- VIDEO LINKS
- MODEMS AND MULTIPLEXERS
- SUITABLE FOR TEMPEST SYSTEMS

Table of Contents

Description

The HFBR-0400 ST Series of components is designed to provide cost effective, high performance fiber optic communication links for information systems and industrial applications. Link distances of up to 4 kilometres, and data rates of up to 50 megabaud are attainable with these components. These transmitter and receiver components can be quickly locked into position with AT&T's ST Connector and bayonet style connectors from a variety of manufacturers. The ST port will accommodate 62.5/125, 100/140, and 50/125 multimode fibers, and mates directly with the ST Connector's precision ferrule. Due to less variation per insertion, the ST connection assures the maximum possible optical power budget for a system designer's fiber optic link design.

A complete ST evaluation kit (HFBR-0410) is available. It contains an HFBR-1412 transmitter, HFBR-2412 receiver, 3 metres of ST connectored 62.5/125 fiber optic cable with plastic ferrules, and technical literature. In addition, one and ten metre lengths of ST connectored cables with ceramic ferrules are available for prototyping purposes.

*ST is a registered trademark of AT&T Lightguide Cable Connectors.

FIGURE B-7 HP Fiber Optic Evaluation Kit. (Reproduced with permission of Hewlett Packard Company.)

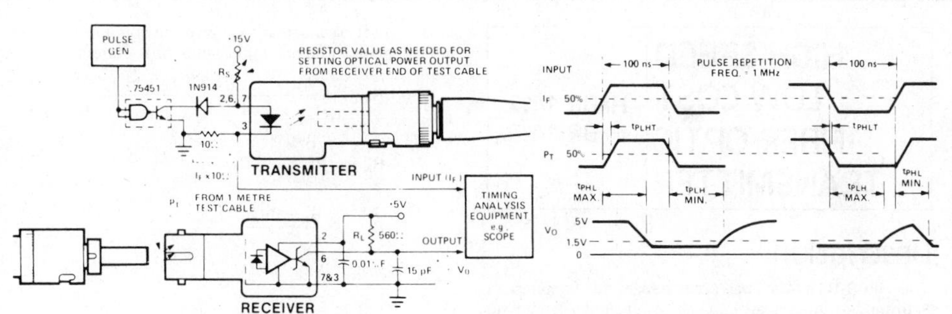

Figure 13. System Propagation Delay Test Circuit and Waveform Timing Definitions.

ST Evaluation Kit

The HFBR-0410 kit is a simple and inexpensive way to demonstrate the performance of Hewlett-Packard's HFBR-0400 ST Series transmitters and receivers.

The HFBR-0410 ST Evaluation Kit contains the following items:

- One HFBR-1412 transmitter
- One HFBR-2412 five megabaud TTL receiver
- Three metres of ST connectored 62.5/125 μm fiber optic cable with low cost plastic ferrules
- HFBR-0400 ST Series data sheets
- HP Application Bulletin 73
- ST connector and cable data sheets

To order an ST Evaluation Kit, please specify HFBR-0410, Quantity 1.

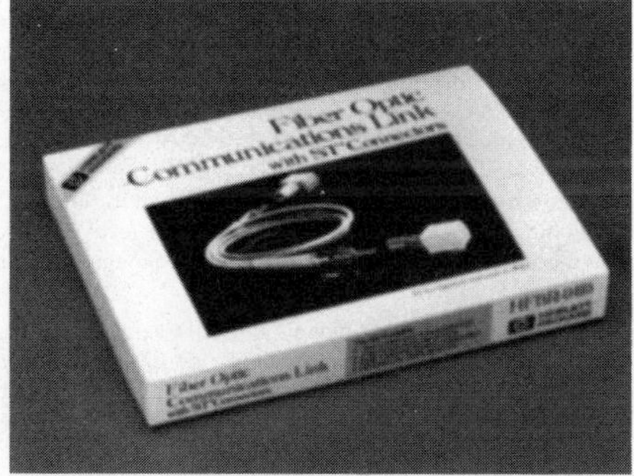

ST Evaluation Cables

Hewlett-Packard offers six different ST connectored cables, available for prototyping purposes. These simplex cables use an ST Connector with a precision ceramic ferrule. One and ten metre simplex cables are available with 62.5/125 μm, 100/140 μm, and 50/125 μm fiber sizes. To order any of these cables, please select the desired part number found below:

For example, to order two connectored simplex cables with 62.5/125 μm fiber, and ST connectors with ceramic ferrules, each ten metres long, specify:

HFBR-BXS010 Quantity: 2

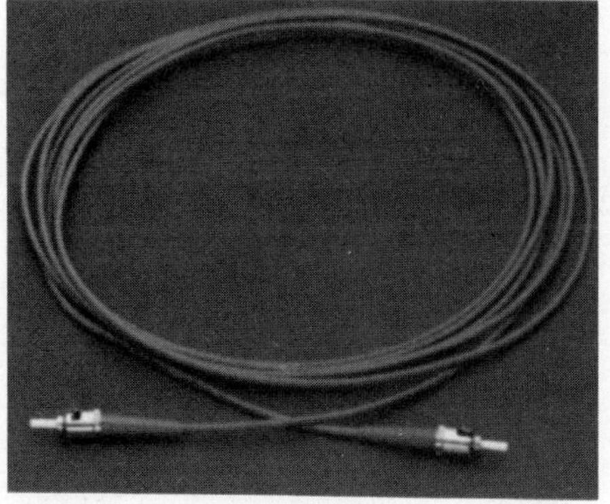

FIGURE B-7 HP Fiber Optic Evaluation Kit (cont'd). (Reproduced with permission of Hewlett Packard Company.)

HIGH SPEED LOW COST FIBER OPTIC TRANSMITTER

HFBR-1412
HFBR-1414

Description

The HFBR-1412/1414 fiber optic transmitter contains an 820 nm GaAlAs emitter capable of efficiently launching optical power into three different optical fiber sizes: 62.5/125 μm, 100/140 μm, and 50/125 μm. This allows the designer flexibility in choosing the fiber size. The HFBR-1412/1414 is designed to operate with the Hewlett-Packard HFBR-2412 and HFBR-2414 fiber optic receivers.

The HFBR-1412/1414 transmitter's high coupling efficiency allows the emitter to be driven at low current levels resulting in low power consumption and increased reliability of the transmitter. The HFBR-1414 high power transmitter is optimized for small size fiber and typically can launch -16.5 dBm optical power into 50/125 μm fiber and -12 dBm into 62.5/125 μm fiber. The HFBR-1412 standard transmitter typically can couple -11.5 dBm of optical power into 100/140 μm fiber cable. It is ideal for large size fiber such as 100/140 μm. The high power level is useful for systems where star couplers, taps, or inline connectors create large fixed losses.

Consistent coupling efficiency is assured by the double-lens optical system (Figure 1). Power coupled into any of the three fiber types varies less than 5 dB from part to part at a given drive current and temperature. The benefit of this is reduced dynamic range requirements on the receiver.

Recommended Drive Circuits

For data rates of 35 MBd or less, the transmitter drive circuit in Figure 7 will be adequate. For greater than 35 MBd operation, shorter rise and fall times are desirable. Rise and fall times can be improved by using a pre-bias current and "speed-up" capacitor. A pre-bias current will significantly reduce the junction capacitance and will not change the extinction ratio appreciably. The recommended TTL compatible drive circuit in Figure 4 using a speed-up capacitor will provide typical rise and fall times of 4 ns. The following set of equations will give the component values for the circuit for different transmitter drive current:

$$R_y = \frac{(V_{CC} - V_F) + 3.2\,(V_{CC} - V_F - 1.4\text{V})}{I_{F_{ON}}}$$

$$R_x = \left(\frac{R_y}{3.2} - 10\,\Omega\right)$$

$$R_{x_1} = \frac{R_x + 10\Omega}{2}$$

$$R_{x_2} = R_{x_1} - 10\Omega$$

$$C = \frac{2.0\text{ nsec}}{R_{x_1}}$$

Example: For $I_{F_{ON}} = 27$ mA, V_F can be obtained from Figure 2 = 1.7 V.

$$R_y = \frac{(5\text{V} - 1.7\text{V}) + 3.2\,(5\text{ V} - 1.7\text{ V} - 1.4\text{ V})}{27\text{ mA}}$$

$$= \frac{3.3\text{ V} + 6.1\text{ V}}{27\text{ mA}} = 348\ \Omega$$

$$R_x = \left(\frac{348\ \Omega}{3.2}\right) - 10\ \Omega = 98.8\ \Omega$$

$$R_{x_1} = \frac{98.8\ \Omega + 10\ \Omega}{2} = 54.4\ \Omega$$

$$R_{x_2} = 54.4 - 10 = 44.4\ \Omega$$

$$C = \frac{2\text{ nsec}}{R_{x_1}} = 36.8\text{ pF}$$

Selected the following standard value components:

$R_y = 330\ \Omega$ $R_{x_1} = 56\ \Omega$ $R_{x_2} = 47\ \Omega$ $C = 39$ pF

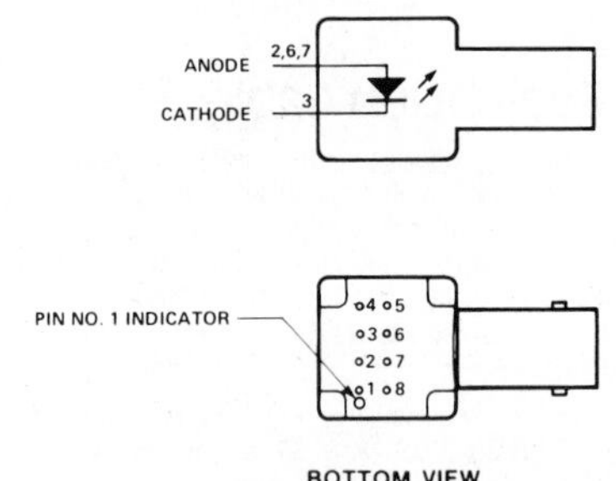

BOTTOM VIEW

PIN	FUNCTION
1	N.C.
2*	ANODE
3	CATHODE
4	N.C.
5	N.C.
6*	ANODE
7*	ANODE
8	N.C.

*PINS 2, 6 AND 7 ELECTRICALLY CONNECTED TO HEADER

Absolute Maximum Ratings

Parameter		Symbol	Min.	Max.	Unit	Notes
Storage Temperature		T_S	-55	+85	°C	
Operating Temperature		T_A	-40	+85	°C	
Lead Soldering Cycle	Temp.			+260	°C	
	Time			10	sec	
Forward Input Current	Peak	I_{FPK}		120	mA	Note 1
	DC	I_{FDC}		60	mA	
Reverse Input Voltage		V_{BR}		1.8	V	

FIGURE B-7 HP Fiber Optic Evaluation Kit (cont'd). (Reproduced with permission of Hewlett Packard Company.)

5 MBd LOW COST FIBER OPTIC RECEIVER

HFBR-2412

Description

The HFBR-2412 fiber optic receiver is designed to operate with the Hewlett-Packard HFBR-1412/1414 fiber optic transmitter and 62.5/125 μm, 100/140 μm, and 50/125 μm fiber optic cable terminated with ST Connectors. Consistent coupling into the receiver is assured by the lensed optical system (Figure 1). Response does not vary with fiber size.

The HFBR-2412 receiver incorporates an integrated photo IC containing a photodetector and dc amplifier driving an open-collector Schottky output transistor. The HFBR-2402 is designed for direct interfacing to popular logic families. The absence of an internal pull-up resistor allows the open-collector output to be used with logic families such as CMOS requiring voltage excursions much higher than V_{CC}.

Both the open-collector "Data" output Pin 6 and V_{CC} Pin 2 are referenced to "Com" Pin 3, 7. The "Data" output allows busing, strobing and wired "OR" circuit configurations. The transmitter is designed to operate from a single +5V supply. It is essential that a bypass capacitor 0.01μF to 0.1 μF ceramic be connected from Pin 2 V_{CC} to Pin 3 circuit common of the receiver.

Absolute Maximum Ratings

Parameter		Symbol	Min.	Max.	Units	Reference
Storage Temperature		T_S	-55	+85	C	
Operating Temperature		T_A	-40	+85	C	
Lead Soldering Cycle	Temp			+260	C	Note 1
	Time			10	sec	
Supply Voltage		V_{CC}	-0.5	7.0	V	
Output Current		I_O		25	mA	
Output Voltage		V_O	-0.5	18.0	V	
Output Collector Power Dissipation		$P_{O\ AV}$		40	mW	
Fan Out (TTL)		N		5		Note 2

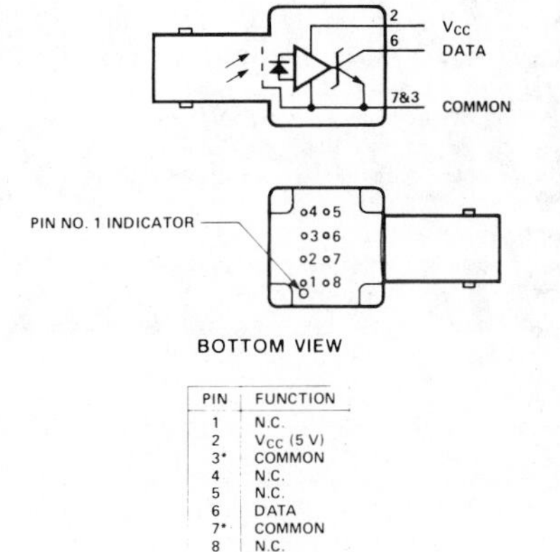

PIN	FUNCTION
1	N.C.
2	V_{CC} (5 V)
3*	COMMON
4	N.C.
5	N.C.
6	DATA
7*	COMMON
8	N.C.

*PINS 3 AND 7 ARE ELECTRICALLY CONNECTED TO HEADER

FIGURE B-7 HP Fiber Optic Evaluation Kit (cont'd). (Reproduced with permission of Hewlett Packard Company.)

Appendix C

Programmable Logic Device Development Systems

C-1 PLD DEVELOPMENT SYSTEMS

The programmable logic devices (PLDs) used throughout this textbook are the GAL16V8 and the GAL16V8A, manufactured by Lattice Semiconductor Corp. The GAL16V8 and GAL16V8A are E^2PLD CMOS devices that emulate all common 20-pin programmable array logic (PAL) devices. The data sheet for the GAL16V8A is shown in Figure 12-6.

PLD development systems are hardware and software systems to program the PLD. One low-cost development system that can be used to program the GAL16V8 is the Logic Lab programmer and the LC9000 logic compiler, both manufactured by Programmable Logic Technologies. The examples in Chapter 12 use the LC9000 compiler and Logic Lab programmer to program the GAL16V8. The LC9000 source files for selected example problems from Chapter 12 are listed for reference in Appendix D.

Numerous hardware programmer systems and software development tools are available with enhanced features beyond what LogicLab and LC9000 are intended to provide. The PLD development systems recommended by Lattice Semiconductor Corp. for use with GAL devices are listed in Table C-1 and C-2. The programmer manufacturers and software developers are listed in Table C-3 and C-4, with addresses and phone numbers to obtain additional information.

TABLE C-1 Programmer/Development Systems Qualified for Lattice GAL Devices

Vendor	Model
Data I/O Corporation	M29B
	PT 303A-011
	Unisite 40
	M60A
Programmable Logic Technologies	Logic Lab
Qwerty Inc.	GPR-1000
	GPR-1000+
Stag Electronic Designs	ZL30A/ZL32

TABLE C-2 Software Development Tools

Vendor	Software Package
Capilano Computing	LPLC
Data I/O	ABEL
	PLD test
	DASH-ABEL
Hewlett-Packard	PLD Design System
Monolithic Memories	PALASM
Personal CAD Systems	CUPL
Pistohl Electronics	ELP
Programmable Logic Technologies	LC9000
Qwerty Inc.	PLAQ

TABLE C-3 Programmer Manufacturers

Data I/O Corp.
10525 Willows Road N.E.
P.O. Box 97046
Redmond, WA 98073-9746
(206) 881-6444

Programmable Logic Technologies
P.O. Box 1567
Longmont, CO 80501
(303) 772-9059

Qwerty Inc.
5346 Bragg Street
San Diego, CA 92122
(619) 455-0500

Stag Electronic Designs
1600 Wyatt Dr.
Santa Clara, CA 95054
(408) 988-1118

TABLE C-4 Software Developers

Capilano Computing
P.O. Box 86971
North Vancouver, BC V7L 4P6
Canada
(604) 669-6343

Data I/O FutureNet
10525 Willows Road N.E.
P.O. Box 97046
Redmond, WA 98073-9746
(206) 881-6444

Personal CAD Systems
1290 Parkmoor Ave.
San Jose, CA 95126
(408) 971-1300

Pistohl Electronics
22560 Alcalde Rd.
Cupertino, CA 95014
(408) 255-2422

Programmable Logic Technologies
P.O. Box 1567
Longmont, CO 80501
(303) 772-9059

Qwerty Inc.
5346 Bragg Street
San Diego, CA 92122
(619) 455-0500

C-2 LOGIC LAB PLD PROGRAMMER

Logic Lab is a basic PLD programmer manufactured by Programmable Logic Technologies that is appropriate for educational or personal use. The Logic Lab system requires an IBM compatible PC with a minimal configuration of 512 KBytes of RAM, one RS-232 serial port, and two floppy disk drives. The Logic Lab programmer has two sockets, one for 20-pin GAL devices such as the GAL16V8, and another for 24-pin GAL devices such as the GAL20V8.

Programming the GAL device requires the use of the LC9000 compiler along with the programmer. The Logic Lab programmer is shipped with the LC9000 compiler.

C-3 LC9000 LOGIC COMPILER

The LC9000 compiler is a PLD software development tool that can program the PLD through the specification of Boolean equations. The LC9000 compiler converts Boolean equations to a JEDEC file to create a fuse map defining the fuse connections of the AND-OR array. The JEDEC file is downloaded from the PC to the buffer in the Logic Lab programmer to program the PLD.

The LC9000 assembler can specify combinational and sequential logic equations. Schematic capture, truth table entry, state transition entry, or logic simulation functions are not performed by LC9000. A more complex logic compiler would be required to perform the enhanced programming functions.

C-4 REFERENCES

Additional information about the GAL devices, Logic Lab programmer, and LC9000 logic compiler can be obtained from the manufacturers.

GAL devices: Lattice Semiconductor Corp.
Customer Service: 1-800-FAST-GAL

Logic Lab and LC9000: Programmable Logic Technologies
(303) 772-9059

References

1. *GAL Handbook*, Lattice Semiconductor Corp.
2. *GAL Data Book*, Lattice Semiconductor Corp.
3. *The Logic Lab with LC9000 Users' Guide*, Programmable Logic Development System, Programmable Logic Technologies, Inc.

Appendix D

Programmable Logic Device Example Problems: LC9000 Source File Listings and LC9000 Document File Listings

Appendix D contains the source files and document files produced by LC9000 logic compiler for selected PLD example problems in Chapter 12. All of the example problems are fully explained in Chapter 12. The PLD source files of all PLD examples are shown in Chapter 12.

The LC9000 source files and document files are included in Appendix D as a reference to those who do not have access to PLD programmers or development systems.

```
DEVICE 16V8;
TITLE Example 12-5;
NAME Decimal-to-Binary Encoder;
/*      This source file defines a decimal-to-binary
priority encoder. The encoder accepts the inputs
from ten active-LOW switches and outputs the
corresponding binary value.      */

/*      Inputs              */

PIN  1 = I0;
PIN  2 = I1;
PIN  3 = I2;
PIN  4 = I3;
PIN  5 = I4;
PIN  6 = I5;
PIN  7 = I6;
PIN  8 = I7;
PIN  9 = I8;
PIN 11 = I9;

/*      Outputs             */

PIN 12 = D;
PIN 13 = C;
PIN 14 = B;
PIN 15 = A;

/*      Power and ground    */

PIN 20 = VCC;
PIN 10 = GND;

/*      Boolean Equations */

D = !I9 ! !I8 & I9 ;

C = !I7 & I8 & I9 ! !I6 & I7 & I8 & I9
      ! !I5 & I6 & I7 & I8 & I9
      ! !I4 & I5 & I6 & I7 & I8 & I9 ;
```

```
B = !I7 & I8 & I9 ! !I6 & I7 & I8 & I9
    ! !I3 & I4 & I5 & I6 & I7 & I8 & I9
    ! !I2 & I3 & I4 & I5 & I6 & I7 & I8 & I9 ;

A = !I9 ! !I7 & I8 & I9
    ! !I5 & I6 & I7 & I8 & I9
    ! !I3 & I4 & I5 & I6 & I7 & I8 & I9
    ! !I1 & I2 & I3 & I4 & I5 & I6 & I7 & I8 & I9 ;
```

Logic Comp by Programmable Logic
EXAMPLE 12-5
DECIMAL-TO-BINARY ENCODER

16V8

I0	01	20	VCC
I1	02	19	unused
I2	03	18	unused
I3	04	17	unused
I4	05	16	unused
I5	06	15	A
I6	07	14	B
I7	08	13	C
I8	09	12	D
GND	10	11	I9

Logic Comp by Programmable Logic
EXAMPLE 12-5
DECIMAL-TO-BINARY ENCODER

Equations translated to Sum of Products form

```
D
  =     !I8
  |     !I9;
```

```
C
    =   !I4 & I8 & I9
    |   !I5 & I8 & I9
    |   !I6 & I8 & I9
    |   !I7 & I8 & I9;

B
    =   !I6 & I8 & I9
    |   !I7 & I8 & I9
    |   !I2 & I4 & I5 & I8 & I9
    |   !I3 & I4 & I5 & I8 & I9;

A
    =   !I7
    |   !I7 & I8
    |   !I5 & I6 & I8
    |   !I3 & I4 & I6 & I8
    |   !I1 & I2 & I4 & I6 & I8;
```

```
DEVICE 16V8;
TITLE Example 12-6;
NAME BCD-to-Excess 3 Code Converter;
/*  This source file defines a BCD-to-Excess 3 code converter.
    It converts BCD-to-Excess 3, as well as convert Excess 3-
    to-BCD.         */

/*  BCD-to-Excess 3 Inputs          */

PIN  1 = D;
PIN  2 = C;
PIN  3 = B;
PIN  4 = A;

/*  BCD-to-Excess 3 Outputs          */

PIN 19 = W;
PIN 18 = X;
PIN 17 = Y;
PIN 16 = Z;

/*  Excess 3-to-BCD Inputs          */

PIN  5 = R;
PIN  6 = S;
PIN  7 = T;
PIN  8 = U;
```

```
/*    Excess 3-to-BCD Outputs              */

PIN 15 = H;
PIN 14 = G;
PIN 13 = F;
PIN 12 = E;

/*    Power and Ground              */

PIN 20 = VCC;
PIN 10 = GND;

/*    BCD-to-Excess 3 Boolean Equations          */

W = !D & C & !B & A ! !D & C & B & !A ! !D & C & B & A
    ! D & !C & !B & !A ! D & !C & !B & A ;

X = !D & !C & !B & A ! !D & !C & B & !A ! !D & !C & B & A
    ! !D & C & !B & !A ! !D & C & !B & A ;

Y = !D & !C & !B & !A ! !D & !C & B & A ! !D & C & !B & !A
    ! !D & C & B & A ! D & !C & !B & !A;

Z = !A;

/*    Excess 3-to-BCD Boolean Equations          */

H = R & !S & T & U ! R & S & !T & !U;

G = !R & S & T & U ! R & !S & !T & !U
    ! R & !S & !T & U ! R & !S & T & !U;

F = !R & S & !T & U ! !R & S & T & !U
    ! R & !S & !T & U ! R & !S & T & !U;

E = !U;
```

Logic Comp by Programmable Logic
EXAMPLE 12-6
BCD-TO-EXCESS 3 CODE CONVERTER

16V8

D	01	20	VCC
C	02	19	W
B	03	18	X
A	04	17	Y
R	05	16	Z
S	06	15	H
T	07	14	G
U	08	13	F
unused	09	12	E
GND	10	11	unused

Logic Comp by Programmable Logic
EXAMPLE 12-6
BCD-TO-EXCESS 3 CODE CONVERTER

Equations translated to Sum of Products form

```
W
    =   !D &  C &  B
    |    D & !C & !B
    |   !D &  C &  A;

X
    =   !D & !C &  B
    |   !D &  C & !B
    |   !D & !B &  A;

Y
    =   !D &  B &  A
    |   !D & !B & !A
    |   !C & !B & !A;

Z
    =   !A;
```

```
H
   =    R & !S & T & U
   |    R & S & !T & !U;
G
   =    R & !S & !T
   |    R & !S & !U
   |   !R & S & T & U;
F
   =   !R & S & !T & U
   |    R & !S & !T & U
   |   !R & S & T & !U
   |    R & !S & T & !U;
E
   =   !U;
```

```
DEVICE 16V8;
TITLE Example 12-8;
NAME Quad 2-input Multiplexer;

/*    This source file defines a four-output
      multiplexer that switches one of two inputs to each
      output.    */

/*    Data Inputs — A Word          */

PIN 2 = A3;
PIN 3 = A2;
PIN 4 = A1;
PIN 5 = A0;

/*    Data Inputs — B Word          */

PIN 6 = B3;
PIN 7 = B2;
PIN 8 = B1;
PIN 9 = B0;

/*    Select Input        */

PIN 19 = S ;

/*    Outputs        */

PIN 15 = Y3;
PIN 14 = Y2;
PIN 13 = Y1;
PIN 12 = Y0;
```

```
/*      Power and Ground             */

PIN 20 = VCC ;
PIN 10 = GND ;

/*      Boolean Equations            */

Y3 = !S & A3 ! S & B3;
Y2 = !S & A2 ! S & B2;
Y1 = !S & A1 ! S & B1;
Y0 = !S & A0 ! S & B0;
```

Logic Comp by Programmable Logic
EXAMPLE 12-8
QUAD 2-INPUT MULTIPLEXER

16V8

unused	01	20	VCC
A3	02	19	S
A2	03	18	unused
A1	04	17	unused
A0	05	16	unused
B3	06	15	Y3
B2	07	14	Y2
B1	08	13	Y1
B0	09	12	Y0
GND	10	11	unused

Logic Comp by Programmable Logic
EXAMPLE 12-8
QUAD 2-INPUT MULTIPLEXER

Equations translated to Sum of Products form

```
Y3
   =    B3 & S
   |    A3 & !S;
```

```
Y2
   =    B2 & S
   |    A2 & !S;

Y1
   =    B1 & S
   |    A1 & !S;

Y0
   =    B0 & S
   |    A0 & !S;
```

```
DEVICE 16V8;
TITLE Example 12-10 for the GAL 16V8;
NAME SR Latch and D Latch;

/*    This source file defines an active-LOW SR latch and
      an active-HIGH D latch.    */

/*    The GAL 16V8 must operate in the complex mode in
      order to have feedback in the combinational output
      logic expressions.    */

/*    SR Latch Inputs    */

PIN  1 = S;
PIN  2 = R;

/*    D Latch Inputs    */

PIN  8 = EN;
PIN  9 = D;

/*    D Latch Outputs    */

PIN 14 = QD;
PIN 13 = QDNOT;

/*    SR Latch Outputs    */

PIN 18 = QRS;
PIN 17 = QRSNOT;

/*    Power and Ground    */

PIN 20 = VCC;
PIN 10 = GND;
```

```
/*      SR Latch Boolean Equations      */

QRS =         !S ! S & R & QRS;

QRSNOT = !R ! S & R & !QRS ;

QRS.OE = VCC;          /*    Output enable function for QRS      */

QRSNOT.OE = VCC;       /*    Output enable function for
                             QRSNOT     */

/*      Gated D Latch Boolean Equations      */

QD =          !EN & QD ! EN & D ;

QDNOT = !EN & !QD ! EN & !D ;

QD.OE = VCC;           /*    Output enable function for QD      */

QDNOT.OE = VCC;        /*    Output enable function for
                             QDNOT      */
```

Logic Comp by Programmable Logic
EXAMPLE 12-10 FOR THE GAL 16V8
SR LATCH AND D LATCH

16V8

S	01	20	VCC
R	02	19	unused
unused	03	18	QRS
unused	04	17	QRSNOT
unused	05	16	unused
unused	06	15	unused
unused	07	14	QD
EN	08	13	QDNOT
D	09	12	unused
GND	10	11	unused

```
Logic Comp by Programmable Logic
EXAMPLE 12-10 for the GAL 16V8
SR LATCH AND D LATCH

Equations translated to Sum of Products form

QRS
  =     !S
  |     S & R &  QRS;

QRSNOT
  =     !R
  |     S & R & !QRS;

QRS.OE
  =     VCC;

QRSNOT.OE
  =     VCC;

QD
  =     !EN &  QD
  |      EN &  D;

QDNOT
  =     !EN & !QD
  |      EN & !D;

QD.OE
  =     VCC;

QDNOT.OE
  =     VCC;
```

```
DEVICE 16V8;
TITLE Example 12-11;
NAME PLD Flip-Flops;

/*     This source file defines a D flip-flop, and toggle
       flip-flop, and a JK flip-flop. Each flip flop
       is a positive edge-triggered device with synchronous
       preset and clear inputs.      */

/*     The output enable is an active-LOW input. A logic-LOW
       on Pin 11 enables all registered outputs. A logic-HIGH on Pin 11
       disables all registered outputs by putting them into
       a high-impedance state.      */
```

```
/*   Clock and Enable Inputs   */

PIN  1 = CLK;
PIN 11 = OE;

/*   Common Preset and Clear Inputs   */

/*   These preset and clear inputs will preset and clear
     all registered outputs on the rising edge of the clock pulse.   */

PIN  2 = PRE;
PIN  3 = CLR;

/*   D Flip-Flop Inputs   */

PIN  4 = D;

/*   D Flip-Flop Outputs   */

PIN 19 = QD;
PIN 18 = QDNOT;

/*   Toggle Flip Flop Inputs   */

PIN  5 = T;

/*   Toggle Flip-Flop Outputs   */

PIN 17 = QT;
PIN 16 = QTNOT;

/*   J-K Flip-Flop Inputs   */

PIN  6 = J;
PIN  7 = K;

/*   J-K Flip-Flop Outputs   */

PIN 15 = QJK;
PIN 14 = QJKNOT;

/*   D Flip-Flop Boolean Equations   */

QD.D =       !PR # CL & D ;

QDNOT.D = !CL # PR & !D ;

/*   Toggle Flip-Flop Boolean Equations   */

QT.D =       !PR # CL & !T &  QT # CL & T & !QT ;

QTNOT.D = !CL # PR & !T & !QT # PR & T &  QT ;
```

```
/*      J-K Flip-Flop Boolean Equations          */

QJK.D =          !PR ! CL & !J & !K & QJK ! CL & J & !K
                 ! CL & J & K & !QJK ;

QJKNOT.D =       !CL ! PR & !J & !K !QJK ! PR & !J & K
                 ! PR & J & K & QJK ;
```

Logic Comp by Programmable Logic
EXAMPLE 12-11
PLD FLIP FLOPS

16V8

CLK	01	20	VCC
PRE	02	19	QD
CLR	03	18	QDNOT
D	04	17	QT
T	05	16	QTNOT
J	06	15	QJK
K	07	14	QJKNOT
unused	08	13	unused
unused	09	12	unused
GND	10	11	OE

Logic Comp by Programmable Logic
EXAMPLE 12-11
PLD FLIP FLOPS

Equations translated to Sum of Products form

```
QD.D
  =     !PR
  |      CL &  D;
```

```
QDNOT.D
   =    !CL
   |     PR & !D;

QT.D
   =    !PR
   |     CL & !T &  QT
   |     CL &  T & !QT

QTNOT.D
   =    !CL
   |     PR &  T &  QT
   |     PR & !T & !QT;

QJK.D
   =    !PR
   |     CL & !K &  QJK
   |     CL &  J  & !QJK;

QJKNOT.D
   =    !CL
   |     PR &  K &  QJK
   |     PR & !J  & !QJK;
```

```
DEVICE 16V8;
TITLE Example 12-12;
NAME Universal Shift Register;

/*    This source file defines a four-bit shift register
      that has four modes of operation. It can hold data,
      shift left, shift right, or parallel load.      */

/*    The shifting takes place on the rising edge of the
      clock pulse.      */

/*    The outputs are enabled when Pin 11 is a logic-LOW.
      The outputs are in a high-impedance state when Pin 11 is a
      logic-HIGH.      */

/*    Clock and Output-Enable Inputs      */

PIN  1 = CLK;
PIN 11 = OE;
```

```
/*     Mode Control Inputs          */

PIN  2 = S2;
PIN  3 = S1;
PIN  4 = S0;

/*     Parallel Data Inputs         */

PIN  5 = P3;
PIN  6 = P2;
PIN  7 = P1;
PIN  8 = P0;

/*     Serial Input for Shifting Right Input     */

PIN  9 = SIR;

/*     Serial Input for Shifting Left Input      */

PIN 12 = SIL;

/*     Parallel Outputs             */

PIN 19 = Q3;
PIN 18 = Q2;
PIN 17 = Q1;
PIN 16 = Q0;

/*     Boolean Equations            */

Q3.D =   !S1 & !S0 & Q3 # !S1 & S0 & Q2
         # S1 & !S0 & SIR # S1 & S0 & P3;

Q2.D =   !S1 & !S0 & Q2 # !S1 & S0 & Q1
         # S1 & !S0 & Q3 # S1 & S0 & P2;

Q1.D =   !S1 & !S0 & Q1 # !S1 & S0 & Q0
         # S1 & !S0 & Q2 # S1 & S0 & P1;

Q0.D =   !S1 & !S0 & Q0 # !S1 & S0 & SIL
         # S1 & !S0 & Q1 # S1 & S0 & P0;
```

Logic Comp by Programmable Logic
EXAMPLE 12-12
UNIVERSAL SHIFT REGISTER

16V8

CLK	01	20	VCC
S2	02	19	Q3
S1	03	18	Q2
S0	04	17	Q1
P3	05	16	Q0
P2	06	15	unused
P1	07	14	unused
P0	08	13	unused
SIR	09	12	SIL
GND	10	11	OE

Logic Comp by Programmable Logic
EXAMPLE 12-12
UNIVERSAL SHIFT REGISTER

Equations translated to Sum of Products form

```
Q3.D
   =    S1 &  S0 & P3
   |    S1 & !S0 & SIR
   |   !S1 &  S0 & Q2
   |   !S1 & !S0 & Q3;

Q2.D
   =    S1 &  S0 & P2
   |   !S1 &  S0 & Q1
   |   !S1 & !S0 & Q2
   |    S1 & !S0 & Q3;

Q1.D
   =    S1 &  S0 & P1
   |   !S1 &  S0 & Q0
   |   !S1 & !S0 & Q1
   |    S1 & !S0 & Q2;
```

```
Q0.D
   =     S1 & S0 & P0
   |    !S1 & S0 & SIL
   |    !S1 & !S0 & Q0
   |     S1 & !S0 & Q1;

DEVICE 16V8;
TITLE Example 12-15;
NAME Binary Sequence Generator;

/*   This source file defines a binary sequence
     generator. The circuit generates a four-bit
     output of the following sequence: 2, 3, 7, 5, 8,
     10, 14, 12, 2, 3, etc. Any unwanted four-bit
     combinations force the sequence generator to
     the count value of 2 so that the circuit is
     self-correcting.  */

/*   The sequence generator changes count states on
     the rising edge of the clock. All outputs are
     active when Pin 11 is a logic-LOW. All outputs
     are in a high-impedance state when Pin 11 is
     a logic-HIGH.          */

/*   Clock and Output-Enable Control Inputs      */

PIN  1 = CLK;
PIN 11 = OE;

/*   Outputs           */

PIN 19 = Q3;
PIN 18 = Q2;
PIN 17 = Q1;
PIN 16 = Q0;

/*   Power and Ground           */

PIN 20 = VCC ;
PIN 10 = GND ;

/*   Boolean Equations          */

Q3.D = !Q3 & Q2 & !Q1 & Q0 ! Q3 & !Q2 & !Q1 & !Q0
     ! Q3 & !Q2 & Q1 & !Q0 ! Q3 & Q2 & Q1 & !Q0 ;

Q2.D = !Q3 & !Q2 & Q1 & Q0 ! !Q3 & Q2 & Q1 & Q0
     ! Q3 & !Q2 & Q1 & !Q0 ! Q3 & Q2 & Q1 & !Q0 ;

!Q1.D = !Q3 & Q2 & !Q1 & Q0 ! !Q3 & Q2 & Q1 & Q0
     ! Q3 & Q2 & Q1 & !Q0 ;

Q0.D = !Q3 & !Q2 & Q1 & !Q0 ! !Q3 & !Q2 & Q1 & Q0
     ! !Q3 & Q2 & Q1 & Q0 ;
```

Logic Comp by Programmable Logic
EXAMPLE 12-15
BINARY SEQUENCE GENERATOR

16V8

CLK	01	20	VCC
unused	02	19	Q3
unused	03	18	Q2
unused	04	17	Q1
unused	05	16	Q0
unused	06	15	unused
unused	07	14	unused
unused	08	13	unused
unused	09	12	unused
GND	10	11	OE

Logic Comp by Programmable Logic
EXAMPLE 12-15
BINARY SEQUENCE GENERATOR

Equations translated to Sum of Products form

```
Q3.D
  =    !Q0 & Q1 & Q3
  |    !Q0 & !Q2 & Q3
  |     Q0 & !Q1 & Q2 & !Q3;

Q2.D
  =    !Q0 & Q1 & Q3
  |     Q0 & Q1 & !Q3;

!Q1.D
  =     Q0 & Q2 & !Q3
  |    !Q0 & Q1 & Q2 & Q3;

Q0.D
  =     Q0 & Q1 & !Q3
  |     Q1 & !Q2 & !Q3;
```

Appendix E

Semiconductor Memory Data Book Specifications

HN62331P/F

131,072 × 8-Bit CMOS MASK Programmable Read Only Memory

■ DESCRIPTION

The HN62331 is a 1-Mbit CMOS mask-programmable ROM organized as 131,072-words × 8-bits. Realizing low power consumption, this memory is allowed for battery operation. In addition, the HN62331, which provides large capacity of 1M bits, is ideally suited for kanji character generators.

(DP-32)

(FP-32D)

■ FEATURES

- Single +5V Power Supply
- Three-State Data Output for OR-Tieing
- TTL Compatible
- Maximum Access Time ....120ns (max.)
- Low Power Consumption ....100mW (typ.) Active
  5μW (typ.) Standby
- Byte-wide Data Organization
- Pin Compatible with JEDEC

■ ORDERING INFORMATION

Type No.	Access Time	Package
HN62331P	120ns	600 mil 32 pin Plastic DIP
HN62331F	120ns	32 pin Plastic SOP

■ PIN ARRANGEMENT

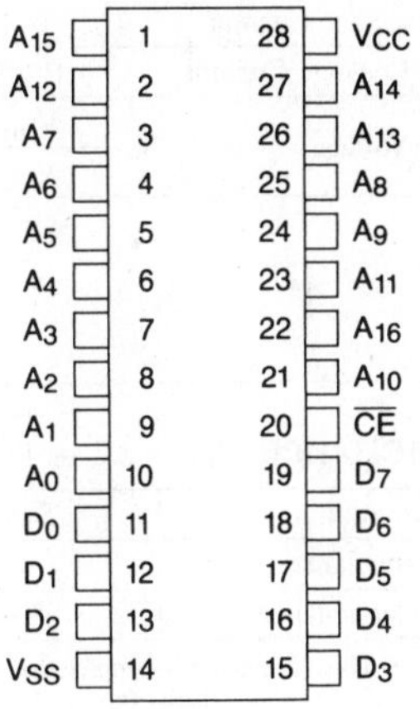

(Top View)

■ BLOCK DIAGRAM

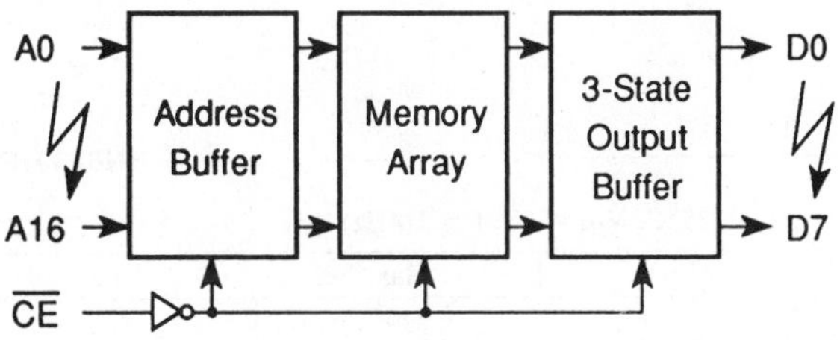

■ ABSOLUTE MAXIMUM RATINGS

Item	Symbol	Value	Unit	Note
Supply Voltage	V_{CC}	-0.3 ~ +7.0	V	1
All Input and Output Voltage	V_T	-3.0 ~ V_{CC} +0.3	V	1
Operating Temperature Range	T_{opr}	0 ~ +70	°C	
Storage Temperature Range	T_{stg}	-55 ~ +125	°C	
Temperature Under Bias	T_{bias}	-20 ~ +85	°C	

NOTE: 1. With respect to V_{SS}.

■ RECOMMENDED OPERATING CONDITIONS (V_{SS} = 0V, T_a = 0 ~ 70°C)

Item	Symbol	Min.	Typ.	Max.	Unit
Supply Voltage	V_{CC}	4.5	5.0	5.5	V
Input Voltage	V_{IH}	2.4	—	V_{CC} + 0.3	V
	V_{IL}	-0.3	—	0.45	V

■ DC ELECTRICAL CHARACTERISTICS (V_{CC} = 5V ± 10%, V_{SS} = 0V, T_a = 0 ~ 70°C)

Item		Symbol	Test Condition	Min.	Max.	Unit
Supply Current	Active	I_{CC}	V_{CC} = 5.5V, ID_{OUT} = 0mA, t_{RC} = Min.	—	50	mA
	Standby	I_{SB}	V_{CC} = 5.5V, $\overline{CE} \geq V_{CC}$ - 0.2V	—	30	μA
Input Leakage Current		$\lvert I_{IL} \rvert$	V_{IN} = 0 ~ V_{CC}	—	10	μA
Output Leakage Current		$\lvert I_{OL} \rvert$	$\overline{CE}$ = 2.4V, V_{OUT} = 0 ~ V_{CC}	—	10	μA
Output Voltage		V_{OH}	I_{OH} = -205μA	2.4	—	V
		V_{OL}	I_{OL} = 1.6mA	—	0.4	V

■ CAPACITANCE (V_{CC} = 5V ± 10%, V_{SS} = 0V, T_a = 25°C, V_{IN} = 0V, f = 1MHz)

Item	Symbol	Min.	Max.	Unit
Input Capacitance	C_{IN}	—	10	pF
Output Capacitance	C_{OUT}	—	15	pF

NOTE: * This parameter is sampled and not 100% tested.

■ AC ELECTRICAL CHARACTERISTICS (V_{CC} = 5V ± 10%, V_{SS} = 0V, T_a = 0 ~ 70°C)

Item	Symbol	Min.	Max.	Unit
Read Cycle Time	t_{RC}	120	—	ns
Address Access Time	t_{AA}	—	120	ns
$\overline{CE}$ Access Time	t_{ACE}	—	120	ns
Output Hold Time From Address Change	t_{DHA}	0	—	ns
Output Hold Time From $\overline{CE}$	t_{DHC}	0	—	ns
$\overline{CE}$ to Output in High Z	t_{CHZ}*	—	60	ns
$\overline{CE}$ to Output in Low Z	t_{CLZ}	5	—	ns

NOTE: * t_{CHZ} and t_{OHZ} are defined as the time at which the output achieves the open circuit conditions and are not referred to output voltage levels.

HN62331P/F

- **Test Conditions**
  - Input Pulse Level: 0.45 ~ 2.4V
  - Input and Output Timing Reference Level: 1.5V
  - Input Rise and Fall Time: 10ns
  - Output Load: 1 TTL gate + CL = 100pF (including scope and jig capacitance)

■ TIMING WAVEFORM

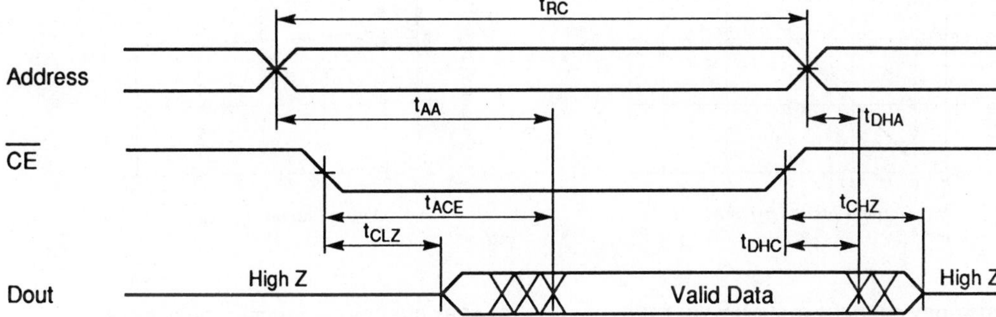

NOTES: 1. t_{DHA}, t_{DHC}; determined by faster.
2. t_{AA}, t_{ACE}; determined by slower.

OUTPUT VOLTAGE vs. OUTPUT CURRENT

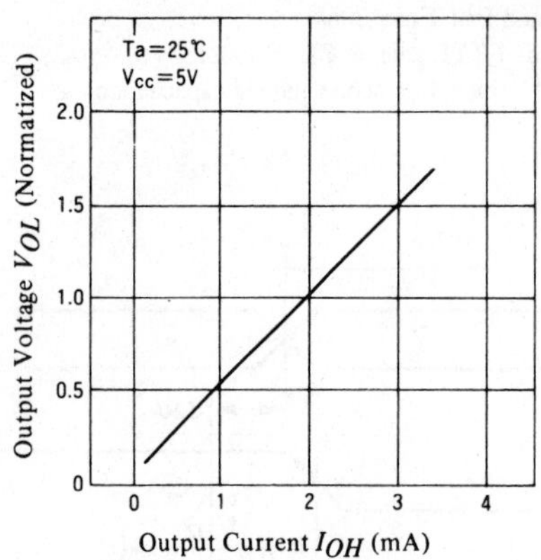

OUTPUT VOLTAGE vs. OUTPUT CURRENT

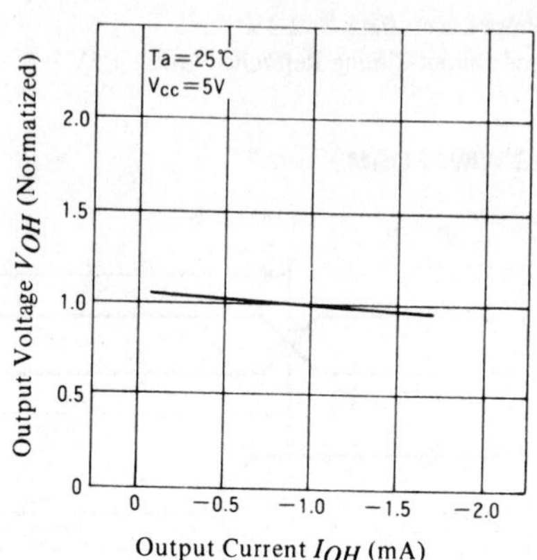

STANDBY CURRENT vs. SUPPLY VOLTAGE

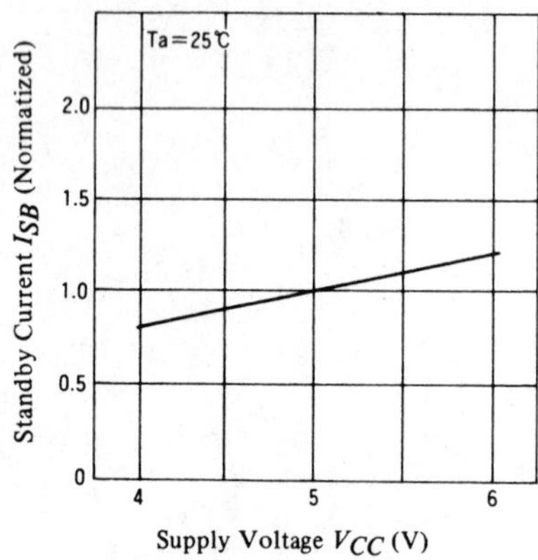

STANDBY CURRENT vs. AMBIENT TEMPERATURE

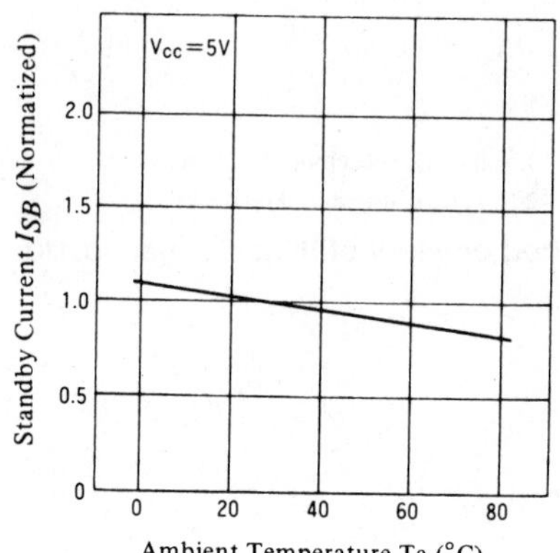

Reproduced courtesy of Hitachi America, Ltd.

HN27512G Series

65536-word x 8-bit UV Erasable and Programmable ROM

The HN27512G is a 65536-word by 8-bit erasable and electrically programmable ROM. This device is packaged in a 28-pin dual in-line package with transparent window. The transparent window allows the user to expose the chip to ultraviolet light to erase the bit pattern, whereby a new pattern can then be written into the device.

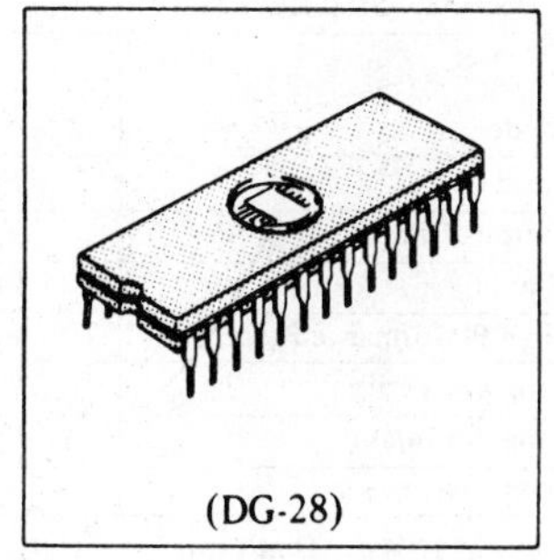

(DG-28)

■ FEATURES

- Single Power Supply . . . . +5V ±5%
- High Performance Programming . . . . Program Voltage: +12.5V D.C. High Performance Programming Operations
- Static . . . . No Clocks Required
- Inputs and Outputs TTL Compatible During Both Read and Program Modes
- Access Time . . . . 250/300ns (max.)
- Absolute Max. Rating of Vpp pin . . . . . 14.0V (max.)
- Low Stand-by Current . . . . 40mA (max.)
- Device Identifier Mode . . . . . . Manufacturer Code and Device Code

■ ORDERING INFORMATION

Type No.	Access Time	Package
HN27512G-25	250ns	600 mil 28 pin Cerdip
HN27512G-30	300ns	

■ BLOCK DIAGRAM

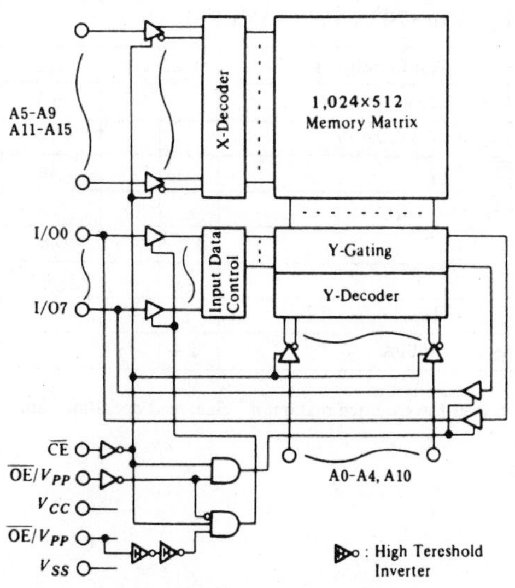

■ PIN ARRANGEMENT

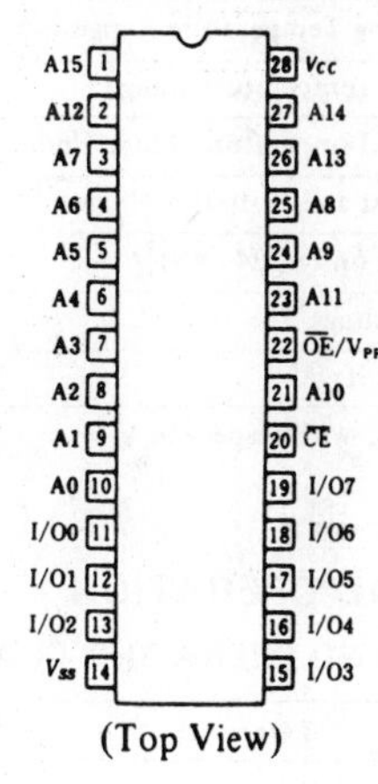

(Top View)

■ MODE SELECTION

Mode \ Pins	$\overline{CE}$ (20)	$\overline{OE}/V_{PP}$ (22)	A9 (24)	V_{CC} (28)	I/O (11 ~ 13, 15 ~ 19)
Read	V_{IL}	V_{IL}	X	V_{CC}	Dout
Output Disable	V_{IL}	V_{IH}	X	V_{CC}	High Z
Standby	V_{IH}	X	X	V_{CC}	High Z
High Performance Program	V_{IL}	V_{PP}	X	V_{CC}	Din
Program Verify	V_{IL}	V_{IL}	X	V_{CC}	Dout
Program Inhibit	V_{IH}	V_{PP}	X	V_{CC}	High Z
Identifier	V_{IL}	V_{IL}	V_H *2	V_{CC}	Code

Notes) *1. X . . . Don't care
*2. V_H: 12.0V ± 0.5V.

■ ABSOLUTE MAXIMUM RATINGS

Item	Symbol	Value	Unit
Operating Temperature Range	T_{opr}	0 to +70	°C
Storage Temperature Range	T_{stg}	−65 to +125	°C
Storage Temperature Range Under Bias	T_{bias}	−10 to +80	°C
All Input and Output Voltages*1	V_{IN}, V_{out}	−0.6 to +7	V
Voltage on Pin 24 (A9)*1	V_{ID}	−0.6 to +13.5	V
V_{PP} Voltage*1	V_{PP}	−0.6 to +14.0	V
V_{CC} Voltage*1	V_{CC}	−0.6 to +7	V

Note) *1. with respect to V_{SS}.

■ READ OPERATION

• DC AND OPERATING CHARACTERISTICS (T_a = 0 to +70°C, V_{CC} = 5V ±5%)

Parameter	Symbol	Test Conditions	min.	typ.	max.	Unit
Input Leakage Current	I_{LI}	V_{IN} = 5.25V	–	–	10	μA
Output Leakage Current	I_{LO}	V_{out} = 5.25V/0.45V	–	–	10	μA
V_{CC} Current (Standby)	I_{CC1}	$\overline{CE}$ = V_{IH}	–	–	40	mA
V_{CC} Current (Active)	I_{CC2}	$\overline{CE}$ = $\overline{OE}$ = V_{IL}	–	45	100	mA
Input Low voltage	V_{IL}		−0.1*1	–	0.8	V
Input High Voltage	V_{IH}		2.0	–	V_{CC}+1*2	V
Output Low Voltage	V_{OL}	I_{OL} = 2.1mA	–	–	0.45	V
Output High Voltage	V_{OH}	I_{OH} = −400μA	2.4	–	–	V

Notes) *1. −0.6V for pulse width ≦ 20ns
*2. V_{CC} + 1.5V for pulse width ≦ 20ns. If V_{IH} is over the specified maximum value, read operation cannot be guaranteed.

HN27512G Series

• AC CHARACTERISTICS (T_a = 0 to +70°C, V_{CC} = 5V ±5%)

Parameter	Symbol	Test Condition	HN27512G-25		HN27512G-30		Unit
			min.	max.	min.	max.	
Addres to Output Delay	t_{ACC}	$\overline{CE} = \overline{OE} = V_{IL}$	–	250	–	300	ns
$\overline{CE}$ to Output Delay	t_{CE}	$\overline{OE} = V_{IL}$	–	250	–	300	ns
$\overline{OE}$ to Output Delay	t_{OE}	$\overline{CE} = V_{IL}$	–	100	–	120	ns
$\overline{OE}$ High Output Float	t_{DF}	$\overline{CE} = V_{IL}$	0	60	0	105	ns
Address to Output Hold	t_{OH}	$\overline{CE} = \overline{OE} = V_{IL}$	0	–	0	–	ns

Note: t_{DF} is defined as the time at which the Output achieves the open circuit condition and Data is no longer driven.

• SWITCHING CHARACTERISTICS

Test Condition

Input Pulse Levels:	0.45V to 2.4V
Input Rise and Fall Time:	≤ 20ns
Output Load:	1 TTL Gate +100pF
Reference Level for Measuring Timing:	0.8V and 2.0V

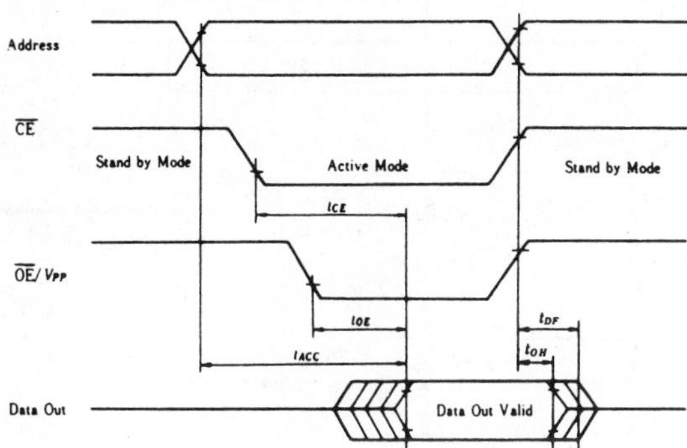

• CAPACITANCE (T_a = 25°C, f = 1MHz)

Parameter		Symbol	Test Condition	min.	typ.	max.	Unit
Input Capacitance	except $\overline{OE}/V_{PP}$	C_{in1}	V_{in} = 0V	–	4	6	pF
	$\overline{OE}/V_{PP}$ Pin	C_{in2}	V_{in} = 0V	–	12	20	pF
Output Capacitance		C_{out}	V_{out} = 0V	–	8	12	pF

■ HIGH PERFORMANCE PROGRAMMING

This device can be applied the High Performance Programming algorithm show in following flowchart. This algorithm allows to obtain faster programming time without any voltage stress to the device nor deterioration in reliability of programmed data.

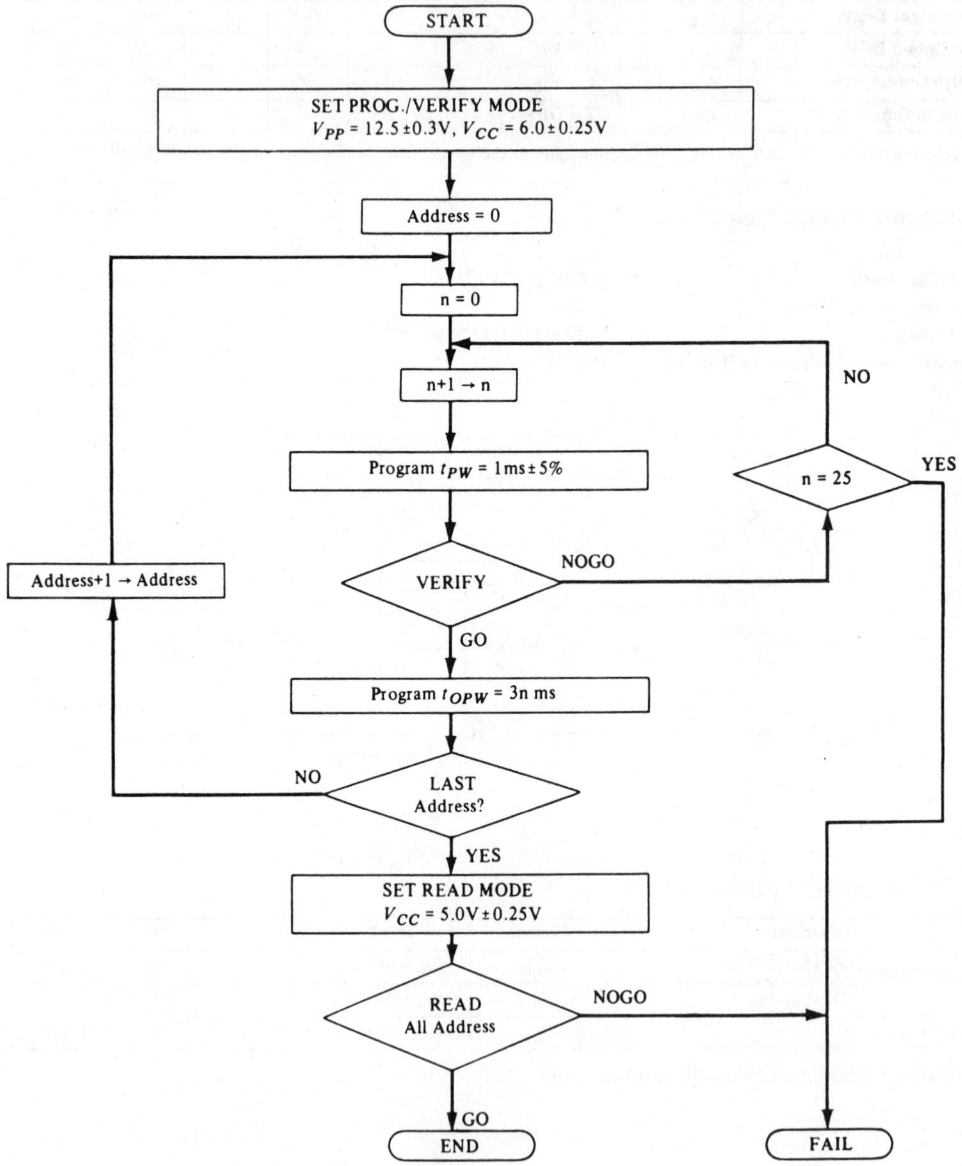

High performance Programming Flowchart

■ HIGH PERFORMANCE PROGRAMMING OPERATION

• DC PROGRAMMING CHARACTERISTICS (T_a = 25°C ±5°C, V_{CC} = 6V ±0.25V, V_{PP} = 12.5V±0.3V)

Parameter	Symbol	Test Condition	min.	typ.	max.	Unit
Input Leakage Current	I_{LI}	V_{IN} = 5.25V	–	–	10	μA
Output Low Voltage During Verify	V_{OL}	I_{OL} = 2.1mA	–	–	0.45	V
Output High Voltage During Verify	V_{OH}	I_{OH} = –400μA	2.4	–	–	V
V_{CC} Current (Active)	I_{CC2}		–	–	100	mA
Input Low Level	V_{IL}		–0.1 *1	–	0.8	V
Input High Level	V_{IH}		2.0	–	V_{CC}+0.5 *2	V
V_{PP} Supply Current	I_{PP}	$\overline{CE}$ = V_{IL}	–	–	50	mA

Notes) *1. –0.6V for pulse width ≦ 20ns.
*2. If V_{IH} is over the specified maximum value, programming operation cannot be guaranteed.

• AC PROGRAMMING CHARACTERISTICS (T_a = 25°C ±5°C, V_{CC} = 6V ± 0.25V, V_{PP} = 12.5V ±0.3V)

Parameter	Symbol	Test Condition	min.	typ.	max.	Unit
Address Setup Time	t_{AS}		2	–	–	μs
Data Setup Time	t_{DS}		2	–	–	μs
Address Hold Time	t_{AH}		0	–	–	μs
Data Hold Time	t_{DH}		2	–	–	μs
$\overline{OE}$ Hold Time	t_{OEH}		2	–	–	μs
$\overline{CE}$ to Output Float Delay	t_{DF} *1		0	–	130	ns
V_{PP} Setup Time	t_{VPS}		2	–	–	μs
V_{CC} Setup Time	t_{VCS}		2	–	–	μs
$\overline{CE}$ Pulse Width During Initial Programming	t_{PW}		0.95	1.0	1.05	ms
$\overline{CE}$ Pulse Width During Overprogramming	t_{OPW} *2		2.85	–	78.75	ms
V_{PP} Recovery Time	t_{VR}		2	–	–	μs
Data Valid from $\overline{CE}$	t_{DV}		–	–	1	μs

Notes: *1. t_{DF} is defined as the time at which the output achieves the open circuit condition and data is no longer driven.
*2. Refer to the programming flowchart for t_{OPW}.

• SWITCHING CHARACTERISTICS

Test Condition
Input Pulse Level: 0.45V to 2.4V
Input Rise and Fall Time: ≤ 20ns
Reference Level for Measuring Timing: 0.8V and 2.0V

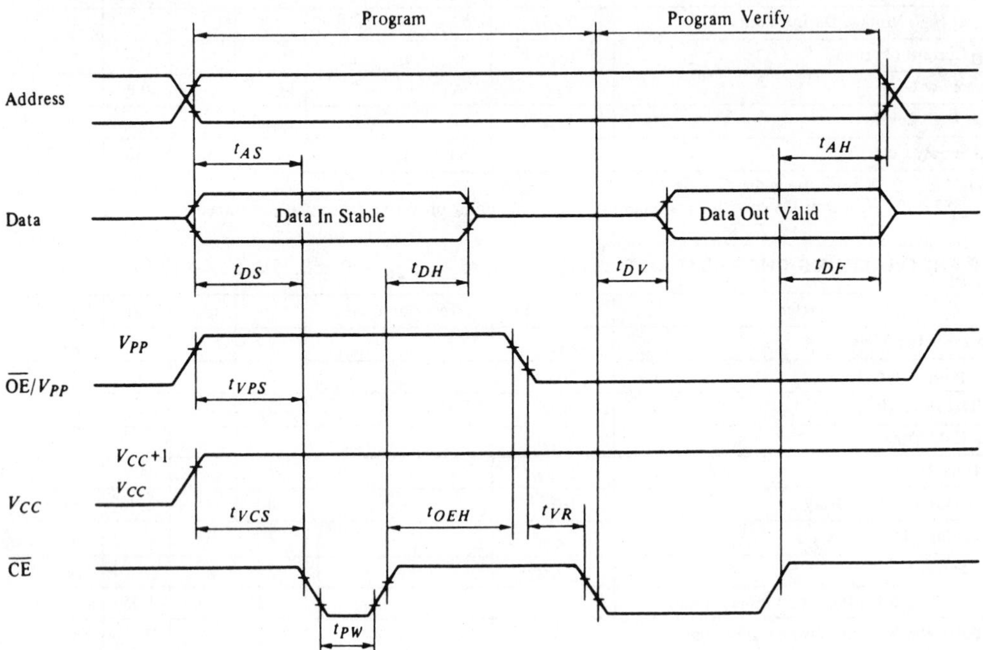

■ ERASE

Erasure of HN27512G is performed by exposure to ultraviolet light of 2537Å and all the output data are changed to "1" after this erasure procedure. The minimum integrated dose (i.e. UV intensity x exposure time) for erasure is 15 W · sec/cm^2.

■ DEVICE IDENTIFIER MODE

The Identifier Mode allows the reading out of binary codes that identify manufacturer and type of device, from outputs of EPROM. By this Mode, the device will be automatically matched its own corresponding programming algorithm, using programming equipment.

• HN27512G SERIES IDENTIFIER CODE

Identifier \ Pins	A_0 (10)	I/O7 (19)	I/O6 (18)	I/O5 (17)	I/O4 (16)	I/O3 (15)	I/O2 (13)	I/O1 (12)	I/O0 (11)	Hex Data
Manufacturer Code	V_{IL}	0	0	0	0	0	1	1	1	07
Device Code	V_{IH}	1	0	0	1	0	1	0	0	94

Notes: 1. $A_9 = 12.0 \pm 0.5V$.
2. $A_1 - A_8, A_{10} - A_{15}, \overline{CE}, \overline{OE}/V_{PP} = V_{IL}$.

SUPPLY CURRENT vs. SUPPLY VOLTAGE

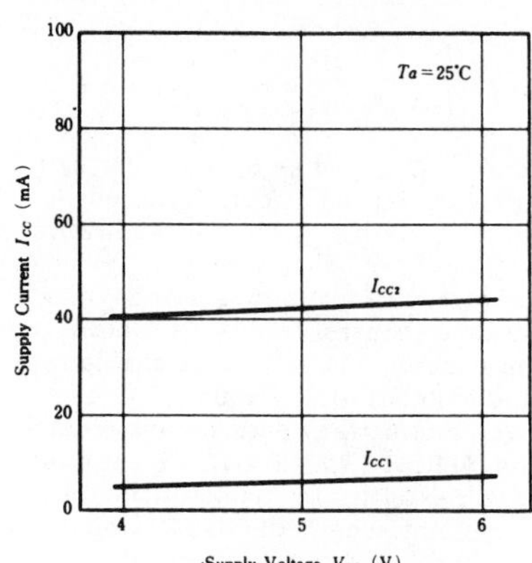

SUPPLY CURRENT vs. AMBIENT TEMPERATURE

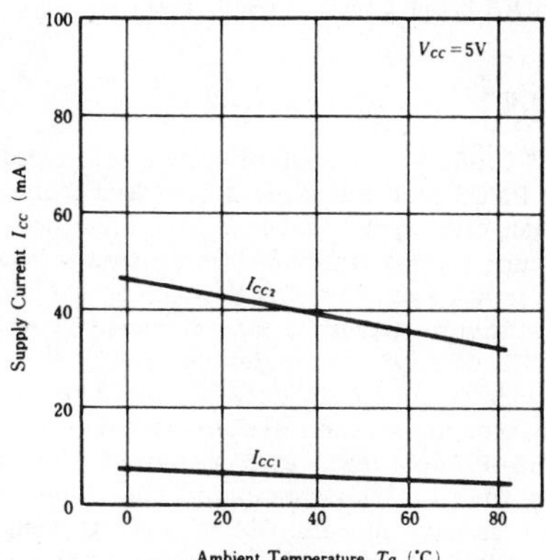

ADDRESS ACCESS TIME vs. SUPPLY VOLTAGE

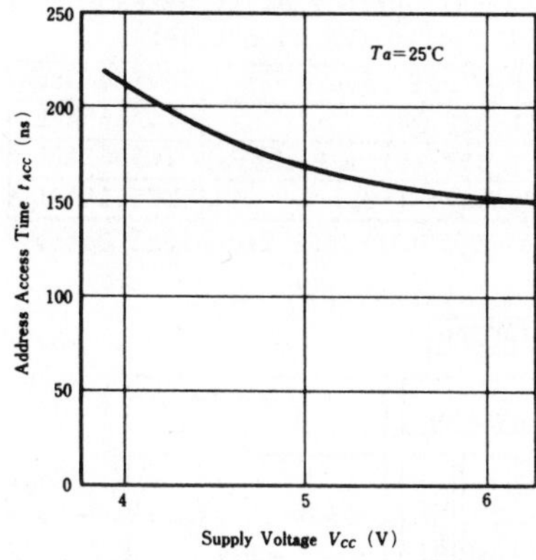

ADDRESS ACCESS TIME vs. AMBIENT TEMPERATURE

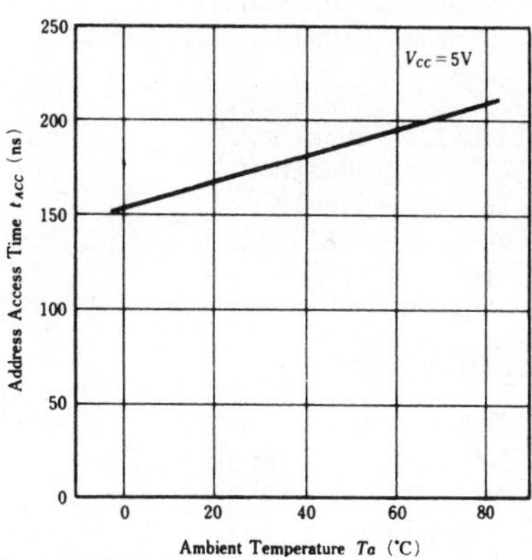

TC5563APL–10, TC5563APL–12, TC5563APL–15

8,192 WORD X 8 BIT CMOS STATIC RAM

DESCRIPTION

The TC5563APL is a 65,536 bit static random access memory organized as 8,192 words by 8 bits using CMOS technology, and operates from a single 5V supply. Advanced circuit techniques provide both high speed and low power features with a maximum operating current of 5mA/MHz and maximum access time of 100ns/120ns/150ns.
When CE2 is a logical low or $\overline{\text{CE1}}$ is a logical high, the device is placed in low power standby mode in which standby current is 2μA typically. The TC5563APL has three control inputs. Two chip enables ($\overline{\text{CE1}}$, CE2) allow for device selection and data retention control, and an output enable input ($\overline{\text{OE}}$) provides fast memory access. Thus the TC5563APL is suitable for use in various microprocessor application systems where high speed, low power, and battery back up are required. The TC5563APL also features pin compatibility with the 64K bit EPROM (TMM2764D). RAM and EPROM are then interchangeable in the same socket, resulting in flexibility in the definition of the quantity of RAM versus EPROM in microprocessor application systems. The TC5563APL is offered in a dual-in-line 28 pin standard 300 mil plastic package.

FEATURES

- Low Power Dissipation
  27.5mW/MHz(Max.) Operating
- Standby Current: 100μA(Max.) Ta=70°C
- Access Time
  TC5563APL-10: 100ns(Max.)
  TC5563APL-12: 120ns(Max.)
  TC5563APL-15: 150ns(Max.)
- 5V Single Power Supply
- Power Down Features: CE2, $\overline{\text{CE1}}$
- Fully Static Operation
- Data Retention Supply Voltage: 2.0 ∿ 5.5V
- Directly TTL Compatible: All Inputs and Outputs
- Pin Compatible with 2764 type EPROM
- TC5565APL Family (Package type)

Package Type	Device Name
600 mil DIP	*TC5565APL
300 mil DIP (Slim Package)	TC5563APL
Flat Package (SOP)	*TC5565AFL

*: See TC5565APL/AFL Technical Data.

PIN CONNECTION (TOP VIEW)

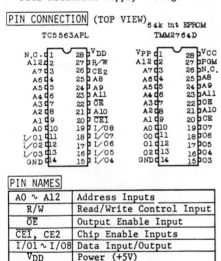

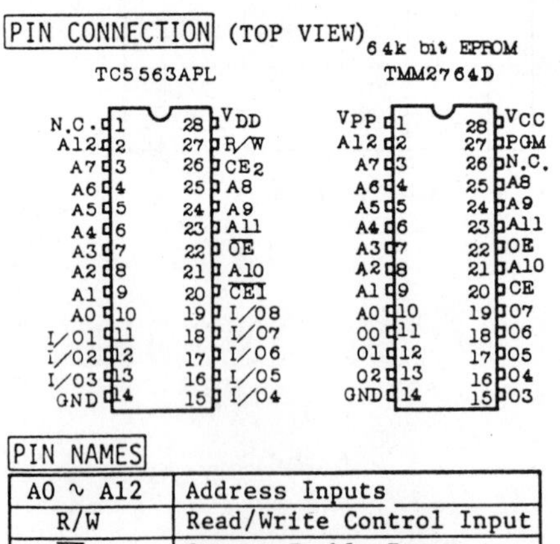

PIN NAMES

A0 ∿ A12	Address Inputs
R/W	Read/Write Control Input
$\overline{\text{OE}}$	Output Enable Input
$\overline{\text{CE1}}$, CE2	Chip Enable Inputs
I/O1 ∿ I/O8	Data Input/Output
V_{DD}	Power (+5V)
GND	Ground
N.C.	No Connection

BLOCK DIAGRAM

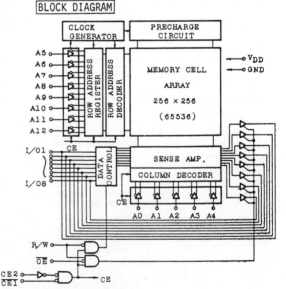

CLOCK GENERATOR
PRECHARGE CIRCUIT
A5 A6 A7 A8 A9 A10 A11 A12
ROW ADDRESS REGISTER
ROW ADDRESS DECODER
MEMORY CELL ARRAY 256 × 256 (65536)
V_{DD}
GND
I/O1 … I/O8
CE
DATA CONTROL
SENSE AMP.
COLUMN DECODER
CE
A0 A1 A2 A3 A4
R/W
$\overline{\text{OE}}$
CE2
$\overline{\text{CE1}}$
CE

TC5563APL–10, TC5563APL–12
TC5563APL–15

OPERATION MODE

OPERATION MODE	$\overline{CE1}$	CE2	$\overline{OE}$	R/W	I/O1 ~ I/O8	POWER
Read	L	H	L	H	D_{OUT}	I_{DDO}
Write	L	H	*	L	D_{IN}	I_{DDO}
Output Deselect	L	H	H	H	High-Z	I_{DDO}
Standby	H	*	*	*	High-Z	I_{DDS}
	*	L	*	*	High-Z	I_{DDS}

*: H or L

MAXIMUM RATINGS

SYMBOL	ITEM	RATING	UNIT
V_{DD}	Power Supply Voltage	-0.3 ~ 7.0	V
V_{IN}	Input Voltage	-0.3* ~ 7.0	V
$V_{I/O}$	Input and Output Voltage	-0.5 ~ V_{DD}+0.5	V
P_D	Power Dissipation	0.8	W
T_{solder}	Soldering Temperature	260 · 10	°C · sec
T_{stg}	Storage Temperature	-55 ~ 150	°C
T_{opr}	Operating Temperature	0 ~ 70	°C

*: -3.0V at pulse width 50ns Max.

D.C. RECOMMENDED OPERATING CONDITIONS

SYMBOL	PARAMETER	MIN.	TYP.	MAX.	UNIT
V_{DD}	Power Supply Voltage	4.5	5.0	5.5	V
V_{IH}	Input High Voltage	2.2	-	V_{DD}+0.3	
V_{IL}	Input Low Voltage	-0.3*	-	0.8	
V_{DH}	Data Retention Supply Voltage	2.0	-	5.5	

*: -3.0V at pulse width 50ns Max.

TC5563APL–10, TC5563APL–12 TC5563APL–15

D.C. and OPERATING CHARACTERISTICS (Ta=0 ∿ 70°C, V_{DD}=5V±10%)

SYMBOL	PARAMETER	TEST CONDITION			MIN.	TYP.	MAX.	UNIT
I_{IL}	Input Leakage Current	V_{IN}=0 ∿ V_{DD}			-	-	±1.0	μA
I_{OH}	Output High Current	V_{OH}=2.4V			-1.0	-	-	mA
I_{OL}	Output Low Current	V_{OL}=0.4V			4.0	-	-	mA
I_{LO}	Output Leakage Current	$\overline{CE1}$=V_{IH} or CE2=V_{IL} or R/W=V_{IL} or $\overline{OE}$=V_{IH} V_{OUT}=0 ∿ V_{DD}			-	-	±1.0	μA
I_{DDO1}	Operating Current	V_{DD}=5.5V $\overline{CE1}$=V_{IL} CE2=V_{IH} Other input= V_{IH}/V_{IL} I_{OUT}=0mA	t_{cycle}=1.0μs		-	-	10	mA
			TC5563APL-10	t_{cycle} =100ns	-	-	45	mA
			TC5563APL-12	t_{cycle} =120ns	-	-	40	mA
			TC5563APL-15	t_{cycle} =150ns	-	-	35	mA
I_{DDO2}		V_{DD}=5.5V $\overline{CE1}$=0.2V CE2=V_{DD}-0.2V Other input= V_{DD}-0.2V/0.2V I_{OUT}=0mA	t_{cycle}=1.0μs		-	-	5	mA
			TC5563APL-10	t_{cycle} =100ns	-	-	40	mA
			TC5563APL-12	t_{cycle} =120ns	-	-	35	mA
			TC5563APL-15	t_{cycle} =150ns	-	-	30	mA
I_{DDS1}	Standby Current	$\overline{CE1}$=V_{IH} or CE2=V_{IL}			-	-	3	mA
* I_{DDS2}	Standby Current	$\overline{CE1}$=V_{DD}-0.2V or CE2=0.2V	V_{DD}=5.5V		-	2	100	μA
			V_{DD}=3.0V		-	1	50	

*: In standby mode with $\overline{CE1}$ ≧ V_{DD}-0.2V, these specification limits are guaranteed under the condition of CE2 ≧ V_{DD}-0.2V or CE2 ≦ 0.2V.

CAPACITANCE (Ta=25°C)

SYMBOL	PARAMETER	TEST CONDITION	MAX.	UNIT
C_{IN}	Input Capacitance	V_{IN}=GND	10	pF
C_{OUT}	Output Capacitance	V_{OUT}=GND	10	

Note: This parameter is periodically sampled and is not 100% tested.

TC5563APL–10, TC5563APL–12
TC5563APL–15

A.C. CHARACTERISTICS (Ta=0 ∼ 70°C, V_{DD}=5V±10%)

READ CYCLE

SYMBOL	PARAMETER	TC5563APL-10L		TC5563APL-12L		TC5563APL-15L		UNIT
		MIN.	MAX.	MIN.	MAX.	MIN.	MAX.	
t_{RC}	Read Cycle Time	100	-	120	-	150	-	ns
t_{ACC}	Address Access Time	-	100	-	120	-	150	
t_{CO1}	$\overline{CE1}$ Access Time	-	100	-	120	-	150	
t_{CO2}	CE2 Access Time	-	100	-	120	-	150	
t_{OE}	Output Enable to Output Valid	-	50	-	60	-	70	
t_{COE}	Chip Enable ($\overline{CE1}$, CE2) to Output in Low-Z	10	-	10	-	15	-	
t_{OEE}	Output Enable to Output in Low-Z	5	-	5	-	5	-	
t_{OD}	Chip Enable ($\overline{CE1}$, CE2) to Output in High-Z	-	35	-	40	-	50	
t_{ODO}	Output Enable to Output in High-Z	-	35	-	40	-	50	
t_{OH}	Output Data Hold Time	20	-	20	-	20	-	

WRITE CYCLE

SYMBOL	PARAMETER	TC5563APL-10L		TC5563APL-12L		TC5563APL-15L		UNIT
		MIN.	MAX.	MIN.	MAX.	MIN.	MAX.	
t_{WC}	Write Cycle Time	100	-	120	-	150	-	ns
t_{WP}	Write Pulse Width	60	-	70	-	90	-	
t_{CW}	Chip Selection to End of Write	80	-	85	-	100	-	
t_{AS}	Address Set up Time	0	-	0	-	0	-	
t_{WR}	Write Recovery Time	0	-	0	-	0	-	
t_{ODW}	R/W to Output High-Z	-	35	-	40	-	50	
t_{OEW}	R/W to Output Low-Z	5	-	5	-	10	-	
t_{DS}	Data Set up Time	40	-	50	-	60	-	
t_{DH}	Data Hold Time	0	-	0	-	0	-	

A.C. TEST CONDITION

Output Load		: 100pF + 1 TTL Gate
Input Pulse Level		: 0.6V, 2.4V
Timing Measurement	V_{IN}	: 0.8V, 2.2V
Reference Level	V_{OUT}	: 0.8V, 2.2V
t_r, t_f		: 5ns

TC5563APL–10, TC5563APL–12 TC5563APL–15

TIMING WAVEFORMS

READ CYCLE (1)

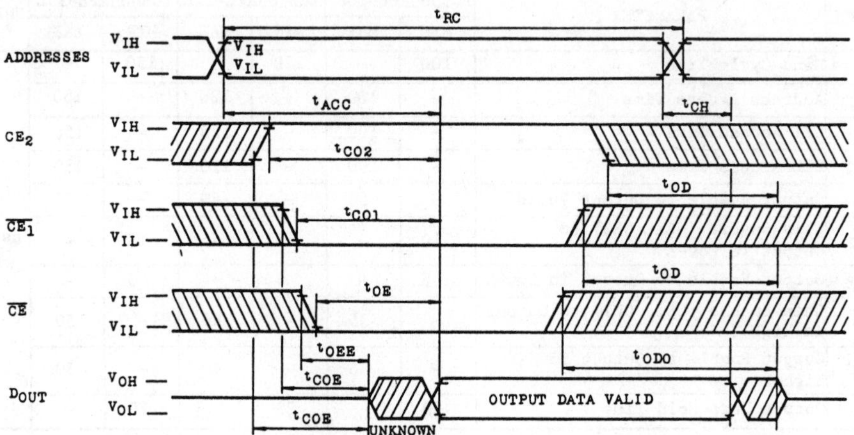

WRITE CYCLE 1 (4) (R/W Controlled Write)

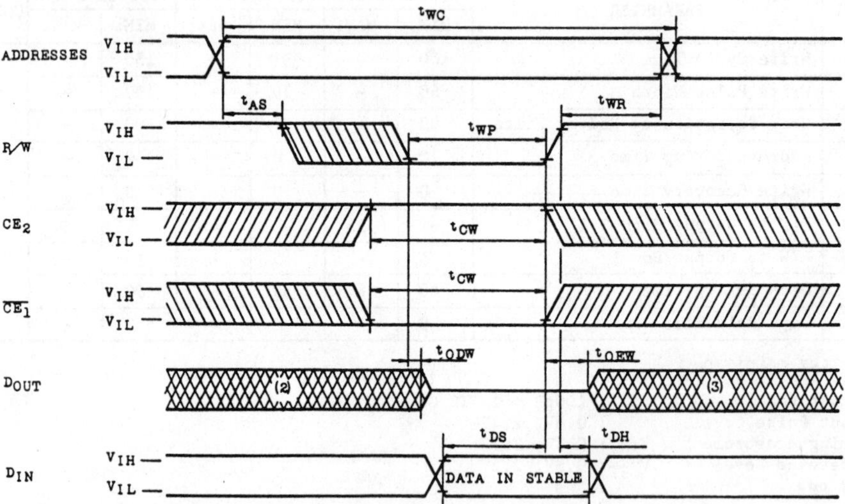

Used with permission from Toshiba America Electronic Components.

TC5563APL–10, TC5563APL–12
TC5563APL–15

WRITE CYCLE 2 (4) ($\overline{CE1}$ Controlled Write)

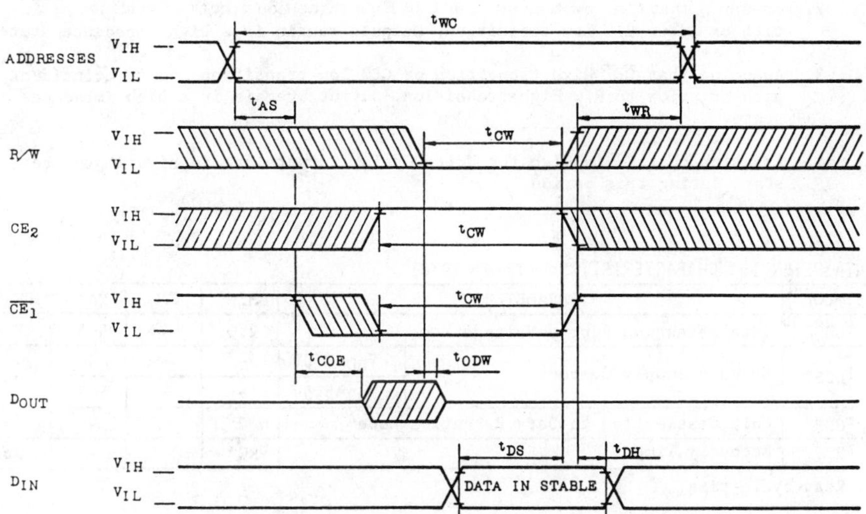

WRITE CYCLE 3 (4) (CE2 Controlled Write)

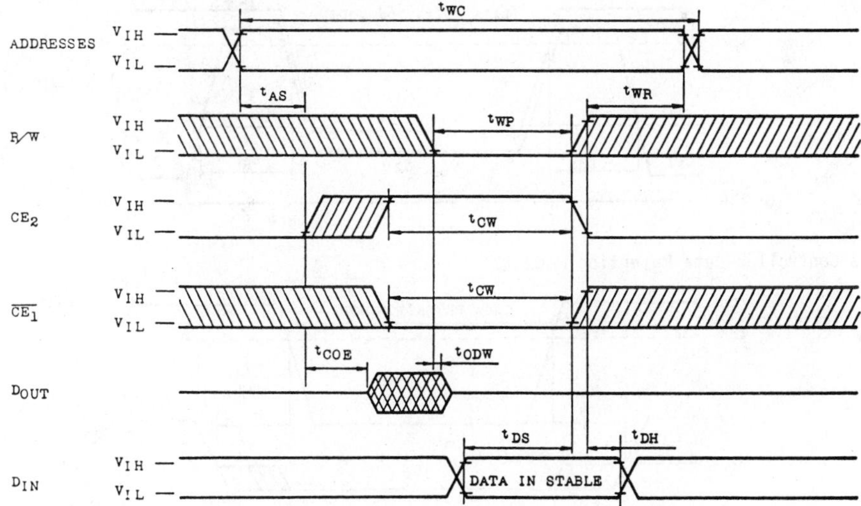

TC5563APL–10, TC5563APL–12
TC5563APL–15

Note 1. R/W is High for Read Cycle.

2. Assuming that $\overline{CE1}$ Low transition or CE2 High transition occurs coincident with or after R/W Low transition, Outputs remain in a high impedance state.

3. Assuming that $\overline{CE1}$ High transition or CE2 Low transition occurs coincident with or prior to R/W High transition, Outputs remain in a high impedance state.

4. Assuming that $\overline{OE}$ is High for Write Cycle, Outputs are in high impedance state during this period.

DATA RETENTION CHARACTERISTICS (Ta=0 ∿ 70°C)

SYMBOL	PARAMETER		MIN.	TYP.	MAX.	UNIT
V_{DH}	Data Retention Supply Voltage		2.0	–	5.5	V
I_{DDS2}	Standby Supply Current	V_{DD}=3.0V	–	–	50	μA
		V_{DD}=5.5V	–	–	100	
t_{CDR}	Chip Deselection to Data Retention Mode		0	–	–	μs
t_R	Recovery Time		t_{RC}*	–	–	μs

*: Read cycle time.

$\overline{CE1}$ Controlled Data Retention Mode (1)

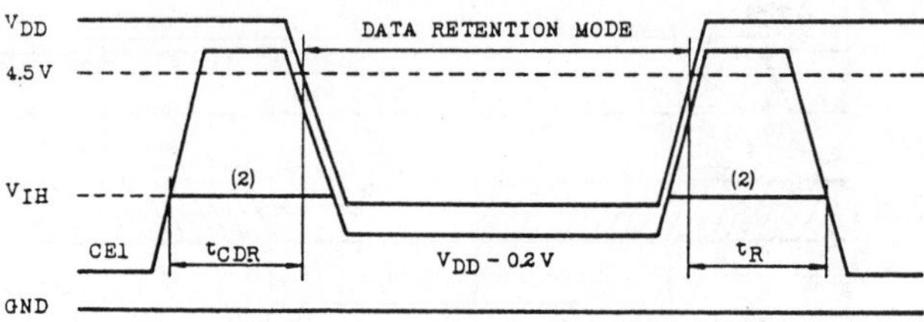

CE2 Controlled Data Retention Mode (3)

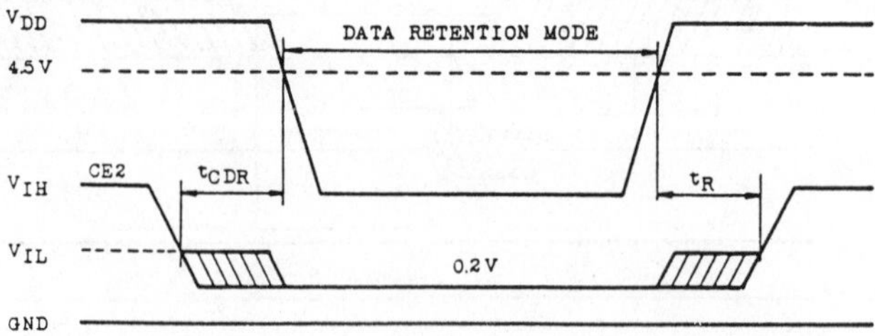

TC5563APL–10, TC5563APL–12
TC5563APL–15

Note 1: In $\overline{CE1}$ controlled data retention mode, minimum standby current mode is achieved under the condition of CE2 ≦ 0.2V or CE2 ≧ V_{DD}-0.2V.

2: If the V_{IH} of $\overline{CE1}$ is 2.2V in active operation, I_{DDS1} current flows during the period that the V_{DD} voltage is going down from 4.5V to 2.4V.

3: In CE2 controlled data retention mode, minimum standby current mode is achieved under the condition of CE2 ≦ 0.2V.

DEVICE INFORMATION

The TC5563APL is an asynchronous RAM using address activated circuit technology, thus the internal operation is synchronous. Then once row address change occur, the precharge operation is executed by internal pulse generated from row address transient. Therefore the peak current flows only after row address change, as shown in the following figure.

This peak current may induce the noise on V_{DD}/GND lines. Thus the use of about 0.1μF decoupling capacitor for every device is recommended to eliminate such noise.

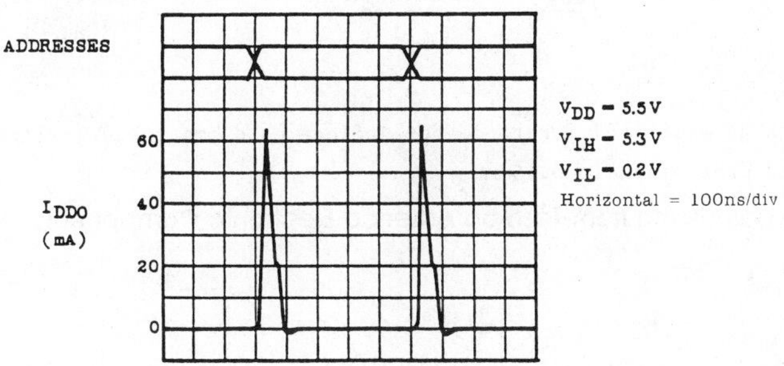

Fig. Typical Current Waveforms

TC5563APL–10, TC5563APL–12
TC5563APL–15

OUTLINE DRAWINGS (DIP28-P-300B)

Unit in mm

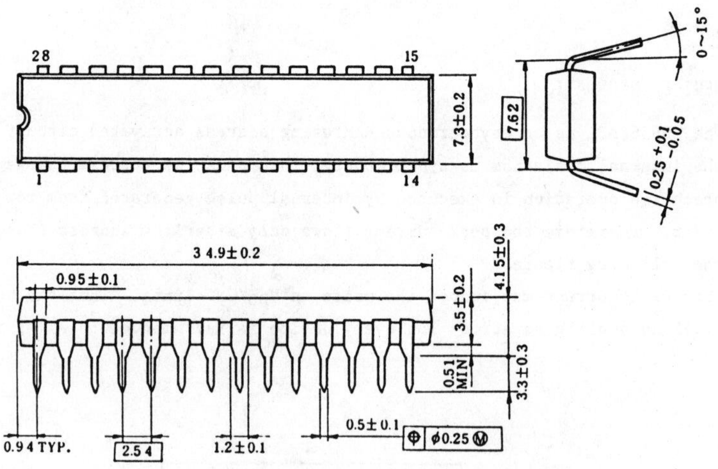

Note: Package width and length do not include mold protrusion, allowable mold protrusion is 0.15mm.

Used with permission from Toshiba America Electronic Components.

TOSHIBA MOS MEMORY PRODUCTS

262,144 WORDS × 4 BIT DYNAMIC RAM
SILICON GATE CMOS

TC514256P/J-10
TC514256P/J-12

DESCRIPTION

The TC514256P/J is the new generation dynamic RAM organized 262,144 words by 4 bit. The TC514256P/J utilizes TOSHIBA's CMOS Silicon gate process technology as well as advanced circuit techniques to provide wide operating margins, both internally and to the system user. Multiplexed address inputs permit the TC514256P/J to be packaged in a standard 20 pin plastic DIP and 20 pin plastic SOJ. The package size provides high system bit densities and is compatible with widely available automated testing and insertion equipment. System oriented features include single power supply of 5V±10% tolerance, direct interfacing capability with high performance logic families such as Schottky TTL.

FEATURES

- 262,144 words by 4 bit organization
- Fast access time and cycle time

		TC514256P/J-10	TC514256P/J-12
t_{RAC}	$\overline{RAS}$ Access Time	100ns	120ns
t_{AA}	Column Address Access Time	50ns	60ns
t_{CAC}	$\overline{CAS}$ Access Time	35ns	45ns
t_{RC}	Cycle Time	190ns	220ns
t_{PC}	Fast Page Mode Cycle Time	55ns	70ns

- Single power supply of 5V±10% with a built-in V_{BB} generator
- Low Power
  - 358mW MAX. Operating(TC514256P/J-10)
  - 303mW MAX. Operating(TC514256P/J-12)
  - 5.5mW MAX. Standby
- Output unlatched at cycle end allows two-dimensional chip selection
- Read-Modify-Write, $\overline{CAS}$ before $\overline{RAS}$ refresh, $\overline{RAS}$-only refresh, Hidden refresh, and Fast Page Mode capability
- All inputs and output TTL compatible
- 512 refresh cycles/8ms
- Package Plastic DIP: TC514256P
  Plastic SOJ: TC514256J

PIN CONNECTION (TOP VIEW)

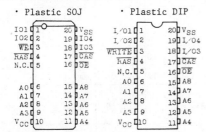

• Plastic SOJ

Pin	Name	Pin	Name
1	IO1	20	V_{SS}
2	IO2	19	IO4
3	$\overline{WE}$	18	IO3
4	$\overline{RAS}$	17	$\overline{CAS}$
5	N.C.	16	$\overline{OE}$
6	A0	15	A8
7	A1	14	A7
8	A2	13	A6
9	A3	12	A5
10	V_{CC}	11	A4

• Plastic DIP

Pin	Name	Pin	Name
1	I/O1	20	V_{SS}
2	I/O2	19	I/O4
3	$\overline{WRITE}$	18	I/O3
4	$\overline{RAS}$	17	$\overline{CAS}$
5	N.C.	16	$\overline{OE}$
6	A0	15	A8
7	A1	14	A7
8	A2	13	A6
9	A3	12	A5
10	V_{CC}	11	A4

PIN NAMES

A0 ~ A8	Address Inputs
$\overline{RAS}$	Row Address Strobe
$\overline{CAS}$	Column Address Strobe
$\overline{WRITE}$	Read/Write Input
$\overline{OE}$	Output Enable
I/O1~I/O4	Data Input/Output
V_{CC}	Power (+5V)
V_{SS}	Ground
N.C.	No Connection

BLOCK DIAGRAM

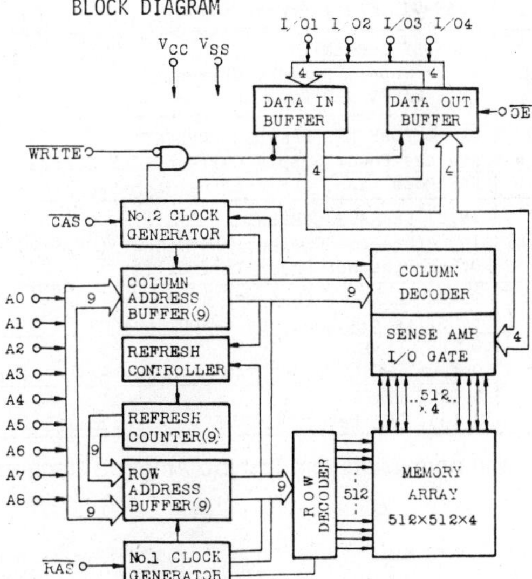

ABSOLUTE MAXIMUM RATINGS

ITEM	SYMBOL	RATING	UNITS	NOTES
Input Voltage	V_{IN}	-1 ∿ 7	V	1
Output Voltage	V_{OUT}	-1 ∿ 7	V	1
Power Supply Voltage	V_{CC}	-1 ∿ 7	V	1
Operating Temperature	T_{OPR}	0 ∿ 70	°C	1
Storage Temperature	T_{STG}	-55 ∿ 150	°C	1
Soldering Temperature · Time	T_{SOLDER}	260 · 10	°C · sec	1
Power Dissipation	P_D	600	mW	1
Short Circuit Output Current	I_{OUT}	50	mA	1

RECOMMENDED DC OPERATING CONDITIONS (Ta=0 ∿ 70°C)

SYMBOL	PARAMETER	MIN.	TYP.	MAX.	UNIT	NOTES
V_{CC}	Supply Voltage	4.5	5.0	5.5	V	2
V_{IH}	Input High Voltage	2.4		6.5	V	2
V_{IL}	Input Low Voltage	-1.0		0.8	V	2

DC ELECTRICAL CHARACTERISTICS (V_{CC}=5V±10%, Ta=0 ∿ 70°C)

SYMBOL	PARAMETER		MIN.	MAX.	UNITS	NOTES
$I_{CC}1$	OPERATING CURRENT Average Power Supply Operating Current ($\overline{RAS}$, $\overline{CAS}$, Address Cycling: t_{RC}=t_{RC} MIN.)	TC514256P/J-10	-	65	mA	3,4
		TC514256P/J-12	-	55	mA	
$I_{CC}2$	STANDBY CURRENT Power Supply Standby Current ($\overline{RAS}$=$\overline{CAS}$=V_{IH})		-	2	mA	
$I_{CC}3$	$\overline{RAS}$ ONLY REFRESH CURRENT Average Power Supply Current, $\overline{RAS}$ Only Mode ($\overline{RAS}$ Cycling, $\overline{CAS}$=V_{IH}: t_{RC}=t_{RC} MIN.)	TC514256P/J-10	-	65	mA	3
		TC514256P/J-12	-	55	mA	
$I_{CC}4$	FAST PAGE MODE CURRENT Average Power Supply Current, Fast Page Mode ($\overline{RAS}$=VIL,$\overline{CAS}$,Address Cycling: t_{PC}=t_{PC} MIN.)	TC514256P/J-10	-	45	mA	3,4
		TC514256P/J-12	-	35	mA	
$I_{CC}5$	STANDBY CURRENT Power Supply Standby Current ($\overline{RAS}$=$\overline{CAS}$=V_{CC}-0.2V)		-	1	mA	
$I_{CC}6$	$\overline{CAS}$ BEFORE RAS REFRESH CURRENT Average Power Supply Current, $\overline{CAS}$ Before $\overline{RAS}$ Mode ($\overline{RAS}$, $\overline{CAS}$ Cycling: t_{RC}=t_{RC} MIN.)	TC514256P/J-10	-	65	mA	3
		TC514256P/J-12	-	55	mA	
$I_I(L)$	INPUT LEAKAGE CURRENT Input Leakage Current, any input (0V≦V_{IN}≦6.5V, All Other Pins Not Under Test=0V)		-10	10	μA	
$I_O(L)$	OUTPUT LEAKAGE CURRENT (D_{OUT} is disabled, 0V ≦ V_{OUT} ≦ V_{CC})		-10	10	μA	
V_{OH}	OUTPUT LEVEL Output "H" Level VOLTAGE (I_{OUT}=-5mA)		2.4	-	V	
V_{OL}	OUTPUT LEVEL Output "L" Level VOLTAGE (I_{OUT}=4.2mA)		-	0.4	V	

ELECTRICAL CHARACTERISTICS AND RECOMMENDED AC OPERATING CONDITIONS

(V_{CC} =5V±10%, Ta = 0∿70°C)(Notes 5, 6, 7)

SYMBOL	PARAMETER	TC514256P/-10		TC514256P/J12		UNIT	NOTES
		MIN.	MAX.	MIN.	MAX.		
t_{RC}	Random Read or Write Cycle Time	190		220		ns	
t_{RWC}	Read-Write Cycle Time	255		295		ns	
t_{PC}	Fast Page Mode Cycle Time	55		70		ns	
t_{PRWC}	Fast Page Mode Read-Write Cycle Time	115	-	140		ns	
t_{RAC}	Access Time from $\overline{RAS}$		100		120	ns	8,13
t_{CAC}	Access Time from $\overline{CAS}$		35		45	ns	8,13
t_{AA}	Access Tire from Column Address		50		60	ns	8,14
t_{CPA}	Access Time from $\overline{CAS}$ Precharge		50		65	ns	8,
t_{CLZ}	$\overline{CAS}$ to output in Low-Z	5		5		ns	5
t_{OFF}	Output Buffer Turn-off Delay	0	30	0	35	ns	9
t_{T}	Transition Time (Rise and Fall)	3	50	3	50	ns	7
t_{RP}	$\overline{RAS}$ Precharge Time	80		90		ns	
t_{RAS}	$\overline{RAS}$ Pulse Width	100	10,000	120	10,000	ns	
t_{RASP}	$\overline{RAS}$ Pulse Width (Fast Page Mode)	100	100,000	120	100,000	ns	
t_{RSH}	$\overline{RAS}$ Hold Time	35		45		ns	
t_{CSH}	$\overline{CAS}$ Hold Time	100		120		ns	
t_{CAS}	$\overline{CAS}$ Pulse Width	35		45		ns	
t_{RCD}	$\overline{RAS}$ to $\overline{CAS}$ Delay Time	25	65	25	75	ns	13
t_{RAD}	$\overline{RAS}$ to Column Address Delay Time	20	50	20	60	ns	14
t_{CRP}	$\overline{CAS}$ to $\overline{RAS}$ Precharge Time	10		10		ns	
t_{CP}	$\overline{CAS}$ Precharge Time	10		15		ns	
t_{ASR}	Row Address Set-Up Time	0		0		ns	
t_{RAH}	Row Address Hold Time	15		15		ns	
t_{ASC}	Column Address Set-Up Time	0		0		ns	
t_{CAH}	Column Address Hold Time	20		25		ns	
t_{AR}	Column Address Hold Time referenced to $\overline{RAS}$	75		90		ns	
t_{RAL}	Column Address to $\overline{RAS}$ Lead Time	50		60		ns	
t_{RCS}	Read Command Set-Up Time	0		0		ns	
t_{RCH}	Read Command Hold Time	0		0		ns	10
t_{RRH}	Read Command Hold Time referenced to $\overline{RAS}$	0		0		ns	10

SYMBOL	PARAMETER	TC514256P-10		TC514256P-12		UNITS	NOTES
		MIN.	MAX.	MIN.	MAX.		
t_{WCH}	Write Command Hold Time	20		25		ns	
t_{WCR}	Write Command Hold Time referenced to $\overline{RAS}$	75		90		ns	
t_{WP}	Write Command Pulse Width	20		25		ns	
t_{RWL}	Write Command to $\overline{RAS}$ Lead Time	25		30		ns	
t_{CWL}	Write Command to $\overline{CAS}$ Lead Time	25		30		ns	
t_{DS}	Data Set-Up Time	0		0		ns	11
t_{DH}	Data Hold Time	20		25		ns	11
t_{DHR}	Data Hold Time Referenced to $\overline{RAS}$	75		90		ns	
t_{REF}	Refresh Period		8		8	ms	
t_{WCS}	Write Command Set-Up Time	0		0		ns	12
t_{CWD}	$\overline{CAS}$ to $\overline{WRITE}$ Delay Time	70		85		ns	12
t_{RWD}	$\overline{RAS}$ to $\overline{WRITE}$ Delay Time	135		160		ns	12
t_{AWD}	Column Address to $\overline{WRITE}$ Delay Time	85		100		ns	12
t_{CSR}	$\overline{CAS}$ Set-Up Time (CAS before $\overline{RAS}$ Cycle)	10		10		ns	
t_{CHR}	CAS Hold Time ($\overline{CAS}$ before $\overline{RAS}$ cycle)	30		30		ns	
t_{RPC}	$\overline{RAS}$ to $\overline{CAS}$ Precharge Time	0		0		ns	
t_{CPT}	$\overline{CAS}$ Precharge Time ($\overline{CAS}$ before $\overline{RAS}$ Counter Test Cycle)	50		60		ns	
t_{ROH}	$\overline{OE}$ Hold Time	0		0		ns	
t_{OEA}	$\overline{OE}$ Access Time		25		30	ns	
t_{OED}	$\overline{OE}$ to Data Delay	25		30		ns	
t_{OEZ}	Output buffer turn off Delay Time from $\overline{OE}$	0	25	0	30	ns	
t_{OEH}	$\overline{OE}$ Command Hold Time	25		30		ns	

CAPACITANCE (V_{CC} = 5V±10%, f = 1MHz, Ta = 0∿70°C)

SYMBOL	PARAMETER	MIN.	MAX.	UNIT
C_{I1}	Input Capacitance (A_0 - A_8)		5	pF
C_{I2}	Input Capacitance ($\overline{RAS}$,$\overline{CAS}$,$\overline{WRITE}$)		7	pF
C_O	Output Capacitance (I/O_1 - I/O_4)		7	pF

NOTES:

1. Stresses greater than those listed under "Absolute Maximum Ratings" may cause permanent damage to the device.

2. All voltage are reference to V_{SS}.

3. Icc1, Icc3, Icc4, Icc6 depend on cycle rate.

4. Icc1, Icc4 depend on output loading. Specified value are obtained with the output open.

5. An initial pause of 200μs is required after power-up followed by 8 $\overline{RAS}$ cycles before proper device operation is achieved. In case of using internal refresh counter, a minimum of 8 $\overline{CAS}$ Before $\overline{RAS}$ initialization cycles instead of 8 $\overline{RAS}$ cycles are required.

6. AC measurements assume t_T=5ns.

7. V_{IH}(min.) and V_{IL}(max.) are reference levels for measuring timing of input signals. Also, transition times are measured between V_{IH} and V_{IL}.

8. Measured with a load equivalent to 2 TTL loads and 100pF.

9. t_{OFF}(max.) defines the time at which the output achieves the open circuit condition and is not referenced to output voltage levels.

10. Either t_{RCH} to t_{RRH} must be satisfied for a read cycle.

11. These parameters are referenced to $\overline{CAS}$ leading edge in early write cycles and to $\overline{WRITE}$ leading edge in read-write or read-modify-write cycles.

12. t_{WCS}, t_{RWD}, t_{CWD} and t_{AWD} are not restrictive operating parameters. They are included the data sheet as electrical characteristics only. If $t_{WCS} \geqq t_{WCS}$(min.) the cycle is an early write cycle and data out pin will remain open circuit (high impedance) through the entire cycle; If $t_{RWD} \geqq t_{RWD}$(min.), $t_{CWD} \geqq t_{CWD}$(min.) and $t_{AWD} \geqq t_{AWD}$(min.), the cycle is a read-write or read-modify-write cycle and data out will contain data read from the selected cell : If neither of the above sets of conditions is satisfied, the condition of the data out (at access time) is indeterminate.

13. Operation within the t_{RCD}(max.) limit insures that t_{RAC}(max.) can be met. t_{RCD}(max.) is specified as a reference point only: If t_{RCD} is greater than the specified t_{RCD}(max.) limit, then access time is controlled by t_{CAC}.

14. Operation within the t_{RAD}(max.) limit insures that t_{RAC}(max.) can be met. t_{RAD}(max.) is specified as a reference point only: If t_{RAD} is greater than the specified t_{RAD}(max.) limit, then access time is controlled by t_{AA}.

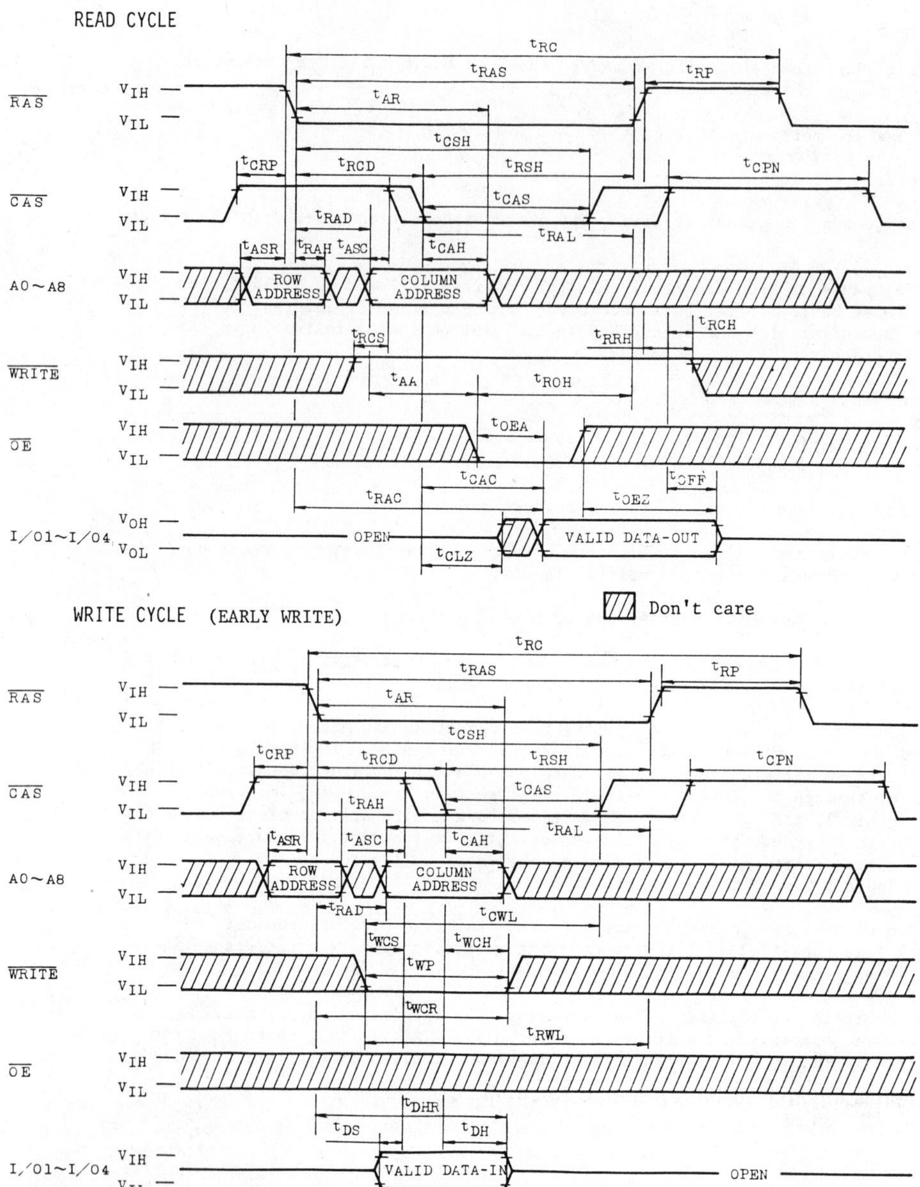

Used with permission from Toshiba America Electronic Components.

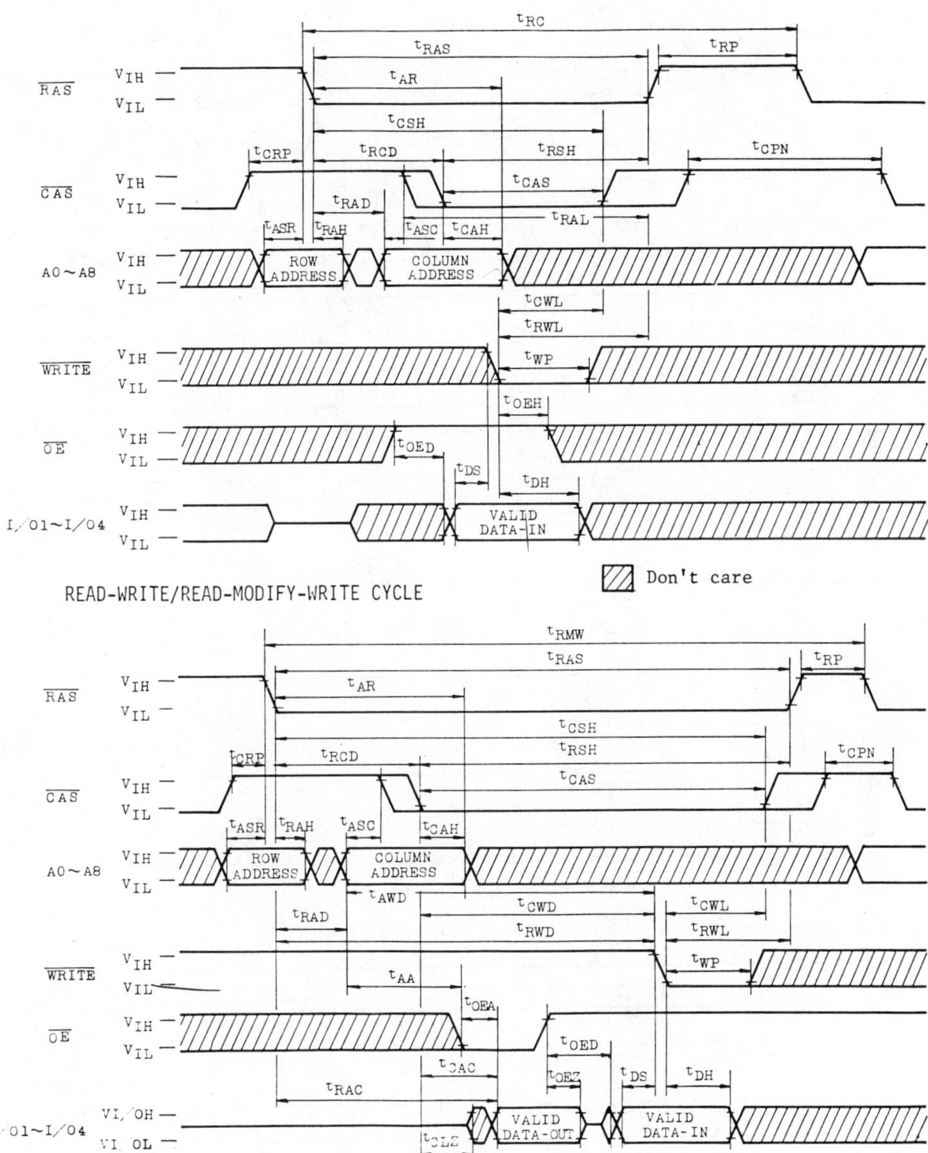

Used with permission from Toshiba America Electronic Components.

FAST PAGE MODE READ CYCLE

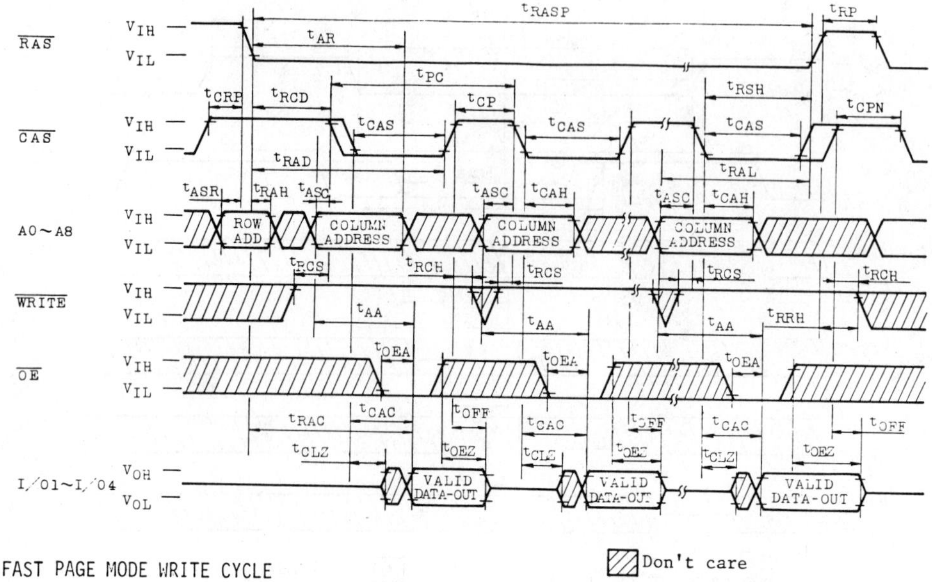

FAST PAGE MODE WRITE CYCLE

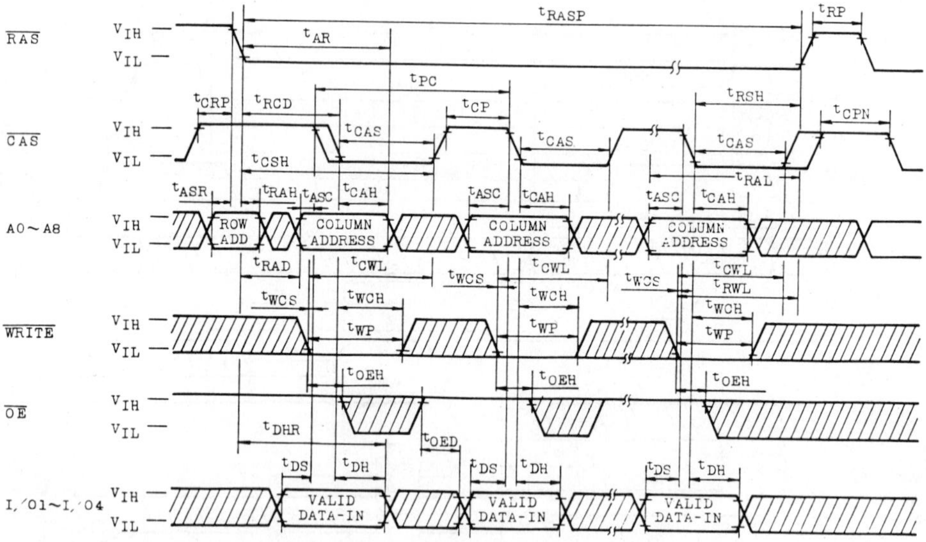

Don't care

Used with permission from Toshiba America Electronic Components.

FAST PAGE MODE READ-WRITE CYCLE

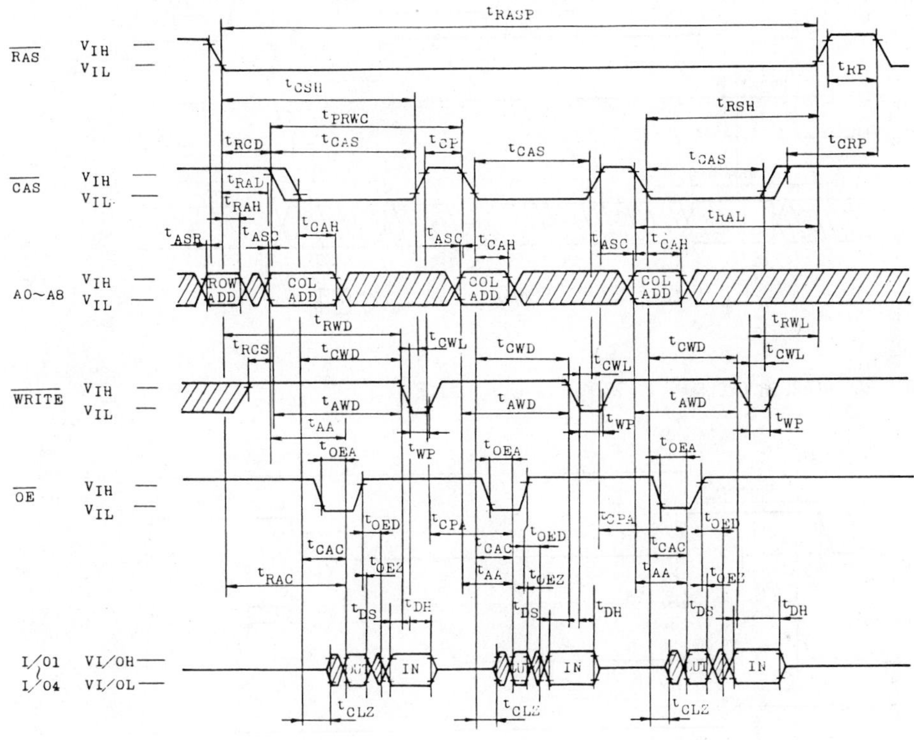

Used with permission from Toshiba America Electronic Components.

$\overline{\text{RAS}}$ ONLY REFRESH CYCLE

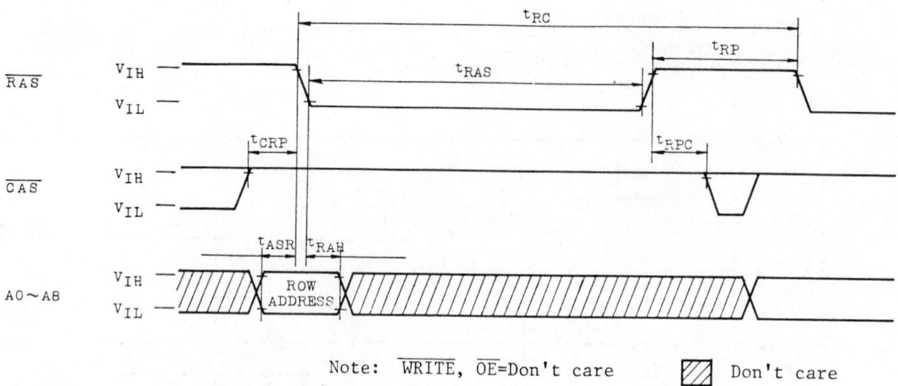

Note: $\overline{\text{WRITE}}$, $\overline{\text{OE}}$=Don't care ▨ Don't care

$\overline{\text{CAS}}$ BEFORE $\overline{\text{RAS}}$ REFRESH CYCLE

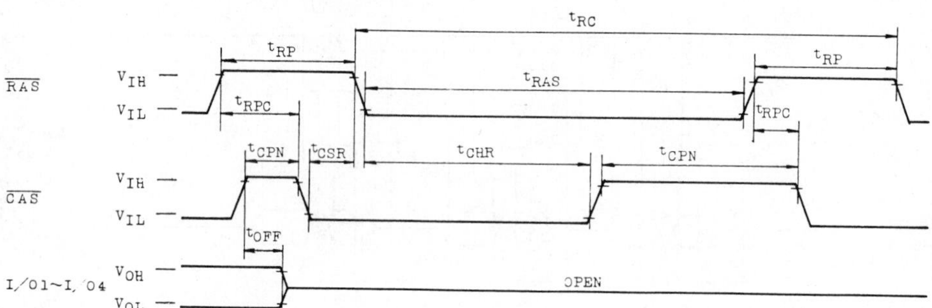

Note: $\overline{\text{WRITE}}$, $\overline{\text{OE}}$, A0 ∿ A7=Don't care

Used with permission from Toshiba America Electronic Components.

HIDDEN REFRESH CYCLE (READ)

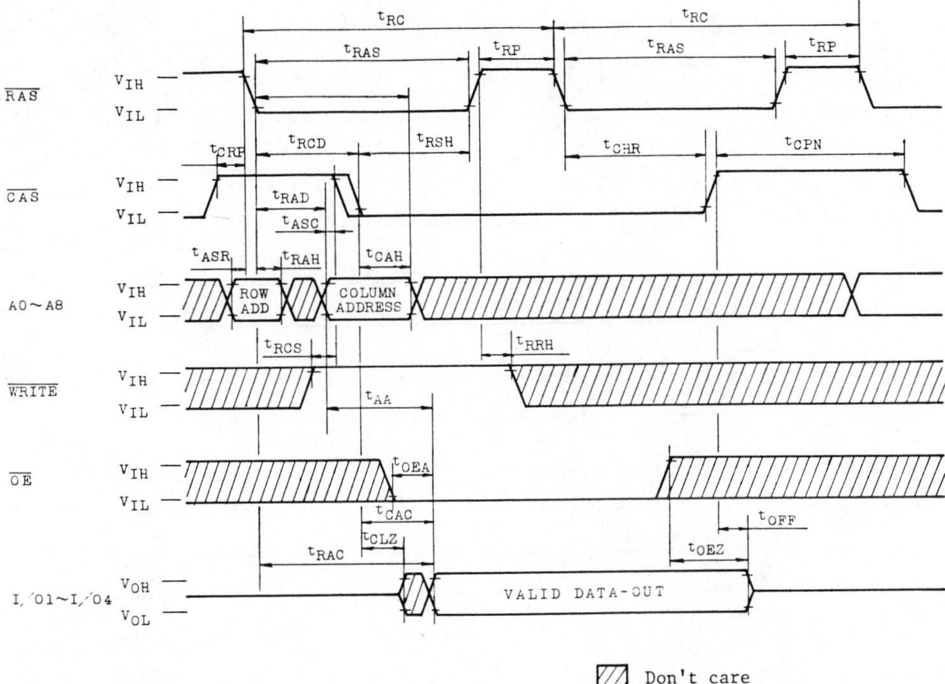

Used with permission from Toshiba America Electronic Components.

HIDDEN REFRESH CYCLE (WRITE)

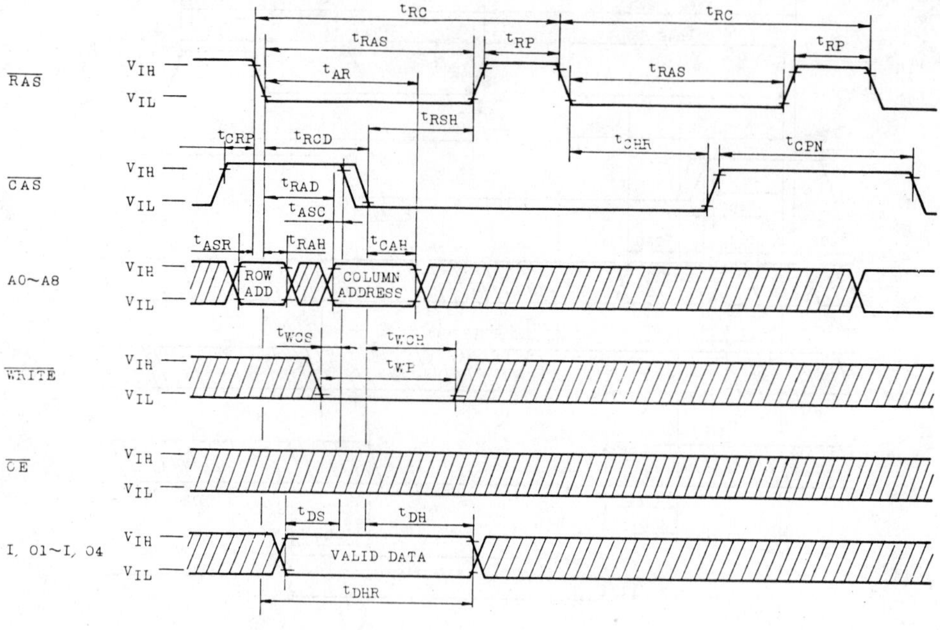

CAS BEFORE RAS REFRESH COUNTER TEST CYCLE

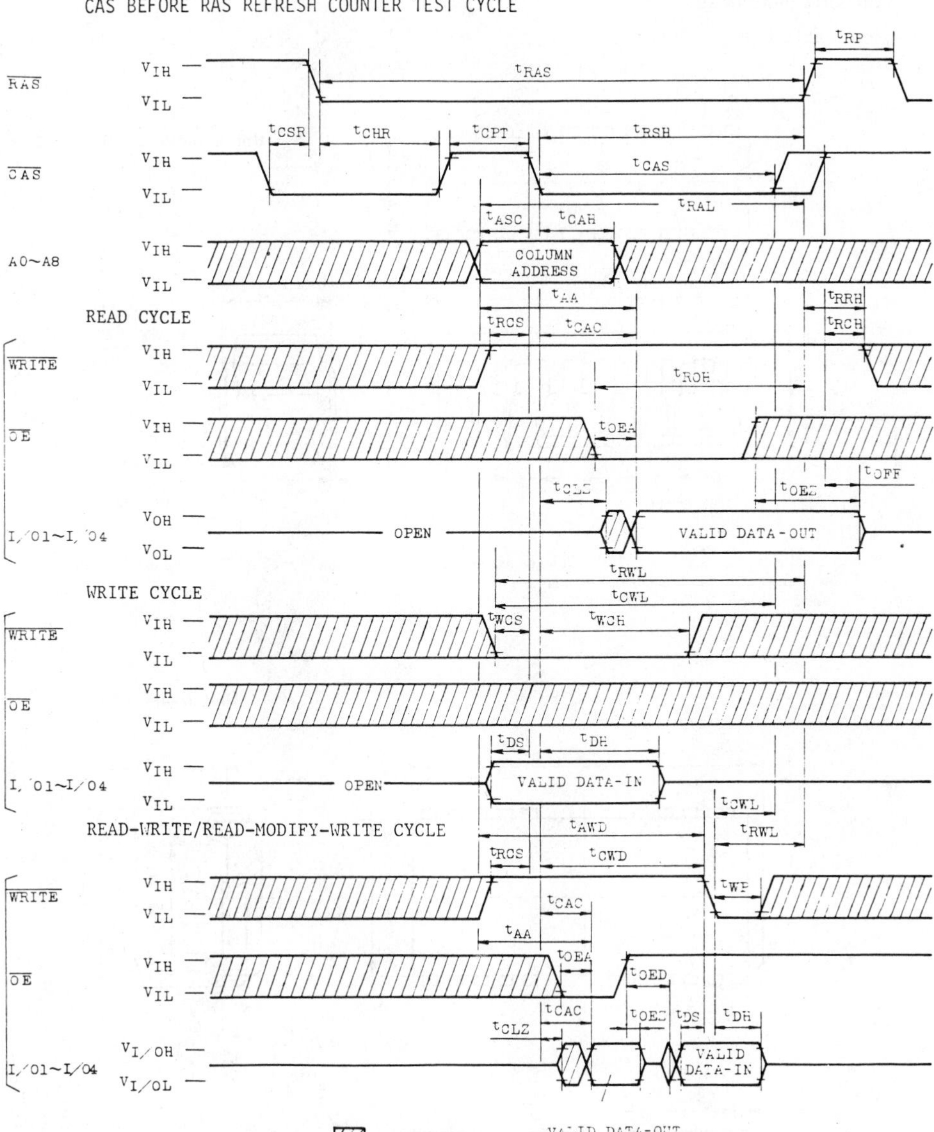

OUTLINE DRAWINGS

• Plastic DIP

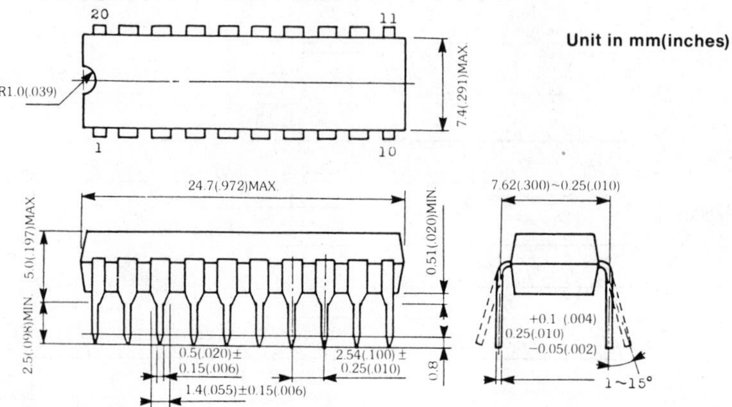

Note: Each lead pitch is 2.54mm(.100). All leads are located within 0.25mm of their true longitudinal position with respect to No.1 and No.20 leads.
All dimensions are in millimeters.

• Plastic SOJ

Unit in mm(inches)

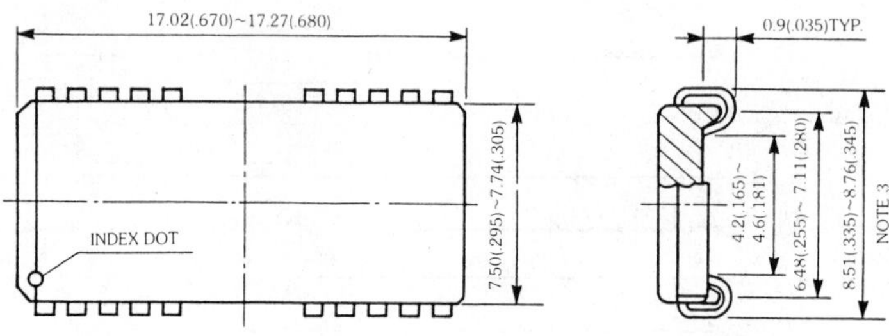

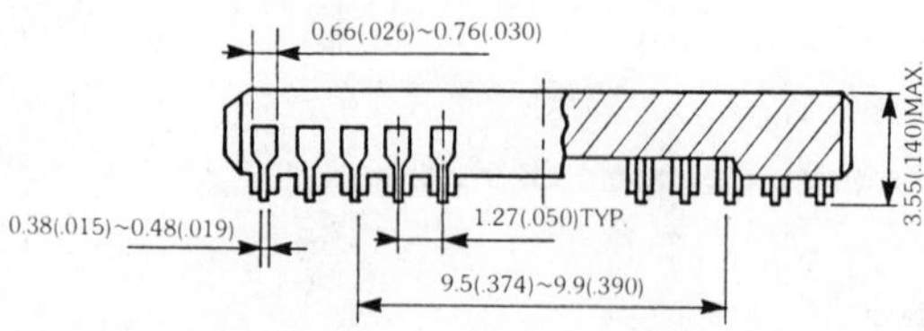

Note: Each lead pitch 1.27(.050)mm.

Note: Toshiba does not assume any responsibility for use of any circuitry described; no circuit patent licenses are implied, and Toshiba reserves the right, at any time without notice, to change said circuitry.

Note: This dimension is subject to change.

Appendix F

Answers to Selected Problems

Chapter 1

4. **(a)** and **(c)**

8. **(a)** VLSI or ULSI **(b)** MSI **(c)** MSI
   (d) SSI **(e)** VLSI or ULSI

10. **(a)** 1 ms **(b)** .1 ms **(c)** .01 ms **(d)** 1 μs

12. f = 20 Hz $\Rightarrow$ T = 50 ms

    f = 20 KHz $\Rightarrow$ T = 50 μs

16. **(a)**

1	2	3	4	5	6	7	8	9	10	11	12
1	0	1	0	1	0	1	0	1	0	1	0

(b) 100 μs **(c)** $f = \dfrac{1}{100\ \mu s} = 10$ KHz **(d)** $t_H = t_L$; therefore, duty cycle = 50% **(e)** square wave **(f)** $T_{new} = 50\ \mu s$

19. T = 10 μs t_{LOW} = 20% of 10 μs = 2 μs
    t_{HIGH} = 8 μs

2 μs ← 10 μs →

22. Square wave = 50% duty cycle f = 25 KHz

    $T = 1/f = \dfrac{1}{25\text{ KHz}} = 40\ \mu s$ 50% of 40 μs = 20 μs

    $t_w = 20\ \mu s$

Chapter 2

2. 9, 13, 12, 14, 15, 11, 0, 1, 3, 6, 4, 12, 13, 5, 1

4. Eleven bits; $2^{11} = 2048$, therefore, $(2000)_{10}$ requires 11 bits to be represented in binary.

10. (a) $(56.879)_{10}$

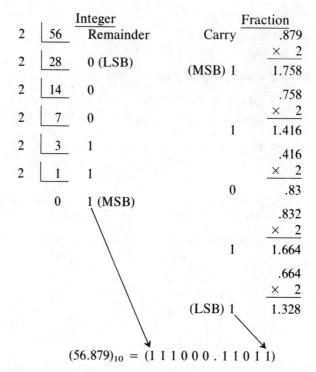

	Integer	Remainder		Carry	Fraction
2	56				.879
					× 2
2	28	0 (LSB)		(MSB) 1	1.758
2	14	0			.758
					× 2
2	7	0		1	1.416
2	3	1			.416
					× 2
2	1	1		0	.83
	0	1 (MSB)			.832
					× 2
				1	1.664
					.664
					× 2
				(LSB) 1	1.328

$$(56.879)_{10} = (1\,1\,1\,0\,0\,0\,.\,1\,1\,0\,1\,1)$$

12. (a) $(23F.45)_{16} = (0\,0\,1\,0 \quad 0\,0\,1\,1 \quad 1\,1\,1\,1\,.\,0\,1\,0\,0 \quad 0\,1\,0\,1)_2$
(b) $(A040.51)_{16} = (1\,1\,0\,0 \quad 0\,0\,0\,0 \quad 0\,1\,0\,0 \quad 0\,0\,0\,0\,.\,0\,1\,0\,1 \quad 0\,0\,0\,1)_2$

17. (a) $(500)_{10} = (1\,0\,0\,0 \quad 0\,0\,1\,1 \quad 0\,0\,1\,1)_{\text{Excess-3 BCD}}$
(b) $(59)_{10} = (1\,0\,0\,0 \quad 1\,1\,0\,0)_{\text{Excess-3 BCD}}$
(c) $(56.879)_{10} = (1\,0\,0\,0 \quad 1\,0\,0\,1\,.\,1\,0\,1\,1 \quad 1\,0\,1\,0 \quad 1\,1\,0\,0)_{\text{Excess-3 BCD}}$

20. $(1\,0\,0\,1 \quad 1\,0\,0\,1 \quad 1\,0\,0\,1)_{\text{8421 BCD}} = (999)_{10}$
Maximum 12-bit 8421 BCD Value

24. (a)

```
  1 0 0 1 0 0 1
×           1 0
---------------
1 0 0 1 0 0 1 0
```

(b)

```
        1 0 0 1 . 1 1 0 0 1
    -----------------------
101)1 1 0 0 0 1 . 0 0 0 0 0
    1 0 1
    -----------------------
      1 0 0 1
        1 0 1
    -----------------------
        1 0 0  0
          1 0  1
    -----------------------
              1  1 0
              1  0 1
    -----------------------
                   1 0 0 0
```

35. (a)

```
  F 8 4       1111 1000 0100
 -A 0 9      -1010 0000 1001
 ------      ----------------
  5 7 B
```

Two's complement arithmetic

```
  1111           1
  1111 1000 0100
 +0101 1111 0111
 ----------------
 X0101 0111 1011
  (5    7    B)16
```

(b)

```
  2 9 E 6     0010 1001 1110 0110
 -5 F 5 8    -0101 1111 0101 1000
 --------    ---------------------
  C A 8 E
```

Two's complement arithmetic

```
  1          11   11
  0010 1001 1110 0110
 +1010 0000 1010 1000
 ---------------------
  1100 1010 1000 1110
   (C    A    8    E)16
```

Chapter 3

5.

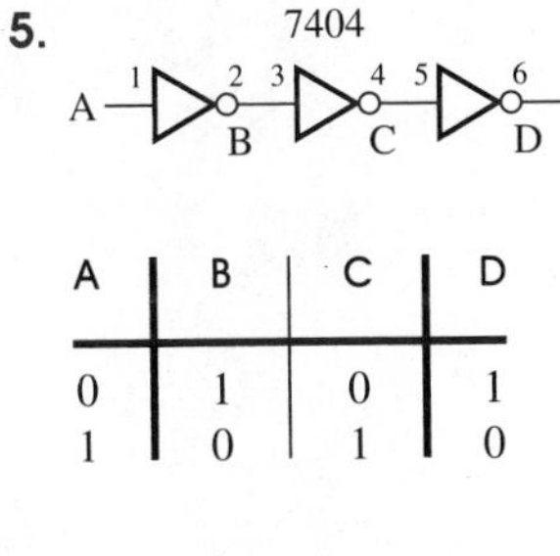

A	B	C	D
0	1	0	1
1	0	1	0

11.

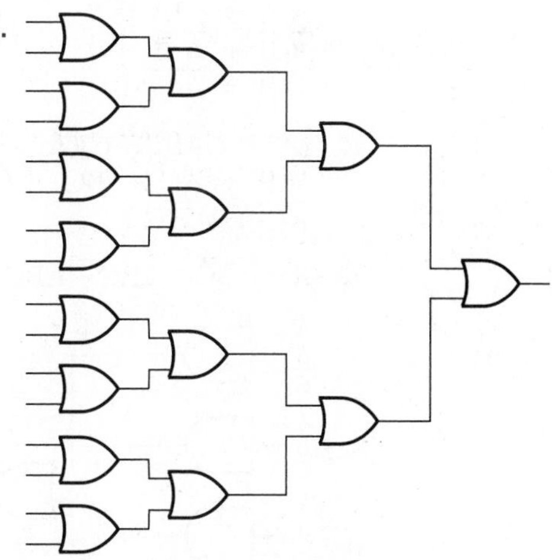

Four 7432 ICs are required.

16.

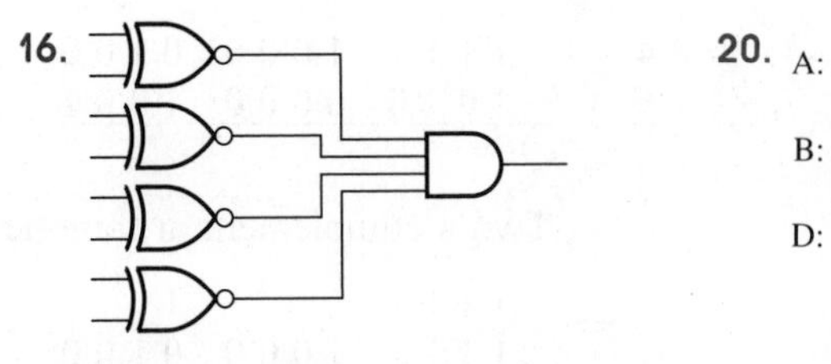

20.

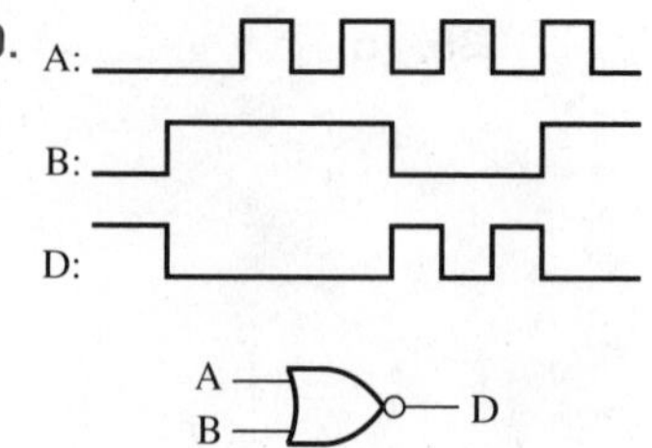

24.

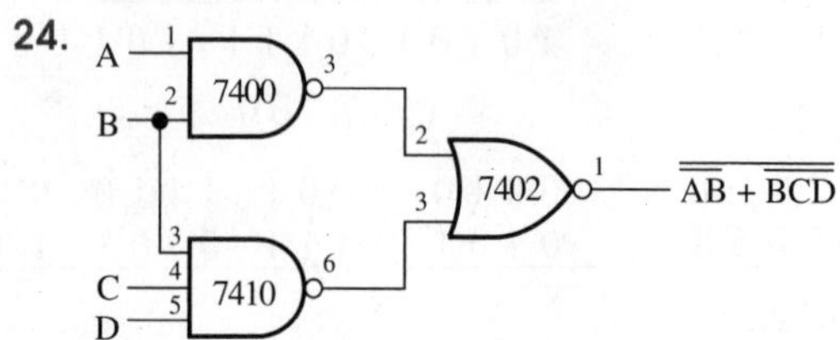

30. Two levels in Figure 3-79

39. $A(\overline{A} + B) = AB$

A	B	$\overline{A}$	$\overline{A} + B$	$(\overline{A} + B)A$	AB
0	0	1	1	0	0
0	1	1	1	0	0
1	0	0	0	0	0
1	1	0	1	1	1

45. $\overline{(A + B)}(\overline{A} + \overline{B})$
$\overline{A} \cdot \overline{B}(\overline{A} + \overline{B})$
$\overline{A}\,\overline{A}\,\overline{B} + \overline{A}\,\overline{B}\,\overline{B}$
$\overline{A}\,\overline{B} + \overline{A}\,\overline{B}$
$\overline{A}\,\overline{B} = \overline{A + B}$

50. $(A + C)(B + C)(\overline{A} + \overline{C})$
$(AB + AC + BC + C)(\overline{A} + \overline{C})$
$\overline{A}C + A\overline{B}\,\overline{C}$

52. $X = \overline{A}B\overline{C} + \overline{A}BC + A\overline{B}C + AB\overline{C}$

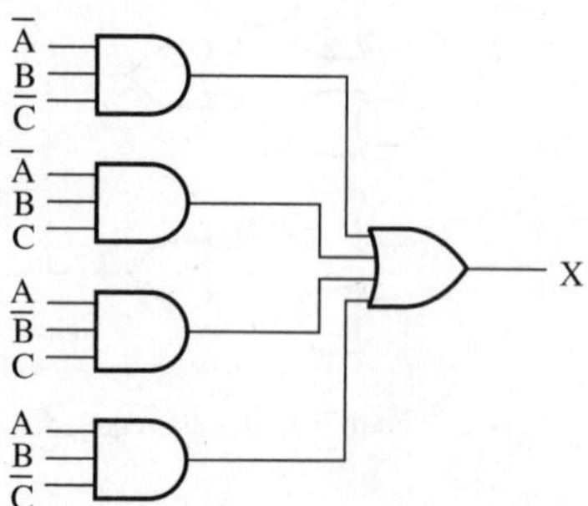

61.

$$X = \overline{A}BC\overline{D}$$
$$X = \overline{\overline{\overline{A}BC\overline{D}}}$$
$$X = \overline{\overline{(\overline{A \cdot 1}) \cdot B \cdot C \cdot (\overline{D \cdot 1})} \cdot 1}$$

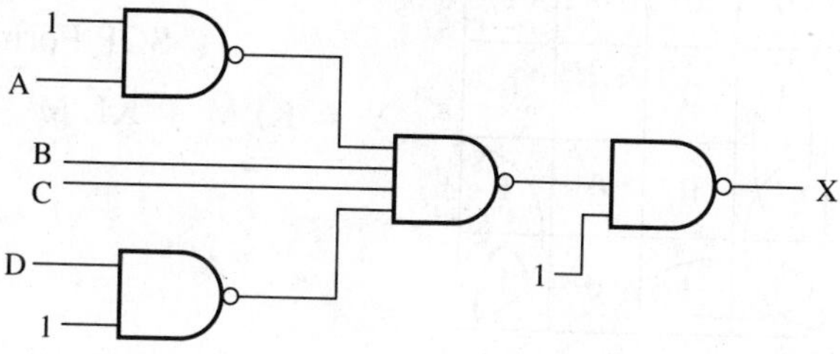

69. See Figure 3-79. Truth table derived in Problem 3-26.

A B C D	M
0 0 0 0	0
0 0 0 1	1
0 0 1 0	1
0 0 1 1	0
0 1 0 0	1
0 1 0 1	0
0 1 1 0	0
0 1 1 1	1
1 0 0 0	1
1 0 0 1	0
1 0 1 0	0
1 0 1 1	1
1 1 0 0	0
1 1 0 1	1
1 1 1 0	1
1 1 1 1	0

$$M = (\overline{A \oplus B}) \oplus (\overline{C \oplus D})$$

$$\begin{aligned} M = {} & (A + B + C + D)(A + B + \overline{C} + \overline{D}) \\ & (A + \overline{B} + C + \overline{D})(A + \overline{B} + \overline{C} + D) \\ & (\overline{A} + B + C + \overline{D})(\overline{A} + B + \overline{C} + D) \\ & \cdot(\overline{A} + \overline{B} + C + D)(\overline{A} + \overline{B} + \overline{C} + \overline{D}) \end{aligned}$$

74. See Figure 3-84.

JK \ LM	00	01	11	10
00	0	0	0	1
01	1	0	0	0
11	1	0	0	1
10	1	1	0	1

SOP Form

$$Y = \overline{K}L\overline{M} + K\overline{L}\,\overline{M} + J\overline{M} + J\overline{K}\,\overline{L}$$

JK \ LM	00	01	11	10
00	0	0	0	1
01	1	0	0	0
11	1	0	0	1
10	1	1	0	1

POS Form

$$Y = (J + K + L)(J + \overline{M})(\overline{K} + \overline{M}) \cdot (\overline{L} + \overline{M})(J + \overline{K} + \overline{L})$$

86.
$$\begin{aligned} A \oplus B &= \overline{A}B + A\overline{B} \\ &= \overline{\overline{\overline{A}B + A\overline{B}}} \\ &= \overline{\overline{\overline{A}B} \cdot \overline{A\overline{B}}} \end{aligned}$$

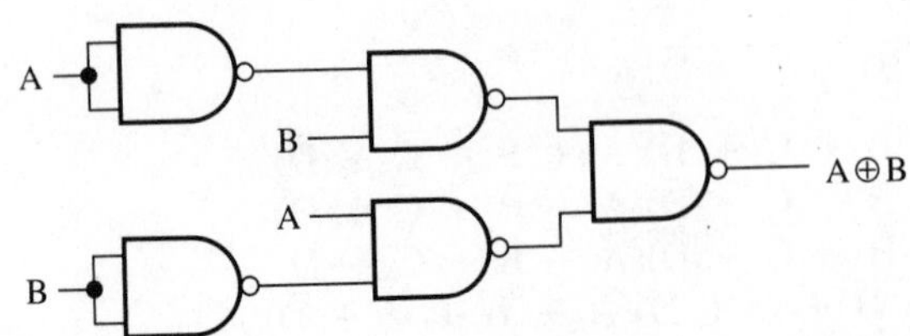

92. (See Figure 3-81.) Truth table derived in Problem 3-28:

A B C D	P
0 0 0 0	1
0 0 0 1	1
0 0 1 0	1
0 0 1 1	1
0 1 0 0	1
0 1 0 1	1
0 1 1 0	1
0 1 1 1	0
1 0 0 0	1
1 0 0 1	1
1 0 1 0	1
1 0 1 1	0
1 1 0 0	1
1 1 0 1	0
1 1 1 0	1
1 1 1 1	1

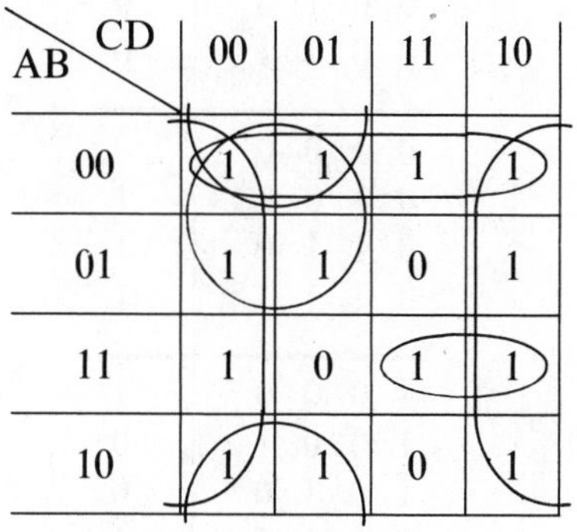

AB \ CD	00	01	11	10
00	1	1	1	1
01	1	1	0	1
11	1	0	1	1
10	1	1	0	1

(a) SOP form:

$$P = \overline{D} + \overline{A}\overline{B} + \overline{A}\overline{C} + \overline{B}\overline{C} + ABC$$

AB \ CD	00	01	11	10
00	1	1	1	1
01	1	1	0	1
11	1	0	1	1
10	1	1	0	1

(b) POS Form (no simplification):

$$P = (A + \overline{B} + \overline{C} + \overline{D})(\overline{A} + \overline{B} + C + \overline{D})(\overline{A} + B + \overline{C} + \overline{D})$$

97. Convert the waveforms in Figure 3-86 to a truth table:

D C B A	Z
0 0 0 0	0
0 0 0 1	0
0 0 1 0	0
0 0 1 1	0
0 1 0 0	0
0 1 0 1	1
0 1 1 0	1
0 1 1 1	1
1 0 0 0	1
1 0 0 1	0
1 0 1 0	0
1 0 1 1	1
1 1 0 0	1
1 1 0 1	1
1 1 1 0	0
1 1 1 1	1

DC \ AB	00	01	11	10
00	0	0	0	0
01	0	1	1	1
11	1	1	1	0
10	1	0	1	0

$Z = (D + C)(D + B + A)(\overline{D} + \overline{B} + A)(C + B +$

$Z = CA + \overline{D}CB + D\overline{B}\,\overline{A} + DBA$

Both the SOP and POS forms are equivalent (in terms of simplification).

114.

A B	C D	J K L M
0 0	0 0	0 0 0 0
0 0	0 1	0 0 0 0
0 0	1 0	0 0 0 0
0 0	1 1	0 0 0 0
0 1	0 0	0 0 0 0
0 1	0 1	0 0 0 1
0 1	1 0	0 0 1 0
0 1	1 1	0 0 1 1
1 0	0 0	0 0 0 0
1 0	0 1	0 0 1 0
1 0	1 0	0 1 0 0
1 0	1 1	0 1 1 0
1 1	0 0	0 0 0 0
1 1	0 1	0 0 1 1
1 1	1 0	0 1 1 0
1 1	1 1	1 0 0 1

$$\begin{array}{r} AB \\ \times\ CD \\ \hline JKLM \end{array}$$

J = ABCD, by inspection

K-Map for K Output

AB \ CD	00	01	11	10
00	0	0	0	0
01	0	0	0	0
11	0	0	0	1
10	0	0	1	1

$K = A\overline{B}C + AC\overline{D}$

K-Map for L Output

AB \ CD	00	01	11	10
00	0	0	0	0
01	0	0	1	1
11	0	1	0	1
10	0	1	1	0

$L = A\overline{C}D + A\overline{B}D + \overline{A}BC + BC\overline{D}$

K-Map for M Output

AB \ CD	00	01	11	10
00	0	0	0	0
01	0	1	1	0
11	0	1	1	0
10	0	0	0	0

$M = BD$

Circuit for Problem 114: Binary Multiplier

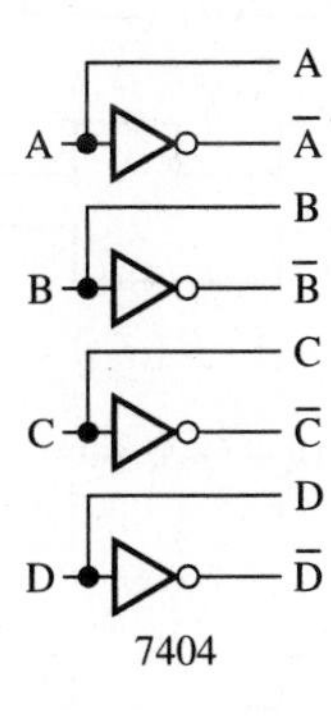

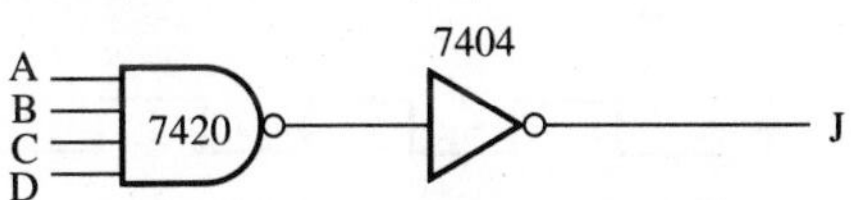

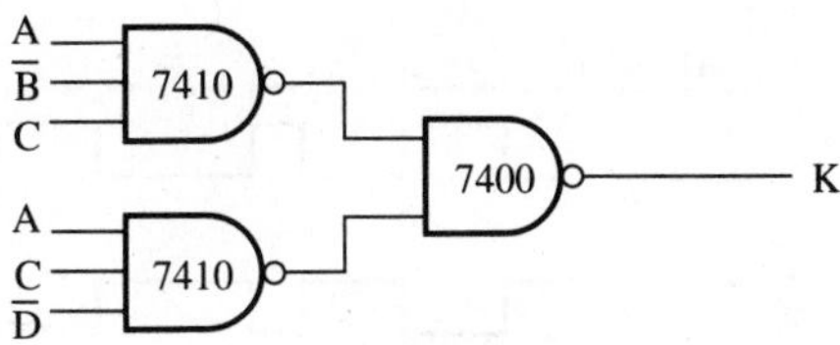

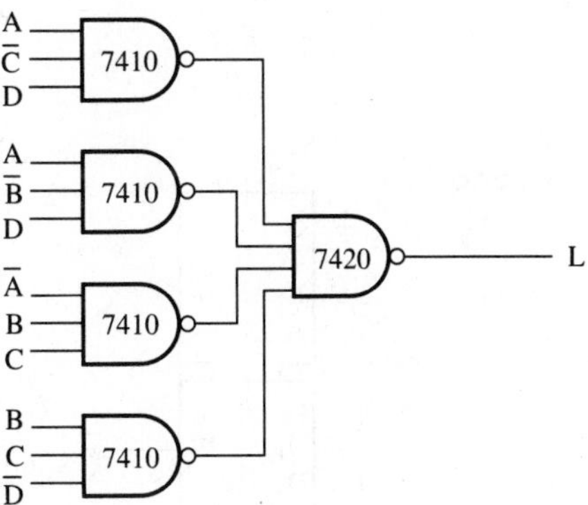

ICs Used:
1-7404
1-7420
2-7410
1-7400

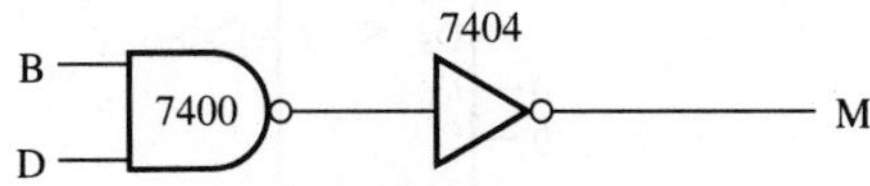

Chapter 4

2. **(a)** 18 ns typically; 27 ns maximum
   (b) t_{PHL} *Note:* $t_{PHL} > t_{PLH}$ in this example.
   (c) The data on the D_0 through D_7 inputs cannot change faster than
   $$\frac{1}{27 \text{ ns}} = 37 \text{ MHz}$$

10. 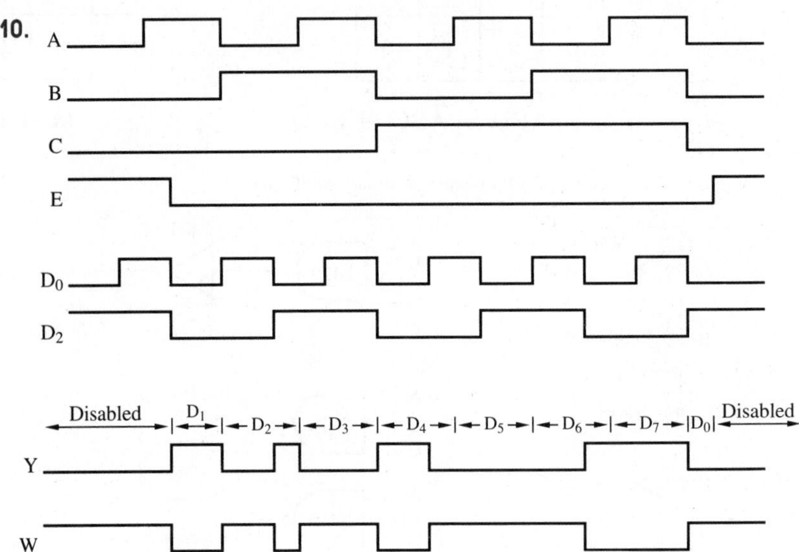

13. and 14. 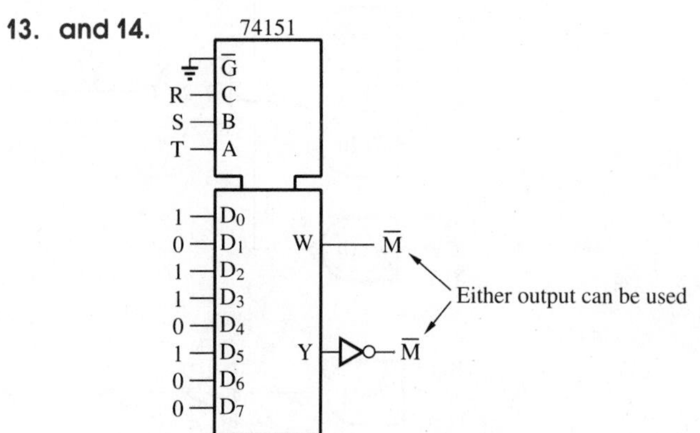

18.

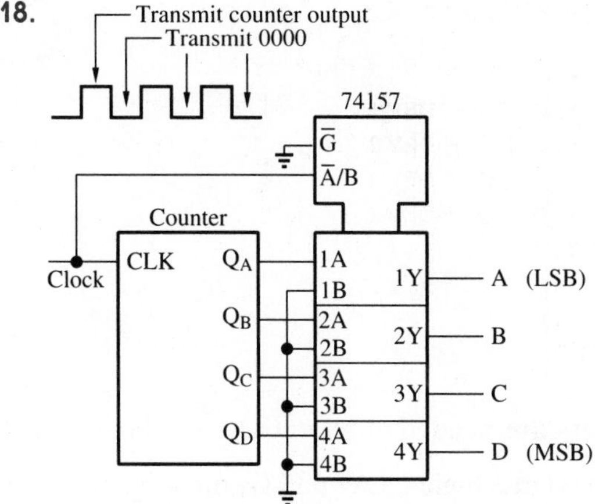

22.

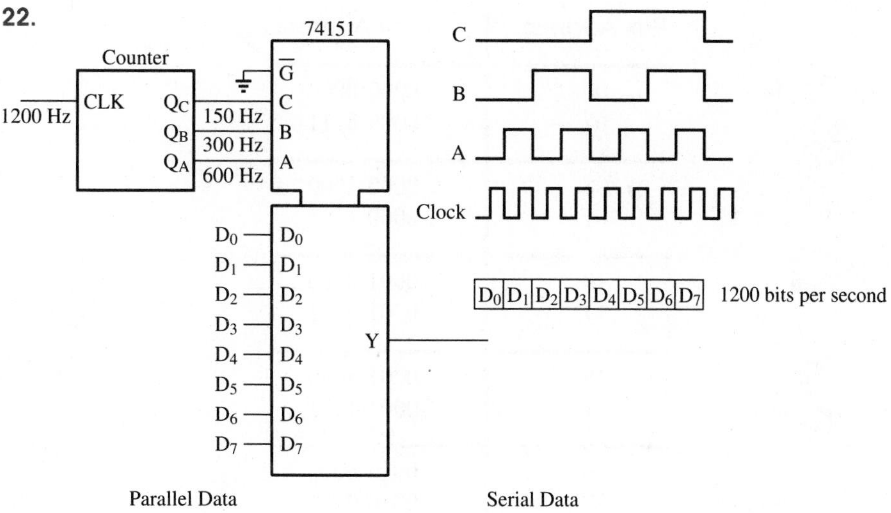

26.

Strobe $\overline{G}$	Select Inputs D C B A	Output W
0	Unconnected	$\overline{E_{15}}$
1	Unconnected	1

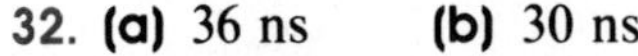

32. **(a)** 36 ns **(b)** 30 ns

39.

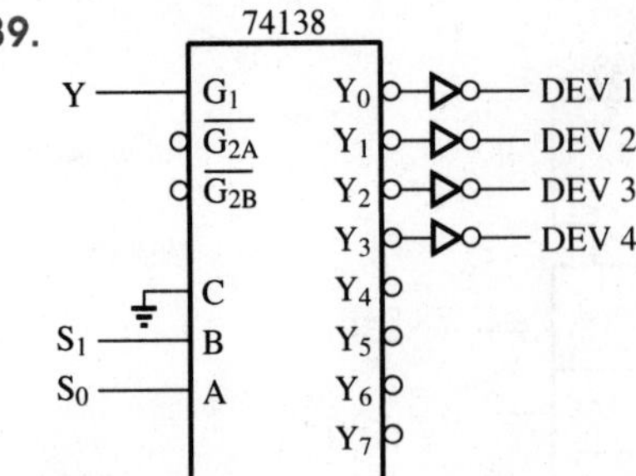

44. Pull-up resistors are needed at all outputs to obtain a logic-HIGH.

49. $\overline{G_{2B}}$ must be held at a logic-LOW and G_1 must be held at a logic-HIGH.

Chapter 5

2. **(a)** 36 ns **(b)** 36 ns + 22 ns = 58 ns **(c)** 22 ns + 22 ns = 44 ns

7.

Hex Address	Binary Address
00	0000 0000
07	0000 0111
08	0000 1000
0F	0000 1111
10	0001 0000
17	0001 0111
18	0001 1000
1F	0001 1111
20	0010 0000
27	0010 0111
28	0010 1000
2F	0010 1111
30	0011 0000
37	0011 0111
38	0011 1000
3F	0011 1111

Eight 74138 ICs are required.

10. 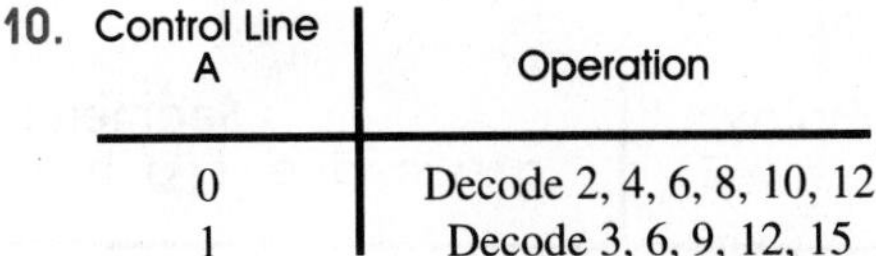

Control Line A	Operation
0	Decode 2, 4, 6, 8, 10, 12
1	Decode 3, 6, 9, 12, 15

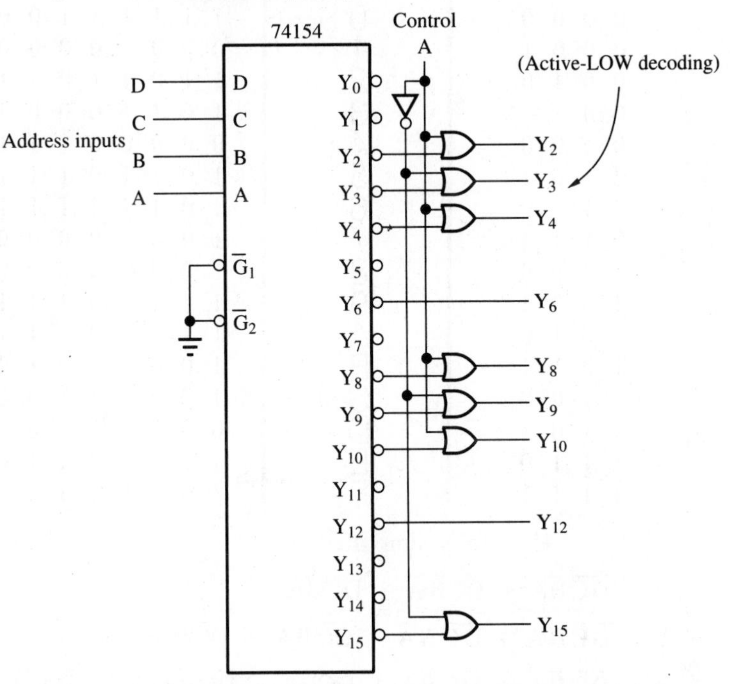

Note: Y_6 and Y_{12} are decoded independently of A, so no gating control is required for those outputs.

15.

A	B	C	D	L	K	M
0	0	0	0	0	0	0
0	0	0	1	1	0	0
0	0	1	0	0	0	1
0	0	1	1	0	0	1
0	1	0	0	0	0	0
0	1	0	1	1	0	0
0	1	1	0	1	1	0
0	1	1	1	1	1	0
1	0	0	0	0	0	1
1	0	0	1	1	1	1
1	0	1	0	0	0	1
1	0	1	1	1	1	1
1	1	0	0	0	1	0
1	1	0	1	1	1	0
1	1	1	0	0	1	0
1	1	1	1	1	1	0

23. See Figure 5-40.

Input Code D C B A	Display	a	b	c	d	e	f	g	h	j	k	l	m	n	p
0 0 0 0	0	1	1	1	1	1	1	0	0	0	0	0	0	0	0
0 0 0 1	1	0	0	0	0	0	0	0	0	1	0	0	1	0	0
0 0 1 0	2	1	1	0	1	1	0	1	1	0	0	0	0	0	0
0 0 1 1	3	1	0	1	1	0	0	0	1	0	1	0	0	0	0
0 1 0 0	4	0	0	0	0	0	1	1	1	1	0	0	1	0	0
0 1 0 1	5	1	0	1	1	0	1	1	1	0	0	0	0	0	0
0 1 1 0	6	1	0	1	1	1	1	1	1	0	0	0	0	0	0
0 1 1 1	7	1	0	0	1	0	0	0	0	0	1	0	0	1	0
1 0 0 0	8	1	0	0	1	0	0	0	0	0	1	1	0	1	1
1 0 0 1	9	1	1	1	0	0	1	1	1	0	0	0	0	0	0
1 0 1 0	A	1	1	1	0	0	1	1	1	0	0	0	0	0	0
1 0 1 1	B	1	0	0	1	1	1	1	0	0	1	1	0	0	0
1 1 0 0	C	1	0	0	1	1	1	0	0	0	0	0	0	0	0
1 1 0 1	D	0	0	0	1	1	1	0	0	0	0	1	0	0	1
1 1 1 0	E	1	0	0	1	1	1	1	0	0	0	0	0	0	0
1 1 1 1	F	1	0	0	0	1	1	1	0	0	0	0	0	0	0

(Not fully simplified)

$\bar{a} = \bar{D}\bar{C}\bar{B}A + \bar{D}C\bar{B}\bar{A} + DC\bar{B}A$

$b = \bar{D}\bar{C}\bar{B}\bar{A} + \bar{D}\bar{C}B\bar{A} + D\bar{C}\bar{B}A + D\bar{C}B\bar{A}$

$c = \bar{D}\bar{C}\bar{B}\bar{A} + \bar{D}\bar{C}BA + \bar{D}C\bar{B}A + \bar{D}CB\bar{A} + D\bar{C}\bar{B}A + D\bar{C}B\bar{A}$

$\bar{d} = \bar{D}\bar{C}\bar{B}A + \bar{D}C\bar{B}\bar{A} + D\bar{C}\bar{B}A + D\bar{C}B\bar{A} + DCBA$

$e = DC + DBA + \bar{D}B\bar{A} + \bar{D}\bar{C}\bar{B}\bar{A}$

$f = DC + D\bar{C}BA + \bar{D}C\bar{B} + \bar{D}C\bar{A} + \bar{D}\bar{C}\bar{B}\bar{A}$

$g = DCB + D\bar{C}B + D\bar{C}A + \bar{D}C\bar{A} + \bar{D}C\bar{B}A + \bar{D}\bar{C}B\bar{A}$

$h = \bar{D}\bar{C}B + \bar{D}C\bar{B} + \bar{D}CB\bar{A} + D\bar{C}\bar{B}A + D\bar{C}B\bar{A}$

$j = \bar{D}\bar{C}\bar{B}A + \bar{D}C\bar{B}\bar{A}$

$k = \bar{D}BA + D\bar{C}\bar{B}\bar{A} + D\bar{C}BA$

$l = D\bar{C}\bar{B}\bar{A} + D\bar{C}BA + DC\bar{B}A$

$m = j = \bar{D}\bar{C}\bar{B}A + \bar{D}C\bar{B}\bar{A}$

$n = \bar{D}CBA + D\bar{C}\bar{B}\bar{A}$

$p = D\bar{C}\bar{B}\bar{A} + DC\bar{B}A$

24. **(a)** 19 ns **(b)** 33 ns

28. **(a)** 80 ns (two decades) **(b)** 280 ns (four decades) **(c)** (1 0 0 1 1 0 0 1 1 0 0 1 1 0 0 1 1 0 0 1 1 0 0 1)$_{BCD}$ **(d)** Eleven packages are required (four decades).

34.

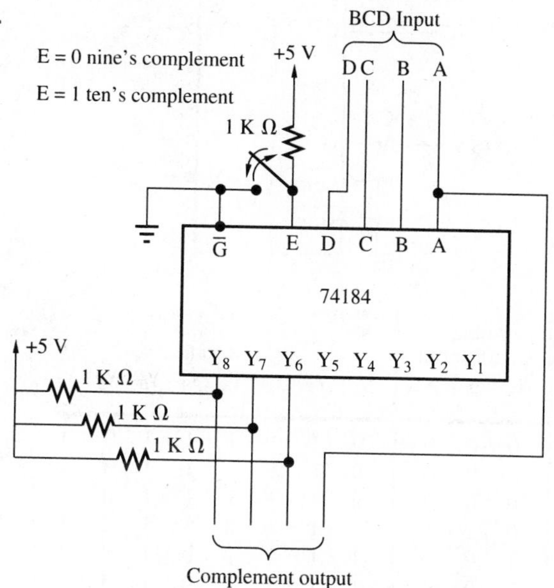

37.

Character	ASCII	ASCII with Even Parity
"	0 0 1 0 0 0 1 0	0 0 0 1 0 0 0 1 0
D	0 1 0 0 0 1 0 0	0 0 1 0 0 0 1 0 0
i	0 1 1 0 1 0 0 1	0 0 1 1 0 1 0 0 1
g	0 1 1 0 0 1 1 1	1 0 1 1 0 0 1 1 1
i	0 1 1 0 1 0 0 1	0 0 1 1 0 1 0 0 1
t	0 1 1 1 0 1 0 0	0 0 1 1 1 0 1 0 0
a	0 1 1 0 0 0 0 1	1 0 1 1 0 0 0 0 1
l	0 1 1 0 1 1 0 0	0 0 1 1 0 1 1 0 0
space	0 0 1 0 0 0 0 0	1 0 0 1 0 0 0 0 0
L	0 1 0 0 1 1 0 0	1 0 1 0 0 1 1 0 0
o	0 1 1 0 1 1 1 1	0 0 1 1 0 1 1 1 1
g	0 1 1 0 0 1 1 1	1 0 1 1 0 0 1 1 1
i	0 1 1 0 1 0 0 1	0 0 1 1 0 1 0 0 1
c	0 1 1 0 0 0 1 1	0 0 1 1 0 0 0 1 1
"	0 0 1 0 0 0 1 0	0 0 0 1 0 0 0 1 0

Circuit is shown in Figure 5-35.

39.

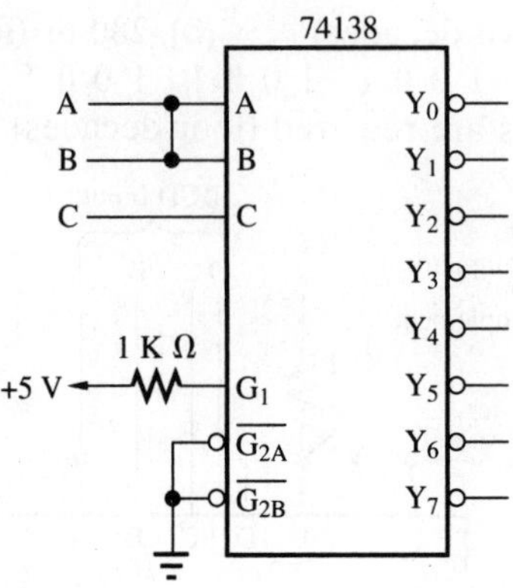

Input Switches			Actual Circuit Input			Output							
C	B	A	C	B	A	Y_0	Y_1	Y_2	Y_3	Y_4	Y_5	Y_6	Y_7
0	0	0	0	0	0	0	1	1	1	1	1	1	1
0	0	1	0	0	0	0	1	1	1	1	1	1	1
0	1	0	0	0	0	0	1	1	1	1	1	1	1
0	1	1	0	1	1	1	1	1	0	1	1	1	1
1	0	0	1	0	0	1	1	1	1	0	1	1	1
1	0	1	1	0	0	1	1	1	1	0	1	1	1
1	1	0	1	0	0	1	1	1	1	0	1	1	1
1	1	1	1	1	1	1	1	1	1	1	1	1	0

Chapter 6

1. Unsigned numbers, 0 to 255

5. Nine-bit adder-subtracter

$$\begin{array}{r} A_9\,A_8\,A_7\,A_6\,A_5\,A_4\,A_3\,A_2\,A_1 \\ \pm\ B_9\,B_8\,B_7\,B_6\,B_5\,B_4\,B_3\,B_2\,B_1 \\ \hline R_9\,R_8\,R_7\,R_6\,R_5\,R_4\,R_3\,R_2\,R_1 \end{array}$$

$$\text{Overflow} = A_9\,B_9\,\overline{R}_9 + \overline{A}_9 \cdot \overline{B}_9 \cdot R_9$$

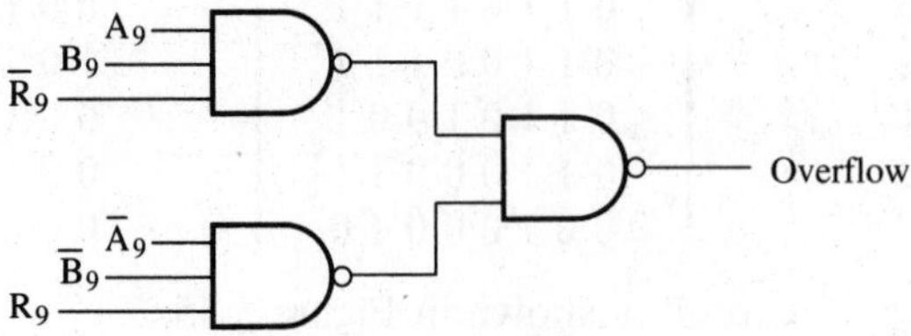

10.

				A_4	A_3	A_2	A_1
			×	B_4	B_3	B_2	B_1
				A_4B_1	A_3B_1	A_2B_1	A_1B_1
			A_4B_2	A_3B_2	A_2B_2	A_1B_2	
		A_4B_3	A_3B_3	A_2B_3	A_1B_3		
	A_4B_4	A_3B_4	A_2B_4	A_1B_4			
P_8	P_7	P_6	P_5	P_4	P_3	P_2	P_1

4-7408s
3-74284s
7 ICs total for this design

13. Maximum propagation delay of the 7485 is 35 ns.

17.

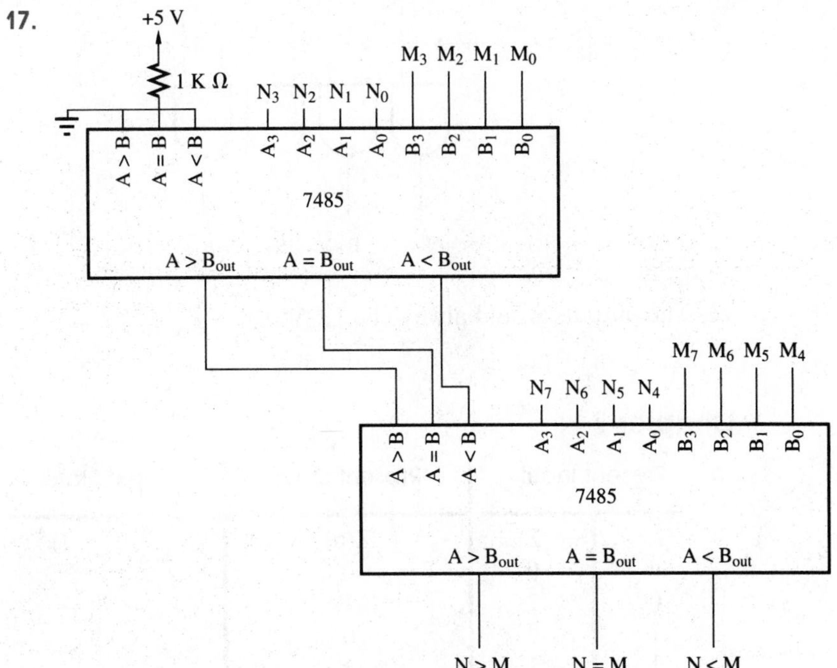

23.

Inputs			Operation	74283 Inputs								
G	M	N		A_4	A_3	A_2	A_1	B_4	B_3	B_2	B_1	C_0
0	0	0	BCD	D	C	B	A	0	0	0	0	0
0	0	1	Excess-3	D	C	B	A	0	0	1	1	0
0	1	X	Binary	D	C	B	A	0	0	0	0	0
1	X	X	Zero	X	X	X	X	X	X	X	X	X

Input Equations for the 74283

$A_4 = D \quad B_4 = 0$

$A_3 = C \quad B_3 = 0$

$A_2 = B \quad B_2 = \overline{M}N$

$A_1 = A \quad B_1 = \overline{M}N$

$C_0 = 0$

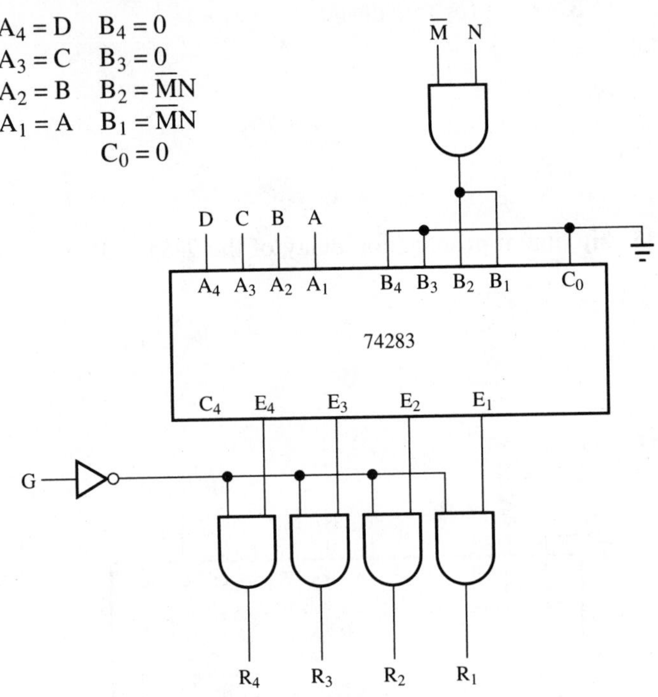

26. The outputs would always be LOW.

Chapter 7

5.

Present Input		Present State	Next State	
A	Z	Z(n)	Z(n + 1)	
0	0	0	1	Unstable
0	1	1	0	Unstable
1	0	0	0	Stable
1	1	1	1	Stable

7. Using Shottky TTL logic gates:

	t_{PLH}	t_{PHL}
Typical	10 ns	9.5 ns
Maximum	15 ns	15 ns

11.

	t_{PLH}	t_{PHL}
Typical	15 ns	15 ns
Maximum	22 ns	22 ns

15. 330 μs

21. C = 1000 pF; R = 6.8K Ω

27. R_A = 9.9K Ω; C = .1 μF

31. C = .1 μF; R_A = 360 Ω; R_B = 2880 Ω

37. (a) 3.33 V (b) 6.67 V

43.

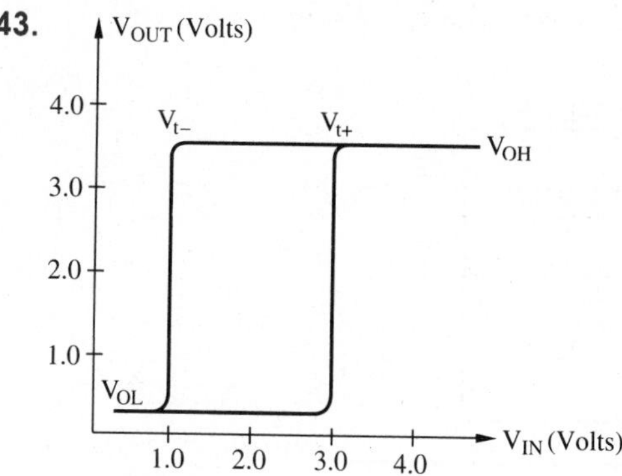

48. 24.2 KHz

51. 446 ms

Chapter 8

6.

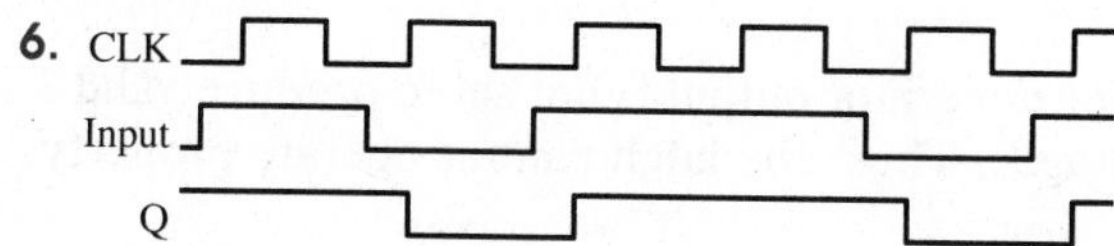

12. (a)

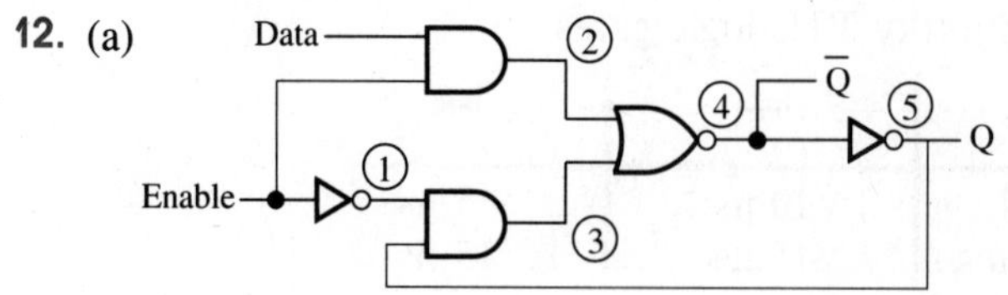

Enable	Data	Q	①	②	③	④ $\overline{Q}$	⑤ Q
0	0	0	1	0	0	1	0
0	0	1	1	0	1	0	1
0	1	0	1	0	0	1	0
0	1	1	1	0	1	0	1
1	0	0	0	0	0	1	0
1	0	1	0	0	0	1	0
1	1	0	0	1	0	0	1
1	1	1	0	1	0	0	1

16.

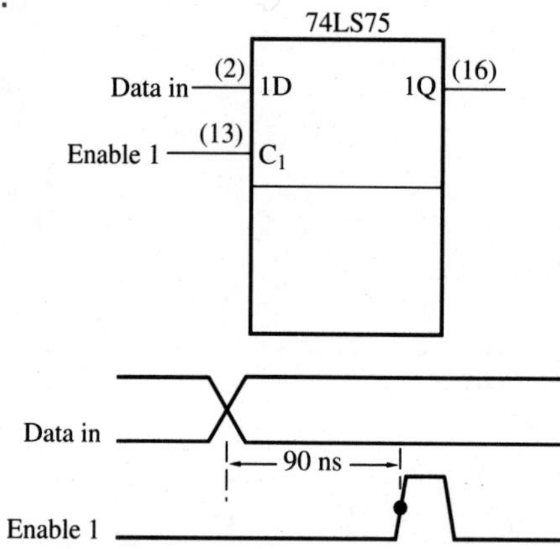

22. The 3C/4C enable input can be floating or tied LOW, disabling the two latches.

24. The function generator output is not set to produce valid TTL LOW and HIGH voltages. Thus, the latch cannot operate property.

Chapter 9

7.

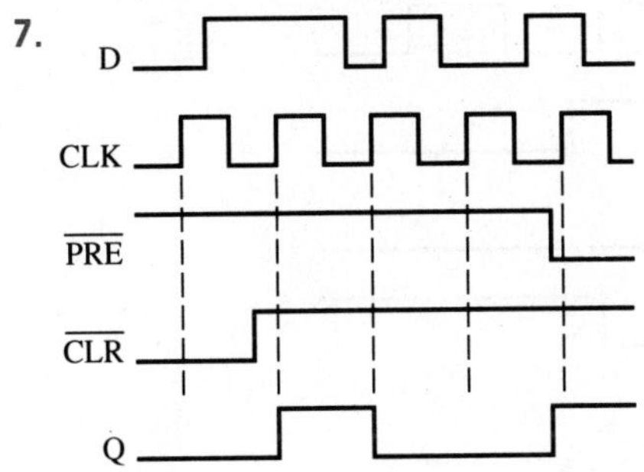

15.

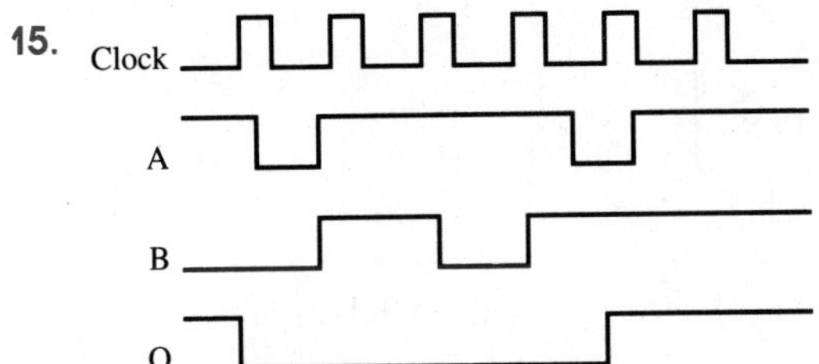

17.

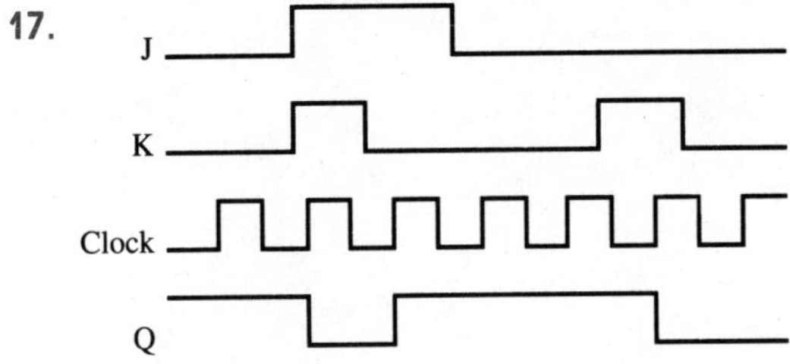

18.

19.

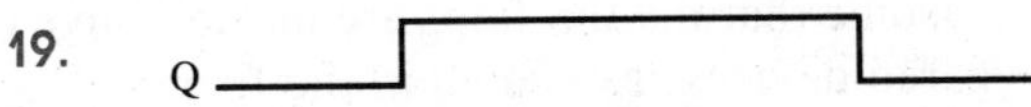

23. **(a)**

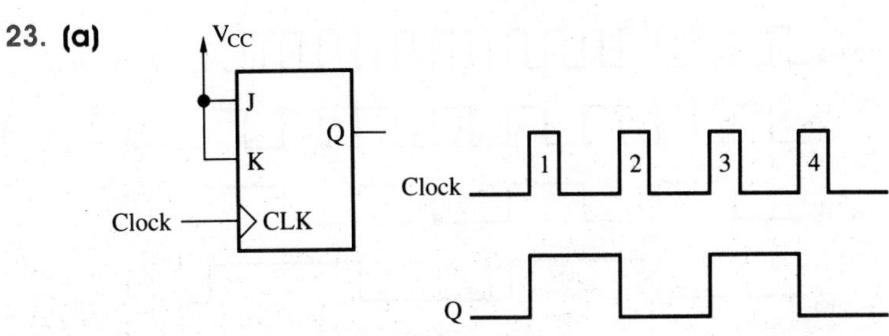

(b) 5 KHz **(c)** 15 MHz

30. **(a)** 25 ns **(b)** 21 ns

32.

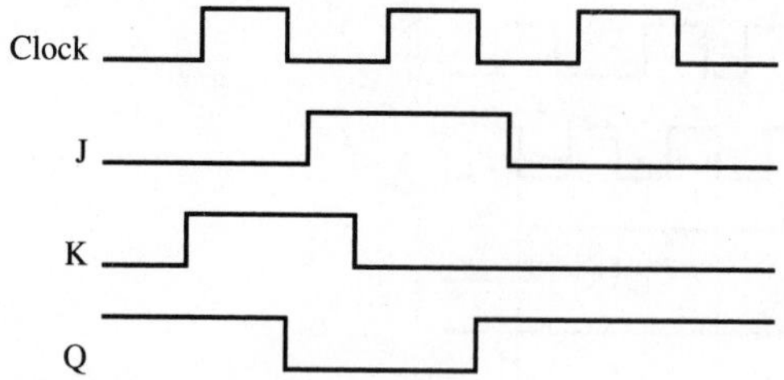

39. **(a)**

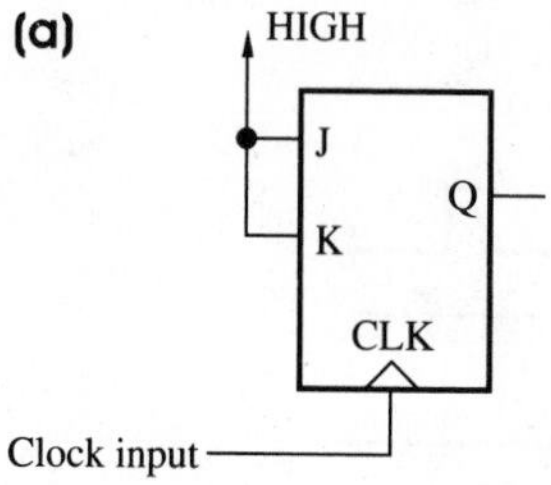

(b) 50 KHz **(c)** 50% **(d)** 25 KHz, 50%

Chapter 10

3. See Figure 10-1. D is 125 Hz.

5. See Figure 10-4. Assume that the flip-flops are master-slave devices (not positive edge-triggered devices, as shown in the figure).

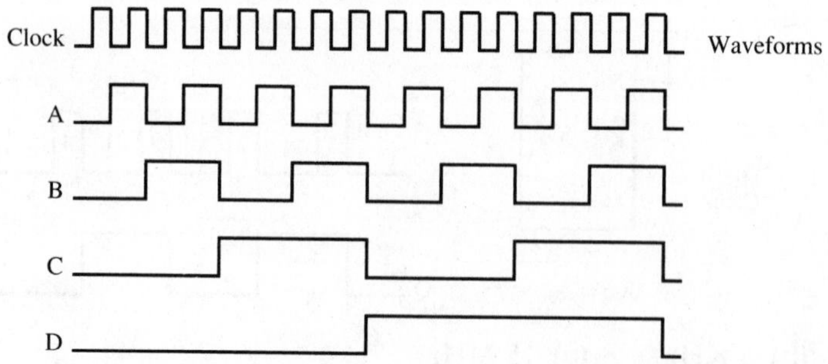

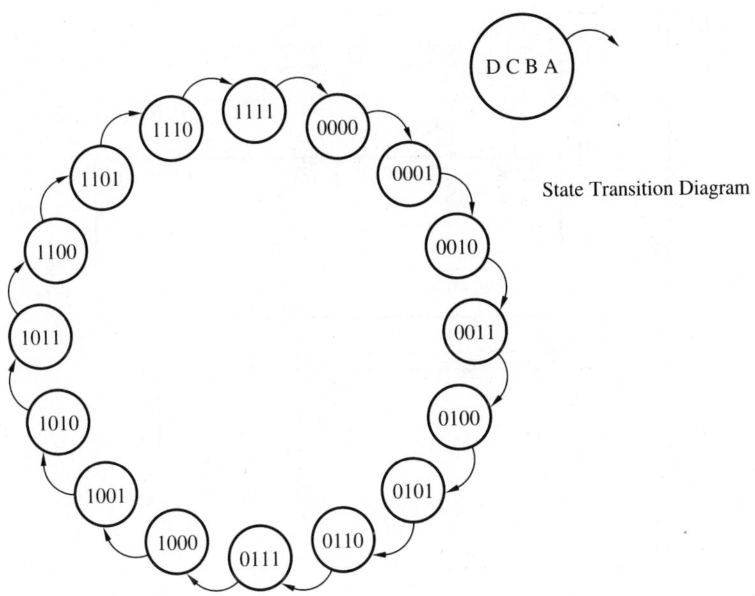

State Transition Diagram

8.

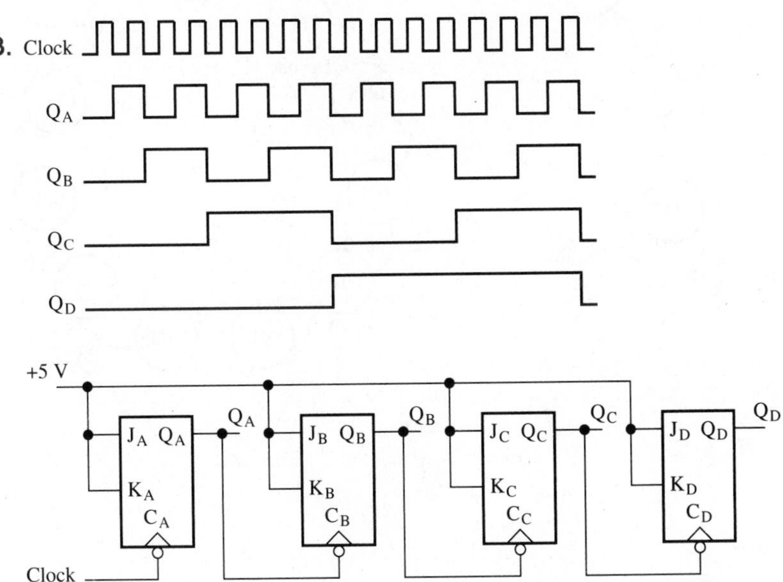

4-Bit Counter — Block Diagram

Use two 74LS76A J-K negative edge-triggered flip-flops.

13.

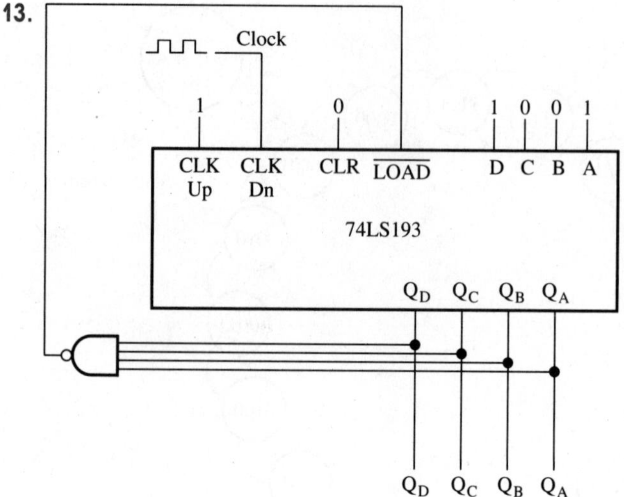

Clock
1
0
1 0 0 1
CLK Up
CLK Dn
CLR
LOAD
D C B A
74LS193
QD QC QB QA
QD QC QB QA

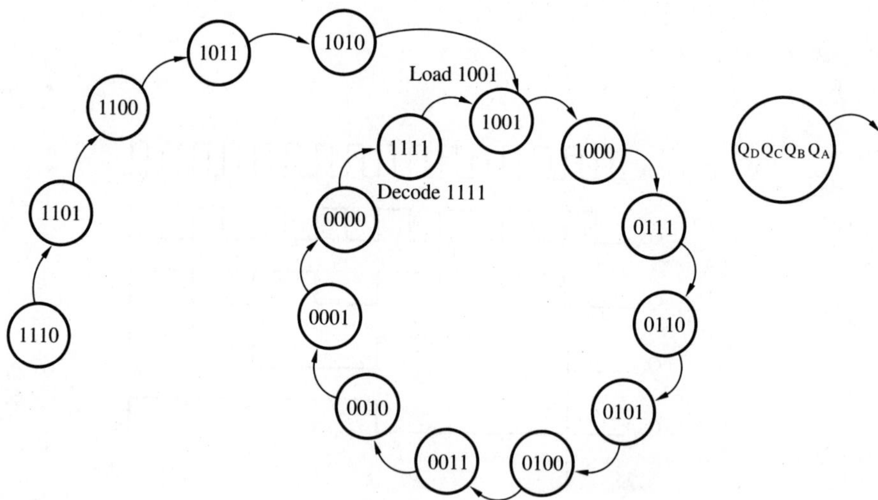

1110
1101
1100
1011
1010
Load 1001
1001
1000
0111
0110
0101
0100
0011
0010
0001
0000
Decode 1111
1111
QD QC QB QA

17.

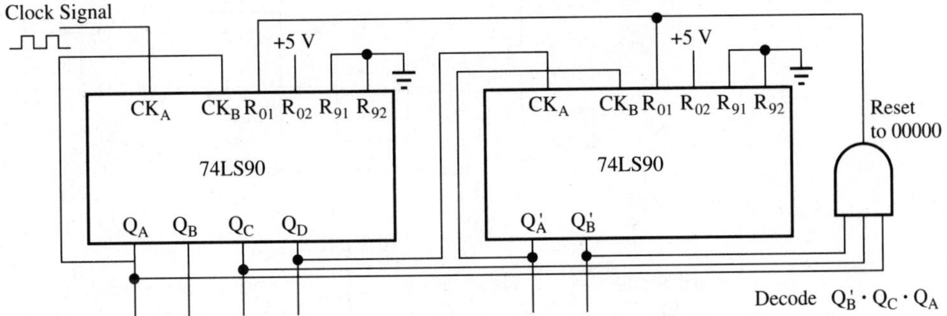

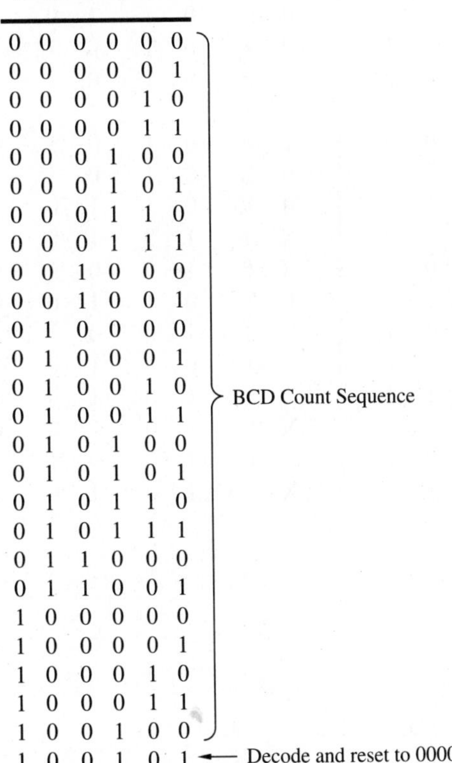

Q'_B	Q'_A	Q_D	Q_C	Q_B	Q_A	
0	0	0	0	0	0	BCD Count Sequence
0	0	0	0	0	1	
0	0	0	0	1	0	
0	0	0	0	1	1	
0	0	0	1	0	0	
0	0	0	1	0	1	
0	0	0	1	1	0	
0	0	0	1	1	1	
0	0	1	0	0	0	
0	0	1	0	0	1	
0	1	0	0	0	0	
0	1	0	0	0	1	
0	1	0	0	1	0	
0	1	0	0	1	1	
0	1	0	1	0	0	
0	1	0	1	0	1	
0	1	0	1	1	0	
0	1	0	1	1	1	
0	1	1	0	0	0	
0	1	1	0	0	1	
1	0	0	0	0	0	
1	0	0	0	0	1	
1	0	0	0	1	0	
1	0	0	0	1	1	
1	0	0	1	0	0	
1	0	0	1	0	1	← Decode and reset to 00000

19. Circuit:

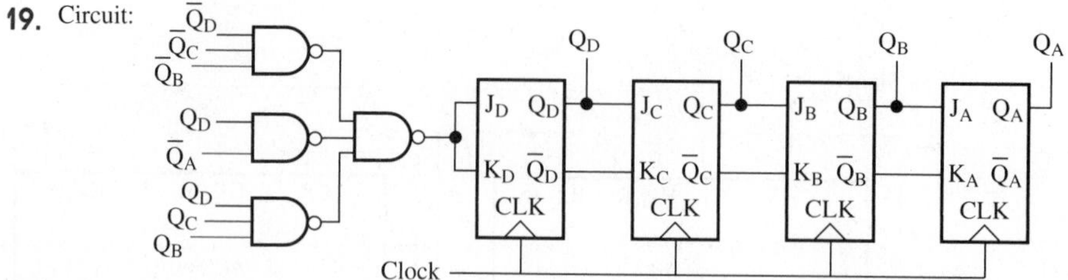

See Figure 10-44.

Design

Present State Q_D	Q_C	Q_B	Q_A	Next State Q_D	Q_C	Q_B	Q_A	Excitation—Present Inputs J_D	K_D	J_C	K_C	J_B	K_B	J_A	K_A
1	0	0	0	0	1	0	0	X	1	1	0	0	1	0	1
0	1	0	0	0	0	1	0	0	X	0	1	1	0	0	1
0	0	1	0	0	0	0	1	0	X	0	1	0	1	1	0
0	0	0	1	1	0	0	0	1	X	0	1	0	1	0	1
0	0	0	0	1	0	0	0	1	X	0	1	0	1	0	1
0	0	1	1	0	0	0	1	0	X	0	1	0	1	1	0
0	1	1	0	0	0	1	1	0	X	0	1	1	0	1	0
1	1	0	0	0	1	1	0	X	1	1	0	1	0	0	1
1	0	0	1	1	1	0	0	X	0	1	0	0	1	0	1
0	1	0	1	0	0	1	0	0	X	0	1	1	0	0	1
1	0	1	0	0	1	0	1	X	1	1	0	0	1	1	0
0	1	1	1	0	0	1	1	0	X	0	1	1	0	1	0
1	1	1	0	0	1	1	1	X	1	1	0	1	0	1	0
1	1	0	1	1	1	1	0	X	0	1	0	1	0	0	1
1	0	1	1	1	1	0	1	X	0	1	0	0	1	1	0
1	1	1	1	0	1	1	1	X	1	1	0	1	0	1	0

Present States

Q_BQ_A / Q_DQ_C	00	01	11	10
00	1	1	0	0
01	0	0	0	0
11	1	0	1	1
10	1	0	0	1

$J_D = K_D$ $\quad J_C = Q_D$ $\quad J_B = Q_C$ $\quad J_A$

$\quad K_C = \overline{Q_D}$ $\quad K_B = \overline{Q_C}$ $\quad K_A$

Present inputs are functions of the present st outputs.

$$J_D = K_D = \overline{Q_D}\,\overline{Q_C}\,\overline{Q_B} + Q_D\overline{Q_A} + Q_DQ_CQ_B$$

Chapter 11

2. See Figure 11-19.

Control Inputs S_1	S_0	Present State Q_D	Q_C	Q_B	Q_A	Next State Q_D	Q_C	Q_B	Q_A
0	0	Q_{D_n}	Q_{C_n}	Q_{B_n}	Q_{A_n}	Q_{D_n}	Q_{C_n}	Q_{B_n}	Q_{A_n}
0	1	Q_{D_n}	Q_{C_n}	Q_{B_n}	Q_{A_n}	SIR	Q_{D_n}	Q_{C_n}	Q_{A_n}
1	0	Q_{D_n}	Q_{C_n}	Q_{B_n}	Q_{A_n}	Q_{C_n}	Q_{B_n}	Q_{A_n}	SIL
1	1	Q_{D_n}	Q_{C_n}	Q_{B_n}	Q_{A_n}	D	C	B	A

- Parallel inputs: D, C, B, A
- Serial input right: SIR
- Serial input left: SIL

5. Input clock frequency = 100 KHz

$$\text{Input clock period} = \frac{1}{100 \times 10^3} = 10^{-5} = 10\,\mu\text{s}$$

Required time delay = .1 ms = 100 µs

$$\text{Number of stages required} = \frac{100\,\mu\text{s}}{10\,\mu\text{s}} = 10 \text{ stages}$$

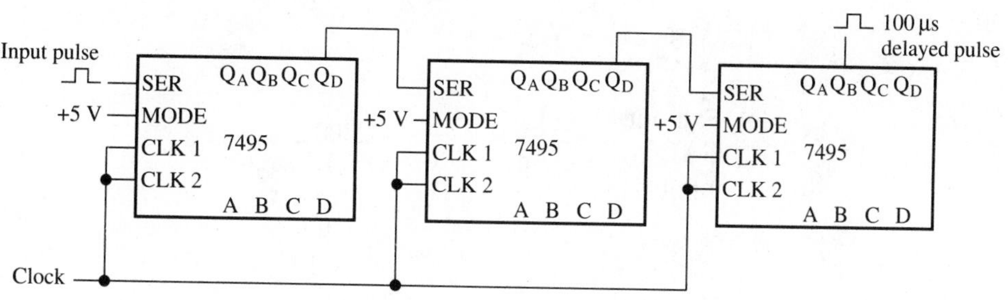

9. Eight-bit Johnson counter; 8-bit twisted ring counter

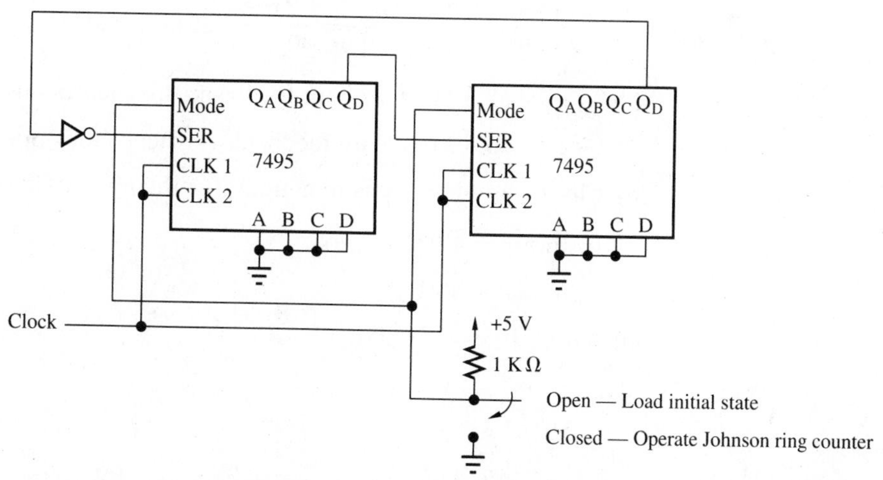

15. With CLK_1 tied to a constant logic-HIGH, the basic ring counter circuit in Figure 11-15 would load 1, 0, 0, 0 into the A, B, C, D inputs, respectively. The outputs would then remain always at 1, 0, 0, 0 once the capacitor charged to +5 V, keeping the mode at a logic-LOW level.

Chapter 12

1. **(a)** 4.75–5.25 V **(b)** 1.5 V

(c) $V_{OL(max)} = 0.5$ V

$V_{OH(min)} = 2.4$ V

(d) $V_{IL(min)} = V_{SS} - 0.5$ V

$V_{IL(max)} = 0.8$ V

$V_{IH(min)} = 2.0$ V

$V_{IH(max)} = V_{CC} + 1$ V

(e) Fan out to GAL inputs

$$\frac{I_{OL}}{I_{IL}} = \frac{24\text{ mA}}{10\ \mu\text{A}} = 2300$$

$$\frac{I_{OH}}{I_{IH}} = \frac{3.2\text{ mA}}{10\ \mu\text{A}} = 320$$

← 320 is the limiting fan-out.

Fan out to unit loads:

$$\frac{I_{OL}}{I_{UL\ (LOW)}} = \frac{24\text{ mA}}{1.6\text{ mA}} = 15\text{ unit loads}$$

$$\frac{I_{OH}}{I_{UL\ (HIGH)}} = \frac{3.2\text{ mA}}{40\ \mu\text{A}} = 80\text{ unit loads}$$

← 15 unit loads is the limiting fan-out.

(f) $f_{CLK} = 62.5$ MHz without feedback—asynchronous operation

$f_{CLK} = 55.5$ MHz with feedback—synchronous operation

(g) Clock period = 16 ns minimum (for the 69.5 MHz operation)

$t_{W(HIGH)} = 8$ ns

$t_{W(LOW)} = 8$ ns

(h) $t_{SU} = 10$ ns

3. Design: 8-bit gray-to-binary code converter

Discrete gate circuit:

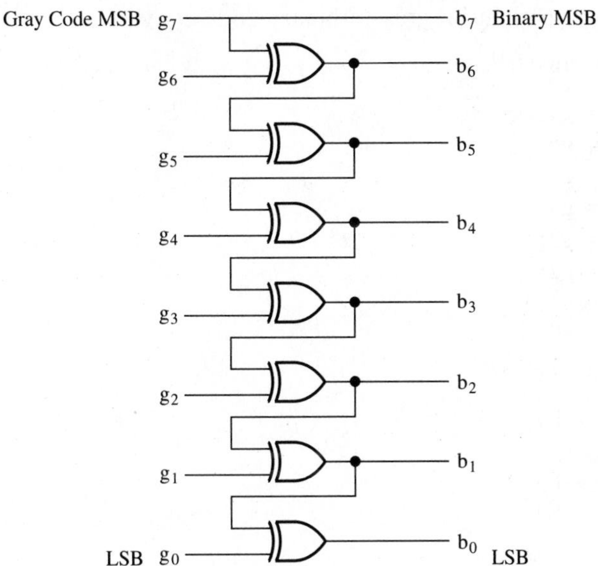

Logic equations:

$b_7 = g_7$
$b_6 = b_7 \oplus g_6$
$b_5 = b_6 \oplus g_5$
$b_4 = b_5 \oplus g_4$
$b_3 = b_4 \oplus g_3$
$b_2 = b_3 \oplus g_2$
$b_1 = b_2 \oplus g_1$
$b_0 = b_1 \oplus g_0$
$b_n = b_{(n+1)} \oplus g_n$

Pin assignments:

g_7 = pin 1
g_6 = pin 2
g_5 = pin 3
g_4 = pin 4
g_3 = pin 5
g_2 = pin 6
g_1 = pin 7
g_0 = pin 8
b_7 = pin 16
b_6 = pin 19
b_5 = pin 18
b_4 = pin 17
b_3 = pin 14
b_2 = pin 13
b_1 = pin 12
b_0 = pin 15

```
DEVICE 16V8;
TITLE Problem 12-3;
NAME Gray-to-Binary Code Converter;

/* Design an eight-bit gray-to-binary code converter */

/* Input Pins */

PIN 1 = g7;
PIN 2 = g6;
PIN 3 = g5;
PIN 4 = g4;
PIN 5 = g3;
PIN 6 = g2;
PIN 7 = g1;
PIN 8 = g0;
/* Output Pins */

PIN 19 = b7;
PIN 18 = b6;
PIN 17 = b5;
PIN 16 = b4;
PIN 15 = b3;
PIN 14 = b2;
PIN 13 = b1;
PIN 12 = b0;

/* VCC and Ground Connections */

PIN 20 = VCC;
PIN 10 = GND;

/*Boolean Equations */

b7 = g7;
b6 = !b7 & g6 | b7 & !g6;
b5 = !b6 & g5 | b6 & !g5;
b4 = !b5 & g4 | b5 & !g4;
b3 = !b4 & g3 | b4 & !g3;
b2 = !b3 & g2 | b3 & !g2;
b1 = !b2 & g1 | b2 & !g1;
b0 = !b1 & g0 | b1 & !g0;

b6.oe = vcc;
b5.oe = vcc;
b4.oe = vcc;
b3.oe = vcc;
b2.oe = vcc;
b1.oe = vcc;
```

16V8

G7	01	20	VCC
G6	02	19	B7
G5	03	18	B6
G4	04	17	B5
G3	05	16	B4
G2	06	15	B3
G1	07	14	B2
G0	08	13	B1
unused	09	12	B0
GND	10	11	unused

Equations translated to Sum of Products form

```
B7
   =      G7;

B6
   =     !G6 &  B7
   |      G6 & !B7;

B5
   =     !G5 &  B6
   |      G5 & !B6;

B4
   =     !G4 &  B5
   |      G4 & !B5;

B3
   =     !G3 &  B4
   |      G3 & !B4;

B2
   =     !G2 &  B3
   |      G2 & !B3;

B1
   =     !G1 &  B2
   |      G1 & !B2;

B0
   =     !G0 &  B1
   |      G0 & !B1;
```

```
B6.OE
  =        VCC;

B5.OE
  =        VCC;

B4.OE
  =        VCC;

B3.OE
  =        VCC;

B2.OE
  =        VCC;

B1.OE
  =        VCC;

/* Design an eight-bit gray-to-binary code converter */

/* Input Pins */

PIN 1 = g7;
PIN 2 = g6;
PIN 3 = g5;
PIN 4 = g4;
PIN 5 = g3;
PIN 6 = g2;
PIN 7 = g1;
PIN 8 = g0;

/* Output Pins */

PIN 19 = b7;
PIN 18 = b6;
PIN 17 = b5;
PIN 16 = b4;
PIN 15 = b3;
PIN 14 = b2;
PIN 13 = b1;
PIN 12 = b0;

/* VCC and Ground Connections */

PIN 20 = VCC;
PIN 10 = GND;

/* Boolean Equations */

b7 = g7;
b6 = !b7 & g6 | b7 & !g6;
b5 = !b6 & g5 | b6 & !g5;
b4 = !b5 & g4 | b5 & !g4;
```

```
b3 = !b4 & g3 | b4 & !g3;
b2 = !b3 & g2 | b3 & !g2;
b1 = !b2 & g1 | b2 & !g1;
b0 = !b1 & g0 | b1 & !g0;

b6.oe = vcc;
b5.oe = vcc;
b4.oe = vcc;
b3.oe = vcc;
b2.oe = vcc;
b1.oe = vcc;
```

6. Design: A quad, 3-input MUX.

Functional Block
(one possible solution)

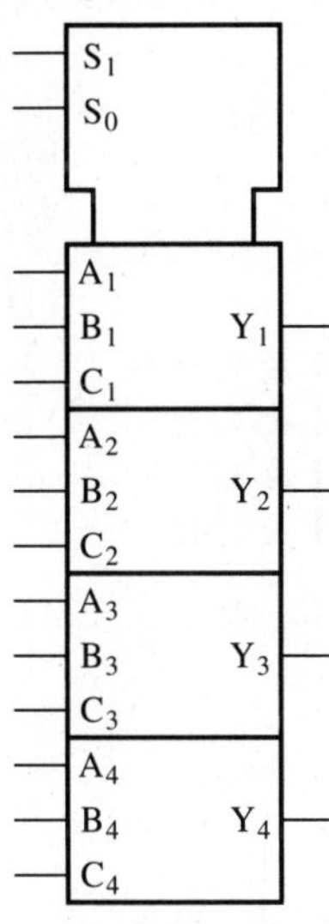

Function Table
(one possible solution)

S_1	S_0	Y_1	Y_2	Y_3	Y_4
0	0	A_1	A_2	A_3	A_4
0	1	B_1	B_2	B_3	B_4
1	X	C_1	C_2	C_3	C_4
X	X	0	0	0	0

Logic equations:

$$Y_1 = \bar{S}_1 \cdot \bar{S}_0 \cdot A_1 + \bar{S}_1 \cdot S_0 \cdot B_1 + S_1 \cdot C_1$$
$$Y_2 = \bar{S}_1 \cdot \bar{S}_0 \cdot A_2 + \bar{S}_1 \cdot S_0 \cdot B_2 + S_1 \cdot C_2$$
$$Y_3 = \bar{S}_1 \cdot \bar{S}_0 \cdot A_3 + \bar{S}_1 \cdot S_0 \cdot B_3 + S_1 \cdot C_3$$
$$Y_4 = \bar{S}_1 \cdot \bar{S}_0 \cdot A_4 + \bar{S}_1 \cdot S_0 \cdot B_4 + S_1 \cdot C_4$$

Pin assignments:

S_1 = pin 1	C_1 = pin 12
S_0 = pin 2	C_2 = pin 13
A_1 = pin 3	C_3 = pin 14
A_2 = pin 4	C_4 = pin 19
A_3 = pin 5	Y_1 = pin 18
A_4 = pin 6	Y_2 = pin 17
B_1 = pin 7	Y_3 = pin 16
B_2 = pin 8	Y_4 = pin 15
B_3 = pin 9	
B_4 = pin 11	

```
/*Input Pins */

PIN 1 = S1;
PIN 2 = S0;
PIN 3 = A1;
PIN 4 = A2;
PIN 5 = A3;
PIN 6 = A4;
```

```
PIN 7 = B1;
PIN 8 = B2;
PIN 9 = B3;
PIN 11 = B4;

PIN 12 = C1;
PIN 13 = C2;
PIN 14 = C3;
PIN 19 = C4;

/* Output Pins */

PIN 18 = Y1;
PIN 17 = Y2;
PIN 16 = Y3;
PIN 15 = Y4;

/* VCC and Ground */

PIN 20 = VCC;
PIN 10 = GND;

/* Boolean Equations */

Y1 = !S1 & !S0 & A1 | !S1 & S0 & B1 | S1 & C1;
Y2 = !S1 & !S0 & A2 | !S1 & S0 & B2 | S1 & C2;
Y3 = !S1 & !S0 & A3 | !S1 & S0 & B3 | S1 & C3;
Y4 = !S1 & !S0 & A4 | !S1 & S0 & B4 | S1 & C4;
```

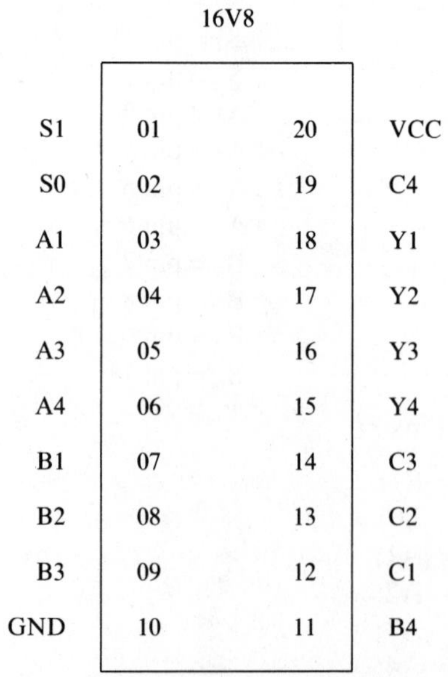

16V8

S1	01	20	VCC
S0	02	19	C4
A1	03	18	Y1
A2	04	17	Y2
A3	05	16	Y3
A4	06	15	Y4
B1	07	14	C3
B2	08	13	C2
B3	09	12	C1
GND	10	11	B4

Equations translated to Sum of Products form

```
Y1
   =      S1 &  C1
   |     !S1 & !S0 &  A1
   |     !S1 &  S0 &  B1;

Y2
   =      S1 &  C2
   |     !S1 & !S0 &  A2
   |     !S1 &  S0 &  B2;

Y3
   =      S1 &  C3
   |     !S1 & !S0 &  A3
   |     !S1 &  S0 &  B3;

Y4
   =      S1 &  C4
   |     !S1 & !S0 &  A4
   |     !S1 &  S0 &  B4;
```

13. Design: 5-bit RS latch PLD with true outputs

RS Latch Present Input-Present State-Next State Table

R S	Q_n	Q_{n+1}	
0 0	0	0	Hold
0 0	1	1	
0 1	0	1	Set
0 1	1	1	
1 0	0	0	Reset
1 0	1	0	
1 1	0	1	Invalid
1 1	1	1	

Logic diagram:

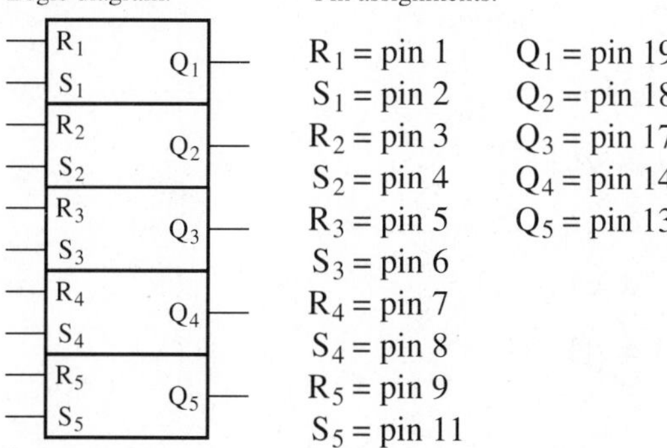

Pin assignments:

R_1 = pin 1
S_1 = pin 2
R_2 = pin 3
S_2 = pin 4
R_3 = pin 5
S_3 = pin 6
R_4 = pin 7
S_4 = pin 8
R_5 = pin 9
S_5 = pin 11

Q_1 = pin 19
Q_2 = pin 18
Q_3 = pin 17
Q_4 = pin 14
Q_5 = pin 13

Logic equations:

$$Q_1 = \bar{R}_1 \cdot \bar{S}_1 \cdot Q_1 + S_1$$
$$Q_2 = \bar{R}_2 \cdot \bar{S}_2 \cdot Q_2 + S_2$$
$$Q_3 = \bar{R}_3 \cdot \bar{S}_3 \cdot Q_3 + S_3$$
$$Q_4 = \bar{R}_4 \cdot \bar{S}_4 \cdot Q_4 + S_4$$
$$Q_5 = \bar{R}_5 \cdot \bar{S}_5 \cdot Q_5 + S_5$$

```
DEVICE 16V8;
TITLE Problem 12-13;
NAME 5-bit RS latch with true outputs;

/* Input Pins */

PIN 1 = r1;
PIN 2 = s1;

PIN 3 = r2;
PIN 4 = s2;

PIN 5 = r3;
PIN 6 = s3;

PIN 7 = r4;
PIN 8 = s4;

PIN 9 = r5;
PIN 11 = s5;

/* Output Pins */

PIN 19 = q1;
PIN 18 = q2;
PIN 17 = q3;
PIN 14 = q4;
PIN 13 = q5;

/* Boolean Equations */

q1 = !r1 & !s1 & q1 | s1;

q2 = !r2 & !s2 & q2 | s2;

q3 = !r3 & !s3 & q3 | s3;

q4 = !r4 & !s4 & q4 | s4;
```

16V8

R1	01	20	VCC
S1	02	19	Q1
R2	03	18	Q2
S2	04	17	Q3
R3	05	16	unused
S3	06	15	unused
R4	07	14	Q4
S4	08	13	Q5
R5	09	12	unused
GND	10	11	S5

Equations translated to Sum of Products form

```
Q1
  =   S1
  |   !R1 & Q1;

Q2
  =   S2
  |   !R2 & Q2;

Q3
  =   S3
  |   !R3 & Q3;

Q4
  =   S4
  |   !R4 & Q4;
```

17. Design: 4-bit decade up/down counter

Function Table

Mode Control	Count Operation
0	Up
1	Down

Input M	Present State D	C	B	A	Next State D C B A
0	0	0	0	0	0 0 0 1
0	0	0	0	1	0 0 1 0
0	0	0	1	0	0 0 1 1
0	0	0	1	1	0 1 0 0
0	0	1	0	0	0 1 0 1
0	0	1	0	1	0 1 1 0
0	0	1	1	0	0 1 1 1
0	0	1	1	1	1 0 0 0
0	1	0	0	0	1 0 0 1
0	1	0	0	1	0 0 0 0
0	1	0	1	X	0 0 0 0
0	1	1	X	X	0 0 0 0
1	0	0	0	0	1 0 0 1
1	0	0	0	1	0 0 0 0
1	0	0	1	0	0 0 0 1
1	0	0	1	1	0 0 1 0
1	0	1	0	0	0 0 1 1
1	0	1	0	1	0 1 0 0
1	0	1	1	0	0 1 0 1
1	0	1	1	1	0 1 1 0
1	1	0	0	0	0 1 1 1
1	1	0	0	1	1 0 0 0
1	1	0	1	X	1 0 0 1
1	1	1	X	X	1 0 0 1

Pin assignments:

Pin 1 = CLK
Pin 11 = OE
Pin 2 = M
Pin 19 = D
Pin 18 = C
Pin 17 = B
Pin 16 = A

Logic equations:

$$\begin{aligned}
D.D = {} & \overline{M}\,\overline{D}CBA + \overline{M}D\overline{C}\,\overline{B}\,\overline{A} + \\
& M\overline{D}\,\overline{C}\,\overline{B}\,\overline{A} + MD\overline{C}\,\overline{B}A + \\
& MD\overline{C}B + MDC
\end{aligned}$$

$$\begin{aligned}
C.D = {} & \overline{M}\,\overline{D}\,\overline{C}BA + \overline{M}\,\overline{D}C\overline{B}\,\overline{A} + \\
& \overline{M}\,\overline{D}C\overline{B}A + \overline{M}\,\overline{D}CB\overline{A} + \\
& M\overline{D}C\overline{B}A + M\overline{D}CB\overline{A} + \\
& M\overline{D}CBA + MD\overline{C}\,\overline{B}\,\overline{A}
\end{aligned}$$

$$\begin{aligned}
B.D = {} & \overline{M}\,\overline{D}\,\overline{C}\,\overline{B}A + \overline{M}\,\overline{D}\,\overline{C}B\overline{A} + \\
& \overline{M}\,\overline{D}C\overline{B}A + \overline{M}\,\overline{D}CB\overline{A} + \\
& M\overline{D}\,\overline{C}BA + M\overline{D}C\overline{B}\,\overline{A} + \\
& M\overline{D}CBA + MD\overline{C}\,\overline{B}\,\overline{A}
\end{aligned}$$

$$\begin{aligned}
A.D = {} & \overline{M}\,\overline{D}\,\overline{A} + \overline{M}D\overline{C}\,\overline{B}\,\overline{A} + M\overline{D}\,\overline{A} + \\
& MD\overline{C}\,\overline{B}\,\overline{A} + MD\overline{C}B + MDC
\end{aligned}$$

```
DEVICE 16V8;
TITLE Problem 12-17;
NAME 4-bit decade up/down counter;

/*        Clock and enable output control */

PIN 1 = CLOCK;
PIN 11 = OE;

/*        Count operation mode control */

PIN 2 = M;

/*        Counter outputs */

PIN 19 = D;
PIN 18 = C;
PIN 17 = B;
PIN 16 = A;

/*        Boolean Equations */

D.D = !M & !D & C & B & A | !M & D & !C & !B & !A
      | M & !D & !C & !B & !A | M & D & !C & !B & A
      | M & D & !C & B | M & D & C;

C.D = !M & !D & !C & B & A | !M & !D & C & !B & !A
      | !M & !D & C & !B & A | !M & !D & C & B & !A
      | M & !D & C & !B & A | M & !D & C & B & !A
      | M & !D & C & B & A | M & D & !C & !B & !A;
```

```
B.D = !M & !D & !C & !B & A | !M & !D & !C & B & !A
      | !M & !D & C & !B & A | !M & !D & C & B & !A
      | M & !D & !C & B & A | M & !D & C & !B & A
      | M & !D & C & B & A | M & D & !C & !B & !A;

A.D = !M & !D & !A | !M & D & !C & !B & !A
      | M & !D & !A | M & D & !C & !B & !A
      | M & D & !C & B | M & D & C;
```

16V8

CLOCK	01	20	VCC
M	02	19	D
unused	03	18	C
unused	04	17	B
unused	05	16	A
unused	06	15	unused
unused	07	14	unused
unused	08	13	unused
unused	09	12	unused
GND	10	11	OE

Equations translated to Sum of Products form

```
D.D
  =    M & A & D
  |    M & B & D
  |    M & C & D
  |   !M & !A & !B & !C & D
  |   !M & A & B & C & !D
  |    M & !A & !B & !C & !D;

C.D
  =   !M & !A & C & !D
  |    M & B & C & !D
  |    A & !B & C & !D
  |    M & !A & !B & !C & D
  |   !M & A & B & !C & !D;
```

```
B.D
  =     M &  A &  B & !D
  |    !M & !A &  B & !D
  |    !M &  A & !B & !D
  |     A & !B &  C & !D
  |     M & !A & !B & !C &  D;

A.D
  =    !A & !D
  |    !A & !B & !C
  |     M &  B &  D
  |     M &  C &  D;
```

22. Design: 6-bit Johnson counter

Preset	Present State A B C D E F	Next State Feedback A_{n+1}
0	0 0 0 0 0 0	1
0	1 0 0 0 0 0	1
0	1 1 0 0 0 0	1
0	1 1 1 0 0 0	1
0	1 1 1 1 0 0	1
0	1 1 1 1 1 0	1
0	1 1 1 1 1 1	0
0	0 1 1 1 1 1	0
0	0 0 1 1 1 1	0
0	0 0 0 1 1 1	0
0	0 0 0 0 1 1	0
0	0 0 0 0 0 1	0
1	X X X X X X	Preset to: 0 0 0 0 0 0

$$A.D = (\overline{A}\,\overline{B}\,\overline{C}\,\overline{D}\,\overline{E}\,\overline{F} + A\overline{B}\,\overline{C}\,\overline{D}\,\overline{E}\,\overline{F} + AB\overline{C}\,\overline{D}\,\overline{E}\,\overline{F} + ABC\overline{D}\,\overline{E}\,\overline{F} + ABCD\overline{E}\,\overline{F} + ABCDE\overline{F})\cdot\overline{PRE}$$

$$B.D = A\cdot\overline{PRE}$$
$$C.D = B\cdot\overline{PRE}$$
$$D.D = C\cdot\overline{PRE}$$
$$E.D = D\cdot\overline{PRE}$$
$$F.D = E\cdot\overline{PRE}$$

Pin assignments:

Pin 1 = CLK
Pin 11 = OE
Pin 2 = PRE
Pin 19 = A
Pin 18 = B

Pin 17 = C
Pin 16 = D
Pin 15 = E
Pin 14 = F

```
DEVICE 16V8;
TITLE Problem 12-22;
NAME 6-bit Johnson counter (twisted ring counter);

/*      Clock and output enable control */

PIN 1 = CLOCK;
PIN 11 = OE;

/*      Preset control */

PIN 2 = PRE;

/*      Outputs pins */

PIN 19 = A;
PIN 18 = B;
PIN 17 = C;
PIN 16 = D;
PIN 15 = E;
PIN 14 = F;

/*      Boolean Equations        */

A.D = (!A & !B & !C & !D & !E & !F
      | A & !B & !C & !D & !E & !F
      | A & !B & !C & !D & !E & !F
      | A & B & C & !D & !E & !F
      | A & B & C & D & !E & !F
      | A & B & C & D & E & !F) & PRE;

B.D = A & !PRE;

C.D = B & !PRE;

D.D = C & !PRE;

E.D = D & !PRE;

F.D = E & !PRE;
```

16V8

CLOCK	01	20	VCC
PRE	02	19	A
unused	03	18	B
unused	04	17	C
unused	05	16	D
unused	06	15	E
unused	07	14	F
unused	08	13	unused
unused	09	12	unused
GND	10	11	OE

Equations translated to Sum of Products form

```
A.D
   =    PRE & !F & !E & !D & !C & !B
   |    PRE & !F & !E &  C &  B &  A
   |    PRE & !F &  D &  C &  B &  A;

B.D
   =    !PRE &  A;

C.D
   =    !PRE &  B;

D.D
   =    !PRE &  C;

E.D
   =    !PRE &  D;

F.D
   =    !PRE &  E;
```

Chapter 13

8. **(a)** Serial, 16 **(b)** Parallel (nibble), 18 **(c)** Serial, 20 **(d)** Parallel (byte), 17

9. **(a)** 65,536 bits **(b)** 1,048,576 bits **(c)** 1,048,576 bits **(d)** 1,048,576 bits

12. **(a)** Processing steps used to fabricate all semiconductor memories **(b)** UVEPROM erasure **(c)** EEPROM erasure **(d)** Required for DRAMS **(e)** Memory cell characteristic of DRAMS

20. **(a)** 17 minutes **(b)** Comparable

27. **(a)** 7FFH **(b)** 3FFFH **(c)** 3FFFFH **(d)** 3FFFFH **(e)** FFFFFH **(f)** FFFFFFH

31. **(a)** 32,768 bits **(b)** 393,216 bits **(c)** 524,288 bits **(d)** 2,097,152 bits **(e)** 8,388,608 bits **(f)** 67,108,864 bits

33. 16, assuming one decoder output for each IC.

39. **(a)** 10 ns **(b)** 640 ns **(c)** 955 ns

Chapter 14

3. **(a)** Logic arithmetic; input/output; register and data transfer; memory; program control; status

8. **(a)** Processing unit; memory; input/output

   (b) Address bus ⇒ unidirectional from microprocessor

   Data bus ⇒ bidirectional

   Control bus ⇒ unidirectional lines going both to and from the microprocessor

   (c)

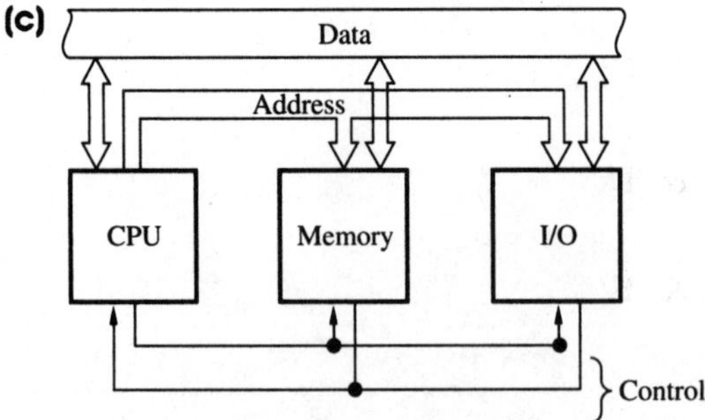

11. **(a)** The first data stored in the stack is the first data retrieved from the stack memory. (first-in, first-out)
    (b) 05 H

18.

Frequency (MHz)		Time (ns)
12	⇒	80
15	⇒	70
20	⇒	50
25	⇒	40

21. $$T = \frac{1}{10\text{ MHz}} = 100\text{ ns}$$

$$\begin{aligned} 90 \times 6 \times 100\text{ ns} &= 50{,}000\text{ ns} \\ 110 \times 8 \times 100\text{ ns} &= 90{,}000\text{ ns} \\ 60 \times 10 \times 100\text{ ns} &= \underline{60{,}000\text{ ns}} \\ & 200{,}000\text{ ns} \end{aligned}$$

$$\boxed{200\ \mu\text{s}}$$

33. 1. Build a shift register of 12-bits.
2. Two GAL 16V8A's are needed; no additional logic ICs are needed.
3/4. Use an editor to define the PLD pin list and program. Assemble for no errors.
5. Try a known working program; program the PLD to determine if the PLD is functional. Then download the shift register program.
6. Modify PLD program, as needed.
7. Reprogram, and verify working shift register.
8. Generate a description of the problem, circuit, and its PLD documentation, and test data.

38. The two LSBs of the port may be incorrectly connected together (shorted).

Chapter 15

4.

	TYPICAL		MAXIMUM	
	t_{PHL} (ns)	t_{PLH} (ns)	t_{PHL} (ns)	t_{PLH} (ns)
(a)	7	11	15	22
(b)	10	9	15	15
(c)	21	23	30	30
(d)	3	3	5	45
(e)	2 (min)	3 (min)	8	11

16. **(a)** 20 **(b)** 400 (considering only currents) **(c)** 5 **(d)** 4

18. 20

23. **(a)** 5 to 10 pF **(b)** 50 to 100 pF **(c)** Since propagation delays are quoted in a data book for Ci = 15 pF, a >15 pF load will result in slower switching speeds than those shown in the data book. Therefore, propagation delay increases.

29. $V_{IH(min)} = 3.85$ V
$V_{IL(max)} = 1.1$ V

35. 400 μW

36. **(a)** 135 pF, typical **(b)** Used to calculate the no-load dynamic power dissipation.

44. **(a)** Emitter coupled logic. A very fast bipolar logic family **(b)** High speed oscilloscopes; supercomputers; LAN (local area network) hardware **(c)** 0.2 ns typical P_D for ECL; 8 ns typical P_D for LSTTL; 3900% faster (approximately 40 times faster)

49. **(a)** 10 ns **(b)** 8 ns **(c)** 10 ns **(d)** 13 ns

52. As frequency increases, power increases.

59. 10

75. **(a)** 563 Ω, or larger

(b)

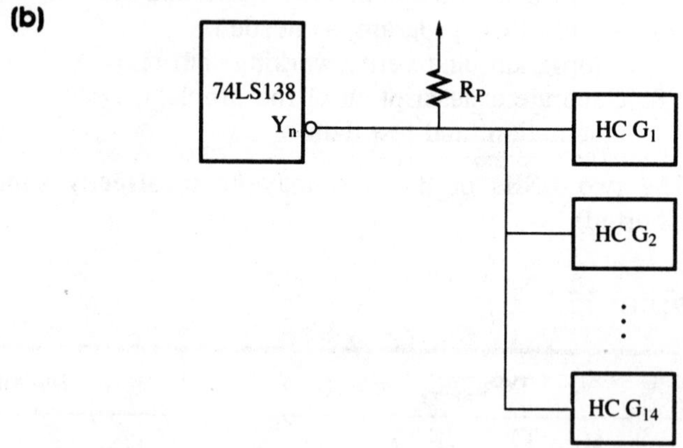

79. **(a)** 282 Ω, or greater

86. 300 ns

91. $R = 200\ \Omega$

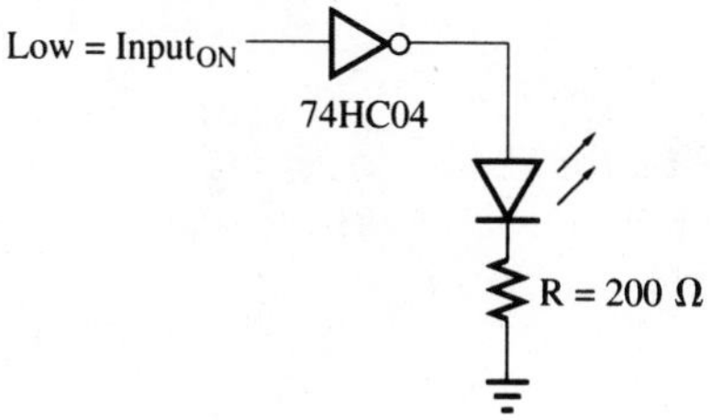

Low = Input_{ON}

74HC04

$R = 200\ \Omega$

Chapter 16

1. $2^{12} = 4096$ quantization levels

2. 256 quantization levels → 8-bits of encoding

$$\%\ \text{resolution} = \frac{1}{2^n - 1} = \frac{1}{256 - 1} = \frac{1}{255} \times 100\%$$

$$= .392\%$$

3. 16-bit CD system → 65,536 quantization levels

Input voltage range = 2 V

$$\frac{2\ \text{V}}{2^n - 1} = \frac{2\ \text{V}}{65{,}535} = \begin{array}{l}30.518\ \mu\text{V}\\ \text{voltage resolution}\end{array}$$

6. See Figure 16-9. **(a)** 8-bit resolution **(b)** 1.5 μs maximum settling time **(c)** 48 dB dynamic response **(d)** 125 mW power dissipation

14. See Figure 16-20. **(a)** 8-bit resolution **(b)** 100 μs conversion time **(c)** 8770 cycles per second, maximum conversion rate **(d)** 48 dB dynamic response **(e)** 100 KHz minimum input clock frequency **(f)** 1.2 MHz maximum input clock frequency **(g)** 416.6 ns minimum clock pulse width **(h)** 5 μs maximum clock pulse width **(i)** 875 mW maximum power dissipation

16. See Figure 16-22. Minimum sampling frequency = 2 KHz

$$\frac{f_{clock}}{73} \geq 2\ \text{KHz} \qquad f_{clock} \geq 146\ \text{KHz}$$

Set clock frequency to ~300 KHz

$$f_{clock} = \frac{1}{1.1\ RC}$$

Select C = 220 pF, calculate R = 13.7 KΩ. (No information is given about the voltage range.)

Glossary

8421 Binary Coded Decimal Binary code for decimal digits.
8421 BCD Arithmetic Arithmetic procedures for decimal values encoded in 8421 BCD code.
access time The time it takes to read or write data to a memory device.
accumulator A special microprocessor data register involved in many of the arithmetic and logical operations.
active mode The switching mode of a logic device; typically the mode of the device that consumes the most power.
active-HIGH The logic HIGH value is the active condition.
active-LOW The logic LOW value is the active condition.
adder/subtracter circuits Logic circuits that perform binary addition or subtraction.
address bus The circuit path that carries the address information in a memory or microprocessor system.
aliasing Distortion that occurs when a signal is sampled at less than twice its highest frequency.
alphanumeric binary codes Binary codes that encode alphabetic and numeric characters.
ALS TTL Advanced Low Power Schottky TTL devices.
alternative gates Logic gates that can perform the equivalent function.
ALU Arithmetic logic unit; part of a microprocessor CPU.
AM Amplitude modulation, an analog modulation technique.
analog Continuous with an infinite number of values.
analog-to-digital conversion (A/D) Conversion of an analog quantity to a digital value.
analysis Systematic evaluation of the circuit operation.
AND A logic function that is a 1 only when all inputs are 1.
AND-OR array A logic circuit comprised of AND gates and an output OR gate.
antialiasing filter A bandlimiting filter used in A/D ICs to limit the input signal bandwidth and to prevent aliasing.
aperiodic waveform A waveform with no repeating pattern.
Application Specific ICs (ASIC) Custom ICs for a specific application.
Arithmetic Logic Unit (ALU) A special purpose IC or a special section in a microprocessor that performs many arithmetic and logic functions.
arithmetic circuits Logic circuits that perform arithmetic functions.
AS TTL Advanced Schottky TTL logic family.
ASCII American Standard Code for Information Interchange, a seven-bit binary code.
assembly language A type of computer language specifically designed for microprocessors.
astable A device that oscillates between 1 and 0 because it has no stable state.
asynchronous Not synchronous; not dependent on one timing signal.
asynchronous counter circuits Counters that do not have one common clock controlling all stages.

BCD Binary coded decimal, usually referring to the 8421 BCD code.
bidirectional A counter that can count up or down.
binary addition Addition of binary numbers.
binary number system The base-2 number system.
binary arithmetic Addition, subtraction, multiplication, and division of binary numbers.
binary word multiplexing Multiplexing binary words rather than individual bits.
binary codes Binary number system used for encoding.
binary digits The binary digits, one and zero; bits.
bipolar transistor A transistor fabricated on TTL devices, consisting of an n-p-n or an p-n-p semiconductor material.
bipolar Operation depends on the flow of electrons and holes through the semiconductor material.
bistable A device that has two stable states, 1 and 0.

bit Binary digit.
bit weight expansion A technique used to convert binary numbers to decimal numbers.
bit time The time period (slot) allotted to one bit.
Boolean The algebra techniques used to construct and manipulate digital logic equations.
buffer A logic gate or circuit where the input logic value equals the output logic value; used to isolate circuitry or provide greater current fan-out.
bus A grouping of signal lines such as address or data lines.
bus receiver A type of device that receives signals on a bus.
bus contention A condition that occurs when more than one device try to simultaneously transmit on a common bus.
bus transceiver A device that can transmit or receive.
bus driver A type of device that transmits signals on a bus.
byte Eight binary bits.
byte organized 8-bit organization in a memory system.

capacity The total bit storage in a memory device or system.
CAS Column Address Select; a memory IC address signal.
cascaded counters Counters connected together to expand the count sequence.
cascaded decoders Decoders connected together to expand the number of addresses that can be decoded.
cascaded operation Devices connected together to expand their operation.
cascaded encoders Encoders connected together to expand the number of inputs that can be encoded.
cell area The semiconductor area required for a memory cell in a memory IC.
cell libraries A library of circuits that perform a specific operation or logic function.
cell retention The amount of time a dynamic RAM memory cell stores charge before losing its contents due to charge leakage.
central processing unit (CPU) The block of a microprocessor system responsible for calculations and system control.
chip An integrated circuit.
CLEAR Changing the true output of a flip-flop or related device to a LOW.
clock A digital waveform used for timing in many circuits.
clock cycle The period of the clock signal.
CMOS to TTL Interfacing between a CMOS driver device and TTL load devices.
CMOS (1) Complementary Metal Oxide Semiconductor, a type of semiconductor processing that contains both NMOS and PMOS FET transistors. (2) a type of logic family.
code converters Devices that convert from one digital code to another.
combinational logic Logic circuits whose output depends on the combination of the input logic states; circuit without memory or feedback.
common-anode LED displays with all anodes tied common.
common-cathode LED displays with all cathodes tied common.
commutative law A Boolean law.
comparator operations Greater than, less than, equal to, not equal to, greater than or equal to, less than or equal to.
comparators Logic devices that compare two digital numbers.
compiler A type of computer program that converts a software code into a code executable by a computer.
complement arithmetic Arithmetic performed by adding the complement of negative numbers.
complex mode A mode of operation of PLDs.
complement a representation of negative numbers.
Complimentary Metal-Oxide Semiconductor (See CMOS).
control bus A transmission path on which control signals are transmitted in a microprocessor system.
conversion time The time required for an A/D converter to complete the measurement process.
coprocessor A microprocessor that works in conjunction with the main microprocessor to speed up computations.
cost analysis Examining all expenses associated with a project.
count state decoding An operation to decode the states of a counter.
count modulus The number of states that a counter repeatedly generates.
counter stages or bits The flip flop stages or output bits of a counter.
coprocessor A microprocessor used in parallel with another processor to subdivide computational tasks.
CPU Central processor unit.
cross-couple Two circuits or gates, with the output of each fed back to the input of the other circuit.
current limiting resistors Resistors used to limit the amount of current that flows in a circuit.
current sinking Current flowing into a logic device whose output is a logic-LOW state.
Current Mode Logic (CML) A type of logic family.
current sourcing Current flowing out of a logic device whose output is a logic HIGH state.
custom logic Logic devices fabricated for a single application.
cycle time The total time required for a memory or microprocessor IC to perform a read or write operation and restore its circuitry to be able to perform the next read or write operation.

D latch A latch whose output Q follows the input D.
D flip-flop A flip-flop whose output Q follows the input D.

data bus A set of transmission lines on which the data signals are transmitted in a microprocessor system.
data selection A multiplexing application of selecting one data input to transmit to the output of the multiplexer.
data inputs Inputs containing data signals.
data rate The number of bits that are transmitted per second.
data outputs Outputs containing data signals.
data routing A demultiplexing technique where an input is routed to a specific data output.
data lockout A special feature on some master-slave flip flops where changes in data inputs do not affect the output.
DC offset The amount of voltage by which a digital pulse waveform is shifted from a reference position of 0 Volts.
debounce (switch) A switch that transmits only a single pulse; additional circuitry added to a switch to eliminate the effect of switch bounce.
decimal Base-10 number system.
decoders Logic circuits that decode an address to activate a specific output.
DeMorgan's Theorems Boolean algebra techniques.
demultiplexers Logic circuits that separate an input signal and route it to separate outputs.
depletion mode A type of FET transistor operation.
device programmers Hardware systems used to program PLDs and memory devices.
digital Having a finite number of allowed states.
digital electronics Electronic devices that accept inputs of only defined logic states and output signals with only defined logic states.
digital-to-analog conversion (D/A) Conversion of a digital number to an analog quantity.
DIP Dual in-line package; standard TTL and CMOS SSI/MSI IC package.
discrete Consisting of individual resistors, capacitors, diodes, and inductors.
display decoder drivers Decoders that convert an input number to a code appropriate for a seven-segment display and drive the display.
display multiplexing Driving more than one display with a single decoder driver by multiplexing the inputs.
distributive law A Boolean law.
dmux Demultiplexer.
don't care states An output logic state that can be a zero or a one; an output that corresponds to input combinations that cannot occur in a logic system.
doping The process of adding electrons or holes to semiconductor material so that it is positively or negatively charged.
downloading The transfer of a computer program or data from a computer system to an individual computer or control device.
DRAM Dynamic Random Access Memory; a read-write memory with one device cell memory storage that require periodic data refresh.
drive device The device in a circuit providing the current for load devices to operate.
DTL Diode-Transistor-Logic.
duty cycle The percentage of time a waveform is in its active state.

E^{2}PLD Electrically Erasable Programmable Logic Device.
EAPROM Electrically Alterable Programmable Read Only Memory.
EBCDIC Extended Binary Coded Decimal Information Code.
edge-triggered Devices which change states on the edge of an input clock.
EEPROM Electrically Erasable Programmable Read Only Memory.
embedded An application for a microcontroller with specific functional requirements; a specific application within the context of a system.
Emitter-Coupled Logic (ECL) A type of high speed bipolar logic family.
EN Enable input.
enable inputs Inputs used to put a device in a ready state.
encoders Devices that encode a single activated input as a binary code.
enhancement mode A type of FET semiconductor transistor operation.
ENIAC The first electronic digital computer, circa 1946.
EPROM Erasable Programmable Read Only Memory.
Equivalent gates Gates that perform the same logic function.
erase To remove (clear) the data in a memory device.
ESD Electro-static discharge; a high voltage condition that can damage CMOS ICs.
Excess-3 A binary code for decimal digital.
excitation table A table of input values the resulting output state of sequential logic devices.
Exclusive NOR A logic gate whose output is HIGH when the two inputs are equal to each other.
Exclusive OR A logic gate whose output is HIGH when the two inputs are not equal to each other.
External memory System memory in addition to memory already contained within a microprocessor IC.

fall time The time it takes a pulse to fall from 90% to 10% of its maximum value.
fanout A measure of the number of inputs that a single logic output can reliably drive.
feedback Connecting the output of a logic gate back to an input of that gate.
FET Field Effect Transistor.
flags Special purpose bit registers used to indicate the status of microprocessor operations.
flash A/D conversion High-speed analog-to-digital conversion technique.
flat pack A type of IC packaging.

flip-flop A bistable edge-triggered storage device.
floating input An input that is left unconnected in a logic circuit.
floppy disks Magnetic storage medium used in PC systems.
FM Frequency modulation.
fmax Maximum device operating frequency.
four-quadrant multiplication a digital-to-analog conversion technique.
free running Mode of continuous operation often associated with a clock generated by an oscillator circuit.
frequency The number of cycles per second of a waveform.
frequency division Dividing the frequency of a waveform by an integer.
full adder Adder circuit that adds three bits.
full-scale error Error of an analog-to-digital converter over the entire operating range.
function table Table specifying all input combinations and the resulting output of a particular logic function or IC.
functional block diagram Block diagram of major operating functions in a digital or analog system.

GAL16V8 Generic Array Logic 20-pin PLD.
GAL16V8A Improved Generic Array Logic 20-pin PLD.
gate arrays A type of VLSI semiconductor logic.
gated latch A latch with an enable input.
Generic Array Logic (GAL) PLDs that perform combinational or sequential logic operations as defined by the program.
glue logic Logic gates that are used to interface between logic circuits in a digital system.
Gray Code Binary code where only one bit changes from one count to the next.

half adders Adder circuits that add two bits.
hardware Circuits, devices.
hard-wired Permanently connected.
HC CMOS A CMOS logic subfamily.
HCT CMOS A CMOS logic subfamily that is TTL voltage compatible.
HEX Hexadecimal base-16 number system.
HEX to binary conversion Conversion from the hexadecimal number system to the binary number system.
HEX file A binary file encoded in the hexadecimal code.
HEX to decimal conversion Conversion from the hexadecimal number system to the decimal number system.
hexadecimal arithmetic Arithmetic operations on hexadecimal numbers.
high Z high impedance; electrically disconnected.
high level language A software language with instructions that are descriptive in nature and can perform multiple functions per instruction.
hold time The amount of time address signals must be supplied to a device after the device operation has occurred.
HOLD A latch, flip-flop or circuit input condition in which the device output does not change state.
hysteresis The voltage difference between the two switching states of Schmitt trigger devices.

I/O requirements Input/output requirements.
IC Integrated circuit; transistors, capacitors, and resistors fabricated into a silicon circuit.
ideal waveform A pulse waveform with instantaneous transitions between logic levels that does not take into account rise and fall times.
IEEE/ANSI gate symbols The Institute of Electrical and Electronic Engineers/American National Standards Institute standardized logic gate symbols.
initial state Beginning logic state.
instruction set The software commands for a particular microprocessor.
Integrated Injection Logic (IIL) A high speed logic family.
interfacing Proper connection of devices with differing current and voltage requirements.
internal memory Semiconductor memory that is contained within a microprocessor IC.
interrupt A signal request from a peripheral device to a microprocessor.
invalid state Logic levels or binary codes that are not allowed.
inverted SOP Active-LOW Sum-of-Products logic equation.
inverter Logic gate whose output logic level is the opposite of the input logic level.

JEDEC An international standard for IC packaging.
J-K flip-flop A type of flip-flop with four modes of operation.
Johnson counter Another name for a twisted ring counter.

Karnaugh map Graphical technique to minimize Boolean functions.

L TTL Low-Power TTL circuit.
latch a level triggered bistable storage device.
latchup An unwanted circuit condition in CMOS circuits that prevents the circuit from functioning.
LC9000 PLD logic compiler by Programmable Logic Devices.
LCD Liquid crystal display.
leading edge triggered Sequential logic device that changes state on the rising edge of the input trigger clock.
leading edge Rising edge of a pulse.
level triggered Device that is triggered by an input voltage level rather than by an input clock transition.
level shifter a type of circuit that changes input and/or output interface voltage levels.
levels (of logic) Number of gates through which the signal must pass to reach the output.

load device The gates or devices attached to a driver output.
load Inputs driven by an output.
logic probe Test device that determines the logic state of a node in the circuit.
Logic Lab PLD programming software by Programmable Logic Devices.
logic equation A Boolean equation that defines a logic function.
logic symbol Unique symbol that depicts a logic gate or device.
logic analyzer Test equipment that displays voltage waveforms.
logic gate Basic logic functions of NOT, AND, NAND, OR, NOR, XOR, XNOR.
logic HIGH Allowed high voltage state; a logic 1.
logic LOW Allowed low voltage state; a logic 0.
look-ahead carry a method for speeding the carry out of an addition.
LS TTL Low Power Schottky TTL device family.
LSB Least significant bit; the rightmost binary bit which has the lowest binary weight of a given number.
LSI Large Scale Integration.

mask level A processing step in the fabrication of semiconductor ICs.
master The first internal circuit stage of a master-slave flip-flop.
master-slave flip-flop A type of flip-flop that requires a leading and trailing edge to trigger; a pulse triggered flip-flop.
max terms OR terms in a POS equation.
maximum length ring counter N-bit ring counter with 2^N-1 states.
memory array The memory cell area of a semiconductor chip.
memory cell The transistor circuitry necessary to store one bit of information.
microcontroller A specialized type of microprocessor.
microprocessor A software controlled multifunction logic IC with processing, storage and I/O capabilities.
min terms The AND terms in an SOP equation.
mixed logic The use of several different types of logic families in one logic circuit or system.
mnemonic A microprocessor software acronym.
modified twisted ring counter N-bit ring counter with 2^N-1 states.
monostable a device with one stable logic state.
MOS Metal Oxide Semiconductor; a type of semiconductor processing.
MSB Most significant bit; the leftmost binary bit which has the highest binary weight of a given number.
MSI Medium Scale Integration.
multiplexer Digital device that routes several sources to a single output.
multivibrator A logic device that can switch between two logic states.
multitasking The use of multiple microprocessors to perform tasks under the control of a main microprocessor.
MUX Multiplexer.

NAND equivalent Equivalent logic function constructed solely of NAND gates; corresponds to SOP equations.
NAND A logic function that is LOW only when all inputs are HIGH.
negative edge-triggered A device whose output changes on the negative edge of an input clock.
negative edge The falling edge of a pulse.
negative logic Logic convention when the logic 1 is the LOW voltage and logic 0 is the HIGH voltage.
next state The logic state that immediately follows the present logic state.
nibble Four binary bits.
nibble organized A memory that has four data input/outputs.
nine's complement An unsigned representation of a negative number in the decimal system.
NMOS A type of semiconductor process used to produce n-channel transistor circuits.
noise margin Voltage margin between the allowed input voltages and the output voltage.
non-ideal waveform Pulse waveform with a rise time and fall time.
non-retriggerable A type of circuit that will ignore any additional trigger inputs while in an active trigger output state.
non-volatile A type of memory that will not lose its stored information if power is removed.
NOR Logic gate that is HIGH only when all inputs are LOW.
NOR equivalent Equivalent logic function constructed solely of NOR gates; associated with POS equations.
NOT Logic function that is LOW when the input is HIGH and HIGH when the input is LOW.
n-channel A type a semiconductor FET.

object file A computer file that contains instruction code that can be processed by a microprocessor.
octal A number system that has a base of eight.
one shot A monostable multivibrator.
one's complement method Subtraction method when negative numbers are represented in their one's complement form.
one's complement Representation of negative numbers.
one-time-programmable A PLD or PROM that can only be programmed one time.
open-collector outputs Devices where the output stage has no connection to Vcc at the collector of the output transistor and require an external pull-up resistor.

open-drain outputs The CMOS equivalent of open-collector outputs.
operation code The hexadecimal software code that corresponds to a microprocessor instruction.
optical receiver PIN diode or avalanche photodiode that receives an optical signal and converts it to an electrical signal.
optical interface Interface between the electrical and optical components.
optical detector Optical receiver.
optocouplers A type of optical transistor switch used to electrically isolate one part of an electronic circuit from another.
optoisolators Another name for an optocoupler.
oscillator A circuit that switches back and forth between two states; also known as an astable multivibrator.
OR Logic function that is HIGH when any input is HIGH.
oscilloscope Test equipment that displays waveforms.
overflow A condition that occurs during the addition of quantities where the sign bit of the sum is correct.
overflow detection circuitry Circuitry that detects an overflow condition that occurs during an arithmetic operation.
oversampling Sampling at more than twice the maximum analog frequency.

packaging The type of plastic or ceramic enclosure for an IC.
parallel memory Memory that has more than one bit of organization.
parallel I/O Input/output of more than one bit at a time.
parity encoding Encoding to detect single bit errors.
parity generator/checker circuits Circuit to check or generate parity bits for error detection.
periodic waveform A waveform that has a repeatable pattern of a fixed time increment (period).
photo-transistor The type of transistor used in optocoupler devices.
PISO Parallel in, serial out; type of shift register.
PLCC Plastic lead chip carrier; a type of IC package.
PLD Programmable Logic Device; a type of semiconductor logic IC.
PMOS P-type metal oxide semiconductor; a type of semiconductor processing used to produce p-type transistors.
port One or more bits of microprocessor or computer input/output.
POS Product-of-Sums; a logic equation in a special form with sum terms ANDed together. Can be implemented with two levels of NOR gates.
positive logic Logic convention where the logic 1 is the HIGH voltage and the logic 0 is the LOW voltage.
positive edge-triggered Device whose output changes state on the positive edge of an input trigger clock.
positive edge The rising edge of a pulse.
power dissipation The amount of electrical power than a circuit or device consumes.
present state-next state table Table used for sequential circuit analysis that lists the present state and next state for all possible combinations.
present input-present state next-state table Table used for sequential circuit analysis that lists the present input, present state, and next state for all possible input combinations.
present state The output state of a device at the current time period.
preset (PRE) An asynchronous input that will cause a device output to SET.
previous state The output state of a device one time period before the present state.
priority encoding Encoding that sets a higher priority for large input numbers.
pro bono [Latin, literally, for the good] Any work or service done free of charge.
product terms AND terms.
Programmable Read Only Memory (PROM) A memory device that can be programmed out of a circuit with a programmer and then placed back into a circuit to function as a read-only memory.
programmable logic devices Devices that can be programmed for specific combinational or sequential logic functions.
Programmable Array Logic (PAL) A type of application specific IC.
PROM Programmable Read Only Memory.
propagation delay Time delay caused by gate or device; the smaller the propagation delay, the faster the device switches logic states.
PRR Pulse Repetition Rate; another term for waveform frequency.
pull-up resistor Resistor connected to V_{CC} to provide adequate V_{OH} levels, required on open-collector outputs.
pulse triggered Type of device that triggers with an input pulse.
pulse code modulation (PCM) Digital encoding technique often used for voice and audio.
pulse width Time duration of a pulse.
pulsed operation Operation of a logic circuit with a varying input.
p-channel Type of semiconductor FET transistor with p-type semiconductor material used for the conductor between an n-type gate and drain.

qualifying symbols IEEE/ANSI symbols on a logic block that designate the operation of inputs and outputs.
quantization error The error resulting from quantizing an analog signal to convert it to a digital code.

R/2R ladder network Analog-to-digital conversion technique.

RAS Row address select; one of the address signals of a semiconductor memory device.
refresh Required rewriting of data stored in a DRAM to prevent memory loss.
register Group of flip-flops used for temporary data storage.
registered outputs Type of output on GAL PLDs.
registered mode One type of operation associated with GAL PLDs.
removal time A logic or memory waveform parametric.
repeated division by 2 Technique to convert decimal integers numbers to binary integers.
repeated multiplication by 2 Technique to convert decimal fractions to binary fractions.
RESET Clearing the output of a flip-flop or related device.
resolution Accuracy of the analog-to-digital conversion system.
retrieve The read operation for a memory device.
retriggerable A characteristic of some monostable multivibrators that allows the device trigger and begin its pulse again even if already triggered and in its unstable output mode.
ring counter A type of shift register with the output of the last flip-flop connected to the input of the first flip-flop, n-bit counter with n states.
ripple counter An asynchronous counter.
rise time Time required for a pulse to rise from 10% of its maximum value to 90% of its maximum value.
ROM Read Only Memory; a type of semiconductor memory that can only be read from in a circuit application.
RWM Read Write Memory; another term for RAM memory.

sampling rate The frequency of sampling or measuring of a signal.
Schmitt trigger A special type of input circuit that causes a digital device to abruptly switch logic states at the positive and negative threshold points.
select inputs Inputs that are used for address inputs.
self-complementing A code that can form its complement by inverting the bits.
semiconductors Electronic devices fabricated on electrically doped elements or compounds; predominately silicon.
sequential logic Logic devices whose output depends on the present inputs and the present state of the device; output depends on the sequence of inputs.
serial memory A memory device that has only one input/output for data.
serial I/O An I/O device that has only one input/output for data.
serial/parallel format conversion Data is converted from a serial format to a parallel format.
SET Changing the true output of a flip-flop or related device to a HIGH.
setup time A device parametric that defines the amount of time one signal must be valid before another signal can be applied to the device.
Set-Reset flip-flop (S-R flip-flop) A two-input bistable multivibrator with three valid input combinations and one invalid input combination.
shift register Sequential logic device consisting of a series of D flip flop stages that shift the data from one stage to the next.
signature analyzer A special type of test equipment used for logic analysis and troubleshooting.
signed binary arithmetic Arithmetic operations on positive or negative binary numbers.
signed binary numbers Positive or negative binary numbers.
Sign-and-Magnitude Form of representing signed binary numbers.
silicon A common semiconductor material.
SIPO Serial in, parallel out; a type of shift register.
slave The internal second stage of a master-slave flip-flop.
SMD Surface mount device; a special type of IC packaging for surface soldering of the component to the printed circuit board.
software A program of instructions stored for use by a computer.
SOIC Small outline integrated circuit; a type of surface mount IC.
SOP Sum-of-Products; a special form of logic equation consisting of product terms ORed together that can be implemented with two levels of NAND gates.
source device A device that is supplying current or driving other devices.
source file A file of data that will be read by a program.
SRAM Static Random Access Memory.
SSI Small Scale Integration.
stable state A device logic output state that will not change unless the device is triggered into the next state.
stack Temporary memory storage used by microprocessors and other computational devices.
standard logic (7400 Series) A TTL subfamily.
Standard TTL Standard logic.
standby mode The mode of a device not in use; powered but not actively switching logic states.
state transition diagrams Diagrams that depict the input and the resulting output states of a sequential device.
state The output logic condition of a device or circuit.
static timing Theoretical timing waveforms for a device.
static operation Device operation with constant input values.
static-unchanging storage characteristics The data retention characteristics of memory devices.
store To save data into a memory device.
strobe inputs Inputs used to enable a device; can also be referred to as enable inputs.

subroutine A set of instructions within a program to perform a specific task.
successive approximation A/D converters A technique for analog-to-digital conversion.
sum terms AND terms in an SOP equation.
surface mount A type of device packaging.
synchronization Timing control using a common clock.
synchronous Devices operating from a common clock.
synchronous counters Counters where all flip flop stages operate from a common clock.
S-R latch a set-reset latch.
S-R flip-flop a set-reset flip-flop.

TDM Time Division Multiplexing.
ten's complement Complement of a decimal number.
threshold A limiting value; MOS transistors have voltage thresholds that control transistor operation.
time division multiplexing A technique to combine multiple signals so that they share a common transmission line timing parameters.
timing diagram Waveforms showing the timing relationship between critical signals.
timing The sequence of signals.
timing clock The clock that controls the timing of a circuit.
TOGGLE A condition where the output of a device changes state with each clock trigger.
toggle flip flop A flip flop device that alternates output states between HIGH and LOW with each clock pulse; occurs with a J-K flip-flop when both inputs are 1.
totem pole Output stage on a TTL device.
t_{PHL} Propagation delay as the output waveform transitions from HIGH to LOW.
t_{PLH} Propagation delay as the output waveform transitions from LOW to HIGH.
trailing edge The negative edge of a pulse.
transfer characteristic Output vs. input switching characteristics of a device in graphical form.
transistor Semiconductor device that can effectively work as an open or closed switch.
Transistor-Transistor Logic (TTL) A family of bipolar digital devices.
transparent A mode of operation for a latch or other device where the operation of the device is undetectable by the user.
trigger A signal that causes a device to operate.
trigger voltage The voltage level necessary to trigger a device.
tristate Devices that can be HIGH, LOW, or have a HIGH IMPEDANCE output state.
troubleshooting Technique to debug circuit problems.
truth table Table listing all input combinations and the resulting output state for a circuit.
TTL compatible A device having input and output voltage characteristics compatible with TTL devices.
TTL Transistor Transistor Logic; a bipolar transistor circuitry used to build TTL logic family ICs.
twisted ring counter N-bit ring counter with 2N count states.
two's complement A representation of negative binary numbers.
two's complement method Arithmetic procedures used with negative numbers are represented in their two's complement form.

UHF Ultra High Frequency.
ULSI Ultra large scale integration; the largest scale of integration defined for semiconductor chips.
unidirectional Signals that are transmitted in only one direction.
unit load A figure of merit associated with device fan-out.
unsigned arithmetic Arithmetic procedures to use when dealing with numbers that represent magnitudes.
unstable state A state that the device will not remain in a stable state.
UV-PLD A PLD that can be erased with ultraviolet light.
UVEPROM Ultraviolet Erasable Programmable Read Only Memory.

variables The symbolic designations of the inputs or outputs of digital circuits or signals.
VHF Very High Frequency.
VLSI Very Large Scale Integration.
volatile A memory device characteristic which indicates that memory contents will be lost if the device loses its power connections.
V_{t+} The upper hysteresis switching point for Schmitt trigger devices.
V_{t-} The lower hysteresis switching point for Schmitt trigger devices.

wafer A slice of semiconductor material on which multiple ICs are fabricated.
waveform analysis Analyzing the operation of a device or system by interpreting the operational waveforms produced by the device.
weighted base-16 Hexadecimal number system.
weighted base-2 Binary number system.
weighted base-10 Decimal number system.
wired-AND Open-collector outputs connected together to form an AND function.
wired gates Gates whose outputs can be connected directly and that perform a logic function.
write The storage of data into a memory device.

XNOR Exclusive NOR; logic function that is HIGH when the two inputs are equal.
XOR Exclusive OR; logic function that is HIGH when the two inputs are not equal.

Index